ADVANCED ENGINEERING DYNAMICS

Second Edition

R. Valéry Roy

University of Delaware

Advanced Engineering Dynamics

 ISBN-13: 978-0990696926 (R. Valery Roy)
Published by Hyperbolic Press

First printing, February 2015

Contents

Preface

ADVANCED ENGINEERING DYNAMICS was written for graduate students and scientists in Mechanical Engineering. It covers a wide range of fundamental and advanced topics which can be taught in a two-course sequence. The book deals with the treatment of many aspects of engineering dynamics usually not found in a single tome. Indeed, our goal was to write as complete a book as possible, in a compact, concise and rigorous style. The methods, tools and notations advocated in this book will appear to be novel to most readers. They mirror the style of the book in their efficiency, coherence and compactness. They are illustrated by many example problems which are essential to full comprehension of the subject. It should also be noted that this book is not specific to a particular field of application, such as robotics, spacecraft mechanics, or biomechanics. Many books are already available in these specialized fields.

In light of the ever increasing sophistication of Kinematics and Motion Simulation modeling and computing software, one may ask: why learn Dynamics? While they undoubtedly have their place in the engineering profession, these tools cannot be used properly without a thorough understanding of the subject matter. It can also be argued that too much reliance on a machine to do engineering analysis may limit the understanding of the user.

OVERVIEW OF THE BOOK. The book is structured in sixteen chapters which can be broadly classified in two parts. The first part of the book deals with kinematic aspects at the level of particles (Chapter 2), rigid body (Chapters 3, 5, 6) and systems of rigid bodies (Chapters 7 and 8). This first part starts with a preliminary chapter (Chapter 1) devoted to the definition of position of a rigid body, mostly through the parametrization of its orientation. Chapter 4 is pivotal to this book: the concept of screws is relevant not only to kinematics but also to all aspects of kinetics. Before the start of the second part of the book, two preliminary chapters will be found to cover the topics of mass distribution (Chapter 9) and of mechanical actions (Chapter 10). The remainder of the book is devoted to kinetics, that is, to the exposition of methods devised to formulate the equations of motions and to determine unknown mechanical actions, as applied to a single rigid body or systems of rigid bodies. More specifically,

Chapter 11 presents the vectorial formalism of Newton-Euler with its central result known as the Fundamental Theorem of Dynamics.

Chapter 12 presents notions of power, kinetic energy, and potential energy leading to the derivation of the Kinetic Energy Theorem.

Chapter 13 is an introduction to analytical dynamics, starting with Lagrange and Painlevé equations.

Chapter 14 is a continuation of analytical dynamics with an introduction to Gibbs-Appell and Kane equations.

The book ends with two chapters specific to gyroscopic phenomena (Chapter 15) and to the generalization of theorems relative to non-Newtonian referentials (Chapter 16).

METHODOLOGY. Throughout this book, we will make extensive use of mathematical objects called *screws*. They will provide a simple yet powerful formalism which will unify all aspects of rigid body mechanics. Specifically, we take advantage of the fact that all relevant vector fields in rigid body mechanics have the following form

$$\mathbf{v}: \begin{cases} \mathcal{E} \to E \\ P \mapsto \mathbf{v}_P \end{cases} \text{ such that } \mathbf{v}_Q = \mathbf{v}_P + \mathbf{V} \times \mathbf{r}_{PQ}$$

Such fields define screws which will be denoted in a simple array form:

$$\{\mathcal{V}\} = \begin{Bmatrix} \mathbf{V} \\ \mathbf{v}_A \end{Bmatrix}$$

Various operations (addition, multiplication, scalar product, ...) on screws can then be defined and their essential properties will be determined. Four fundamental screws will be introduced:

- $\{\mathcal{V}_{\mathcal{B}/\mathcal{E}}\}$ as the *kinematic screw* of a rigid body $\mathcal{B}$ (Chapter 5) and $\{\mathcal{V}^{q_i}_{\mathcal{B}/\mathcal{E}}\}$ as its *partial kinematic screw* in analytical dynamics (Chapters 13 and 14),
- $\{\mathcal{H}_{\mathcal{B}/\mathcal{E}}\}$ as the *kinetic screw* $\{\mathcal{H}_{\mathcal{B}/\mathcal{E}}\}$ of a rigid body $\mathcal{B}$, and $\{\mathcal{H}_{\Sigma/\mathcal{E}}\}$ as kinetic screw of a system of rigid body Σ (Chapter 9),
- $\{\mathcal{D}_{\mathcal{B}/\mathcal{E}}\}$ as the *dynamic screw* of a rigid body $\mathcal{B}$, and $\{\mathcal{D}_{\Sigma/\mathcal{E}}\}$ as the dynamic screw of a system of rigid bodies Σ (Chapter 9),
- $\{\mathcal{A}_{\Sigma_1\to\Sigma_2}\}$ as the *action screw* of material system Σ_1 on material system Σ_2 (Chapter 10).

The theorems underlying the methods of this book will all be derived and put to practical use by employing the formalism of screws. The starting point will be D'Alembert Principle of Virtual Power, which, in the language of screws can be stated as follows:

$$\underbrace{\{\mathcal{D}_{\Sigma/\mathcal{E}}\}}_{\text{dynamic screw}} \cdot \underbrace{\{\mathcal{V}^*\}}_{\text{virtual velocity screw}} = \underbrace{\{\mathcal{A}_{\overline{\Sigma}\to\Sigma}\}}_{\text{action screw}} \cdot \underbrace{\{\mathcal{V}^*\}}_{\text{virtual velocity screw}}$$

in a Newtonian referential $\mathcal{E}$. By specifying the virtual velocity screw $\{\mathcal{V}^*\}$, various theorems are obtained:

- choosing $\{\mathcal{V}^*\}$ arbitrary yields the Fundamental Theorem of Dynamics of the Newton-Euler formalism relative to a Newtonian referential (Chapter 11) or to a non-Newtonian referential (Chapter 16),
- choosing $\{\mathcal{V}^*\}$ as the kinematic screw $\{\mathcal{V}_{\mathcal{B}/\mathcal{E}}\}$ of rigid body $\mathcal{B}$ yields the Kinetic Energy Theorem (Chapter 12),
- choosing $\{\mathcal{V}^*\}$ as the partial kinematic screws $\{\mathcal{V}^{q_i}_{\mathcal{B}/\mathcal{E}}\}$ of rigid body $\mathcal{B}$ yields Lagrange equations (Chapter 13) or Gibbs-Appell equations (Chapter 14),
- choosing $\{\mathcal{V}^*\}$ as the generalized partial kinematic screws $\{\mathcal{V}^{u_i}_{\mathcal{B}/\mathcal{E}}\}$ of rigid body $\mathcal{B}$ yields Kane equations (Chapter 14),
- choosing $\{\mathcal{V}^*\}$ as the kinematic screw $\{\mathcal{V}_{\mathcal{B}/\mathcal{E}}\}$ relative to a non-Newtonian referential yields the Kinetic Energy Theorem in a non-Newtonian referential (Chapter 16).

HOW TO USE THIS BOOK. Dynamics is a rational discipline, and thus requires a certain mathematical rigor both in the presentation of the subject matter and in the approach to problem-solving. Although Dynamics does not require advanced mathematical tools, it is necessary for students to be familiar with basic geometry, vector calculus and concepts of linear algebra. If students are unfamiliar with these notions, it is strongly recommended that they first review the material presented in Appendix A.

As with other subjects, learning Dynamics requires a great deal of practice. In order to master the subject matter, the student is encouraged to work and re-work all example problems. The solutions of these problems are not meant to be simply read, but to be worked through. It is only by attempting each problem by himself, instead of passively reading the solution provided in the book, that the student will gain lasting benefits.

Nomenclature

$\mathcal{E}, \mathcal{F}, \mathcal{B}, \ldots$	rigid body or referential
$A, B, \ldots, P, Q$	points or particles
G, G_1, G_Σ	mass center (of body 1 or system Σ).
Σ	system of particles or rigid bodies, material system
AB	line joining point A to point B
$\mathbf{r}_{AB}$	position vector directed from point A to point B
$\|AB\|$	distance measured from point A to point B
$\mathbf{U}, \mathbf{V}, \mathbf{W}, \ldots$	vectors
$\hat{\mathbf{u}}, \hat{\mathbf{v}}, \ldots$	unit vectors
$b(\hat{\mathbf{e}}_1, \hat{\mathbf{e}}_2, \hat{\mathbf{e}}_3)$	orthonormal right-handed basis.
$\alpha = (\hat{\mathbf{u}}, \hat{\mathbf{v}})$	oriented angle between $\hat{\mathbf{u}}$ and $\hat{\mathbf{v}}$
Δ, $(O, \hat{\mathbf{u}})$	line, line passing through O directed along $\hat{\mathbf{u}}$.
Π, $(O, \hat{\mathbf{u}}, \hat{\mathbf{v}})$	plane, plane passing through O directed along $\hat{\mathbf{u}}$ and $\hat{\mathbf{v}}$.
$\mathcal{E}(O, \hat{\mathbf{e}}_1, \hat{\mathbf{e}}_2, \hat{\mathbf{e}}_3)$	three-dimensional space $\mathcal{E}$ (referential) passing through O of basis $(\hat{\mathbf{e}}_1, \hat{\mathbf{e}}_2, \hat{\mathbf{e}}_3)$.
$\mathcal{R}_{\alpha,\hat{\mathbf{u}}}$	rotation operator of angle α about unit vector $\hat{\mathbf{u}}$.
$\mathcal{L}$	linear operator.
$[\mathcal{L}]_b$	matrix representation of linear operator $\mathcal{L}$ on basis b.
Q_1, Q_2	quaternions.
$\mathbf{v}_A, \mathbf{v}_{A\in 1/0}, \mathbf{v}_{A\in\mathcal{B}}$	velocity vector of a point or particle
$\mathbf{a}_A, \mathbf{a}_{A\in 1/0}, \mathbf{a}_{A\in\mathcal{B}}$	acceleration vector of a point or particle
$\omega, \omega_{\mathcal{B}/\mathcal{A}}, \omega_{2/1}$	angular velocity of a rigid body
$\boldsymbol{\alpha}, \boldsymbol{\alpha}_{\mathcal{B}}, \boldsymbol{\alpha}_{2/1}$	angular acceleration of a rigid body

$\{\mathcal{U}\}, \{\mathcal{V}\}$	screws
$\{\mathcal{V}_{\mathcal{B}_2/\mathcal{B}_1}\}, \{\mathcal{V}_{2/1}\}$	kinematic screw of body $\mathcal{B}_1$ relative to body (referential) $\mathcal{B}_2$
$\{\mathcal{H}_{\mathcal{B}/\mathcal{E}}\}, \{\mathcal{H}_{1/0}\}, \{\mathcal{H}_{\Sigma/0}\}$	kinetic screw of body $\mathcal{B}$ (or system Σ) relative to referential $\mathcal{E}$
$\mathbf{H}_O, \mathbf{H}_{O,\mathcal{B}}, \mathbf{H}_{O,\Sigma/\mathcal{E}}$	angular momentum about O of rigid body $\mathcal{B}$ (or system Σ) relative to referential $\mathcal{E}$.
$\{\mathcal{D}_{\mathcal{B}/\mathcal{E}}\}, \{\mathcal{D}_{1/0}\}, \{\mathcal{D}_{\Sigma/0}\}$	dynamic screw of body $\mathcal{B}$ (or system Σ) relative to referential $\mathcal{E}$
$\mathbf{D}_O, \mathbf{D}_{O,\mathcal{B}}, \mathbf{D}_{O,\Sigma/\mathcal{E}}$	dynamic moment about O of rigid body $\mathcal{B}$ (or system Σ) relative to referential $\mathcal{E}$.
$\mathcal{I}_O, \mathcal{I}_{O,\mathcal{B}}, \mathcal{I}_{O,1}$	inertia operator about O of body $\mathcal{B}$ (body $\mathcal{B}_1$).
$\{\mathcal{A}_{\Sigma_1\to\Sigma_2}\}, \{\mathcal{A}^c_{\mathcal{B}_1\to\mathcal{B}_2}\}, \{\mathcal{A}^c_{1\to 2}\}$	action screw exerted by system (rigid body) Σ_1 on system Σ_2.
$\mathbf{R}_{\mathcal{A}\to\mathcal{B}}, \mathbf{R}_{\Sigma\to\mathcal{B}}, \mathbf{R}_{1\to 2}$	resultant force exerted by rigid body $\mathcal{A}$ on rigid body $\mathcal{B}$
$\mathbf{M}_{O,\overline{\Sigma}\to\Sigma}, \mathbf{M}_{O,1\to 2}$	resultant moment about O of external action on system Σ)
$\mathbb{K}_{\mathcal{B}/\mathcal{E}}, \mathbb{K}_{1/0}, K_{\Sigma/0}$	kinetic energy of rigid body $\mathcal{B}$ (or system Σ) relative to referential $\mathcal{E}$.
$\mathbb{P}_{\Sigma_1\to\Sigma/\mathcal{E}}, \mathbb{P}_{\mathcal{B}_1\leftrightarrow\mathcal{B}_2}$	power of external action, power of interaction.
$\mathbb{U}_{\Sigma_1\to\Sigma/\mathcal{E}}, \mathbb{U}_{\mathcal{B}_1\leftrightarrow\mathcal{B}_2}$	potential energy
$\mathbb{Q}_{\Sigma_1\to C/\mathcal{E}}, \mathbb{Q}_{\mathcal{B}_1\leftrightarrow\mathcal{B}_2}$	power coefficient
$\mathbb{S}_{\mathcal{B}/\mathcal{E}}, \mathbb{S}_{\Sigma/0}$	Gibbs S-function of rigid body $\mathcal{B}$ (system Σ).

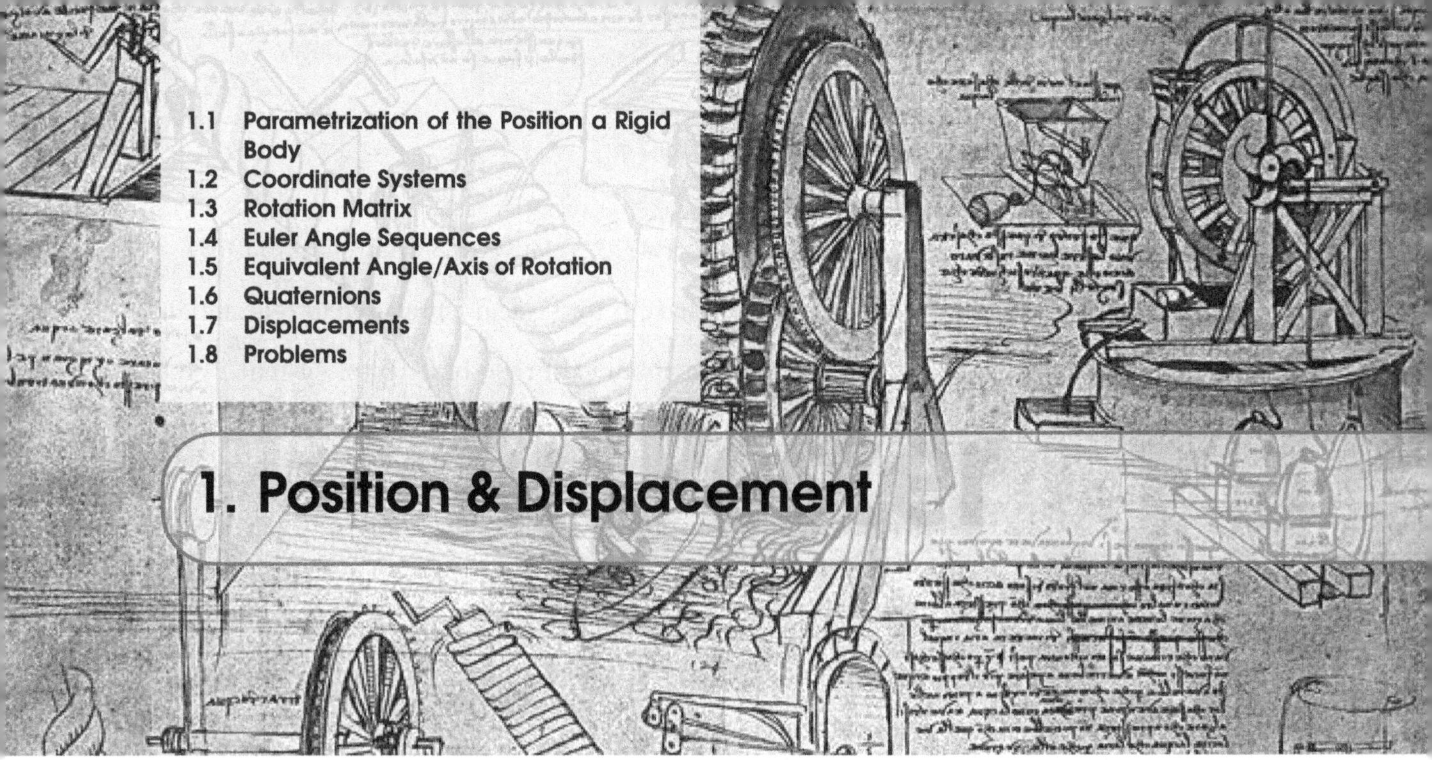

1. Position & Displacement

Prior to studying the kinematics of rigid bodies, we must address the problem of defining their position in space. Parametrizing the position of a rigid body is equivalent to parametrizing the position of one of its points and to parametrizing its orientation (or attitude). The first task is accomplished by adopting one of several coordinate systems. Much of this chapter will be devoted to the second task. We shall show that the orientation of a rigid body is parametrized by at most three independent parameters which can be defined by employing one of three methods:

1. by using rotation operators whose matrix representations rely on direction cosines,
2. by using one of several Euler sequences defined in terms of three angles,
3. by using a single rotation defined in terms an equivalent angle/direction,

We shall show how these methods relate to each other, and point out their relative benefits and drawbacks. We shall also show that quaternions are useful tools to represent spatial rotations. Finally, we end this chapter with the study of finite displacements of rigid bodies.

1.1 Parametrization of the Position a Rigid Body

In mechanics, motions are observed relative to a referential $\mathcal{E}$, that is, a Euclidean physical space[1]. A particular point O of $\mathcal{E}$ is chosen to define an origin of $\mathcal{E}$. Referential $\mathcal{E}$ is also equipped with an orthonormal right-handed basis [2] $(\hat{\mathbf{e}}_1, \hat{\mathbf{e}}_2, \hat{\mathbf{e}}_3)$. A rigid body $\mathcal{B}$ is a mathematical abstraction, defined as a connected subset of points which remain at a constant distance from each other. Body $\mathcal{B}$ is equipped with an orthonormal right-handed basis $(\hat{\mathbf{b}}_1, \hat{\mathbf{b}}_2, \hat{\mathbf{b}}_3)$ which remains attached to $\mathcal{B}$ at all time. An origin B of $\mathcal{B}$ is chosen as a point fixed in $\mathcal{B}$ at all time. In this chapter, we seek to parametrize the position of $\mathcal{B}$ relative to

[1] There is a one-to-one mapping between $\mathcal{E}$ and $\mathbb{R}^3$ once an origin of $\mathcal{E}$ is chosen.

[2] All orthonormal bases, whether fixed or mobile, will always be chosen right-handed.

$\mathcal{E}$, that is, to define a set of parameters which would enable us to find the positions of all points attached to $\mathcal{B}$ relative to $\mathcal{E}$. Since body $\mathcal{B}$ is rigid, this requires a parametrization of the set $(B, \hat{\mathbf{b}}_1, \hat{\mathbf{b}}_2, \hat{\mathbf{b}}_3)$ relative to the set $(O, \hat{\mathbf{e}}_1, \hat{\mathbf{e}}_2, \hat{\mathbf{e}}_3)$: indeed the position of an arbitrary point P attached to $\mathcal{B}$ relative to $\mathcal{E}$ is defined by the equation $\mathbf{r}_{OP} = \mathbf{r}_{OB} + \mathbf{r}_{BP}$ as seen in Figure 1.1. Defining the position of $\mathcal{B}$ relative to $\mathcal{E}$ is then equivalent to:

(i) defining the position of origin B in $\mathcal{E}$, thus allowing for the determination of position vector $\mathbf{r}_{OB}$,

(ii) defining the orientation of basis $(\hat{\mathbf{b}}_1, \hat{\mathbf{b}}_2, \hat{\mathbf{b}}_3)$ relative to basis $(\hat{\mathbf{e}}_1, \hat{\mathbf{e}}_2, \hat{\mathbf{e}}_3)$: this would allow for the determination of position vector $\mathbf{r}_{BP}$ if P is at a specified location relative to B.

The position of B in $\mathcal{B}$ is defined by adopting a coordinate system (Section 1.2). The orientation of $\mathcal{B}$ can be defined in three possible ways: (i) by the direction cosines of basis of $\mathcal{B}$ relative to basis of $\mathcal{E}$ (Section 1.3), (ii) by one of twelve possible Euler sequences (Section 1.4) , and (iii) by a single equivalent rotation (Section 1.5) represented in terms of an angle and a direction or in terms of a quaternion (Section 1.6).

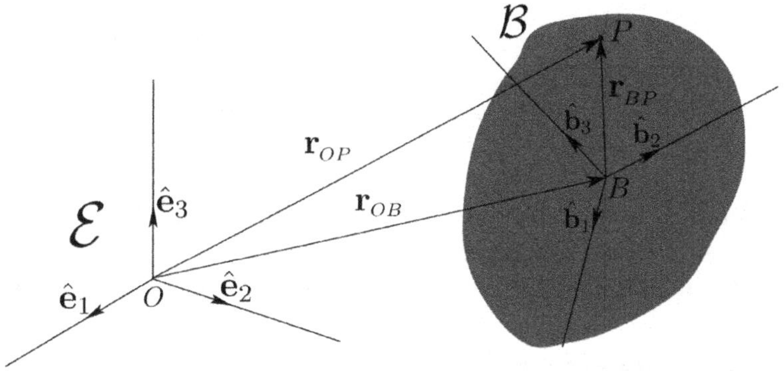

Figure 1.1

1.2 Coordinate Systems

We first seek to define the position of origin B of $\mathcal{B}$ relative to referential $\mathcal{E}$. This is done by defining a coordinate system, that is, a mapping $P \in \mathcal{E} \mapsto (q_1, q_2, q_3) \in \mathbb{R}^3$.

Definition 1.1 — Coordinate System. The position of a point P in a referential $\mathcal{E}$ is defined by a coordinate system, that is, a set a three scalar parameters (q_1, q_2, q_3), called *coordinates* of P. Given an origin O of $\mathcal{E}$, the *position vector* $\mathbf{r}_{OP}$ is a vector function of (q_1, q_2, q_3):

$$\mathbf{r}_{OP} = \mathbf{r}(q_1, q_2, q_3) \tag{1.1}$$

There are several practical ways to parametrize the position of a point relative to a given referential. We describe below the Cartesian, cylindrical and spherical coordinate systems. Other ways can be devised by mixing various coordinates taken from these three systems.

1.2.1 Cartesian Coordinate System

Consider three axes fixed in referential $\mathcal{E}$, intersecting at origin O, and mutually perpendicular. We orient these axes by the unit vectors $\hat{\mathbf{e}}_1$, $\hat{\mathbf{e}}_2$ and $\hat{\mathbf{e}}_3$, such that the triplet $(\hat{\mathbf{e}}_1, \hat{\mathbf{e}}_2, \hat{\mathbf{e}}_3)$ defines a right-handed orthonormal basis. See Figure 1.2.

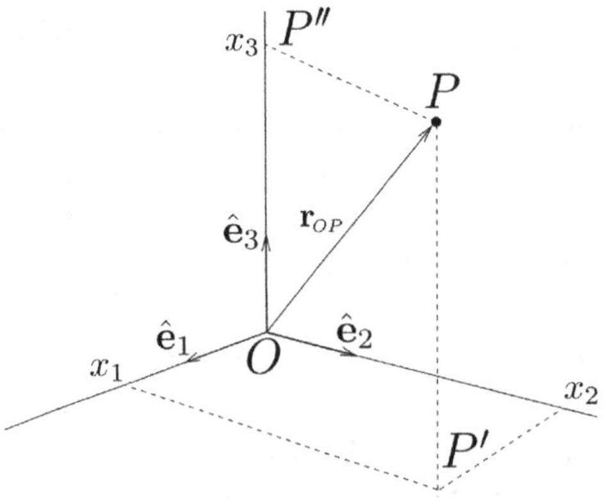

Figure 1.2

Definition 1.2 The Cartesian coordinates (x_1, x_2, x_3) of point P are the components of position vector $\mathbf{r}_{OP}$ on basis $(\hat{\mathbf{e}}_1, \hat{\mathbf{e}}_2, \hat{\mathbf{e}}_3)$:

$$\mathbf{r}_{OP} = \mathbf{r}_{OP'} + \mathbf{r}_{OP''} = x_1\hat{\mathbf{e}}_1 + x_2\hat{\mathbf{e}}_2 + x_3\hat{\mathbf{e}}_3 \tag{1.2}$$

where points P' and P'' are the projections of P onto plane $(O, \hat{\mathbf{e}}_1, \hat{\mathbf{e}}_2)$ and line $(O, \hat{\mathbf{e}}_3)$, respectively.

We often identify a referential $\mathcal{E}$ with a set $(O, \hat{\mathbf{e}}_1, \hat{\mathbf{e}}_2, \hat{\mathbf{e}}_3)$ chosen fixed in $\mathcal{E}$. However one should not confuse the notion of referential with that of coordinate system. In particular, more than one Cartesian coordinate system can be defined within a given referential.

1.2.2 Cylindrical Coordinate System

Let $(O, \hat{\mathbf{e}}_1, \hat{\mathbf{e}}_2, \hat{\mathbf{e}}_3)$ define three Cartesian axes $(O, \hat{\mathbf{e}}_1)$, $(O, \hat{\mathbf{e}}_2)$ and $(O, \hat{\mathbf{e}}_3)$ attached to referential $\mathcal{E}$.

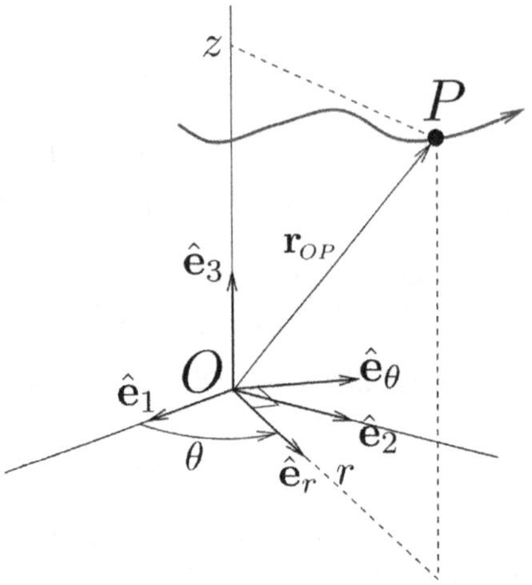

Figure 1.3

Definition 1.3 The *cylindrical* coordinates of point P are defined as the triplet $(r, \theta, z = x_3)$ in the following way (see Figure 1.3):

(i) radial coordinate r is the magnitude of position vector $\mathbf{r}_{OP'}$, P' projection of P onto plane $(O, \hat{\mathbf{e}}_1, \hat{\mathbf{e}}_2)$.

(ii) θ is the oriented angle between axis $(O, \hat{\mathbf{e}}_1)$ and line OP'.

(iii) $z = x_3$ is the component of position vector $\mathbf{r}_{OP}$ on unit vector $\hat{\mathbf{e}}_z = \hat{\mathbf{e}}_3$.

The position vector of P can then be written as

$$\mathbf{r}_{OP} = r\hat{\mathbf{e}}_r + z\hat{\mathbf{e}}_z \tag{1.3}$$

where $\hat{\mathbf{e}}_r$ is the radial unit vector, pointing from O to P'.

Note that $\hat{\mathbf{e}}_r$ is a function of angle θ. A third unit vector $\hat{\mathbf{e}}_\theta$ can be defined such that the triplet $(\hat{\mathbf{e}}_r, \hat{\mathbf{e}}_\theta, \hat{\mathbf{e}}_z)$ forms a right-handed basis.

1.2.3 Spherical Coordinate System

Let $(O, \hat{\mathbf{e}}_1, \hat{\mathbf{e}}_2, \hat{\mathbf{e}}_3)$ define three Cartesian axes $(O, \hat{\mathbf{e}}_1)$, $(O, \hat{\mathbf{e}}_2)$ and $(O, \hat{\mathbf{e}}_3)$ attached to referential $\mathcal{E}$.

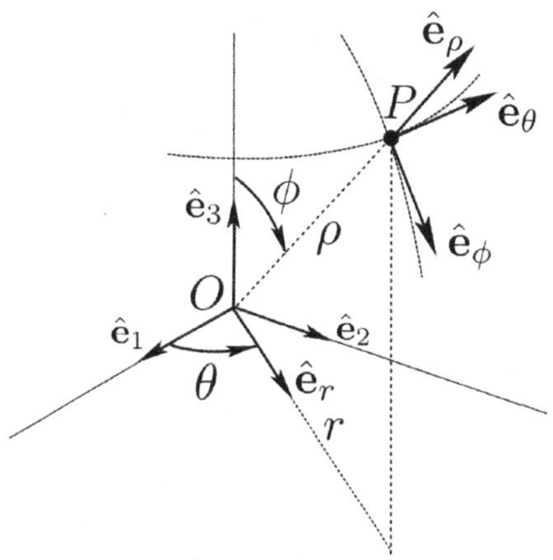

Figure 1.4

Definition 1.4 The *spherical* coordinates (ρ, ϕ, θ) of point P are defined in the following way (see Figure 1.4):

(i) define coordinate ρ as the distance from point O to point P.

(ii) project P onto plane $(O, \hat{\mathbf{e}}_1, \hat{\mathbf{e}}_2)$ to obtain point P' and define the *azimuthal* (or *longitude*) angle θ as the angle measured between axis $(O, \hat{\mathbf{e}}_1)$ and line OP'.

(iii) define *colatitude* angle ϕ as the angle measured from axis $(O, \hat{\mathbf{e}}_3)$ and line OP.

Then the position of P is given by

$$\mathbf{r}_{OP} = \rho\hat{\mathbf{e}}_\rho \tag{1.4}$$

where $\hat{\mathbf{e}}_\rho$ is the unit vector pointing from O to P.

Note that unit vector $\hat{\mathbf{e}}_\rho$ is a function of both angles ϕ and θ. Two additional units vectors can be defined from the spherical coordinates of P:

- unit vector $\hat{\mathbf{e}}_\phi$ tangential to the line of constant θ at P in the direction of increasing ϕ,
- unit vector $\hat{\mathbf{e}}_\theta$ tangential to the line of constant ϕ at P in the direction of increasing θ.

1.3 Rotation Matrix

Our next task is to parametrize the orientation [3] of body $\mathcal{B}$ relative to referential $\mathcal{E}$, or equivalently the orientation of basis $(\hat{\mathbf{b}}_1, \hat{\mathbf{b}}_2, \hat{\mathbf{b}}_3)$ of $\mathcal{B}$ relative to basis $(\hat{\mathbf{e}}_1, \hat{\mathbf{e}}_2, \hat{\mathbf{e}}_3)$ of $\mathcal{E}$. One possible way to achieve this task is to determine the direction cosines between the two bases.

Definition 1.5 The *direction cosines* of basis $(\hat{\mathbf{b}}_1, \hat{\mathbf{b}}_2, \hat{\mathbf{b}}_3)$ on basis $(\hat{\mathbf{e}}_1, \hat{\mathbf{e}}_2, \hat{\mathbf{e}}_3)$ are the scalars c_{ij} defined as

$$c_{ij} = \hat{\mathbf{e}}_i \cdot \hat{\mathbf{b}}_j, \qquad (i,j = 1,2,3) \tag{1.5}$$

The matrix $[\mathcal{C}_{EB}] \equiv [c_{ij}] = [\hat{\mathbf{b}}_1|\hat{\mathbf{b}}_2|\hat{\mathbf{b}}_3]_{(\hat{\mathbf{e}}_1,\hat{\mathbf{e}}_2,\hat{\mathbf{e}}_3)}$ is called *direction cosine matrix*: its column vectors are obtained by writing each basis vector $\hat{\mathbf{b}}_j$ of $\mathcal{B}$ on the basis of $\mathcal{E}$.

Each unit vector $\hat{\mathbf{b}}_j$ can be written as

$$\hat{\mathbf{b}}_j = c_{1j}\hat{\mathbf{e}}_1 + c_{2j}\hat{\mathbf{e}}_2 + c_{3j}\hat{\mathbf{e}}_3 \qquad (j = 1,2,3) \tag{1.6}$$

The nine direction cosines c_{ij} are not independent since the basis vectors $(\hat{\mathbf{b}}_1, \hat{\mathbf{b}}_2, \hat{\mathbf{b}}_3)$ satisfy the six independent equations

$$\hat{\mathbf{b}}_j \cdot \hat{\mathbf{b}}_k = \delta_{jk} = \begin{cases} 0, & j \neq k \\ 1, & j = k \end{cases}, \qquad (j,k = 1,2,3)$$

Hence for $j = k = 1,2,3$ we have

$$c_{11}^2 + c_{21}^2 + c_{31}^2 = 1 \tag{1.7}$$
$$c_{12}^2 + c_{22}^2 + c_{32}^2 = 1 \tag{1.8}$$
$$c_{13}^2 + c_{23}^2 + c_{33}^2 = 1 \tag{1.9}$$

and for $j \neq k$

$$c_{11}c_{12} + c_{21}c_{22} + c_{31}c_{32} = 0 \tag{1.10}$$
$$c_{11}c_{13} + c_{21}c_{23} + c_{31}c_{33} = 0 \tag{1.11}$$
$$c_{13}c_{12} + c_{23}c_{22} + c_{33}c_{32} = 0 \tag{1.12}$$

Therefore, *only three independent direction cosines are necessary to define the orientation of $\mathcal{B}$ relative to $\mathcal{E}$.*

We can also express basis vector $\hat{\mathbf{e}}_i$ on basis $(\hat{\mathbf{b}}_1, \hat{\mathbf{b}}_2, \hat{\mathbf{b}}_3)$ in the following way

$$\hat{\mathbf{e}}_i = c_{i1}\hat{\mathbf{b}}_1 + c_{i2}\hat{\mathbf{b}}_2 + c_{i3}\hat{\mathbf{b}}_3, \quad (i = 1,2,3) \tag{1.13}$$

This implies that the direction cosine matrix $[\mathcal{C}_{BE}] = [\hat{\mathbf{e}}_1|\hat{\mathbf{e}}_2|\hat{\mathbf{e}}_3]_{(\hat{\mathbf{b}}_1,\hat{\mathbf{b}}_2,\hat{\mathbf{b}}_3)}$ is given by $[c_{ji}]$, and that the inverse of matrix $[\mathcal{C}_{EB}]$ is equal to its transpose:

$$[\mathcal{C}_{EB}]^{-1} = [\mathcal{C}_{EB}]^T = [\mathcal{C}_{BE}], \qquad [\mathcal{C}_{BE}]^{-1} = [\mathcal{C}_{BE}]^T = [\mathcal{C}_{EB}] \tag{1.14}$$

[3] In some fields, such as aeronautics or celestial mechanics, the orientation is often referred to as the *attitude*.

The condition $[\mathcal{C}_{EB}][\mathcal{C}_{EB}]^T = [\mathcal{I}]$ characterizes an *orthogonal matrix* and is in fact equivalent to equations (1.7-1.12). Furthermore, the determinant of the direction cosine matrix is necessarily equal to $+1$ since both bases are right-handed. Matrix $[\mathcal{C}_{BE}]$ allows for the determination of the components (v_1, v_2, v_3) of any vector $\mathbf{V}$ on basis $(\hat{\mathbf{b}}_1, \hat{\mathbf{b}}_2, \hat{\mathbf{b}}_3)$ from its components (V_1, V_2, V_3) on basis $(\hat{\mathbf{e}}_1, \hat{\mathbf{e}}_2, \hat{\mathbf{e}}_3)$

$$\begin{pmatrix} v_1 \\ v_2 \\ v_3 \end{pmatrix} = [\mathcal{C}_{BE}] \begin{pmatrix} V_1 \\ V_2 \\ V_3 \end{pmatrix}$$

and conversely

$$\begin{pmatrix} V_1 \\ V_2 \\ V_3 \end{pmatrix} = [\mathcal{C}_{EB}] \begin{pmatrix} v_1 \\ v_2 \\ v_3 \end{pmatrix} = [\mathcal{C}_{BE}]^T \begin{pmatrix} v_1 \\ v_2 \\ v_3 \end{pmatrix}$$

where we have used $[\mathcal{C}_{EB}] = [\mathcal{C}_{BE}]^T$.

Direction cosine matrix $[\mathcal{C}_{EB}]$ also allows us to relate the matrix representations of any linear operator $\mathcal{L} : \mathbf{V} \mapsto \mathbf{W} = \mathcal{L}(\mathbf{V})$ in the bases of $\mathcal{E}$ and $\mathcal{B}$ as follows:

$$\begin{pmatrix} w_1 \\ w_2 \\ w_3 \end{pmatrix} = [\mathcal{C}_{BE}] \begin{pmatrix} W_1 \\ W_2 \\ W_3 \end{pmatrix} = [\mathcal{L}]_B \begin{pmatrix} v_1 \\ v_2 \\ v_3 \end{pmatrix} = [\mathcal{L}]_B [\mathcal{C}_{BE}] \begin{pmatrix} V_1 \\ V_2 \\ V_3 \end{pmatrix}$$

giving

$$\begin{pmatrix} W_1 \\ W_2 \\ W_3 \end{pmatrix} = [\mathcal{C}_{BE}]^T [\mathcal{L}]_B [\mathcal{C}_{BE}] \begin{pmatrix} V_1 \\ V_2 \\ V_3 \end{pmatrix}$$

This yields the following relationship between matrices $[\mathcal{L}]_B$ and $[\mathcal{L}]_E$ on bases $(\hat{\mathbf{b}}_1, \hat{\mathbf{b}}_2, \hat{\mathbf{b}}_3)$ and $(\hat{\mathbf{e}}_1, \hat{\mathbf{e}}_2, \hat{\mathbf{e}}_3)$:

$$[\mathcal{L}]_E = [\mathcal{C}_{EB}][\mathcal{L}]_B[\mathcal{C}_{EB}]^T \tag{1.15}$$

A special class of linear operators are rotations:

Definition 1.6 — Rotation. The *rotation* $\mathcal{R}_{EB}$ is the linear operator which maps basis $(\hat{\mathbf{e}}_1, \hat{\mathbf{e}}_2, \hat{\mathbf{e}}_3)$ of $\mathcal{E}$ to basis $(\hat{\mathbf{b}}_1, \hat{\mathbf{b}}_2, \hat{\mathbf{b}}_3)$ of $\mathcal{B}$:

$$\hat{\mathbf{b}}_i = \mathcal{R}_{EB}(\hat{\mathbf{e}}_i) \tag{1.16}$$

Remark 1. Determination of $\mathcal{R}_{EB}$ is tantamount to the determination of the orientation of $\mathcal{B}$ relative to $\mathcal{E}$.

Remark 2. The inverse of operator $\mathcal{R}_{EB}$ is $\mathcal{R}_{EB}^{-1} = \mathcal{R}_{BE}$.

Remark 3. The set of rotations is a *group* denoted $SO(3)$.

Remark 4. Rotations are not commutative: given two rotations $\mathcal{R}_1$ and $\mathcal{R}_2$, the rotation $\mathcal{R}_1 \circ \mathcal{R}_2$ is not, in general, equal to rotation $\mathcal{R}_2 \circ \mathcal{R}_1$.

Rotations and direction cosines are related according to the following result:

Corollary 1.1 The matrix representation of rotation $\mathcal{R}_{EB}$ on basis $(\hat{\mathbf{e}}_1, \hat{\mathbf{e}}_2, \hat{\mathbf{e}}_3)$ or basis $(\hat{\mathbf{b}}_1, \hat{\mathbf{b}}_2, \hat{\mathbf{b}}_3)$ is the direction cosine matrix $[\mathcal{C}_{EB}]$:

$$[\mathcal{R}_{EB}]_E = [\mathcal{C}_{EB}] = [\mathcal{R}_{EB}]_B \tag{1.17}$$

Furthermore, the rotations $\mathcal{R}_{EB}$ and $\mathcal{R}_{BE}$ are related by the equation

$$\mathcal{R}_{BE} = \mathcal{R}_{EB}^T \tag{1.18}$$

Proof. Matrix $[\mathcal{R}_{EB}]_E$ has ijth element $\mathcal{R}_{EB}(\hat{\mathbf{e}}_j) \cdot \hat{\mathbf{e}}_i = \hat{\mathbf{b}}_j \cdot \hat{\mathbf{e}}_i$ which is equal to c_{ij} by definition. The second equality is more surprising: the ijth element of the matrix $[\mathcal{R}_{EB}]_B$ is given by

$$\mathcal{R}_{EB}(\hat{\mathbf{b}}_j) \cdot \hat{\mathbf{b}}_i = \mathcal{R}_{EB}(c_{kj}\hat{\mathbf{e}}_k) \cdot \hat{\mathbf{b}}_i = c_{kj}\mathcal{R}_{EB}(\hat{\mathbf{e}}_k) \cdot \hat{\mathbf{b}}_i = c_{kj}\hat{\mathbf{b}}_k \cdot \hat{\mathbf{b}}_i = c_{kj}\delta_{ki} = c_{ij}$$

where we have used the summation convention for repeated indices. To show (1.18), we use (1.17):

$$[\mathcal{R}_{BE}]_E = [\mathcal{C}_{BE}] = [\mathcal{C}_{EB}]^T = [\mathcal{R}_{EB}]_E^T$$

■

It is of interest to consider composition of rotations: consider a third rigid body (or referential) $\mathcal{A}$ of basis $(\hat{\mathbf{a}}_1, \hat{\mathbf{a}}_2, \hat{\mathbf{a}}_3)$ and consider the rotations $\mathcal{R}_{EA}$ and $\mathcal{R}_{AB}$ which satisfy

$$\hat{\mathbf{a}}_i = \mathcal{R}_{EA}(\hat{\mathbf{e}}_i), \qquad \hat{\mathbf{b}}_i = \mathcal{R}_{AB}(\hat{\mathbf{a}}_i) \qquad (i = 1, 2, 3)$$

The rotation which maps $(\hat{\mathbf{e}}_1, \hat{\mathbf{e}}_2, \hat{\mathbf{e}}_3)$ to $(\hat{\mathbf{b}}_1, \hat{\mathbf{b}}_2, \hat{\mathbf{b}}_3)$ is given by

$$\mathcal{R}_{EB} = \mathcal{R}_{AB} \circ \mathcal{R}_{EA} \tag{1.19}$$

However, their matrix representations follow the rule

$$[\mathcal{R}_{EB}]_E = [\mathcal{R}_{EA}]_E [\mathcal{R}_{AB}]_A \tag{1.20}$$

Proof. Equation (1.20) is equivalent to

$$[\mathcal{C}_{EB}] = [\mathcal{C}_{EA}]\,[\mathcal{C}_{AB}]$$

in terms of direction cosine matrices, according to (1.17). To prove this result, consider an arbitrary vector $\mathbf{V}$ and denote by $[V]_E$, $[V]_A$ and $[V]_B$ the components of $\mathbf{V}$ on the basis of $\mathcal{E}$, $\mathcal{A}$ and $\mathcal{B}$, respectively: we know that $[V]_E = [\mathcal{C}_{EA}][V]_A$ and $[V]_A = [\mathcal{C}_{AB}][V]_B$ leading to

$$[V]_E = [\mathcal{C}_{EA}][\mathcal{C}_{AB}][V]_B = [\mathcal{C}_{EB}][V]_B$$

■

Example 1.1 Given the configuration shown below, find the matrix of the rotation which maps basis $(\hat{\mathbf{e}}_1, \hat{\mathbf{e}}_2, \hat{\mathbf{e}}_3)$ to basis $(\hat{\mathbf{b}}_1, \hat{\mathbf{b}}_2, \hat{\mathbf{b}}_3)$.

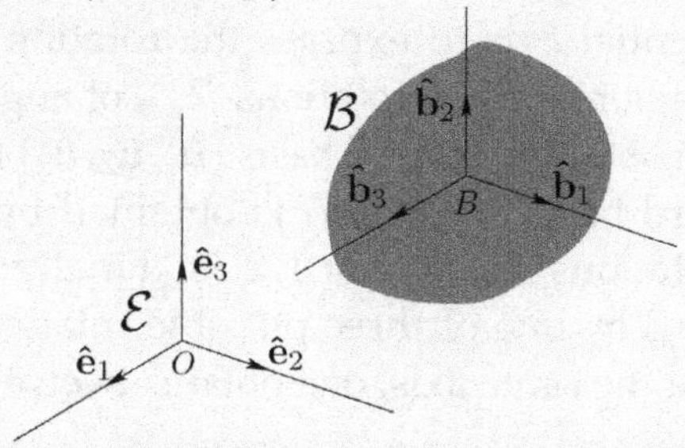

Conversely, find out if the following matrices correspond to rotations:

$$\begin{bmatrix} -1 & 0 & 0 \\ 0 & 1 & 0 \\ 0 & 0 & 1 \end{bmatrix} \qquad \frac{1}{4}\begin{bmatrix} 3 & 1 & \sqrt{6} \\ 1 & 3 & -\sqrt{6} \\ -\sqrt{6} & \sqrt{6} & 2 \end{bmatrix}$$

■

With $\mathcal{R}(\hat{\mathbf{e}}_1) = \hat{\mathbf{b}}_1 = \hat{\mathbf{e}}_2$, $\mathcal{R}(\hat{\mathbf{e}}_2) = \hat{\mathbf{b}}_2 = \hat{\mathbf{e}}_3$, and $\mathcal{R}(\hat{\mathbf{e}}_3) = \hat{\mathbf{b}}_3 = \hat{\mathbf{e}}_1$, we immediately obtain

$$[\mathcal{R}]_E = \begin{bmatrix} 0 & 0 & 1 \\ 1 & 0 & 0 \\ 0 & 1 & 0 \end{bmatrix}_E$$

For the first given matrix, the set $(\hat{\mathbf{b}}_1, \hat{\mathbf{b}}_2, \hat{\mathbf{b}}_3) = (-\hat{\mathbf{e}}_1, \hat{\mathbf{e}}_2, \hat{\mathbf{e}}_3)$ forms a basis of orthonormal unit vectors. However, it is not right-handed since $\hat{\mathbf{b}}_1 \times \hat{\mathbf{b}}_2 = -\hat{\mathbf{b}}_3$: this is not a rotation matrix. For the second matrix, it is easy to verify that $\hat{\mathbf{b}}_i \cdot \hat{\mathbf{b}}_j = \delta_{ij}$ and that $\hat{\mathbf{b}}_1 \times \hat{\mathbf{b}}_2 = \hat{\mathbf{b}}_3$: this is a rotation matrix. ■

Example 1.2 Given θ $(0 \leq \theta < 2\pi)$, consider the rotation, denoted $\mathcal{R}_{\theta,\hat{\mathbf{e}}_3}$, of angle θ about unit vector $\hat{\mathbf{e}}_3$. Construct the matrix representation $\left[\mathcal{R}_{\theta,\hat{\mathbf{e}}_3}\right]_E$ of $\mathcal{R}_{\theta,\hat{\mathbf{e}}_3}$.

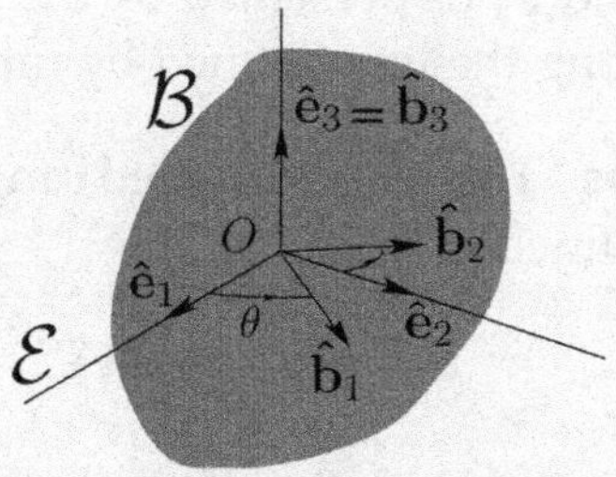

■

With $\hat{\mathbf{b}}_1 = \cos\theta \hat{\mathbf{e}}_1 + \sin\theta \hat{\mathbf{e}}_2$, $\hat{\mathbf{b}}_2 = -\sin\theta \hat{\mathbf{e}}_1 + \cos\theta \hat{\mathbf{e}}_2$, and $\hat{\mathbf{b}}_3 = \hat{\mathbf{e}}_3$, we find

$$[\mathcal{R}_{\theta,\hat{\mathbf{e}}_3}]_E = \begin{bmatrix} \cos\theta & -\sin\theta & 0 \\ \sin\theta & \cos\theta & 0 \\ 0 & 0 & 1 \end{bmatrix}_E$$

■

Although direction cosines naturally define rotations, they are not convenient in practice due to their redundancy.

1.4 Euler Angle Sequences

A convenient way to parametrize the orientation of basis $(\hat{\mathbf{b}}_1, \hat{\mathbf{b}}_2, \hat{\mathbf{b}}_3)$ of body $\mathcal{B}$ relative to basis $(\hat{\mathbf{e}}_1, \hat{\mathbf{e}}_2, \hat{\mathbf{e}}_3)$ of referential $\mathcal{E}$ is to express the rotation $\mathcal{R}_{EB}$ which maps $(\hat{\mathbf{e}}_1, \hat{\mathbf{e}}_2, \hat{\mathbf{e}}_3)$ to $(\hat{\mathbf{b}}_1, \hat{\mathbf{b}}_2, \hat{\mathbf{b}}_3)$ as the composition of three rotations $\mathcal{R}_{\alpha,\hat{\mathbf{u}}}$ of angle α about unit vector $\hat{\mathbf{u}}$. Starting with basis $(\hat{\mathbf{e}}_1, \hat{\mathbf{e}}_2, \hat{\mathbf{e}}_3)$, one obtains a second basis $(\hat{\mathbf{u}}_1, \hat{\mathbf{u}}_2, \hat{\mathbf{u}}_3)$ by one of three possible rotations $\mathcal{R}_{\alpha_i,\hat{\mathbf{e}}_i}$ $(i = 1,2,3)$. A third basis $(\hat{\mathbf{v}}_1, \hat{\mathbf{v}}_2, \hat{\mathbf{v}}_3)$ is obtained by the mapping of $(\hat{\mathbf{u}}_1, \hat{\mathbf{u}}_2, \hat{\mathbf{u}}_3)$ by one of three possible rotations $\mathcal{R}_{\beta_i,\hat{\mathbf{u}}_i}$ $(i = 1,2,3)$. Finally basis $(\hat{\mathbf{b}}_1, \hat{\mathbf{b}}_2, \hat{\mathbf{b}}_3)$ is obtained by the mapping of $(\hat{\mathbf{v}}_1, \hat{\mathbf{v}}_2, \hat{\mathbf{v}}_3)$ by one of three possible rotations $\mathcal{R}_{\gamma_i,\hat{\mathbf{v}}_i}$ $(i = 1,2,3)$. Ruling out successive rotations about the same axis, one obtains twelve possible transformations known as *Euler angle sequences.*

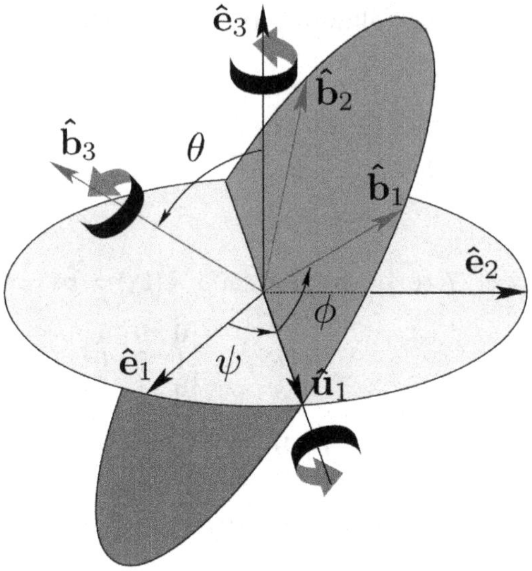

Figure 1.5

One such sequence, known as the *zxz*-convention, is defined by considering the two planes perpendicular to $\hat{\mathbf{e}}_3$ and $\hat{\mathbf{b}}_3$ (represented by the two circles in Figure 1.5). In general, these two planes intersect along the line defined by unit vector $\hat{\mathbf{u}}_1$.

Definition 1.7 — Euler Angles. The three oriented[4] angles ψ (*precession angle*), θ (*nutation angle*) and ϕ (*spin angle*) defined as

$$\psi = (\hat{\mathbf{e}}_1, \hat{\mathbf{u}}_1)$$

$$\theta = (\hat{\mathbf{e}}_3, \hat{\mathbf{b}}_3)$$

$$\phi = (\hat{\mathbf{u}}_1, \hat{\mathbf{b}}_1)$$

are known as *Euler angles.* The rotation $\mathcal{R}_{EB}$ which maps basis $(\hat{\mathbf{e}}_1, \hat{\mathbf{e}}_2, \hat{\mathbf{e}}_3)$ to basis $(\hat{\mathbf{b}}_1, \hat{\mathbf{b}}_2, \hat{\mathbf{b}}_3)$ is obtained as $\mathcal{R}_{\phi,\hat{\mathbf{b}}_3} \circ \mathcal{R}_{\theta,\hat{\mathbf{u}}_1} \circ \mathcal{R}_{\psi,\hat{\mathbf{e}}_3}$:

$$(\hat{\mathbf{e}}_1, \hat{\mathbf{e}}_2, \hat{\mathbf{e}}_3) \xrightarrow{\mathcal{R}_{\psi,\hat{\mathbf{e}}_3}} (\hat{\mathbf{u}}_1, \hat{\mathbf{u}}_2, \hat{\mathbf{u}}_3) \xrightarrow{\mathcal{R}_{\theta,\hat{\mathbf{u}}_1}} (\hat{\mathbf{v}}_1, \hat{\mathbf{v}}_2, \hat{\mathbf{v}}_3) \xrightarrow{\mathcal{R}_{\phi,\hat{\mathbf{b}}_3}} (\hat{\mathbf{b}}_1, \hat{\mathbf{b}}_2, \hat{\mathbf{b}}_3) \tag{1.21}$$

with $\hat{\mathbf{u}}_3 = \hat{\mathbf{e}}_3$, $\hat{\mathbf{v}}_1 = \hat{\mathbf{u}}_1$ and $\hat{\mathbf{b}}_3 = \hat{\mathbf{v}}_3$.

This sequence of transformations can be more clearly displayed on the following diagrams:

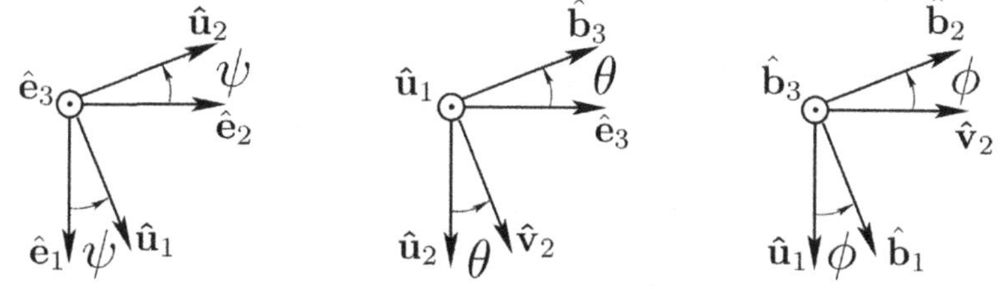

Figure 1.6

SPECIAL CASE. When the axes defined by unit vectors $\hat{\mathbf{e}}_3$ and $\hat{\mathbf{b}}_3$ coincide, i.e. whenever $\hat{\mathbf{b}}_3 = \pm\hat{\mathbf{e}}_3$, then there is an indetermination in the definition of unit vector $\hat{\mathbf{u}}_1$ and angles ψ and ϕ. One can choose any unit vector $\hat{\mathbf{u}}_1$ perpendicular to $\hat{\mathbf{e}}_3$. Then if $\hat{\mathbf{b}}_3 = \hat{\mathbf{e}}_3$, angle θ is equal to zero, the angles ψ and ϕ must satisfy $(\hat{\mathbf{e}}_1, \hat{\mathbf{b}}_1) = \psi + \phi$, but *cannot be specified uniquely* (if $\hat{\mathbf{b}}_3 = -\hat{\mathbf{e}}_3$, then $\theta = \pi$ and $(\hat{\mathbf{e}}_1, \hat{\mathbf{b}}_1) = \psi - \phi$). Due to this indetermination, Euler angles are precluded in certain applications, such as in satellite attitude dynamics.

DIRECTION COSINE MATRIX. The direction cosines of basis $(\hat{\mathbf{b}}_1, \hat{\mathbf{b}}_2, \hat{\mathbf{b}}_3)$ on basis $(\hat{\mathbf{e}}_1, \hat{\mathbf{e}}_2, \hat{\mathbf{e}}_3)$ can easily be found in terms of Euler angles by expressing each vector $\hat{\mathbf{b}}_j$ on basis $(\hat{\mathbf{e}}_1, \hat{\mathbf{e}}_2, \hat{\mathbf{e}}_3)$:

$$\begin{aligned}
\hat{\mathbf{b}}_1 &= c_\phi \hat{\mathbf{u}}_1 + s_\phi \hat{\mathbf{v}}_2 = c_\phi(c_\psi \hat{\mathbf{e}}_1 + s_\psi \hat{\mathbf{e}}_2) + s_\phi(c_\theta \hat{\mathbf{u}}_2 + s_\theta \hat{\mathbf{e}}_3) \\
&= (c_\phi c_\psi - s_\phi c_\theta s_\psi)\hat{\mathbf{e}}_1 + (c_\phi s_\psi + s_\phi c_\theta c_\psi)\hat{\mathbf{e}}_2 + s_\phi s_\theta \hat{\mathbf{e}}_3 \\
\hat{\mathbf{b}}_2 &= -s_\phi \hat{\mathbf{u}}_1 + c_\phi \hat{\mathbf{v}}_2 \\
&= (-s_\phi c_\psi - c_\phi c_\theta s_\psi)\hat{\mathbf{e}}_1 + (-s_\phi s_\psi + c_\phi c_\theta c_\psi)\hat{\mathbf{e}}_2 + c_\phi s_\theta \hat{\mathbf{e}}_3 \\
\hat{\mathbf{b}}_3 &= -s_\theta \hat{\mathbf{u}}_2 + c_\theta \hat{\mathbf{e}}_3 \\
&= s_\psi s_\theta \hat{\mathbf{e}}_1 - c_\psi s_\theta \hat{\mathbf{e}}_2 + c_\theta \hat{\mathbf{e}}_3
\end{aligned}$$

using the notation $c_\theta = \cos\theta$, $s_\theta = \sin\theta$, etc. This leads to the direction cosine matrix

$$[\mathcal{C}_{EB}] = [\hat{\mathbf{e}}_i \cdot \hat{\mathbf{b}}_j] = \begin{bmatrix} c_\phi c_\psi - s_\phi c_\theta s_\psi & -s_\phi c_\psi - c_\phi c_\theta s_\psi & s_\psi s_\theta \\ c_\phi s_\psi + s_\phi c_\theta c_\psi & -s_\phi s_\psi + c_\phi c_\theta c_\psi & -c_\psi s_\theta \\ s_\phi s_\theta & c_\phi s_\theta & c_\theta \end{bmatrix}$$

Recall that matrix $[\mathcal{C}_{EB}] = [\mathcal{C}_{EU}]\,[\mathcal{C}_{UV}]\,[\mathcal{C}_{VB}]$ represents the rotation $\mathcal{R}_{EB} = \mathcal{R}_{\phi,\hat{\mathbf{b}}_3} \circ \mathcal{R}_{\theta,\hat{\mathbf{u}}_1} \circ \mathcal{R}_{\psi,\hat{\mathbf{e}}_3}$ on basis $(\hat{\mathbf{b}}_1, \hat{\mathbf{b}}_2, \hat{\mathbf{b}}_3)$ or basis $(\hat{\mathbf{e}}_1, \hat{\mathbf{e}}_2, \hat{\mathbf{e}}_3)$. It can be shown that this matrix only depends on the sum $\psi + \phi$ for $\theta = 0$. Hence, the mapping $(\psi, \theta, \phi) \to [\mathcal{C}_{EB}]$ is singular for $\theta = 0$ (or $\theta = \pi$).

BRYANT (CARDAN) ANGLES. Whenever the referential $\mathcal{E}$ is attached to Earth with $\hat{\mathbf{e}}_3$ directed along the vertical upward, Euler angles of the *zxz*-convention are inadequate in applications (such as in aerospace engineering) for which angle θ crosses the values $\theta = 0$ or $\theta = \pi$ (in

[4]Here the notation $\theta = (\hat{\mathbf{u}}, \hat{\mathbf{v}})$ stands for oriented angle θ, that is, angle θ is measured positively according to the right-hand rule, by pointing the right hand's thumb in the direction of $\hat{\mathbf{u}} \times \hat{\mathbf{v}}$.

which case $\hat{\mathbf{b}}_3$ is also directed along the vertical). These angles can be replaced by the angles ψ, θ and ϕ defined as follows:

$$(\hat{\mathbf{e}}_1, \hat{\mathbf{e}}_2, \hat{\mathbf{e}}_3) \xrightarrow{\mathcal{R}_{\psi,\hat{\mathbf{e}}_3}} (\hat{\mathbf{u}}_1, \hat{\mathbf{u}}_2, \hat{\mathbf{e}}_3) \xrightarrow{\mathcal{R}_{\theta,\hat{\mathbf{u}}_2}} (\hat{\mathbf{v}}_1 = \hat{\mathbf{b}}_1, \hat{\mathbf{v}}_2 = \hat{\mathbf{u}}_2, \hat{\mathbf{v}}_3) \xrightarrow{\mathcal{R}_{\phi,\hat{\mathbf{b}}_1}} (\hat{\mathbf{b}}_1, \hat{\mathbf{b}}_2, \hat{\mathbf{b}}_3) \tag{1.22}$$

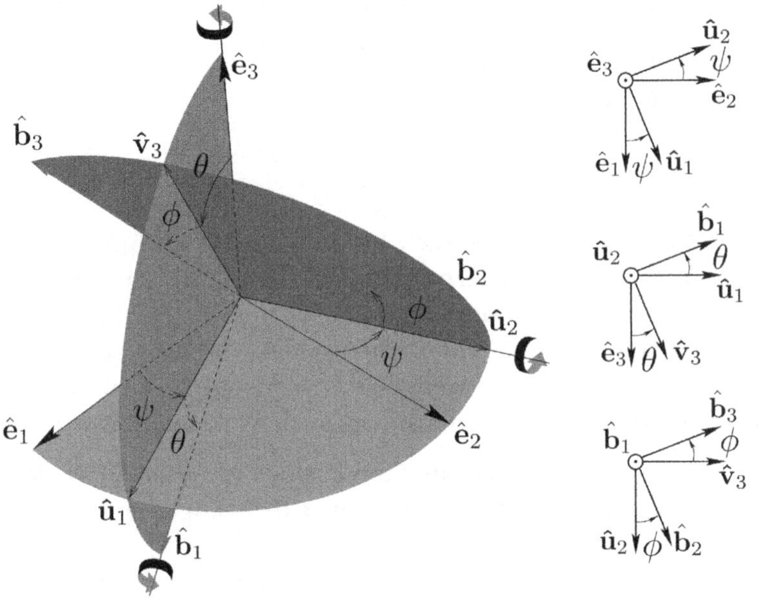

Figure 1.7

This sequence is referred to as the *zyx*-convention, or the *yaw-pitch-roll* convention. The corresponding angles are referred to as Bryant (or Cardan) angles. See Figure 1.7. The rotation matrix $[\mathcal{R}_{EB}]_E = [\mathcal{R}_{EB}]_B = [\mathcal{C}_{EB}]$ takes the expression

$$\begin{aligned}
[\mathcal{C}_{EB}] &= [\mathcal{C}_{EU}][\mathcal{C}_{UV}][\mathcal{C}_{VB}] = \begin{pmatrix} c_\psi & -s_\psi & 0 \\ s_\psi & c_\psi & 0 \\ 0 & 0 & 1 \end{pmatrix} \begin{pmatrix} c_\theta & 0 & s_\theta \\ 0 & 1 & 0 \\ -s_\theta & 0 & c_\theta \end{pmatrix} \begin{pmatrix} 1 & 0 & 0 \\ 0 & c_\phi & -s_\phi \\ 0 & s_\phi & c_\phi \end{pmatrix} \\
&= \begin{pmatrix} c_\psi c_\theta & c_\psi s_\theta s_\phi - s_\psi c_\phi & c_\psi s_\theta c_\phi + s_\psi s_\phi \\ s_\psi c_\theta & s_\psi s_\theta s_\phi + c_\psi c_\phi & s_\psi s_\theta c_\phi - c_\psi s_\phi \\ -s_\theta & c_\theta s_\phi & c_\theta c_\phi \end{pmatrix}
\end{aligned}$$

The angles ψ and ϕ are indeterminate for the configurations $\theta = \pm\pi/2$.

1.5 Equivalent Angle/Axis of Rotation

Despite their simple physical interpretations, the use of Euler sequences defined in Section 1.4 leads to significant difficulties for trajectories with large angle variations across singularities. Another drawback is the appearance of nonlinearities in the equations of motion and the inevitable numerical difficulties which ensue during integration. The use of rotation matrix expressed in terms of the nine direction cosines presented in Section 1.3 has the advantage of resolving the indetermination of Euler sequences, but has the disadvantage of having to account for six (nonlinear) relationships between these quantities.

An alternative method consists of representing any rotation in terms of its so-called Euler parameters. Euler showed that an arbitrary composition of rotations can be realized by a single rotation $\mathcal{R}_{\alpha,\hat{\mathbf{u}}}$ of angle $\alpha \in [0, 2\pi)$ about a unit vector $\hat{\mathbf{u}}$. The parameters $(\alpha, \hat{\mathbf{u}})$ are called Euler parameters or the *equivalent angle and axis* of the rotation. See Figure 1.8.

First, we give a formal definition of operator $\mathcal{R}_{\alpha,\hat{\mathbf{u}}}$:

Definition 1.8 Given a unit vector $\hat{\mathbf{u}}$, there always exist two unit vectors $(\hat{\mathbf{v}}, \hat{\mathbf{w}})$ such that $(\hat{\mathbf{u}}, \hat{\mathbf{v}}, \hat{\mathbf{w}})$ forms a orthonormal, right-handed basis. Then, given $\alpha \in \mathbb{R}$, the rotation of angle α about $\hat{\mathbf{u}}$ is the linear operator $\mathcal{R}_{\alpha,\hat{\mathbf{u}}}$ such that:

$$\mathcal{R}_{\alpha,\hat{\mathbf{u}}}(\hat{\mathbf{u}}) = \hat{\mathbf{u}}, \quad \mathcal{R}_{\alpha,\hat{\mathbf{u}}}(\hat{\mathbf{v}}) = \cos\alpha\hat{\mathbf{v}} + \sin\alpha\hat{\mathbf{w}}, \quad \mathcal{R}_{\alpha,\hat{\mathbf{u}}}(\hat{\mathbf{w}}) = -\sin\alpha\hat{\mathbf{v}} + \cos\alpha\hat{\mathbf{w}} \tag{1.23}$$

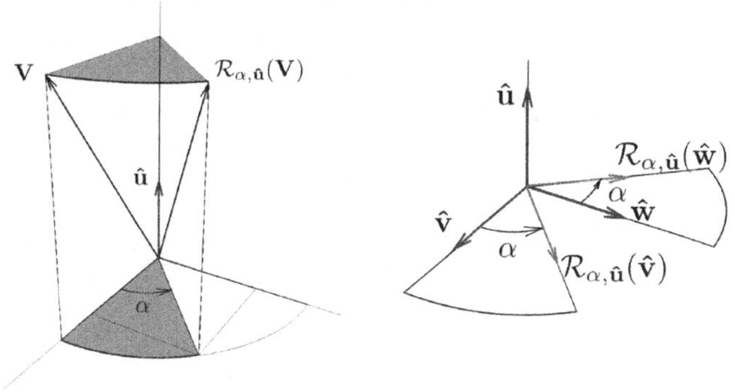

Figure 1.8

PROPERTIES:

1. The rotation $\mathcal{R}_{\alpha,\hat{\mathbf{u}}}$ does not depend on the choice of $\hat{\mathbf{v}}$ and $\hat{\mathbf{w}}$ which form basis $(\hat{\mathbf{u}}, \hat{\mathbf{v}}, \hat{\mathbf{w}})$.
2. The rotations $\mathcal{R}_{\alpha,\hat{\mathbf{u}}}$ and $\mathcal{R}_{-\alpha,-\hat{\mathbf{u}}}$ coincide.
3. The rotations of angle α and $\alpha + 2n\pi$ ($n \in \mathbb{Z}$) about unit vector $\hat{\mathbf{u}}$ coincide.
4. $\mathcal{R}_{0,\hat{\mathbf{u}}} = \mathcal{I}$. $\mathcal{R}_{\alpha,\hat{\mathbf{u}}} \circ \mathcal{R}_{\beta,\hat{\mathbf{u}}} = \mathcal{R}_{\alpha+\beta,\hat{\mathbf{u}}}$ and $\mathcal{R}_{\alpha,\hat{\mathbf{u}}}^{-1} = \mathcal{R}_{-\alpha,\hat{\mathbf{u}}}$.
5. The matrix representation of $\mathcal{R}_{\alpha,\hat{\mathbf{u}}}$ on basis $(\hat{\mathbf{u}}, \hat{\mathbf{v}}, \hat{\mathbf{w}})$ is given by

$$\begin{bmatrix} 1 & 0 & 0 \\ 0 & \cos\alpha & -\sin\alpha \\ 0 & \sin\alpha & \cos\alpha \end{bmatrix}_{(\hat{\mathbf{u}},\hat{\mathbf{v}},\hat{\mathbf{w}})}$$

This matrix expression of $\mathcal{R}_{\alpha,\hat{\mathbf{u}}}$ is not useful in practice. It would be much more practical to obtain a basis-free and coordinate-free expression of $\mathcal{R}_{\alpha,\hat{\mathbf{u}}}$. This is provided by **Rodrigues formula** which gives an intrinsic representation of rotations:

Theorem 1.1 — **Rodrigues formula.** The rotation $\mathcal{R}_{\alpha,\hat{\mathbf{u}}}$ of angle α about unit vector $\hat{\mathbf{u}}$ can be represented in the form

$$\mathcal{R}_{\alpha,\hat{\mathbf{u}}}(\mathbf{V}) = \mathbf{V} + \sin\alpha\hat{\mathbf{u}} \times \mathbf{V} + (1 - \cos\alpha)\hat{\mathbf{u}} \times (\hat{\mathbf{u}} \times \mathbf{V}) \tag{1.24}$$

for any vector $\mathbf{V}$.

Proof. We can always write an arbitrary vector $\mathbf{V}$ as a sum of a vector collinear to $\hat{\mathbf{u}}$ and a vector normal to $\hat{\mathbf{u}}$:

$$\mathbf{V} = \lambda\hat{\mathbf{u}} + \mathbf{V}^{\perp}, \qquad \mathbf{V}^{\perp}\cdot\hat{\mathbf{u}} = 0$$

with $\lambda = \hat{\mathbf{u}}\cdot\mathbf{V}$. The rotation operator $\mathcal{R}_{\alpha,\hat{\mathbf{u}}}$ satisfies

$$\mathcal{R}_{\alpha,\hat{\mathbf{u}}}(\hat{\mathbf{u}}) = \hat{\mathbf{u}}, \qquad \mathcal{R}_{\alpha,\hat{\mathbf{u}}}(\mathbf{V}^{\perp}) = \cos\alpha\mathbf{V}^{\perp} + \sin\alpha\hat{\mathbf{u}}\times\mathbf{V}^{\perp}$$

Hence the mapping of $\mathbf{V}$ by $\mathcal{R}_{\alpha,\hat{\mathbf{u}}}$ is given by

$$\mathcal{R}_{\alpha,\hat{\mathbf{u}}}(\mathbf{V}) = \lambda\hat{\mathbf{u}} + \cos\alpha\mathbf{V}^{\perp} + \sin\alpha\hat{\mathbf{u}}\times\mathbf{V}^{\perp}$$

If we then replace $\mathbf{V}^{\perp}$ by $\mathbf{V} - \lambda\hat{\mathbf{u}}$, we obtain

$$\begin{aligned}\mathcal{R}_{\alpha,\hat{\mathbf{u}}}(\mathbf{V}) &= \lambda\hat{\mathbf{u}} + \cos\alpha(\mathbf{V}-\lambda\hat{\mathbf{u}}) + \sin\alpha\hat{\mathbf{u}}\times(\mathbf{V}-\lambda\hat{\mathbf{u}})\\ &= (1-\cos\alpha)(\hat{\mathbf{u}}\cdot\mathbf{V})\hat{\mathbf{u}} + \cos\alpha\mathbf{V} + \sin\alpha\hat{\mathbf{u}}\times\mathbf{V}\end{aligned}$$

Finally if we use the identity $\hat{\mathbf{u}}\times(\hat{\mathbf{u}}\times\mathbf{V}) = (\hat{\mathbf{u}}\cdot\mathbf{V})\hat{\mathbf{u}} - \mathbf{V}$, we obtain Rodrigues formula (1.24). ∎

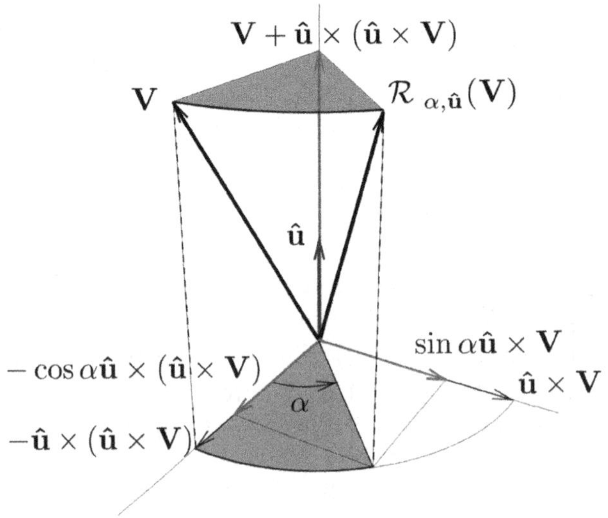

Figure 1.9

A geometric interpretation of Rodrigues formula is shown in Figure 1.9: by considering the projections of vector $\mathbf{V}$ on $\hat{\mathbf{u}}$ and on a plane perpendicular to $\hat{\mathbf{u}}$, vector $\mathcal{R}_{\alpha,\hat{\mathbf{u}}}(\mathbf{V})$ can be seen to be the sum of three contributions:

1. a contribution along $\hat{\mathbf{u}}$: $(\mathbf{V}\cdot\hat{\mathbf{u}})\hat{\mathbf{u}} = \mathbf{V} + \hat{\mathbf{u}}\times(\hat{\mathbf{u}}\times\mathbf{V})$,
2. a contribution along vector $-\hat{\mathbf{u}}\times(\hat{\mathbf{u}}\times\mathbf{V})$: $-\cos\alpha\hat{\mathbf{u}}\times(\hat{\mathbf{u}}\times\mathbf{V})$
3. a contribution along vector $\hat{\mathbf{u}}\times\mathbf{V}$: $\sin\alpha\hat{\mathbf{u}}\times\mathbf{V}$.

Remark 5. The axis of rotation $\mathcal{R}$ can be found by solving for the vectors which remain invariant by $\mathcal{R}$, that is, satisfying $\mathcal{R}(\mathbf{V}) = \mathbf{V}$.

Remark 6. Once the unit vector $\hat{\mathbf{u}}$ of the axis has been determined, the angle α of rotation $\mathcal{R}$

can be found from a unit vector $\hat{\mathbf{v}}$ normal to $\hat{\mathbf{u}}$ and its mapping by $\mathcal{R}$:

$$\cos\alpha = \hat{\mathbf{v}} \cdot \mathcal{R}(\hat{\mathbf{v}}), \qquad \sin\alpha = \hat{\mathbf{u}} \cdot (\hat{\mathbf{v}} \times \mathcal{R}(\hat{\mathbf{v}})) \tag{1.25}$$

as shown by Rodrigues formula.

This is illustrated with the following examples.

Example 1.3 Consider the operator whose matrix in basis $(\hat{\mathbf{e}}_1, \hat{\mathbf{e}}_2, \hat{\mathbf{e}}_3)$ of $\mathcal{E}$ is given by

$$[\mathcal{L}]_E = \frac{1}{9}\begin{pmatrix} 4 & 1 & -8 \\ 7 & 4 & 4 \\ 4 & -8 & 1 \end{pmatrix}$$

a. Show that $[\mathcal{L}]_E$ is the matrix of a rotation.
b. Find the equivalent angle/axis of this rotation. ■

a. It is easy to verify that $[\mathcal{L}]_E$ is an orthogonal matrix, that is, $[\mathcal{L}]_E[\mathcal{L}]_E^T = [\mathcal{I}]$. It is equivalent to show that the column vectors $(\mathbf{c}_1, \mathbf{c}_2, \mathbf{c}_3)$ of $[\mathcal{L}]_E$ are unit vectors and mutually orthogonal and that $\mathbf{c}_3 = \mathbf{c}_1 \times \mathbf{c}_2$. Hence operator $\mathcal{L}$ is necessarily a rotation.
b. To find the axis of the rotation we look for the solution of $\mathcal{L}(\mathbf{V}) = \mathbf{V}$ (the eigenspace corresponding to eigenvalue $+1$), that is, we solve the equations

$$\begin{cases} 4x_1 + x_2 - 8x_3 = 9x_1 \\ 7x_1 + 4x_2 + 4x_3 = 9x_2 \\ 4x_1 - 8x_2 + x_3 = 9x_3 \end{cases}$$

Simplifications yield two independent equations

$$\begin{cases} x_1 + 2x_3 = 0 \\ x_1 - x_2 = 0 \end{cases}$$

This is the line directed along unit vector

$$\hat{\mathbf{u}} = \frac{2}{3}\hat{\mathbf{e}}_1 + \frac{2}{3}\hat{\mathbf{e}}_2 - \frac{1}{3}\hat{\mathbf{e}}_3$$

To find the unique angle α corresponding to this choice of $\hat{\mathbf{u}}$, we identify a unit vector normal to $\hat{\mathbf{u}}$: we choose $\hat{\mathbf{v}} = \frac{1}{\sqrt{2}}(\hat{\mathbf{e}}_1 - \hat{\mathbf{e}}_2)$ (it satisfies $\hat{\mathbf{u}} \cdot \hat{\mathbf{v}} = 0$). Angle α can be determined from

$$\cos\alpha = \hat{\mathbf{v}} \cdot \mathcal{R}(\hat{\mathbf{v}}) = 0, \qquad \sin\alpha = (\hat{\mathbf{v}}, \mathcal{R}(\hat{\mathbf{v}}), \hat{\mathbf{u}}) = -1$$

(Note that $\cos\alpha$ can also be found from the trace of $[\mathcal{L}]_E$: $2\cos\alpha + 1 = \mathrm{tr}([\mathcal{L}]_E) = 1$). We find $\alpha = \frac{3\pi}{2}$. In conclusion, $\mathcal{L} = \mathcal{R}_{\frac{3\pi}{2},\hat{\mathbf{u}}}$. ■

Example 1.4 Find the matrix of the rotation $\mathcal{R}_{\pi,\hat{\mathbf{u}}}$ with $\hat{\mathbf{u}} = -\frac{1}{3}\hat{\mathbf{e}}_1 + \frac{2}{3}\hat{\mathbf{e}}_2 - \frac{2}{3}\hat{\mathbf{e}}_3$ on basis $(\hat{\mathbf{e}}_1, \hat{\mathbf{e}}_2, \hat{\mathbf{e}}_3)$. ■

Method 1: We use Rodrigues formula for $\mathbf{V} = \hat{\mathbf{e}}_1, \hat{\mathbf{e}}_2, \hat{\mathbf{e}}_2$ with $\alpha = \pi$: this will give the column vectors of matrix $[\mathcal{R}_{\pi,\hat{\mathbf{u}}}]_E$:

$$\mathcal{R}_{\pi,\hat{\mathbf{u}}}(\hat{\mathbf{e}}_1) = \hat{\mathbf{e}}_1 + 2\hat{\mathbf{u}} \times (\hat{\mathbf{u}} \times \hat{\mathbf{e}}_1) = (-7\hat{\mathbf{e}}_1 - 4\hat{\mathbf{e}}_2 + 4\hat{\mathbf{e}}_3)/9$$

$$\mathcal{R}_{\pi,\hat{\mathbf{u}}}(\hat{\mathbf{e}}_2) = \hat{\mathbf{e}}_2 + 2\hat{\mathbf{u}} \times (\hat{\mathbf{u}} \times \hat{\mathbf{e}}_2) = (-4\hat{\mathbf{e}}_1 - \hat{\mathbf{e}}_2 - 8\hat{\mathbf{e}}_3)/9$$

$$\mathcal{R}_{\pi,\hat{\mathbf{u}}}(\hat{\mathbf{e}}_3) = \hat{\mathbf{e}}_3 + 2\hat{\mathbf{u}} \times (\hat{\mathbf{u}} \times \hat{\mathbf{e}}_3) = (4\hat{\mathbf{e}}_1 - 8\hat{\mathbf{e}}_2 - \hat{\mathbf{e}}_3)/9$$

This gives the matrix

$$[\mathcal{R}_{\pi,\hat{\mathbf{u}}}]_E = \frac{1}{9}\begin{pmatrix} -7 & -4 & 4 \\ -4 & -1 & -8 \\ 4 & -8 & -1 \end{pmatrix}$$

Method 2: We can find the matrix of $\mathcal{R}_{\pi,\hat{\mathbf{u}}}$ by exploiting the fact that for $\alpha = \pi$, we have the properties that $\mathbf{V} + \mathcal{R}_{\pi,\hat{\mathbf{u}}}(\mathbf{V})$ is collinear to $\hat{\mathbf{u}}$ and $\mathbf{V} - \mathcal{R}_{\pi,\hat{\mathbf{u}}}(\mathbf{V})$ is normal to $\hat{\mathbf{u}}$: denoting $\mathbf{V} = x_1\hat{\mathbf{e}}_1 + x_2\hat{\mathbf{e}}_2 + x_3\hat{\mathbf{e}}_3$ and $\mathcal{R}_{\pi,\hat{\mathbf{u}}}(\mathbf{V}) = x_1'\hat{\mathbf{e}}_1 + x_2'\hat{\mathbf{e}}_2 + x_3'\hat{\mathbf{e}}_3$ we find four equations by expressing the conditions $\mathbf{V} + \mathcal{R}_{\pi,\hat{\mathbf{u}}}(\mathbf{V}) = \lambda\hat{\mathbf{u}}$ ($\lambda \in \mathbb{R}$) and $(\mathbf{V} - \mathcal{R}_{\pi,\hat{\mathbf{u}}}(\mathbf{V})) \cdot \hat{\mathbf{u}} = 0$

$$\begin{cases} x_1 + x_1' = -\lambda \\ x_2 + x_2' = 2\lambda \\ x_3 + x_3' = -2\lambda \\ (x_1 - x_1') - 2(x_2 - x_2') + 2(x_3 - x_3') = 0 \end{cases}$$

We solve for λ:

$$9\lambda = -2x_1 + 4x_2 - 4x_3$$

This expression can then be used to find (x_1', x_2', x_3') vs (x_1, x_2, x_3):

$$\begin{cases} 9x_1' = -7x_1 - 4x_2 + 4x_3 \\ 9x_2' = -4x_1 - x_2 - 8x_3 \\ 9x_3' = 4x_1 - 8x_2 - x_3 \end{cases}$$

We find the same matrix as with method 1. ∎

It is straightforward to obtain a matrix representation of $\mathcal{R}_{\alpha,\hat{\mathbf{u}}}$ on an arbitrary basis $(\hat{\mathbf{a}}_1, \hat{\mathbf{a}}_2, \hat{\mathbf{a}}_3)$: denoting $\hat{\mathbf{u}} = u_1\hat{\mathbf{a}}_1 + u_2\hat{\mathbf{a}}_2 + u_3\hat{\mathbf{a}}_3$, we find

$$\begin{aligned} [\mathcal{R}_{\alpha,\hat{\mathbf{u}}}]_A &= \begin{bmatrix} 1 & 0 & 0 \\ 0 & 1 & 0 \\ 0 & 0 & 1 \end{bmatrix} + \sin\alpha \begin{bmatrix} 0 & -u_3 & u_2 \\ u_3 & 0 & -u_1 \\ -u_2 & u_1 & 0 \end{bmatrix} + (1-\cos\alpha) \begin{bmatrix} u_1^2 - 1 & u_1u_2 & u_1u_3 \\ u_1u_2 & u_2^2 - 1 & u_2u_3 \\ u_1u_3 & u_2u_3 & u_3^2 - 1 \end{bmatrix} \\ &= \begin{bmatrix} \cos\alpha + (1-\cos\alpha)u_1^2 & (1-\cos\alpha)u_1u_2 - u_3\sin\alpha & (1-\cos\alpha)u_1u_3 + u_2\sin\alpha \\ (1-\cos\alpha)u_1u_2 + u_3\sin\alpha & \cos\alpha + (1-\cos\alpha)u_2^2 & (1-\cos\alpha)u_2u_3 - u_1\sin\alpha \\ (1-\cos\alpha)u_1u_3 - u_2\sin\alpha & (1-\cos\alpha)u_2u_3 + u_1\sin\alpha & \cos\alpha + (1-\cos\alpha)u_3^2 \end{bmatrix} \end{aligned}$$

Denoting the operator $\mathcal{U} : \mathbf{V} \mapsto \hat{\mathbf{u}} \times \mathbf{V}$ and $\mathcal{I} : \mathbf{V} \mapsto \mathbf{V}$ the identity operator, we note from this result that $\mathcal{I} + (1-\cos\alpha)\mathcal{U}^2$ is the symmetric part of operator $\mathcal{R}_{\alpha,\hat{\mathbf{u}}}$ and that $(\sin\alpha)\mathcal{U}$ represents its skew-symmetric part.

Conversely, given a rotation $\mathcal{R}$, it is of interest to find its equivalent representation in terms of its Euler parameters $(\alpha, \hat{\mathbf{u}})$. Since $\mathcal{R}$ can always be written as the sum of its symmetric part $\frac{1}{2}(\mathcal{R} + \mathcal{R}^T)$ and skew-symmetric part $\frac{1}{2}(\mathcal{R} - \mathcal{R}^T)$, we can relate $\mathcal{R}$ to its equivalent representation $\mathcal{R}_{\alpha,\hat{\mathbf{u}}}$ according to:

$$\tfrac{1}{2}(\mathcal{R} + \mathcal{R}^T) = \mathcal{I} + (1-\cos\alpha)\mathcal{U}^2 \qquad (1.26)$$

$$\tfrac{1}{2}(\mathcal{R} - \mathcal{R}^T) = (\sin\alpha)\mathcal{U} \qquad (1.27)$$

From (1.26) we obtain equality of the traces:

$$\mathrm{tr}(\mathcal{R}) = 3 + (1-\cos\alpha)\mathrm{tr}(\mathcal{U}^2) = 1 + 2\cos\alpha$$

since the trace of operator $\mathcal{U}^2$ is -2. In particular for the rotation $\mathcal{R}_{EB}$ which maps basis $(\hat{\mathbf{e}}_1, \hat{\mathbf{e}}_2, \hat{\mathbf{e}}_3)$ of $\mathcal{E}$ to basis $(\hat{\mathbf{b}}_1, \hat{\mathbf{b}}_2, \hat{\mathbf{b}}_3)$ of body $\mathcal{B}$ we find that the equivalent angle α satisfies

$$1 + 2\cos\alpha = c_{11} + c_{22} + c_{33}$$

with $c_{ij} = \hat{\mathbf{e}}_i \cdot \hat{\mathbf{b}}_j$. To find the equivalent axis we use (1.27)

$$\sin\alpha \begin{bmatrix} 0 & -u_3 & u_2 \\ u_3 & 0 & -u_1 \\ -u_2 & u_1 & 0 \end{bmatrix} = \frac{1}{2}\begin{bmatrix} 0 & c_{12}-c_{21} & c_{13}-c_{31} \\ c_{21}-c_{12} & 0 & c_{23}-c_{32} \\ c_{31}-c_{13} & c_{32}-c_{23} & 0 \end{bmatrix}$$

which gives

$$2\sin\alpha\,\hat{\mathbf{u}} = (c_{32}-c_{23})\hat{\mathbf{e}}_1 + (c_{13}-c_{31})\hat{\mathbf{e}}_2 + (c_{21}-c_{12})\hat{\mathbf{e}}_3$$

relative to basis $(\hat{\mathbf{e}}_1, \hat{\mathbf{e}}_2, \hat{\mathbf{e}}_3)$. We summarize these two results with the following theorem.

Theorem 1.2 The rotation $\mathcal{R}_{EB}$ which maps basis $(\hat{\mathbf{e}}_1, \hat{\mathbf{e}}_2, \hat{\mathbf{e}}_3)$ of $\mathcal{E}$ to basis $(\hat{\mathbf{b}}_1, \hat{\mathbf{b}}_2, \hat{\mathbf{b}}_3)$ of body $\mathcal{B}$ admits the unique equivalent representation $\mathcal{R}_{\alpha,\hat{\mathbf{u}}}$ given by

$$1 + 2\cos\alpha = c_{11} + c_{22} + c_{33} \tag{1.28}$$

and

$$2\sin\alpha\,\hat{\mathbf{u}} = (c_{32}-c_{23})\hat{\mathbf{e}}_1 + (c_{13}-c_{31})\hat{\mathbf{e}}_2 + (c_{21}-c_{12})\hat{\mathbf{e}}_3 \tag{1.29}$$

where $c_{ij} = \hat{\mathbf{e}}_i \cdot \hat{\mathbf{b}}_j$.

Remark 7. The trace of an operator is an *invariant*: if $\mathcal{R}_{EB}$ is represented by the matrix $[r_{ij}]_b$ in some particular basis b, then (1.28) can be written as

$$1 + 2\cos\alpha = r_{11} + r_{22} + r_{33}$$

Remark 8. Recall that $[\mathcal{C}_{EB}] = [\mathcal{R}_{EB}]_E = [\mathcal{R}_{EB}]_B$, hence the equality $(\mathcal{R}_{EB} - \mathcal{R}_{EB}^T) = 2\sin\alpha\,\mathcal{U}$ can be written on basis $(\hat{\mathbf{b}}_1, \hat{\mathbf{b}}_2, \hat{\mathbf{b}}_3)$:

$$2\sin\alpha\hat{\mathbf{u}} = (c_{32}-c_{23})\hat{\mathbf{b}}_1 + (c_{13}-c_{31})\hat{\mathbf{b}}_2 + (c_{21}-c_{12})\hat{\mathbf{b}}_3$$

If $\mathcal{R}_{EB}$ is represented by the matrix $[r_{ij}]$ on a basis $(\hat{\mathbf{a}}_1, \hat{\mathbf{a}}_2, \hat{\mathbf{a}}_3)$, then $\hat{\mathbf{u}}$ is obtained on this basis:

$$2\sin\alpha\hat{\mathbf{u}} = (r_{32}-r_{23})\hat{\mathbf{a}}_1 + (r_{13}-r_{31})\hat{\mathbf{a}}_2 + (r_{21}-r_{12})\hat{\mathbf{a}}_3$$

Remark 9. If α is close to π, then (1.29) should not be used since it may lead to a large error for $\hat{\mathbf{u}}$. Another method must be used. See Problem 1.5.

Remark 10. One can show that (1.29) leads to the formula (see Problem 1.6)

$$2\sin\alpha\,\hat{\mathbf{u}} = \hat{\mathbf{e}}_1 \times \hat{\mathbf{b}}_1 + \hat{\mathbf{e}}_2 \times \hat{\mathbf{b}}_2 + \hat{\mathbf{e}}_3 \times \hat{\mathbf{b}}_3$$

Example 1.5 Consider the rotation $\mathcal{R}_{\alpha,\hat{\mathbf{u}}}$ of angle α about unit vector $\hat{\mathbf{u}}$ whose orientation is given by angle (ψ, θ) relative to basis $(\hat{\mathbf{e}}_1, \hat{\mathbf{e}}_2, \hat{\mathbf{e}}_3)$ of $\mathcal{E}$ as shown in Figure 1.10.

a. Find the matrix $[\mathcal{R}_{\alpha,\hat{\mathbf{u}}}]_E$ in basis $(\hat{\mathbf{e}}_1, \hat{\mathbf{e}}_2, \hat{\mathbf{e}}_3)$ by using Rodrigues formula.

b. Two bases can be defined from $(\hat{\mathbf{e}}_1, \hat{\mathbf{e}}_2, \hat{\mathbf{e}}_3)$ by two consecutive rotations:

$$(\hat{\mathbf{e}}_1, \hat{\mathbf{e}}_2, \hat{\mathbf{e}}_3) \xrightarrow{\mathcal{R}_{\psi,\hat{\mathbf{e}}_3}} (\hat{\mathbf{u}}_1, \hat{\mathbf{u}}_2, \hat{\mathbf{u}}_3 = \hat{\mathbf{e}}_3) \xrightarrow{\mathcal{R}_{\theta,\hat{\mathbf{u}}_2}} (\hat{\mathbf{v}}_1, \hat{\mathbf{v}}_2 = \hat{\mathbf{u}}_2, \hat{\mathbf{v}}_3 = \hat{\mathbf{u}})$$

Find matrix $[\mathcal{R}_{\alpha,\hat{\mathbf{u}}}]_V$ in basis $(\hat{\mathbf{v}}_1, \hat{\mathbf{v}}_2, \hat{\mathbf{v}}_3)$, then find the matrix $[\mathcal{R}_{\alpha,\hat{\mathbf{u}}}]_E$ by using $[\mathcal{C}_{EV}]$. ■

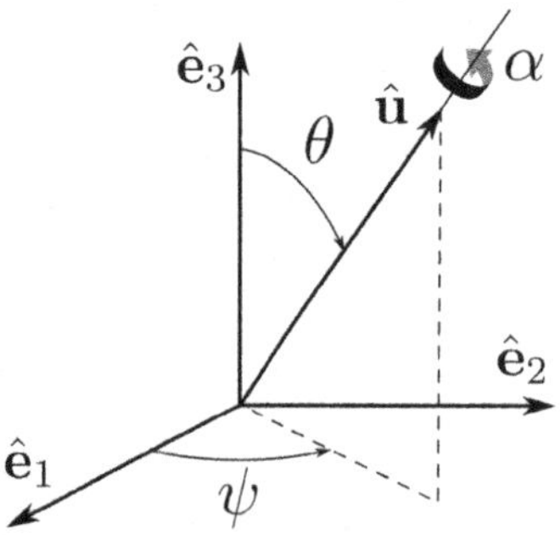

Figure 1.10

a. We can write the components of unit vector $\hat{\mathbf{u}}$ on basis $(\hat{\mathbf{e}}_1, \hat{\mathbf{e}}_2, \hat{\mathbf{e}}_3)$ in terms of angles ψ and θ:

$$\hat{\mathbf{u}} = s_\theta c_\psi \hat{\mathbf{e}}_1 + s_\theta s_\psi \hat{\mathbf{e}}_2 + c_\theta \hat{\mathbf{e}}_3$$

We can then apply (1.24) to find $[\mathcal{R}_{\alpha,\hat{\mathbf{u}}}]_E$:

$$[\mathcal{R}_{\alpha,\hat{\mathbf{u}}}]_E = \begin{bmatrix} 1 & 0 & 0 \\ 0 & 1 & 0 \\ 0 & 0 & 1 \end{bmatrix} + s_\alpha \begin{bmatrix} 0 & -c_\theta & s_\theta s_\psi \\ c_\theta & 0 & -s_\theta c_\psi \\ -s_\theta s_\psi & s_\theta c_\psi & 0 \end{bmatrix} + (1 - c_\alpha) \begin{bmatrix} s_\theta^2 c_\psi^2 - 1 & s_\theta^2 c_\psi s_\psi & s_\theta c_\theta c_\psi \\ s_\theta^2 c_\psi s_\psi & s_\theta^2 s_\psi^2 - 1 & s_\theta c_\theta s_\psi \\ s_\theta c_\theta c_\psi & s_\theta c_\theta s_\psi & c_\theta^2 - 1 \end{bmatrix}$$

b. Matrix $[\mathcal{R}_{\alpha,\hat{\mathbf{u}}}]_V$ takes a simple expression in basis $(\hat{\mathbf{v}}_1, \hat{\mathbf{v}}_2, \hat{\mathbf{v}}_3)$ since $\hat{\mathbf{v}}_3 = \hat{\mathbf{u}}$ is invariant by rotation $\mathcal{R}_{\alpha,\hat{\mathbf{u}}}$:

$$[\mathcal{R}_{\alpha,\hat{\mathbf{u}}}]_V = \begin{bmatrix} c_\alpha & -s_\alpha & 0 \\ s_\alpha & c_\alpha & 0 \\ 0 & 0 & 1 \end{bmatrix}$$

Then matrix $[\mathcal{R}_{\alpha,\hat{\mathbf{u}}}]_E$ is obtained in basis $(\hat{\mathbf{e}}_1, \hat{\mathbf{e}}_2, \hat{\mathbf{e}}_3)$ by using the direction cosine matrix $[\mathcal{C}_{EV}]$ according to formula (1.15)

$$[\mathcal{R}_{\alpha,\hat{\mathbf{u}}}]_E = [\mathcal{C}_{EV}][\mathcal{R}_{\alpha,\hat{\mathbf{u}}}]_V[\mathcal{C}_{EV}]^T$$

with

$$[\mathcal{C}_{EV}] = [\mathcal{C}_{EU}][\mathcal{C}_{UV}] = \begin{bmatrix} c_\psi & -s_\psi & 0 \\ s_\psi & c_\psi & 0 \\ 0 & 0 & 1 \end{bmatrix} \begin{bmatrix} c_\theta & 0 & s_\theta \\ 0 & 1 & 0 \\ -s_\theta & 0 & c_\theta \end{bmatrix} = \begin{bmatrix} c_\psi c_\theta & -s_\psi & c_\psi s_\theta \\ s_\psi c_\theta & c_\psi & s_\psi s_\theta \\ -s_\theta & 0 & c_\theta \end{bmatrix}$$

The reader will check that the same result is obtained. ■

Finally, we end this section with the following question. Given two rotations $\mathcal{R}_{\alpha,\hat{\mathbf{u}}}$ and $\mathcal{R}_{\beta,\hat{\mathbf{v}}}$, can the angle γ and direction $\hat{\mathbf{w}}$ be found for their composition $\mathcal{R}_{\gamma,\hat{\mathbf{w}}} = \mathcal{R}_{\beta,\hat{\mathbf{v}}} \circ \mathcal{R}_{\alpha,\hat{\mathbf{u}}}$? We may seek expressions for $(\gamma, \hat{\mathbf{w}})$ by applying Rodrigues formula. The derivations are very tedious. However, we shall see in the next section that they can be performed in a straightforward manner by the use of quaternions.

1.6 Quaternions

Quaternions are to spatial rotations what complex numbers are to planar rotations. The set of quaternions [5], denoted as $\mathbb{H}$, is the set of elements Q defined as

$$Q = q_0 + \mathbf{q} = q_0 + q_1\hat{\mathbf{e}}_1 + q_2\hat{\mathbf{e}}_2 + q_3\hat{\mathbf{e}}_3$$

[5] J.B. Kuipers, *Quaternions and Rotation Sequences*, Princeton University Press, Princeton (1999).

given four real numbers q_0, q_1, q_2, q_3 and a right-handed basis $(\hat{\mathbf{e}}_1, \hat{\mathbf{e}}_2, \hat{\mathbf{e}}_3)$ of orthonormal vectors of a referential $\mathcal{E}$. Hence a quaternion $Q \in \mathbb{H}$ is defined by its scalar part q_0 and its vector part $\text{Vect}(Q) = \mathbf{q} = q_1\hat{\mathbf{e}}_1 + q_2\hat{\mathbf{e}}_2 + q_3\hat{\mathbf{e}}_3$. A pure quaternion $Q = 0 + \mathbf{q}$ is a quaternion whose scalar part is zero. The set of pure quaternions forms a subset of $\mathbb{H}$ denoted $\mathbb{H}_0$.

Quaternion algebra is governed by the following fundamental rules:

$$\begin{aligned} \hat{\mathbf{e}}_1^2 = \hat{\mathbf{e}}_2^2 = \hat{\mathbf{e}}_3^2 = \hat{\mathbf{e}}_1\hat{\mathbf{e}}_2\hat{\mathbf{e}}_3 &= -1 \\ \hat{\mathbf{e}}_3 = \hat{\mathbf{e}}_1\hat{\mathbf{e}}_2 &= -\hat{\mathbf{e}}_2\hat{\mathbf{e}}_1 \\ \hat{\mathbf{e}}_2 = \hat{\mathbf{e}}_3\hat{\mathbf{e}}_1 &= -\hat{\mathbf{e}}_1\hat{\mathbf{e}}_3 \\ \hat{\mathbf{e}}_1 = \hat{\mathbf{e}}_2\hat{\mathbf{e}}_3 &= -\hat{\mathbf{e}}_3\hat{\mathbf{e}}_2 \end{aligned} \tag{1.30}$$

known as Hamilton rules. Quaternions form a 4-dimensional vector space over $\mathbb{R}$: given two elements Q, Q' of $\mathbb{H}$ and a real scalar λ, addition and scalar multiplication can be defined as

$$Q + Q' = (q_0 + q_0') + (q_1 + q_1')\hat{\mathbf{e}}_1 + (q_2 + q_2')\hat{\mathbf{e}}_2 + (q_3 + q_3')\hat{\mathbf{e}}_3$$

$$\lambda Q = \lambda q_0 + \lambda q_1\hat{\mathbf{e}}_1 + \lambda q_2\hat{\mathbf{e}}_2 + \lambda q_3\hat{\mathbf{e}}_3.$$

Quaternions can be multiplied according to the rules (1.30). It can be shown that the product $QQ' = (q_0 + \mathbf{q})(q_0' + \mathbf{q}')$ of two quaternions is given by

$$QQ' = q_0q_0' - \mathbf{q}\cdot\mathbf{q}' + q_0\mathbf{q}' + q_0'\mathbf{q} + \mathbf{q}\times\mathbf{q}' \tag{1.31}$$

Note that the multiplication of quaternions is not commutative: formula (1.31) shows that in general $QQ' \neq Q'Q$. Also note that the product of two pure quaternions $Q = 0 + \mathbf{q}$ and $Q' = 0 + \mathbf{q}'$ of $\mathbb{H}_0$ is not a pure quaternion:

$$QQ' = (0 + \mathbf{q})(0 + \mathbf{q}') = -\mathbf{q}\cdot\mathbf{q}' + \mathbf{q}\times\mathbf{q}'$$

The *inverse* of a quaternion can be defined by first defining the *conjugate* $\overline{Q}$ of a quaternion Q:

$$\overline{Q} = \overline{q_0 + \mathbf{q}} = q_0 - \mathbf{q} = q_0 - q_1\hat{\mathbf{e}}_1 - q_2\hat{\mathbf{e}}_2 - q_3\hat{\mathbf{e}}_3$$

Note that for $Q \in \mathbb{H}_0$, $\overline{Q} = -Q$ and that $\overline{QQ'} = \overline{Q'}\,\overline{Q}$ for any two arbitrary quaternions Q and Q'. The *norm* $|Q|$ of a quaternion Q is then defined by $(Q\overline{Q})^{1/2} = (\overline{Q}Q)^{1/2}$. Formula (1.31) shows that this expression has a meaning since

$$|Q|^2 = Q\overline{Q} = \overline{Q}Q = q_0^2 + q_1^2 + q_2^2 + q_3^2$$

Then the *inverse* of a non-zero quaternion Q is the quaternion Q^{-1} defined as $QQ^{-1} = Q^{-1}Q = 1$: it can be shown that Q^{-1} is given by

$$Q^{-1} = \frac{\overline{Q}}{|Q|^2}$$

A *unit* quaternion is a quaternion Q of norm $|Q| = 1$. It can be readily shown that all unit quaternions can be written in the form

$$Q = \cos\theta + \sin\theta\,\hat{\mathbf{u}}$$

where angle θ satisfies $0 \leq \theta < 2\pi$ and $\hat{\mathbf{u}}$ is a unit vector. If Q is a unit quaternion, its inverse is given by $Q^{-1} = \overline{Q}$.

Example 1.6
a. Given two quaternions Q_1 and Q_2, show that $Q_1Q_2 - Q_2Q_1 = 2\mathbf{q}_1 \times \mathbf{q}_2$.
b. Given two pure quaternions $Q_1 = 0 + \mathbf{q}_1$ and $q_2 = 0 + \mathbf{q}_2$, show that

$$Q_1Q_2 + Q_2Q_1 = -2\mathbf{q}_1 \cdot \mathbf{q}_2$$

■

a. According to (1.31) we can write

$$Q_1Q_2 = q_{10}q_{20} - \mathbf{q}_1 \cdot \mathbf{q}_2 + q_{10}\mathbf{q}_2 + q_{20}\mathbf{q}_1 + \mathbf{q}_1 \times \mathbf{q}_2$$

$$Q_2Q_1 = q_{10}q_{20} - \mathbf{q}_1 \cdot \mathbf{q}_2 + q_{10}\mathbf{q}_2 + q_{20}\mathbf{q}_1 + \mathbf{q}_2 \times \mathbf{q}_1$$

which leads to

$$Q_1Q_2 - Q_2Q_1 = 2\mathbf{q}_1 \times \mathbf{q}_2$$

b. For two pure quaternions we have

$$Q_1Q_2 = -\mathbf{q}_1 \cdot \mathbf{q}_2 + \mathbf{q}_1 \times \mathbf{q}_2, \qquad Q_2Q_1 = -\mathbf{q}_1 \cdot \mathbf{q}_2 + \mathbf{q}_2 \times \mathbf{q}_1$$

leading to

$$Q_1Q_2 + Q_2Q_1 = -2\mathbf{q}_1 \cdot \mathbf{q}_2$$

We see in particular that the square of a pure quaternion $Q = 0 + \mathbf{v}$ is the scalar $Q^2 = -\mathbf{v} \cdot \mathbf{v} = -\mathbf{v}^2$. ■

The usefulness of quaternions stems from their connection to rotations as shown by the following theorem.

Theorem 1.3 Given a unit quaternion $Q = \cos\frac{\alpha}{2} + \sin\frac{\alpha}{2}\,\hat{\mathbf{u}}$, the operator

$$\mathcal{R}_Q : \mathbf{V} \in \mathbb{H}_0 \mapsto Q\mathbf{V}\overline{Q} \in \mathbb{H}_0$$

corresponds to a rotation $\mathcal{R}_{\alpha,\hat{\mathbf{u}}}$ of angle α about unit vector $\hat{\mathbf{u}}$.

Remark 11. The correspondence between unit quaternions and rotations is not one-to-one since both Q and $-Q$ correspond to the same rotation.

Proof. To show this, we first find that for any $Q \in \mathbb{H}$ and any $\mathbf{V} \in \mathbb{H}_0$ we have

$$Q\mathbf{V}\overline{Q} = (q_0^2 - \mathbf{q}^2)\mathbf{V} + 2(\mathbf{q} \cdot \mathbf{V})\mathbf{q} + 2q_0\mathbf{q} \times \mathbf{V}$$

by two consecutive uses of (1.31). Hence $Q\mathbf{V}\overline{Q}$ is an element of $\mathbb{H}_0$. Then with $Q = \cos\frac{\alpha}{2} + \sin\frac{\alpha}{2}\,\hat{\mathbf{u}}$ we find

$$\mathcal{R}_Q(\mathbf{V}) = \cos\alpha\mathbf{V} + (1 - \cos\alpha)(\hat{\mathbf{u}} \cdot \mathbf{V})\hat{\mathbf{u}} + \sin\alpha\hat{\mathbf{u}} \times \mathbf{V}$$

Upon using the identity $\hat{\mathbf{u}} \times (\hat{\mathbf{u}} \times \mathbf{V}) = (\hat{\mathbf{u}} \cdot \mathbf{V})\hat{\mathbf{u}} - \mathbf{V}$ we find

$$\mathcal{R}_Q(\mathbf{V}) = \mathbf{V} + \sin\alpha\hat{\mathbf{u}} \times \mathbf{V} + (1 - \cos\alpha)\hat{\mathbf{u}} \times (\hat{\mathbf{u}} \times \mathbf{V})$$

This is exactly the expression of the mapping of vector $\mathbf{V}$ by rotation $\mathcal{R}_{\alpha,\hat{\mathbf{u}}}$ as given by Rodrigues formula (1.24). ■

Hence rotations of vectors can be performed by simple quaternion multiplications as illustrated by the following example.

Example 1.7 Find the mapping of $\mathbf{V} = \hat{\mathbf{e}}_3$ by the rotation of angle $\alpha = \pi/3$ about $\hat{\mathbf{u}} = (\hat{\mathbf{e}}_1 + \hat{\mathbf{e}}_2 + \hat{\mathbf{e}}_3)/\sqrt{3}$. ■

First we define the quaternion $Q = \cos\frac{\alpha}{2} + \sin\frac{\alpha}{2}\,\hat{\mathbf{u}}$

$$Q = \frac{\sqrt{3}}{2} + \frac{\hat{\mathbf{e}}_1 + \hat{\mathbf{e}}_2 + \hat{\mathbf{e}}_3}{2\sqrt{3}}$$

Then $\mathcal{R}_Q(\mathbf{V})$ is given as the product $Q\mathbf{V}\overline{Q}$:

$$\begin{aligned}\mathcal{R}_Q(\mathbf{V}) &= (\frac{\sqrt{3}}{2} + \frac{\hat{\mathbf{e}}_1 + \hat{\mathbf{e}}_2 + \hat{\mathbf{e}}_3}{2\sqrt{3}})\hat{\mathbf{e}}_3(\frac{\sqrt{3}}{2} - \frac{\hat{\mathbf{e}}_1 + \hat{\mathbf{e}}_2 + \hat{\mathbf{e}}_3}{2\sqrt{3}}) \\ &= \frac{\sqrt{3}}{6}(-1 + \hat{\mathbf{e}}_1 - \hat{\mathbf{e}}_2 + \hat{\mathbf{e}}_3)(\frac{\sqrt{3}}{2} - \frac{\hat{\mathbf{e}}_1 + \hat{\mathbf{e}}_2 + \hat{\mathbf{e}}_3}{2\sqrt{3}}) = \frac{2}{3}\hat{\mathbf{e}}_1 - \frac{1}{3}\hat{\mathbf{e}}_2 + \frac{2}{3}\hat{\mathbf{e}}_3\end{aligned}$$

■

Composition of rotations corresponds to product of quaternions: given two unit quaternions Q_1 and Q_2, consider the following sequence

$$\mathbf{V} \in \mathbb{H}_0 \xrightarrow{\mathcal{R}_{Q_1}} \mathbf{V}_1 = Q_1\mathbf{V}\overline{Q}_1 \xrightarrow{\mathcal{R}_{Q_2}} \mathbf{V}_2 = Q_2\mathbf{V}_1\overline{Q}_2$$

Then we can write $\mathbf{V}_2 = \mathcal{R}_Q(\mathbf{V}) = \mathcal{R}_{Q_2} \circ \mathcal{R}_{Q_1}(\mathbf{V}) = Q\mathbf{V}\overline{Q}$ with $Q = Q_2Q_1$. Hence quaternion Q_2Q_1 corresponds to rotation $\mathcal{R}_2 \circ \mathcal{R}_1$.

Example 1.8 Consider the sequence of two rotations $\mathcal{R}_{\alpha_1,\hat{\mathbf{e}}_3}$ and $\mathcal{R}_{\alpha_2,\hat{\mathbf{e}}_3}$:

$$\mathbf{V} \xrightarrow{\mathcal{R}_{\alpha_1,\hat{\mathbf{e}}_3}} \mathbf{V}_1 \xrightarrow{\mathcal{R}_{\alpha_2,\hat{\mathbf{e}}_3}} \mathbf{V}_2$$

By using quaternions, find the equivalent rotation which maps $\mathbf{V}$ to $\mathbf{V}_2$. ■

We first introduce the unit quaternions $Q_1 = \cos\frac{\alpha_1}{2} + \sin\frac{\alpha_1}{2}\hat{\mathbf{e}}_3$ and $Q_2 = \cos\frac{\alpha_2}{2} + \sin\frac{\alpha_2}{2}\hat{\mathbf{e}}_3$. Then $\mathbf{V}_2 = \mathcal{R}_Q(\mathbf{V})$ with Q given by

$$\begin{aligned}Q = Q_2Q_1 &= (\cos\frac{\alpha_1}{2} + \sin\frac{\alpha_1}{2}\hat{\mathbf{e}}_3)(\cos\frac{\alpha_2}{2} + \sin\frac{\alpha_2}{2}\hat{\mathbf{e}}_3) \\ &= \cos\frac{\alpha_1}{2}\cos\frac{\alpha_2}{2} - \sin\frac{\alpha_1}{2}\sin\frac{\alpha_2}{2} + (\cos\frac{\alpha_1}{2}\sin\frac{\alpha_2}{2} + \cos\frac{\alpha_2}{2}\sin\frac{\alpha_1}{2})\hat{\mathbf{e}}_3 \\ &= \cos\frac{\alpha_1+\alpha_2}{2} + \sin\frac{\alpha_1+\alpha_2}{2}\hat{\mathbf{e}}_3\end{aligned}$$

As expected this corresponds to the rotation $\mathcal{R}_{\alpha_1+\alpha_2,\hat{\mathbf{e}}_3}$ ■

Example 1.9 Consider the Euler sequence of three rotations $\mathcal{R}_{\psi,\hat{\mathbf{e}}_3}$, $\mathcal{R}_{\theta,\hat{\mathbf{u}}_1}$ and $\mathcal{R}_{\phi,\hat{\mathbf{b}}_3}$ which maps a basis $(\hat{\mathbf{e}}_1, \hat{\mathbf{e}}_2, \hat{\mathbf{e}}_3)$ of $\mathcal{E}$ to $(\hat{\mathbf{b}}_1, \hat{\mathbf{b}}_1, \hat{\mathbf{b}}_3)$ of a rigid body $\mathcal{B}$:

$$(\hat{\mathbf{e}}_1, \hat{\mathbf{e}}_2, \hat{\mathbf{e}}_3) \xrightarrow{\mathcal{R}_{\psi,\hat{\mathbf{e}}_3}} (\hat{\mathbf{u}}_1, \hat{\mathbf{u}}_2, \hat{\mathbf{e}}_3) \xrightarrow{\mathcal{R}_{\theta,\hat{\mathbf{u}}_1}} (\hat{\mathbf{u}}_1, \hat{\mathbf{v}}_2, \hat{\mathbf{z}}_3) \xrightarrow{\mathcal{R}_{\phi,\hat{\mathbf{b}}_3}} (\hat{\mathbf{b}}_1, \hat{\mathbf{b}}_2, \hat{\mathbf{b}}_3)$$

Find the equivalent rotation using quaternions.

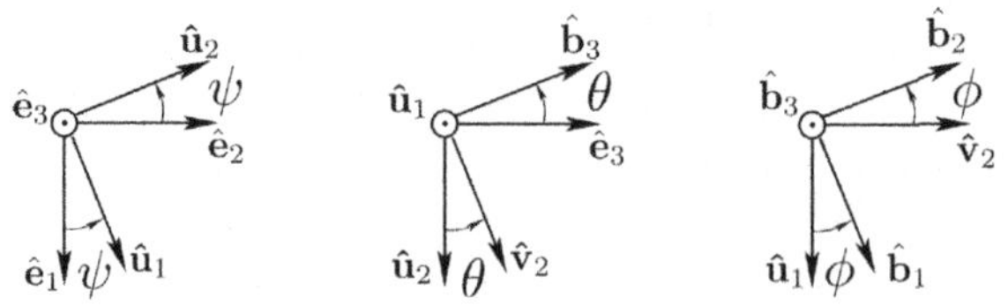

The three unit quaternions associated with $\mathcal{R}_{\psi,\hat{e}_3}$, $\mathcal{R}_{\theta,\hat{u}_1}$ and $\mathcal{R}_{\phi,\hat{b}_3}$ are

$$Q_\psi = \cos\frac{\psi}{2} + \sin\frac{\psi}{2}\hat{\mathbf{e}}_3, \quad Q_\theta = \cos\frac{\theta}{2} + \sin\frac{\theta}{2}\hat{\mathbf{u}}_1, \quad Q_\phi = \cos\frac{\phi}{2} + \sin\frac{\phi}{2}\hat{\mathbf{b}}_3$$

In order to find the product $Q_\phi Q_\theta Q_\psi$, the three quaternions must be expressed on the same basis. It is most convenient to use basis $(\hat{\mathbf{u}}_1, \hat{\mathbf{u}}_2, \hat{\mathbf{e}}_3)$, then we must express Q_ϕ as

$$Q_\phi = \cos\frac{\phi}{2} + \sin\frac{\phi}{2}(\cos\theta\hat{\mathbf{e}}_3 - \sin\theta\hat{\mathbf{u}}_2)$$

First, we find the product $Q_\theta Q_\psi$ using (1.31)

$$\begin{aligned} Q_\theta Q_\psi &= (\cos\frac{\theta}{2} + \sin\frac{\theta}{2}\hat{\mathbf{u}}_1)(\cos\frac{\psi}{2} + \sin\frac{\psi}{2}\hat{\mathbf{e}}_3) \\ &= \cos\frac{\psi}{2}\cos\frac{\theta}{2} + \cos\frac{\psi}{2}\sin\frac{\theta}{2}\hat{\mathbf{u}}_1 - \sin\frac{\psi}{2}\sin\frac{\theta}{2}\hat{\mathbf{u}}_2 + \sin\frac{\psi}{2}\cos\frac{\theta}{2}\hat{\mathbf{e}}_3 \end{aligned}$$

Then we find the product $Q_\phi Q_\theta Q_\psi$

$$\begin{aligned} Q_\phi Q_\theta Q_\psi &= c_{\phi/2}c_{\psi/2}c_{\theta/2} - s_{\psi/2}s_{\phi/2}s_\theta s_{\theta/2} - s_{\psi/2}s_{\psi/2}c_\theta c_{\theta/2} \\ &\quad +(c_{\psi/2}s_{\theta/2}c_{\psi/2} - s_{\psi/2}s_{\phi/2}s_\theta c_{\theta/2} + s_{\psi/2}s_{\psi/2}c_\theta s_{\theta/2})\hat{\mathbf{u}}_1 \\ &\quad -(s_{\psi/2}s_{\theta/2}c_{\phi/2} + c_{\psi/2}s_{\phi/2}s_\theta c_{\theta/2} - c_{\psi/2}s_{\phi/2}c_\theta s_{\theta/2})\hat{\mathbf{u}}_2 \\ &\quad +(s_{\psi/2}c_{\theta/2}c_{\phi/2} + c_{\psi/2}s_{\phi/2}c_\theta c_{\theta/2} + c_{\psi/2}s_{\phi/2}s_\theta s_{\theta/2})\hat{\mathbf{e}}_3 \end{aligned}$$

using the notation $c_\theta = \cos\theta$, $s_\theta = \sin\theta$, etc. After simplifications, this gives

$$Q_\phi Q_\theta Q_\psi = c_{\theta/2}c_{(\psi+\phi)/2} + s_{\theta/2}c_{(\psi+\phi)/2}\hat{\mathbf{u}}_1 - s_{\theta/2}s_{(\psi+\phi)/2}\hat{\mathbf{u}}_2 + c_{\theta/2}s_{(\psi+\phi)/2}\hat{\mathbf{e}}_3$$

We can then express $Q_\phi Q_\theta Q_\psi$ on basis $(\hat{\mathbf{e}}_1, \hat{\mathbf{e}}_2, \hat{\mathbf{e}}_3)$ to find

$$\begin{aligned} Q_\phi Q_\theta Q_\psi &= \cos\tfrac{\theta}{2}\cos\left(\tfrac{\psi+\phi}{2}\right) + \sin\tfrac{\theta}{2}\cos\left(\tfrac{\psi-\phi}{2}\right)\hat{\mathbf{e}}_1 + \sin\tfrac{\theta}{2}\sin\left(\tfrac{\psi-\phi}{2}\right)\hat{\mathbf{e}}_2 \\ &\quad + \cos\tfrac{\theta}{2}\sin\left(\tfrac{\psi+\phi}{2}\right)\hat{\mathbf{e}}_3 \end{aligned}$$

We can equate $Q_\phi Q_\theta Q_\psi$ to unit quaternion $\cos\frac{\alpha}{2} + \sin\frac{\alpha}{2}\widehat{\mathbf{U}}$ where angle α and unit vector $\widehat{\mathbf{U}}$ are given by

$$\cos\frac{\alpha}{2} = \cos\frac{\theta}{2}\cos\left(\frac{\psi+\phi}{2}\right)$$

$$\sin\frac{\alpha}{2}\widehat{\mathbf{U}} = \sin\frac{\theta}{2}\cos\left(\frac{\psi-\phi}{2}\right)\hat{\mathbf{e}}_1 + \sin\frac{\theta}{2}\sin\left(\frac{\psi-\phi}{2}\right)\hat{\mathbf{e}}_2 + \cos\frac{\theta}{2}\sin\left(\frac{\psi+\phi}{2}\right)\hat{\mathbf{e}}_3$$

The sequence of three rotations $\mathcal{R}_{\psi,\hat{e}_3}$, $\mathcal{R}_{\theta,\hat{u}_1}$ and $\mathcal{R}_{\phi,\hat{b}_3}$ is then equivalent to the rotation $\mathcal{R}_{\alpha,\widehat{U}}$. ■

Quaternions are also helpful to derive interesting properties of rotations. The following result relates to the so-called *rotation vector* of a rotation $\mathcal{R}_{\alpha,\hat{\mathbf{u}}}$ defined as the vector $\boldsymbol{\tau} = \tan\frac{\alpha}{2}\,\hat{\mathbf{u}}$.

Theorem 1.4 Given two rotations $\mathcal{R}_{\alpha,\hat{\mathbf{u}}}$ and $\mathcal{R}_{\beta,\hat{\mathbf{v}}}$ of rotation vectors $\boldsymbol{\tau}_u = \tan\frac{\alpha}{2}\,\hat{\mathbf{u}}$ and $\boldsymbol{\tau}_v = \tan\frac{\beta}{2}\,\hat{\mathbf{v}}$, the rotation vector $\boldsymbol{\tau}_w = \tan\frac{\gamma}{2}\,\hat{\mathbf{w}}$ of rotation $\mathcal{R}_{\gamma,\hat{\mathbf{w}}} = \mathcal{R}_{\beta,\hat{\mathbf{v}}} \circ \mathcal{R}_{\alpha,\hat{\mathbf{u}}}$ is given by

$$\boldsymbol{\tau}_w = \frac{\boldsymbol{\tau}_u + \boldsymbol{\tau}_v + \boldsymbol{\tau}_v \times \boldsymbol{\tau}_u}{1 - \boldsymbol{\tau}_u \cdot \boldsymbol{\tau}_v} \tag{1.32}$$

Proof. Rotation $\mathcal{R}_{\gamma,\hat{\mathbf{w}}}$ corresponds to quaternion Q_w given by

$$\begin{aligned} Q_w &= Q_v Q_u = (c_{\beta/2} + s_{\beta/2}\hat{\mathbf{v}})(c_{\alpha/2} + s_{\alpha/2}\hat{\mathbf{u}}) \\ &= c_{\beta/2}c_{\alpha/2} - s_{\beta/2}s_{\alpha/2}(\hat{\mathbf{u}}\cdot\hat{\mathbf{v}}) + c_{\beta/2}s_{\alpha/2}\hat{\mathbf{u}} + c_{\alpha/2}s_{\beta/2}\hat{\mathbf{v}} + s_{\beta/2}s_{\alpha/2}\hat{\mathbf{v}}\times\hat{\mathbf{u}} \end{aligned}$$

We then equate the real parts and the vector parts to obtain two equations:

$$\cos\frac{\gamma}{2} = \cos\frac{\beta}{2}\cos\frac{\alpha}{2} - \sin\frac{\beta}{2}\sin\frac{\alpha}{2}(\hat{\mathbf{u}}\cdot\hat{\mathbf{v}})$$

$$\sin\frac{\gamma}{2}\hat{\mathbf{w}} = \cos\frac{\beta}{2}\sin\frac{\alpha}{2}\hat{\mathbf{u}} + \cos\frac{\alpha}{2}\sin\frac{\beta}{2}\hat{\mathbf{v}} + \sin\frac{\beta}{2}\sin\frac{\alpha}{2}\hat{\mathbf{v}}\times\hat{\mathbf{u}}$$

We factor $\cos\frac{\beta}{2}\cos\frac{\alpha}{2}$ in the second equation:

$$\sin\frac{\gamma}{2}\hat{\mathbf{w}} = \cos\frac{\beta}{2}\cos\frac{\alpha}{2}(\boldsymbol{\tau}_u + \boldsymbol{\tau}_v + \boldsymbol{\tau}_v \times \boldsymbol{\tau}_u)$$

then divide by $\cos\frac{\gamma}{2}$ and use the first equation to obtain the final result

$$\boldsymbol{\tau}_w = \frac{\cos\frac{\beta}{2}\cos\frac{\alpha}{2}}{\cos\frac{\gamma}{2}}(\boldsymbol{\tau}_u + \boldsymbol{\tau}_v + \boldsymbol{\tau}_v \times \boldsymbol{\tau}_u) = \frac{1}{1 - \boldsymbol{\tau}_u \cdot \boldsymbol{\tau}_v}(\boldsymbol{\tau}_u + \boldsymbol{\tau}_v + \boldsymbol{\tau}_v \times \boldsymbol{\tau}_u)$$

■

Given a unit quaternion $Q = q_0 + \mathbf{q} = q_0 + q_1\hat{\mathbf{e}}_1 + q_2\hat{\mathbf{e}}_2 + q_3\hat{\mathbf{e}}_3$, we can find the matrix $[\mathcal{R}_{\alpha,\hat{\mathbf{u}}}]_E$ of the rotation associated with quaternion Q on basis $(\hat{\mathbf{e}}_1, \hat{\mathbf{e}}_2, \hat{\mathbf{e}}_3)$ in terms of (q_0, q_1, q_2, q_3). According to Rodrigues formula, operator $\mathcal{R}_{\alpha,\hat{\mathbf{u}}}$ takes the form

$$\mathcal{R}_{\alpha,\hat{\mathbf{u}}} = \mathcal{I} + (\sin\alpha)\mathcal{U} + (1-\cos\alpha)\mathcal{U}^2 = \mathcal{I} + 2q_0\mathcal{V} + 2\mathcal{V}^2$$

where $\mathcal{U}$ is the operator $\mathbf{V} \mapsto \hat{\mathbf{u}} \times \mathbf{V}$ and $\mathcal{V}$ is the operator given by

$$\mathcal{V}: \quad \mathbf{V} \mapsto \sin\frac{\alpha}{2}\hat{\mathbf{u}} \times \mathbf{V} = \mathbf{q} \times \mathbf{V}$$

We can use our previous derivations to find the matrix of $\mathcal{R}_{\alpha,\hat{\mathbf{u}}}$ on basis $(\hat{\mathbf{e}}_1, \hat{\mathbf{e}}_2, \hat{\mathbf{e}}_3)$:

$$\begin{aligned} [\mathcal{R}_{\alpha,\hat{\mathbf{u}}}]_E &= \begin{pmatrix} 1 & 0 & 0 \\ 0 & 1 & 0 \\ 0 & 0 & 1 \end{pmatrix} + 2q_0 \begin{pmatrix} 0 & -q_3 & q_2 \\ q_3 & 0 & -q_1 \\ -q_2 & q_1 & 0 \end{pmatrix} + 2 \begin{pmatrix} q_0^2 + q_1^2 - 1 & q_1q_2 & q_1q_3 \\ q_1q_2 & q_0^2 + q_2^2 - 1 & q_2q_3 \\ q_1q_3 & q_2q_3 & q_0^2 + q_3^2 - 1 \end{pmatrix} \\ &= \begin{pmatrix} 2q_0^2 + 2q_1^2 - 1 & 2(q_1q_2 - q_0q_3) & 2(q_1q_3 + q_0q_2) \\ 2(q_1q_2 + q_0q_3) & 2q_0^2 + 2q_2^2 - 1 & 2(q_2q_3 - q_0q_1) \\ 2(q_1q_3 - q_0q_2) & 2(q_2q_3 + q_0q_1) & 2q_0^2 + 2q_3^2 - 1 \end{pmatrix} \end{aligned} \tag{1.33}$$

Conversely, given a rotation matrix $[r_{ij}]_E$, we can find the corresponding quaternion $Q = q_0 + q_1\hat{\mathbf{e}}_1 + q_2\hat{\mathbf{e}}_2 + q_3\hat{\mathbf{e}}_3$. The previous derivations show that the symmetric and skew-symmetric parts of matrix $[r_{ij}]_E$ are given by

$$[\frac{r_{ij}+r_{ji}}{2}]_E = [\mathcal{I} + 2\mathcal{V}^2]_E \quad , \qquad [\frac{r_{ij}-r_{ji}}{2}]_E = [2q_0\mathcal{V}]_E$$

Equality of the skew-symmetric parts gives three equations

$$q_0q_1 = \frac{1}{4}(r_{32} - r_{23}), \quad q_0q_2 = \frac{1}{4}(r_{13} - r_{31}), \quad q_0q_3 = \frac{1}{4}(r_{21} - r_{12}) \tag{1.34}$$

Equality of the symmetric parts yields four equations

$$\begin{aligned} q_0^2 &= \tfrac{1}{4}(1 + r_{11} + r_{22} + r_{33}) \\ q_1^2 &= \tfrac{1}{4}(1 + r_{11} - r_{22} - r_{33}) \\ q_2^2 &= \tfrac{1}{4}(1 - r_{11} + r_{22} - r_{33}) \\ q_3^2 &= \tfrac{1}{4}(1 - r_{11} - r_{22} + r_{33}) \end{aligned} \tag{1.35}$$

after taking into account $q_0^2 + q_1^2 + q_2^2 + q_3^2 = 1$. Since both $\pm Q$ give the same rotation, one of two possible values for q_0 can be found from the first equation of (1.35). Then the values of (q_1, q_2, q_3) are found uniquely from (1.34).

1.7 Displacements

We propose in this section to study here the finite displacements of rigid bodies, that is, mappings which take a configuration of rigid body $\mathcal{B}$ into new configurations in referential $\mathcal{E}$. We start with a definition of displacements.

Definition 1.9 Displacements are mappings of $\mathcal{E}$ which conserve distance and orientation.

See Figure 1.11. Hence each point P of $\mathcal{B}$ is mapped by displacement $\mathcal{D}$ into a point P', with the following requirements:

(i) distances between points of $\mathcal{B}$ are conserved by $\mathcal{D}$

$$|\mathbf{p} - \mathbf{q}| = |\mathbf{p}' - \mathbf{q}'|$$

denoting $\mathbf{p} = \mathbf{r}_{OP}$, $\mathbf{q} = \mathbf{r}_{OQ}$, $\mathbf{p}' = \mathbf{r}_{OP'}$, and $\mathbf{q}' = \mathbf{r}_{OQ'}$.

(ii) oriented angles are conserved by $\mathcal{D}$:

$$(\mathbf{q} - \mathbf{p}, \mathbf{r} - \mathbf{p}) = (\mathbf{q}' - \mathbf{p}', \mathbf{r}' - \mathbf{p}')$$

for any three points P, Q and R attached to $\mathcal{B}$.

Remark 12. The set of displacements constitutes a group. It is a subgroup of the group of isometries of $\mathcal{E}$ (mappings in $\mathcal{E}$ which conserve distance).

Remark 13. The set of all possible displacements is comprised of translations, rotations and their compositions.

Remark 14. It will be useful to define the field of displacements $P \in \mathcal{B} \mapsto \mathbf{d}_P = \mathbf{p}' - \mathbf{p} = \mathbf{r}_{PP'}$.

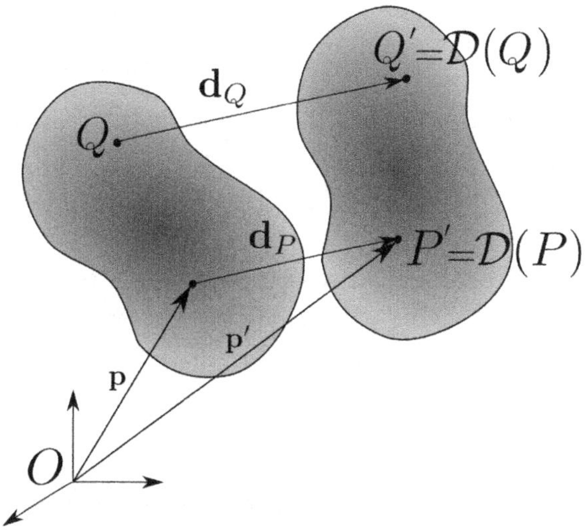

Figure 1.11

1.7.1 Translation

Definition 1.10 — Translation. The *translation* $\mathcal{T}_l$ of vector $\boldsymbol{l}$ is the transformation defined by

$$\mathcal{T}_l: \; P \in \mathcal{B} \mapsto P' = \mathcal{T}_l(P) \quad \text{such that} \quad \mathbf{p}' = \mathbf{p} + \boldsymbol{l} \tag{1.36}$$

Hence the field of displacements is invariant: $\mathbf{d}_P = \boldsymbol{l}$ for all points of $\mathcal{B}$. The transformation can be written in Cartesian coordinates on a basis $(\hat{\mathbf{e}}_1, \hat{\mathbf{e}}_2, \hat{\mathbf{e}}_3)$ in the following form

$$x_1' = x_1 + l_1$$
$$x_2' = x_2 + l_2$$
$$x_3' = x_3 + l_3$$

or in array form

$$\begin{bmatrix} x_1' \\ x_2' \\ x_3' \\ 1 \end{bmatrix} = [\mathcal{T}_l] \begin{bmatrix} x_1 \\ x_2 \\ x_3 \\ 1 \end{bmatrix}, \qquad [\mathcal{T}_l] = \begin{bmatrix} 1 & 0 & 0 & l_1 \\ 0 & 1 & 0 & l_2 \\ 0 & 0 & 1 & l_3 \\ 0 & 0 & 0 & 1 \end{bmatrix}$$

The composition of two translations $\mathcal{T}_{l_1}$ and $\mathcal{T}_{l_2}$ is given by

$$\mathcal{T}_{l_1} \circ \mathcal{T}_{l_2} = \mathcal{T}_{l_1 + l_2}$$

The translation of infinitesimal vector $d\boldsymbol{l}$ is represented by the matrix

$$[\mathcal{T}_{dl}] = \begin{bmatrix} 1 & 0 & 0 & dl_1 \\ 0 & 1 & 0 & dl_2 \\ 0 & 0 & 1 & dl_3 \\ 0 & 0 & 0 & 1 \end{bmatrix} = [\mathcal{I}] + dl_1[\mathcal{T}_1] + dl_2[\mathcal{T}_2] + dl_3[\mathcal{T}_3]$$

with

$$[\mathcal{I}] = \begin{bmatrix} 1 & 0 & 0 & 0 \\ 0 & 1 & 0 & 0 \\ 0 & 0 & 1 & 0 \\ 0 & 0 & 0 & 0 \end{bmatrix} \quad [\mathcal{T}_1] = \begin{bmatrix} 0 & 0 & 0 & 1 \\ 0 & 0 & 0 & 0 \\ 0 & 0 & 0 & 0 \\ 0 & 0 & 0 & 0 \end{bmatrix} \quad [\mathcal{T}_2] = \begin{bmatrix} 0 & 0 & 0 & 0 \\ 0 & 0 & 0 & 1 \\ 0 & 0 & 0 & 0 \\ 0 & 0 & 0 & 0 \end{bmatrix} \quad [\mathcal{T}_3] = \begin{bmatrix} 0 & 0 & 0 & 0 \\ 0 & 0 & 0 & 0 \\ 0 & 0 & 0 & 1 \\ 0 & 0 & 0 & 0 \end{bmatrix}$$

It is easy to verify that

$$[\mathcal{T}_i][\mathcal{T}_j] = [0] \qquad (i,j = 1,2,3)$$

which leads to the property

$$e^{l_1[\mathcal{T}_1]+l_2[\mathcal{T}_2]+l_3[\mathcal{T}_3]} = [\mathcal{I}] + l_i[\mathcal{T}_i]) + \frac{1}{2}l_il_j[\mathcal{T}_i][\mathcal{T}_j] + \ldots = [\mathcal{I}] + l_1[\mathcal{T}_1] + l_2[\mathcal{T}_2] + l_3[\mathcal{T}_3]$$

This shows that matrix $[\mathcal{T}_l]$ can be expressed in terms of the components $[\mathcal{T}_i]$ according to:

$$[\mathcal{T}_l] = e^{l_1[\mathcal{T}_1]+l_2[\mathcal{T}_2]+l_3[\mathcal{T}_3]} \tag{1.37}$$

1.7.2 Rotation

Definition 1.11 — Rotation. A rotation is a transformation which leaves a point O of $\mathcal{B}$ invariant and conserves the orientation of a basis of $\mathcal{B}$. The rotation $\mathcal{R}_O$ about O, of angle α, and direction $\hat{\mathbf{u}}$ is characterized by

$$\mathcal{R}_O : P \in \mathcal{B} \mapsto P' = \mathcal{R}_O(P) \quad \text{such that} \quad \mathbf{p}' = \mathcal{R}_{\alpha,\hat{\mathbf{u}}}(\mathbf{p})$$

The displacement field can be described by $\mathbf{d}_P = \sin\alpha\hat{\mathbf{u}} \times \mathbf{p} + (1-\cos\alpha)\hat{\mathbf{u}} \times (\hat{\mathbf{u}} \times \mathbf{p})$ according to Rodrigues formula. All points of the axis of rotation $\Delta(O, \hat{\mathbf{u}})$ are invariant by the rotation: $\mathbf{d}_P = 0$ for all $P \in \Delta$. The transformation can be written in Cartesian coordinates on a basis $(\hat{\mathbf{e}}_1, \hat{\mathbf{e}}_2, \hat{\mathbf{e}}_3)$ in various forms

$$\begin{bmatrix} x_1' \\ x_2' \\ x_3' \end{bmatrix} = [\mathcal{R}_O] \begin{bmatrix} x_1 \\ x_2 \\ x_3 \end{bmatrix}, \qquad [\mathcal{R}_O] = \begin{bmatrix} r_{11} & r_{12} & r_{13} \\ r_{21} & r_{22} & r_{23} \\ r_{31} & r_{32} & r_{33} \end{bmatrix}$$

where the coefficients r_{ij} can be expressed in terms of the direction cosines $c_{ij} = \hat{\mathbf{e}}_i \cdot \hat{\mathbf{e}}_i'$ (Section 1.3), in terms of Euler angles (Section 1.4), or in terms of Euler parameters $(\alpha, \hat{\mathbf{u}})$ (Section 1.5).

The infinitesimal rotation $\mathcal{R}_{d\alpha,\hat{\mathbf{u}}}$ of angle $d\alpha$ about $\hat{\mathbf{u}}$ maps point P to P' according to

$$\mathcal{R}_{d\alpha,\hat{\mathbf{u}}}(\mathbf{p}) = \mathbf{p} + d\alpha\hat{\mathbf{u}} \times \mathbf{p}$$

and the corresponding matrix on basis $b(\hat{\mathbf{e}}_1, \hat{\mathbf{e}}_2, \hat{\mathbf{e}}_3)$

$$[\mathcal{R}_{d\alpha,\hat{\mathbf{u}}}]_b = [\mathcal{I}] + d\alpha \begin{bmatrix} 0 & -u_3 & u_2 \\ u_3 & 0 & u_1 \\ -u_2 & -u_1 & 0 \end{bmatrix} = [\mathcal{I}] + d\alpha(u_1[\mathcal{R}_1]_b + u_2[\mathcal{R}_2]_b + u_3[\mathcal{R}_3]_b)$$

where (u_1, u_2, u_3) are the components of $\hat{\mathbf{u}}$ on basis b and with

$$[\mathcal{R}_1]_b = \begin{bmatrix} 0 & 0 & 0 \\ 0 & 0 & 1 \\ 0 & -1 & 0 \end{bmatrix}, \quad [\mathcal{R}_2]_b = \begin{bmatrix} 0 & 0 & 1 \\ 0 & 0 & 0 \\ -1 & 0 & 0 \end{bmatrix}, \quad [\mathcal{R}_3]_b = \begin{bmatrix} 0 & -1 & 0 \\ 1 & 0 & 0 \\ 0 & 0 & 0 \end{bmatrix}$$

1.7.3 Screw Displacement

The most general displacement can be considered to be a composition of a translation and a rotation. Using Rodrigues formula, it is possible to obtain a coordinate-free expressions of displacements.

Theorem 1.5 The most general displacement can be characterized by the following mapping

$$\mathcal{D} : P \in \mathcal{B} \mapsto P' = \mathcal{D}(P) = \mathcal{T}_l \circ \mathcal{R}_O(P) \quad \text{such that} \quad \mathbf{p}' = \boldsymbol{l} + e^{\alpha \mathbf{U}}(\mathbf{p}) \tag{1.38}$$

where $\mathbf{U}$ is the operator defined by $\mathbf{U}(\mathbf{V}) = \hat{\mathbf{u}} \times \mathbf{V}$.

Proof. Consider a particular point A of $\mathcal{B}$ which is mapped into A'. Then consider the mapping $\mathbf{p} - \mathbf{a} \mapsto \mathbf{p}' - \mathbf{a}'$. This map leaves A invariant. Hence the vector $\mathbf{p}' - \mathbf{a}'$ can be obtained from $\mathbf{p} - \mathbf{a}$ by a (vectorial) rotation $\mathcal{R}$ such that:

$$\mathbf{p}' - \mathbf{a}' = \mathcal{R}(\mathbf{p} - \mathbf{a})$$

which gives

$$\mathbf{p}' = \mathbf{a}' - \mathcal{R}(\mathbf{a}) + \mathcal{R}(\mathbf{p}) = \boldsymbol{l} + \mathcal{R}(\mathbf{p})$$

It is easy to show that $\mathcal{R}$ is not a function of the choice of A. Using Rodrigues formula, there exist an angle α and a unit vector $\hat{\mathbf{u}}$ such that

$$\mathcal{R}(\mathbf{p}) = \mathbf{p} + \sin\alpha \hat{\mathbf{u}} \times \mathbf{p} + (1 - \cos\alpha)\hat{\mathbf{u}} \times (\hat{\mathbf{u}} \times \mathbf{p}) \tag{1.39}$$

We then need to show that the operator $e^{\alpha\mathcal{U}}$ is equivalent to Rodrigues formula. This operator can be defined as the expansion

$$e^{\alpha\mathcal{U}} = \mathcal{I} + \alpha\mathcal{U} + \frac{\alpha^2}{2!}\mathcal{U}^2 + \frac{\alpha^3}{3!}\mathcal{U}^3 + \cdots$$

It is easy to show that operator $\mathcal{U}$ satisfies:

$$\mathcal{U}^{2k} = (-1)^{k-1}\mathcal{U}^2, \qquad \mathcal{U}^{2k-1} = (-1)^{k-1}\mathcal{U} \qquad (k \geq 1)$$

We can then express operator $e^{\alpha\mathcal{U}}$ as

$$e^{\alpha\mathcal{U}} = \mathcal{I} + (\alpha - \frac{\alpha^3}{3!} + \frac{\alpha^5}{5!} + \cdots)\mathcal{U} + (\frac{\alpha^2}{2!} - \frac{\alpha^4}{4!} + \cdots)\mathcal{U}^2 = \mathcal{I} + \sin\alpha\,\mathcal{U} + (1 - \cos\alpha)\mathcal{U}^2$$

■

Remark 15. In general, a displacement which is not a rotation ($\boldsymbol{l} \neq \mathbf{0}$) does not have any fixed points, that is, points undergoing no displacement. Such points would satisfy $(\mathcal{R} - \mathcal{I})(\mathbf{p}) = \boldsymbol{l}$. However the operator $\mathcal{R} - \mathcal{I}$ is singular since $\lambda = 1$ is an eigenvalue of $\mathcal{R}$. There are no such points.

An important characterization of displacements can be established by seeking the set of points which have minimal displacement, that is, which minimize

$$|\mathbf{p}' - \mathbf{p}|^2 = |(\mathcal{R} - \mathcal{I})\mathbf{p} + \boldsymbol{l}|^2$$

The minimization yields the solution $(\mathcal{R} - \mathcal{I})(\mathbf{p}' - \mathbf{p}) = 0$: since the eigenvectors of $\mathcal{R}$ corresponding to eigenvalue $\lambda = 1$ are the vectors collinear to $\hat{\mathbf{u}}$, we find that the points with minimum-norm displacement satisfy

$$\mathbf{p}' - \mathbf{p} = \mu\hat{\mathbf{u}}, \qquad \mu \in \mathbb{R}$$

Hence the minimum-norm displacement lies along the axis of rotation $\mathcal{R}$. Conversely, the points whose displacements are parallel to the rotation axis lie on an axis parallel to $\hat{\mathbf{u}}$. Indeed, let point Q satisfy $\mathbf{q} = \mathbf{p} + \nu\hat{\mathbf{u}}$ where ν is an arbitrary scalar and where $\mathbf{p}$ satisfy $\mathbf{p}' - \mathbf{p} = \mu\hat{\mathbf{u}}$. Then $\mathbf{q}' - \mathbf{q} = \mathcal{R}(\mathbf{q}) + \boldsymbol{l} - \mathbf{q} = \mathcal{R}(\mathbf{p}) + \boldsymbol{l} - \mathbf{p} = \mathbf{p}' - \mathbf{p} = \mu\hat{\mathbf{u}}$. Hence all points of this axis have the same displacement. In conclusion,

> **Theorem 1.6** The set of points with minimum-norm displacement is a line Δ, called *screw axis*, directed along the rotation axis $\hat{\mathbf{u}}$. All points of the screw axis have the same displacement $\mu\hat{\mathbf{u}}$.

It is then possible to derive a coordinate-free expression of the displacement, independent of the choice of origin O. First we need to find a particular point of the screw axis: such points are solution of the equation

$$\mathbf{d}_P = \mathbf{p}' - \mathbf{p} = \mu\hat{\mathbf{u}} = \sin\alpha\hat{\mathbf{u}} \times \mathbf{p} + (1 - \cos\alpha)\hat{\mathbf{u}} \times (\hat{\mathbf{u}} \times \mathbf{p}) + \boldsymbol{l} \tag{1.40}$$

We eliminate the unknown $\mu\hat{\mathbf{u}}$ by taking the cross-product of this equation with $\hat{\mathbf{u}}$ to obtain

$$\mathbf{0} = \sin\alpha\hat{\mathbf{u}} \times (\hat{\mathbf{u}} \times \mathbf{p}) + (1 - \cos\alpha)\hat{\mathbf{u}} \times \big(\hat{\mathbf{u}} \times (\hat{\mathbf{u}} \times \mathbf{p})\big) + \hat{\mathbf{u}} \times \boldsymbol{l} \tag{1.41}$$

Let P^* the point of the screw axis satisfying $\mathbf{p}^* \cdot \hat{\mathbf{u}}$: P^* is the foot of the perpendicular drawn from origin O to the screw axis. Then equation (1.41) becomes, using $\hat{\mathbf{u}} \times (\hat{\mathbf{u}} \times \mathbf{p}^*) = -\mathbf{p}^*$,

$$\sin\alpha\mathbf{p}^* + (1 - \cos\alpha)\hat{\mathbf{u}} \times \mathbf{p}^* - \hat{\mathbf{u}} \times \boldsymbol{l} = \mathbf{0} \tag{1.42}$$

and after taking the cross-product with $\hat{\mathbf{u}}$

$$\sin\alpha\hat{\mathbf{u}} \times \mathbf{p}^* - (1 - \cos\alpha)\mathbf{p}^* - \hat{\mathbf{u}} \times (\hat{\mathbf{u}} \times \boldsymbol{l}) = \mathbf{0} \tag{1.43}$$

Now we can solve for $\mathbf{p}^*$:

$$\mathbf{p}^* = \frac{1}{2}\cot\frac{\alpha}{2}\,\hat{\mathbf{u}} \times \boldsymbol{l} - \frac{1}{2}\hat{\mathbf{u}} \times (\hat{\mathbf{u}} \times \boldsymbol{l}) \tag{1.44}$$

The screw axis Δ is then the set of points defined by

$$\Delta = \{Q \,|\, \mathbf{q} = \mathbf{p}^* + \nu\hat{\mathbf{u}}, \quad \nu \in \mathbb{R}\}$$

The general expression of the displacement is then

$$\mathbf{p}' = \boldsymbol{l} + e^{\alpha\mathbf{U}}(\mathbf{p}) = \boldsymbol{l} + e^{\alpha\mathbf{U}}(\mathbf{p}^*) + e^{\alpha\mathbf{U}}(\mathbf{q} - \mathbf{p}^*) + e^{\alpha\mathbf{U}}(\mathbf{p} - \mathbf{q})$$

where Q is an arbitrary point of Δ. We then find

$$e^{\alpha\mathbf{U}}(\mathbf{q} - \mathbf{p}^*) = (\mathbf{q} - \mathbf{p}^*), \qquad e^{\alpha\mathbf{U}}(\mathbf{p}^*) = \hat{\mathbf{u}} \times (\hat{\mathbf{u}} \times \boldsymbol{l}) + \mathbf{p}^*$$

Finally we obtain

$$\mathbf{p}' - \mathbf{q} = \lambda\hat{\mathbf{u}} + e^{\alpha\mathbf{U}}(\mathbf{p} - \mathbf{q}) \tag{1.45}$$

with $\lambda = \hat{\mathbf{u}} \cdot \boldsymbol{l}$. We conclude that the most general displacement of a rigid body is entirely defined by the following geometric quantities:

1. the screw displacement λ,
2. a point P^* of the screw axis Δ whose position is defined by (1.44),
3. the direction $\hat{\mathbf{u}}$ of Δ along and about which the body translates and rotates,
4. the angle of rotation α.

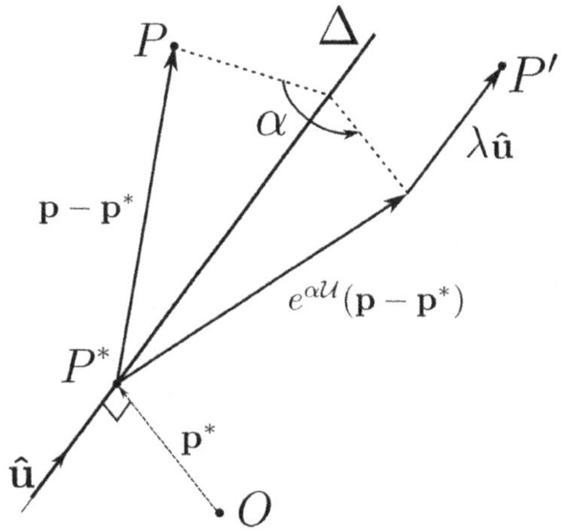

Figure 1.12

These results can be summarized by the following theorem (see Figure 1.12).

Theorem 1.7 — Mozzi-Chasles Theorem. Any displacement $\mathcal{D}$ of rigid body $\mathcal{B}$ can be expressed as an *helicoidal* or *screw displacement*, along a particular axis $\Delta(P^*, \hat{\mathbf{u}})$. If the displacement is not a translation, then the mapping $P \mapsto P'$ by $\mathcal{D}$ can be expressed as

$$\mathbf{p}' - \mathbf{q} = h\frac{\alpha}{2\pi}\hat{\mathbf{u}} + e^{\alpha \mathbf{U}}(\mathbf{p} - \mathbf{q}) \tag{1.46}$$

where Q is an arbitrary point of Δ, scalar h is called *pitch* of the screw, and $\mathcal{U}$ is the operator defined by $\mathbf{U}(\mathbf{V}) = \hat{\mathbf{u}} \times \mathbf{V}$. Hence a displacement which is not a translation, is fully characterized by its screw axis Δ, its angle α and its pitch h.

Remark 16. The displacement of all points of Δ is the quantity $\lambda = \hat{\mathbf{u}} \cdot \boldsymbol{l} = h\alpha/2\pi$.

Remark 17. The position of the screw axis changes relative to both $\mathcal{B}$ and $\mathcal{E}$ from one configuration to the next.

Remark 18. Displacements can be classified according to the set of their fixed points, that is, of points satisfying $\mathcal{D}(P) = P$: (i) if all points are fixed points, $\mathcal{D}$ is the identity, (ii) if there are no fixed points, $\mathcal{D}$ is either a translation or a screw displacement, (iii) if the set of fixed points is a line, then $\mathcal{D}$ is a rotation.

Example 1.10 Consider the mapping $P(x_1, x_2, x_3) \in \mathcal{B} \mapsto P'(x'_1, x'_2, x'_3)$ defined by the following equations

$$\begin{cases} x'_1 &= \frac{1}{4}(x_1 + 3x_2 - \sqrt{6}x_3) + 1 \\ x'_2 &= \frac{1}{4}(3x_1 + x_2 + \sqrt{6}x_3) + 1 \\ x'_3 &= \frac{1}{4}(\sqrt{6}x_1 - \sqrt{6}x_2 - 2x_3) - 1 \end{cases}$$

Show that this mapping corresponds to a screw displacement. Find the characteristics of this displacement (screw axis, angle and pitch). ■

The mapping can be written in the following form:

$$\mathbf{p}' = \boldsymbol{l} + \mathcal{R}(\mathbf{p}), \qquad [\boldsymbol{l}]_E = \begin{bmatrix} 1 \\ 1 \\ -1 \end{bmatrix} \qquad [\mathcal{R}]_E = \frac{1}{4}\begin{bmatrix} 1 & 3 & -\sqrt{6} \\ 3 & 1 & \sqrt{6} \\ \sqrt{6} & -\sqrt{6} & -2 \end{bmatrix}$$

We must check that matrix $[\mathcal{R}]_E$ corresponds to a rotation: if we denote the column vectors $(\mathbf{c}_1, \mathbf{c}_2, \mathbf{c}_3)$ we can verify that $\mathbf{c}_i \cdot \mathbf{c}_j = \delta_{ij}$ and that $\mathbf{c}_3 = \mathbf{c}_1 \times \mathbf{c}_2$. Since $\boldsymbol{l} \neq 0$, this mapping is necessarily a displacement.

We can find the direction of the corresponding screw axis by determining the set of invariant vectors by $\mathcal{R}$, that is, satisfying $\mathcal{R}(\mathbf{V}) = \mathbf{V}$:

$$\begin{cases} x_1 + 3x_2 - \sqrt{6}x_3 = 4x_1 \\ 3x_1 + x_2 + \sqrt{6}x_3 = 4x_2 \\ \sqrt{6}x_1 - \sqrt{6}x_2 - 2x_3 = 4x_3 \end{cases}$$

These equations are equivalent to

$$x_1 = x_2, \qquad x_3 = 0$$

We may choose $\hat{\mathbf{u}} = (\hat{\mathbf{e}}_1 + \hat{\mathbf{e}}_2)/\sqrt{2}$ as the direction of the screw axis. The corresponding angle α is found by finding $\cos\alpha$ and $\sin\alpha$:

$$2\cos\alpha + 1 = \mathrm{tr}(\mathcal{R}) = 0, \qquad \sin\alpha = (\hat{\mathbf{v}}, \mathcal{R}(\hat{\mathbf{v}}), \hat{\mathbf{u}}) = -\frac{\sqrt{3}}{2}$$

by choosing $\hat{\mathbf{v}} = \hat{\mathbf{e}}_3$ (normal to $\hat{\mathbf{u}}$). This gives $\alpha = 4\pi/3$. Finally $\mathcal{R} = \mathcal{R}_{4\pi/3,\hat{\mathbf{u}}}$.

The screw displacement is given by $\lambda = \boldsymbol{l} \cdot \hat{\mathbf{u}} = \sqrt{2}$: since $\lambda \neq 0$, the displacement is a screw displacement. To find the screw axis, we can find point P^* by applying formula (1.44), or we can find the set of points P whose displacement is $\sqrt{2}\hat{\mathbf{u}}$, that is, such that $\mathbf{p}' - \mathbf{p} = \sqrt{2}\hat{\mathbf{u}}$:

$$\begin{cases} -3x_1 + 3x_2 - \sqrt{6}x_3 = 0 \\ 3x_1 - 3x_2 + \sqrt{6}x_3 = 0 \\ \sqrt{6}x_1 - \sqrt{6}x_2 - 6x_3 = -1 \end{cases}$$

This gives the axis $\Delta(A, \hat{\mathbf{u}})$ with $A(1/\sqrt{6}, 0, -1/2)$. It is easy to verify that the point P^* given by

$$\mathbf{r}_{OP^*} = \frac{1}{2}\cot\frac{\alpha}{2}\,\hat{\mathbf{u}} \times \boldsymbol{l} - \frac{1}{2}\hat{\mathbf{u}} \times (\hat{\mathbf{u}} \times \boldsymbol{l}) = \left(\frac{\hat{\mathbf{e}}_1}{2\sqrt{6}} - \frac{\hat{\mathbf{e}}_2}{2\sqrt{6}} - \frac{\hat{\mathbf{e}}_3}{2}\right)$$

lies on axis Δ.

■

1.7.4 Displacements Under Small Rotations

Consider a rigid body $\mathcal{B}(B, \hat{\mathbf{b}}_1, \hat{\mathbf{b}}_2, \hat{\mathbf{b}}_3)$ in a referential $\mathcal{E}(O, \hat{\mathbf{e}}_1, \hat{\mathbf{e}}_2, \hat{\mathbf{e}}_3)$. Assume that body $\mathcal{B}$ undergoes a displacement $\mathcal{D}$ which takes every point P to a new position P'. We can then write the following equation between the positions of any two points P and Q of $\mathcal{B}$:

$$\mathbf{q}' - \mathbf{q} = (\mathcal{R} - \mathcal{I})(\mathbf{q} - \mathbf{p}) + \mathbf{p}' - \mathbf{p}$$

The displacements of P and Q are then related by the equation

$$\mathbf{d}_Q = \mathbf{d}_P + (\mathcal{R} - \mathcal{I})(\mathbf{q} - \mathbf{p})$$

The operator $\mathcal{R} = \mathcal{R}_{EB}$ is the rotation which maps basis $(\hat{\mathbf{e}}_1, \hat{\mathbf{e}}_2, \hat{\mathbf{e}}_3)$ of $\mathcal{E}$ to basis $(\hat{\mathbf{b}}_1, \hat{\mathbf{b}}_2, \hat{\mathbf{b}}_3)$ of $\mathcal{B}$. Assume that the orientation of $\mathcal{B}$ is parametrized by Bryant angles according to the transforms

$$(\hat{\mathbf{e}}_1, \hat{\mathbf{e}}_2, \hat{\mathbf{e}}_3) \xrightarrow{\mathcal{R}_{\psi,\hat{\mathbf{e}}_3}} (\hat{\mathbf{u}}_1, \hat{\mathbf{u}}_2, \hat{\mathbf{u}}_3 = \hat{\mathbf{e}}_3) \xrightarrow{\mathcal{R}_{\theta,\hat{\mathbf{u}}_2}} (\hat{\mathbf{v}}_1, \hat{\mathbf{v}}_2 = \hat{\mathbf{u}}_2, \hat{\mathbf{v}}_3) \xrightarrow{\mathcal{R}_{\phi,\hat{\mathbf{v}}_1}} (\hat{\mathbf{b}}_1 = \hat{\mathbf{v}}_1, \hat{\mathbf{b}}_2, \hat{\mathbf{b}}_3)$$

According to Section 1.4, the corresponding rotation matrix is found to be

$$[\mathcal{R}_{EB}]_E = [\mathcal{C}_{EB}] = \begin{bmatrix} c_\psi c_\theta & c_\psi s_\theta s_\phi - s_\psi c_\phi & c_\psi s_\theta c_\phi + s_\psi s_\phi \\ s_\psi c_\theta & s_\psi s_\theta s_\phi + c_\psi c_\phi & s_\psi s_\theta c_\phi - c_\psi s_\phi \\ -s_\theta & c_\theta s_\phi & c_\theta c_\phi \end{bmatrix}$$

Let us assume a small rotation, that is, small values of the angles (ψ, θ, ϕ): by keeping only the terms of order 1 in (ψ, θ, ϕ) we find that the rotation matrix takes the following form

$$[\mathcal{R}_{EB}]_E = [\mathcal{C}_{EB}] = \begin{bmatrix} 1 & -\psi & \theta \\ \psi & 1 & -\phi \\ -\theta & \phi & 1 \end{bmatrix}$$

Hence, matrix $[\mathcal{R}_{EB} - \mathcal{I}]_E$ takes the form:

$$[\mathcal{R}_{EB} - \mathcal{I}]_E = \begin{bmatrix} 0 & -\psi & \theta \\ \psi & 0 & -\phi \\ -\theta & \phi & 0 \end{bmatrix}$$

We conclude that the operator $\mathcal{R}_{EB} - \mathcal{I}$ is skew-symmetric and that it can be expressed as

$$(\mathcal{R}_{EB} - \mathcal{I})(\mathbf{q} - \mathbf{p}) = \mathbf{\Omega} \times \mathbf{r}_{PQ} \tag{1.47}$$

with $\mathbf{\Omega} = \phi \hat{\mathbf{e}}_1 + \theta \hat{\mathbf{e}}_2 + \psi \hat{\mathbf{e}}_3$. This leads to the following theorem.

Theorem 1.8 The displacement field $\mathbf{d}_P = \mathbf{p}' - \mathbf{p} = \mathbf{r}_{PP'}$ of a rigid body satisfies the property

$$\mathbf{d}_Q = \mathbf{d}_P + \mathbf{\Omega} \times \mathbf{r}_{PQ} \tag{1.48}$$

for small rotations of the body. The vector $\mathbf{\Omega}$ is known as the *rotation vector* of the body.

Remark 19. It can be seen that the rotation vector is an invariant of the body (for small rotations): it is not a function of position or of the chosen coordinate system.

Remark 20. Vector fields satisfying the property $\mathbf{v}_Q = \mathbf{v}_P + \mathbf{V} \times \mathbf{r}_{PQ}$ play a central role in rigid-body mechanics. They will be studied in Chapter 4.

1.8 Problems

Problem 1.1 Which of the two matrices

$$\begin{pmatrix} -1 & 0 & 0 \\ 0 & 1 & 0 \\ 0 & 0 & 1 \end{pmatrix} \qquad \frac{1}{25}\begin{pmatrix} 9 & 12 & -20 \\ 12 & 16 & 15 \\ 20 & -15 & 0 \end{pmatrix}$$

represents a rotation?

Problem 1.2 Find symmetric and skew-symmetric parts of the matrix of rotation $\mathcal{R}_{\frac{\pi}{3},\hat{\mathbf{u}}}$ with $\hat{\mathbf{u}} = (\hat{\mathbf{e}}_1 + \hat{\mathbf{e}}_2 + \hat{\mathbf{e}}_3)/\sqrt{3}$.

Problem 1.3 If the given matrix is a rotation matrix, find its equivalent angle/axis representation in each case:

$$\begin{pmatrix} 0 & 0 & 1 \\ 1 & 0 & 0 \\ 0 & 1 & 0 \end{pmatrix} \qquad \frac{1}{25}\begin{pmatrix} 9 & 12 & -20 \\ 12 & 16 & 15 \\ 20 & -15 & 0 \end{pmatrix}$$

$$\frac{1}{3}\begin{pmatrix} -1 & 2 & 2 \\ 2 & -1 & 2 \\ 2 & 2 & -1 \end{pmatrix}$$

Problem 1.4 Given three real scalars a, b, and c, consider the following matrix

$$[A]_E = \begin{pmatrix} a & b & c \\ c & a & b \\ b & c & a \end{pmatrix}$$

Show that $[A]_E$ is a rotation matrix if and only if a, b and c are the roots of the polynomial $p(x) = x^3 - x^2 + k$, with $0 \leq k \leq 4/27$. Describe the axis of this rotation.

Problem 1.5 Consider the equivalent rotation $\mathcal{R}_{\alpha,\hat{\mathbf{u}}}$ corresponding to rotation $\mathcal{R}_{BE}$ which maps a basis of $\mathcal{E}$ to a basis of $\mathcal{B}$. When the equivalent angle α is close to π, show that the equations

$$u_k^2 = \frac{c_{kk} - \cos\alpha}{1 - \cos\alpha}, \quad k = 1,2,3$$

can be used to determine $\hat{\mathbf{u}} = u_1\hat{\mathbf{e}}_1 + u_2\hat{\mathbf{e}}_2 + u_3\hat{\mathbf{e}}_3$, with $c_{ij} = \hat{\mathbf{e}}_i \cdot \hat{\mathbf{b}}_j$.

Problem 1.6 Consider the equivalent rotation $\mathcal{R}_{\alpha,\hat{\mathbf{u}}}$ which maps basis $(\hat{\mathbf{e}}_1, \hat{\mathbf{e}}_2, \hat{\mathbf{e}}_3)$ of $\mathcal{E}$ to basis $(\hat{\mathbf{b}}_1, \hat{\mathbf{b}}_2, \hat{\mathbf{b}}_3)$ of body $\mathcal{B}$. Let $(\hat{\mathbf{a}}_1, \hat{\mathbf{a}}_2, \hat{\mathbf{a}}_3)$ be an auxiliary basis.

a. Show that the skew-symmetric operator $\mathcal{U} : \mathbf{V} \mapsto \hat{\mathbf{u}} \times \mathbf{V}$ satisfies

$$2\sin\alpha\, \mathcal{U} = \mathcal{R}_{AB} \circ \mathcal{R}_{EA}^T - \mathcal{R}_{EA} \circ \mathcal{R}_{AB}^T$$

b. Deduce that the equivalent axis and angle satisfy

$$2\sin\alpha\ \hat{\mathbf{u}} = \hat{\mathbf{e}}_1 \times \hat{\mathbf{b}}_1 + \hat{\mathbf{e}}_2 \times \hat{\mathbf{b}}_2 + \hat{\mathbf{e}}_3 \times \hat{\mathbf{b}}_3$$

Problem 1.7 Find the mapping of $\mathbf{V} = x\hat{\mathbf{e}}_1 + y\hat{\mathbf{e}}_2 + z\hat{\mathbf{e}}_3$ by the rotation of angle $\alpha = 2\pi/3$ about $(\hat{\mathbf{e}}_1 + \hat{\mathbf{e}}_2 + \hat{\mathbf{e}}_3)$. Describe the mapping of the unit cube by this rotation.

Problem 1.8 Prove the identity

$$\mathbf{U} \times (\mathbf{V} \times \mathbf{W}) = (\mathbf{U} \cdot \mathbf{W})\mathbf{V} - (\mathbf{U} \cdot \mathbf{V})\mathbf{W}$$

given 3 vectors $\mathbf{U}, \mathbf{V}$ and $\mathbf{W}$ by a quaternion calculus.

Problem 1.9 Consider the quaternion $Q = \frac{1}{2} + \frac{1}{2}\hat{\mathbf{e}}_1 + \frac{1}{2}\hat{\mathbf{e}}_2 + \frac{1}{2}\hat{\mathbf{e}}_3$.

a. Find $Q + \overline{Q}$ and $Q\overline{Q}$: deduce Q^2.

b. Find $Q^2 - Q + 1$: deduce Q^3.

Problem 1.10 Given two real numbers q_0 and q_1,

a. find the quaternions Q which satisfy $Q\hat{\mathbf{e}}_1 = \hat{\mathbf{e}}_1(q_0 + q_1\hat{\mathbf{e}}_1)$. Deduce the value of $Q_\theta\hat{\mathbf{e}}_1\overline{Q}_\theta$ for $Q_\theta = \cos\frac{\theta}{2} + \hat{\mathbf{e}}_1 \sin\frac{\theta}{2}$.

b. find the quaternions Q which satisfy $Q\hat{\mathbf{e}}_2 = \hat{\mathbf{e}}_2(q_0 + q_1\hat{\mathbf{e}}_1)$. Deduce the value of $Q_\theta\hat{\mathbf{e}}_2\overline{Q}_\theta$ for $Q_\theta = \cos\frac{\theta}{2} + \hat{\mathbf{e}}_1 \sin\frac{\theta}{2}$.

Problem 1.11 a. Show that the multiplication of quaternions is associative, that is, $Q_1(Q_2Q_3) = (Q_1Q_2)Q_3$ for any three quaternions Q_1, Q_2 and Q_3.

b. Find the quaternions Q which satisfy $QQ_0 = Q_0Q$ for all $Q_0 \in \mathbb{H}$.

Problem 1.12 We define quaternion e^Q as the formal expansion $1+Q+\frac{1}{2}Q^2+\cdots+\frac{Q^n}{n!}+\cdots$. Given a pure unit quaternion $0+\hat{\mathbf{u}}$ and a real number θ, show that

$$e^{\theta\hat{\mathbf{u}}} = \cos\theta + \sin\theta\hat{\mathbf{u}}$$

Conclude that any unit quaternion can be put in the form $e^{\theta\hat{\mathbf{u}}}$. Is $e^{\theta\hat{\mathbf{u}}}e^{\phi\hat{\mathbf{v}}}$ equal to $e^{\theta\hat{\mathbf{u}}+\phi\hat{\mathbf{v}}}$?

Problem 1.13 Show that the set S^3 of unit quaternions forms a group under the multiplication rule, that is,
(i) if $P,Q\in S^3$, then $PQ\in S^3$ (closure),
(ii) for all $P,Q,R\in S^3$, $P(QR)=(PQ)R$ (associativity),
(iii) $1\in S^3$ and for all $Q\in S^3$, $1Q=Q1$ (identity element),
(iv) For each $Q\in S^3$ there exists $Q^{-1}\in S^3$ such that $QQ^{-1}=Q^{-1}Q=1$ (inverse).

Problem 1.14 Show that for all non-zero quaternion Q there exist a unique a positive real number λ and a unique unit quaternion R such that $Q=\lambda R$.

Problem 1.15 Given two quaternions $Q=q_0+\mathbf{q}$ and $Q'=q_0+\mathbf{q}$, consider the bilinear form $\langle Q,Q'\rangle = q_0q_0'+\mathbf{q}\cdot\mathbf{q}'$.

a. Show that $\langle .,. \rangle$ defines a scalar product in $\mathbb{H}$.

b. Given two quaternions Q and R, show that the following three statements are equivalent:
(i) Q and R are orthogonal, that is, $\langle Q,R\rangle=0$
(ii) $Q\bar{R}$ is a pure quaternion,
(iii) $Q\bar{R}+R\bar{Q}=0$.

Problem 1.16 In referential $\mathcal{E}(O,\hat{\mathbf{e}}_1,\hat{\mathbf{e}}_2,\hat{\mathbf{e}}_3)$, consider the rotations $\mathcal{R}_{\alpha,\hat{\mathbf{e}}_1}$, $\mathcal{R}_{\beta,\hat{\mathbf{e}}_2}$ and $\mathcal{R}_{\gamma,\hat{\mathbf{e}}_3}$.

a. Find the equivalent angle and axis of rotation $\mathcal{R}_{\alpha,\hat{\mathbf{e}}_1}\circ\mathcal{R}_{\beta,\hat{\mathbf{e}}_2}$.

b. Find the quaternion associated with rotation $\mathcal{R}_{\alpha,\hat{\mathbf{e}}_1}\circ\mathcal{R}_{\beta,\hat{\mathbf{e}}_2}\circ\mathcal{R}_{\gamma,\hat{\mathbf{e}}_3}$.

Problem 1.17 Let $Q=q_0+q_1\hat{\mathbf{e}}_1+q_2\hat{\mathbf{e}}_2+q_3\hat{\mathbf{e}}_3$ be a quaternion. Define the 4x4 matrix $[\mathcal{M}]$ as follows

$$[\mathcal{M}] = \begin{pmatrix} q_0 & -q_1 & -q_2 & -q_3 \\ q_1 & q_0 & -q_3 & q_2 \\ q_2 & q_3 & q_0 & -q_1 \\ q_3 & -q_2 & q_1 & q_0 \end{pmatrix}$$

a. Show that $Q=1$ corresponds to the diagonal matrix $[\mathcal{M}]=\text{diag}(1,1,1,1)$.

b. Show that the conjugate $\overline{Q}$ of Q corresponds to $[\mathcal{M}]^T$, and that the inverse Q^{-1} of Q corresponds to $[\mathcal{M}]^{-1}=\frac{1}{|Q|^2}[\mathcal{M}]^T$.

c. Show that if Q is a unit quaternion, then $[\mathcal{M}]^{-1}=[\mathcal{M}]^T$.

d. Show that if $Q_3=Q_1Q_2$ corresponds to $[\mathcal{M}_3]=[\mathcal{M}_1][\mathcal{M}_2]$.

Problem 1.18 In basis $(\hat{\mathbf{e}}_1,\hat{\mathbf{e}}_2,\hat{\mathbf{e}}_3)$ of referential $\mathcal{E}$ a rigid body is subject to the displacement $P\in\mathcal{B}\mapsto P'$ described by the equations

$$x_1'=x_3,\qquad x_2'=x_1,\qquad x_3'=x_2$$

Show that this displacement is a rotation about O. Find its equivalent angle and direction.

Problem 1.19 In basis $(\hat{\mathbf{e}}_1,\hat{\mathbf{e}}_2,\hat{\mathbf{e}}_3)$ of referential $\mathcal{E}$ a rigid body is subject to the displacement $P\in\mathcal{B}\mapsto P'$ described by the equations

$$\begin{aligned} x_1' &= -\frac{2}{3}x_1-\frac{1}{3}x_2+\frac{2}{3}x_3+1 \\ x_2' &= \frac{2}{3}x_1-\frac{2}{3}x_2+\frac{1}{3}x_3+1 \\ x_3' &= \frac{1}{3}x_1+\frac{2}{3}x_2+\frac{2}{3}x_3+3 \end{aligned}$$

Show that this is a valid displacement and find the corresponding screw parameters (screw axis, angle and pitch).

Problem 1.20 Repeat Problem 1.19 for the following transformation

$$\begin{aligned} x_1' &= \frac{1}{2}x_1+\frac{1}{2}x_2-\frac{\sqrt{2}}{2}x_3+\frac{-3+\sqrt{2}}{2} \\ x_2' &= \frac{1}{2}x_1+\frac{1}{2}x_2+\frac{\sqrt{2}}{2}x_3-\frac{1+\sqrt{2}}{2} \\ x_3' &= \frac{\sqrt{2}}{2}x_1+\frac{\sqrt{2}}{2}x_2+x_3++\frac{\sqrt{2}}{2} \end{aligned}$$

Problem 1.21 Show that it is not possible to find a displacement of the unit sphere which keeps its center fixed and displaces every point of its surface.

Problem 1.22 Figure 1.13 shows two configurations of a rigid body in the shape of a unit cube, where A is mapped into A_1, B into B_1, etc. Consider the rotation which maps basis $(\hat{\imath}, \hat{\jmath}, \hat{\mathbf{k}})$ into $(\hat{\imath}_1, \hat{\jmath}_1, \hat{\mathbf{k}}_1)$.

a. Find its matrix representation on basis $(\hat{\imath}, \hat{\jmath}, \hat{\mathbf{k}})$, then on basis $(\hat{\imath}_1, \hat{\jmath}_1, \hat{\mathbf{k}}_1)$.

b. Find its equivalent representation $\mathcal{R}_{\alpha,\hat{\mathbf{u}}}$ and the corresponding unit quaternion.

c. Find the screw parameters (screw axis, angle and pitch) of the displacement which takes the body from the initial configuration to its final configuration.

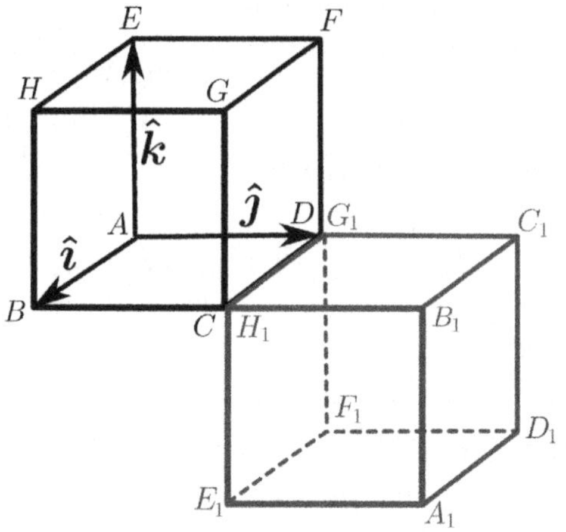

Figure 1.13

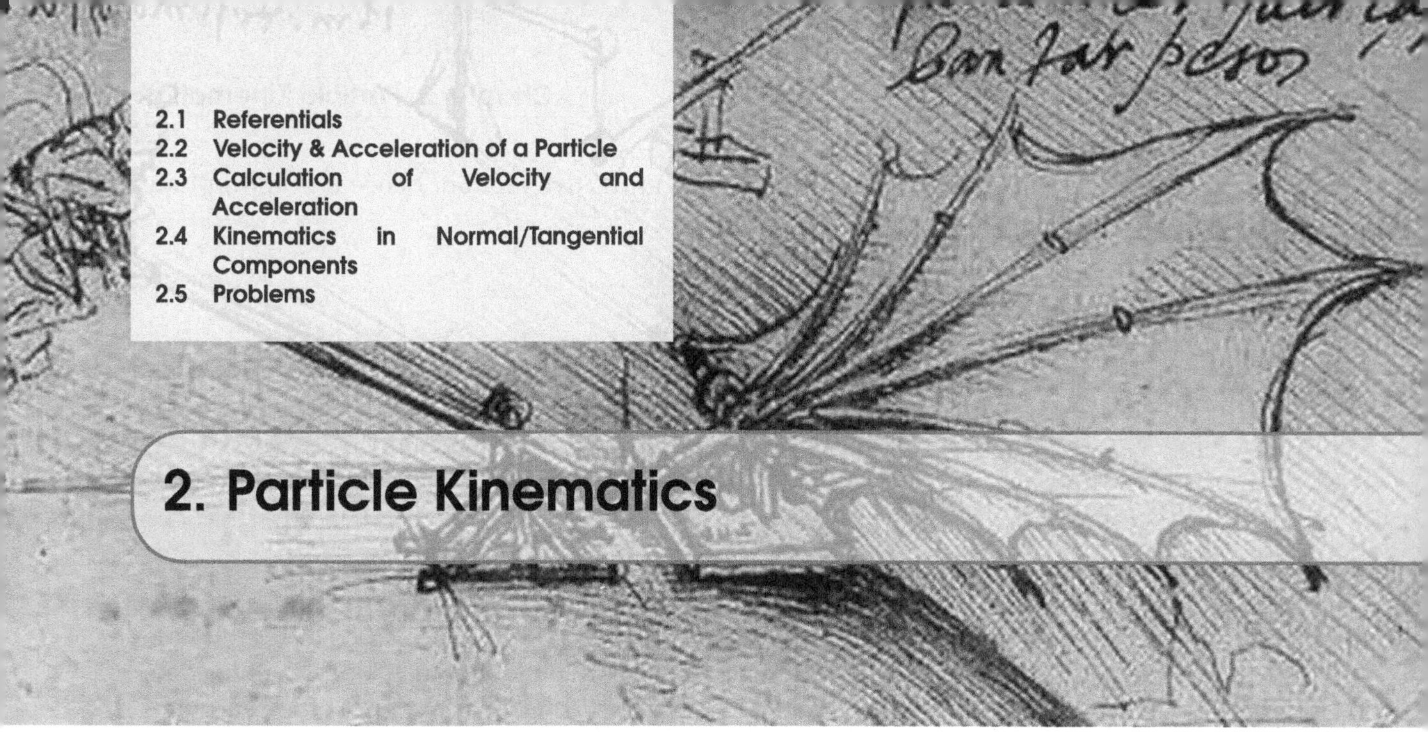

2. Particle Kinematics

KINEMATICS is the study of motions in themselves, that is, without consideration of their causes. In this chapter, we consider the motion of *particles*, that is, of points in motion in a three-dimensional referential $\mathcal{E}$, relative to which the observer is attached. A particle P describes a *trajectory* relative to $\mathcal{E}$. At any time, one can define the *velocity* and *acceleration* vectors of P. These kinematic quantities depend on the choice of referential. Relative to another referential $\mathcal{F}$ (itself in motion relative to $\mathcal{E}$) the trajectory of P (and the corresponding kinematics) will be different. We shall learn how to determine the kinematics of a particle in a variety of ways, given a particular description of its trajectory, or conversely, learn how to find the trajectory of a particle, given a description of its kinematics.

2.1 Referentials

We have defined in Section 1.1 a referential $\mathcal{E}$ as a three-dimensional space, typically associated with the rigid extension of a physical body. A referential is equipped with a clock allowing the measurements of the time t of occurrence of (simultaneous) events at various locations of $\mathcal{E}$. Now consider another referential $\mathcal{F}$ in motion relative to $\mathcal{E}$. In each referential, an observer is equipped with a clock to record the occurrence of events. We assume that the clocks of $\mathcal{E}$ and $\mathcal{F}$ have been synchronized. In classical mechanics, we make the fundamental assumption that *two events which occur simultaneously in $\mathcal{E}$ must occur simultaneously in $\mathcal{F}$*: this implies that the clocks of $\mathcal{E}$ and $\mathcal{F}$ indicate identical times of occurrence of a specific event. Similarly, we assume that *the distances measured in $\mathcal{E}$ and $\mathcal{F}$ between two simultaneous events are identical*. In particular, the length measured between any two points of a referential (or rigid body) remains constant relative to any other referential.

The main task we face in mechanics is the determination the time rate of change $d\mathbf{V}/dt$ of vector functions $\mathbf{V}(t)$. However, vector functions, as opposed to scalar functions, have different time-derivatives in different referentials in relative motion: hence it is appropriate to denote $d\mathbf{V}/dt$ relative to referential $\mathcal{E}$ as

$$\left(\frac{d\mathbf{V}}{dt}\right)_{\mathcal{E}}$$

in order to specify the dependence upon referential. *We will always do so whenever necessary.* [1]

In practice, the calculation of the time-derivative of $\mathbf{V}$ relative to $\mathcal{E}$ can be done by resolving $\mathbf{V}$ on a basis $(\hat{\mathbf{e}}_1, \hat{\mathbf{e}}_2, \hat{\mathbf{e}}_3)$ of unit vectors fixed in $\mathcal{E}$: $\mathbf{V} = V_1\hat{\mathbf{e}}_1 + V_2\hat{\mathbf{e}}_2 + V_3\hat{\mathbf{e}}_3$. If $\mathbf{V}$ is a function of time, its components should also be functions of time. Then since $(\hat{\mathbf{e}}_1, \hat{\mathbf{e}}_2, \hat{\mathbf{e}}_3)$ are constant in $\mathcal{E}$, $d\mathbf{V}/dt$ is given by [2]

$$\left(\frac{d\mathbf{V}}{dt}\right)_{\mathcal{E}} = \frac{d}{dt}(V_1\hat{\mathbf{e}}_1 + V_2\hat{\mathbf{e}}_2 + V_3\hat{\mathbf{e}}_3) = \dot{V}_1\hat{\mathbf{e}}_1 + \dot{V}_2\hat{\mathbf{e}}_2 + \dot{V}_3\hat{\mathbf{e}}_3 \tag{2.1}$$

This approach is adequate for most applications in particle kinematics, but it will become quickly laborious in rigid body kinematics. We shall learn in Chapter 3 how the concept of angular velocity will allow us to perform time derivatives of vector functions.

Let us mention properties of the time-differentiation w.r.t. to a given referential

$$\frac{d}{dt}(\mathbf{V}+\mathbf{W}) = \frac{d\mathbf{V}}{dt} + \frac{d\mathbf{V}}{dt} \tag{2.2}$$

$$\frac{d}{dt}(\lambda\mathbf{V}) = \dot{\lambda}\mathbf{V} + \lambda\frac{d\mathbf{V}}{dt} \tag{2.3}$$

$$\frac{d}{dt}(\mathbf{V}\cdot\mathbf{W}) = \frac{d\mathbf{V}}{dt}\cdot\mathbf{W} + \mathbf{V}\cdot\frac{d\mathbf{W}}{dt} \tag{2.4}$$

$$\frac{d}{dt}(\mathbf{V}\times\mathbf{W}) = \frac{d\mathbf{V}}{dt}\times\mathbf{W} + \mathbf{V}\times\frac{d\mathbf{W}}{dt} \tag{2.5}$$

for two arbitrary vectors $\mathbf{V}$ and $\mathbf{W}$. Here $\mathbf{V}\cdot\mathbf{W}$ and $\mathbf{V}\times\mathbf{W}$ are the scalar product and vector product between $\mathbf{V}$ and $\mathbf{W}$, respectively.

Remark 1. In equation (2.4) the derivative of scalar $\mathbf{V}\cdot\mathbf{W}$ is independent of the choice of referential: however, one must choose the same referential to evaluate the expression $\mathbf{W}\cdot d\mathbf{V}/dt + \mathbf{V}\cdot d\mathbf{W}/dt$.

As an application of these properties, here are two useful theorems:

Theorem 2.1 A vector $\mathbf{V}(t)$ remains of constant magnitude if and only if $\mathbf{V}$ remains perpendicular to its derivative $d\mathbf{V}/dt$ (relative to any referential $\mathcal{E}$).

Proof. The time-derivative of the scalar $|\mathbf{V}|^2 = \mathbf{V}\cdot\mathbf{V}$ vanishes since vector $\mathbf{V}$ has a constant magnitude. This gives

$$\frac{d\mathbf{V}}{dt}\cdot\mathbf{V} + \mathbf{V}\cdot\frac{d\mathbf{V}}{dt} = 0$$

Hence $\mathbf{V}\cdot(d\mathbf{V}/dt) = 0$: $\mathbf{V}$ and $d\mathbf{V}/dt$ are orthogonal. ■

[1] If only one referential is involved in a particular context, we omit its dependence upon time-derivatives.

[2] We will always denote the derivative of a scalar function $u(t)$ as $\dot{u}$.

Theorem 2.2 A non-zero vector $\mathbf{V}(t)$ remains of constant direction in a referential $\mathcal{E}$ if and only if $\mathbf{V}$ remains collinear to its time-derivative $d\mathbf{V}/dt$ in $\mathcal{E}$.

Proof. To prove this property, introduce the unit vector $\hat{\mathbf{v}} = \mu\mathbf{V}$ with $\mu = 1/|\mathbf{V}|$ ($\mathbf{V}$ is not zero) which is collinear to $\mathbf{V}$. If $\mathbf{V}(t)$ remains of constant direction, then $\hat{\mathbf{v}}(t)$ is constant vector. We then take the cross-product of both sides of $d\hat{\mathbf{v}}/dt = \dot{\mu}\mathbf{V} + \mu(d\mathbf{V}/dt) = \mathbf{0}$ with vector $\mathbf{V}$ to find

$$\mathbf{V} \times \frac{d\mathbf{V}}{dt} = 0 \tag{2.6}$$

which shows that $\mathbf{V}$ and $d\mathbf{V}/dt$ are collinear. Conversely, assume (2.6) holds, then it is easy to show that $\hat{\mathbf{v}} \times d\hat{\mathbf{v}}/dt = 0$. Hence $\hat{\mathbf{v}}$ is collinear to $d\hat{\mathbf{v}}/dt$. Furthermore, from theorem 2.1, $\hat{\mathbf{v}}$ is also orthogonal to $d\hat{\mathbf{v}}/dt$, since $\hat{\mathbf{v}}$ is a unit vector. Then necessarily $d\hat{\mathbf{v}}/dt = \mathbf{0}$, that is, $\hat{\mathbf{v}}$ is a constant vector in $\mathcal{E}$: $\mathbf{V}$ remains of constant direction. ■

2.2 Velocity & Acceleration of a Particle

Consider a particle P in motion relative to a referential $\mathcal{E}$. Its position in $\mathcal{E}$ is defined by its *position vector* $\mathbf{r}_{OP}$ relative to an origin O (an arbitrary point fixed in $\mathcal{E}$).

Definition 2.1 — Velocity/Acceleration. The *velocity* of P, denoted $\mathbf{v}_{P/\mathcal{E}}$, is the vector defined as

$$\mathbf{v}_{P/\mathcal{E}} = \left(\frac{d\mathbf{r}_{OP}}{dt}\right)_{\mathcal{E}} \tag{2.7}$$

The *speed* of point P, denoted $v_{P/\mathcal{E}}$, is the magnitude of its velocity vector. The acceleration of P, denoted $\mathbf{a}_{P/\mathcal{E}}$, is the vector defined as

$$\mathbf{a}_{P/\mathcal{E}} = \left(\frac{d\mathbf{v}_{P/\mathcal{E}}}{dt}\right)_{\mathcal{E}} \tag{2.8}$$

In applications where only one referential is present, we generally omit to specify the dependence upon $\mathcal{E}$, and we simply write the velocity and acceleration of P as $\mathbf{v}_P$ and $\mathbf{a}_P$. But we must keep in mind that if $\mathcal{F}$ is another referential in motion relative to $\mathcal{E}$, we expect $\mathbf{v}_{P/\mathcal{F}}$ to be different from $\mathbf{v}_{P/\mathcal{E}}$.

Note that the velocity of P does not depend on the choice of origin of $\mathcal{E}$. Consider O' another point attached to $\mathcal{E}$. Then we can write $\mathbf{r}_{O'P} = \mathbf{r}_{O'O} + \mathbf{r}_{OP}$. This equality can be differentiated (in $\mathcal{E}$) to give

$$\frac{d\mathbf{r}_{O'P}}{dt} = \frac{d\mathbf{r}_{O'O}}{dt} + \frac{d\mathbf{r}_{OP}}{dt} = \frac{d\mathbf{r}_{OP}}{dt},$$

since vector $\mathbf{r}_{O'O}$ remains constant relative to $\mathcal{E}$.

The acceleration of P characterizes the time rate-of-change of both the magnitude and direction of its velocity. In particular, the acceleration of a point with constant speed is not, in general, zero. The motion of P is said to be *accelerated* if $\mathbf{v}_P \cdot \mathbf{a}_P > 0$. Conversely, it is said to be *decelerated* if $\mathbf{v}_P \cdot \mathbf{a}_P < 0$. The *trajectory* of P in referential $\mathcal{E}$ is the locus described by $P(t)$ as time varies from an instant t_0 to an instant $t_1 > t_0$. The velocity vector of P is tangent to the trajectory at point P, and is oriented in the sense of the trajectory.

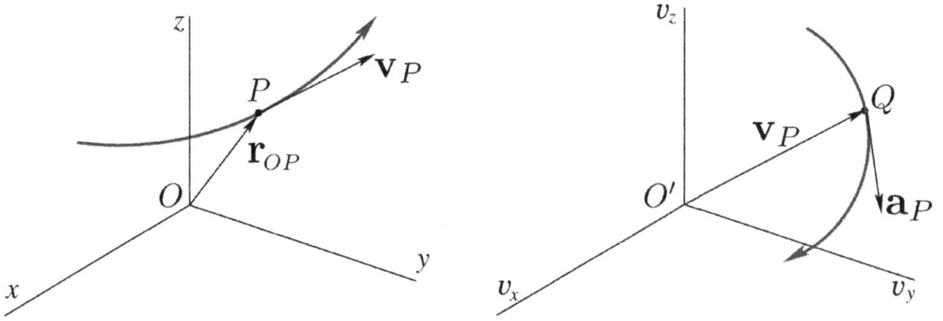

Figure 2.1 – *Trajectory and hodograph of a point P.*

The acceleration of P is graphically less intuitive. We can visualize this vector in the following way: consider the fictitious point Q moving in the velocity space $Ov_xv_yv_z$ and whose position vector is defined by the velocity of P

$$\mathbf{r}_{OQ} = \mathbf{v}_P$$

The trajectory of point Q as P moves in referential $\mathcal{E}$ is called the *hodograph* of P. The velocity of Q is $\mathbf{a}_P$: hence, the acceleration of P, $\mathbf{a}_P$, is tangent to the hodograph at point Q. See Figure 2.1.

In practice, the velocity and acceleration of P can be determined in a variety of ways depending on the chosen coordinate system within the same referential. As will be seen in the following sections, we can express the same velocity vector $\mathbf{v}_P$ (or any other vectorial quantity associated with the motion of P) in various ways depending on the choice of unit vectors which may be fixed or in motion relative to $\mathcal{E}$.

2.3 Calculation of Velocity and Acceleration

In this section, we determine the components of velocity and acceleration on the three coordinate systems defined in Section 1.2.

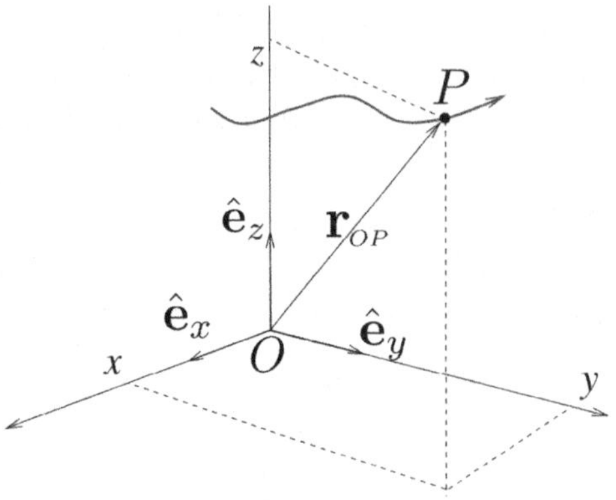

Figure 2.2

2.3.1 Cartesian Coordinates of Velocity and Acceleration

Consider three Cartesian axes Ox, Oy and Oz fixed in referential $\mathcal{E}$ and mutually perpendicular, directed on unit vectors $\hat{\mathbf{e}}_x$, $\hat{\mathbf{e}}_y$ and $\hat{\mathbf{e}}_z$, respectively. Let (x, y, z) define the Cartesian coordinates of a particle P in motion in $\mathcal{E}$. See Figure 2.2. The position of P is then defined by

$$\mathbf{r}_{OP} = x\hat{\mathbf{e}}_x + y\hat{\mathbf{e}}_y + z\hat{\mathbf{e}}_z \tag{2.9}$$

Then, the velocity of P is given by time-differentiation of $\mathbf{r}_{OP}$ relative to $\mathcal{E}$:

$$\mathbf{v}_{P/\mathcal{E}} = \dot{x}\hat{\mathbf{e}}_x + \dot{y}\hat{\mathbf{e}}_y + \dot{z}\hat{\mathbf{e}}_z \tag{2.10}$$

Example 2.1 In WW1, German high-velocity 77mm shells were known as "whizz-bangs" as soldiers would first hear the high-pitched noise of the shell before its explosion[3]. To study this phenomenon, consider shell P fired from a cannon located at the origin O of a plane Oxy. Assume that P travels at constant speed v along axis Ox. A fixed observer located in plane Oxy at point Q at distance r from O can hear the explosion and whistling sound of P along its trajectory. Denote by c the speed of sound and by θ the angle of line OQ with line Ox ($0 < \theta \leq \pi$) and assume $v > c$.

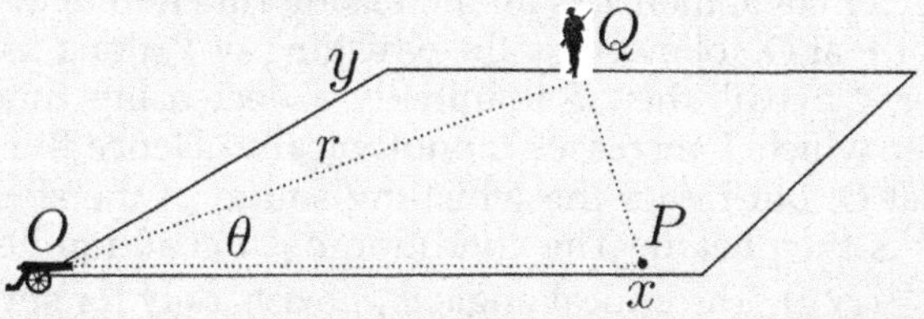

Show that the explosion is not necessarily the first event heard by the observer if $\theta < \theta_{crit}$. ■

At a given time t, the position of P is defined by coordinate x. Since the speed of P is constant, we have

$$x = vt$$

setting $t = 0$ at $x = 0$. The passage of P at position x creates a sound wave which travels to Q (or any other point) at speed c. At any given position of P, the sound travels at constant speed c along line PQ: it takes the time $|PQ|/c$ for the sound to travel the distance $|PQ|$. Hence the time taken for the sound to reach position Q corresponding to the passage of P at position x (that is, at time t) is given by

$$T = t + \frac{|PQ|}{c}$$

We can express distance $|PQ|$ in terms of x, r, and θ by examination of triangle OPQ:

$$|PQ|^2 = x^2 + r^2 - 2rx\cos\theta$$

Finally time T takes the expression

$$T = \frac{x}{v} + \frac{1}{c}\sqrt{x^2 + r^2 - 2rx\cos\theta} \qquad [1]$$

To relate this result to the actual sequence of events perceived by observer Q, we sketch function $T(x)$ for $x \geq 0$. First we note that for large x, T is a linear function of x:

$$T \sim (\frac{1}{v} + \frac{1}{c})x, \qquad x \to \infty$$

However, T is not necessarily a monotonic function of x as is seen by the expansion near $x = 0$:

$$T \sim \frac{r}{c} + (\frac{1}{v} - \frac{1}{c}\cos\theta)x, \qquad x \to 0$$

[3] Most soldiers in the cannon line of sight would unfortunately only hear the "whizz".

We must distinguish two cases (see Figure 2.3) if $v > c$:

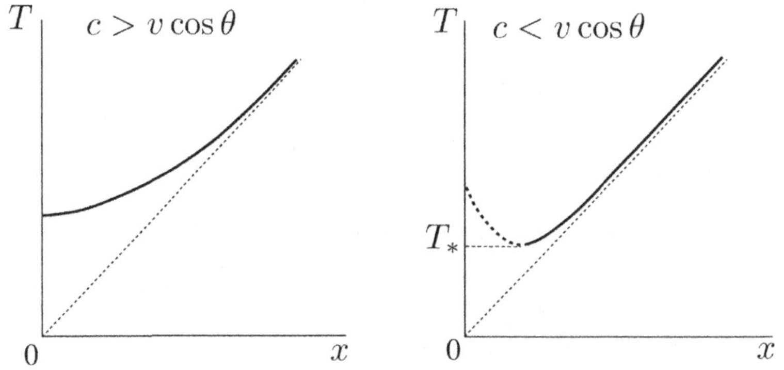

Figure 2.3

Case 1: if $c > v\cos\theta$, then T is an increasing function of x. The first event heard by Q is the explosion of P at O, followed by the whistling of P along its trajectory.

Case 2: if $c < v\cos\theta$, then T is initially a decreasing function of x until the value T_* is reached, after which T increases monotonically. Hence the first event heard by Q is not the explosion at O, but rather the whistling sound of the shell! [4] At time $T(0) > T_*$, the explosion of P is then heard. The condition $c < v\cos\theta$ implies that Q is inside the region $\theta < \theta_{crit} = \cos^{-1}(c/v)$. The critical angle θ_{crit} exists only for supersonic shells ($v > c$).

■

Cartesian coordinates are not always well-suited for the kinematics of particles, especially, for curvilinear motion. The cylindrical and spherical coordinate systems are the most widely used curvilinear coordinate systems. But other coordinate systems can be devised.

2.3.2 Cylindrical Coordinate System

Given Cartesian axes $Oxyz$ attached to referential $\mathcal{E}$, let (r, θ, z) define the cylindrical coordinates of a particle P in motion in $\mathcal{E}$. See Figure 2.4. On basis $(\hat{\mathbf{e}}_r, \hat{\mathbf{e}}_\theta, \hat{\mathbf{e}}_z)$, the position vector of P takes the expression

$$\mathbf{r}_{OP} = r\hat{\mathbf{e}}_r + z\hat{\mathbf{e}}_z \tag{2.11}$$

Both unit vectors $\hat{\mathbf{e}}_r$ and $\hat{\mathbf{e}}_\theta$ are function of angle θ and are time-dependent. The velocity $\mathbf{v}_P$ and acceleration $\mathbf{a}_P$ are obtained in basis $(\hat{\mathbf{e}}_r, \hat{\mathbf{e}}_\theta, \hat{\mathbf{e}}_z)$ by time-differentiation of $\mathbf{r}_{OP}$:

$$\mathbf{v}_P = \dot{r}\hat{\mathbf{e}}_r + r\frac{d\hat{\mathbf{e}}_r}{dt} + \dot{z}\hat{\mathbf{e}}_z$$

with

$$\frac{d\hat{\mathbf{e}}_r}{dt} = \frac{d}{dt}(\cos\theta\hat{\mathbf{e}}_x + \sin\theta\hat{\mathbf{e}}_y) = \dot{\theta}(-\sin\theta\hat{\mathbf{e}}_x + \cos\theta\hat{\mathbf{e}}_y) = \dot{\theta}\hat{\mathbf{e}}_\theta$$

Hence we obtain the expression of $\mathbf{v}_P$ on basis $(\hat{\mathbf{e}}_r, \hat{\mathbf{e}}_\theta, \hat{\mathbf{e}}_z)$:

$$\mathbf{v}_P = \dot{r}\hat{\mathbf{e}}_r + r\dot{\theta}\hat{\mathbf{e}}_\theta + \dot{z}\hat{\mathbf{e}}_z \tag{2.12}$$

[4] Actually, two whistling sounds would appear to exist: however one sound (solid line in Figure 2.3) corresponds to the forward motion of P, the other (dashed line) corresponds to the backward motion of P toward O. This last solution must be rejected. Only one sound is heard.

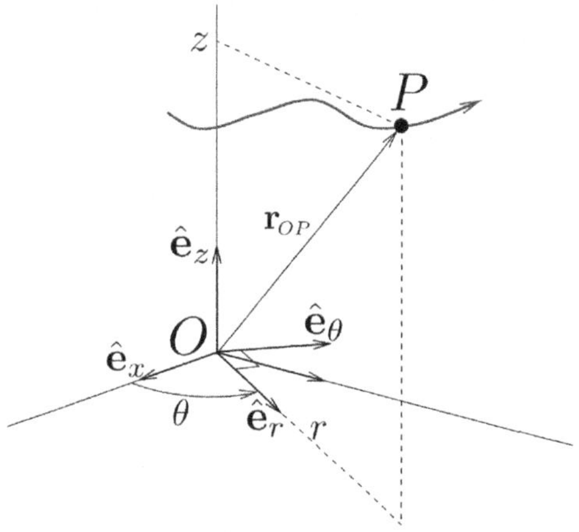

Figure 2.4

The expression of acceleration $\mathbf{a}_P$ is obtained by time-differentiation of equation (2.12), and recalling that $d\hat{\mathbf{e}}_\theta/dt = -\dot{\theta}\hat{\mathbf{e}}_r$:

$$\mathbf{a}_P = \ddot{r}\hat{\mathbf{e}}_r + \dot{r}\frac{d\hat{\mathbf{e}}_r}{dt} + (\dot{r}\dot{\theta} + r\ddot{\theta})\hat{\mathbf{e}}_\theta + r\dot{\theta}\frac{d\hat{\mathbf{e}}_\theta}{dt} + \ddot{z}\hat{\mathbf{e}}_z = \ddot{r}\hat{\mathbf{e}}_r + \dot{r}\dot{\theta}\hat{\mathbf{e}}_\theta + (\dot{r}\dot{\theta} + r\ddot{\theta})\hat{\mathbf{e}}_\theta - r\dot{\theta}^2\hat{\mathbf{e}}_r + \ddot{z}\hat{\mathbf{e}}_z$$

Finally we obtain, by regrouping the components,

$$\mathbf{a}_P = (\ddot{r} - r\dot{\theta}^2)\hat{\mathbf{e}}_r + (2\dot{r}\dot{\theta} + r\ddot{\theta})\hat{\mathbf{e}}_\theta + \ddot{z}\hat{\mathbf{e}}_z \tag{2.13}$$

In central force motions, the following expression for the $\hat{\mathbf{e}}_\theta$-component of $\mathbf{a}_P$ is useful:

$$a_\theta = \mathbf{a}_P \cdot \hat{\mathbf{e}}_\theta = \frac{1}{r}(2r\dot{r}\dot{\theta} + r^2\ddot{\theta}) = \frac{1}{r}\frac{d}{dt}(r^2\dot{\theta}) \tag{2.14}$$

valid as long as $r \neq 0$.

Example 2.2 Three boys A, B and C are initially located at the vertices of an equilateral triangle of side length d. They simultaneously begin to run at the same constant speed v_0, A chasing B, B chasing C and C chasing A, in the counterclockwise direction.

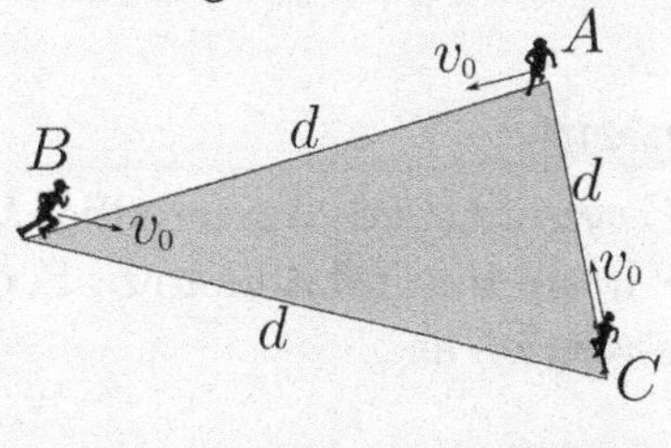

Find the trajectory of each boy. Then find the time taken for the boys to meet. Sketch their trajectories. ■

We take advantage of the symmetry of the problem.. At any given time, the three particles still form an equilateral triangle since they chase each other at constant speed. This simplifies their configuration: we use polar coordinates (r, θ) to parametrize the position of, say, A w.r.t. center O of triangle ABC, with $r = |OA| = |OB| = |OC|$. See Figure 2.5. The trajectory of A is obtained by imposing the magnitude and direction of its velocity $\mathbf{v}_A$. Once the trajectory of A is obtained, the trajectories of B and C are found by a counterclockwise rotation of angle $2\pi/3$ and $4\pi/3$ from that of A, respectively.

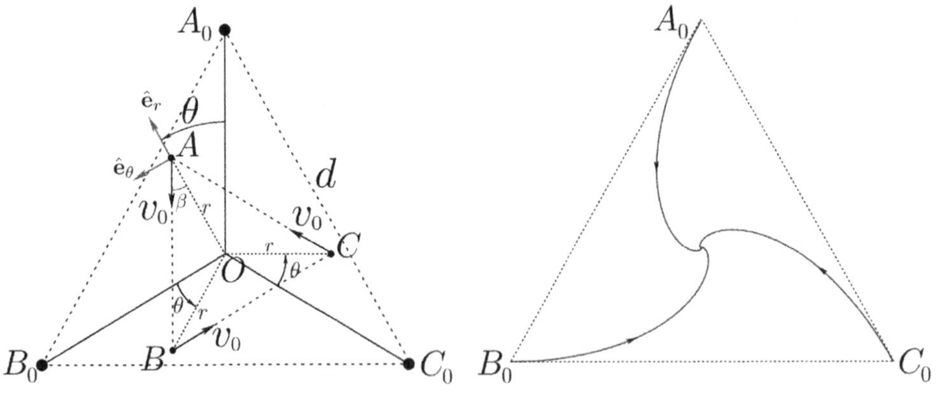

Figure 2.5

The velocity $\mathbf{v}_A$ of A makes the constant angle $\beta = \pi/6$ relative to the radial line OA as shown. Since its magnitude is the constant v_0, we can write

$$\mathbf{v}_A = \dot{r}\hat{\mathbf{e}}_r + r\dot{\theta}\hat{\mathbf{e}}_\theta = v_0(-\hat{\mathbf{e}}_r \cos\frac{\pi}{6} + \hat{\mathbf{e}}_\theta \sin\frac{\pi}{6})$$

giving

$$\dot{r} = -v_0 \cos\frac{\pi}{6}, \qquad r\dot{\theta} = v_0 \sin\frac{\pi}{6}$$

This gives $r d\theta/dr = -\tan(\pi/6) = -1/\sqrt{3}$ and by integration

$$r = \frac{d}{\sqrt{3}} \exp(-\theta\sqrt{3})$$

since $r = r_0 = d/\sqrt{3}$ at $\theta = 0$ (at time $t = 0$). This is the polar equation of a logarithmic spiral. We can also obtain a parametrization of the trajectory versus t: we integrate $\dot{r} = -(\sqrt{3}/2)v_0$ to get

$$r(t) = \frac{d}{\sqrt{3}} - \frac{\sqrt{3}}{2}v_0 t, \qquad \theta(t) = \frac{1}{\sqrt{3}} \ln \frac{1}{1 - \frac{3v_0}{2d}t}$$

The three particles will meet at point O at time $t_f = 2d/3v_0$ (by setting $r = 0$). To find the total distance traveled by A, we use $ds/dt = v_0$, where s is the arc length measured on the trajectory of A. By integration, the total distance traveled by A is then $d_f = v_0 t_f = 2d/3$. ∎

2.3.3 Spherical Coordinate System

Given a Cartesian system $Oxyz$ attached to referential $\mathcal{E}$, we denote by (ρ, ϕ, θ) the spherical coordinates of a particle P in motion relative to $\mathcal{E}$. See Figure 2.6. On basis $(\hat{\mathbf{e}}_\rho, \hat{\mathbf{e}}_\phi, \hat{\mathbf{e}}_\theta)$ the position vector of P can be written as

$$\mathbf{r}_{OP} = \rho\hat{\mathbf{e}}_\rho \tag{2.15}$$

The spherical basis vectors $(\hat{\mathbf{e}}_\rho, \hat{\mathbf{e}}_\phi, \hat{\mathbf{e}}_\theta)$ become vector functions of time, just as angles ϕ and θ are scalar functions of time. The velocity of P is obtained by taking the time-derivative of the position vector $\mathbf{r}_{OP}$:

$$\mathbf{v}_P = \dot{\rho}\hat{\mathbf{e}}_\rho + \rho\frac{d\hat{\mathbf{e}}_\rho}{dt}$$

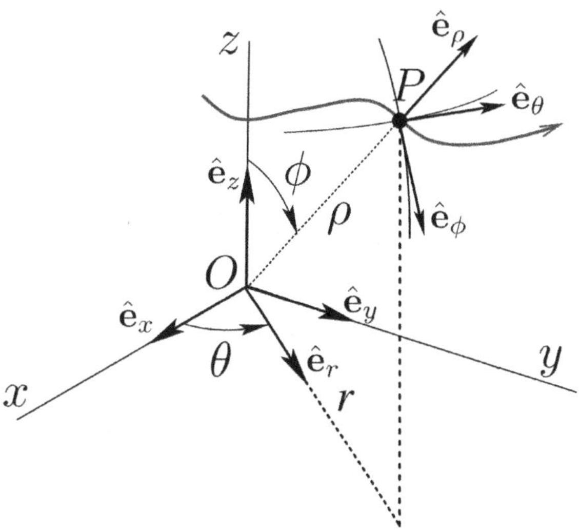

Figure 2.6

To determine the derivative of $\hat{\mathbf{e}}_\rho$, we first write $\hat{\mathbf{e}}_\rho$ on unit vector $\hat{\mathbf{e}}_r$ and $\hat{\mathbf{e}}_z$: $\hat{\mathbf{e}}_\rho = \cos\phi\hat{\mathbf{e}}_z + \sin\phi\hat{\mathbf{e}}_r$. We then obtain [5]

$$\frac{d\hat{\mathbf{e}}_\rho}{dt} = -\dot{\phi}\sin\phi\hat{\mathbf{e}}_z + \dot{\phi}\cos\phi\hat{\mathbf{e}}_r + \sin\phi\frac{d\hat{\mathbf{e}}_r}{dt} = \dot{\phi}(-\sin\phi\hat{\mathbf{e}}_z + \cos\phi\hat{\mathbf{e}}_r) + \dot{\theta}\sin\phi\hat{\mathbf{e}}_\theta$$

where we have used $d\hat{\mathbf{e}}_r/dt = \dot{\theta}\hat{\mathbf{e}}_\theta$. Then we recognize that $(-\sin\phi\hat{\mathbf{e}}_z + \cos\phi\hat{\mathbf{e}}_r) = \hat{\mathbf{e}}_\phi$. Finally, we obtain

$$\frac{d\hat{\mathbf{e}}_\rho}{dt} = \dot{\phi}\hat{\mathbf{e}}_\phi + \dot{\theta}\sin\phi\hat{\mathbf{e}}_\theta \tag{2.16}$$

and we verify that $\hat{\mathbf{e}}_\rho \cdot (d\hat{\mathbf{e}}_\rho/dt) = 0$. The velocity vector in spherical coordinates is then given by

$$\mathbf{v}_P = \dot{\rho}\,\hat{\mathbf{e}}_\rho + \rho\dot{\phi}\,\hat{\mathbf{e}}_\phi + \rho\dot{\theta}\sin\phi\,\hat{\mathbf{e}}_\theta \tag{2.17}$$

The expression of the acceleration of P in spherical coordinates is obtained by differentiating equation (2.17). Thus we need the time-derivative of unit vector $\hat{\mathbf{e}}_\phi$. Proceeding like $\hat{\mathbf{e}}_\rho$, we easily obtain

$$\frac{d\hat{\mathbf{e}}_\phi}{dt} = -\dot{\phi}\hat{\mathbf{e}}_\rho + \dot{\theta}\cos\phi\hat{\mathbf{e}}_\theta \tag{2.18}$$

The components of $\mathbf{a}_P = a_\rho\hat{\mathbf{e}}_\rho + a_\phi\hat{\mathbf{e}}_\phi + a_\theta\hat{\mathbf{e}}_\theta$ on basis $(\hat{\mathbf{e}}_\rho, \hat{\mathbf{e}}_\phi, \hat{\mathbf{e}}_\theta)$ are then given by

$$\begin{aligned} a_\rho &= \ddot{\rho} - \rho\dot{\phi}^2 - \rho\dot{\theta}^2\sin^2\phi \\ a_\phi &= 2\dot{\rho}\dot{\phi} + \rho\ddot{\phi} - \rho\dot{\theta}^2\cos\phi\sin\phi \\ a_\theta &= 2\dot{\rho}\dot{\theta}\sin\phi + 2\rho\dot{\phi}\dot{\theta}\cos\phi + \rho\ddot{\theta}\sin\phi \end{aligned} \tag{2.19}$$

Example 2.3 A ship P travels at a constant speed v_0 between two points on the surface of the Earth in the following way: the ship's captain draws a straight line on the map (assuming that this map is a Mercator projection of the Earth) connecting the two points so that his ship crosses the meridians at a constant angle α (in the ab-

[5] See Example 3.1 of Chapter 3 for an alternate derivation.

sence of a map, the ship's captain keeps his compass pointing in a constant direction).

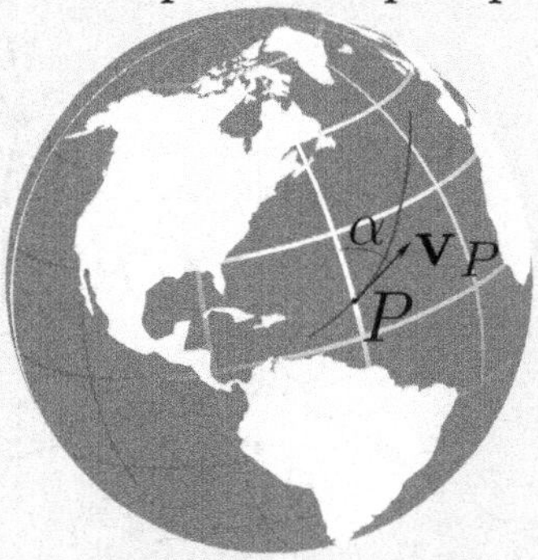

Find the trajectory (known as *rhumb line* in navigation) of the ship on the surface of the Earth. Find the acceleration of P. ■

Particle P moves on the surface of a sphere of center O (Earth's center) and radius R (Earth's radius). Hence we adopt a spherical coordinate system $(\rho = R, \theta, \phi)$. The trajectory of P is obtained by imposing a constant angle α between unit vector $\hat{\mathbf{e}}_\phi$ (tangent to the meridian at P) and the velocity $\mathbf{v}_P$ of P. Hence $\mathbf{v}_P$ takes the following expression of the spherical unit vectors $(\hat{\mathbf{e}}_\rho, \hat{\mathbf{e}}_\theta, \hat{\mathbf{e}}_\phi)$:

$$\mathbf{v}_P = v_0(\cos\alpha\hat{\mathbf{e}}_\phi + \sin\alpha\hat{\mathbf{e}}_\theta)$$

The spherical expression of $\mathbf{v}_P$ yields

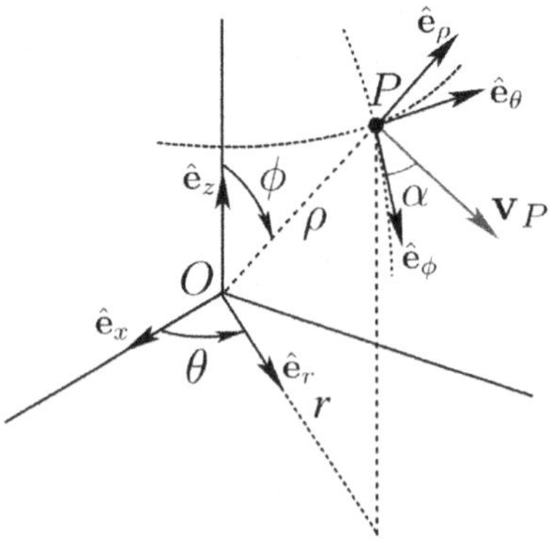

Figure 2.7

$$\mathbf{v}_P = \dot{\rho}\hat{\mathbf{e}}_\rho + \rho\dot{\phi}\hat{\mathbf{e}}_\phi + \rho\dot{\theta}\sin\phi\hat{\mathbf{e}}_\theta = R(\dot{\phi}\hat{\mathbf{e}}_\phi + \dot{\theta}\sin\phi\hat{\mathbf{e}}_\theta)$$

Equating these expressions of $\mathbf{v}_P$ we obtain two equations

$$\dot{\phi} = \frac{v_0}{R}\cos\alpha, \qquad \dot{\theta}\sin\phi = \frac{v_0}{R}\sin\alpha$$

These equations are readily integrated assuming the initial conditions $\phi = \phi_0$ and $\theta = \theta_0$ at $t = 0$:

$$\phi = \phi_0 + \frac{v_0 t}{R}\cos\alpha, \qquad \theta = \theta_0 + \tan\alpha \ln\left(\frac{\tan\frac{\phi}{2}}{\tan\frac{\phi_0}{2}}\right)$$

as long as $\alpha \neq \pi/2$. For $\alpha = \pi/2$, we get $\phi = \phi_0$ and $\theta = \theta_0 + (v_0/R\sin\phi_0)t$ and the trajectory of P is a meridian (a circle). The acceleration of P is determined from equation (2.19) taking into account the constraints

$$\rho = R, \qquad \dot{\phi} = \frac{v_0}{R}\cos\alpha, \qquad \dot{\theta}\sin\phi = \frac{v_0}{R}\sin\alpha$$

which are valid at all time. We then get the expressions

$$a_\rho = -R(\dot{\phi}^2 + \dot{\theta}^2 \sin^2 \phi) = -\frac{v_0^2}{R}, \qquad a_\phi = R(\ddot{\phi} - \dot{\theta}^2 \cos\phi \sin\phi) = \frac{v_0^2}{R} \sin^2 \alpha \cot\phi$$

and

$$a_\theta = R(2\dot{\phi}\dot{\theta}\cos\phi + \ddot{\theta}\sin\phi) = \frac{v_0^2}{R} \cos\alpha \sin\alpha \cot\phi$$

■

2.4 Kinematics in Normal/Tangential Components

The trajectory $\mathcal{C}$ of a particle P observed in a referential $\mathcal{E}$ is completely specified once a parametrization of the position vector $\mathbf{r}_{OP}(u)$ has been found where parameter' u is a known function of time. For instance, the trajectory of P can be defined by a parametric representation $(x(u), y(u), z(u))$ in Cartesian coordinates, or $(r(u), \theta(u), z(u))$ in cylindrical coordinates. As a possible choice for parameter u, we may use the length s of the arc of trajectory P_0P from an arbitrary origin P_0 of $\mathcal{C}$ which *we orient in the sense of the motion*. Coordinate s is *intrinsic* to the curve $\mathcal{C}$, that is, it does not depend on coordinate axes defined in $\mathcal{E}$, or even the chosen referential itself.

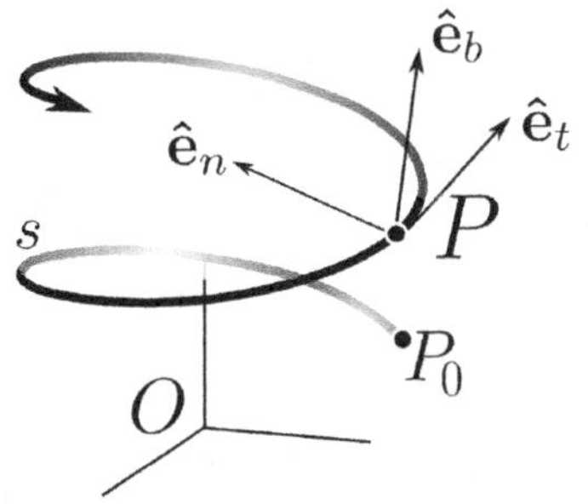

Figure 2.8 – *The Frenet basis at P.*

As P moves along $\mathcal{C}$, the arc length s is an increasing function of time. We can find the velocity of P in $\mathcal{E}$ in the following manner:

$$\mathbf{v}_P = \frac{d}{dt}\mathbf{r}_{OP}(s(t)) = \frac{ds}{dt}\frac{d\mathbf{r}_{OP}}{ds}$$

If we write $d\mathbf{r}_{OP}/ds$ as the limit

$$\lim_{\Delta s \to 0} \frac{(\mathbf{r}_{OP}(s + \Delta s) - \mathbf{r}_{OP}(s))}{\Delta s}$$

we obtain a unit vector $\hat{\mathbf{e}}_t$ since the magnitude of $\Delta\mathbf{r} = \mathbf{r}_{OP}(s + \Delta s) - \mathbf{r}_{OP}(s)$ tends to the arc length Δs in the limit $\Delta s \to 0$. This unit vector also tends to the tangent direction of $\mathcal{C}$ at P, and is directed in the sense of the motion. It depends only upon $\mathcal{C}$ and its orientation, and not upon the particular evolution of P on $\mathcal{C}$.

Definition 2.2 — Unit tangent vector. The unit tangent vector at P is the vector $\hat{\mathbf{e}}_t$ defined by

$$\hat{\mathbf{e}}_t = \frac{d}{ds}\mathbf{r}_{OP} \tag{2.20}$$

It points in the direction of motion. Then the velocity vector of P is given by

$$\mathbf{v}_P = v_P\,\hat{\mathbf{e}}_t = \dot{s}\,\hat{\mathbf{e}}_t \tag{2.21}$$

The instantaneous rate of change ds/dt of the arc length is the speed of P.

The acceleration $\mathbf{a}_P$ is obtained by differentiating (2.21):

$$\mathbf{a}_P = \frac{d}{dt}(v_P\,\hat{\mathbf{e}}_t) = \dot{v}_P\,\hat{\mathbf{e}}_t + v_P\,\frac{ds}{dt}\frac{d\hat{\mathbf{e}}_t}{ds} = \dot{v}_P\,\hat{\mathbf{e}}_t + v_P^2\,\frac{d\hat{\mathbf{e}}_t}{ds}$$

We note that the vector $d\hat{\mathbf{e}}_t/ds$ is necessarily orthogonal to $\hat{\mathbf{e}}_t$ since $\hat{\mathbf{e}}_t$ is a unit vector. Hence, we have decomposed the acceleration into a component $\mathbf{a}_{Pt} = \dot{v}_P\hat{\mathbf{e}}_t = \ddot{s}\hat{\mathbf{e}}_t$ along the tangential direction and a component $\mathbf{a}_{Pn} = v_P^2\,d\hat{\mathbf{e}}_t/ds$ normal to the trajectory. Clearly, $\mathbf{a}_{Pt}$ reflects the time rate of change of the magnitude of the velocity vector $\mathbf{v}_P$. Therefore $\mathbf{a}_{Pn}$ must reflect the time rate of change of the direction of $\mathbf{v}_P$. We define the normal direction as follows:

Definition 2.3 — principal normal. The *principal unit normal* vector $\hat{\mathbf{e}}_n$ to the trajectory at P is defined by the equation

$$\frac{d\hat{\mathbf{e}}_t}{ds} = \frac{1}{\rho}\,\hat{\mathbf{e}}_n \tag{2.22}$$

where the *positive scalar* ρ is referred to as *the radius of curvature* of the trajectory at P.

The curvature $\kappa(s) = 1/\rho = |\frac{d\hat{\mathbf{e}}_t}{ds}|$ measures the deviation of $\mathcal{C}$ from a straight line. Equation (2.22) gives the following expression of the normal acceleration

$$\mathbf{a}_{Pn} = \frac{v_P^2}{\rho}\,\hat{\mathbf{e}}_n$$

The plane $(P, \hat{\mathbf{e}}_t, \hat{\mathbf{e}}_n)$ is called the *osculating plane*: it contains the trajectory $\mathcal{C}$ in a small neighborhood of P. The circle of center C and radius ρ defined by $\mathbf{r}_{PC} = \rho\hat{\mathbf{e}}_n$ is called the *osculating circle* at P: it is the circle that best approximates the trajectory of P in a small neighborhood of P. Point C is called the *center of curvature* of $\mathcal{C}$ at P.

In order to gain more insight into equation (2.22), consider the case of a plane curve $\mathcal{C}$. Let $\varphi = (\hat{\mathbf{e}}_x, \hat{\mathbf{e}}_t)$ be the angle made by vector $\hat{\mathbf{e}}_t$ with axis Ox. Angle φ is referred to the *tangential angle* or *turning angle*. Then we can write

$$\frac{d\hat{\mathbf{e}}_t}{ds} = \frac{d\varphi}{ds}\frac{d\hat{\mathbf{e}}_t}{d\varphi}.$$

The ratio $|ds/d\varphi|$ is recognized as the radius of curvature ρ of a planar curve, that is, the radius of the osculating circle to the trajectory. Whether $d\varphi/ds$ is positive or not, one can readily see that $d\hat{\mathbf{e}}_t/ds$ and hence $\hat{\mathbf{e}}_n = \rho(d\hat{\mathbf{e}}_t/ds)$ (since ρ is always positive by convention) is always directed toward the center of curvature of the trajectory. Hence with the sign of $\dot{v}_P$ and the curvature of the curve at a particular position P, one can get an idea of the direction of the acceleration vector $\mathbf{a}_P$ at any location of the trajectory.

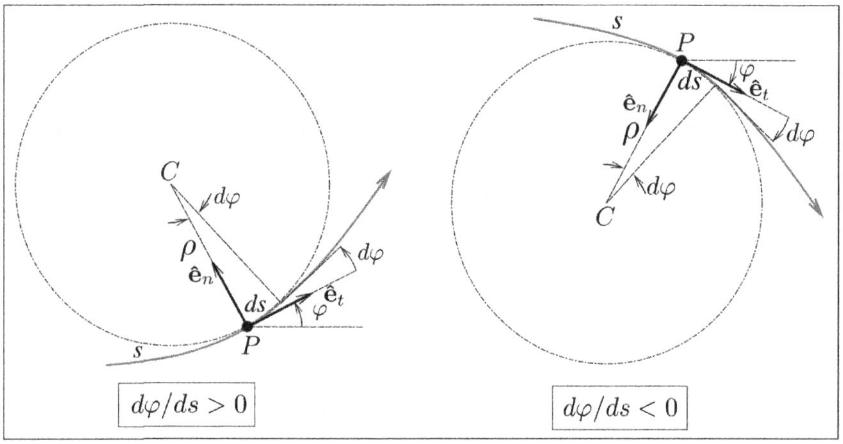

Figure 2.9 – *The position of particle P is defined by intrinsic coordinates s (arc length) and φ (turning angle).*

For a particle P moving along a space curve, a third unit vector can be defined as $\hat{\mathbf{e}}_b = \hat{\mathbf{e}}_t \times \hat{\mathbf{e}}_n$. Being normal to $\hat{\mathbf{e}}_t$, unit vector $\hat{\mathbf{e}}_b$ is also normal to the trajectory at P which we call *binormal unit vector*. Hence a right-handed basis $(\hat{\mathbf{e}}_t, \hat{\mathbf{e}}_n, \hat{\mathbf{e}}_b)$ of unit vectors, called the *Frenet basis*, is defined at every location of P along its trajectory. The variation of these unit vectors along $\mathcal{C}$ is given by the *Serret-Frenet* formulas.

Theorem 2.3 — Serret-Frenet formulas. The time-rate of change of unit vectors $(\hat{\mathbf{e}}_t, \hat{\mathbf{e}}_n, \hat{\mathbf{e}}_b)$ are given by the formulas

$$\frac{d\hat{\mathbf{e}}_t}{ds} = \frac{1}{\rho}\hat{\mathbf{e}}_n, \qquad \frac{d\hat{\mathbf{e}}_n}{ds} = -\frac{1}{\rho}\hat{\mathbf{e}}_t + \frac{1}{\tau}\hat{\mathbf{e}}_b, \qquad \frac{d\hat{\mathbf{e}}_b}{ds} = -\frac{1}{\tau}\hat{\mathbf{e}}_n \tag{2.23}$$

where τ is known as the *radius of torsion* of $\mathcal{C}$ at P and is given by

$$\frac{1}{\tau} = \rho^2 \frac{d\mathbf{r}_{OP}}{ds} \cdot \left(\frac{d^2\mathbf{r}_{OP}}{ds^2} \times \frac{d^3\mathbf{r}_{OP}}{ds^3}\right) \tag{2.24}$$

Proof. To prove the last two Serret-Frenet formulas, we first use the fact that $\hat{\mathbf{e}}_n$ and $\hat{\mathbf{e}}_b$, being unit vectors, are orthogonal to their derivatives. Hence there exist four scalars a, b, c and d such that

$$\frac{d\hat{\mathbf{e}}_n}{ds} = a\hat{\mathbf{e}}_t + b\hat{\mathbf{e}}_b, \qquad \frac{d\hat{\mathbf{e}}_b}{ds} = c\hat{\mathbf{e}}_t + d\hat{\mathbf{e}}_n$$

To find these scalars, we differentiate the relations $\hat{\mathbf{e}}_t \cdot \hat{\mathbf{e}}_n = 0$, $\hat{\mathbf{e}}_n \cdot \hat{\mathbf{e}}_b = 0$, and $\hat{\mathbf{e}}_t \cdot \hat{\mathbf{e}}_b = 0$ w.r.t. arc length s and upon replacing $d\hat{\mathbf{e}}_t/ds$ by $\hat{\mathbf{e}}_n/\rho$, $d\hat{\mathbf{e}}_n/ds$ by $a\hat{\mathbf{e}}_t + b\hat{\mathbf{e}}_b$, and $d\hat{\mathbf{e}}_b/ds$ by $c\hat{\mathbf{e}}_t + d\hat{\mathbf{e}}_n$ we obtain

$$a + 1/\rho = 0, \quad b + d = 0, \quad c = 0$$

Hence, we obtain (2.23) after writing $b = 1/\tau = -d$. Equation (2.24) is found from the expression of $d\hat{\mathbf{e}}_n/ds$:

$$1/\tau = \hat{\mathbf{e}}_b \cdot \frac{d\hat{\mathbf{e}}_n}{ds} = \rho(\mathbf{r}' \times \mathbf{r}'') \cdot (\rho\mathbf{r}''' + \rho'\mathbf{r}'') = \rho^2\mathbf{r}''' \cdot (\mathbf{r}' \times \mathbf{r}'') = \rho^2\mathbf{r}' \cdot (\mathbf{r}'' \times \mathbf{r}''')$$

denoting $\mathbf{r} = \mathbf{r}_{OP}$ and $(\cdot)' = d(\cdot)/ds$. ■

Note that the radius of torsion, as opposed to the radius of curvature, is not necessarily positive. It measures the deviation of $\mathcal{C}$ from a planar curve.

We can summarize the results of this section with the following theorem.

Theorem 2.4 — **Kinematics in N-T Components.** At any given time, it is possible to define two unit vectors $(\hat{\mathbf{e}}_t, \hat{\mathbf{e}}_n)$, called *tangential and principal normal* unit vectors to the path at P. Then the velocity and acceleration of P take the expressions

$$\mathbf{v}_P = v_P \hat{\mathbf{e}}_t, \qquad v_P = \dot{s} \tag{2.25}$$

$$\mathbf{a}_P = \dot{v}_P \hat{\mathbf{e}}_t + \frac{v_P^2}{\rho}\hat{\mathbf{e}}_n \tag{2.26}$$

where s and ρ are the arc length and the radius of curvature of the path at P.

The formulas (2.25) and (2.26) are fundamental in particle kinematics. They are expressed in terms of the local, intrinsic characteristics s, ρ, $\hat{\mathbf{e}}_t$, and $\hat{\mathbf{e}}_n$ of the curve described by P.

Example 2.4 Use the expression of the acceleration $\mathbf{a}_P$ on the Frenet basis to find the expression of the radius of curvature ρ of a planar curve $y \equiv y(x)$ in Cartesian coordinates. Repeat for a planar curve $r \equiv r(\theta)$ in polar coordinates. ■

The radius of curvature of a curve can be found from equation (2.26): $1/\rho = |\mathbf{a}_P \cdot \hat{\mathbf{e}}_n|/v_P^2$. So we start with the velocity and the acceleration of P in Cartesian coordinates:

$$\mathbf{v}_P = \frac{d}{dt}[x\hat{\mathbf{e}}_x + y(x)\hat{\mathbf{e}}_y] = \dot{x}(\hat{\mathbf{e}}_x + y'\hat{\mathbf{e}}_y), \quad \mathbf{a}_P = \frac{d\mathbf{v}_P}{dt} = \ddot{x}\hat{\mathbf{e}}_x + (y'\ddot{x} + y''\dot{x}^2)\hat{\mathbf{e}}_y$$

denoting $y' = dy/dx$, and $y'' = d^2y/dx^2$. From the expression of $\mathbf{v}_P$, we obtain the unit tangential vector

$$\hat{\mathbf{e}}_t = \frac{1}{(1+y'^2)^{1/2}}(\hat{\mathbf{e}}_x + y'\hat{\mathbf{e}}_y)$$

assuming $\dot{x} > 0$ without loss of generality. This then leads to an expression of the unit normal vector $\hat{\mathbf{e}}_n = \pm(-y'\hat{\mathbf{e}}_x + \hat{\mathbf{e}}_y)/(1+y'^2)^{1/2}$, the direction of which depending on the curvature at P (or the sign of y''). [6] Then we find

$$\frac{1}{\rho} = \frac{|\mathbf{a}_P \cdot \hat{\mathbf{e}}_n|}{v_P^2} = \frac{|y''|}{(1+y'^2)^{3/2}}$$

We proceed the same way for a curve $r(\theta)$ in polar coordinates:

$$\mathbf{v}_P = \dot{\theta}(r'\hat{\mathbf{e}}_r + r\hat{\mathbf{e}}_\theta), \qquad \mathbf{a}_P = (r'\ddot{\theta} + r''\dot{\theta}^2 - r\dot{\theta}^2)\hat{\mathbf{e}}_r + (r\ddot{\theta} + 2r'\dot{\theta}^2)\hat{\mathbf{e}}_\theta$$

denoting $r' = dr/d\theta$, $r'' = d^2\theta/d\theta^2$. This leads to $\hat{\mathbf{e}}_t = (r'\hat{\mathbf{e}}_r + r\hat{\mathbf{e}}_\theta)/(r^2 + r'^2)^{1/2}$ (assuming

[6] The unit vectors normal to unit vector $\mathbf{u} = u_x\hat{\mathbf{e}}_x + u_y\hat{\mathbf{e}}_y$ are $\mathbf{v} = \pm(-u_x\hat{\mathbf{e}}_x + u_y\hat{\mathbf{e}}_y)$ and $\pm\hat{\mathbf{e}}_z$.

$\dot{\theta} > 0$), and $\hat{\mathbf{e}}_n = \pm(-r\hat{\mathbf{e}}_r + r'\hat{\mathbf{e}}_\theta)/(r^2 + r'^2)^{1/2}$. Finally we obtain

$$\frac{1}{\rho} = \frac{|\mathbf{a}_P \cdot \hat{\mathbf{e}}_n|}{v_P^2} = \frac{|rr'' - 2r'^2 - r^2|}{(r^2 + r'^2)^{3/2}}$$

In both cases, we can see from these expressions that the radius of curvature does not depend on the manner in which P travels on curve $\mathcal{C}$. ∎

Example 2.5 The trajectory of a particle P in a referential $Oxyz$ is a regular circular helix whose Cartesian coordinates are described by

$$x(t) = R\cos\omega t, \qquad y(t) = R\sin\omega t, \qquad z(t) = h\omega t$$

where R, h, and ω are three positive constants.

a. Find the velocity vector $\mathbf{v}_P$ of P in Cartesian and cylindrical coordinates. Show that the motion of P is uniform.

b. By first showing that the inclination of $\mathbf{v}_P$ with plane Oxy remains constant, find the hodograph associated with the motion of P.

c. Determine the distance traveled by P between two instants t_1 and $t_2 > t_1$.

d. Determine the Frenet basis $(\hat{\mathbf{e}}_t, \hat{\mathbf{e}}_n, \hat{\mathbf{e}}_b)$ on the cylindrical basis associated with P. Determine the radius of curvature ρ and the radius of torsion τ.

e. Determine the acceleration $\mathbf{a}_P$ of P in Cartesian and cylindrical coordinates. Express $\mathbf{a}_P$ on the Frenet basis $(\hat{\mathbf{e}}_t, \hat{\mathbf{e}}_n, \hat{\mathbf{e}}_b)$ of P. ∎

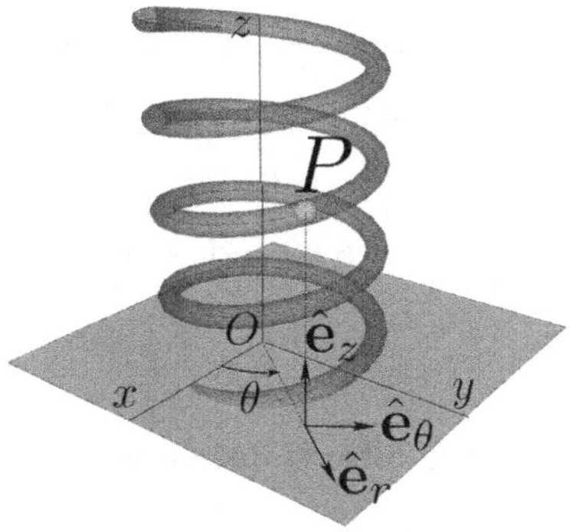

a. If the introduce the angle $\theta = \omega t = (\hat{\mathbf{e}}_x, \hat{\mathbf{e}}_r) = (\hat{\mathbf{e}}_y, \hat{\mathbf{e}}_\theta)$, then the position vector of P can be written as

$$\mathbf{r}_{OP} = R\hat{\mathbf{e}}_r + h\theta\hat{\mathbf{e}}_z.$$

By differentiation w.r.t. time, we obtain the velocity of P in cylindrical coordinates, and then in Cartesian coordinates:

$$\mathbf{v}_P = \dot{\theta}(R\hat{\mathbf{e}}_\theta + h\hat{\mathbf{e}}_z) = \omega(R\hat{\mathbf{e}}_\theta + h\hat{\mathbf{e}}_z) = \omega(-R\sin\theta\hat{\mathbf{e}}_x + R\cos\theta\hat{\mathbf{e}}_y + h\hat{\mathbf{e}}_z).$$

The square of its speed $v_P^2 = \omega^2(R^2 + h^2) = v_0^2$ is a constant: the motion of P is uniform.

b. To show that the angle of $\mathbf{v}_P$ with plane Oxy remains constant, it is equivalent to show that the angle $\alpha = (\hat{\mathbf{e}}_z, \mathbf{v}_P)$ is also constant. The cosine of this angle is given by $\hat{\mathbf{e}}_z \cdot \mathbf{v}_P = v_0 \cos\alpha = h\omega$. It is constant, and since the speed v_P is constant, angle α is also constant. The hodograph is the motion of the point Q satisfying $\mathbf{r}_{OQ} = \mathbf{v}_P$: with the properties of $\mathbf{v}_P$ just shown, the hodograph is necessarily the circle of axis Ov_z and radius $v_0 \sin\alpha = \omega R$.

c. The distance traveled by P in the time dt is $ds = v_P dt$. Since $v_P = v_0$ is constant, the time traveled between two instants t_1 and $t_2 > t_1$ is then $s(t_2) - s(t_1) = v_0(t_2 - t_1)$.

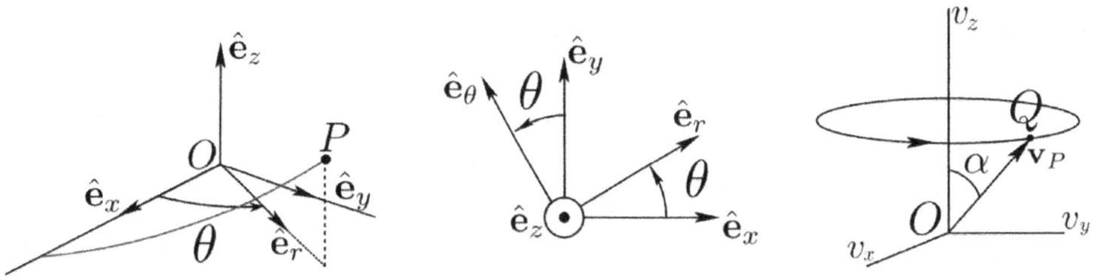

d. The unit tangential vector is found according to

$$\hat{\mathbf{e}}_t = \frac{\mathbf{v}_P}{v_0} = \frac{R\hat{\mathbf{e}}_\theta + h\hat{\mathbf{e}}_z}{(R^2+h^2)^{1/2}}$$

To find the principal unit normal vector, we first find

$$\frac{d\hat{\mathbf{e}}_t}{ds} = \frac{1}{v_0}\frac{d\hat{\mathbf{e}}_t}{dt} = -\frac{1}{v_0}\frac{R\omega\hat{\mathbf{e}}_r}{(R^2+h^2)^{1/2}} = -\frac{R}{(R^2+h^2)}\hat{\mathbf{e}}_r$$

(we have used $ds = v_0 dt$). Using equation (2.22), we can identify the radius of curvature ρ and $\hat{\mathbf{e}}_n$ (recall that $\rho > 0$ by convention):

$$\hat{\mathbf{e}}_n = -\hat{\mathbf{e}}_r, \qquad \rho = \frac{R^2+h^2}{R}$$

Finally the binormal unit vector is simply

$$\hat{\mathbf{e}}_b = \hat{\mathbf{e}}_t \times \hat{\mathbf{e}}_n = \frac{R\hat{\mathbf{e}}_z - h\hat{\mathbf{e}}_\theta}{(R^2+h^2)^{1/2}}$$

To find the torsion, we use the last of the Serret-Frenet formulas (2.23): hence we need

$$\frac{d\hat{\mathbf{e}}_b}{ds} = \frac{1}{v_0}\frac{d\hat{\mathbf{e}}_b}{dt} = \frac{1}{v_0}\frac{h\omega\hat{\mathbf{e}}_r}{(R^2+h^2)^{1/2}} = -\frac{h\hat{\mathbf{e}}_n}{(R^2+h^2)}$$

We do indeed get $d\hat{\mathbf{e}}_b/ds$ collinear to $\hat{\mathbf{e}}_n$ and we can now identify the radius of torsion

$$\tau = \frac{R^2+h^2}{h}$$

e. We obtain the acceleration by differentiating $\mathbf{v}_P$:

$$\mathbf{a}_P = \omega\frac{d}{dt}(R\hat{\mathbf{e}}_\theta + h\hat{\mathbf{e}}_z) = -R\omega\dot{\theta}\hat{\mathbf{e}}_r = -R\omega^2\hat{\mathbf{e}}_r = -R\omega^2(\cos\theta\hat{\mathbf{e}}_x + R\sin\theta\hat{\mathbf{e}}_y).$$

On the Serret-Frenet basis, we obtain

$$\mathbf{a}_P = -R\omega^2\hat{\mathbf{e}}_r = R\omega^2\hat{\mathbf{e}}_n = \frac{v_0^2}{\rho}\hat{\mathbf{e}}_n$$

The tangential component of $\mathbf{a}_P$ is of course zero since the motion is uniform. ■

Example 2.6 Determine the curvature at any point of the rhumb curve of Example 2.3. Conclude that this trajectory cannot be a great circle which is known to be the curve of shortest length connecting two points on a sphere. ■

To obtain the radius of curvature r_c of the trajectory of P, we use the spherical components $(a_\rho, a_\phi, a_\theta)$ of the acceleration of P found in Example 2.3. The acceleration of P can also be expressed on the unit vectors $(\hat{\mathbf{e}}_t, \hat{\mathbf{e}}_n)$

$$\mathbf{a}_P = \frac{dv_P}{dt}\hat{\mathbf{e}}_t + \frac{v_P^2}{r_c}\hat{\mathbf{e}}_n = \frac{v_0^2}{r_c}\hat{\mathbf{e}}_n$$

since the speed of P is constant. This shows that r_c can be obtained as the ratio $v_0^2/|\mathbf{a}_P|$:

$$r_c = \frac{v_0^2}{(a_\rho^2 + a_\phi^2 + a_\theta^2)^{1/2}} = \frac{R}{(1 + \sin^2\alpha \cot^2\phi)^{1/2}}$$

Hence we see that in general the radius of curvature r_c is always less than radius R, unless

- $\alpha = 0$, in which case $\theta = constant = \theta_0$, the trajectory is a meridian, and hence a great circle.
- $\alpha = \pi/2$ and $\phi_0 = \pi/2$, the trajectory of P is the equator, hence a great circle.

This implies that in general the rhumb curve cannot be a great circle, and the distance traveled by P will not be the shortest between two points.

■

Example 2.7 In the design of highway interchanges, one is faced with the problem of connecting straight paths with appropriate curved paths. Consider a vehicle P traveling at constant speed v_0 on a straight road Δ_1. If, in order to join straight road Δ_2 perpendicular to Δ_1, one uses an arc of circle of radius R, despite the smooth connections at points O and A, the vehicle would exhibit a discontinuity of the normal acceleration v_0^2/ρ since the curvature $\kappa = 1/\rho$ passes from the value 0 to the value $1/R$ while crossing point O (and similarly at point A). Such a connecting path can be the cause of discomfort and even of accident. The same issue arises in the design of railroad tracks or of roller-coaster loops.

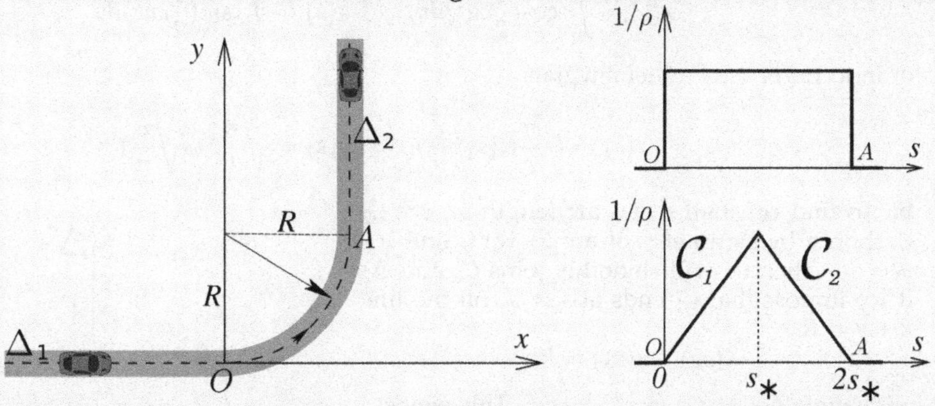

To find an alternative to the arc of circle joining O to A, we look for the path whose curvature κ linearly increases along C_1 from O with the arc length s, then linearly decreases along arc C_2 to reach the value 0 at point A. Hence the curvature must follow the equation

$$\kappa(s) = \begin{cases} cs, & 0 \leq s \leq s_* \quad (\text{on } C_1) \\ c(2s_* - s), & s_* \leq s \leq 2s_* \quad (\text{on } C_2) \end{cases}$$

where c is a positive constant, and $2s_*$ is the total length of the arc joining O to A.

a. Show that arc of trajectory C_1 is given by

$$x(s) = \sqrt{\frac{\pi}{c}}C(s\sqrt{\frac{c}{\pi}}), \qquad y(s) = \sqrt{\frac{\pi}{c}}S(s\sqrt{\frac{c}{\pi}})$$

with $s = v_0 t$, and where the functions C and S are the Fresnel cosine and sine integrals

$$C(z) = \int_0^z \cos(\frac{\pi}{2}u^2)\,du, \qquad S(z) = \int_0^z \sin(\frac{\pi}{2}u^2)\,du$$

This trajectory is known as an arc of *clothoid*.

b. Find constant c so that the second arc C_2 joins Δ_2 smoothly at point A.

c. Determine the length ratio $2s_*/(\frac{1}{2}\pi R)$ of two the paths. ■

a. First the arc length is found by integrating $\dot{s} = v_0$, yielding $s = v_0 t$ setting $s = 0$ and $t = 0$ at point O. Denote by ϕ the turning angle of the tangent:

$$\frac{dx}{ds} = \cos\phi, \qquad \frac{dy}{ds} = \sin\phi \qquad [1]$$

with $\kappa = cs = d\phi/ds$ This last equation can be integrated to give

$$\phi = \phi_0 + \frac{1}{2}cs^2$$

We must impose value $\phi_0 = 0$ at $s = 0$ corresponding to point O, so that the path is smooth to line Δ_1. We can now integrate [1] to find

$$x(s) = \int_0^s \cos(\frac{1}{2}cu^2)du, \qquad y(s) = \int_0^s \sin(\frac{1}{2}cu^2)du$$

or in terms of the Fresnel integrals

$$x(s) = \sqrt{\frac{\pi}{c}}C(s\sqrt{\frac{c}{\pi}}), \qquad y(s) = \sqrt{\frac{\pi}{c}}S(s\sqrt{\frac{c}{\pi}})$$

b. To find constant c and arc length s_*, arc C_2 is chosen by symmetry of arc C_1 w.r.t. line $x + y = R$. Then C_2 will smoothly joins C_1 and Δ_2 if we impose that C_1 ends at $s = s_*$ on the line $x + y = R$

$$x(s_*) + y(s_*) = R$$

with angle $\phi(s_*) = \pi/4$: $\frac{\pi}{4} = \frac{1}{2}cs_*^2$. This yields

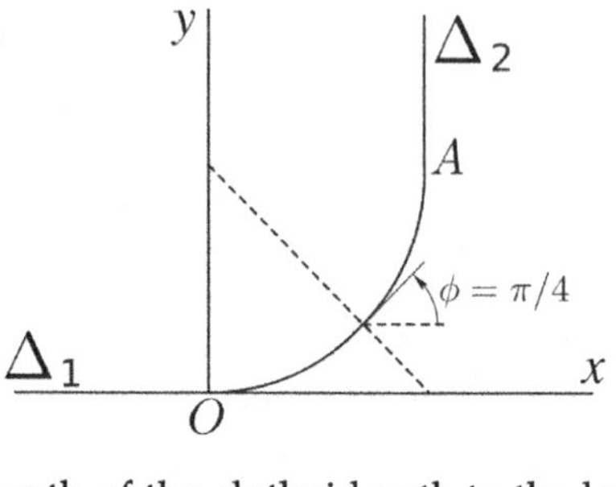

$$\sqrt{\frac{\pi}{c}}\left(C(\frac{1}{\sqrt{2}}) + S(\frac{1}{\sqrt{2}})\right) = R$$

c. From the results of b) we find the ratio of the length of the clothoid path to the length of the arc of circle

$$\frac{2s_*}{\frac{1}{2}\pi R} = \frac{2\sqrt{2}}{\pi\left(C(\frac{1}{\sqrt{2}}) + S(\frac{1}{\sqrt{2}})\right)} \approx 1.069$$

■

2.5 Problems

Problem 2.1 A hiker A is walking beside a lake when he notices a swimmer B crying for help. He runs at speed u and swims at speed $v < u$ to reach B along straight paths. The paths make the angle α and β relative to the line normal to the shore. Assume u and v constant.

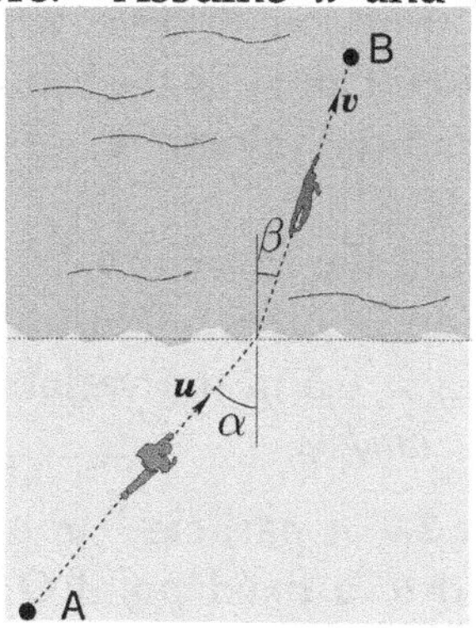

Show that the angles α and β must satisfy the equation

$$\frac{\sin\beta}{\sin\alpha} = \frac{v}{u}$$

for A to reach B in the shortest time.

Problem 2.2 A particle P of polar coordinates (r, θ) is in motion in a plane Oxy. Its motion is characterized by the following properties:

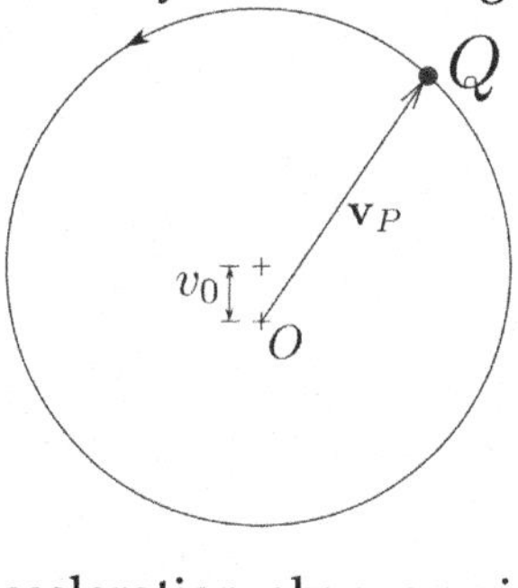

(i) its acceleration always points toward O, that is, $a_\theta = 0$,
(ii) its hodograph is the circle centered at point $(0, v_0)$.

Show that the radial acceleration of P satisfies $a_r = k/r^2$ where k is a constant.

Problem 2.3 A satellite P of polar coordinates (r, θ) is in motion around the Earth O along the ellipse of equation:

$$r = \frac{p}{1 + e\cos\theta}$$

where p and e are constant parameters ($0 < e < 1$). At time $t = 0$, P has speed v_0 at the position $\theta = 0$.

a. Show that the velocity $\mathbf{v}_P$ of P can be written as the sum of two vectors $\mathbf{A}$ and $\mathbf{B}$ of constant magnitude, with $\mathbf{A}$ directed along the y-axis and $\mathbf{B}$ directed along the transverse direction. Find the expressions of $\mathbf{A}$ and $\mathbf{B}$.

b. Using the expression of $\mathbf{v}_P$ found in a), find the acceleration $\mathbf{a}_P$ of P as a function of r. Then find the hodograph of P.

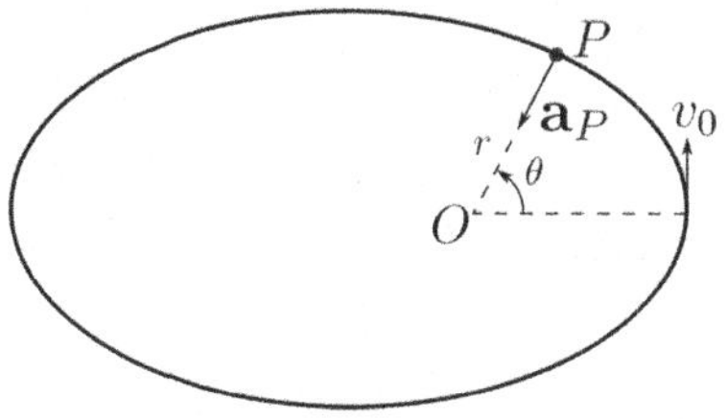

Problem 2.4 A particle P moves into a plane Oxy in such a way that its velocity can be expressed at any given time as the sum of two vectors $\mathbf{U}$ and $\mathbf{V}$: $\mathbf{U} = U\hat{\mathbf{e}}_x$ is constant, and $\mathbf{V}$ has a constant magnitude and remains perpendicular to the position vector $\mathbf{r}_{OP}$ of particle P.

a. Find a polar coordinate representation (r, θ) of the trajectory of P. Denote by $e = V/U$, where $U = |\mathbf{U}|$ and $V = |\mathbf{V}|$, and by (r_0, θ_0) the polar coordinates of P at $t = 0$. Sketch the trajectory of P depending on the value of e.

b. Find a relationship between time t and polar angle θ.

c. Show that the acceleration of P points toward O at all time. Express $\mathbf{a}_P$ in terms of V, r_0 and $r = |\mathbf{r}_{OP}|$. Comment.

Problem 2.5 A particle P moves in the plane Oxy in such a way that its hodograph is described by the half circle OAB of radius v_0 tangent to axis Ov_x. In addition, its speed increases linearly with time: $v = 2v_0 t/T$, T being the time taken to travel from O to B.

Find the trajectory of point P assuming that P is located at O at $t = 0$. Plot this trajectory. Find the acceleration of P.

Problem 2.6 A semi-infinite string is wrapped around a disk of center O and radius r. Its endpoint is located at point A on axis Ox. The string is then unwound from the disk, remaining taunt at all time. The position of the string's detachment point I is defined by angle $\theta = \omega t$, ω being a constant.

a. Find a parametric representation of the trajectory of P. Then plot this curve, along with the circle.

b. Find the velocity of P. Show that $\mathbf{v}_P$ is parallel to OI.

c. Find the acceleration of P.
The resulting curve is called the *involute* of the circle.

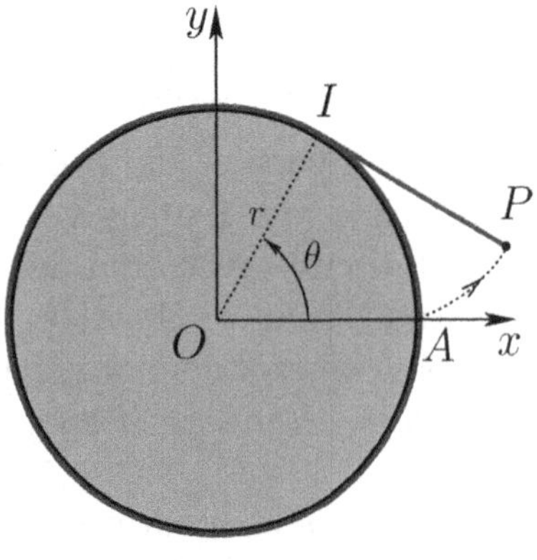

Problem 2.7 A particle P is in motion in a plane Oxy in such a way that
(i) its acceleration always points toward O,
(ii) its velocity keeps a constant angle α with the radial line.
At time $t = 0$, the position of P is defined by $r = r_0$ and $\theta = 0$.

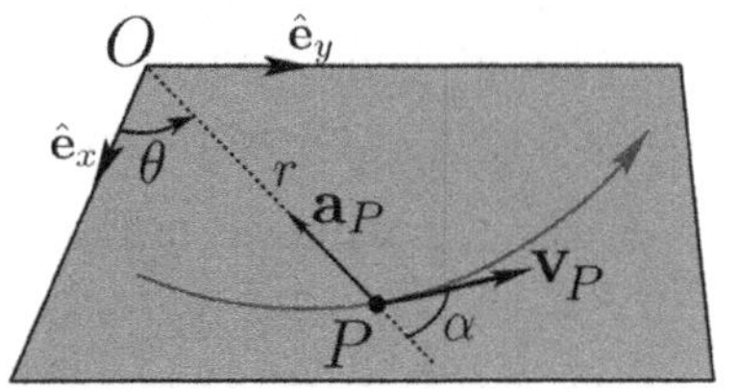

a. Show that the radial acceleration of P follows a $1/r^3$ law.

b. Find and sketch the trajectory of P.

Problem 2.8 The motion of a particle P in plane Oxy is characterized by the conditions
(i) P is at O and $\mathbf{v}_P = v_0 \hat{\mathbf{e}}_x$ at time $t = 0$,
(ii) the tangential acceleration a_T takes the constant value a_0 at all time,
(iii) the normal acceleration takes the expression $a_N = \omega^2 \rho$ at all time, where ω is a positive constant and ρ is the radius of curvature.

a. Find the velocity $\mathbf{v}_P$ of P as a function of time t.

b. Find the trajectory $(x(t), y(t))$ of P as a function of time t. Plot the XY-curve for $(a_0/\omega v_0) = 0.5$ in the variables $X = \omega x/v_0$ and $Y = \omega y/v_0$.

Problem 2.9 A particle P in planar motion is attracted to a fixed point O in such a way that its velocity $\mathbf{v}_P$ makes the angle $\theta/2$ with respect to transverse unit vector $\hat{\mathbf{e}}_\theta$ when the radial unit vector $\hat{\mathbf{e}}_r$ makes the angle θ with respect to axis Ox. Furthermore P moves at constant speed v_0 and is initially at point A on axis Ox at distance $r = r_0$ from O.

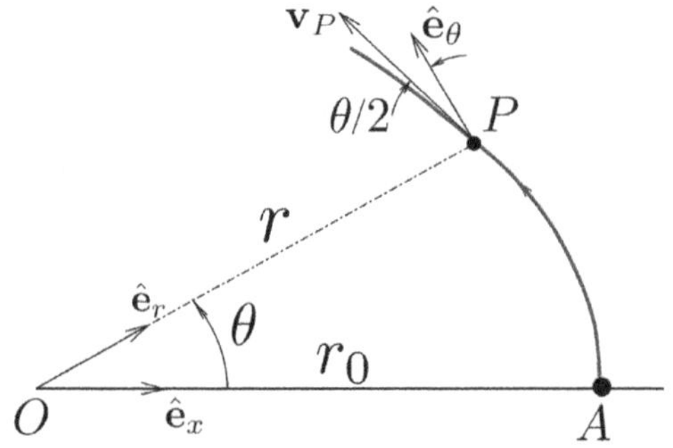

a. Show that the path of P is given in polar coordinates by the curve

$$r = \frac{r_0}{2}(1 + \cos\theta)$$

and find θ versus t. Sketch this path. Find the time taken to reach O.

b. Determine the acceleration $\mathbf{a}_P$ of P in polar coordinates, then find the normal and tangential components of $\mathbf{a}_P$.

c. Deduce the radius of curvature at any location of the path.

Problem 2.10 Two particles A and B connected by a rod of length l are in motion in a horizontal plane Oxy. A moves along axis Ox at constant speed v_0. The orientation of the rod defined by angle θ must be such that the speed of B must be equal to v_0 at all time. At time $t = 0$, $\theta = \pi/2$ so that B lies on axis Oy.

a. Find the equation which gives $\dot{\theta}$ versus θ. Show that two possible trajectories are possible. Find the trajectories of B in the form $(x_B(t), y_B(t))$. Sketch these trajectories.

b. Show that $\mathbf{v}_A$ and $\mathbf{v}_B$ have equal projections on line AB.

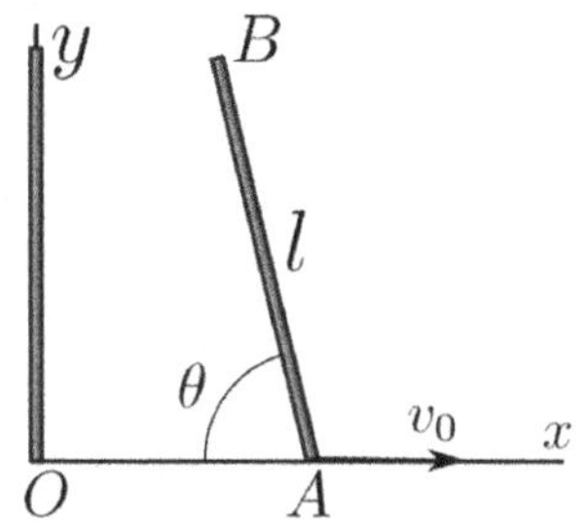

Problem 2.11 We seek to describe the trajectory of the contact point J of the back wheel of a bicycle, given that the contact point I of the front wheel travels at constant speed v_0 along the axis Ox.

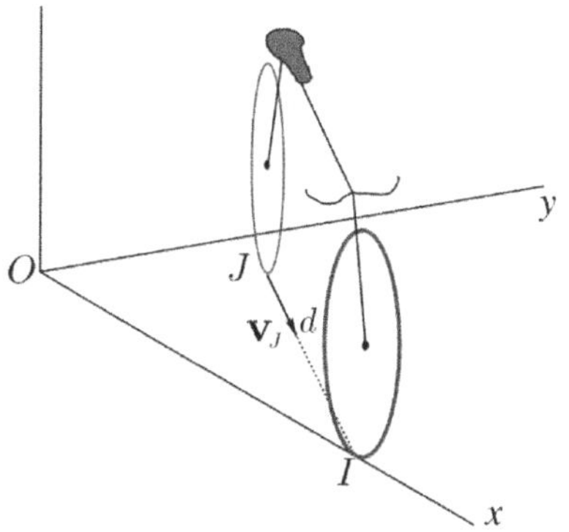

Find the trajectory of J by imposing a constant distance a between I and J and by the requiring that the velocity $\mathbf{v}_J$ is always directed along line IJ (which is kinematically correct if the back wheel rolls without slipping on the road). Assume that at time $t = 0$, point I is located at O while J is on axis Oy.

Find velocity $\mathbf{v}_J$ and acceleration $\mathbf{a}_J$ on the intrinsic unit vectors $(\hat{\mathbf{e}}_t, \hat{\mathbf{e}}_n)$.

The resulting curve was first studied by Huygens in 1692, who gave it the name *tractrix*.

Problem 2.12 A dog B is chasing a robber A which runs at constant speed v_A along straight line $y = D$ of plane Oxy. At time $t = 0$, B is at origin O at a distance D from A. B chases A at constant speed v_B so that its velocity vector $\mathbf{v}_B$ points toward A at all time. Denote by λ the speed ratio v_A/v_B. We seek to determine the dog's trajectory, and whether the dog can catch up with the robber.

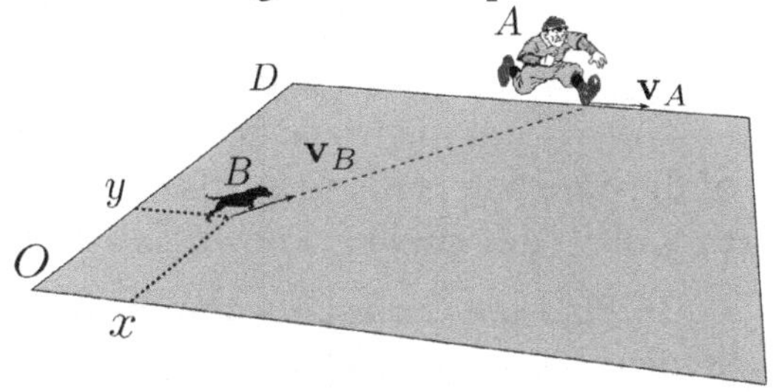

a. Denoting by $(x(t), y(t))$ the Cartesian coordinates of B, show that the dog's trajectory is governed by the equation $xy'' = \lambda(1 + y'^2)^{1/2}$ where y' and y'' denote dy/dx and d^2y/dx^2 respectively.

b. Integrate this equation to show that the dog's trajectory is given by

$$2\left(y - \frac{\lambda D}{1-\lambda^2}\right) = x\left(\frac{1}{1+\lambda}\left(\frac{x}{D}\right)^{\lambda} - \frac{1}{1-\lambda}\left(\frac{D}{x}\right)^{\lambda}\right)$$

Conclude by showing that (i) if $\lambda > 1$, the dog cannot reach the robber, (ii) if $\lambda < 1$, the dog can reach the robber in finite time. In case (ii), find the time taken by B to reach A. Then treat the case $\lambda = 1$.

Problem 2.13 Consider a particular point P of a bicycle wheel of radius R and center C. At $t = 0$, point P is in contact with the road. Center C moves at constant speed v_0. We assume that the wheel does not slip: hence the distance x traveled by C is equal to the arc length $|IP| = R\theta$, where θ is the angle between line CI and line CP.

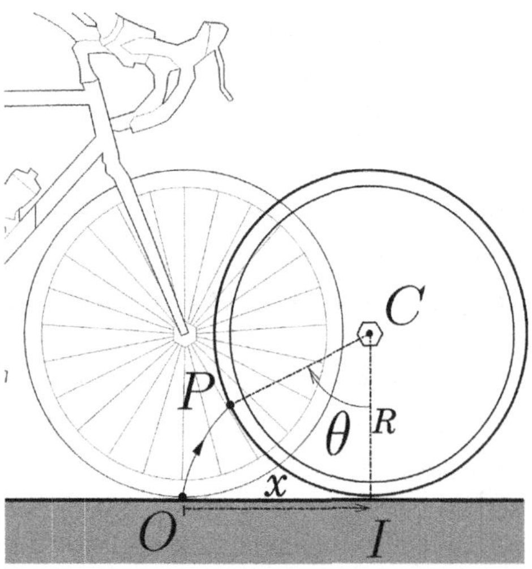

a. Find the Cartesian coordinates $(x(t), y(t))$ parametrized by time t in terms of the parameters R and v_0. Sketch the trajectory of P (this curve is known as a *cycloid*).

b. Find the Cartesian components of the velocity and acceleration of P. Show that the angle between the acceleration and the velocity is $\theta/2$.

c. From the previous results, find the velocity of P at the instants P comes in contact with the road.

d. Show that the radius of curvature of the path of P is given by

$$\rho = 4R \left| \sin\left(\frac{v_0 t}{2R}\right) \right|$$

Show that the center of curvature K is given by $\mathbf{r}_{PK} = 2\mathbf{r}_{PI}$. Sketch the trajectories described by both P and K. Conclude that the path of K is also a cycloid.

Problem 2.14 Three particles P_1, P_2 and P_3 are in motion in a plane with the velocities

$$\mathbf{v}_1 = k\mathbf{r}_{P_1P_2},\ \mathbf{v}_2 = k\mathbf{r}_{P_2P_3},\ \mathbf{v}_3 = k\mathbf{r}_{P_3P_1}$$

where k is a positive constant.

a. Show that the centroid of triangle $P_1P_2P_3$ is fixed.

b. Show that the area A of triangle $P_1P_2P_3$ satisfies

$$A = A_0 \exp(-3kt)$$

c. Show that, if the triangle is initially equilateral, it remains equilateral. If so, find the trajectories of the particles.

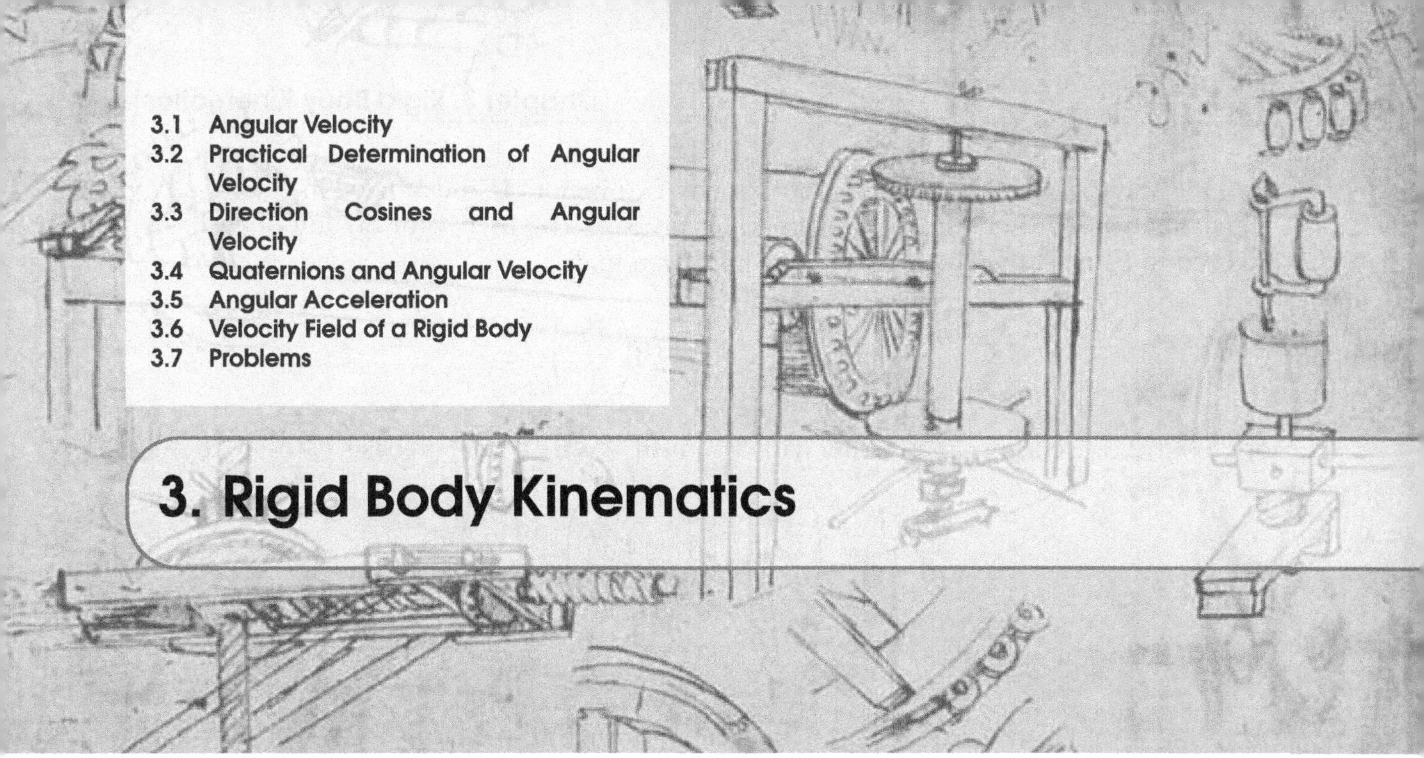

3. Rigid Body Kinematics

THE GOAL of this chapter is to study the kinematics of a rigid body $\mathcal{B}$ in motion relative to a referential (or rigid body) $\mathcal{A}$. We wish to characterize the velocity field $P \in \mathcal{B} \mapsto \mathbf{v}_{P/\mathcal{A}}$ of body $\mathcal{B}$ relative to $\mathcal{A}$. We shall find out that this vector field behaves like a *field of moments*, that is, as a vector field satisfying the property $\mathbf{u}_Q = \mathbf{u}_P + \mathbf{U} \times \mathbf{r}_{PQ}$, where $\mathbf{U}$ is an invariant of the field. We shall show that the velocity field $P \in \mathcal{B} \mapsto \mathbf{v}_{P/\mathcal{A}}$ is entirely specified at any instant by the knowledge of two quantities: (i) the velocity of a particular point of $\mathcal{B}$ and (ii) a vector independent of position, called *angular velocity*, characterizing the change of orientation of $\mathcal{B}$ relative to $\mathcal{A}$. We shall learn to determine the angular velocity in terms of the various parameters introduced in Chapter 1 for the definition of the orientation of a rigid body. The notion of angular velocity is pivotal not only in kinematics but also in all tasks involving the time-differentiation of vectors.

3.1 Angular Velocity

CONSIDER an arbitrary vector $\mathbf{V}$ attached to $\mathcal{B}$. The components (v_1, v_2, v_3) of $\mathbf{V}$ on basis $(\hat{\mathbf{b}}_1, \hat{\mathbf{b}}_2, \hat{\mathbf{b}}_3)$ of $\mathcal{B}$ are constant. However, the components (V_1, V_2, V_3) of $\mathbf{V}$ on basis $(\hat{\mathbf{a}}_1, \hat{\mathbf{a}}_2, \hat{\mathbf{a}}_3)$ of $\mathcal{A}$ are necessarily (scalar) functions of time due to the motion of $\mathcal{B}$ relative to $\mathcal{A}$.

We seek an expression for the derivative $(d\mathbf{V}/dt)_\mathcal{A}$ relative to $\mathcal{A}$, by a method more tractable than that which consists of differentiating $\mathbf{V} = V_1\hat{\mathbf{a}}_1 + V_2\hat{\mathbf{a}}_2 + V_3\hat{\mathbf{a}}_3$ resolved on basis $(\hat{\mathbf{a}}_1, \hat{\mathbf{a}}_2, \hat{\mathbf{a}}_3)$ of $\mathcal{A}$. To this end, we introduce the following operator

$$\left(\frac{d}{dt}\right)_\mathcal{A} : \quad \mathbf{V} \mapsto \left(\frac{d\mathbf{V}}{dt}\right)_\mathcal{A} \tag{3.1}$$

defined on the set of vectors fixed in $\mathcal{B}$. This operator is clearly *linear*. Furthermore, it is *skew-symmetric*:

$$\mathbf{U} \cdot \left(\frac{d\mathbf{V}}{dt}\right)_\mathcal{A} = -\mathbf{V} \cdot \left(\frac{d\mathbf{U}}{dt}\right)_\mathcal{A} .$$

since the scalar product $\mathbf{U} \cdot \mathbf{V}$ is constant for any two vectors $\mathbf{U}$ and $\mathbf{V}$ fixed in $\mathcal{B}$.

The matrix representation of this operator on basis $(\hat{\mathbf{b}}_1, \hat{\mathbf{b}}_2, \hat{\mathbf{b}}_3)$ (or on any other basis attached to $\mathcal{B}$) must then be skew-symmetric[1] given that

$$\hat{\mathbf{b}}_i \cdot \left(\frac{d\hat{\mathbf{b}}_j}{dt}\right)_{\mathcal{A}} = -\hat{\mathbf{b}}_j \cdot \left(\frac{d\hat{\mathbf{b}}_i}{dt}\right)_{\mathcal{A}}$$

for $i, j = 1, 2, 3$. Hence we may write, with $\mathbf{V} = v_1\hat{\mathbf{b}}_1 + v_2\hat{\mathbf{b}}_2 + v_3\hat{\mathbf{b}}_3$ on basis $b_B(\hat{\mathbf{b}}_1, \hat{\mathbf{b}}_2, \hat{\mathbf{b}}_3)$

$$\left(\frac{d\mathbf{V}}{dt}\right)_{\mathcal{A}} = \begin{pmatrix} 0 & -\omega_3 & \omega_2 \\ \omega_3 & 0 & -\omega_1 \\ -\omega_2 & \omega_1 & 0 \end{pmatrix}_{b_B} \begin{pmatrix} v_1 \\ v_2 \\ v_3 \end{pmatrix}$$

In expanded form, this gives

$$\begin{aligned} \left(\frac{d\mathbf{V}}{dt}\right)_{\mathcal{A}} &= (-\omega_3 v_2 + \omega_2 v_3)\hat{\mathbf{b}}_1 + (\omega_3 v_1 - \omega_1 v_3)\hat{\mathbf{b}}_2 + (-\omega_2 v_1 + \omega_1 v_2)\hat{\mathbf{b}}_3 \\ &= (\omega_1\hat{\mathbf{b}}_1 + \omega_2\hat{\mathbf{b}}_2 + \omega_3\hat{\mathbf{b}}_3) \times (v_1\hat{\mathbf{b}}_1 + v_2\hat{\mathbf{b}}_2 + v_3\hat{\mathbf{b}}_3) \end{aligned}$$

We can now state:

Theorem 3.1 — **Angular Velocity.** There exists a unique vector denoted $\boldsymbol{\omega}_{\mathcal{B}/\mathcal{A}}$, called *angular velocity* of $\mathcal{B}$ relative to $\mathcal{A}$ such that

$$\left(\frac{d\mathbf{V}}{dt}\right)_{\mathcal{A}} = \boldsymbol{\omega}_{\mathcal{B}/\mathcal{A}} \times \mathbf{V} \tag{3.2}$$

for any vector $\mathbf{V}$ fixed in $\mathcal{B}$. Vector $\boldsymbol{\omega}_{\mathcal{B}/\mathcal{A}}$ is independent of $\mathbf{V}$ and of the choice of basis of $\mathcal{B}$.

Proof. Uniqueness is easily shown: consider two vectors $\boldsymbol{\omega}_1$ and $\boldsymbol{\omega}_2$ satisfying (3.2), then $(\boldsymbol{\omega}_1 - \boldsymbol{\omega}_2) \times \mathbf{V} = \mathbf{0}$ for all vectors $\mathbf{V}$ fixed in $\mathcal{B}$. This necessarily implies $\boldsymbol{\omega}_1 = \boldsymbol{\omega}_2$. Furthermore formula (3.2) is independent of the choice of basis of $\mathcal{B}$. ■

Remark 1. It can be shown that all skew-symmetric operators $\mathcal{U}$ of 3-dimensional oriented vector spaces must be of the type $\mathcal{U}(\mathbf{V}) = \mathbf{U} \times \mathbf{V}$.

Remark 2. Vector $\boldsymbol{\omega}_{\mathcal{B}/\mathcal{A}}$ is not expected to be constant in $\mathcal{B}$ nor in $\mathcal{A}$.

We can generalize formula (3.2) for arbitrary vector functions $\mathbf{V}$, that is, varying relative to both $\mathcal{A}$ and $\mathcal{B}$:

$$\left(\frac{d\mathbf{V}}{dt}\right)_{\mathcal{A}} = \dot{v}_1\hat{\mathbf{b}}_1 + \dot{v}_2\hat{\mathbf{b}}_2 + \dot{v}_3\hat{\mathbf{b}}_3 + v_1\left(\frac{d\hat{\mathbf{b}}_1}{dt}\right)_{\mathcal{A}} + v_2\left(\frac{d\hat{\mathbf{b}}_2}{dt}\right)_{\mathcal{A}} + v_3\left(\frac{d\hat{\mathbf{b}}_3}{dt}\right)_{\mathcal{A}}$$

We recognize that $(d\hat{\mathbf{b}}_i/dt)_{\mathcal{A}} = \boldsymbol{\omega}_{\mathcal{B}/\mathcal{A}} \times \hat{\mathbf{b}}_i$, and that $\dot{v}_1\hat{\mathbf{b}}_1 + \dot{v}_2\hat{\mathbf{b}}_2 + \dot{v}_3\hat{\mathbf{b}}_3 = (d\mathbf{V}/dt)_{\mathcal{B}}$.

[1]Recall that the ijth element of this matrix is the scalar $\hat{\mathbf{b}}_i \cdot \left(d\hat{\mathbf{b}}_j/dt\right)_{\mathcal{A}}$.

Theorem 3.2 The time-derivatives of an arbitrary vector $\mathbf{V}$ relative to referentials $\mathcal{A}$ and $\mathcal{B}$ are related by

$$\left(\frac{d\mathbf{V}}{dt}\right)_{\mathcal{A}} = \left(\frac{d\mathbf{V}}{dt}\right)_{\mathcal{B}} + \omega_{\mathcal{B}/\mathcal{A}} \times \mathbf{V} \tag{3.3}$$

This fundamental formula shows that the time-derivative of $\mathbf{V}$ relative to $\mathcal{A}$ can be found from that relative to $\mathcal{B}$ by evaluating the term $\omega_{\mathcal{B}/\mathcal{A}} \times \mathbf{V}$ which accounts for the change of orientation of $\mathcal{B}$ relative to $\mathcal{A}$. The consequence of this formula is that it offers a practical way to calculate the time-derivatives of vectors. If angular velocities can be determined for arbitrary motions, we have an efficient means of calculating $(d\mathbf{V}/dt)_{\mathcal{A}}$ by simple cross-product evaluations of vectors, *without having to resolve vector* $\mathbf{V}$ *into components on the chosen basis of referential* $\mathcal{A}$.

Note that the components of angular velocity $\omega_{\mathcal{B}/\mathcal{A}}$ on basis $(\hat{\mathbf{b}}_1, \hat{\mathbf{b}}_2, \hat{\mathbf{b}}_3)$ of $\mathcal{B}$ can be expressed as, according to matrix representation of operator $(d \cdot /dt)_{\mathcal{A}}$ on the same basis,

$$\omega_1 = \left(\frac{d\hat{\mathbf{b}}_2}{dt}\right)_{\mathcal{A}} \cdot \hat{\mathbf{b}}_3, \quad \omega_2 = \left(\frac{d\hat{\mathbf{b}}_3}{dt}\right)_{\mathcal{A}} \cdot \hat{\mathbf{b}}_1, \quad \omega_3 = \left(\frac{d\hat{\mathbf{b}}_1}{dt}\right)_{\mathcal{A}} \cdot \hat{\mathbf{b}}_2 \tag{3.4}$$

But these expressions do not offer a practical way of calculating $\omega_{\mathcal{B}/\mathcal{A}}$ since the time derivatives $(d\hat{\mathbf{b}}_i/dt)_{\mathcal{A}}$ $(i = 1, 2, 3)$ are not easily found. They could be evaluated by expressing each basis vector $\hat{\mathbf{b}}_i$ on a basis of $\mathcal{A}$: this is not only unpractical, but we would lose all benefits of formula (3.2). In fact, *the simplest representation of* $\omega_{\mathcal{B}/\mathcal{A}}$ *is most often resolved on neither a basis of* $\mathcal{A}$ *nor a basis of* $\mathcal{B}$.

3.2 Practical Determination of Angular Velocity

A PRACTICAL way of determining angular velocities is to introduce a sequence of *auxiliary referentials* $\mathcal{A}_1$, $\mathcal{A}_2$, ..., $\mathcal{A}_n$ so that a basis $b_{\mathcal{A}}$ of $\mathcal{A}$ is mapped onto a basis $b_{\mathcal{B}}$ of $\mathcal{B}$ by a sequence of rotations

$$b_{\mathcal{A}} \xrightarrow{\mathcal{R}_0} b_{\mathcal{A}_1} \xrightarrow{\mathcal{R}_1} \dots b_{\mathcal{A}_n} \xrightarrow{\mathcal{R}_n} b_{\mathcal{B}}$$

If such a sequence can be found, and if each angular velocity $\omega_{\mathcal{A}_{k+1}/\mathcal{A}_k}$ can be determined, then the angular velocity $\omega_{\mathcal{B}/\mathcal{A}}$ can be found by using the following result.

Theorem 3.3 Given three referentials $\mathcal{A}$, $\mathcal{B}$ and $\mathcal{C}$, the pairwise angular velocities satisfy the loop equation

$$\omega_{\mathcal{B}/\mathcal{C}} + \omega_{\mathcal{C}/\mathcal{A}} + \omega_{\mathcal{A}/\mathcal{B}} = \mathbf{0} \tag{3.5}$$

As a consequence of (3.5) we have two simple identities:

$$\omega_{\mathcal{B}/\mathcal{A}} = -\omega_{\mathcal{A}/\mathcal{B}} \tag{3.6}$$

and

$$\omega_{\mathcal{A}/\mathcal{A}} = \mathbf{0} \tag{3.7}$$

Proof. Given an arbitrary vector $\mathbf{V}$, we have according to (3.3)

$$\left(\frac{d\mathbf{V}}{dt}\right)_{\mathcal{A}} = \left(\frac{d\mathbf{V}}{dt}\right)_{\mathcal{B}} + \boldsymbol{\omega}_{\mathcal{B}/\mathcal{A}} \times \mathbf{V}$$

$$\left(\frac{d\mathbf{V}}{dt}\right)_{\mathcal{C}} = \left(\frac{d\mathbf{V}}{dt}\right)_{\mathcal{A}} + \boldsymbol{\omega}_{\mathcal{A}/\mathcal{C}} \times \mathbf{V}$$

$$\left(\frac{d\mathbf{V}}{dt}\right)_{\mathcal{B}} = \left(\frac{d\mathbf{V}}{dt}\right)_{\mathcal{C}} + \boldsymbol{\omega}_{\mathcal{C}/\mathcal{B}} \times \mathbf{V}$$

Then, by summing these equations, we find $(\boldsymbol{\omega}_{\mathcal{B}/\mathcal{A}} + \boldsymbol{\omega}_{\mathcal{A}/\mathcal{C}} + \boldsymbol{\omega}_{\mathcal{C}/\mathcal{B}}) \times \mathbf{V} = \mathbf{0}$ for all vectors $\mathbf{V}$. Hence $\boldsymbol{\omega}_{\mathcal{B}/\mathcal{A}} + \boldsymbol{\omega}_{\mathcal{A}/\mathcal{C}} + \boldsymbol{\omega}_{\mathcal{C}/\mathcal{B}} = \mathbf{0}$. First let $\mathcal{C}$ coincide with $\mathcal{A}$: we obtain the identity $\boldsymbol{\omega}_{\mathcal{B}/\mathcal{A}} = -\boldsymbol{\omega}_{\mathcal{A}/\mathcal{B}}$ given that $\boldsymbol{\omega}_{\mathcal{A}/\mathcal{A}} = \mathbf{0}$. ■

The simplest motion between two referentials $\mathcal{A}$ and $\mathcal{B}$ is a rotational motion about a common axis: assume that the basis $(\hat{\mathbf{a}}_1, \hat{\mathbf{a}}_2, \hat{\mathbf{a}}_3)$ of $\mathcal{A}$ can be mapped onto basis $(\hat{\mathbf{b}}_1, \hat{\mathbf{b}}_2, \hat{\mathbf{b}}_3 = \hat{\mathbf{a}}_3)$ of $\mathcal{B}$ by the rotation $\mathcal{R}_{\theta,\hat{\mathbf{a}}_3}$ of angle θ about unit vector $\hat{\mathbf{a}}_3 = \hat{\mathbf{b}}_3$ fixed in both $\mathcal{A}$ and $\mathcal{B}$:

$$(\hat{\mathbf{a}}_1, \hat{\mathbf{a}}_2, \hat{\mathbf{a}}_3) \xrightarrow{\mathcal{R}_{\theta,\hat{\mathbf{a}}_3}} (\hat{\mathbf{b}}_1, \hat{\mathbf{b}}_2, \hat{\mathbf{b}}_3 = \hat{\mathbf{a}}_3)$$

The orientation of $\mathcal{B}$ relative to $\mathcal{A}$ is then characterized by the oriented angle $\theta = (\hat{\mathbf{a}}_1, \hat{\mathbf{b}}_1) = (\hat{\mathbf{a}}_2, \hat{\mathbf{b}}_2)$. By convention, the positive sense of rotation about vector $\hat{\mathbf{a}}_3$ is given by the right-hand-rule. See Figure 3.1. Then the angular velocity of $\mathcal{B}$ relative to $\mathcal{B}$ is given by

$$\boldsymbol{\omega}_{\mathcal{B}/\mathcal{A}} = \dot{\theta}\hat{\mathbf{a}}_3 \tag{3.8}$$

Indeed, it is easy to show that $(d\hat{\mathbf{b}}_1/dt)_{\mathcal{A}} = \dot{\theta}\hat{\mathbf{b}}_2 = \dot{\theta}\hat{\mathbf{a}}_3 \times \hat{\mathbf{b}}_1$ and $(d\hat{\mathbf{b}}_2/dt)_{\mathcal{A}} = -\dot{\theta}\hat{\mathbf{b}}_1 = \dot{\theta}\hat{\mathbf{a}}_3 \times \hat{\mathbf{b}}_2$.

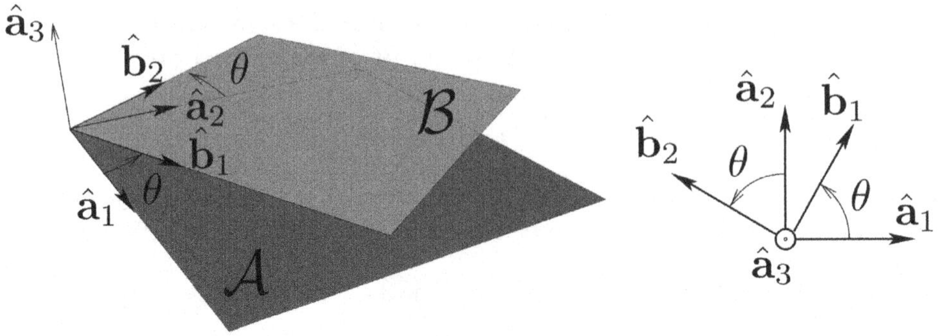

Figure 3.1

For a general motion $\mathcal{B}/\mathcal{A}$, a practical way of determining $\boldsymbol{\omega}_{\mathcal{B}/\mathcal{A}}$ is to map a basis of $\mathcal{A}$ into a basis of $\mathcal{B}$ by $n+1$ consecutive rotations of angle θ_i about unit vector $\hat{\mathbf{k}}_i$, each rotation defining an auxiliary referential $\mathcal{A}_i$:

$$b_{\mathcal{A}} \xrightarrow{\mathcal{R}_{\theta_0,\hat{\mathbf{k}}_0}} b_{\mathcal{A}_1} \xrightarrow{\mathcal{R}_{\theta_1,\hat{\mathbf{k}}_1}} b_{\mathcal{A}_2} \rightarrow \cdots \rightarrow b_{\mathcal{A}_n} \xrightarrow{\mathcal{R}_{\theta_n,\hat{\mathbf{k}}_n}} b_{\mathcal{B}} \tag{3.9}$$

when unit vector $\hat{\mathbf{k}}_i$ is fixed in both $\mathcal{A}_i$ and $\mathcal{A}_{i+1}$. Then, according to (3.5), we have

$$\boldsymbol{\omega}_{\mathcal{B}/\mathcal{A}} = \dot{\theta}_0\,\hat{\mathbf{k}}_0 + \dot{\theta}_1\,\hat{\mathbf{k}}_1 + \cdots + \dot{\theta}_n\,\hat{\mathbf{k}}_n \tag{3.10}$$

Remark 3. The determination of $\omega_{\mathcal{B}/\mathcal{A}}$ is intimately related to the parametrization of the orientation of $\mathcal{B}$ relative to $\mathcal{A}$. In particular, Euler sequences introduced in Section 1.4 correspond to (3.9).

Remark 4. A representation of $\omega_{\mathcal{B}/\mathcal{A}}$ such as (3.10) yields an expression which is generally resolved neither on a basis of $\mathcal{A}$ nor on a basis of $\mathcal{B}$.

The remainder of this section demonstrates through examples the efficiency of formula (3.3) for the determination of time-derivatives of vectors by the use of angular velocities.

Example 3.1 A point P is in motion in a referential $\mathcal{E}$ of Cartesian axes $Oxyz$. Its position is defined by the spherical coordinates (ρ, ϕ, θ) as defined in Section 1.2.3.

Find the velocity $\mathbf{v}_{P/\mathcal{E}}$ of P relative to $\mathcal{E}$ by defining a fictitious referential $\mathcal{F}$ relative to which the unit vectors $(\hat{\mathbf{e}}_\rho, \hat{\mathbf{e}}_\phi, \hat{\mathbf{e}}_\theta)$ are attached. See Figure 3.2. ■

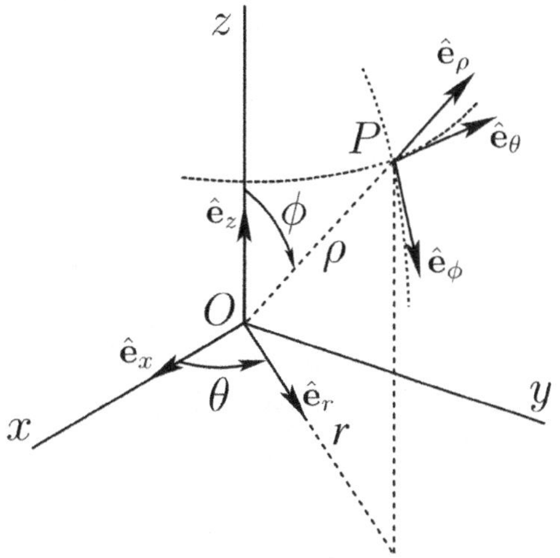

Figure 3.2

To the spherical coordinates (ρ, ϕ, θ) corresponds the moving basis of unit vectors $(\hat{\mathbf{e}}_\rho, \hat{\mathbf{e}}_\phi, \hat{\mathbf{e}}_\theta)$. The velocity of point P is obtained by differentiating the position vector $\mathbf{r}_{OP} = \rho\,\hat{\mathbf{e}}_\rho$ relative to $\mathcal{E}$:

$$\mathbf{v}_{P/\mathcal{E}} = \dot{\rho}\,\hat{\mathbf{e}}_\rho + \rho \left(\frac{d\hat{\mathbf{e}}_\rho}{dt}\right)_{\mathcal{E}}.$$

Hence, we need to find the derivative of $\hat{\mathbf{e}}_\rho$: according to (3.3) we have

$$\left(\frac{d\hat{\mathbf{e}}_\rho}{dt}\right)_{\mathcal{E}} = \omega_{\mathcal{F}/\mathcal{E}} \times \hat{\mathbf{e}}_\rho$$

where $\mathcal{F}$ denotes a fictitious referential relative to which basis $(\hat{\mathbf{e}}_\rho, \hat{\mathbf{e}}_\phi, \hat{\mathbf{e}}_\theta)$ is fixed. The angular velocity $\omega_{\mathcal{F}/\mathcal{E}}$ is found by two consecutive rotations:

1. the rotation of angle θ about $\hat{\mathbf{e}}_z$ maps basis $(\hat{\mathbf{e}}_x, \hat{\mathbf{e}}_y, \hat{\mathbf{e}}_z)$ to basis $(\hat{\mathbf{e}}_r, \hat{\mathbf{e}}_\theta, \hat{\mathbf{e}}_z)$ of an auxiliary referential $\mathcal{E}_1$.
2. the rotation of angle ϕ about $\hat{\mathbf{e}}_\theta$ maps basis $(\hat{\mathbf{e}}_r, \hat{\mathbf{e}}_\theta, \hat{\mathbf{e}}_z)$ to basis $(\hat{\mathbf{e}}_\phi, \hat{\mathbf{e}}_\theta, \hat{\mathbf{e}}_\rho)$ of referential $\mathcal{F}$.

$$(\hat{\mathbf{e}}_x, \hat{\mathbf{e}}_y, \hat{\mathbf{e}}_z) \xrightarrow{\mathcal{R}_{\theta,\hat{\mathbf{e}}_z}} (\hat{\mathbf{e}}_r, \hat{\mathbf{e}}_\theta, \hat{\mathbf{e}}_z) \xrightarrow{\mathcal{R}_{\phi,\hat{\mathbf{e}}_\theta}} (\hat{\mathbf{e}}_\phi, \hat{\mathbf{e}}_\theta, \hat{\mathbf{e}}_\rho)$$

These transformations are summarized on the following rotation diagrams:

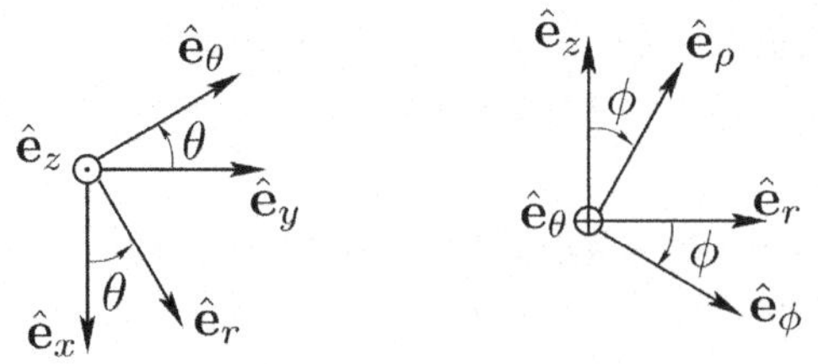

We can now write

$$\boldsymbol{\omega}_{\mathcal{F}/\mathcal{E}} = \boldsymbol{\omega}_{\mathcal{F}/\mathcal{E}_1} + \boldsymbol{\omega}_{\mathcal{E}_1/\mathcal{E}} = \dot{\phi}\,\hat{\mathbf{e}}_\theta + \dot{\theta}\hat{\mathbf{e}}_z$$

The velocity of P can then be found as the straightforward determination of cross-products

$$\mathbf{v}_{P/\mathcal{E}} = \dot{\rho}\,\hat{\mathbf{e}}_\rho + \rho\boldsymbol{\omega}_{\mathcal{F}/\mathcal{E}} \times \hat{\mathbf{e}}_\rho = \dot{\rho}\,\hat{\mathbf{e}}_\rho + \rho\,(\dot{\phi}\,\hat{\mathbf{e}}_\theta + \dot{\theta}\hat{\mathbf{e}}_z) \times \hat{\mathbf{e}}_\rho = \dot{\rho}\,\hat{\mathbf{e}}_\rho + \rho\,(\dot{\phi}\,\hat{\mathbf{e}}_\phi + \dot{\theta}\sin\phi\,\hat{\mathbf{e}}_\theta)$$

where we have determined the cross-products $\hat{\mathbf{e}}_\theta \times \hat{\mathbf{e}}_\rho$ and $\hat{\mathbf{e}}_z \times \hat{\mathbf{e}}_\rho$ by direct inspection of the rotation diagrams: $\hat{\mathbf{e}}_\theta \times \hat{\mathbf{e}}_\rho = \hat{\mathbf{e}}_\phi$, $\hat{\mathbf{e}}_z \times \hat{\mathbf{e}}_\rho = \sin\phi\,\hat{\mathbf{e}}_\theta$.

In order to find the acceleration of P, one would need the derivative of unit vector $\hat{\mathbf{e}}_\phi$. It is found in the following way:

$$\left(\frac{d\hat{\mathbf{e}}_\phi}{dt}\right)_{\mathcal{E}} = \boldsymbol{\omega}_{\mathcal{F}/\mathcal{E}} \times \hat{\mathbf{e}}_\phi = (\dot{\phi}\,\hat{\mathbf{e}}_\theta + \dot{\theta}\hat{\mathbf{e}}_z) \times \hat{\mathbf{e}}_\phi = -\dot{\phi}\,\hat{\mathbf{e}}_\rho + \dot{\theta}\cos\phi\,\hat{\mathbf{e}}_\theta$$

Remark 5. We could have found $\mathbf{v}_{P/\mathcal{E}}$ by using formula (3.3) between $\mathcal{E}$ and $\mathcal{F}$ applied to $\mathbf{V} = \mathbf{r}_{OP}$:

$$\mathbf{v}_{P/\mathcal{E}} = \left(\frac{d}{dt}(\rho\hat{\mathbf{e}}_\rho)\right)_{\mathcal{F}} + \boldsymbol{\omega}_{\mathcal{F}/\mathcal{E}} \times \rho\hat{\mathbf{e}}_\rho$$

The same result is found.

Remark 6. To fully appreciate the efficiency of this approach, compare it with the method which would consist of first resolving $\hat{\mathbf{e}}_\rho$ on basis $(\hat{\mathbf{e}}_x, \hat{\mathbf{e}}_y, \hat{\mathbf{e}}_z)$, then differentiating each component, and finally expressing the final answer on basis $(\hat{\mathbf{e}}_\phi, \hat{\mathbf{e}}_\theta, \hat{\mathbf{e}}_\rho)$.

■

Example 3.2 Determine the angular velocity $\boldsymbol{\omega}_{\mathcal{B}/\mathcal{E}}$ of the referential $\mathcal{B}$ whose orientation is parametrized in terms of Euler angles (ψ, θ, ϕ) shown in Figure 3.3. Express $(\dot{\psi}, \dot{\theta}, \dot{\phi})$ in terms of the components (p, q, r) of $\boldsymbol{\omega}_{\mathcal{B}/\mathcal{A}}$ on basis $(\hat{\mathbf{b}}_1, \hat{\mathbf{b}}_2, \hat{\mathbf{b}}_3)$. Then find the derivatives of $\hat{\mathbf{b}}_i$ $(i = 1, 2, 3)$ relative to referential $\mathcal{E}$. ■

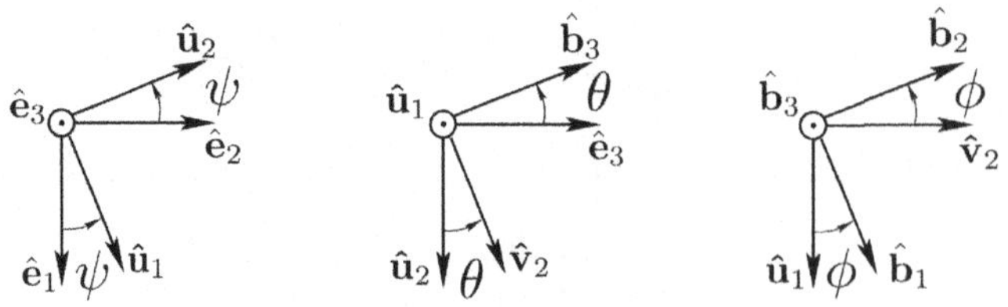

Figure 3.3 – *Euler angles*

The sequence of transformations which maps basis $(\hat{\mathbf{e}}_1, \hat{\mathbf{e}}_2, \hat{\mathbf{e}}_3)$ of $\mathcal{E}$ into basis $(\hat{\mathbf{b}}_1, \hat{\mathbf{b}}_2, \hat{\mathbf{b}}_3)$ of $\mathcal{B}$ leads to

$$\boldsymbol{\omega}_{\mathcal{B}/\mathcal{E}} = \dot{\psi}\hat{\mathbf{e}}_3 + \dot{\theta}\hat{\mathbf{u}}_1 + \dot{\phi}\hat{\mathbf{b}}_3$$

We can resolve $\boldsymbol{\omega}_{\mathcal{B}/\mathcal{E}}$ on basis $(\hat{\mathbf{b}}_1, \hat{\mathbf{b}}_2, \hat{\mathbf{b}}_3)$ to obtain (p, q, r)

$$\begin{aligned} p &= \dot{\psi} \sin\theta \sin\phi + \dot{\theta}\cos\phi \\ q &= \dot{\psi} \sin\theta \cos\phi - \dot{\theta}\sin\phi \\ r &= \dot{\psi}\cos\theta + \dot{\phi} \end{aligned}$$

We can then express $(\dot{\psi}, \dot{\theta}, \dot{\phi})$ in terms of (p, q, r)

$$\begin{aligned} \dot{\psi} &= (p\sin\phi + q\cos\phi)/\sin\theta \\ \dot{\theta} &= p\cos\phi - q\sin\phi \\ \dot{\phi} &= r - \cot\theta(p\sin\phi + q\cos\phi) \end{aligned}$$

To differentiate $\hat{\mathbf{b}}_1$, we apply formula (3.3) (recall that $\hat{\mathbf{b}}_1$ is attached to $\mathcal{B}$)

$$\begin{aligned} \left(\frac{d\hat{\mathbf{b}}_1}{dt}\right)_{\mathcal{E}} &= \left(\frac{d\hat{\mathbf{b}}_1}{dt}\right)_{\mathcal{B}} + \boldsymbol{\omega}_{\mathcal{B}/\mathcal{E}} \times \hat{\mathbf{b}}_1 = (\dot{\psi}\hat{\mathbf{e}}_3 + \dot{\theta}\hat{\mathbf{u}}_1 + \dot{\phi}\hat{\mathbf{b}}_3) \times \hat{\mathbf{b}}_1 \\ &= \dot{\psi}(\cos\theta\hat{\mathbf{b}}_2 - \sin\theta\cos\phi\hat{\mathbf{b}}_3) + \dot{\theta}\sin\phi\hat{\mathbf{b}}_3 + \dot{\phi}\hat{\mathbf{b}}_2 \end{aligned}$$

where we have found the following cross-products from the rotations diagrams displayed above

$$\hat{\mathbf{e}}_3 \times \hat{\mathbf{b}}_1 = \cos\theta\hat{\mathbf{b}}_2 - \sin\theta\cos\phi\hat{\mathbf{b}}_3, \quad \hat{\mathbf{u}}_1 \times \hat{\mathbf{b}}_1 = \sin\phi\hat{\mathbf{b}}_3, \quad \hat{\mathbf{b}}_3 \times \hat{\mathbf{b}}_1 = \hat{\mathbf{b}}_2$$

Regroup likewise terms to obtain

$$\left(\frac{d\hat{\mathbf{b}}_1}{dt}\right)_{\mathcal{E}} = (\dot{\psi}\cos\theta + \dot{\phi})\hat{\mathbf{b}}_2 + (\dot{\theta}\sin\phi - \dot{\psi}\sin\theta\cos\phi)\hat{\mathbf{b}}_3$$

Note that since $\hat{\mathbf{b}}_1$ is a unit vector, its derivative is normal to itself. The reader will verify the following results

$$\left(\frac{d\hat{\mathbf{b}}_2}{dt}\right)_{\mathcal{E}} = -(\dot{\psi}\cos\theta + \dot{\phi})\hat{\mathbf{b}}_1 + (\dot{\theta}\cos\phi + \dot{\psi}\sin\theta\sin\phi)\hat{\mathbf{b}}_3$$

(which can be found from the derivative of $\hat{\mathbf{b}}_1$ by changing ϕ to $\phi + \pi/2$),

$$\left(\frac{d\hat{\mathbf{b}}_3}{dt}\right)_{\mathcal{E}} = \dot{\psi}\sin\theta\hat{\mathbf{u}}_1 + \dot{\theta}\hat{\mathbf{v}}_2$$

Note the singularity at $\theta = 0, \pi$ in the expression $\dot{\psi} = (p\sin\phi + q\cos\phi)/\sin\theta$ consistent with the indetermination of Euler angles described in Section 1.4. ■

Example 3.3 Two rigid bodies $\mathcal{A}$ and $\mathcal{B}$ are in motion in a referential $\mathcal{E}$ of origin O and basis $(\hat{\mathbf{e}}_1, \hat{\mathbf{e}}_2, \hat{\mathbf{e}}_3)$. Body $\mathcal{A}(O, \hat{\mathbf{a}}_1, \hat{\mathbf{a}}_2, \hat{\mathbf{a}}_3)$ is in rotation about axis $(O, \hat{\mathbf{e}}_3)$ of $\mathcal{E}$. Its orientation is parametrized by angle $\alpha = (\hat{\mathbf{e}}_1, \hat{\mathbf{a}}_1)$. Denote by A the point of $\mathcal{A}$ defined by $\mathbf{r}_{OA} = a\hat{\mathbf{a}}_1$. Body $\mathcal{B}(A, \hat{\mathbf{b}}_1, \hat{\mathbf{b}}_2, \hat{\mathbf{b}}_3)$ rotates relative to $\mathcal{A}$ about axis $(A, \hat{\mathbf{a}}_2)$. Its orientation is parametrized by angle $\beta = (\hat{\mathbf{a}}_1, \hat{\mathbf{b}}_1)$. Finally, a collar P slides along body $\mathcal{B}$: its position is defined by $\mathbf{r}_{AP} = \rho(t)\hat{\mathbf{b}}_3$. See Figure 3.4.

a. Find the time-derivative of unit vectors $\hat{\mathbf{b}}_1$ and $\hat{\mathbf{b}}_3$ relative to $\mathcal{E}$.

b. Find the velocity and acceleration of P in referential $\mathcal{E}$ in terms of ρ, α, β and their derivatives. ■

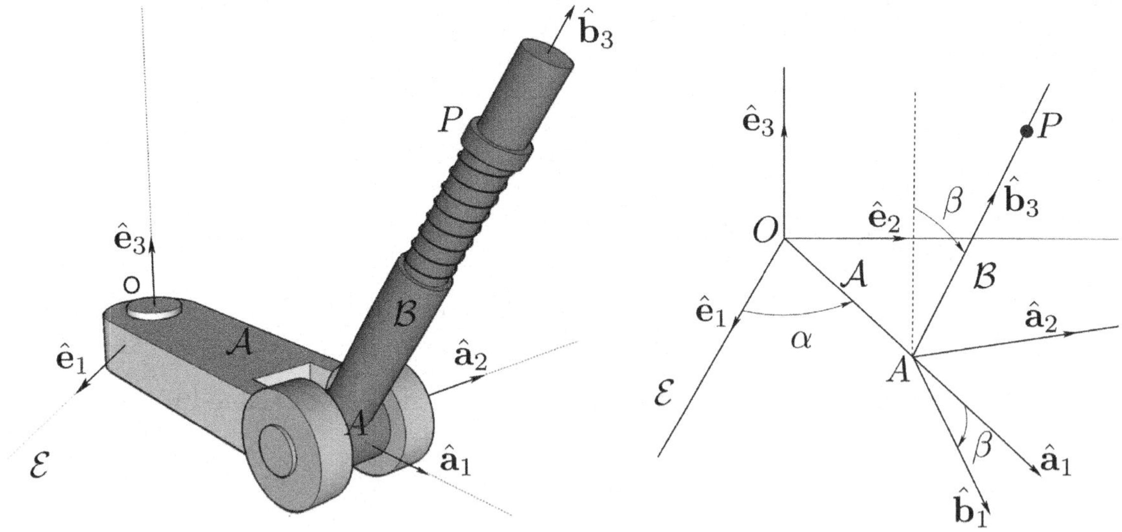

Figure 3.4

a. We have the following transformations between referentials $\mathcal{E}$, $\mathcal{A}$ and $\mathcal{B}$:

$$(\hat{\mathbf{e}}_1, \hat{\mathbf{e}}_2, \hat{\mathbf{e}}_3) \xrightarrow{\mathcal{R}_{\alpha,\hat{\mathbf{e}}_3}} (\hat{\mathbf{a}}_1, \hat{\mathbf{a}}_2, \hat{\mathbf{a}}_3 = \hat{\mathbf{e}}_3) \xrightarrow{\mathcal{R}_{\beta,\hat{\mathbf{a}}_2}} (\hat{\mathbf{b}}_1, \hat{\mathbf{b}}_2 = \hat{\mathbf{a}}_2, \hat{\mathbf{b}}_3)$$

and we can sketch the corresponding rotation diagrams leading to the corresponding angular

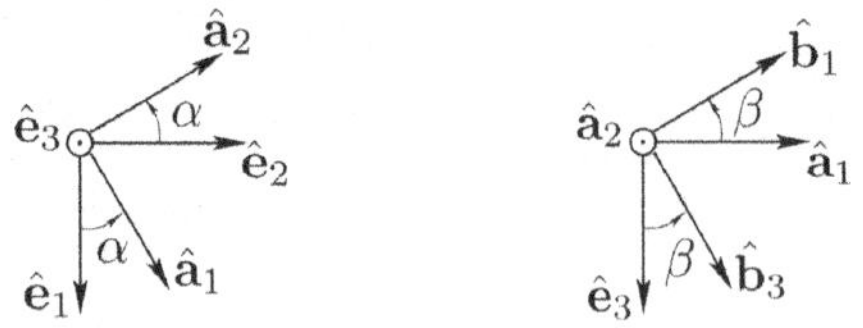

velocities $\boldsymbol{\omega}_{\mathcal{A}/\mathcal{E}} = \dot{\alpha}\hat{\mathbf{e}}_3$, $\boldsymbol{\omega}_{\mathcal{B}/\mathcal{A}} = \dot{\beta}\hat{\mathbf{a}}_2$, and $\boldsymbol{\omega}_{\mathcal{B}/\mathcal{E}} = \dot{\alpha}\hat{\mathbf{e}}_3 + \dot{\beta}\hat{\mathbf{a}}_2$. We can now find $(d\hat{\mathbf{b}}_1/dt)_{\mathcal{E}}$ and $(d\hat{\mathbf{b}}_3/dt)_{\mathcal{E}}$:

$$\left(\frac{d\hat{\mathbf{b}}_1}{dt}\right)_{\mathcal{E}} = \boldsymbol{\omega}_{\mathcal{B}/\mathcal{E}} \times \hat{\mathbf{b}}_1 = \dot{\alpha}\cos\beta\hat{\mathbf{a}}_2 - \dot{\beta}\hat{\mathbf{b}}_3$$

$$\left(\frac{d\hat{\mathbf{b}}_3}{dt}\right)_{\mathcal{E}} = \boldsymbol{\omega}_{\mathcal{B}/\mathcal{E}} \times \hat{\mathbf{b}}_3 = \dot{\alpha}\sin\beta\hat{\mathbf{a}}_2 + \dot{\beta}\hat{\mathbf{b}}_1$$

where the cross-products $\hat{\mathbf{e}}_3 \times \hat{\mathbf{b}}_3$, $\hat{\mathbf{e}}_3 \times \hat{\mathbf{b}}_1$ and $\hat{\mathbf{a}}_2 \times \hat{\mathbf{b}}_3$ are determined directly from the rotation diagrams.

b. The velocity of particle P in $\mathcal{E}$ is obtained by differentiating (relative to $\mathcal{E}$) the position vector $\mathbf{r}_{OP} = a\hat{\mathbf{a}}_1 + \rho\hat{\mathbf{b}}_3$ one term at a time:

$$\begin{aligned}
\mathbf{v}_{P/\mathcal{E}} &= a\left(\frac{d\hat{\mathbf{a}}_1}{dt}\right)_{\mathcal{E}} + \dot{\rho}\,\hat{\mathbf{b}}_3 + \rho\left(\frac{d\hat{\mathbf{b}}_3}{dt}\right)_{\mathcal{E}} = a\dot{\alpha}\,\hat{\mathbf{a}}_2 + \dot{\rho}\,\hat{\mathbf{b}}_3 + \rho(\dot{\alpha}\sin\beta\,\hat{\mathbf{a}}_2 + \dot{\beta}\,\hat{\mathbf{b}}_1) \\
&= (a\dot{\alpha} + \rho\dot{\alpha}\sin\beta)\hat{\mathbf{a}}_2 + \dot{\rho}\,\hat{\mathbf{b}}_3 + \rho\dot{\beta}\,\hat{\mathbf{b}}_1
\end{aligned}$$

The mistake to avoid here is to write $\mathbf{v}_{P/\mathcal{E}} = \boldsymbol{\omega}_{\mathcal{B}/\mathcal{E}} \times \mathbf{r}_{OP}$ since $\mathbf{r}_{OP}$ is not fixed to referential $\mathcal{B}$. However we could write $\mathbf{v}_{P/\mathcal{E}} = (d\mathbf{r}_{OP}/dt)_{\mathcal{B}} + \boldsymbol{\omega}_{\mathcal{B}/\mathcal{E}} \times \mathbf{r}_{OG}$ but this is not practical since $\mathbf{r}_{OP}$ varies relative to both $\mathcal{E}$ and $\mathcal{B}$.

The acceleration of P in $\mathcal{E}$ is found the same way: we differentiate $\mathbf{v}_{P/\mathcal{E}}$ term by term to find

$$\mathbf{a}_{P/\mathcal{E}} = \dot{\overline{\dot{\alpha}(a+\rho\sin\beta)}}\ \hat{\mathbf{a}}_2 - (a+\rho\sin\beta)\dot{\alpha}^2\,\hat{\mathbf{a}}_1 + \ddot{\rho}\hat{\mathbf{b}}_3 + \dot{\rho}(\dot{\alpha}\sin\beta\hat{\mathbf{a}}_2 + \dot{\beta}\hat{\mathbf{b}}_1) + \dot{\overline{\rho\dot{\beta}}}\,\hat{\mathbf{b}}_1 + \rho\dot{\beta}(\dot{\alpha}\cos\beta\hat{\mathbf{a}}_2 - \dot{\beta}\hat{\mathbf{b}}_3)$$

Regrouping similar terms we find

$$\mathbf{a}_{P/\mathcal{E}} = (\ddot{\rho} - \rho\dot{\beta}^2)\hat{\mathbf{b}}_3 + (2\dot{\rho}\dot{\beta} + \rho\ddot{\beta})\hat{\mathbf{b}}_1 + (a+\rho\sin\beta)(\ddot{\alpha}\hat{\mathbf{a}}_2 - \dot{\alpha}^2\hat{\mathbf{a}}_1) + 2\dot{\alpha}(\dot{\rho}\sin\beta + \rho\dot{\beta}\cos\beta)\hat{\mathbf{a}}_2$$

We may leave the expression of $\mathbf{a}_{P/\mathcal{E}}$ in this form. An expression entirely resolved on basis $(\hat{\mathbf{a}}_1, \hat{\mathbf{a}}_2, \hat{\mathbf{a}}_3)$ is easily obtained. ■

Example 3.4 A gyroscopic system consists of three interconnected rigid bodies $\mathcal{A}$, $\mathcal{B}$, and $\mathcal{C}$ in motion in a referential $\mathcal{E}(O, \hat{\mathbf{e}}_1, \hat{\mathbf{e}}_2, \hat{\mathbf{e}}_3)$. The outer gimbal $\mathcal{A}(O, \hat{\mathbf{a}}_1, \hat{\mathbf{a}}_2, \hat{\mathbf{a}}_3 = \hat{\mathbf{e}}_3)$ is in rotation relative to referential $\mathcal{E}$ about fixed axis $(O, \hat{\mathbf{e}}_3)$. Connected to $\mathcal{A}$ is the inner gimbal $\mathcal{B}(O, \hat{\mathbf{b}}_1 = \hat{\mathbf{a}}_1, \hat{\mathbf{b}}_2, \hat{\mathbf{b}}_3)$ which is free to rotate relative to $\mathcal{A}$ about axis $(O, \hat{\mathbf{a}}_1)$. Finally rotor $\mathcal{C}(O, \hat{\mathbf{c}}_1, \hat{\mathbf{c}}_2 = \hat{\mathbf{b}}_2, \hat{\mathbf{c}}_3)$ can rotate relative to $\mathcal{B}$ about axis $(O, \hat{\mathbf{b}}_2)$. The rotation diagrams mapping basis $(\hat{\mathbf{e}}_1, \hat{\mathbf{e}}_2, \hat{\mathbf{e}}_3)$ to basis $(\hat{\mathbf{c}}_1, \hat{\mathbf{c}}_2, \hat{\mathbf{c}}_3)$ are shown in Figure 3.5.

Find the velocity and acceleration of point P of $\mathcal{C}$ defined by $\mathbf{r}_{OP} = \hat{\mathbf{c}}_1$. ■

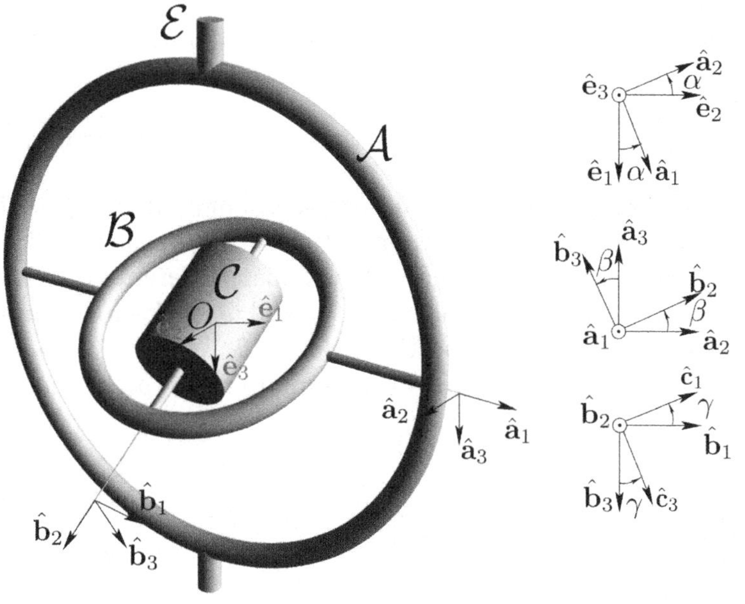

Figure 3.5

Each of the motions $\mathcal{A}/\mathcal{E}$, $\mathcal{B}/\mathcal{A}$, and $\mathcal{C}/\mathcal{B}$ is a rotation. The corresponding angular velocities are then easily found from the diagrams showing the configurations of the bases of $\mathcal{E}$, $\mathcal{A}$, $\mathcal{B}$ and $\mathcal{C}$: $\boldsymbol{\omega}_{\mathcal{A}/\mathcal{E}} = \dot{\alpha}\hat{\mathbf{e}}_3$, $\boldsymbol{\omega}_{\mathcal{B}/\mathcal{A}} = \dot{\beta}\hat{\mathbf{a}}_1$ and $\boldsymbol{\omega}_{\mathcal{C}/\mathcal{B}} = \dot{\gamma}\hat{\mathbf{b}}_2$. Hence we have $\boldsymbol{\omega}_{\mathcal{C}/\mathcal{E}} = \dot{\alpha}\hat{\mathbf{e}}_3 + \dot{\beta}\hat{\mathbf{a}}_1 + \dot{\gamma}\hat{\mathbf{b}}_2$. Velocity $\mathbf{v}_{P/\mathcal{E}}$ is found by time-differentiating position vector $\mathbf{r}_{OP} = \hat{\mathbf{c}}_1$ relative to $\mathcal{E}$:

$$\begin{aligned}
\mathbf{v}_{P/\mathcal{E}} &= \boldsymbol{\omega}_{\mathcal{C}/\mathcal{E}} \times \hat{\mathbf{c}}_1 = (\dot{\alpha}\hat{\mathbf{e}}_3 + \dot{\beta}\hat{\mathbf{a}}_1 + \dot{\gamma}\hat{\mathbf{b}}_2) \times \hat{\mathbf{c}}_1 = \dot{\alpha}\hat{\mathbf{e}}_3 \times \hat{\mathbf{c}}_1 + \dot{\beta}\hat{\mathbf{a}}_1 \times \hat{\mathbf{c}}_1 - \dot{\gamma}\hat{\mathbf{c}}_3 \\
&= \dot{\alpha}(\cos\beta\cos\gamma\hat{\mathbf{c}}_2 - \sin\beta\hat{\mathbf{c}}_3) + \dot{\beta}\sin\gamma\hat{\mathbf{c}}_2 - \dot{\gamma}\hat{\mathbf{c}}_3 \\
&= (\dot{\beta}\sin\gamma + \dot{\alpha}\cos\beta\cos\gamma)\hat{\mathbf{c}}_2 - (\dot{\gamma} + \dot{\alpha}\sin\beta)\hat{\mathbf{c}}_3
\end{aligned}$$

Note that, as expected, $(d\hat{\mathbf{c}}_1/dt)_{\mathcal{E}}$ is orthogonal to $\hat{\mathbf{c}}_1$. By using the concept of angular velocity, we have determined in an efficient manner the simplest expression of the time-derivative of $\hat{\mathbf{c}}_1$

relative to $\mathcal{E}$. The acceleration of P is found by first determining the derivatives $(d\hat{\mathbf{c}}_2/dt)_\mathcal{E}$ and $(d\hat{\mathbf{c}}_3/dt)_\mathcal{E}$:

$$\left(\frac{d\hat{\mathbf{c}}_2}{dt}\right)_\mathcal{E} = \boldsymbol{\omega}_{\mathcal{B}/\mathcal{E}} \times \hat{\mathbf{c}}_2 = -\dot{\alpha}\cos\beta\,\hat{\mathbf{b}}_1 + \dot{\beta}\,\hat{\mathbf{b}}_3$$

$$\left(\frac{d\hat{\mathbf{c}}_3}{dt}\right)_\mathcal{E} = \boldsymbol{\omega}_{\mathcal{C}/\mathcal{E}} \times \hat{\mathbf{c}}_3 = (\dot{\alpha}\sin\beta - \dot{\beta}\sin\gamma + \dot{\gamma})\hat{\mathbf{c}}_1 + (\dot{\alpha}\cos\beta\sin\gamma + \dot{\beta}\cos\gamma)\hat{\mathbf{c}}_2$$

This leads to

$$\begin{aligned}\mathbf{a}_{P/\mathcal{E}} = {} & \dot{\overline{(\dot{\beta}\sin\gamma + \dot{\alpha}\cos\beta\cos\gamma)}}\;\hat{\mathbf{c}}_2 + (\dot{\beta}\sin\gamma + \dot{\alpha}\cos\beta\cos\gamma)(-\dot{\alpha}\cos\beta\,\hat{\mathbf{b}}_1 + \dot{\beta}\,\hat{\mathbf{b}}_3) \\ & - \dot{\overline{(\dot{\gamma} + \dot{\alpha}\sin\beta)}}\;\hat{\mathbf{c}}_3 - (\dot{\gamma} + \dot{\alpha}\sin\beta)[(\dot{\alpha}\sin\beta - \dot{\beta}\sin\gamma + \dot{\gamma})\hat{\mathbf{c}}_1 + (\dot{\alpha}\cos\beta\sin\gamma + \dot{\beta}\cos\gamma)\hat{\mathbf{c}}_2]\end{aligned}$$

■

Example 3.5 A referential $\mathcal{A}(A, \hat{\imath}, \hat{\jmath}, \hat{\mathbf{k}})$ is in motion relative to a referential $\mathcal{E}(O, \hat{\mathbf{x}}, \hat{\mathbf{y}}, \hat{\mathbf{z}})$ according to the following conditions (valid at all time):
- a line $\mathcal{L}$ of $\mathcal{A}$ is constrained to lie into the plane $(O, \hat{\mathbf{x}}, \hat{\mathbf{y}})$ of $\mathcal{E}$,
- a point Q attached to $\mathcal{A}$ and located at a distance a from line $\mathcal{L}$ is constrained to lie on axis $(O, \hat{\mathbf{z}})$ of $\mathcal{E}$.

Line $\mathcal{L}$ is defined by unit vector $\hat{\mathbf{k}}$ and point A defined as the projection of Q onto $\mathcal{L}$. The orientation of line $\mathcal{L}$ is defined by angle ψ such that

$$\hat{\mathbf{u}} = \hat{\mathbf{x}}\cos\psi + \hat{\mathbf{y}}\sin\psi, \qquad \hat{\mathbf{k}} = \hat{\mathbf{x}}\sin\psi - \hat{\mathbf{y}}\cos\psi$$

Unit vector $\hat{\jmath}$ is directed along line AQ whose orientation is defined by angle θ such that $\hat{\jmath} = \hat{\mathbf{z}}\cos\theta - \hat{\mathbf{u}}\sin\theta$. Finally define unit vector $\hat{\mathbf{k}} = \hat{\imath} \times \hat{\jmath}$. The set $(\hat{\imath}, \hat{\jmath}, \hat{\mathbf{k}})$ defines a basis of unit vectors attached to $\mathcal{A}$. $\mathcal{F}$ denotes the auxiliary referential $(O, \hat{\mathbf{k}}, \hat{\mathbf{u}}, \hat{\mathbf{z}})$. See Figure 3.6.

a. Find the angular velocities $\boldsymbol{\omega}_{\mathcal{A}/\mathcal{F}}$, $\boldsymbol{\omega}_{\mathcal{F}/\mathcal{E}}$ and $\boldsymbol{\omega}_{\mathcal{A}/\mathcal{E}}$ from the defined parametrization. Find the velocities of points A and Q relative to $\mathcal{E}$.

b. A point P moves relative to $\mathcal{A}$ according to $\mathbf{r}_{AP} = \rho(t)\hat{\imath}$. Find the velocity $\mathbf{v}_{P/\mathcal{E}}$. ■

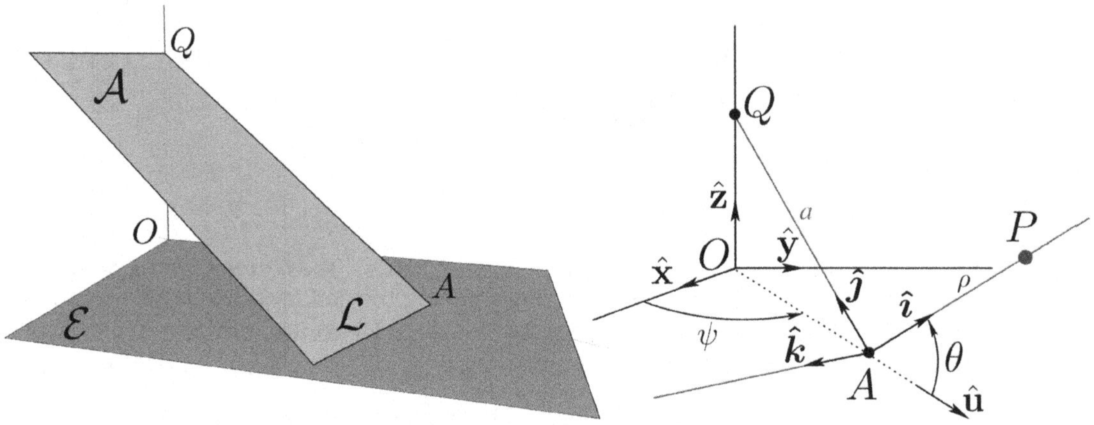

Figure 3.6

a. First we sketch the rotation diagrams corresponding to the transformations

$$(\hat{\mathbf{x}},\hat{\mathbf{y}},\hat{\mathbf{z}}) \xrightarrow{\mathcal{R}_{\psi,\hat{\mathbf{z}}}} (\hat{\mathbf{u}},-\hat{\mathbf{k}},\hat{\mathbf{z}}) \xrightarrow{\mathcal{R}_{\theta,\hat{\mathbf{k}}}} (\hat{\imath},-\hat{\mathbf{k}},\hat{\jmath})$$

leading to the expressions of the angular velocities

$$\boldsymbol{\omega}_{\mathcal{A}/\mathcal{F}} = \dot{\theta}\hat{\mathbf{k}}, \quad \boldsymbol{\omega}_{\mathcal{F}/\mathcal{E}} = \dot{\psi}\hat{\mathbf{z}}, \quad \boldsymbol{\omega}_{\mathcal{A}/\mathcal{E}} = \boldsymbol{\omega}_{\mathcal{A}/\mathcal{F}} + \boldsymbol{\omega}_{\mathcal{F}/\mathcal{E}} = \dot{\psi}\hat{\mathbf{z}} + \dot{\theta}\hat{\mathbf{k}}$$

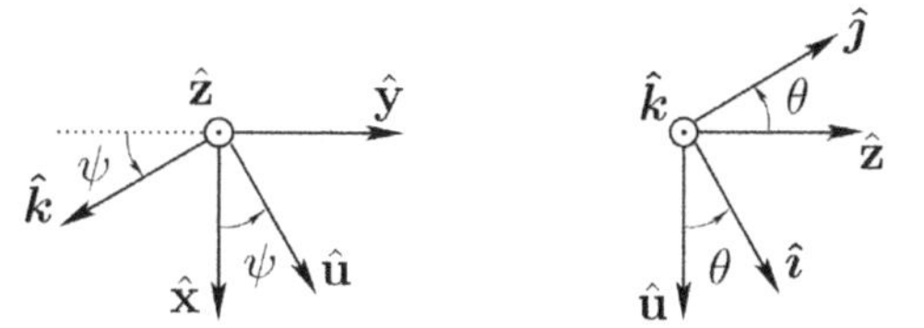

From the expressions of $\mathbf{r}_{OA} = a\sin\theta\hat{\mathbf{u}}$ and $\mathbf{r}_{OQ} = a\cos\theta\hat{\mathbf{z}}$ we find

$$\mathbf{v}_{A/\mathcal{E}} = a\dot{\theta}\cos\theta\hat{\mathbf{u}} + a\sin\theta(\dot{\psi}\hat{\mathbf{z}}\times\hat{\mathbf{u}}) = a\dot{\theta}\cos\theta\hat{\mathbf{u}} - a\dot{\psi}\sin\theta\hat{\mathbf{k}}, \quad \mathbf{v}_{Q/\mathcal{E}} = -a\dot{\theta}\sin\theta\hat{\mathbf{z}}$$

b. To find $\mathbf{v}_{P/\mathcal{E}}$, we differentiate the position vector $\mathbf{r}_{OP} = \mathbf{r}_{OA} + \mathbf{r}_{AP} = a\sin\theta\hat{\mathbf{u}} + \rho\hat{\imath}$ relative to $\mathcal{E}$ to find

$$\mathbf{v}_{P/\mathcal{E}} = a(\dot{\theta}\cos\theta\hat{\mathbf{u}} - \dot{\psi}\sin\theta\hat{\mathbf{k}}) + \dot{\rho}\hat{\imath} + \rho(\dot{\psi}\hat{\mathbf{z}} + \dot{\theta}\hat{\mathbf{k}})\times\hat{\imath} = a(\dot{\theta}\cos\theta\hat{\mathbf{u}} - \dot{\psi}\sin\theta\hat{\mathbf{k}}) + \dot{\rho}\hat{\imath} + \rho(-\dot{\psi}\cos\theta\hat{\mathbf{k}} + \dot{\theta}\hat{\jmath})$$

Note: do not find $\mathbf{v}_{P/\mathcal{E}}$ as $\boldsymbol{\omega}_{\mathcal{A}/\mathcal{E}}\times\mathbf{r}_{OP}$! ■

3.3 Direction Cosines and Angular Velocity

If the orientation of referential $\mathcal{B}$ relative to $\mathcal{A}$ is defined in terms of the direction cosines $c_{ij} = \hat{\mathbf{a}}_i\cdot\hat{\mathbf{b}}_j$ between basis $(\hat{\mathbf{a}}_1,\hat{\mathbf{a}}_2,\hat{\mathbf{a}}_3)$ of $\mathcal{A}$ and basis $(\hat{\mathbf{b}}_1,\hat{\mathbf{b}}_2,\hat{\mathbf{b}}_3)$ of $\mathcal{B}$, then it should be possible to relate the components of angular velocity $\boldsymbol{\omega}_{\mathcal{B}/\mathcal{A}}$ on either basis to the time-derivatives of these quantities.

First we resolve $\boldsymbol{\omega}_{\mathcal{B}/\mathcal{A}}$ on the bases of $\mathcal{A}$ and $\mathcal{B}$ in the following way

$$\boldsymbol{\omega}_{\mathcal{B}/\mathcal{A}} = \Omega_1\hat{\mathbf{a}}_1 + \Omega_2\hat{\mathbf{a}}_2 + \Omega_3\hat{\mathbf{a}}_3 = \omega_1\hat{\mathbf{b}}_1 + \omega_2\hat{\mathbf{b}}_2 + \omega_3\hat{\mathbf{b}}_3$$

We then determine $\dot{c}_{ij}$ by differentiating $\hat{\mathbf{a}}_i\cdot\hat{\mathbf{b}}_j$ relative to referential $\mathcal{A}$:

$$\begin{aligned}\dot{c}_{ij} &= \hat{\mathbf{a}}_i\cdot\left(\frac{d\hat{\mathbf{b}}_j}{dt}\right)_{\mathcal{A}} = (c_{i1}\hat{\mathbf{b}}_1 + c_{i2}\hat{\mathbf{b}}_2 + c_{i3}\hat{\mathbf{b}}_3)\cdot(\boldsymbol{\omega}_{\mathcal{B}/\mathcal{A}}\times\hat{\mathbf{b}}_j)\\ &= \boldsymbol{\omega}_{\mathcal{B}/\mathcal{A}}\cdot\left(c_{i1}\hat{\mathbf{b}}_j\times\hat{\mathbf{b}}_1 + c_{i2}\hat{\mathbf{b}}_j\times\hat{\mathbf{b}}_2 + c_{i3}\hat{\mathbf{b}}_j\times\hat{\mathbf{b}}_3\right)\end{aligned}$$

where we have used the property $(\mathbf{u}\times\mathbf{v})\cdot\mathbf{w} = \mathbf{u}\cdot(\mathbf{v}\times\mathbf{w})$ of the triple scalar product. Then letting $j = 1,2,3$ we find:

Theorem 3.4 If $c_{ij} = \hat{\mathbf{a}}_i\cdot\hat{\mathbf{b}}_j$ denotes the ijth direction cosines between basis $(\hat{\mathbf{a}}_1,\hat{\mathbf{a}}_2,\hat{\mathbf{a}}_3)$ of $\mathcal{A}$ and basis $(\hat{\mathbf{b}}_1,\hat{\mathbf{b}}_2,\hat{\mathbf{b}}_3)$ of $\mathcal{B}$, then

$$\begin{aligned}\dot{c}_{i1} &= c_{i2}\omega_3 - c_{i3}\omega_2\\ \dot{c}_{i2} &= c_{i3}\omega_1 - c_{i1}\omega_3 \qquad (i = 1,2,3) \qquad (3.11)\\ \dot{c}_{i3} &= c_{i1}\omega_2 - c_{i2}\omega_1\end{aligned}$$

with $\omega_i = \boldsymbol{\omega}_{\mathcal{B}/\mathcal{A}} \cdot \hat{\mathbf{b}}_i$.

Alternatively, we can express $\dot{c}_{ij}$ in terms of the components $(\Omega_1, \Omega_2, \Omega_3)$:

$$\begin{aligned} \dot{c}_{1j} &= c_{3j}\Omega_2 - c_{2j}\Omega_3 \\ \dot{c}_{2j} &= c_{1j}\Omega_3 - c_{3j}\Omega_1 \qquad (j = 1,2,3) \\ \dot{c}_{3j} &= c_{2j}\Omega_1 - c_{1j}\Omega_2 \end{aligned} \tag{3.12}$$

In practical applications such as spacecraft attitude dynamics, the evolution of $\boldsymbol{\omega}_{\mathcal{B}/\mathcal{A}}$ is obtained as a vector resolved into the "body basis", that is, in terms of components $(\omega_1, \omega_2, \omega_3)$: the orientation of $\mathcal{B}$ relative to $\mathcal{A}$ is then obtained by integration of the system of equations (3.11).

3.4 Quaternions and Angular Velocity

Consider the rotation which maps a basis $(\hat{\mathbf{a}}_1, \hat{\mathbf{a}}_2, \hat{\mathbf{a}}_3)$ of referential $\mathcal{A}$ to a basis $(\hat{\mathbf{b}}_1, \hat{\mathbf{b}}_2, \hat{\mathbf{b}}_3)$ of a referential $\mathcal{B}$ in motion relative to $\mathcal{A}$. To this rotation corresponds to a time-varying unit quaternion which we denote as $Q_{B/A}(t)$. A vector $\mathbf{V}_0$ fixed in $\mathcal{A}$ is mapped into a vector $\mathbf{V}$ fixed in $\mathcal{B}$ according to the quaternion relationship

$$\mathbf{V}(t) = Q_{B/A}(t)\mathbf{V}_0\overline{Q}_{B/A}(t)$$

where $\overline{Q}_{B/A}$ is the conjugate of $Q_{B/A}$. We can find the derivative of $\mathbf{V}$ relative to $\mathcal{A}$ according to (3.2):

$$\left(\frac{d\mathbf{V}}{dt}\right)_{\mathcal{A}} = \boldsymbol{\omega}_{\mathcal{B}/\mathcal{A}} \times \mathbf{V}$$

If we view both $\boldsymbol{\omega}_{\mathcal{B}/\mathcal{A}}$ and $\mathbf{V}$ as pure quaternions, the cross-product $\boldsymbol{\omega}_{\mathcal{B}/\mathcal{A}} \times \mathbf{V}$ can be written as $\frac{1}{2}(\boldsymbol{\omega}_{\mathcal{B}/\mathcal{A}}\mathbf{V} - \mathbf{V}\boldsymbol{\omega}_{\mathcal{B}/\mathcal{A}})$ (see Example 1.6). This gives

$$\frac{d}{dt}(Q_{B/A}\mathbf{V}_0\overline{Q}_{B/A}) = \frac{1}{2}(\boldsymbol{\omega}_{\mathcal{B}/\mathcal{A}}\mathbf{V} - \mathbf{V}\boldsymbol{\omega}_{\mathcal{B}/\mathcal{A}})$$

A unit quaternion satisfies $Q\overline{Q} = \overline{Q}Q = 1$ and time-differentiation (relative to $\mathcal{A}$) leads to $(d\overline{Q}/dt) = -\overline{Q}(dQ/dt)\overline{Q}$. So the last equation becomes

$$\frac{dQ_{B/A}}{dt}\mathbf{V}_0\overline{Q}_{B/A} - Q_{B/A}\mathbf{V}_0\overline{Q}_{B/A}\frac{dQ_{B/A}}{dt}\overline{Q}_{B/A} = \frac{1}{2}(\boldsymbol{\omega}_{\mathcal{B}/\mathcal{A}}\mathbf{V} - \mathbf{V}\boldsymbol{\omega}_{\mathcal{B}/\mathcal{A}})$$

Then using $\mathbf{V}_0 = \overline{Q}_{B/A}\mathbf{V}Q_{B/A}$ we obtain

$$\frac{dQ_{B/A}}{dt}\overline{Q}_{B/A}\mathbf{V} - \mathbf{V}\frac{dQ_{B/A}}{dt}\overline{Q}_{B/A} = \frac{1}{2}(\boldsymbol{\omega}_{\mathcal{B}/\mathcal{A}}\mathbf{V} - \mathbf{V}\boldsymbol{\omega}_{\mathcal{B}/\mathcal{A}})$$

which can be written in the form

$$\left(\boldsymbol{\omega}_{\mathcal{B}/\mathcal{A}} - 2\frac{dQ_{B/A}}{dt}\overline{Q}_{B/A}\right)\mathbf{V} - \mathbf{V}\left(\boldsymbol{\omega}_{\mathcal{B}/\mathcal{A}} - 2\frac{dQ_{B/A}}{dt}\overline{Q}_{B/A}\right) = 0$$

or, in vector form, as

$$\left(\boldsymbol{\omega}_{\mathcal{B}/\mathcal{A}} - 2\frac{dQ_{B/A}}{dt}\overline{Q}_{B/A}\right) \times \mathbf{V} = 0$$

Since this last equation holds true for all $\mathbf{V}$, we obtain

$$\omega_{\mathcal{B}/\mathcal{A}} = 2\frac{dQ_{\mathcal{B}/\mathcal{A}}}{dt}\overline{Q}_{\mathcal{B}/\mathcal{A}} \tag{3.13}$$

Remark 7. It is can be verified that the quantity $(dQ_{\mathcal{B}/\mathcal{A}}/dt)\overline{Q}_{\mathcal{B}/\mathcal{A}}$ is a pure quaternion.

It is also possible to express angular velocity $\omega_{\mathcal{B}/\mathcal{A}}$ in terms of the derivative of Euler parameters: substitution of $Q_{\mathcal{B}/\mathcal{A}} = \cos\frac{\alpha}{2} + \sin\frac{\alpha}{2}\hat{\mathbf{u}}$ in equation (3.13) gives

$$\omega_{\mathcal{B}/\mathcal{A}} = \dot{\alpha}\hat{\mathbf{u}} + \sin\alpha\frac{d\hat{\mathbf{u}}}{dt} + (1-\cos\alpha)\hat{\mathbf{u}}\times\frac{d\hat{\mathbf{u}}}{dt} \tag{3.14}$$

where $(\alpha, \hat{\mathbf{u}})$ are the equivalent angle/direction of the rotation $\mathcal{R}_{\alpha,\hat{\mathbf{u}}}$ which maps a basis of $\mathcal{A}$ to a basis of $\mathcal{B}$. This result can also be recast in terms of rotation vector $\boldsymbol{\tau} = \tan\frac{\alpha}{2}\hat{\mathbf{u}}$ and its time-derivative

$$\omega_{\mathcal{B}/\mathcal{A}} = \frac{2}{1+\boldsymbol{\tau}^2}\Big(\frac{d\boldsymbol{\tau}}{dt} + \boldsymbol{\tau}\times\frac{d\boldsymbol{\tau}}{dt}\Big) \tag{3.15}$$

In equations (3.13), (3.14) and (3.15) the time-derivatives of $Q_{\mathcal{B}/\mathcal{A}}$, $\hat{\mathbf{u}} = \hat{\mathbf{u}}_{\mathcal{B}/\mathcal{A}}$ and $\boldsymbol{\tau} = \boldsymbol{\tau}_{\mathcal{B}/\mathcal{A}}$ are performed relative to $\mathcal{A}$.

3.5 Angular Acceleration

Definition 3.1 The angular acceleration of rigid body $\mathcal{B}$ relative to referential (or rigid body) $\mathcal{A}$, denoted by $\boldsymbol{\alpha}_{\mathcal{B}/\mathcal{A}}$, is defined as

$$\boldsymbol{\alpha}_{\mathcal{B}/\mathcal{A}} = \Big(\frac{d}{dt}\omega_{\mathcal{B}/\mathcal{A}}\Big)_{\mathcal{A}} \tag{3.16}$$

Remark 8. We can apply formula (3.3) to arrive at the following identity:

$$\boldsymbol{\alpha}_{\mathcal{B}/\mathcal{A}} = \Big(\frac{d}{dt}\omega_{\mathcal{B}/\mathcal{A}}\Big)_{\mathcal{B}} + \omega_{\mathcal{B}/\mathcal{A}}\times\omega_{\mathcal{B}/\mathcal{A}} = \Big(\frac{d}{dt}\omega_{\mathcal{B}/\mathcal{A}}\Big)_{\mathcal{B}} \tag{3.17}$$

so that the differentiation of $\omega_{\mathcal{B}/\mathcal{A}}$ can also be performed with respect to $\mathcal{B}$ to find $\boldsymbol{\alpha}_{\mathcal{B}/\mathcal{A}}$.

Note that the loop identity for angular velocities does not extend to angular accelerations, that is

$$\boldsymbol{\alpha}_{\mathcal{A}/\mathcal{B}} + \boldsymbol{\alpha}_{\mathcal{B}/\mathcal{C}} + \boldsymbol{\alpha}_{\mathcal{C}/\mathcal{A}} \neq \mathbf{0} \tag{3.18}$$

for general motions between $\mathcal{A}$, $\mathcal{B}$, and $\mathcal{C}$.

It is also possible to express angular acceleration $\boldsymbol{\alpha}_{\mathcal{B}/\mathcal{A}}$ in terms of unit quaternion $Q_{\mathcal{B}/\mathcal{A}}$ and its second derivative: by differentiating (3.13) we find that $\boldsymbol{\alpha}_{\mathcal{B}/\mathcal{A}}$ is given by

$$\boldsymbol{\alpha}_{\mathcal{B}/\mathcal{A}} = 2\,\mathrm{Vect}\Big(\frac{d^2Q_{\mathcal{B}/\mathcal{A}}}{dt^2}\overline{Q}_{\mathcal{B}/\mathcal{A}}\Big) \tag{3.19}$$

where $\mathrm{Vect}(Q)$ denotes the vector part of quaternion Q.

Proof. We take the time-derivative of (3.13) to obtain

$$\boldsymbol{\alpha}_{\mathcal{B}/\mathcal{A}} = 2\frac{d^2Q}{dt^2}\overline{Q} + 2\frac{dQ}{dt}\frac{d\overline{Q}}{dt}$$

We then need to show that quaternion $R = \frac{dQ}{dt}\frac{d\overline{Q}}{dt}$ is a scalar: we find $R = -\frac{dQ}{dt}\overline{Q}\frac{dQ}{dt}\overline{Q}$. It is easily shown that $\overline{R} = R$. ■

Example 3.6 Find $\boldsymbol{\alpha}_{\mathcal{C}/\mathcal{E}}$ for the gyroscopic system of Example 3.4. Compare $\boldsymbol{\alpha}_{\mathcal{C}/\mathcal{E}}$ with $\boldsymbol{\alpha}_{\mathcal{C}/\mathcal{B}} + \boldsymbol{\alpha}_{\mathcal{B}/\mathcal{A}} + \boldsymbol{\alpha}_{\mathcal{A}/\mathcal{E}}$. ■

With $\boldsymbol{\omega}_{\mathcal{C}/\mathcal{E}} = \dot{\alpha}\hat{\mathbf{e}}_3 + \dot{\beta}\hat{\mathbf{a}}_1 + \dot{\gamma}\hat{\mathbf{b}}_2$, we find

$$\begin{aligned}
\boldsymbol{\alpha}_{\mathcal{C}/\mathcal{E}} &= \ddot{\alpha}\hat{\mathbf{e}}_3 + \ddot{\beta}\hat{\mathbf{a}}_1 + \dot{\beta}\boldsymbol{\omega}_{\mathcal{A}/\mathcal{E}} \times \hat{\mathbf{a}}_1 + \ddot{\gamma}\hat{\mathbf{b}}_2 + \dot{\gamma}\boldsymbol{\omega}_{\mathcal{B}/\mathcal{E}} \times \hat{\mathbf{b}}_2 \\
&= \ddot{\alpha}\hat{\mathbf{a}}_3 + \ddot{\beta}\hat{\mathbf{a}}_1 + \dot{\beta}\dot{\alpha}\hat{\mathbf{a}}_2 + \ddot{\gamma}\hat{\mathbf{b}}_2 + \dot{\gamma}(\dot{\beta}\hat{\mathbf{b}}_3 + \dot{\alpha}\sin\beta\hat{\mathbf{a}}_1)
\end{aligned}$$

One can easily verify that $\boldsymbol{\alpha}_{\mathcal{C}/\mathcal{E}}$ is not equal to the sum $\boldsymbol{\alpha}_{\mathcal{C}/\mathcal{B}} + \boldsymbol{\alpha}_{\mathcal{B}/\mathcal{A}} + \boldsymbol{\alpha}_{\mathcal{A}/\mathcal{E}}$, since $\boldsymbol{\alpha}_{\mathcal{C}/\mathcal{B}} = \ddot{\gamma}\,\hat{\mathbf{b}}_1$, $\boldsymbol{\alpha}_{\mathcal{B}/\mathcal{A}} = \ddot{\beta}\,\hat{\mathbf{a}}_2$, and $\boldsymbol{\alpha}_{\mathcal{A}/\mathcal{E}} = \ddot{\alpha}\,\hat{\mathbf{a}}_3$. ■

3.6 Velocity Field of a Rigid Body

Consider two rigid bodies (or referentials) $\mathcal{A}$ (of origin A) and $\mathcal{B}$ (of origin B) in relative motion. See Figure 3.7. We wish to characterize the velocity field $P \in \mathcal{B} \mapsto \mathbf{v}_{P/\mathcal{A}}$ of points fixed in $\mathcal{B}$ in motion relative to $\mathcal{A}$. Specifically, we ask whether velocities of points of $\mathcal{B}$ relative to $\mathcal{A}$ are related to one another.

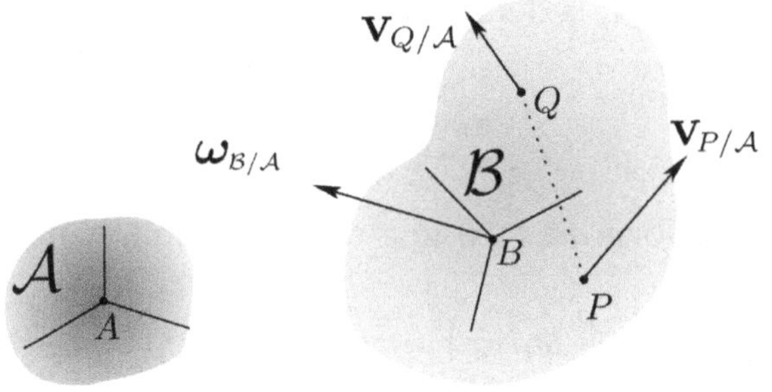

Figure 3.7

Consider two points P and Q *fixed in $\mathcal{B}$ at all times*. The motion of $\mathcal{B}$ relative to $\mathcal{A}$ is characterized by angular velocity $\boldsymbol{\omega}_{\mathcal{B}/\mathcal{A}}$: recall that for any vector $\mathbf{V}$ fixed in $\mathcal{B}$ the time-derivative of $\mathbf{V}$ relative to $\mathcal{A}$ can be expressed as $(d\mathbf{V}/dt)_{\mathcal{A}} = \boldsymbol{\omega}_{\mathcal{B}/\mathcal{A}} \times \mathbf{U}$. By choosing $\mathbf{V} = \mathbf{r}_{PQ}$ which is constant in $\mathcal{B}$, we can write

$$\left(\frac{d\mathbf{r}_{PQ}}{dt}\right)_{\mathcal{A}} = \boldsymbol{\omega}_{\mathcal{B}/\mathcal{A}} \times \mathbf{r}_{PQ}.$$

But since $\mathbf{r}_{PQ} = \mathbf{r}_{AQ} - \mathbf{r}_{AP}$, we have

$$\left(\frac{d\mathbf{r}_{PQ}}{dt}\right)_{\mathcal{A}} = \mathbf{v}_{Q/\mathcal{A}} - \mathbf{v}_{P/\mathcal{A}}$$

Theorem 3.5 The velocity field $P \in \mathcal{B} \mapsto \mathbf{v}_{P/\mathcal{A}}$ of points attached to $\mathcal{B}$ in motion relative to $\mathcal{A}$ satisfies the fundamental relationship

$$\mathbf{v}_{Q/\mathcal{A}} = \mathbf{v}_{P/\mathcal{A}} + \boldsymbol{\omega}_{\mathcal{B}/\mathcal{A}} \times \mathbf{r}_{PQ} \tag{3.20}$$

Hence, at any given time, it is entirely characterized by the knowledge of
- the angular velocity $\boldsymbol{\omega}_{\mathcal{B}/\mathcal{A}}$ and
- the velocity of a particular point, say B, attached to $\mathcal{B}$.

Two particular motions can be examined in the context of formula (3.20):

(i) If $\mathcal{B}$ is in *translational motion* relative to $\mathcal{A}$, its angular velocity vanishes at all times ($\boldsymbol{\omega}_{\mathcal{B}/\mathcal{A}} = \mathbf{0}$). $\mathcal{B}$ keeps the same orientation relative to $\mathcal{A}$. Then equation (3.20) shows that $\mathbf{v}_{Q/\mathcal{A}} = \mathbf{v}_{P/\mathcal{A}}$. All points of $\mathcal{B}$ have the same velocity.

(ii) If $\mathcal{B}$ is in *rotational motion* relative to $\mathcal{A}$ about axis $\Delta(A, \hat{\mathbf{a}}_3 = \hat{\mathbf{b}}_3)$, its angular velocity is directed along $\hat{\mathbf{a}}_3$ at all times: $\boldsymbol{\omega}_{\mathcal{B}/\mathcal{A}} = \dot{\theta}\hat{\mathbf{a}}_3$. Then $\mathbf{v}_{P/\mathcal{A}} = \dot{\theta}\hat{\mathbf{a}}_3 \times \mathbf{r}_{AP} = \dot{\theta}\hat{\mathbf{a}}_3 \times \mathbf{r}_{HP}$ where H is the projection of P onto axis Δ.

Remark 9. Vector fields $P \mapsto \mathbf{v}_P$ satisfying the relationship $\mathbf{v}_Q = \mathbf{v}_P + \mathbf{V} \times \mathbf{r}_{PQ}$ play a central role in rigid-body mechanics. They possess important properties which result from their simple structure. Their study will be devoted to Chapter 4.

We end this section by examining two examples to illustrate the use of equation (3.20).

Example 3.7 Consider the system of Example 3.3 which defines two interconnected bodies $\mathcal{A}(O, \hat{\mathbf{a}}_1, \hat{\mathbf{a}}_2, \hat{\mathbf{a}}_3 = \hat{\mathbf{e}}_3)$ and $\mathcal{B}(A, \hat{\mathbf{b}}_1, \hat{\mathbf{b}}_2 = \hat{\mathbf{a}}_2, \hat{\mathbf{b}}_3)$ in motion relative to referential $\mathcal{E}(O, \hat{\mathbf{e}}_1, \hat{\mathbf{e}}_1, \hat{\mathbf{e}}_3)$. Point A of $\mathcal{A}$ is defined by $\mathbf{r}_{OA} = a\hat{\mathbf{a}}_1$. Point B attached to $\mathcal{B}$ such that $\mathbf{r}_{AB} = b\hat{\mathbf{b}}_3$ (a and b are positive constants.

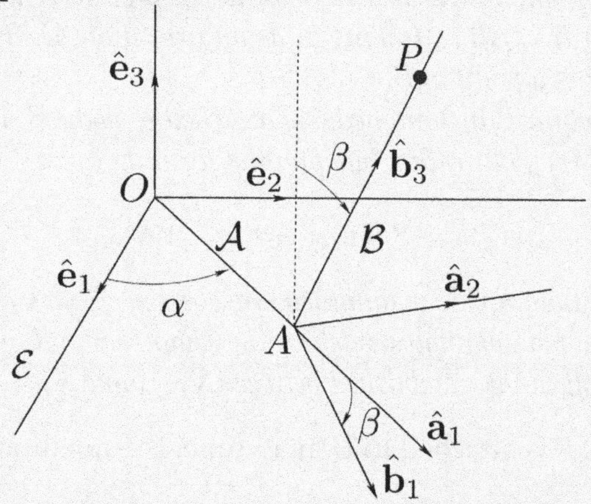

a. Find the velocity $\mathbf{v}_{A/\mathcal{E}}$ of point A. Then find the velocity of $\mathbf{v}_{B/\mathcal{E}}$ using $\mathbf{v}_{A/\mathcal{E}}$ and formula (3.20). Compare with the direct approach obtained by taking the time derivative of $\mathbf{r}_{OB} = a\hat{\mathbf{a}}_1 + b\hat{\mathbf{b}}_3$ relative to $\mathcal{E}$.

b. Consider the point P which slides along axis $(A, \hat{\mathbf{b}}_3)$ according to $\mathbf{r}_{AP} = \rho(t)\hat{\mathbf{b}}_3$. Find velocity $\mathbf{v}_{P/\mathcal{E}}$ and compare with the expression obtained by determining $\mathbf{v}_{A/\mathcal{E}} + \boldsymbol{\omega}_{\mathcal{B}/\mathcal{E}} \times \mathbf{r}_{AP}$ by applying (3.20) between points A and P. Comment. ■

a. We find velocity of B from that of A according to (3.20) by considering A and B two points attached to $\mathcal{B}$. First we find $\mathbf{v}_{A/\mathcal{E}}$ by taking the time-derivative of position vector $\mathbf{r}_{OA} = a\hat{\mathbf{a}}_1$:

$$\mathbf{v}_{A/\mathcal{E}} = a\boldsymbol{\omega}_{\mathcal{A}/\mathcal{E}} \times \hat{\mathbf{a}}_1 = a\dot{\alpha}\hat{\mathbf{a}}_2$$

We can now find $\mathbf{v}_{B/\mathcal{E}}$ with $\boldsymbol{\omega}_{\mathcal{B}/\mathcal{E}} = \dot{\alpha}\hat{\mathbf{e}}_3 + \dot{\beta}\hat{\mathbf{a}}_2$:

$$\mathbf{v}_{B/\mathcal{E}} = \mathbf{v}_{A/\mathcal{E}} + \boldsymbol{\omega}_{\mathcal{B}/\mathcal{E}} \times \mathbf{r}_{AB} = a\dot{\alpha}\hat{\mathbf{a}}_2 + (\dot{\alpha}\hat{\mathbf{e}}_3 + \dot{\beta}\hat{\mathbf{a}}_2) \times b\hat{\mathbf{b}}_3 = (a\dot{\alpha} + b\dot{\alpha}\sin\beta)\hat{\mathbf{a}}_2 + b\dot{\beta}\,\hat{\mathbf{b}}_1$$

We find the same result by time-differentiating the position vector $\mathbf{r}_{OB} = a\hat{\mathbf{a}}_1 + b\hat{\mathbf{b}}_3$ relative to $\mathcal{E}$:

$$\mathbf{v}_{B/\mathcal{E}} = a\left(\frac{d\hat{\mathbf{a}}_1}{dt}\right)_{\mathcal{E}} + b\left(\frac{d\hat{\mathbf{b}}_3}{dt}\right)_{\mathcal{E}} = a\dot{\alpha}\hat{\mathbf{a}}_2 + b(\dot{\alpha}\hat{\mathbf{e}}_3 + \dot{\beta}\hat{\mathbf{a}}_2) \times \hat{\mathbf{b}}_3 = a\dot{\alpha}\hat{\mathbf{a}}_2 + b(\dot{\alpha}\sin\beta\hat{\mathbf{a}}_2 + \dot{\beta}\hat{\mathbf{b}}_1)$$

b. We found the expression of $\mathbf{v}_{P/\mathcal{E}}$ in Example 3.3:

$$\mathbf{v}_{P/\mathcal{E}} = (a\dot{\alpha} + \rho\dot{\alpha}\sin\beta)\hat{\mathbf{a}}_2 + \dot{\rho}\,\hat{\mathbf{b}}_3 + \rho\dot{\beta}\,\hat{\mathbf{b}}_1$$

Next we find $\mathbf{v}_{A/\mathcal{E}} + \boldsymbol{\omega}_{\mathcal{B}/\mathcal{E}} \times \mathbf{r}_{AP}$ by applying (3.20) between A and P

$$\mathbf{v}_{A/\mathcal{E}} + \boldsymbol{\omega}_{\mathcal{B}/\mathcal{E}} \times \mathbf{r}_{AP} = a\dot{\alpha}\hat{\mathbf{a}}_2 + (\dot{\alpha}\hat{\mathbf{e}}_3 + \dot{\beta}\hat{\mathbf{a}}_2) \times \rho\hat{\mathbf{b}}_3 = (a\dot{\alpha} + \rho\dot{\alpha}\sin\beta)\hat{\mathbf{a}}_2 + \rho\dot{\beta}\,\hat{\mathbf{b}}_1$$

Comparing with the previous expression, we notice that we do not obtain the expression of $\mathbf{v}_{P/\mathcal{E}}$: this is not unexpected since point P is not attached to body $\mathcal{B}$ at all time. However we may denote this expression as $\mathbf{v}_{P\in\mathcal{B}/\mathcal{E}}$ to represent the velocity of the point of $\mathcal{B}$ which coincides with P. In fact we find $\mathbf{v}_{P/\mathcal{E}} - \mathbf{v}_{P\in\mathcal{B}/\mathcal{E}} = \dot{\rho}\,\hat{\mathbf{b}}_3$. For a point such as P we have

$$\mathbf{v}_{P/\mathcal{E}} \neq \mathbf{v}_{P\in\mathcal{B}/\mathcal{E}}$$

■

Notation 3.1. *In view of the previous problem, the notation* $\mathbf{v}_{P\in\mathcal{B}/\mathcal{A}}$ *will be used to denote*

- *the velocity of a point P attached to body $\mathcal{B}$ (in motion relative to $\mathcal{A}$) at all time, in which case* $\mathbf{v}_{P\in\mathcal{B}/\mathcal{A}} = (d\mathbf{r}_{AP}/dt)_{\mathcal{A}}$ *(taking A as an origin of $\mathcal{A}$). This notation serves as a way to emphasize that P is a point of $\mathcal{B}$.*
- *the velocity of a point P instantaneously attached to body $\mathcal{B}$, in which case* $\mathbf{v}_{P\in\mathcal{B}/\mathcal{A}}$ *cannot be found as* $(d\mathbf{r}_{AP}/dt)_{\mathcal{A}}$ *but rather by applying formula (3.20)*

$$\mathbf{v}_{P\in\mathcal{B}/\mathcal{A}} = \mathbf{v}_{B/\mathcal{A}} + \boldsymbol{\omega}_{\mathcal{B}/\mathcal{A}} \times \mathbf{r}_{BP}$$

In this case, the notation is mandatory since $\mathbf{v}_{P\in\mathcal{B}/\mathcal{A}} \neq \mathbf{v}_{P/\mathcal{A}}$. *The concepts of coinciding point and relative motion analysis defined in Chapter 6 will give a better understanding of the relationship which can be established between* $\mathbf{v}_{P/\mathcal{A}}$ *and* $\mathbf{v}_{P\in\mathcal{B}/\mathcal{A}}$.

Remark 10. Whenever P is attached to $\mathcal{B}$ at all time, the notation $P\in$ is redundant: $\mathbf{v}_{P\in\mathcal{B}/\mathcal{A}} = \mathbf{v}_{P/\mathcal{A}}$.

Remark 11. We shall learn in Chapter 6 that the difference $\mathbf{v}_{P/\mathcal{A}} - \mathbf{v}_{P\in\mathcal{B}/\mathcal{A}}$ is nothing but $\mathbf{v}_{P/\mathcal{B}}$.

Remark 12. In practice, the only way to determine the velocity $\mathbf{v}_{P\in\mathcal{B}/\mathcal{A}}$ for a point P which is not attached to $\mathcal{B}$ at all time is to apply formula (3.20) by relating P to a particular point attached to $\mathcal{B}$ at all times.

Here is a final example to illustrate this point.

Example 3.8 The motion of a referential $\mathcal{A}(A, \hat{\imath}, \hat{\jmath}, \hat{\mathbf{k}})$ relative to a referential $\mathcal{E}(O, \hat{\mathbf{x}}, \hat{\mathbf{y}}, \hat{\mathbf{z}})$ is characterized by the following conditions at all time:
- line $(A, \hat{\mathbf{k}})$ attached of $\mathcal{A}$ is constrained to lie into the plane $(O, \hat{\mathbf{x}}, \hat{\mathbf{y}})$ of $\mathcal{E}$,
- line $(A, \hat{\jmath})$ attached to $\mathcal{A}$ is constrained to pass through a point Q located on axis $(O, \hat{\mathbf{z}})$ at a constant distance h from O.

Unit vector $\hat{\mathbf{k}}$ is defined as $\hat{\imath} \times \hat{\jmath}$. The set $(\hat{\imath}, \hat{\jmath}, \hat{\mathbf{k}})$ defines a basis of unit vectors attached to $\mathcal{A}$. Its orientation relative to $(\hat{\mathbf{x}}, \hat{\mathbf{y}}, \hat{\mathbf{z}})$ is defined by angles ψ and θ. See Figure 3.8.
a. Find the angular velocity of $\mathcal{A}$ and the velocity $\mathbf{v}_{A/\mathcal{E}}$ of point A (relative to $\mathcal{E}$).
b. Find the velocity $\mathbf{v}_{Q\in\mathcal{A}/\mathcal{E}}$, and compare with velocities $\mathbf{v}_{Q/\mathcal{E}} = (d\mathbf{r}_{OQ}/dt)_{\mathcal{E}}$ and $\mathbf{v}_{Q/\mathcal{A}} = (d\mathbf{r}_{AQ}/dt)_{\mathcal{A}}$. ■

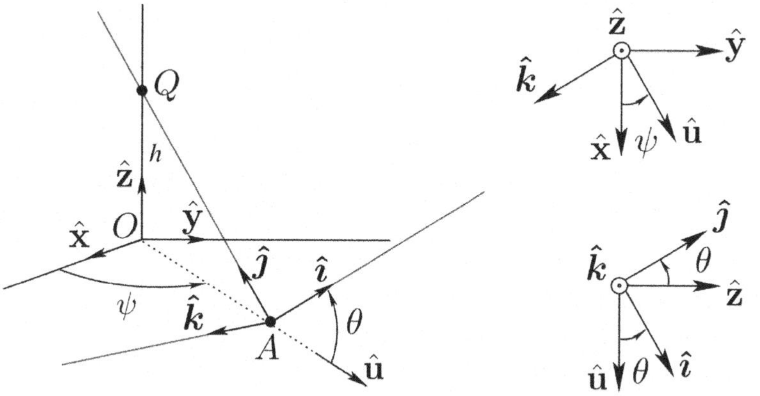

Figure 3.8

a. After sketching the rotation diagrams which map basis $(\hat{\mathbf{x}}, \hat{\mathbf{y}}, \hat{\mathbf{z}})$ to basis $(\hat{\imath}, \hat{\jmath}, \hat{\mathbf{k}})$ we find the angular velocity of $\mathcal{A}$ relative to $\mathcal{E}$ as

$$\boldsymbol{\omega}_{\mathcal{A}/\mathcal{E}} = \dot{\psi}\hat{\mathbf{z}} + \dot{\theta}\hat{\mathbf{k}}.$$

The velocity of point A can be found by differentiating $\mathbf{r}_{OA} = h \tan\theta \hat{\mathbf{u}}$:

$$\mathbf{v}_{A/\mathcal{E}} = h(\dot{\theta}/\cos^2\theta)\hat{\mathbf{u}} - h\dot{\psi}\tan\theta\hat{\mathbf{k}}$$

where we have used $(d\hat{\mathbf{u}}/dt)_{\mathcal{E}} = -\dot{\psi}\hat{\mathbf{k}}$.
b. Point Q is not attached to $\mathcal{A}$, and hence, the velocity $\mathbf{v}_{Q\in\mathcal{A}/\mathcal{E}}$ cannot be found by differentiating $\mathbf{r}_{OQ}$ relative to $\mathcal{E}$. It can be found by relating it to the velocity of point A relative to $\mathcal{E}$:

$$\begin{aligned} \mathbf{v}_{Q\in\mathcal{A}/\mathcal{E}} &= \mathbf{v}_{A/\mathcal{E}} + \boldsymbol{\omega}_{\mathcal{A}/\mathcal{E}} \times \mathbf{r}_{AQ} = \mathbf{v}_{A/\mathcal{E}} + (\dot{\psi}\hat{\mathbf{z}} + \dot{\theta}\hat{\mathbf{k}}) \times (h/\cos\theta)\hat{\jmath} \\ &= h\dot{\theta}\tan^2\theta\hat{\mathbf{u}} - h\dot{\theta}\tan\theta\hat{\mathbf{z}} = -h\dot{\theta}(\sin\theta/\cos^2\theta)\hat{\jmath} \end{aligned}$$

First we find $\mathbf{v}_{Q/\mathcal{E}} = (d\mathbf{r}_{OQ}/dt)_{\mathcal{E}} = \mathbf{0}$ since vector $\mathbf{r}_{OQ}$ is fixed relative to $\mathcal{E}$. Then to find $\mathbf{v}_{Q/\mathcal{A}}$ we need to differentiate vector $\mathbf{r}_{AQ} = (h/\cos\theta)\hat{\jmath}$ relative to $\mathcal{A}$:

$$\mathbf{v}_{Q/\mathcal{A}} = h\dot{\theta}(\sin\theta/\cos^2\theta)\hat{\jmath}$$

since unit vector $\hat{\jmath}$ is attached to $\mathcal{A}$. Hence we recognize that

$$\mathbf{v}_{Q\in\mathcal{A}/\mathcal{E}} = \mathbf{v}_{Q/\mathcal{E}} - \mathbf{v}_{Q/\mathcal{A}}$$

This identity is in fact true for all points, as will be shown in Chapter 6. ■

3.7 Problems

Problem 3.1 Given three referentials $\mathcal{A}$, $\mathcal{B}$ and $\mathcal{C}$, show that

$$\boldsymbol{\alpha}_{\mathcal{A}/\mathcal{B}} + \boldsymbol{\alpha}_{\mathcal{B}/\mathcal{C}} + \boldsymbol{\alpha}_{\mathcal{C}/\mathcal{A}} = \boldsymbol{\omega}_{\mathcal{A}/\mathcal{C}} \times \boldsymbol{\omega}_{\mathcal{B}/\mathcal{C}}$$

Then find conditions for the loop equation $\boldsymbol{\alpha}_{\mathcal{A}/\mathcal{B}} + \boldsymbol{\alpha}_{\mathcal{B}/\mathcal{C}} + \boldsymbol{\alpha}_{\mathcal{C}/\mathcal{A}} = \mathbf{0}$ to be valid.

Problem 3.2 Show that the angular velocity of rigid body $\mathcal{B}$ relative to referential $\mathcal{A}$ can be expressed as

$$\boldsymbol{\omega}_{\mathcal{B}/\mathcal{A}} = \frac{1}{2}\left(\hat{\mathbf{b}}_1 \times \frac{d\hat{\mathbf{b}}_1}{dt} + \hat{\mathbf{b}}_2 \times \frac{d\hat{\mathbf{b}}_2}{dt} + \hat{\mathbf{b}}_3 \times \frac{d\hat{\mathbf{b}}_3}{dt}\right)$$

where $(\hat{\mathbf{b}}_1, \hat{\mathbf{b}}_2, \hat{\mathbf{b}}_3)$ is a basis of $\mathcal{B}$, and where the time-derivatives are taken relative to $\mathcal{A}$.

Problem 3.3 Assume that the motion of body $\mathcal{B}$ relative to referential $\mathcal{A}$ is characterized by the rotation $\mathcal{R}_{\theta,\hat{\mathbf{u}}}$ of angle α about unit vector $\hat{\mathbf{u}}$. Recall that any vector $\mathbf{V}_0$ attached to $\mathcal{A}$ is mapped to a vector $\mathbf{V}$ attached to $\mathcal{B}$ according to Rodrigues formula:

$$\mathbf{V} = \mathbf{V}_0 + \sin\alpha\hat{\mathbf{u}} \times \mathbf{V}_0 + (1-\cos\alpha)\hat{\mathbf{u}} \times (\hat{\mathbf{u}} \times \mathbf{V}_0)$$

Show that angular velocity $\boldsymbol{\omega}_{\mathcal{B}/\mathcal{A}}$ can be found according to

$$\boldsymbol{\omega}_{\mathcal{B}/\mathcal{A}} = \dot{\alpha}\hat{\mathbf{u}} + \sin\alpha\frac{d\hat{\mathbf{u}}}{dt} + (1-\cos\alpha)\hat{\mathbf{u}} \times \frac{d\hat{\mathbf{u}}}{dt}$$

Problem 3.4 A rigid body in the shape of an isosceles triangle AOB ($OA = OB$) rotates about the origin O of a referential $\mathcal{E}$. Show that the velocities of vertices A and B satisfy the following property: $\mathbf{v}_A \cdot \mathbf{r}_{OB} = -\mathbf{v}_B \cdot \mathbf{r}_{OA}$

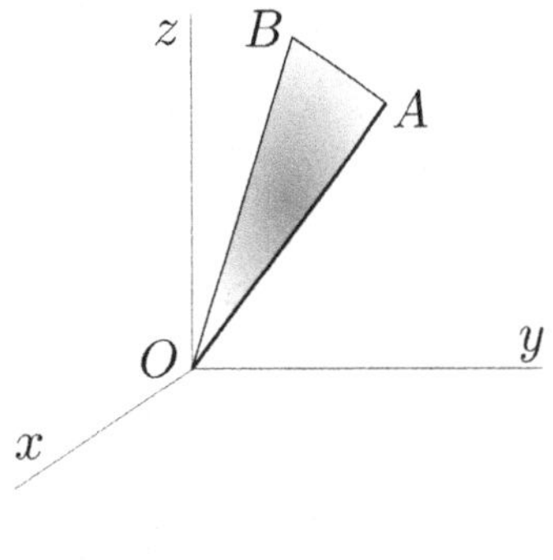

Problem 3.5 Consider a rigid body $\mathcal{B}$ in motion relative to a referential $\mathcal{E}$. Given a unit vector $\hat{\mathbf{z}}$ attached to $\mathcal{B}$, show that the angular velocity of $\mathcal{B}$ relative to $\mathcal{E}$ can be written in the following form

$$\boldsymbol{\omega}_{\mathcal{B}/\mathcal{E}} = \omega_z\hat{\mathbf{z}} + \hat{\mathbf{z}} \times \left(\frac{d\hat{\mathbf{z}}}{dt}\right)_{\mathcal{E}}$$

where $\omega_z = \hat{\mathbf{z}} \cdot \boldsymbol{\omega}_{\mathcal{B}/\mathcal{E}}$.

Problem 3.6 In the Eulerian formulation of continuum mechanics, the velocity field $\mathbf{v}(x_1, x_2, x_3, t)$ of a material system is defined at every point (x_1, x_2, x_3) of a referential $\mathcal{E}(O, \hat{\mathbf{e}}_1, \hat{\mathbf{e}}_2, \hat{\mathbf{e}}_3)$. Show that the velocity field $\mathbf{v}(x_1, x_2, x_3, t)$ is that of a rigid body $\mathcal{F}$ if and only if $\partial_i v_j + \partial_j v_i = 0$ $(i, j = 1, 2, 3)$ where $\partial_i = \partial/\partial x_i$ and $v_i = \mathbf{v} \cdot \hat{\mathbf{e}}_i$. When this condition is satisfied, find the corresponding angular velocity $\boldsymbol{\omega}_{\mathcal{F}/\mathcal{E}}$.

Problem 3.7 Consider at a given time the velocities $\mathbf{v}_P$, $\mathbf{v}_Q$ and $\mathbf{v}_R$ of three points attached to the same rigid body $\mathcal{B}$ in motion relative to a referential $\mathcal{A}$. Then consider the plane passing through the endpoints of the three vectors $\mathbf{v}_P$, $\mathbf{v}_Q$ and $\mathbf{v}_R$ originating from a common arbitrary point O.
Show that the normal to this plane is directed along the angular velocity $\boldsymbol{\omega}_{\mathcal{B}/\mathcal{A}}$ of $\mathcal{B}$.

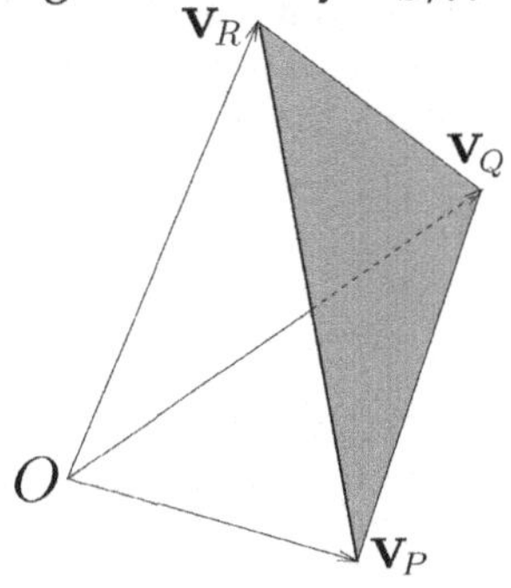

Problem 3.8 A rigid body $\mathcal{B}$ is in motion relative to a referential $\mathcal{E}$. Consider three points P_1, P_2 and P_3 attached to $\mathcal{B}$ and assumed to be non-aligned. Suppose that the velocities $\mathbf{v}_i \equiv \mathbf{v}_{P_i/\mathcal{E}}$, $i = 1, 2, 3$, are known at any given

time. Show that the angular velocity $\omega_{\mathcal{B}/\mathcal{E}}$ can be obtained from the formula

$$\omega_{\mathcal{B}/\mathcal{E}} = \frac{(\mathbf{v}_2 - \mathbf{v}_1) \times (\mathbf{v}_3 - \mathbf{v}_1)}{(\mathbf{v}_2 - \mathbf{v}_1) \cdot \mathbf{r}_{13}}$$

Show that a better expression, symmetric in the role played by the three points, is given by

$$\omega_{\mathcal{B}/\mathcal{E}} = 2\,\frac{\mathbf{v}_1 \times \mathbf{v}_2 + \mathbf{v}_2 \times \mathbf{v}_3 + \mathbf{v}_3 \times \mathbf{v}_1}{\mathbf{v}_1 \cdot \mathbf{r}_{32} + \mathbf{v}_2 \cdot \mathbf{r}_{13} + \mathbf{v}_3 \cdot \mathbf{r}_{21}}$$

where $\mathbf{r}_{ij} \equiv \mathbf{r}_{P_iP_j}$.

Problem 3.9 A rigid body $\mathcal{B}$ is in motion relative to a referential $\mathcal{E}$. We are interested to study the field $\mathbf{v}_{P\in\mathcal{B}/\mathcal{E}}$ *at a particular instant* when the points P lie on a line $\mathcal{L}$. Call ω the angular velocity of $\mathcal{B}$ at this instant. Also denote by $\mathbf{v}_A = \mathbf{v}_{A\in\mathcal{B}/\mathcal{E}}$ the velocity of a particular point A of $\mathcal{L}$.

a. Show that in general the magnitude of $\mathbf{v}_{P\in\mathcal{B}/\mathcal{E}}$ must reach a minimum along line $\mathcal{L}$. Find the point P_* where this minimum is reached.

b. Is there a point of $\mathcal{L}$ for which $\mathbf{v}_{P\in\mathcal{B}/\mathcal{E}}$ is collinear to a unit vector $\hat{\delta}$ directed along $\mathcal{L}$?

Problem 3.10 A rigid body $\mathcal{B}$ of basis $(\hat{\mathbf{b}}_1, \hat{\mathbf{b}}_2, \hat{\mathbf{b}}_3)$ and origin B is in motion relative to a referential $\mathcal{E}$. Consider the three points P, Q and R fixed in $\mathcal{B}$ defined by the position vectors $\mathbf{r}_{BP} = a\hat{\mathbf{b}}_1$, $\mathbf{r}_{BQ} = a\hat{\mathbf{b}}_2$, and $\mathbf{r}_{BR} = a\hat{\mathbf{b}}_3$ (a is a positive constant). The motion of $\mathcal{B}$ relative to $\mathcal{E}$ is characterized by the following conditions valid at all time

$$\mathbf{v}_P \cdot \hat{\mathbf{b}}_2 = 2a\omega, \ \mathbf{v}_P \cdot \hat{\mathbf{b}}_3 = -a\omega$$

$$\mathbf{v}_Q \cdot \hat{\mathbf{b}}_1 = a\omega, \ \mathbf{v}_Q \cdot \hat{\mathbf{b}}_3 = 0$$

$$\mathbf{v}_R \cdot \hat{\mathbf{b}}_1 = a\omega, \ \mathbf{v}_R \cdot \hat{\mathbf{b}}_2 = a\omega$$

where ω is a positive constant.

Find the angular velocity $\omega_{\mathcal{B}/\mathcal{E}}$, the velocity and acceleration of point B. Show that the motion of $\mathcal{B}$ relative to $\mathcal{E}$ cannot be a rotation.

Problem 3.11 Consider a linear operator $\mathcal{L} : \mathbf{V} \mapsto \mathbf{W} = \mathcal{L}(\mathbf{V})$. Show that

$$\frac{d}{dt}\Big|_{\mathcal{A}}(\mathcal{L}) = \frac{d}{dt}\Big|_{\mathcal{B}}(\mathcal{L}) + \Omega_{\mathcal{B}/\mathcal{A}} \circ \mathcal{L} - \mathcal{L} \circ \Omega_{\mathcal{B}/\mathcal{A}}$$

where $\Omega_{\mathcal{B}/\mathcal{A}}$ is the operator: $\mathbf{V} \mapsto \omega_{\mathcal{A}/\mathcal{B}} \times \mathbf{V}$.

Problem 3.12 Human centrifuges are large ground-based centrifuges used to submit pilots to g-force environment they would encounter during the maneuvers of high-performance aircraft. They provide a testing and training platform for pilots subjected to the adverse effects (such as loss of consciousness) of large accelerations. A model of a 3-axis human centrifuge displayed in Figure 3.9 is comprised of the following rigid bodies:
(i) the arm $\mathcal{A}(O, \hat{\mathbf{a}}_1, \hat{\mathbf{a}}_2, \hat{\mathbf{a}}_3 = \hat{\mathbf{e}}_3)$ is rotation about vertical axis $(O, \hat{\mathbf{e}}_3)$ of referential $\mathcal{E}(O, \hat{\mathbf{e}}_1, \hat{\mathbf{e}}_2, \hat{\mathbf{e}}_3)$.
(ii) the gimbal $\mathcal{B}(A, \hat{\mathbf{b}}_1, \hat{\mathbf{b}}_2 = \hat{\mathbf{a}}_2, \hat{\mathbf{b}}_3)$ in rotation about axis $(A, \hat{\mathbf{a}}_2)$ of arm $\mathcal{A}$. Position of point A is defined by $\mathbf{r}_{OA} = L\hat{\mathbf{a}}_1$ where L is a constant.
(iii) the cab $\mathcal{C}(A, \hat{\mathbf{c}}_1 = \hat{\mathbf{b}}_1, \hat{\mathbf{c}}_2, \hat{\mathbf{c}}_3)$ including its passenger in rotation about axis $(A, \hat{\mathbf{b}}_1)$ of gimbal $\mathcal{B}$.
Hence the cab is allowed to pitch and roll relative to the arm. From the point of view of the passenger, the axes $(A, \hat{\mathbf{c}}_1)$, $(A, \hat{\mathbf{c}}_2)$ and $(A, \hat{\mathbf{c}}_3)$ points from side to side, back to front, and toe to head, respectively. The point C whose position is defined by $\mathbf{r}_{AC} = l\hat{\mathbf{c}}_3$ is located at the level of the passenger's head. The acceleration felt by the pilot is the vector $\mathbf{G} = \mathbf{g} - \mathbf{a}_{C\in\mathcal{C}/\mathcal{E}}$ where $\mathbf{g} = -g\hat{\mathbf{e}}_3$ is the gravitational acceleration, and $\mathbf{a}_{C\in\mathcal{C}/\mathcal{E}}$ is the acceleration of point C attached to body $\mathcal{C}$.

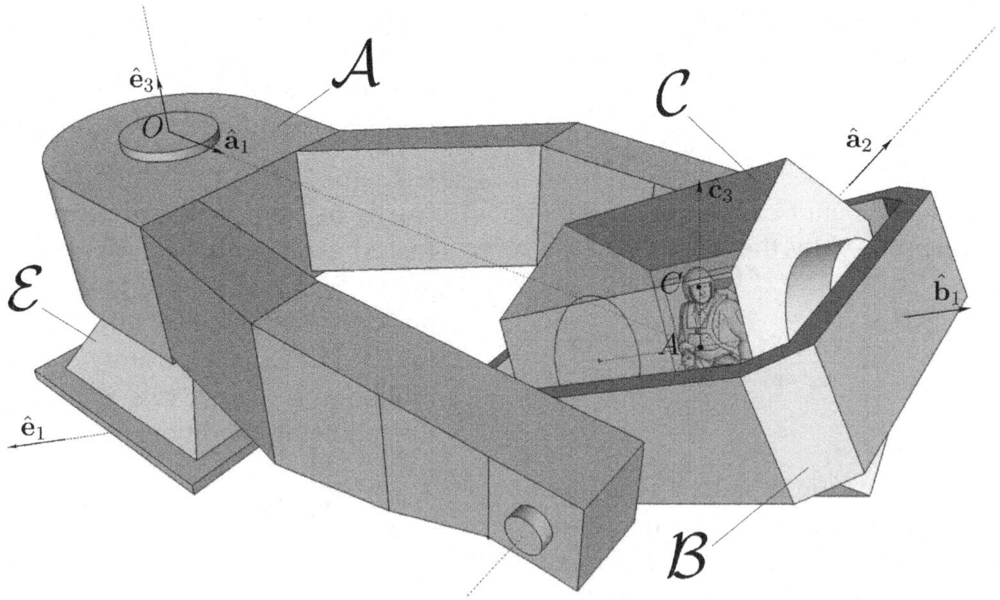

Figure 3.9

The centrifuge has three degrees of freedom modeled by the angles ψ, θ and ϕ which define the orientations of the bases of $\mathcal{A}$, $\mathcal{B}$ and $\mathcal{C}$ as defined in the figure below:

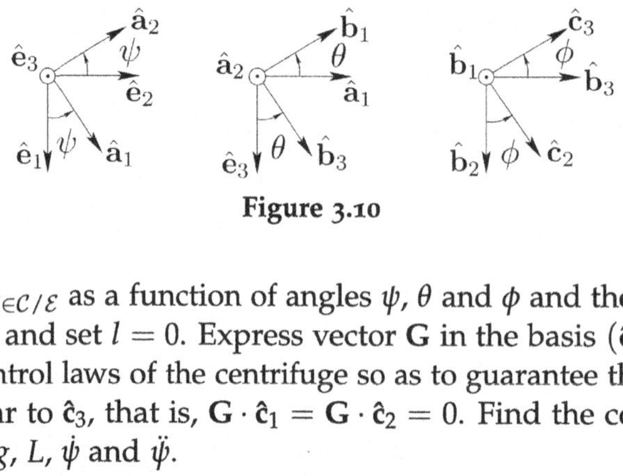

Figure 3.10

a. Find the velocity $\mathbf{v}_{C\in\mathcal{C}/\mathcal{E}}$ as a function of angles ψ, θ and ϕ and their time-derivatives.
b. Assume that $l \ll L$ and set $l = 0$. Express vector $\mathbf{G}$ in the basis $(\hat{\mathbf{c}}_1, \hat{\mathbf{c}}_2, \hat{\mathbf{c}}_3)$ attached to $\mathcal{C}$. It is desired to find control laws of the centrifuge so as to guarantee that the acceleration felt by the pilot is collinear to $\hat{\mathbf{c}}_3$, that is, $\mathbf{G}\cdot\hat{\mathbf{c}}_1 = \mathbf{G}\cdot\hat{\mathbf{c}}_2 = 0$. Find the corresponding angles θ and ϕ as functions of g, L, $\dot{\psi}$ and $\ddot{\psi}$.

Problem 3.13 Figure 3.11 displayed below shows a carousel commonly found in amusement parks and often referred to as the "grasshopper". It is comprised of a central mast $\mathcal{A}(O, \hat{\mathbf{a}}_1, \hat{\mathbf{a}}_2, \hat{\mathbf{a}}_3)$, a system of arms such as $\mathcal{B}(A, \hat{\mathbf{b}}_1, \hat{\mathbf{b}}_2, \hat{\mathbf{b}}_3)$ extending radially from the mast and supporting a passenger-carrying seat $\mathcal{C}(B, \hat{\mathbf{c}}_1, \hat{\mathbf{c}}_2, \hat{\mathbf{c}}_3)$.
The mast $\mathcal{A}$ is in rotation of angle ψ about a vertical axis $(O, \hat{\mathbf{e}}_3 = \hat{\mathbf{a}}_3)$ relative to a referential $\mathcal{E}(O, \hat{\mathbf{e}}_1, \hat{\mathbf{e}}_2, \hat{\mathbf{e}}_3)$ attached to the ground. The arm $\mathcal{B}$ can rotate about axis $(A, \hat{\mathbf{a}}_2 = \hat{\mathbf{b}}_2)$ of $\mathcal{A}$ with angle θ relative to $\mathcal{A}$. An actuator (pneumatic jack) mounted between $\mathcal{A}$ and $\mathcal{B}$ is able to create sudden lifting or lowering motions of arm $\mathcal{B}$. Finally seat $\mathcal{C}$ supported by arm $\mathcal{B}$ can rotate about an axis $(B, \hat{\mathbf{c}}_3 = \hat{\mathbf{b}}_3)$ with angle ϕ relative to arm $\mathcal{B}$. The points A and B are defined by $\mathbf{r}_{OA} = h\hat{\mathbf{e}}_3 + R\hat{\mathbf{a}}_1$ and $\mathbf{r}_{AB} = L\hat{\mathbf{b}}_1$ (h, R, and L are constant).
a. Sketch the three rotation diagrams between the bases of $\mathcal{E}$, $\mathcal{A}$, $\mathcal{B}$ and $\mathcal{C}$.
b. Find the time-derivative of unit vectors $\hat{\mathbf{a}}_1$, $\hat{\mathbf{b}}_1$ relative to referential $\mathcal{E}$.

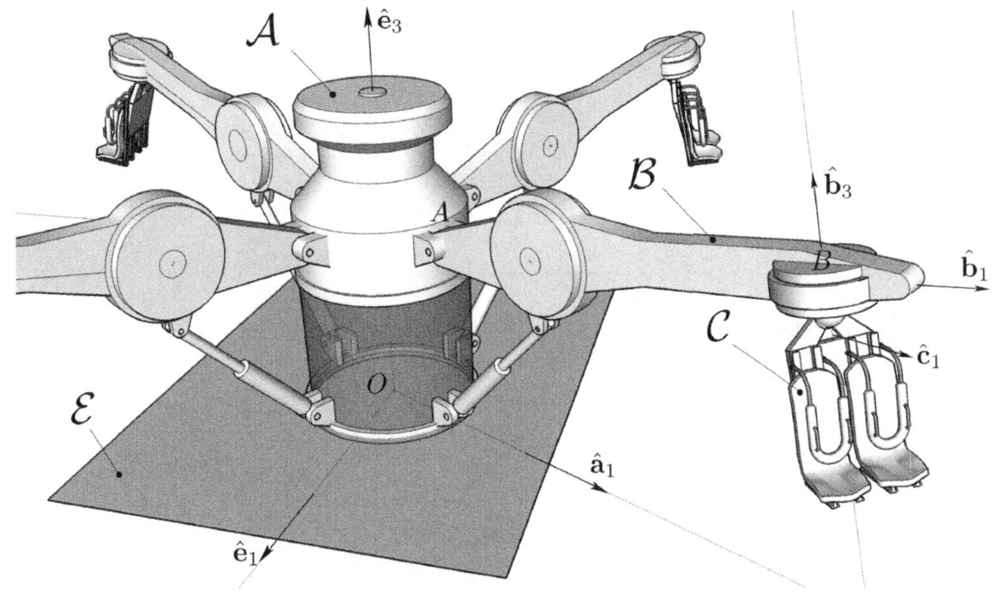

Figure 3.11

c. The position of the head H of a passenger is defined by the vector $\mathbf{r}_{BH} = b\hat{\mathbf{b}}_3 + c\hat{\mathbf{c}}_2$. Find $\mathbf{v}_{H/\mathcal{E}}$.

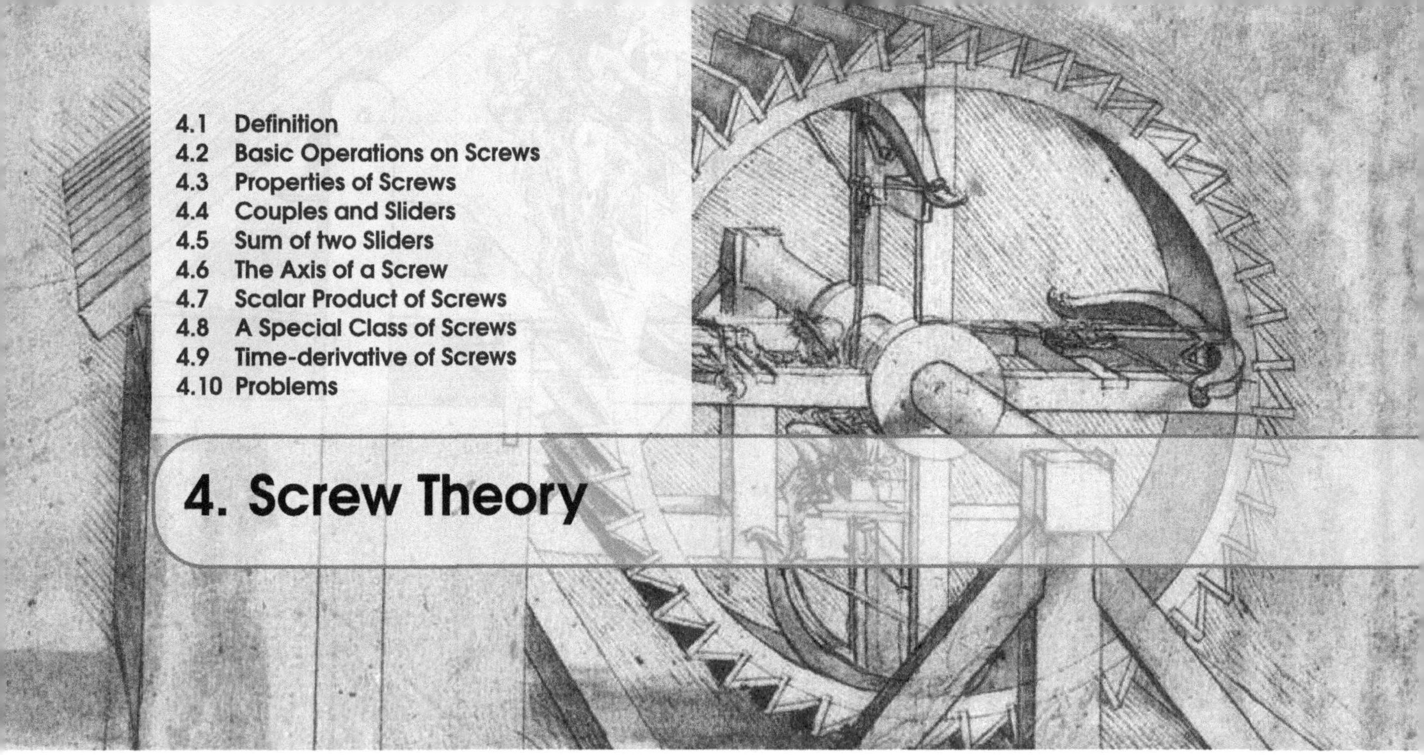

4. Screw Theory

IN THIS CHAPTER, we take a pause from our study of rigid body kinematics to introduce a mathematical object called *screw*. Screws form a special class of vector fields which satisfy the relationship $\mathbf{v}_Q = \mathbf{v}_P + \mathbf{V} \times \mathbf{r}_{PQ}$, where P and Q are any two points of space $\mathcal{E}$ (whether $\mathcal{E}$ is in motion or not is irrelevant here). They will be used throughout this book to provide a simple formalism which unifies all aspects of rigid body mechanics. We have seen in Chapter 3 that the velocity field of a rigid body $\mathcal{B}$ defines a screw. However, other relevant vector fields share this characteristic. Historically, they find their origin in the work of Chasles (in kinematics) and Poinsot[1] (for systems of forces). The concept of screws was defined by astronomer Ball[2], but is also present in the work of Plücker, Klein, and von Mises. The definition and notations adopted here were first proposed by Glaymann[3].

4.1 Definition

Definition 4.1 A *screw*, denoted $\{\mathcal{V}\}$, is a vector field $P \in \mathcal{E} \mapsto \mathbf{v}_P$ satisfying the equation

$$\mathbf{v}_Q = \mathbf{v}_P + \mathbf{V} \times \mathbf{r}_{PQ} \tag{4.1}$$

Vector $\mathbf{V}$ is called the *resultant* of screw $\{\mathcal{V}\}$. The vector $\mathbf{v}_P$ is called *moment* of screw $\{\mathcal{V}\}$ about point P.

Hence screws can be construed as short-hand notations of vector fields which satisfy equation (4.1) (field of moments). A screw is entirely specified by its resultant $\mathbf{V}$ and by a moment $\mathbf{v}_A$

[1]Poinsot L., *The Elements of Statics*, Cambridge University Press, Cambridge, 1877.

[2]Ball R.B., *A Treatise on the Theory of Screws*, Cambridge University Press, Cambridge, 1900.

[3]Glaymann M. *Théorie des torseurs. Leurs applications à la cinématique et à la dynamique du solide*, Vuibert, Paris, 1962.

at a particular point A. The two quantities $(\mathbf{V}, \mathbf{v}_A)$ are called the *elements of reduction* of the screw. To take this feature into account, a screw is written in the following array form

$$\{\mathcal{V}\} = \left\{ \begin{array}{c} \mathbf{V} \\ \mathbf{v}_A \end{array} \right\} = \left\{ \begin{array}{c} V_1\hat{\mathbf{e}}_1 + V_2\hat{\mathbf{e}}_2 + V_3\hat{\mathbf{e}}_3 \\ v_{A1}\hat{\mathbf{e}}_1 + v_{A2}\hat{\mathbf{e}}_2 + v_{A3}\hat{\mathbf{e}}_3 \end{array} \right\}_A \tag{4.2}$$

The upper element in this array is the resultant vector $\mathbf{V}$ of the screw. The lower element denotes the moment about the particular chosen point A. It is often necessary to specify (for instance, in the lower left side of the array) the particular point about which the moment has been determined. This is shown in the second equality of (4.2) where screw $\{\mathcal{V}\}$ is written in terms of the components of $\mathbf{V}$ and $\mathbf{v}_A$ on a particular orthonormal basis $(\hat{\mathbf{e}}_1, \hat{\mathbf{e}}_2, \hat{\mathbf{e}}_3)$ of $\mathcal{E}$. We then say that screw $\{\mathcal{V}\}$ is resolved at point A.

Example 4.1 Consider the following vector field $P \mapsto \mathbf{v}_P$ defined in space $\mathcal{E}(O, \hat{\mathbf{e}}_1, \hat{\mathbf{e}}_2, \hat{\mathbf{e}}_3)$ by

$$v_1 = 1 + x_2 + \lambda x_3, \quad v_2 = 2\lambda - \lambda x_3 - x_1, \quad v_3 = -1 - \lambda x_1 + \lambda^2 x_2$$

where (x_1, x_2, x_3) are the Cartesian coordinates of point P and where λ is a parameter. Show that there exist values of λ for which this vector field defines a screw. In each case, find the corresponding resultant $\mathbf{V}$. ■

Note that the mapping $P(x_1, x_2, x_3) \mapsto \mathbf{v}_P$ must necessarily be linear in (x_1, x_2, x_3) to define a screw. Indeed field $\mathbf{v}$ must satisfy $\mathbf{v}_P = \mathbf{v}_O + \mathbf{V} \times \mathbf{r}_{OP}$. Of course, being linear is not sufficient. We must show the fundamental property (4.1). Given two arbitrary points $P(x_1, x_2, x_3)$ and $P'(x'_1, x'_2, x'_3)$, the identity $\mathbf{v}_{P'} - \mathbf{v}_P = \mathbf{V} \times \mathbf{r}_{PP'}$ can be written as

$$\begin{array}{r} \lambda(x'_3 - x_3) + (x'_2 - x_2) = V_2(x'_3 - x_3) - V_3(x'_2 - x_2) \\ -\lambda(x'_3 - x_3) - (x'_1 - x_1) = V_3(x'_1 - x_1) - V_1(x'_3 - x_3) \\ -\lambda(x'_1 - x_1) + \lambda^2(x'_2 - x_2) = V_1(x'_2 - x_2) - V_2(x'_1 - x_1) \end{array}$$

where (V_1, V_2, V_3) are the components of vector $\mathbf{V}$. We can easily see by inspection that these equations are satisfied for arbitrary P and P' if only if $\lambda = 0$ or $\lambda = 1$. For these values of λ, the vector field $\mathbf{v}_P$ defines a screw $\{\mathcal{V}\}$ whose resultant is

$$\mathbf{V} = -\hat{\mathbf{e}}_3 \quad (\lambda = 0), \qquad \mathbf{V} = \hat{\mathbf{e}}_1 + \hat{\mathbf{e}}_2 - \hat{\mathbf{e}}_3 \quad (\lambda = 1)$$

Screw $\{\mathcal{V}\}$ can then be written as

$$\{\mathcal{V}\} = \left\{ \begin{array}{c} -\hat{\mathbf{e}}_3 \\ \hat{\mathbf{e}}_1 - \hat{\mathbf{e}}_3 \end{array} \right\}_O \quad (\lambda = 0), \qquad \{\mathcal{V}\} = \left\{ \begin{array}{c} \hat{\mathbf{e}}_1 + \hat{\mathbf{e}}_2 - \hat{\mathbf{e}}_3 \\ \hat{\mathbf{e}}_1 + 2\hat{\mathbf{e}}_2 - \hat{\mathbf{e}}_3 \end{array} \right\}_O \quad (\lambda = 1)$$

where we have chosen point O to resolve $\{\mathcal{V}\}$, although any other point can be considered. ■

4.2 Basic Operations on Screws

We can define basic operations of the set of screws.

Definition 4.2 (Equality of two Screws) Two screws $\{\mathcal{V}\}$ and $\{\mathcal{W}\}$ are *equal* if their resultants are equal and if there exists a point P about which their moments are the same

$$\mathbf{V} = \mathbf{W}, \qquad \mathbf{v}_P = \mathbf{w}_P \tag{4.3}$$

It is easy to show then that $\mathbf{v}_Q = \mathbf{w}_Q$ at any other point Q of $\mathcal{E}$.

Definition 4.3 (Sum of two Screws) The *sum* $\{\mathcal{V}\}+\{\mathcal{W}\}$ of two screws is defined as the screw of resultant $\mathbf{V}+\mathbf{W}$ and whose moment at a particular point P is $\mathbf{v}_P+\mathbf{w}_P$.

$\{\mathcal{V}\}+\{\mathcal{W}\}$ is indeed a screw since it is readily shown that equation (4.1) is satisfied.

Definition 4.4 (Multiplication by a scalar) Given a real scalar λ and a screw $\{\mathcal{V}\}$ of resultant $\mathbf{V}$ and moment $\mathbf{v}_P$ about point P, screw $\lambda\{\mathcal{V}\}$ is defined as the screw of resultant $\lambda\mathbf{V}$ and moment $\lambda\mathbf{v}_P$ about point P.

These operations endow the set of screws with the structure of a *vector space* (of dimension 6). In this space, the zero element (corresponding to the vector field $P \mapsto \mathbf{0}$) is denoted $\{0\}$.

Example 4.2 Consider the following two screws defined on the Euclidean space $\mathcal{E}(O,\hat{\mathbf{e}}_1,\hat{\mathbf{e}}_2,\hat{\mathbf{e}}_3)$

$$\{\mathcal{V}\} = \left\{ \begin{array}{c} \hat{\mathbf{e}}_1+\hat{\mathbf{e}}_3 \\ \hat{\mathbf{e}}_1 \end{array} \right\}_O, \text{ and } \{\mathcal{W}\} = \left\{ \begin{array}{c} 4\hat{\mathbf{e}}_1-\hat{\mathbf{e}}_3 \\ \hat{\mathbf{e}}_1+2\hat{\mathbf{e}}_3 \end{array} \right\}_A$$

where point A is defined by $\mathbf{r}_{OA}=\hat{\mathbf{e}}_1$. Find screw $\{\mathcal{V}\}+2\{\mathcal{W}\}$ resolved at O. ■

The resultant is found to be $\mathbf{V}+2\mathbf{W}=9\hat{\mathbf{e}}_1-\hat{\mathbf{e}}_3$. To find a moment, we may choose point O or A: if we choose O, we need to find $\mathbf{w}_O=\mathbf{w}_A+\mathbf{W}\times\mathbf{r}_{AO}=\hat{\mathbf{e}}_1+2\hat{\mathbf{e}}_3+(4\hat{\mathbf{e}}_1-\hat{\mathbf{e}}_3)\times(-\hat{\mathbf{e}}_1)=\hat{\mathbf{e}}_1+\hat{\mathbf{e}}_2+2\hat{\mathbf{e}}_3$. Then, the moment of $\{\mathcal{V}\}+2\{\mathcal{W}\}$ about O is $\mathbf{v}_O+2\mathbf{w}_O=3\hat{\mathbf{e}}_1+2\hat{\mathbf{e}}_2+4\hat{\mathbf{e}}_3$:

$$\{\mathcal{V}\}+2\{\mathcal{W}\} = \left\{ \begin{array}{c} 9\hat{\mathbf{e}}_1-\hat{\mathbf{e}}_3 \\ 3\hat{\mathbf{e}}_1+2\hat{\mathbf{e}}_2+4\hat{\mathbf{e}}_3 \end{array} \right\}_O$$

The error to avoid is to determine the moment of $\{\mathcal{V}\}+2\{\mathcal{W}\}$ about O as the sum $\mathbf{v}_O+2\mathbf{w}_A$.

■

4.3 Properties of Screws

Theorem 4.1 — Scalar Invariant. The scalar quantity $\mathbf{V}\cdot\mathbf{v}_P$ is an invariant of screw $\{\mathcal{V}\}$, that is, it is independent of point P.

Proof. To show that $\mathbf{V}\cdot\mathbf{v}_P$ is independent of point P, we take the scalar product of both sides of (4.1) with $\mathbf{V}$: this leads to $\mathbf{V}\cdot\mathbf{v}_Q=\mathbf{V}\cdot\mathbf{v}_P$ for any two points P and Q since $\mathbf{V}\times\mathbf{r}_{PQ}$ is orthogonal to $\mathbf{V}$. ■

Theorem 4.2 — Equiprojectivity. The vector field $\mathbf{v}_P$ associated with screw $\{\mathcal{V}\}$ is *equiprojective*, that is, it satisfies the property:

$$\mathbf{v}_P\cdot\mathbf{r}_{PQ}=\mathbf{v}_Q\cdot\mathbf{r}_{PQ} \tag{4.4}$$

Hence, the projections of the moments about P and Q on the line joining P and Q are identical. Equiprojectivity is quite fundamental to screws: it can be shown (see Problem 4.1) that, to every equiprojective vector field $\mathbf{v}: P\in\mathcal{E}\mapsto\mathbf{v}_P$, that is, satisfying $\mathbf{v}_P\cdot\mathbf{r}_{PQ}=\mathbf{v}_Q\cdot\mathbf{r}_{PQ}$, corresponds a unique screw. The study of screws and the study of equiprojective fields are one and the same thing.

4.4 Couples and Sliders

Two classes of screws, couples and sliders, play a special role in screw theory.

Definition 4.5 A screw $\{\mathcal{V}\}$ is said to be a *couple* if its resultant $\mathbf{V}$ is zero and if there exists a point A whose moment $\mathbf{v}_A$ is not zero.

Hence the corresponding vector field $\mathbf{v}_P$ is constant, that is, independent of point P: $\mathbf{v}_P = \mathbf{v}_A$ for all points.

Definition 4.6 A screw $\{\mathcal{S}\}$ is said to be a *slider* if its resultant $\mathbf{S}$ is not zero, and if there exists a point A of $\mathcal{E}$ about which moment $\mathbf{s}_A = \mathbf{0}$. The moment of a slider about any point P is then given by $\mathbf{s}_P = \mathbf{S} \times \mathbf{r}_{AP}$:

$$\{\mathcal{S}\} = \left\{ \begin{matrix} \mathbf{S} \\ \mathbf{0} \end{matrix} \right\}_A = \left\{ \begin{matrix} \mathbf{S} \\ \mathbf{S} \times \mathbf{r}_{AP} \end{matrix} \right\}_P \tag{4.5}$$

This implies that the moment of slider $\{\mathcal{S}\}$ about any point of line $\Delta = (A, \mathbf{S})$ passing through A (for which $\mathbf{s}_A = 0$) and parallel to $\mathbf{S}$ is also zero. Δ is called the *axis* of slider $\{\mathcal{S}\}$. Figure 4.1 shows the organization of the vector field about Δ.

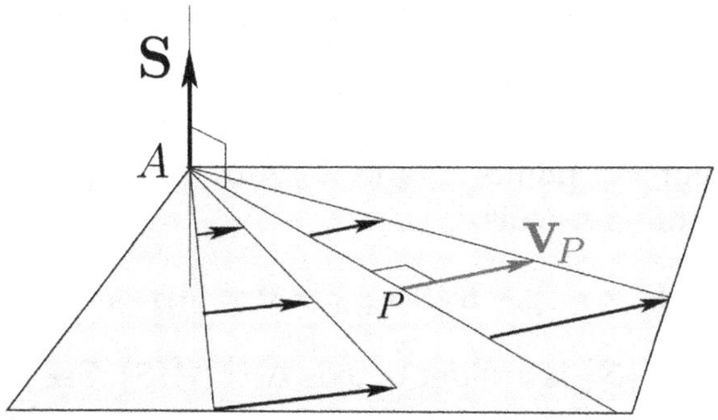

Figure 4.1 – *Geometry of a slider about its axis Δ.*

Corollary 4.1 — Correspondence between sliders and bound vectors. Given a vector $\mathbf{S}$ *bound* at point A, denoted $(A, \mathbf{S})$, recall that the moment about point P of $\mathbf{S}$ is defined as the vector $\mathbf{S} \times \mathbf{r}_{AP}$. The resulting vector field $P \in \mathcal{E} \mapsto \mathbf{S} \times \mathbf{r}_{AP}$ clearly defines a slider $\{\mathcal{S}\}$. Thus there exists a one-to-one correspondence between sliders and bound vectors.

4.5 Sum of two Sliders

Consider the screw $\{\mathcal{S}\} = \{\mathcal{S}_1\} + \{\mathcal{S}_2\}$ defined as the sum of two sliders of axis $(A_1, \mathbf{S}_1)$ and $(A_2, \mathbf{S}_2)$. Its resultant and moment about point P are given by

$$\mathbf{S} = \mathbf{S}_1 + \mathbf{S}_2, \qquad \mathbf{s}_P = \mathbf{S}_1 \times \mathbf{r}_{A_1P} + \mathbf{S}_2 \times \mathbf{r}_{A_2P}$$

It is of interest to ask *under what conditions screw $\{\mathcal{S}\}$ itself defines a slider*. See Figure 4.2. Two non-trivial cases can be found.

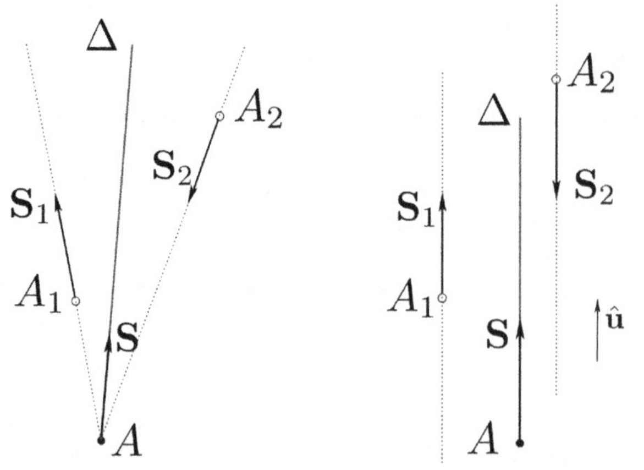

Figure 4.2 – *Sum of Sliders. Case 1: concurrent axes, Case 2: parallel axes.*

Case 1. If the sliders' axes intersect at a common point A, then clearly the moment about A of screw $\{\mathcal{S}\}$ is zero. If in addition $\mathbf{S}$ is not zero, then screw $\{\mathcal{S}\}$ is a slider of axis $\Delta = (A, \mathbf{S} = \mathbf{S}_1 + \mathbf{S}_2)$. See Figure 4.2 (left).
Case 2. If the sliders' axes are parallel along some unit vector $\hat{\mathbf{u}}$, then one can write $\mathbf{S}_i = \alpha_i \hat{\mathbf{u}}$ $(i = 1, 2)$. Assume that the scalar $\alpha_1 + \alpha_2$ is not zero. Then the vector $\mathbf{S}$ is not zero, and one can define a unique point A satisfying the equation

$$\alpha_1 \mathbf{r}_{AA_1} + \alpha_2 \mathbf{r}_{AA_2} = \mathbf{0}$$

Point A is the barycenter of points A_1 and A_2 with the respective weights α_1 and α_2. Then the moment about A of screw $\mathcal{S}$ is

$$\mathbf{s}_A = \mathbf{S}_1 \times \mathbf{r}_{A_1A} + \mathbf{S}_2 \times \mathbf{r}_{A_2A} = \hat{\mathbf{u}} \times (\alpha_1 \mathbf{r}_{AA_1} + \alpha_2 \mathbf{r}_{AA_2}) = \mathbf{0}.$$

We conclude that screw $\{\mathcal{S}\}$ is a slider of axis $\Delta = (A, \mathbf{S})$. See Figure 4.2 (right).
It is possible to show that the converse is true, that is, that the following theorem holds true:

> **Theorem 4.3** The sum of two sliders of resultants $\mathbf{S}_1$ and $\mathbf{S}_2$ satisfying $\mathbf{S}_1 + \mathbf{S}_2 \neq \mathbf{0}$ is a slider if and only if the sliders' axes intersect or are parallel.

> **Example 4.3** In a Euclidean space $\mathcal{E}(O, \hat{\mathbf{e}}_1, \hat{\mathbf{e}}_2, \hat{\mathbf{e}}_3)$ consider the following sliders: $\{\mathcal{S}_1\}$, $\{\mathcal{S}_2\}$, and $\{\mathcal{S}_3\}$ of axes $(O, \mathbf{S}_1 = \alpha \hat{\mathbf{e}}_1)$, $(A, \mathbf{S}_2 = \beta \hat{\mathbf{e}}_1)$ and $(B, \mathbf{S}_3 = \gamma(\hat{\mathbf{e}}_3 - \hat{\mathbf{e}}_2))$ respectively, where points A and B are defined by $\mathbf{r}_{OA} = \hat{\mathbf{e}}_2 + \hat{\mathbf{e}}_3$ and $\mathbf{r}_{OB} = \hat{\mathbf{e}}_1 + \hat{\mathbf{e}}_2$, and where α, β and γ are three scalars. Define the screw $\{\mathcal{S}\}$ as the sum $\{\mathcal{S}_1\} + \{\mathcal{S}_2\} + \{\mathcal{S}_3\}$. Under what conditions is $\{\mathcal{S}\}$ (i) a couple? (ii) a slider? (iii) $\{0\}$? ■

First we sum the three sliders to obtain

$$\{\mathcal{S}\} = \{\mathcal{S}_1\} + \{\mathcal{S}_2\} + \{\mathcal{S}_3\} = \left\{ \begin{array}{c} \alpha \hat{\mathbf{e}}_1 \\ \mathbf{0} \end{array} \right\}_O + \left\{ \begin{array}{c} \beta \hat{\mathbf{e}}_1 \\ \mathbf{0} \end{array} \right\}_A + \left\{ \begin{array}{c} \gamma(\hat{\mathbf{e}}_3 - \hat{\mathbf{e}}_2) \\ \mathbf{0} \end{array} \right\}_B$$

We can sum them by resolving the moments about the same point. We choose point O

$$\{\mathcal{S}\} = \left\{ \begin{matrix} (\alpha+\beta)\hat{\mathbf{e}}_1 - \gamma\hat{\mathbf{e}}_2 + \gamma\hat{\mathbf{e}}_3 \\ \beta\hat{\mathbf{e}}_1 \times (-\hat{\mathbf{e}}_2 - \hat{\mathbf{e}}_3) + \gamma(\hat{\mathbf{e}}_3 - \hat{\mathbf{e}}_2) \times (-\hat{\mathbf{e}}_1 - \hat{\mathbf{e}}_2) \end{matrix} \right\}_O = \left\{ \begin{matrix} (\alpha+\beta)\hat{\mathbf{e}}_1 - \gamma\hat{\mathbf{e}}_2 + \gamma\hat{\mathbf{e}}_3 \\ \gamma\hat{\mathbf{e}}_1 + (\beta-\gamma)\hat{\mathbf{e}}_2 - (\beta+\gamma)\hat{\mathbf{e}}_3 \end{matrix} \right\}_O$$

Case (i). Screw $\{\mathcal{S}\}$ is a couple if the resultant $\mathbf{S} = (\alpha+\beta)\hat{\mathbf{e}}_1 - \gamma\hat{\mathbf{e}}_2 + \gamma\hat{\mathbf{e}}_3$ is zero. This occurs if $\alpha+\beta = 0$ and $\gamma = 0$. We must also require that the moment $\mathbf{s}_O = \beta\hat{\mathbf{e}}_2 - \beta\hat{\mathbf{e}}_3$ is not zero, that is, $\beta \neq 0$.
Case (ii). Screw $\{\mathcal{S}\}$ is a slider if its resultant is non-zero and if its moment is zero at some point Q: the position of Q is given by $\mathbf{S} \times \mathbf{r}_{OQ} = -\mathbf{s}_O$. A solvability condition of this equation is that $\mathbf{s}_O \cdot \mathbf{S} = \gamma(\alpha - \beta) = 0$, which imposes $\gamma = 0$ or $\alpha = \beta$. We must also impose $\mathbf{S} \neq 0$. This gives these 3 possibilities: (ii-1) $\gamma = 0$ and $\alpha + \beta \neq 0$, (ii-2) $\alpha = \beta \neq 0$, and (ii-3): $\alpha = \beta = 0$ and $\gamma \neq 0$.
Case (iii). Screw $\{\mathcal{S}\}$ is $\{0\}$ if $\mathbf{S} = \mathbf{0}$ and $\mathbf{s}_O = \mathbf{0}$: this imposes $\alpha = \beta = \gamma = 0$. ■

Example 4.4 Find the set of screws whose scalar invariant $\mathbf{V} \cdot \mathbf{v}_P$ is zero. ■

Four cases can be found to satisfy the equation $\mathbf{V} \cdot \mathbf{v}_P = 0$.
Case 1: if $\mathbf{V} = 0$ and there exists a point A such that $\mathbf{v}_A = \mathbf{0}$, then screw $\{\mathcal{V}\}$ is the screw $\{0\}$.
Case 2: if $\mathbf{V} = \mathbf{0}$ and if there exists a point A such that $\mathbf{v}_A \neq \mathbf{0}$, then the screw is a couple.
Case 3: if $\mathbf{V} \neq \mathbf{0}$ and if there exists a point A such that $\mathbf{v}_A = \mathbf{0}$: then the screw is a slider along the axis $\Delta = (A, \mathbf{V})$.
Case 4: if $\mathbf{V} \neq \mathbf{0}$ and if there exists a point A such that $\mathbf{v}_A \neq \mathbf{0}$, then the set of points P satisfying $\mathbf{V} \times \mathbf{r}_{PA} = \mathbf{v}_A$ is not empty, since $\mathbf{v}_A$ and $\mathbf{V}$ are orthogonal. The screw is then necessarily a slider. To find this set of points (the axis of the slider) we must solve the vector equation $\mathbf{V} \times \mathbf{r}_{AP} = -\mathbf{v}_A$. If we find a particular solution $\mathbf{r}_{AB}$, then the general solution is necessarily given by $\mathbf{r}_{AP} = \mathbf{r}_{AB} + \lambda\mathbf{V}$. A particular solution orthogonal to $\mathbf{V}$ is found by cross-multiplying both sides of this equation by $\mathbf{V}$: $\mathbf{V} \times (\mathbf{V} \times \mathbf{r}_{AB}) = -\mathbf{V} \times \mathbf{v}_A$. After expanding the triple product, [2] we find the position of point B as given by: $\mathbf{r}_{AB} = (\mathbf{V} \times \mathbf{v}_A)/\mathbf{V}^2$. We conclude that the screw is a slider of axis $\Delta = (B, \mathbf{V})$. We recover case 3 if $\mathbf{v}_A = \mathbf{0}$.
Hence to show that a screw is a slider it is necessary and sufficient to show that its resultant $\mathbf{V}$ *is non-zero and its scalar invariant* $\mathbf{V} \cdot \mathbf{v}_P$ *is zero.*

■

Next we generalize the notion of axis defined for sliders to arbitrary screws. The axis of a screw plays a fundamental role in the decomposition of a screw as the sum of a couple and a slider, thereby revealing the unique structure of the associated vector field around its axis.

4.6 The Axis of a Screw

Definition 4.7 The *axis* Δ of screw $\{\mathcal{V}\}$ of non-zero resultant $\mathbf{V}$ is defined as the set of points Q about which the moment is collinear to $\mathbf{V}$: hence for all points Q of Δ, there exists a scalar p such that $\mathbf{v}_Q = p\mathbf{V}$.

Note first that couples do not possess an axis. Assuming $\mathbf{V} \neq 0$, the axis Δ of a screw is in fact not an empty set. It can be found by solving for the position vector $\mathbf{r}_{OQ}$ solution of the vector equation

$$\mathbf{V} \times \mathbf{r}_{OQ} = p\mathbf{V} - \mathbf{v}_O \tag{4.6}$$

relative to some arbitrary point O of $\mathcal{E}$. A necessary condition for equation (4.6) to have a solution is that the resultant $\mathbf{V}$ be orthogonal to $(p\mathbf{V} - \mathbf{v}_O)$. This leads to the following

[2] Recall the identity $\mathbf{U} \times (\mathbf{V} \times \mathbf{W}) = (\mathbf{U} \cdot \mathbf{W})\mathbf{V} - (\mathbf{U} \cdot \mathbf{V})\mathbf{W}$ for any three vectors $\mathbf{U}$, $\mathbf{V}$ and $\mathbf{W}$.

expression for scalar p:

$$p = \frac{\mathbf{V} \cdot \mathbf{v}_O}{\mathbf{V}^2} \tag{4.7}$$

We recognize in (4.7) the scalar invariant of $\{\mathcal{V}\}$: p is not a function of point O, but rather is a quantity intrinsic to screw $\{\mathcal{V}\}$.

To solve equation (4.6), we first note that if $\mathbf{r}_{OQ_*}$ is a particular solution, then $\mathbf{r}_{OQ_*} + \lambda\mathbf{V}$ is also solution for all scalars λ: hence the general solution of (4.6) is of the type: $\mathbf{r}_{OQ} = \mathbf{r}_{OQ_*} + \lambda\mathbf{V}$, where $\mathbf{r}_{OQ_*}$ is a particular solution orthogonal to $\mathbf{V}$. This shows that *the axis is a straight line directed along* $\mathbf{V}$.

To find a particular solution, we take the cross-product of both sides of (4.6) with $\mathbf{V}$ to find:

$$(\mathbf{V} \cdot \mathbf{r}_{OQ_*})\mathbf{V} - \mathbf{V}^2\, \mathbf{r}_{OQ_*} = -\mathbf{V} \times \mathbf{v}_O$$

and recalling that $\mathbf{V} \cdot \mathbf{r}_{OQ_*} = 0$

$$\mathbf{r}_{OQ_*} = \frac{\mathbf{V} \times \mathbf{v}_O}{\mathbf{V}^2} \tag{4.8}$$

We conclude with the following theorem:

Theorem 4.4 — Axis of a Screw. The axis Δ of $\{\mathcal{V}\}$ is the straight line defined by the equation

$$\mathbf{r}_{OQ} = \frac{\mathbf{V} \times \mathbf{v}_O}{\mathbf{V}^2} + \lambda\mathbf{V} \tag{4.9}$$

The points Q of Δ satisfy $\mathbf{v}_Q = p\mathbf{V}$ with

$$p = \frac{\mathbf{V} \cdot \mathbf{v}_O}{\mathbf{V}^2} \tag{4.10}$$

We call p the *pitch* of screw $\{\mathcal{V}\}$.

Note that the location of axis Δ is independent of the choice of point O in formula (4.9).

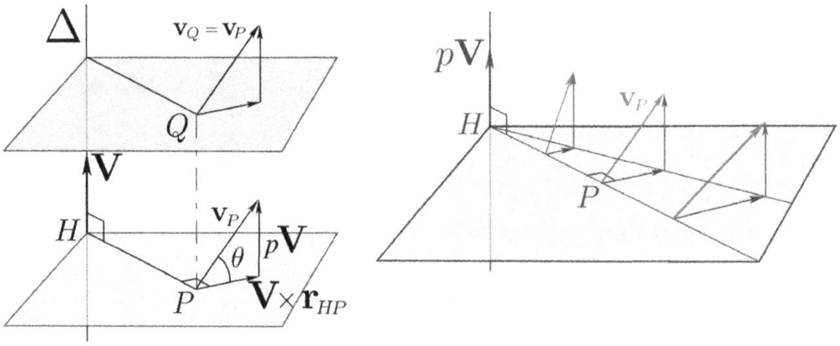

Figure 4.3 – *Axis of a screw.*

The screw axis possesses fundamental properties listed below.

Corollary 4.2 — Properties of the screw axis.
1. Moments are invariant along axis Δ: for all Q of Δ, $\mathbf{v}_Q = p\mathbf{V}$ (recall that the pitch p is an invariant).
2. The notion of axis is an extension to that defined for sliders: in the case of sliders, the pitch is zero, and hence $\mathbf{v}_Q = \mathbf{0}$ for all points of the axis of a slider.
3. The moment about a point P off the axis can be determined from the value of the moment taken on the axis: denoting by H the projection of P on axis Δ, we have (see Figure 4.3)

$$\mathbf{v}_P = p\mathbf{V} + \mathbf{V} \times \mathbf{r}_{HP} \tag{4.11}$$

which shows that the moment about P can be expressed as the sum of two orthogonal vectors, the first being independent of P, the second being proportional to the distance from P to axis Δ.
4. The magnitude of moments take its minimum value on the axis of the screw. As the point P moves farther away from the axis Δ, the angle θ made by $\mathbf{v}_P$ and the plane passing through P and orthogonal to Δ tends to zero: for points far away from Δ, the screw behaves like a slider of axis Δ.
5. According to equation (4.11) any screw $\{\mathcal{V}\}$ of resultant $\mathbf{V} \neq 0$ and axis Δ can be decomposed as the sum of a slider $\{\mathcal{S}\}$ of axis Δ and a couple $\{\mathcal{C}\}$ whose moment is collinear to Δ in the following way

$$\{\mathcal{V}\} = \left\{ \begin{array}{c} \mathbf{V} \\ \mathbf{v}_P \end{array} \right\} = \{\mathcal{C}\} + \{\mathcal{S}\}, \ \{\mathcal{C}\} = \left\{ \begin{array}{c} \mathbf{0} \\ p\mathbf{V} \end{array} \right\}, \ \{\mathcal{S}\} = \left\{ \begin{array}{c} \mathbf{V} \\ \mathbf{0} \end{array} \right\}_{Q_* \in \Delta} \tag{4.12}$$

where p and $\Delta(Q_*, \mathbf{V})$ are the pitch and the axis of $\{\mathcal{V}\}$, respectively.

In conclusion, the knowledge of the pitch p and the axis $\Delta(Q_*, \mathbf{V})$ entirely defines a screw $\{\mathcal{V}\}$: the decomposition of $\{\mathcal{V}\}$ as given by (4.12) is unique. See Figure 4.3 for a graphical representation of $\mathcal{V}\}$ in relation to its axis.

Example 4.5 Consider the screw $\{\mathcal{V}\}$ defined as the sum of the two sliders $\{\mathcal{S}_1\}$ and $\{\mathcal{S}_2\}$ of axes $(A_1, \mathbf{S}_1 = \hat{\mathbf{e}}_1)$ and $(A_2, \mathbf{S}_2 = \hat{\mathbf{e}}_2)$, respectively, where points A_1 and A_2 are defined by $\mathbf{r}_{OA_1} = \hat{\mathbf{e}}_3$ and $\mathbf{r}_{OA_2} = -\hat{\mathbf{e}}_3$. Find the axis of $\{\mathcal{V}\}$ and the corresponding decomposition (4.12). Then find the set of points for which $|\mathbf{v}_P|$ =constant. ■

It is readily seen that $\{\mathcal{V}\}$ is not a slider since the axes of $\{\mathcal{S}_1\}$ and $\{\mathcal{S}_2\}$ are neither parallel nor intersecting. First we express $\{\mathcal{V}\}$ in the form

$$\{\mathcal{V}\} = \left\{ \begin{array}{c} \hat{\mathbf{e}}_1 \\ \mathbf{0} \end{array} \right\}_{A_1} + \left\{ \begin{array}{c} \hat{\mathbf{e}}_2 \\ \mathbf{0} \end{array} \right\}_{A_2} = \left\{ \begin{array}{c} \hat{\mathbf{e}}_1 + \hat{\mathbf{e}}_2 \\ \hat{\mathbf{e}}_1 + \hat{\mathbf{e}}_2 \end{array} \right\}_O$$

We find the pitch of $\{\mathcal{V}\}$ as $p = \mathbf{V} \cdot \mathbf{v}_O / \mathbf{V}^2 = 1$. The axis Δ of $\{\mathcal{V}\}$ is directed along $\mathbf{V} = \hat{\mathbf{e}}_1 + \hat{\mathbf{e}}_2$ and passes through the point B given by

$$\mathbf{r}_{OB} = \frac{\mathbf{V} \times \mathbf{v}_O}{\mathbf{V}^2} = \mathbf{0}$$

Hence the axis passes through O, which is expected since $\mathbf{v}_O = p\mathbf{V}$. According to (4.12) we can write

$$\{\mathcal{V}\} = \left\{ \begin{array}{c} \mathbf{V} \\ \mathbf{0} \end{array} \right\}_O + \left\{ \begin{array}{c} \mathbf{0} \\ \mathbf{V} \end{array} \right\}_O$$

The value of $\mathbf{v}_P$ at any point P can then be written as

$$\mathbf{v}_P = \mathbf{V} + \mathbf{V} \times \mathbf{r}_{HP}$$

where H is the projection of P onto axis Δ. It is seen that $|\mathbf{v}_P|$ =constant for all points equidistant from Δ. The sets on which $|\mathbf{v}_P|$ =constant are cylinders of axis Δ. ■

Example 4.6 Consider the screw $\{\mathcal{V}\}$ of resultant $\mathbf{V} = \hat{\mathbf{e}}_1 + \hat{\mathbf{e}}_2 + \hat{\mathbf{e}}_3$, of pitch $p = 1$, and whose axis passes through point A with $\mathbf{r}_{OA} = \hat{\mathbf{e}}_1$. Find the expression of $\{\mathcal{V}\}$ resolved at point O. ■

The value of $\mathbf{v}_A$ is given by $p\mathbf{V}$ since point A is on axis. This gives

$$\{\mathcal{V}\} = \left\{ \begin{array}{c} \mathbf{V} \\ p\mathbf{V} \end{array} \right\}_A = \left\{ \begin{array}{c} \hat{\mathbf{e}}_1 + \hat{\mathbf{e}}_2 + \hat{\mathbf{e}}_3 \\ \hat{\mathbf{e}}_1 + \hat{\mathbf{e}}_2 + \hat{\mathbf{e}}_3 \end{array} \right\}_A$$

$\{\mathcal{V}\}$ can now be resolved about O:

$$\{\mathcal{V}\} = \left\{ \begin{array}{c} \mathbf{V} \\ p\mathbf{V} + \mathbf{V} \times \mathbf{r}_{AO} \end{array} \right\}_O = \left\{ \begin{array}{c} \hat{\mathbf{e}}_1 + \hat{\mathbf{e}}_2 + \hat{\mathbf{e}}_3 \\ \hat{\mathbf{e}}_1 + 2\hat{\mathbf{e}}_3 \end{array} \right\}_O$$

■

Example 4.7 Given two distinct points A and B, consider the vector field $\mathbf{v}_P = \mathbf{r}_{AP} \times \mathbf{r}_{BP}$. Show that this field is equiprojective, and hence defines a screw. Find its resultant and its axis. ■

We have to show that $\mathbf{v}_P \cdot \mathbf{r}_{PQ} = \mathbf{v}_Q \cdot \mathbf{r}_{PQ}$ for any two points P and Q:

$$\begin{aligned} \mathbf{v}_P \cdot \mathbf{r}_{PQ} &= [(\mathbf{r}_{AQ} + \mathbf{r}_{QP}) \times (\mathbf{r}_{BQ} + \mathbf{r}_{QP})] \cdot \mathbf{r}_{PQ} \\ &= (\mathbf{r}_{AQ} \times \mathbf{r}_{BQ} + \mathbf{r}_{QP} \times \mathbf{r}_{BQ} + \mathbf{r}_{AQ} \times \mathbf{r}_{QP}) \cdot \mathbf{r}_{PQ} \end{aligned}$$

Using the identity $(\mathbf{A} \times \mathbf{B}) \cdot \mathbf{A} = \mathbf{0}$, we find that the last expression gives $\mathbf{v}_Q \cdot \mathbf{r}_{PQ}$. To find the corresponding resultant, we first note that $\mathbf{v}_A = \mathbf{0}$. Hence, we need to find a vector $\mathbf{V}$ independent of P such that $\mathbf{v}_P = \mathbf{V} \times \mathbf{r}_{AP}$: we find

$$\mathbf{v}_P = \mathbf{r}_{AP} \times (\mathbf{r}_{BA} + \mathbf{r}_{AP}) = \mathbf{r}_{AB} \times \mathbf{r}_{AP}$$

which shows that $\mathbf{V} = \mathbf{r}_{AB}$. Field $P \mapsto \mathbf{r}_{AP} \times \mathbf{r}_{BP}$ defines a slider whose axis is line AB. ■

4.7 Scalar Product of Screws

The concept of scalar product of screws is critical to many concepts of rigid body mechanics.

Definition 4.8 The *scalar product*[3] of two screws $\{\mathcal{U}\}$ and $\{\mathcal{V}\}$ is the scalar defined by:

$$\{\mathcal{U}\} \cdot \{\mathcal{V}\} = \mathbf{U} \cdot \mathbf{v}_P + \mathbf{V} \cdot \mathbf{u}_P \tag{4.13}$$

For this definition to be meaningful, we must show that it is independent of the choice of point P: we evaluate (4.13) at a point Q

$$\mathbf{U} \cdot \mathbf{v}_Q + \mathbf{V} \cdot \mathbf{u}_Q = \mathbf{U} \cdot (\mathbf{v}_P + \mathbf{V} \times \mathbf{r}_{PQ}) + \mathbf{V} \cdot (\mathbf{u}_P + \mathbf{U} \times \mathbf{r}_{PQ}) = \mathbf{U} \cdot \mathbf{v}_P + \mathbf{V} \cdot \mathbf{u}_P$$

[3]The mapping $(\{\mathcal{U}\}, \{\mathcal{V}\}) \mapsto \{\mathcal{U}\} \cdot \{\mathcal{V}\}$ is bilinear and symmetric. However it is not positive definite. Hence, it does not define a true scalar product, and an associated norm cannot be defined.

The last equality stems from the fact that the triple scalar product $\mathbf{U} \cdot (\mathbf{V} \times \mathbf{r}_{PQ})$ is equal to $\mathbf{V} \cdot (\mathbf{r}_{PQ} \times \mathbf{U})$.
Note that the scalar invariant of a screw $\{\mathcal{V}\}$ is the scalar product $\frac{1}{2}\{\mathcal{V}\} \cdot \{\mathcal{V}\}$.

Example 4.8 Consider two screws $\{\mathcal{U}\}$ and $\{\mathcal{V}\}$ of non-zero and orthogonal resultants ($\mathbf{U} \cdot \mathbf{V} = 0$). Assume that their scalar product $\{\mathcal{U}\} \cdot \{\mathcal{V}\} = 0$ is zero. Show that their axes must necessarily intersect. Is the converse true? ■

Axis Δ_U of screw $\{\mathcal{U}\}$ is described as the set of points P such that $\mathbf{r}_{AP} = \mathbf{r}_{AI} + \lambda \mathbf{U}$ where λ is an arbitrary real scalar and where point I is given by $\mathbf{r}_{AI} = (\mathbf{U} \times \mathbf{u}_A)/\mathbf{U}^2$ (A arbitrarily chosen). Similarly axis Δ_V of screw $\{\mathcal{V}\}$ is the set of points Q given by $\mathbf{r}_{AQ} = \mathbf{r}_{AJ} + \mu \mathbf{V}$ with $\mathbf{r}_{AJ} = (\mathbf{V} \times \mathbf{v}_A)/\mathbf{V}^2$ (μ is scalar).
For these two axes to intersect there must exist two scalars λ and μ such that

$$\mathbf{r}_{IJ} = \lambda \mathbf{U} - \mu \mathbf{V}$$

Hence a necessary condition to obtain a solution can be stated as

$$\mathbf{r}_{IJ} \cdot (\mathbf{U} \times \mathbf{V}) = 0$$

To show that this condition is satisfied, we use the expressions of $\mathbf{r}_{AI}$ and $\mathbf{r}_{AJ}$:

$$\mathbf{r}_{IJ} \cdot (\mathbf{U} \times \mathbf{V}) = \frac{(\mathbf{V} \times \mathbf{v}_A) \cdot (\mathbf{U} \times \mathbf{V})}{\mathbf{V}^2} - \frac{(\mathbf{U} \times \mathbf{u}_A) \cdot (\mathbf{U} \times \mathbf{V})}{\mathbf{U}^2}$$

We can use the properties of the scalar and vector triple products to find that

$$(\mathbf{V} \times \mathbf{v}_A) \cdot (\mathbf{U} \times \mathbf{V}) = \mathbf{v}_A \cdot (\mathbf{V} \times (\mathbf{U} \times \mathbf{V})) = \mathbf{v}_A \cdot \left(\mathbf{V}^2 \mathbf{U} - (\mathbf{U} \cdot \mathbf{V})\mathbf{V}\right) = \mathbf{V}^2 (\mathbf{v}_A \cdot \mathbf{U})$$

after using $\mathbf{U} \cdot \mathbf{V} = 0$. Likewise we find $(\mathbf{U} \times \mathbf{u}_A) \cdot (\mathbf{U} \times \mathbf{V}) = -\mathbf{U}^2 (\mathbf{u}_A \cdot \mathbf{V})$. This leads to

$$\mathbf{r}_{IJ} \cdot (\mathbf{U} \times \mathbf{V}) = \mathbf{v}_A \cdot \mathbf{U} + \mathbf{u}_A \cdot \mathbf{V} = \{\mathcal{U}\} \cdot \{\mathcal{V}\} = 0$$

Hence the necessary condition to find an intersection point is equivalent to having $\{\mathcal{U}\} \cdot \{\mathcal{V}\} = 0$. If this condition is satisfied then the scalars λ and μ are found to be

$$\lambda = \frac{\mathbf{r}_{IJ} \cdot \mathbf{U}}{\mathbf{U}^2}, \qquad \mu = -\frac{\mathbf{r}_{IJ} \cdot \mathbf{V}}{\mathbf{V}^2}$$

■

4.8 A Special Class of Screws

We can generalize the notion of screw defined as the discrete sum of bound vectors (sliders) to the case of a continuous distribution of bound vectors over a region Σ of a Euclidean space $\mathcal{E}$. In practice, Σ represents a material system (a continuum). Given a vector field $P \in \Sigma \mapsto \mathbf{v}_P$ defined over Σ, consider the following field

$$A \in \mathcal{E} \mapsto \mathbf{M}_A = \int_\Sigma \mathbf{r}_{AP} \times \mathbf{v}_P \, dV \tag{4.14}$$

where dV is an infinitesimal volume element at point P. It is easy to show that equation (4.14) defines a field of moments, and hence a screw whose resultant is given by

$$\mathbf{R} = \int_\Sigma \mathbf{v}_P \, dV \tag{4.15}$$

Indeed, we have

$$\mathbf{M}_B = \int_\Sigma \mathbf{r}_{BP} \times \mathbf{v}_P dV = \int_\Sigma (\mathbf{r}_{BA} + \mathbf{r}_{AP}) \times \mathbf{v}_P dV = \mathbf{M}_A + \mathbf{R} \times \mathbf{r}_{AB}$$

This definition can also be extended to the case of vector fields defined over a surface or a curve of $\mathcal{E}$.
Several fundamental screws of this type will be defined in later chapters, Σ representing one or more rigid bodies.

4.9 Time-derivative of Screws

All vector fields and screws encountered in rigid body mechanics are time-dependent. Thus, it is relevant to examine their time-derivative. Consider screw $\{\mathcal{V}\}$ corresponding to time-dependent vector field $P \mapsto \mathbf{v}_P(t)$ satisfying the equation: $\mathbf{v}_Q = \mathbf{v}_P + \mathbf{V} \times \mathbf{r}_{PQ}$ for any two points P and Q *in motion* relative to a referential $\mathcal{E}$ (of origin O). By time-differentiation relative to $\mathcal{E}$, we obtain

$$\frac{d\mathbf{v}_Q}{dt} = \frac{d\mathbf{v}_P}{dt} + \frac{d\mathbf{V}}{dt} \times \mathbf{r}_{PQ} + \mathbf{V} \times \frac{d\mathbf{r}_{PQ}}{dt}$$

where all time-derivatives are performed relative to $\mathcal{E}$. After substituting $(d\mathbf{r}_{PQ}/dt) = (d\mathbf{r}_{OQ}/dt) - (d\mathbf{r}_{OP}/dt)$ we obtain

$$\left(\frac{d\mathbf{v}_Q}{dt} + \frac{d\mathbf{r}_{OQ}}{dt} \times \mathbf{V}\right) = \left(\frac{d\mathbf{v}_P}{dt} + \frac{d\mathbf{r}_{OP}}{dt} \times \mathbf{V}\right) + \frac{d\mathbf{V}}{dt} \times \mathbf{r}_{PQ}$$

This last result shows that the field $P \mapsto (d\mathbf{v}_P/dt) + (d\mathbf{r}_{OP}/dt) \times \mathbf{V}$ defines a screw of resultant $\frac{d\mathbf{V}}{dt}$.

Definition 4.9 The time-derivative of screw $\{\mathcal{V}\}$ relative to referential $\mathcal{E}$ of origin O, denoted $\{\frac{d}{dt}\mathcal{V}\}_\mathcal{E}$ is the screw defined by

$$\left\{\frac{d}{dt}\mathcal{V}\right\}_\mathcal{E} = \left\{ \begin{array}{c} \dfrac{d\mathbf{V}}{dt} \\ \\ \dfrac{d\mathbf{v}_A}{dt} + \dfrac{d\mathbf{r}_{OA}}{dt} \times \mathbf{V} \end{array} \right\}_A \tag{4.16}$$

where all derivatives are performed relative to $\mathcal{E}$.

4.10 Problems

Problem 4.1 Consider an equiprojective field $P \in \mathcal{E} \mapsto \mathbf{u}_P$, that, a field satisfying $\mathbf{r}_{PQ} \cdot \mathbf{u}_P = \mathbf{r}_{PQ} \cdot \mathbf{u}_Q$ for any two points P and Q. Let O be a given point of $\mathcal{E}$. Consider the linear operator $\mathcal{L} : \mathbf{X} = \mathbf{r}_{OP} \mapsto \mathbf{u}_P - \mathbf{u}_O$.

a. Show that $\mathcal{L}$ is skew-symmetric, that is, $\mathcal{L}(\mathbf{X}) \cdot \mathbf{Y} = -\mathbf{X} \cdot \mathcal{L}(\mathbf{Y})$.

b. Show that $\mathcal{L}$ is necessarily linear.

c. Conclude that there exists a vector $\mathbf{U}$ such that

$$\mathbf{u}_P = \mathbf{u}_O + \mathbf{U} \times \mathbf{r}_{OP}$$

Problem 4.2 Consider the unit cube $OABC$ $O'A'B'C'$. Denote by D the midpoint of side OA and by E the midpoint of side $A'B'$. Consider the three sliders

$$\{\mathcal{S}_1\} = \begin{Bmatrix} \mathbf{r}_{O'E} \\ \mathbf{0} \end{Bmatrix}_{O'}$$

$$\{\mathcal{S}_2\} = \begin{Bmatrix} \mathbf{r}_{CD} \\ \mathbf{0} \end{Bmatrix}_{C}$$

$$\{\mathcal{S}_3\} = \begin{Bmatrix} \mathbf{r}_{C'B} \\ \mathbf{0} \end{Bmatrix}_{C'}$$

Find the elements of screw

$$\{\mathcal{V}\} = \{\mathcal{S}_1\} + \{\mathcal{S}_2\} + \{\mathcal{S}_3\}$$

resolved at O.

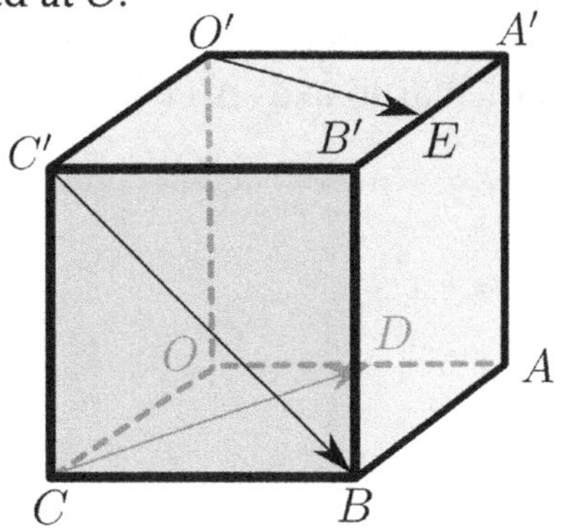

Problem 4.3 Consider four distinct points A, B, C, and D of a Euclidean space $\mathcal{E}$. Show that the vector field $P \in \mathcal{E} \mapsto \mathbf{v}_P = \mathbf{r}_{PA} \times \mathbf{r}_{PB} + \mathbf{r}_{PC} \times \mathbf{r}_{PD}$ defines a screw $\{\mathcal{V}\}$. Find its axis.

Problem 4.4 Consider four points $A(1,0,0)$, $B(-1,0,0)$, $C(0,1,0)$, and $D(0,0,1)$ forming a tetrahedron in a Euclidean space $\mathcal{E}(O, \hat{\mathbf{e}}_x, \hat{\mathbf{e}}_y, \hat{\mathbf{e}}_z)$. Denote by $\{\mathcal{U}\}$, $\{\mathcal{V}\}$, $\{\mathcal{W}\}$ and $\{\mathcal{X}\}$ the sliders corresponding to the bound vectors $(A, a\,\mathbf{r}_{AB})$, $(B, b\,\mathbf{r}_{BC})$, $(C, c\,\mathbf{r}_{CD})$ and $(D, d\,\mathbf{r}_{DA})$, respectively. The quantities a, b, c and d are non-zero scalars. Denote by $\{\mathcal{S}\} = \{\mathcal{U}\} + \{\mathcal{V}\} + \{\mathcal{W}\} + \{\mathcal{X}\}$.

a. Find the condition satisfied by the scalars (a, b, c, d) for screw $\{\mathcal{S}\}$ to be a slider.

b. Find the condition satisfied by the scalars (a, b, c, d) for screw $\{\mathcal{S}\}$ to be a couple.

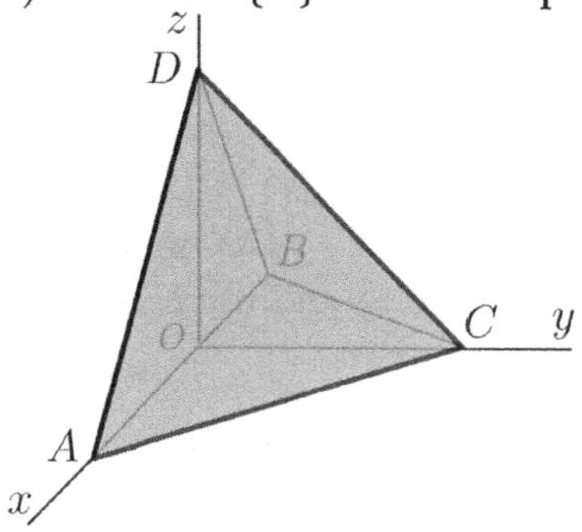

Problem 4.5 Given four points A, B, C, and D forming a regular tetrahedron, consider the sliders $\{\mathcal{U}\}$, $\{\mathcal{V}\}$, and $\{\mathcal{W}\}$ corresponding to the bound vectors $(A, \mathbf{r}_{AB})$, $(B, \mathbf{r}_{BC})$, and $(C, \mathbf{r}_{CD})$, respectively. Find the axis of screw $\{\mathcal{S}\} = \{\mathcal{U}\} + \{\mathcal{V}\} + \{\mathcal{W}\}$.

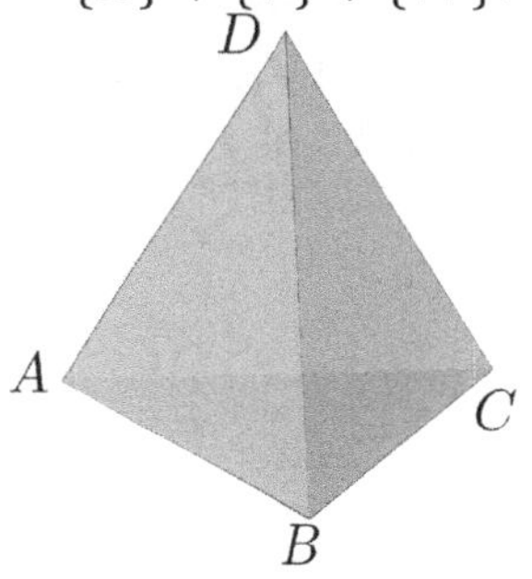

Problem 4.6 Consider the screw

$$\{\mathcal{V}\} = \begin{Bmatrix} \mathbf{V} \\ \mathbf{v}_P \end{Bmatrix}$$

defined over $\mathcal{E}$ and the vector field $P \in \mathcal{E} \mapsto \mathbf{u}_P = \hat{\mathbf{n}} \times (\hat{\mathbf{n}} \times \mathbf{v}_P)$ where $\hat{\mathbf{n}}$ is a given unit vector. Under what condition does this field define a screw?

Problem 4.7 Let $\mathcal{B}$ be a rigid body in motion in a referential $\mathcal{E}$.
a. Show that the velocity field $P \in \mathcal{B} \mapsto \mathbf{v}_{P/\mathcal{E}}$ defines a screw.
b. Show that the acceleration field $P \in \mathcal{B} \mapsto \mathbf{a}_{P/\mathcal{E}}$ does not define a screw.
c. Show that the field $P \in \mathcal{B} \mapsto \mathbf{a}_{P/\mathcal{E}} + \mathbf{v}_{P/\mathcal{E}} \times \boldsymbol{\omega}_{\mathcal{B}/\mathcal{E}}$ defines a screw.

Problem 4.8 — **Lie Algebra.** Consider in a Euclidean space $\mathcal{E}$ two screws $\{\mathcal{U}\}$ and $\{\mathcal{V}\}$ defined as

$$\{\mathcal{U}\} = \left\{ \begin{matrix} \mathbf{U} \\ \mathbf{u}_P \end{matrix} \right\}, \qquad \{\mathcal{V}\} = \left\{ \begin{matrix} \mathbf{V} \\ \mathbf{v}_P \end{matrix} \right\}$$

Consider the vector field

$$P \in \mathcal{E} \mapsto \mathbf{U} \times \mathbf{v}_P - \mathbf{V} \times \mathbf{u}_P$$

a. Show that this vector field is equiprojective, and hence defines a screw. Find the resultant of this screw. Denote this screw as $\{\mathcal{U}\} \times \{\mathcal{V}\}$.
b. Show that

$$\{\mathcal{U}\} \times \{\mathcal{V}\} \cdot \{\mathcal{U}\} = \{\mathcal{U}\} \times \{\mathcal{V}\} \cdot \{\mathcal{V}\} = 0$$

Then show that $\{\mathcal{U}\} \times \{\mathcal{V}\} = -\{\mathcal{V}\} \times \{\mathcal{U}\}$. Now justify the notation $\{\mathcal{U}\} \times \{\mathcal{V}\}$.
c. When $\{\mathcal{U}\} \times \{\mathcal{V}\}$ is not a couple, show that its axis is the common perpendicular to the axis Δ_U of $\{\mathcal{U}\}$ and the axis Δ_V of $\{\mathcal{V}\}$.
d. Show that

$$\{\mathcal{U}\} \times (\{\mathcal{V}\} \times \{\mathcal{W}\}) + \{\mathcal{V}\} \times (\{\mathcal{W}\} \times \{\mathcal{U}\}) + \{\mathcal{W}\} \times (\{\mathcal{U}\} \times \{\mathcal{V}\}) = \{0\}$$

e. Given two vectors $\mathbf{A}$ and $\mathbf{B}$ and two points A and B, show that the vector field defined as

$$P \in \mathcal{E} \mapsto \mathbf{A} \times (\mathbf{B} \times \mathbf{r}_{BP}) + (\mathbf{A} \times \mathbf{r}_{AP}) \times \mathbf{B}$$

defines a screw of the type $\{\mathcal{U}\} \times \{\mathcal{V}\}$. Then show that the axis of this screw, when it exists, is the common perpendicular line to lines $(A, \mathbf{A})$ and $(B, \mathbf{B})$.

Problem 4.9 Given two screws $\{\mathcal{U}\}$ and $\{\mathcal{V}\}$ whose resultants are not collinear, consider $\{\mathcal{W}\} = \{\mathcal{U}\} + \{\mathcal{V}\}$. Show that the common perpendicular to axes Δ_U and Δ_V intersect the axis Δ_W of $\{\mathcal{W}\}$ at a right angle.

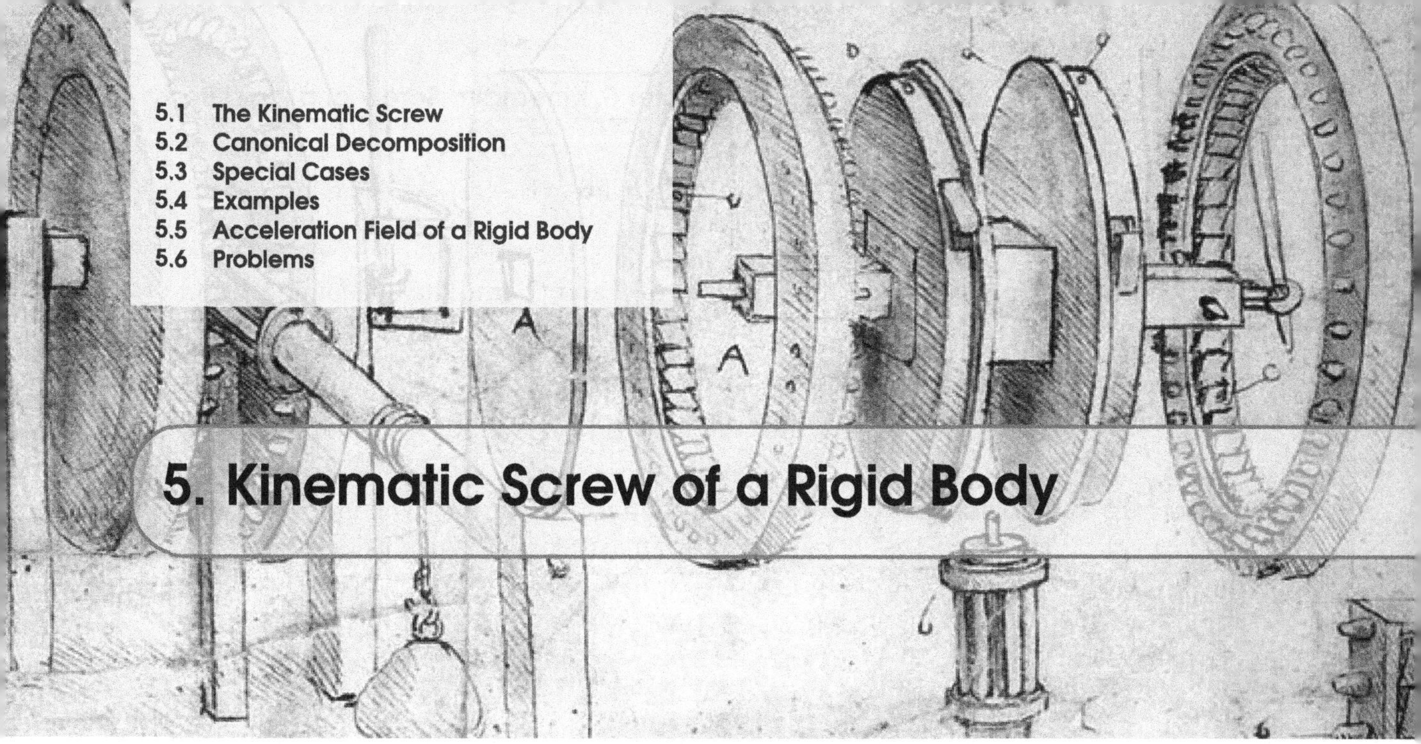

5. Kinematic Screw of a Rigid Body

THIS CHAPTER is devoted to the properties of the velocity field $P \in \mathcal{B} \mapsto \mathbf{v}_{P\in\mathcal{B}/\mathcal{A}}$ of a rigid body $\mathcal{B}$. Using the screw theory of Chapter 4, these properties stem from those of screws, since, as demonstrated in Section 3.6, the velocity field defines a screw, called *kinematic screw*. We shall show that, in general, a rigid body can always be characterized as being in *instantaneous helical* motion about an axis, called *instantaneous screw axis*, directed along the body's angular velocity. We shall also study the acceleration field $P \in \mathcal{B} \mapsto \mathbf{a}_{P\in\mathcal{B}/\mathcal{A}}$. Although it does not, in general, define a screw, it is still characterized by a simple structure.

5.1 The Kinematic Screw

Recall from Section 3.6 that the velocity field $P \in \mathcal{B} \mapsto \mathbf{v}_{P\in\mathcal{B}/\mathcal{A}}$ of a rigid body $\mathcal{B}$ in motion relative to rigid body (or referential) $\mathcal{A}$ satisfies the property $\mathbf{v}_{Q\in\mathcal{B}/\mathcal{A}} = \mathbf{v}_{P\in\mathcal{B}/\mathcal{A}} + \boldsymbol{\omega}_{\mathcal{B}/\mathcal{A}} \times \mathbf{r}_{PQ}$.

Definition 5.1 The velocity field $P \in \mathcal{B} \mapsto \mathbf{v}_{P\in\mathcal{B}/\mathcal{A}}$ defines a screw, called *kinematic screw* of $\mathcal{B}$ relative to $\mathcal{A}$. It is denoted as

$$\{\mathcal{V}_{\mathcal{B}/\mathcal{A}}\} = \begin{Bmatrix} \boldsymbol{\omega}_{\mathcal{B}/\mathcal{A}} \\ \mathbf{v}_{P\in\mathcal{B}/\mathcal{A}} \end{Bmatrix} \tag{5.1}$$

The "resultant" of screw $\{\mathcal{V}_{\mathcal{B}/\mathcal{A}}\}$ is angular velocity $\boldsymbol{\omega}_{\mathcal{B}/\mathcal{A}}$. Its "moment" about point P is velocity $\mathbf{v}_{P\in\mathcal{B}/\mathcal{A}}$. Recall that the velocity of a point P is denoted $\mathbf{v}_{P\in\mathcal{B}/\mathcal{A}}$ to ensure that the velocity P is viewed as that of a point of $\mathcal{B}$.

The properties stated below follow immediately from the general properties of screws.

Corollary 5.1 — Equiprojectivity. The velocity field $P \in \mathcal{B} \mapsto \mathbf{v}_{P\in\mathcal{B}/\mathcal{A}}$ is equiprojective, that is, $\mathbf{v}_{P\in\mathcal{B}/\mathcal{A}} \cdot \mathbf{r}_{PQ} = \mathbf{v}_{Q\in\mathcal{B}/\mathcal{A}} \cdot \mathbf{r}_{PQ}$ for any two points attached to $\mathcal{B}$.

This implies that the projections of the velocities of P and Q onto the line joining P and Q are identical.

Corollary 5.2 — Scalar Invariant. The scalar quantity $\boldsymbol{\omega}_{\mathcal{B}/\mathcal{A}} \cdot \mathbf{v}_{P\in\mathcal{B}/\mathcal{A}}$ is an invariant, that is, it is independent of the chosen point P of $\mathcal{B}$.

Corollary 5.3 — Instantaneous screw axis. At any instant in time, whenever $\boldsymbol{\omega}_{\mathcal{B}/\mathcal{A}} \neq \mathbf{0}$, the kinematic screw $\{\mathcal{V}_{\mathcal{B}/\mathcal{A}}\}$ is characterized by an axis $\Delta_{\mathcal{B}/\mathcal{A}}$ defined as the set of points whose velocity is collinear to the angular velocity $\boldsymbol{\omega}_{\mathcal{B}/\mathcal{A}}$. The velocity field takes the same values along $\Delta_{\mathcal{B}/\mathcal{A}}$, that is, $\mathbf{v}_{Q\in\Delta/\mathcal{A}} = p\,\boldsymbol{\omega}_{\mathcal{B}/\mathcal{A}}$, where the *pitch* p is the (invariant) parameter given by

$$p = \frac{\boldsymbol{\omega}_{\mathcal{B}/\mathcal{A}} \cdot \mathbf{v}_{P\in\mathcal{B}/\mathcal{A}}}{\omega^2_{\mathcal{B}/\mathcal{A}}}. \tag{5.2}$$

Axis $\Delta_{\mathcal{B}/\mathcal{A}}$ (or simply Δ) is referred to as the *instantaneous screw axis* of $\mathcal{B}$ (relative to $\mathcal{A}$).

Remark 1. The instantaneous screw axis Δ is directed along $\boldsymbol{\omega}_{\mathcal{B}/\mathcal{A}}$ and passes through point I whose instantaneous position is given by (given a point B whose velocity $\mathbf{v}_{B\in\mathcal{B}/\mathcal{A}}$ is known)

$$\mathbf{r}_{BI} = \frac{\boldsymbol{\omega}_{\mathcal{B}/\mathcal{A}} \times \mathbf{v}_{B\in\mathcal{B}/\mathcal{A}}}{\omega^2_{\mathcal{B}/\mathcal{A}}} \tag{5.3}$$

Remark 2. In general, *axis Δ is fixed neither in $\mathcal{A}$ nor $\mathcal{B}$*: indeed the direction of Δ is given by the angular velocity $\boldsymbol{\omega}_{\mathcal{B}/\mathcal{A}}$ which in general varies (in the same manner!) relative to both $\mathcal{A}$ and $\mathcal{B}$. Even in the case of $\boldsymbol{\omega}_{\mathcal{B}/\mathcal{A}}$ of constant direction (as in the case of planar motions), the position taken by axis Δ varies in both $\mathcal{A}$ and $\mathcal{B}$. This will be examined in more detail in Section 7.3.4 with the notion of fixed and moving *axodes*.

5.2 Canonical Decomposition

The velocity of any point of $\mathcal{B}$ can be written as the sum of two orthogonal vectors (see Figure 5.1):

$$\mathbf{v}_{P\in\mathcal{B}/\mathcal{A}} = p\,\boldsymbol{\omega}_{\mathcal{B}/\mathcal{A}} + \boldsymbol{\omega}_{\mathcal{B}/\mathcal{A}} \times \mathbf{r}_{HP} \tag{5.4}$$

where point H denotes the projection of P onto instantaneous screw axis Δ. Note that, in the decomposition of equation (5.4),

(i) the first vector is independent of P: it is the (instantaneous) velocity taken along the instantaneous screw axis Δ,

(ii) the second vector is the (instantaneous) velocity of a point in rotation about Δ: any point of Δ can be substituted for point H in equation (5.4).

Theorem 5.1 — Canonical Decomposition. The general motion of $\mathcal{B}$ relative to $\mathcal{A}$ can always be decomposed as the sum of a translation along and a rotation about its instantaneous screw axis, corresponding to the unique decomposition of the kinematic screw

$\{\mathcal{V}_{\mathcal{B}/\mathcal{A}}\}$ according to

$$\{\mathcal{V}_{\mathcal{B}/\mathcal{A}}\} = \underbrace{\begin{Bmatrix} \mathbf{0} \\ p\boldsymbol{\omega}_{\mathcal{B}/\mathcal{A}} \end{Bmatrix}}_{\text{translation along } \Delta} + \underbrace{\begin{Bmatrix} \boldsymbol{\omega}_{\mathcal{B}/\mathcal{A}} \\ \mathbf{0} \end{Bmatrix}_{H\in\Delta}}_{\text{rotation about } \Delta} \tag{5.5}$$

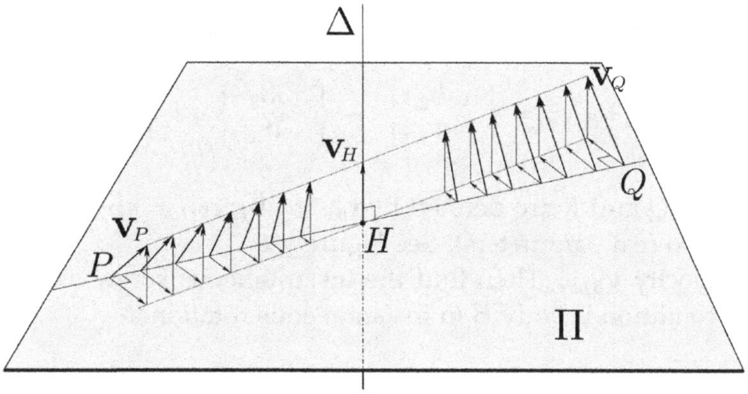

Figure 5.1 – *The velocity field in relation to the instantaneous screw axis.*

Remark 3. At any given time, the minimum speed $|\mathbf{v}_{P\in\mathcal{B}/\mathcal{A}}|$ of points of $\mathcal{B}$ is reached on the instantaneous screw axis Δ.

Remark 4. For points far away from Δ, the contribution of the term $p\,\boldsymbol{\omega}_{\mathcal{B}/\mathcal{A}}$ becomes negligible compared to the term $\boldsymbol{\omega}_{\mathcal{B}/\mathcal{A}} \times \mathbf{r}_{HP}$: far away from Δ, points of $\mathcal{B}$ are nearly in rotation about Δ, that is, $\mathbf{v}_{P\in\mathcal{B}/\mathcal{A}} \approx \boldsymbol{\omega}_{\mathcal{B}/\mathcal{A}} \times \mathbf{r}_{HP}$.

Remark 5. Figure 5.1 shows the distribution of velocity vectors of points along a line PP' of plane Π perpendicular to Δ. This distribution is invariant by translation along Δ. Furthermore, the velocity distribution along any line QQ' of plane Π obtained by rotation about Δ of line PP' is found by the same rotation of the distribution along PP'.

In conclusion, whenever $\boldsymbol{\omega}_{\mathcal{B}/\mathcal{A}} \neq \mathbf{0}$, rigid body $\mathcal{B}$ appears to be in **instantaneous helical motion about axis** Δ relative to $\mathcal{A}$. This characterization of the motion of $\mathcal{B}$ only applies for its velocity field. The acceleration field $P \in \mathcal{B} \mapsto \mathbf{a}_{P\in\mathcal{B}/\mathcal{A}}$ of $\mathcal{B}$ is not that of a helical motion about Δ.

5.3 Special Cases

We can three special cases of "instantaneous" motion:

Case 1. If, at a given time, $\boldsymbol{\omega}_{\mathcal{B}/\mathcal{A}} = \mathbf{0}$ and there exists a point of $\mathcal{B}$ with zero velocity, then $\mathcal{B}$ is *instantaneously at rest* relative to $\mathcal{A}$: $\mathbf{v}_{P\in\mathcal{B}/\mathcal{A}} = \mathbf{0}$ for all P. Keep in mind that the acceleration field of $\mathcal{B}$ may not be zero at this instant.

Case 2. If, at a given time, $\boldsymbol{\omega}_{\mathcal{B}/\mathcal{A}} = \mathbf{0}$ and there exists a point of $\mathcal{B}$ with non-zero velocity, then the velocity field of $\mathcal{B}$ is that of an *instantaneous translational motion* along Δ.

Case 3. If, at a given time, $\boldsymbol{\omega}_{\mathcal{B}/\mathcal{A}}$ is not zero, yet the pitch p is zero, then the velocity field of $\mathcal{B}$ is that of an *instantaneous rotational motion* about axis $\Delta = (I, \boldsymbol{\omega}_{\mathcal{B}/\mathcal{A}})$. Point I is defined by equation (5.3). In this case, axis Δ is referred to as the *instantaneous axis of rotation* of $\mathcal{B}$. Conversely, if there exists a point I such that $\mathbf{v}_{I\in\mathcal{B}/\mathcal{A}} = \mathbf{0}$[1], then I is necessarily located on the instantaneous axis of rotation of $\mathcal{B}$.

5.4 Examples

Example 5.1 A rigid body $\mathcal{B}(B, \hat{\mathbf{b}}_1, \hat{\mathbf{b}}_2, \hat{\mathbf{b}}_3)$ is in motion relative to a referential $\mathcal{E}$. At a particular instant in time, its kinematic screw can be written in the following form

$$\{\mathcal{V}_{\mathcal{B}/\mathcal{E}}\} = \begin{Bmatrix} \omega\hat{\mathbf{b}}_2 \\ \mathbf{0} \end{Bmatrix}_P + \begin{Bmatrix} \omega\hat{\mathbf{b}}_3 \\ \mathbf{0} \end{Bmatrix}_Q + \begin{Bmatrix} \Omega\hat{\mathbf{b}}_1 \\ \mathbf{0} \end{Bmatrix}_R$$

where points P, Q and R are defined by $\mathbf{r}_{BP} = a\hat{\mathbf{b}}_1$, $\mathbf{r}_{BQ} = a\hat{\mathbf{b}}_2$ and $\mathbf{r}_{BR} = a\hat{\mathbf{b}}_3$ (ω and Ω are two non-zero real parameters). See Figure 5.2.

Find the velocity $\mathbf{v}_{B/\mathcal{E}}$. Then find the instantaneous screw axis of $\mathcal{B}$ at this instant. Under what condition is body $\mathcal{B}$ in instantaneous rotation? ■

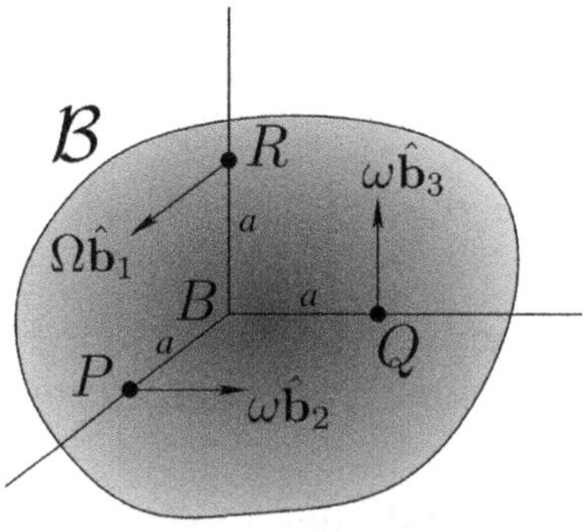

Figure 5.2

The velocity of point B is found by summing the three contributions to $\{\mathcal{V}_{\mathcal{B}/\mathcal{E}}\}$

$$\{\mathcal{V}_{\mathcal{B}/\mathcal{E}}\} = \begin{Bmatrix} \omega\hat{\mathbf{b}}_2 + \omega\hat{\mathbf{b}}_3 + \Omega\hat{\mathbf{b}}_1 \\ \omega\hat{\mathbf{b}}_2 \times \mathbf{r}_{PB} + \omega\hat{\mathbf{b}}_3 \times \mathbf{r}_{QB} + \Omega\hat{\mathbf{b}}_1 \times \mathbf{r}_{RB} \end{Bmatrix}_B$$

This gives

$$\mathbf{v}_{B/\mathcal{E}} = a\omega(\hat{\mathbf{b}}_1 + \hat{\mathbf{b}}_3) + a\Omega\hat{\mathbf{b}}_2$$

The instantaneous screw axis Δ of $\mathcal{B}$ is directed along $\boldsymbol{\omega}_{\mathcal{B}/\mathcal{E}}$ and passes through the point I given by

$$\mathbf{r}_{BI} = \frac{\boldsymbol{\omega}_{\mathcal{B}/\mathcal{E}} \times \mathbf{v}_{B/\mathcal{E}}}{\omega^2_{\mathcal{B}/\mathcal{E}}} = a\frac{(\omega^2 - \omega\Omega)(\hat{\mathbf{b}}_1 + \hat{\mathbf{b}}_2) + (\Omega^2 - \omega^2)\hat{\mathbf{b}}_3}{2\omega^2 + \Omega^2}$$

All points of Δ have the same velocity $p\boldsymbol{\omega}_{\mathcal{B}/\mathcal{E}}$ where the pitch p is given by

$$p = \frac{\boldsymbol{\omega}_{\mathcal{B}/\mathcal{E}} \cdot \mathbf{v}_{B/\mathcal{E}}}{\omega^2_{\mathcal{B}/\mathcal{E}}} = a\frac{\omega^2 + 2\omega\Omega}{2\omega^2 + \Omega^2}$$

which becomes zero when the condition $\omega = -2\Omega$ is satisfied. In this case, body $\mathcal{B}$ is in instantaneous rotation about axis Δ. ■

[1]Note here that the notation $\mathbf{v}_{I\in\mathcal{B}/\mathcal{A}}$ is essential to distinguish this velocity from $\mathbf{v}_{I/\mathcal{A}}$.

Example 5.2 Consider two rigid bodies $\mathcal{A}$ and $\mathcal{B}$ in rotation about parallel axes $(A, \hat{\mathbf{e}}_3)$ and $(B, \hat{\mathbf{e}}_3)$, respectively, relative to a referential $\mathcal{E}(O, \hat{\mathbf{e}}_1, \hat{\mathbf{e}}_2, \hat{\mathbf{e}}_3)$. See Figure 5.3. Denote by $\boldsymbol{\omega}_{\mathcal{A}/\mathcal{E}} = \omega_A \hat{\mathbf{e}}_3$ and $\boldsymbol{\omega}_{\mathcal{B}/\mathcal{E}} = \omega_B \hat{\mathbf{e}}_3$ their angular velocities. The position of A and B are given by $\mathbf{r}_{OA} = a\hat{\mathbf{e}}_1$ and $\mathbf{r}_{OB} = b\hat{\mathbf{e}}_2$. Assume $\omega_B \neq \omega_A$.

a. Find the kinematic screw $\{\mathcal{V}_{\mathcal{B}/\mathcal{A}}\}$.

b. Show that the motion $\mathcal{B}/\mathcal{A}$ admits an instantaneous axis of rotation Δ, that is,

$$\{\mathcal{V}_{\mathcal{B}/\mathcal{A}}\} = \left\{ \begin{array}{c} \boldsymbol{\omega}_{\mathcal{B}/\mathcal{A}} \\ \mathbf{0} \end{array} \right\}_{I \in \Delta}$$

Find the location of Δ by determining the point I which lies in plane $(O, \hat{\mathbf{e}}_1, \hat{\mathbf{e}}_2)$. ∎

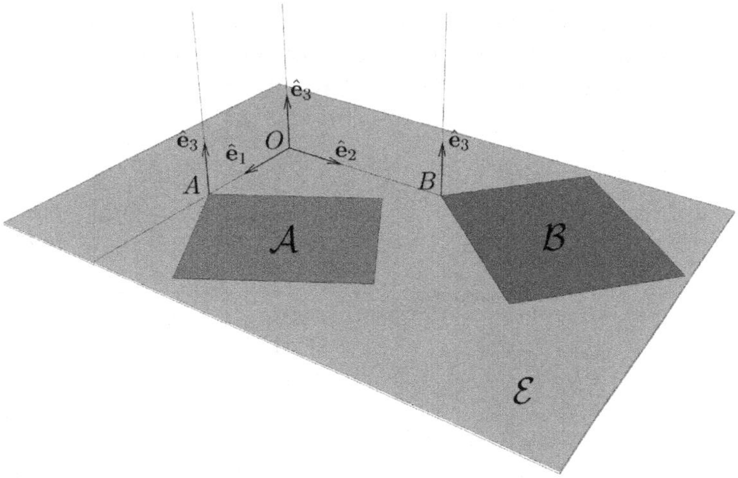

Figure 5.3

a. To find $\{\mathcal{V}_{\mathcal{B}/\mathcal{A}}\}$, we need to find $\boldsymbol{\omega}_{\mathcal{B}/\mathcal{A}}$ and the velocity $\mathbf{v}_{B/\mathcal{A}}$. First we find

$$\boldsymbol{\omega}_{\mathcal{B}/\mathcal{A}} = \boldsymbol{\omega}_{\mathcal{B}/\mathcal{E}} + \boldsymbol{\omega}_{\mathcal{E}/\mathcal{A}} = \boldsymbol{\omega}_{\mathcal{B}/\mathcal{E}} - \boldsymbol{\omega}_{\mathcal{A}/\mathcal{E}} = (\omega_B - \omega_A)\hat{\mathbf{e}}_3$$

Then we find $\mathbf{v}_{B/\mathcal{A}}$ as follows

$$\mathbf{v}_{B/\mathcal{A}} = \left(\frac{d\mathbf{r}_{AB}}{dt}\right)_{\mathcal{A}} = b\left(\frac{d\hat{\mathbf{e}}_2}{dt}\right)_{\mathcal{A}} - a\left(\frac{d\hat{\mathbf{e}}_1}{dt}\right)_{\mathcal{A}} = -b\omega_A \hat{\mathbf{e}}_3 \times \hat{\mathbf{e}}_2 + a\omega_A \hat{\mathbf{e}}_3 \times \hat{\mathbf{e}}_1$$

where we have used $\boldsymbol{\omega}_{\mathcal{E}/\mathcal{A}} = -\boldsymbol{\omega}_{\mathcal{A}/\mathcal{E}} = -\omega_A \hat{\mathbf{e}}_3$. Finally we obtain

$$\mathbf{v}_{B/\mathcal{A}} = \omega_A (a\hat{\mathbf{e}}_2 + b\hat{\mathbf{e}}_1)$$

We summarize the kinematics for $\mathcal{B}$ relative to $\mathcal{A}$ by writing the expression

$$\{\mathcal{V}_{\mathcal{B}/\mathcal{A}}\} = \left\{ \begin{array}{c} (\omega_B - \omega_A)\hat{\mathbf{e}}_3 \\ \omega_A (a\hat{\mathbf{e}}_2 + b\hat{\mathbf{e}}_1) \end{array} \right\}_B$$

b. We first note that the pitch associated with motion $\mathcal{B}/\mathcal{A}$ is $p = 0$ since we have $\boldsymbol{\omega}_{\mathcal{B}/\mathcal{A}} \cdot \mathbf{v}_{B/\mathcal{A}} = 0$. Hence, this motion admits an instantaneous axis of rotation Δ. To find the point I of Δ lying in the plane $(O, \hat{\mathbf{e}}_1, \hat{\mathbf{e}}_2)$, we need to solve for vector $\mathbf{r}_{BI}$ solution of

$$\mathbf{v}_{I \in \mathcal{B}/\mathcal{A}} = \mathbf{0} = \omega_A (a\hat{\mathbf{e}}_2 + b\hat{\mathbf{e}}_1) + (\omega_B - \omega_A)\hat{\mathbf{e}}_3 \times \mathbf{r}_{BI}$$

We then take the cross-product of this equation with $\hat{\mathbf{e}}_3$ to find:

$$\omega_A \hat{\mathbf{e}}_3 \times (a\hat{\mathbf{e}}_2 + b\hat{\mathbf{e}}_1) + (\omega_B - \omega_A)\hat{\mathbf{e}}_3 \times (\hat{\mathbf{e}}_3 \times \mathbf{r}_{BI}) = \mathbf{0}$$

which leads to (using $\hat{\mathbf{e}}_3 \times (\hat{\mathbf{e}}_3 \times \mathbf{r}_{BI}) = (\hat{\mathbf{e}}_3 \cdot \mathbf{r}_{BI})\hat{\mathbf{e}}_3 - \mathbf{r}_{BI} = -\mathbf{r}_{BI}$ and $\hat{\mathbf{e}}_3 \cdot \mathbf{r}_{BI} = 0$):

$$\mathbf{r}_{BI} = \frac{\omega_A}{\omega_B - \omega_A}(b\hat{\mathbf{e}}_2 - a\hat{\mathbf{e}}_1)$$

This result shows that point I lies on line AB (if $\omega_B < \omega_A$, I lies between A and B). Note that if ω_A and ω_B are constant, axis Δ is fixed relative to $\mathcal{E}$. Hence, Δ is fixed neither in $\mathcal{A}$ nor $\mathcal{B}$, as expected. ■

Example 5.3 Figure 5.4 shows a sketch of an amusement park ride known as the Afterburner (designed by KMG). It consists of a pendulum arm $\mathcal{A}$ supported by two A-frames fixed in a referential $\mathcal{E}$. The arm can rotate about a fixed horizontal axis. A rotating hub $\mathcal{B}$ is connected at the end of the arm: it supports six gondolas and can seat 24 passengers. The hub is free to rotate about the axis of arm $\mathcal{A}$.

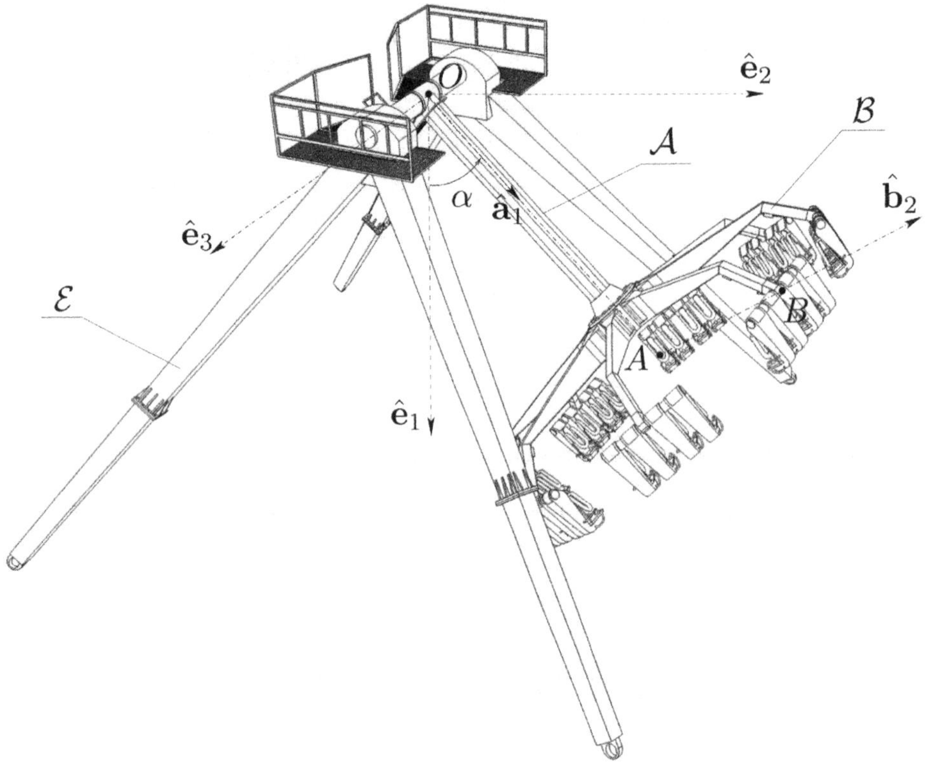

Figure 5.4

Referential $\mathcal{E}$ is defined as $(O, \hat{\mathbf{e}}_1, \hat{\mathbf{e}}_2, \hat{\mathbf{e}}_3)$ where unit vector $\hat{\mathbf{e}}_3$ is chosen as the direction of the axis of rotation of the arm, and $\hat{\mathbf{e}}_1$ is directed downward along the vertical. The arm $\mathcal{A}$ is defined as $(O, \hat{\mathbf{a}}_1, \hat{\mathbf{a}}_2, \hat{\mathbf{a}}_3 = \hat{\mathbf{e}}_3)$. Point A is located on the axis of the arm with $\mathbf{r}_{OA} = a\hat{\mathbf{a}}_1$. Finally the hub $\mathcal{B}$ is defined as $(A, \hat{\mathbf{b}}_1 = \hat{\mathbf{a}}_1, \hat{\mathbf{b}}_2, \hat{\mathbf{b}}_3)$. The location of a typical passenger is defined by point B with $\mathbf{r}_{AB} = R\hat{\mathbf{b}}_2$. Both a and R are constant lengths. The position of referentials $\mathcal{A}$ and $\mathcal{B}$ is defined by the rotation $\mathcal{R}_{\alpha,\hat{\mathbf{e}}_3}$ of angle $\alpha(t)$ which basis $(\hat{\mathbf{e}}_1, \hat{\mathbf{e}}_2, \hat{\mathbf{e}}_3)$ to basis $(\hat{\mathbf{a}}_1, \hat{\mathbf{a}}_2, \hat{\mathbf{a}}_3)$, followed by the rotation $\mathcal{R}_{\beta,\hat{\mathbf{a}}_1}$ of angle $\beta(t)$ which basis $(\hat{\mathbf{a}}_1, \hat{\mathbf{a}}_2, \hat{\mathbf{a}}_3)$ to basis $(\hat{\mathbf{b}}_1, \hat{\mathbf{b}}_2, \hat{\mathbf{b}}_3)$.

a. Sketch the rotation diagrams between bases $(\hat{\mathbf{e}}_1, \hat{\mathbf{e}}_2, \hat{\mathbf{e}}_3)$, $(\hat{\mathbf{a}}_1, \hat{\mathbf{a}}_2, \hat{\mathbf{a}}_3)$ and $(\hat{\mathbf{b}}_1, \hat{\mathbf{b}}_2, \hat{\mathbf{b}}_3)$. Then find the corresponding angular velocities $\boldsymbol{\omega}_{\mathcal{A}/\mathcal{E}}$ and $\boldsymbol{\omega}_{\mathcal{B}/\mathcal{E}}$.

b. Find expressions of the kinematic screws $\{\mathcal{V}_{\mathcal{A}/\mathcal{E}}\}$ and $\{\mathcal{V}_{\mathcal{B}/\mathcal{E}}\}$. Then find the velocity of point B.

c. Find component $\hat{\mathbf{e}}_1 \cdot \mathbf{a}_{B/\mathcal{E}}$ of the acceleration of B. ■

a. The rotation diagrams are defined from the following sequence of rotations

$$(\hat{\mathbf{e}}_1, \hat{\mathbf{e}}_2, \hat{\mathbf{e}}_3) \xrightarrow{\mathcal{R}_{\alpha,\hat{\mathbf{e}}_3}} (\hat{\mathbf{a}}_1, \hat{\mathbf{a}}_2, \hat{\mathbf{a}}_3 = \hat{\mathbf{e}}_3) \xrightarrow{\mathcal{R}_{\beta,\hat{\mathbf{a}}_1}} (\hat{\mathbf{b}}_1 = \hat{\mathbf{a}}_1, \hat{\mathbf{b}}_2, \hat{\mathbf{b}}_3)$$

from which we deduce the angular velocities $\boldsymbol{\omega}_{\mathcal{A}/\mathcal{E}}$ and $\boldsymbol{\omega}_{\mathcal{B}/\mathcal{E}}$:

$$\boldsymbol{\omega}_{\mathcal{A}/\mathcal{E}} = \dot{\alpha}\hat{\mathbf{e}}_3, \quad \boldsymbol{\omega}_{\mathcal{B}/\mathcal{E}} = \boldsymbol{\omega}_{\mathcal{B}/\mathcal{A}} + \boldsymbol{\omega}_{\mathcal{A}/\mathcal{E}} = \dot{\beta}\hat{\mathbf{a}}_1 + \dot{\alpha}\hat{\mathbf{e}}_3$$

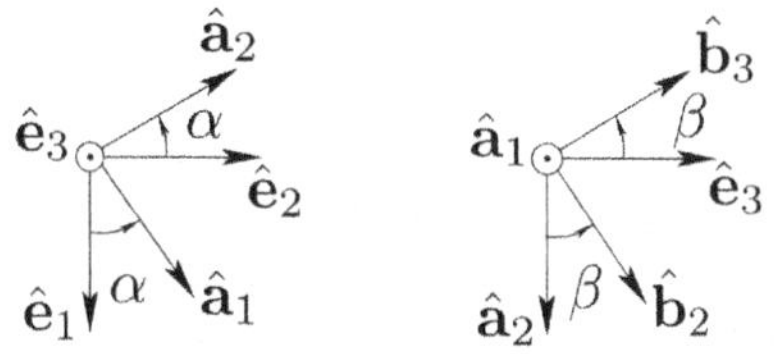

b. To find the expression of kinematic screw $\{\mathcal{V}_{\mathcal{A}/\mathcal{E}}\}$, we need angular velocity $\boldsymbol{\omega}_{\mathcal{A}/\mathcal{E}}$ and the velocity of a point attached to $\mathcal{A}$. Choosing point O we obtain

$$\{\mathcal{V}_{\mathcal{A}/\mathcal{E}}\} = \begin{Bmatrix} \dot{\alpha}\hat{\mathbf{e}}_3 \\ \mathbf{0} \end{Bmatrix}_O$$

representative a body in rotation. Similarly, to find the expression of kinematic screw $\{\mathcal{V}_{\mathcal{B}/\mathcal{E}}\}$, we need the velocity of a point attached to $\mathcal{B}$: choosing point A we obtain

$$\{\mathcal{V}_{\mathcal{B}/\mathcal{E}}\} = \begin{Bmatrix} \dot{\alpha}\hat{\mathbf{e}}_3 + \dot{\beta}\hat{\mathbf{a}}_1 \\ a\dot{\alpha}\hat{\mathbf{a}}_2 \end{Bmatrix}_A$$

Using this expression, we can find $\mathbf{v}_{B/\mathcal{E}}$ since B is another point attached to $\mathcal{B}$:

$$\mathbf{v}_{B/\mathcal{E}} = \mathbf{v}_{B\in\mathcal{B}/\mathcal{E}} = a\dot{\alpha}\hat{\mathbf{a}}_2 + (\dot{\alpha}\hat{\mathbf{e}}_3 + \dot{\beta}\hat{\mathbf{a}}_1) \times R\hat{\mathbf{b}}_2 = a\dot{\alpha}\hat{\mathbf{a}}_2 + R(\dot{\beta}\hat{\mathbf{b}}_3 - \dot{\alpha}\cos\beta\hat{\mathbf{a}}_1)$$

c. We can find the component $\hat{\mathbf{e}}_1$-component of $\mathbf{a}_{B/\mathcal{E}}$ without finding the complete expression of $\mathbf{a}_{B/\mathcal{E}}$ as follows

$$\hat{\mathbf{e}}_1 \cdot \mathbf{a}_{B/\mathcal{E}} = \frac{d}{dt}(\hat{\mathbf{e}}_1 \cdot \mathbf{v}_{B/\mathcal{E}})$$

where $\hat{\mathbf{e}}_1 \cdot \mathbf{v}_{B/\mathcal{E}}$ is obtained from the expression of $\mathbf{v}_{B/\mathcal{E}}$:

$$\hat{\mathbf{e}}_1 \cdot \mathbf{v}_{B/\mathcal{E}} = -a\dot{\alpha}\sin\alpha + R\dot{\beta}\sin\alpha\sin\beta - R\dot{\alpha}\cos\beta\cos\alpha$$

This gives

$$\hat{\mathbf{e}}_1 \cdot \mathbf{a}_{B/\mathcal{E}} = \frac{d}{dt}(-a\dot{\alpha}\sin\alpha + R\dot{\beta}\sin\alpha\sin\beta - R\dot{\alpha}\cos\beta\cos\alpha)$$

■

Example 5.4 Consider the motion $\mathcal{A}$ relative to $\mathcal{E}$ of Example 3.5.

a. Determine the kinematic screw of $\mathcal{A}$ relative to $\mathcal{E}$. Show that $\{\mathcal{V}_{\mathcal{A}/\mathcal{E}}\}$ can be written as the sum of two sliders whose axes are respectively $(O, \hat{\mathbf{z}})$ and a line parallel to line $(A, \hat{\mathbf{k}})$. Conclude that, in general, $\mathcal{A}$ cannot be in instantaneous rotation relative to $\mathcal{E}$.

b. Determine the instantaneous screw axis Δ of $\mathcal{A}$ and the corresponding velocity taken on Δ. ■

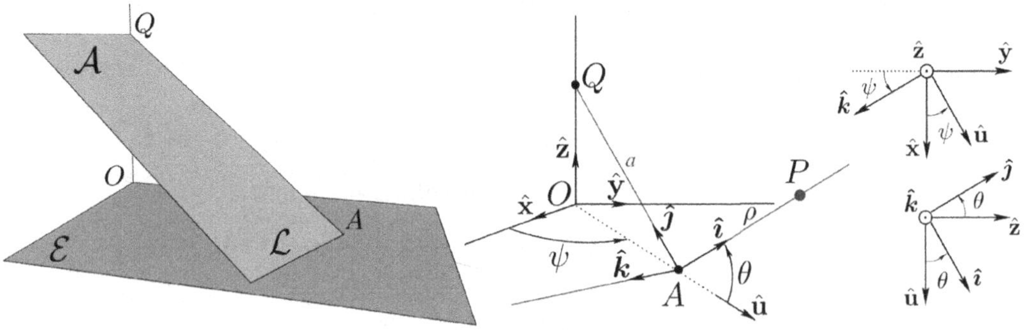

a. With the expressions of the angular velocity $\boldsymbol{\omega}_{\mathcal{A}/\mathcal{E}} = \dot{\psi}\hat{\mathbf{z}} + \dot{\theta}\hat{\mathbf{k}}$ and of the velocity $\mathbf{v}_{A/\mathcal{E}} = a\dot{\theta}\cos\theta\hat{\mathbf{u}} - a\dot{\psi}\sin\theta\hat{\mathbf{k}}$ of point A found in Example 3.5, we find the expression of kinematic screw $\{\mathcal{V}_{\mathcal{A}/\mathcal{E}}\}$ as follows

$$\{\mathcal{V}_{\mathcal{A}/\mathcal{E}}\} = \left\{ \begin{array}{c} \dot{\psi}\hat{\mathbf{z}} + \dot{\theta}\hat{\mathbf{k}} \\ a\dot{\theta}\cos\theta\hat{\mathbf{u}} - a\dot{\psi}\sin\theta\hat{\mathbf{k}} \end{array} \right\}_A = \left\{ \begin{array}{c} \dot{\psi}\hat{\mathbf{z}} + \dot{\theta}\hat{\mathbf{k}} \\ -a\dot{\theta}\sin\theta\hat{\mathbf{z}} \end{array} \right\}_Q$$

We can then write $\{\mathcal{V}_{\mathcal{A}/\mathcal{E}}\}$ as the following sum:

$$\{\mathcal{V}_{\mathcal{A}/\mathcal{E}}\} = \left\{ \begin{array}{c} \dot{\psi}\hat{\mathbf{z}} \\ \mathbf{0} \end{array} \right\}_Q + \left\{ \begin{array}{c} \dot{\theta}\hat{\mathbf{k}} \\ -a\dot{\theta}\sin\theta\hat{\mathbf{z}} \end{array} \right\}_Q = \left\{ \begin{array}{c} \dot{\psi}\hat{\mathbf{z}} \\ \mathbf{0} \end{array} \right\}_O + \left\{ \begin{array}{c} \dot{\theta}\hat{\mathbf{k}} \\ \mathbf{0} \end{array} \right\}_B$$

where the location of point B is yet to be found. If B is on the axis of a slider, it must satisfy

$$-a\dot{\theta}\sin\theta\hat{\mathbf{z}} + \dot{\theta}\hat{\mathbf{k}} \times \mathbf{r}_{QB} = \mathbf{0}$$

We seek a particular solution $\mathbf{r}_{QB}$ perpendicular to $\hat{\mathbf{k}}$: we take the cross-product of the last equation with $\hat{\mathbf{k}}$ to find the location of point B:

$$\mathbf{r}_{QB} = a\sin\theta\hat{\mathbf{u}}$$

Hence B is located at the intersection of lines $(Q, \hat{\mathbf{u}})$ and $(A, \hat{\mathbf{z}})$. We have thus decomposed the motion of $\mathcal{A}$ relative to $\mathcal{E}$ as the sum of two instantaneous rotations whose axes are respectively line $(O, \hat{\mathbf{z}})$ and line $(B, \hat{\mathbf{k}})$. We can verify that, in general, these axes are neither parallel nor intersecting: the sum of these two sliders is not a slider. The motion $\mathcal{A}$ relative to $\mathcal{E}$ is not in general an instantaneous rotation (unless $\theta = 0, \pi$).

b. The instantaneous screw axis Δ of $\mathcal{A}$ relative to $\mathcal{E}$ is the line defined as the set of points $\{\mathbf{r}_{QR} + \lambda\boldsymbol{\omega}_{\mathcal{A}/\mathcal{E}}\}$ where λ is an arbitrary scalar, and where point R is located according to

$$\mathbf{r}_{QR} = \frac{a\dot{\theta}^2\sin\theta}{\dot{\theta}^2 + \dot{\psi}^2}\hat{\mathbf{u}}$$

The velocity of points on Δ is $p\boldsymbol{\omega}_{\mathcal{A}/\mathcal{E}}$ with pitch p given by $p = -a\dot{\theta}\dot{\psi}\sin\theta/(\dot{\theta}^2 + \dot{\psi}^2)$. ■

5.5 Acceleration Field of a Rigid Body

We now seek to relate the accelerations of points of rigid body $\mathcal{B}$ in motion relative to referential $\mathcal{A}$ as we did for velocities. For any two points P and Q fixed in $\mathcal{B}$ at all times, we have according to the kinematic screw formula

$$\mathbf{v}_{Q/\mathcal{A}} = \mathbf{v}_{P/\mathcal{A}} + \boldsymbol{\omega}_{\mathcal{B}/\mathcal{A}} \times \mathbf{r}_{PQ}.$$

Then, by time-differentiation relative to $\mathcal{A}$, we obtain

$$\mathbf{a}_{Q/\mathcal{A}} = \left(\frac{d}{dt}\mathbf{v}_{Q/\mathcal{A}}\right)_{\mathcal{A}} = \mathbf{a}_{P/\mathcal{A}} + \boldsymbol{\alpha}_{\mathcal{B}/\mathcal{A}} \times \mathbf{r}_{PQ} + \boldsymbol{\omega}_{\mathcal{B}/\mathcal{A}} \times \left(\frac{d}{dt}\mathbf{r}_{PQ}\right)_{\mathcal{A}}.$$

But $(d\mathbf{r}_{PQ}/dt)_{\mathcal{A}} = \mathbf{v}_{Q/\mathcal{A}} - \mathbf{v}_{P/\mathcal{A}} = \boldsymbol{\omega}_{\mathcal{B}/\mathcal{A}} \times \mathbf{r}_{PQ}$. Finally we obtain the formula governing the accelerations of any two points attached to $\mathcal{B}$:

Theorem 5.2 The acceleration field $P \in \mathcal{B} \mapsto \mathbf{a}_{P/\mathcal{A}}$ of points attached to $\mathcal{B}$ in motion relative to $\mathcal{A}$ satisfies

$$\mathbf{a}_{Q/\mathcal{A}} = \mathbf{a}_{P/\mathcal{A}} + \boldsymbol{\alpha}_{\mathcal{B}/\mathcal{A}} \times \mathbf{r}_{PQ} + \boldsymbol{\omega}_{\mathcal{B}/\mathcal{A}} \times (\boldsymbol{\omega}_{\mathcal{B}/\mathcal{A}} \times \mathbf{r}_{PQ}) \tag{5.6}$$

for any two points P and Q attached to $\mathcal{B}$.

The presence of the last term $\boldsymbol{\omega}_{\mathcal{B}/\mathcal{A}} \times (\boldsymbol{\omega}_{\mathcal{B}/\mathcal{A}} \times \mathbf{r}_{PQ})$ in equation (5.6) shows that *the acceleration field $P \in \mathcal{B} \mapsto \mathbf{a}_{P/\mathcal{A}}$ of $\mathcal{B}$ relative to $\mathcal{A}$ does not define a screw.*

Remark 6. We can find the time-derivative of $\{\mathcal{V}_{\mathcal{B}/\mathcal{A}}\}$ according to the definition of Section 4.9:

$$\left\{\frac{d}{dt}\mathcal{V}_{\mathcal{B}/\mathcal{A}}\right\}_{\mathcal{A}} = \left\{\begin{matrix} \boldsymbol{\alpha}_{\mathcal{B}/\mathcal{A}} \\ \mathbf{a}_{P/\mathcal{A}} + \mathbf{v}_{P/\mathcal{A}} \times \boldsymbol{\omega}_{\mathcal{B}/\mathcal{A}} \end{matrix}\right\}_P$$

This shows that the field $P \in \mathcal{B} \mapsto \mathbf{a}_{P/\mathcal{A}} + \mathbf{v}_{P/\mathcal{A}} \times \boldsymbol{\omega}_{\mathcal{B}/\mathcal{A}}$ defines a screw. This fact can be used to formulate interesting properties of the acceleration field.

Remark 7. To emphasize that P is a point attached to $\mathcal{B}$, its acceleration may be denoted as $\mathbf{a}_{P\in\mathcal{B}/\mathcal{A}}$. We may also want to find the acceleration of a point P attached to $\mathcal{B}$ only instantaneously: in that case, acceleration $\mathbf{a}_{P\in\mathcal{B}/\mathcal{A}}$ cannot be determined as the time-derivative $(d\mathbf{v}_{P\in\mathcal{B}/\mathcal{A}}/dt)_{\mathcal{A}}$, but rather must be found by using formula (5.6) (by relating it to the known acceleration of a point, say B, attached to $\mathcal{B}$):

$$\mathbf{a}_{P\in\mathcal{B}/\mathcal{A}} = \mathbf{a}_{B/\mathcal{A}} + \boldsymbol{\alpha}_{\mathcal{B}/\mathcal{A}} \times \mathbf{r}_{BP} + \boldsymbol{\omega}_{\mathcal{B}/\mathcal{A}} \times (\boldsymbol{\omega}_{\mathcal{B}/\mathcal{A}} \times \mathbf{r}_{BP})$$

The following example shows that the notation $\mathbf{a}_{P\in\mathcal{B}/\mathcal{A}}$ is vital whenever P is considered a point of $\mathcal{B}$ only in an instantaneous way: in this case $\mathbf{a}_{P\in\mathcal{B}/\mathcal{A}}$ is neither equal to $\mathbf{a}_{P/\mathcal{A}} = (d\mathbf{v}_{P/\mathcal{A}}/dt)_{\mathcal{A}}$ nor equal to $(d\mathbf{v}_{P\in\mathcal{B}/\mathcal{A}}/dt)_{\mathcal{A}}$. We shall learn in Section 6.3 of Chapter 6 how the three vectors $\mathbf{a}_{P\in\mathcal{B}/\mathcal{A}}$, $(d\mathbf{v}_{P\in\mathcal{B}/\mathcal{A}}/dt)_{\mathcal{A}}$, and $(d\mathbf{v}_{P/\mathcal{A}}/dt)_{\mathcal{A}}$ are related to each other.

Example 5.5 Find the acceleration $\mathbf{a}_{Q\in\mathcal{A}/\mathcal{E}}$ of Example 3.8 by relating it to the acceleration $\mathbf{a}_{A/\mathcal{E}}$ using equation (5.6). Then compare this expression with $(d\mathbf{v}_{Q\in\mathcal{A}/\mathcal{E}}/dt)_{\mathcal{E}}$ and $\mathbf{a}_{Q/\mathcal{A}}$. ■

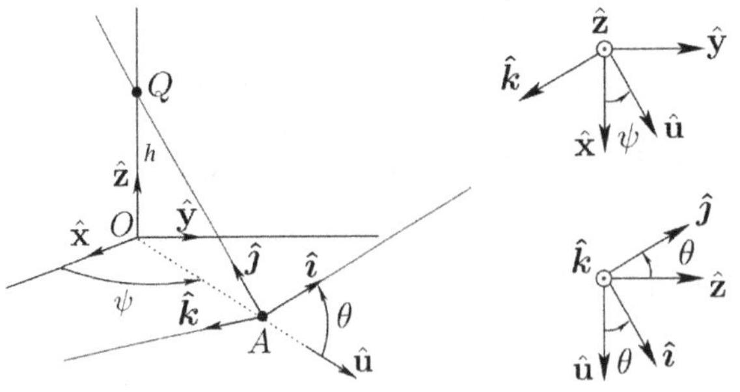

Denote by $r = |\mathbf{r}_{AQ}|$, $\boldsymbol{\omega} = \boldsymbol{\omega}_{\mathcal{A}/\mathcal{E}} = (\dot{\psi}\hat{\mathbf{z}} + \dot{\theta}\hat{\mathbf{k}})$ and $\boldsymbol{\alpha} = \boldsymbol{\alpha}_{\mathcal{A}/\mathcal{E}}$. We can express $\mathbf{v}_{A/\mathcal{E}} = d(\mathbf{r}_{OQ} + \mathbf{r}_{QA})/dt = -d(r\hat{\jmath})/dt$ leading to the expression $\mathbf{v}_{A/\mathcal{E}} = -\dot{r}\hat{\jmath} - r\boldsymbol{\omega} \times \hat{\jmath}$. We find the acceleration of A by differentiating $\mathbf{v}_{A/\mathcal{E}}$ to obtain

$$\mathbf{a}_{A/\mathcal{E}} = -\ddot{r}\hat{\jmath} - 2\dot{r}\boldsymbol{\omega} \times \hat{\jmath} - r\boldsymbol{\alpha} \times \hat{\jmath} - r\boldsymbol{\omega} \times (\boldsymbol{\omega} \times \hat{\jmath})$$

Acceleration $\mathbf{a}_{Q\in\mathcal{A}/\mathcal{E}}$ is obtained by applying (5.6):

$$\begin{aligned} \mathbf{a}_{Q\in\mathcal{A}/\mathcal{E}} &= \mathbf{a}_{A/\mathcal{E}} + \boldsymbol{\alpha} \times r\hat{\jmath} + \boldsymbol{\omega} \times (\boldsymbol{\omega} \times r\hat{\jmath}) \\ &= -\ddot{r}\hat{\jmath} - 2\dot{r}\boldsymbol{\omega} \times \hat{\jmath} = -\ddot{r}\hat{\jmath} - 2\dot{r}(\dot{\psi}\sin\theta\hat{\mathbf{k}} - \dot{\theta}\hat{\imath}) \end{aligned}$$

where $\dot{r}$ and $\ddot{r}$ can be obtained from the expression $r = h/\cos\theta$. We found in Example 3.8 the velocity $\mathbf{v}_{Q\in\mathcal{A}/\mathcal{E}} = -\dot{r}\hat{\jmath}$, leading to

$$\left(\frac{d}{dt}\mathbf{v}_{Q\in\mathcal{A}/\mathcal{E}}\right)_{\mathcal{E}} = -\ddot{r}\hat{\jmath} - \dot{r}\boldsymbol{\omega} \times \hat{\jmath} = -\ddot{r}\hat{\jmath} - \dot{r}(\dot{\psi}\sin\theta\hat{\mathbf{k}} - \dot{\theta}\hat{\imath})$$

Inspection of these results shows that we cannot obtain $\mathbf{a}_{Q\in\mathcal{A}/\mathcal{E}}$ by differentiating $\mathbf{v}_{Q\in\mathcal{A}/\mathcal{E}}$ or $\mathbf{v}_{Q/\mathcal{E}} = \mathbf{0}$. The relationship between $\mathbf{a}_{Q\in\mathcal{A}/\mathcal{E}}$ and $d\mathbf{v}_{Q\in\mathcal{A}/\mathcal{E}}/dt$ will be found in Chapter 6. ■

Example 5.6 Find the acceleration $\mathbf{a}_{I\in\mathcal{B}/\mathcal{A}}$ for the point I of Example 5.2 by relating it to the acceleration $\mathbf{a}_{B/\mathcal{A}}$ using equation (5.6) assuming ω_A and ω_B constant. ■

Point I is not attached to $\mathcal{B}$. We cannot find $\mathbf{a}_{I\in\mathcal{B}/\mathcal{A}}$ as the time-derivative of $\mathbf{v}_{I\in\mathcal{B}/\mathcal{A}}$ relative to $\mathcal{A}$. Instead, we relate point I to point B:

$$\mathbf{a}_{I\in\mathcal{B}/\mathcal{A}} = \mathbf{a}_{B/\mathcal{A}} + \boldsymbol{\alpha}_{\mathcal{B}/\mathcal{A}} \times \mathbf{r}_{BI} + \boldsymbol{\omega}_{\mathcal{B}/\mathcal{A}} \times (\boldsymbol{\omega}_{\mathcal{B}/\mathcal{A}} \times \mathbf{r}_{BI})$$

with acceleration $\mathbf{a}_{B/\mathcal{A}} = (d\mathbf{v}_{B/\mathcal{A}}/dt)_{\mathcal{A}}$ given by

$$\mathbf{a}_{B/\mathcal{A}} = -\omega_A^2(a\hat{\mathbf{e}}_3 \times \hat{\mathbf{e}}_2 + b\hat{\mathbf{e}}_3 \times \hat{\mathbf{e}}_1) = \omega_A^2(a\hat{\mathbf{e}}_1 - b\hat{\mathbf{e}}_2)$$

Taking into account $\boldsymbol{\alpha}_{\mathcal{B}/\mathcal{A}} = \mathbf{0}$, we find

$$\mathbf{a}_{I\in\mathcal{B}/\mathcal{A}} = \omega_A^2(a\hat{\mathbf{e}}_1 - b\hat{\mathbf{e}}_2) - (\omega_B - \omega_A)^2\mathbf{r}_{BI} = \omega_A\omega_B(a\hat{\mathbf{e}}_1 - b\hat{\mathbf{e}}_2)$$

As expected, $\mathbf{a}_{I\in\mathcal{B}/\mathcal{A}} \neq \mathbf{0}$. ■

5.6 Problems

Problem 5.1 A rigid body $\mathcal{B}(B, \hat{\mathbf{b}}_1, \hat{\mathbf{b}}_2, \hat{\mathbf{b}}_3)$ is in motion relative to referential $\mathcal{A}$. At a particular time, its kinematic screw can be written in the following form

$$\{\mathcal{V}_{B/A}\} = \left\{ \begin{array}{c} \hat{\mathbf{b}}_1 + \omega \hat{\mathbf{b}}_2 \\ \mathbf{0} \end{array} \right\}_P + \left\{ \begin{array}{c} \hat{\mathbf{b}}_1 + \Omega \hat{\mathbf{b}}_2 \\ \mathbf{0} \end{array} \right\}_Q$$

where points P and Q are defined by $\mathbf{r}_{BP} = \hat{\mathbf{b}}_3$ and $\mathbf{r}_{BQ} = -\hat{\mathbf{b}}_3$ (ω and Ω are two real parameters).

Find the instantaneous screw axis of $\mathcal{B}$ relative to $\mathcal{A}$ at this instant. Can body $\mathcal{B}$ be in instantaneous rotation?

Problem 5.2 Consider three points A, B, and C in motion relative to a referential $\mathcal{E}(O, \hat{\mathbf{e}}_1, \hat{\mathbf{e}}_2, \hat{\mathbf{e}}_3)$. At a particular time their positions and velocities (relative to $\mathcal{E}$) are known to be

$$\mathbf{r}_{OA} = \hat{\mathbf{e}}_1 + \hat{\mathbf{e}}_2 + \hat{\mathbf{e}}_3, \qquad \mathbf{v}_A = \hat{\mathbf{e}}_1 + \hat{\mathbf{e}}_3$$

$$\mathbf{r}_{OB} = -\hat{\mathbf{e}}_1 + \hat{\mathbf{e}}_3, \qquad \mathbf{v}_B = 2\hat{\mathbf{e}}_1 - 2\hat{\mathbf{e}}_2 + 3\hat{\mathbf{e}}_3$$

$$\mathbf{r}_{OC} = \hat{\mathbf{e}}_1 - \hat{\mathbf{e}}_2, \qquad \mathbf{v}_C = 2\hat{\mathbf{e}}_1 + \hat{\mathbf{e}}_3$$

a. Show that these points belong to the same rigid body $\mathcal{F}$.

b. Find the angular velocity $\boldsymbol{\omega}$ of $\mathcal{F}$ relative to $\mathcal{E}$. Find the kinematic screw of $\mathcal{F}$.

c. Find the instantaneous screw axis of $\mathcal{F}$ at this instant, and the corresponding pitch.

Problem 5.3 It is possible to generalize the fundamental formula

$$\left(\frac{d\mathbf{u}}{dt}\right)_A = \left(\frac{d\mathbf{u}}{dt}\right)_B + \boldsymbol{\omega}_{B/A} \times \mathbf{u}$$

to a time-dependent screw $\{\mathcal{U}\}$. Prove the following identity

$$\left\{\frac{d}{dt}\mathcal{U}\right\}_A = \left\{\frac{d}{dt}\mathcal{U}\right\}_B + \{\mathcal{V}_{B/A}\} \times \{\mathcal{U}\}$$

where the product $\{\mathcal{V}_{B/A}\} \times \{\mathcal{U}\}$ is defined in Problem 4.8. In particular show that the identity

$$\left\{\frac{d}{dt}\mathcal{V}_{B/A}\right\}_A = \left\{\frac{d}{dt}\mathcal{V}_{B/A}\right\}_B$$

is meaningful.

Problem 5.4 In general, the acceleration field of points of a rigid body $\mathcal{B}$ in motion relative to a referential $\mathcal{E}$ does not define a screw, and hence is not equiprojective. Suppose that at a given time, the accelerations of two points A and B attached of $\mathcal{B}$ satisfy the equiprojectivity condition:

$$\mathbf{a}_{A/\mathcal{E}} \cdot \mathbf{r}_{AB} = \mathbf{a}_{B/\mathcal{E}} \cdot \mathbf{r}_{AB}$$

Show that the angular velocity $\boldsymbol{\omega}_{\mathcal{B}/\mathcal{E}}$ is then necessarily parallel to line AB and that $\mathbf{v}_{A/\mathcal{E}} = \mathbf{v}_{B/\mathcal{E}}$ at this instant.

Problem 5.5 Consider rigid body $\mathcal{A}(A, \hat{\mathbf{a}}_1, \hat{\mathbf{a}}_2, \hat{\mathbf{a}}_3)$ in motion relative to a referential $\mathcal{E}$. At a particular instant, the velocity (relative to $\mathcal{E}$) of point A is $\mathbf{v}_A = v(2\hat{\mathbf{a}}_1 + \hat{\mathbf{a}}_2 - 3\hat{\mathbf{a}}_3)$ (v is a positive scalar). Consider two other points B and C attached to $\mathcal{A}$ whose positions and velocities (relative to $\mathcal{E}$) are given by, at this instant,

$$\mathbf{r}_{AB} = a(\hat{\mathbf{a}}_1 + \hat{\mathbf{a}}_2), \quad \mathbf{r}_{AC} = a(\hat{\mathbf{a}}_1 + \hat{\mathbf{a}}_2 + \hat{\mathbf{a}}_3)$$

$$\mathbf{v}_B = v(3\hat{\mathbf{a}}_2 - \hat{\mathbf{a}}_3), \quad \mathbf{v}_C = v(-\hat{\mathbf{a}}_1 + 2\hat{\mathbf{a}}_2 - \hat{\mathbf{a}}_3)$$

where a is a constant.

Determine the kinematic screw of $\mathcal{A}$ relative to $\mathcal{E}$ at this instant. Then find the corresponding instantaneous screw axis, and the equivalent representation of $\{\mathcal{V}_{A/\mathcal{E}}\}$ in terms of the instantaneous screw axis.

Problem 5.6 A point P moves in a referential $\mathcal{E}$ along a curve C at constant speed v_0. The tangential unit vector $\hat{\mathbf{e}}_t$, normal unit vector $\hat{\mathbf{e}}_n$ and binormal unit vector $\hat{\mathbf{e}}_b = \hat{\mathbf{e}}_t \times \hat{\mathbf{e}}_n$ of curve C form a right-handed basis (called Serret-Frenet basis). Consider the referential $\mathcal{F}(P, \hat{\mathbf{e}}_t, \hat{\mathbf{e}}_n, \hat{\mathbf{e}}_b)$ defined by particle P and by the Serret-Frenet basis following the motion of P along C.

Find the angular velocity $\omega_{\mathcal{F}/\mathcal{E}}$ and the instantaneous screw axis Δ of the motion of $\mathcal{F}$ relative to $\mathcal{E}$ in terms of the *radius of curvature* ρ and *radius of torsion* τ of curve $\mathcal{C}$ at P. Find the instantaneous velocity taken on Δ.

Hint: recall from Section 2.4 the Serret-Frenet formulas which give the time-derivatives of unit vectors $(\hat{\mathbf{e}}_t, \hat{\mathbf{e}}_n, \hat{\mathbf{e}}_b)$ along $\mathcal{C}$.

Problem 5.7 Two rigid bodies $\mathcal{F}(O, \hat{\mathbf{u}}, \hat{\mathbf{v}}, \hat{\mathbf{k}})$ and $\mathcal{G}(A, \hat{\mathbf{u}}_1, \hat{\mathbf{v}}, \hat{\mathbf{k}}_1)$ are in motion in a referential $\mathcal{E}(O, \hat{\imath}, \hat{\jmath}, \hat{\mathbf{k}})$. The motion of $\mathcal{F}$ relative to $\mathcal{E}$ is a rotation about axis $(O, \hat{\mathbf{k}})$ of $\mathcal{E}$ with angular velocity $\omega_{\mathcal{F}/\mathcal{E}} = \omega_1 \hat{\mathbf{k}}$. At time $t = 0$, the bases $(\hat{\imath}, \hat{\jmath}, \hat{\mathbf{k}})$ and $(\hat{\mathbf{u}}, \hat{\mathbf{v}}, \hat{\mathbf{k}})$ coincide. The motion of $\mathcal{G}$ relative to $\mathcal{F}$ is a rotation about axis $(A, \hat{\mathbf{v}})$ of $\mathcal{F}$ with angular velocity $\omega_{\mathcal{G}/\mathcal{F}} = \omega_2 \hat{\mathbf{v}}$. Point A is defined by $\mathbf{r}_{OA} = a\hat{\mathbf{u}}$ (a is a constant).

a. Find the kinematic screw of $\mathcal{G}$ relative to $\mathcal{E}$ and the corresponding instantaneous screw axis.

b. Find and sketch the trajectory viewed from $\mathcal{E}$ of the point B attached to $\mathcal{G}$ whose initial position is given by $\mathbf{r}_{OB} = 2a\hat{\mathbf{u}}$.

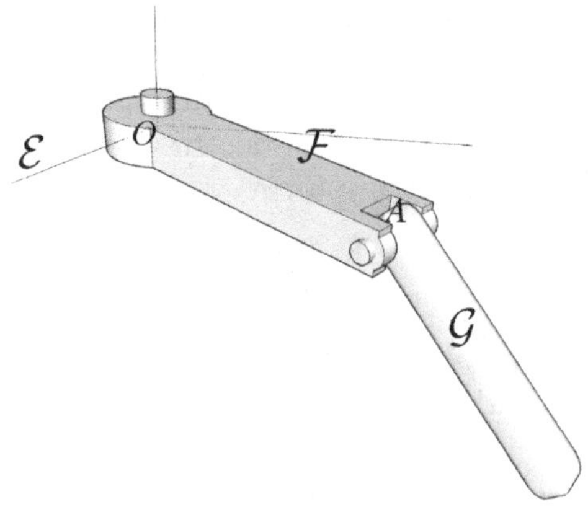

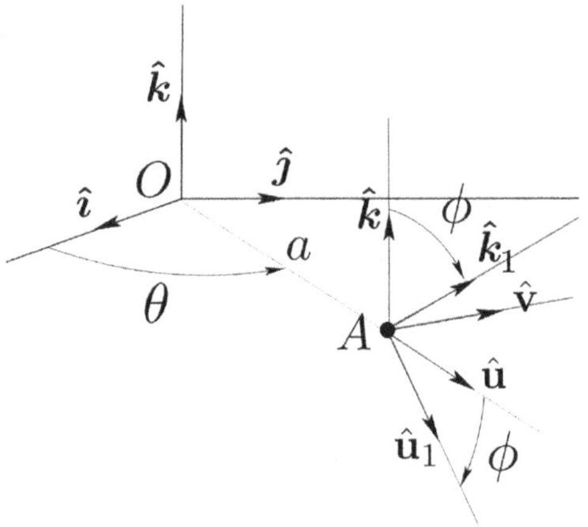

Problem 5.8 Consider three rigid bodies $\mathcal{B}_1$, $\mathcal{B}_2$ and $\mathcal{B}_3$ in relative motion. Denote by $\Delta_{ij} = \Delta_{ji}$ the instantaneous screw axis which characterizes the relative motion between bodies $\mathcal{B}_i$ and $\mathcal{B}_j$.

a. Show that the three axes Δ_{12}, Δ_{23}, Δ_{31} admit a common perpendicular line.

b. Assuming that rigid bodies $\mathcal{B}_1$, $\mathcal{B}_2$ and $\mathcal{B}_3$ are in relative planar motion as shown in Figure 5.5, characterize the property shown in a).

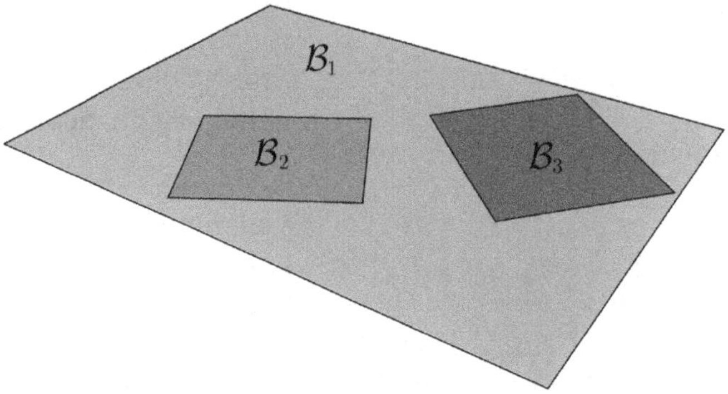

Figure 5.5

Problem 5.9 A helicopter $\mathcal{H}$ is in motion relative to a referential $\mathcal{E}(O, \hat{\mathbf{x}}_0, \hat{\mathbf{y}}_0, \hat{\mathbf{z}}_0)$ attached to the ground so as to remain in a translational motion along the direction of horizontal unit vector $\hat{\mathbf{x}}_0$. The position of a point A of its rotor is defined as $\mathbf{r}_{OA} = H\hat{\mathbf{z}}_0 + x_A(t)\hat{\mathbf{x}}_0$ where H is a constant and $x_A(t)$ is a given function of time. Its blades $\mathcal{B}$ are in rotational motion about the rotor's axis $(A, \hat{\mathbf{z}}_0)$. A point B of $\mathcal{B}$ remains in a horizontal plane and its position is defined as $\mathbf{r}_{AB} = L\hat{\mathbf{x}}_1$ where the orientation of unit vector $\hat{\mathbf{x}}_1$ is defined by angle θ as shown.

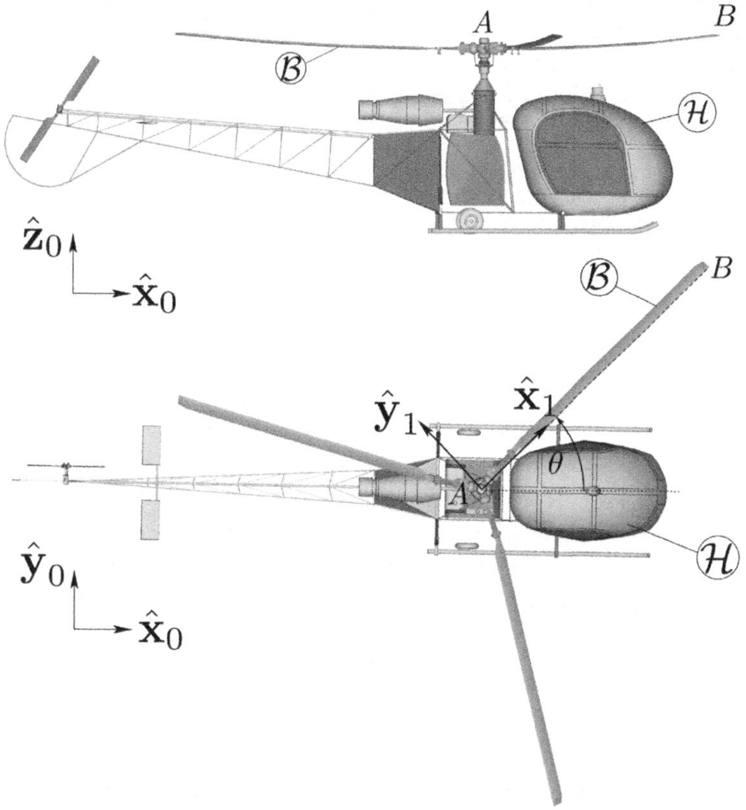

Find as a function of H, L, x_A and θ:

a. velocity $\mathbf{v}_{B/\mathcal{E}}$ by taking the time-derivative of position vector $\mathbf{r}_{OB}$.

b. velocity $\mathbf{v}_{B/\mathcal{H}}$, then $\mathbf{v}_{B/\mathcal{E}}$ from the expression of $\mathbf{v}_{B/\mathcal{H}}$.

c. kinematic screw $\{\mathcal{V}_{B/\mathcal{E}}\}$. Show that $\{\mathcal{V}_{B/\mathcal{E}}\}$ can take the form $\left\{ \begin{matrix} \boldsymbol{\omega}_{\mathcal{B}/\mathcal{E}} \\ \mathbf{0} \end{matrix} \right\}_I$. the location of point I of $\mathcal{B}$ and interpret its physical meaning. Use a graphical construction to find the value of angle θ for which the magnitude of $\mathbf{v}_{B/\mathcal{E}}$ takes its maximum value, assuming $\dot{\theta}$ and $\dot{x}_A$ constant.

d. acceleration $\mathbf{a}_{B/\mathcal{E}}$.

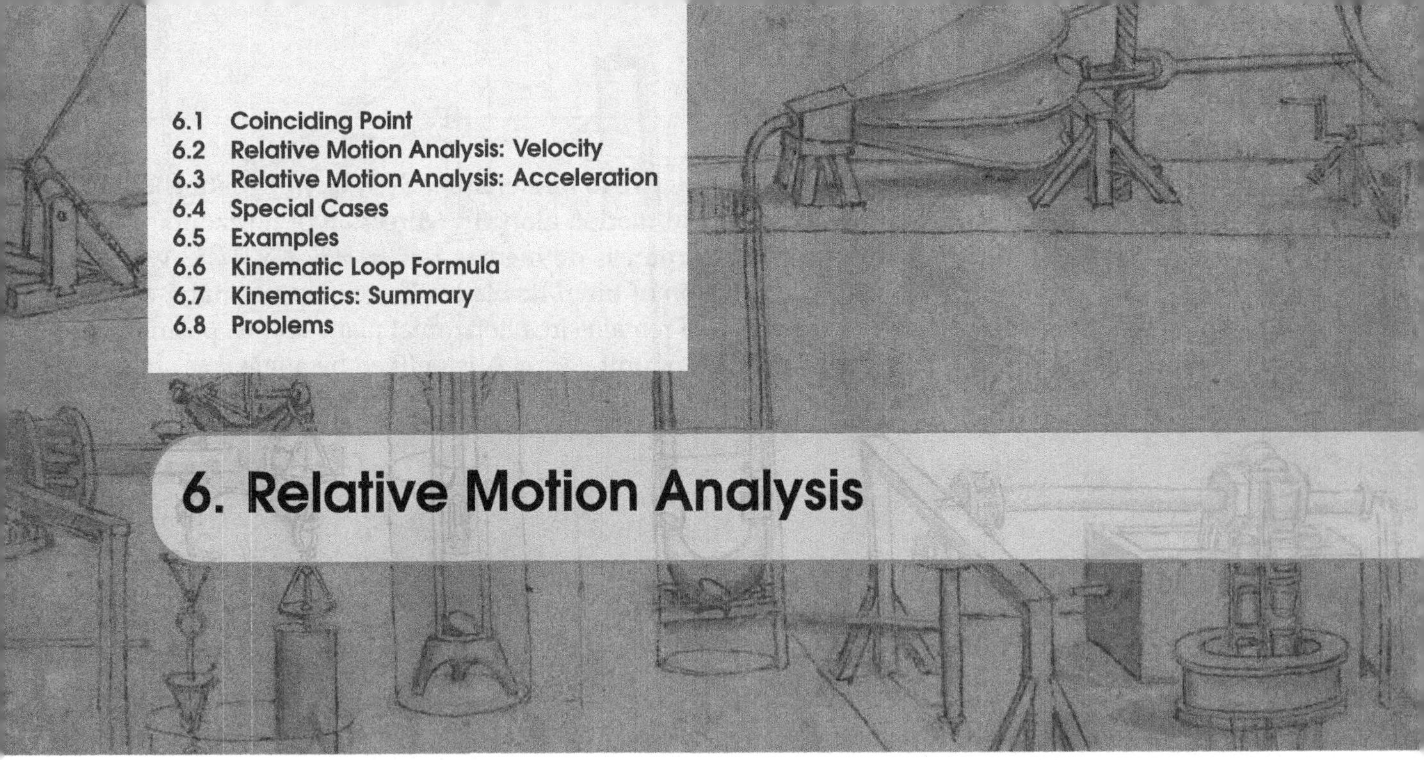

6. Relative Motion Analysis

IN THIS CHAPTER, we return to particle kinematics: we seek to find out how the kinematics of a particle can be obtained from one referential to another. More specifically, we consider a particle P whose motion is observed in two referentials $\mathcal{E}$ and $\mathcal{F}$, which are themselves in relative motion. Assuming that the motion of $\mathcal{F}$ relative to $\mathcal{E}$ is entirely known and that the kinematics (the velocity and acceleration) of P relative to $\mathcal{F}$ has been obtained, we ask whether the kinematics of P relative to $\mathcal{E}$ can be found. By defining the concept of *coinciding point*, we shall elucidate the relationship between velocities $\mathbf{v}_{P/\mathcal{E}}$ and $\mathbf{v}_{P\in\mathcal{F}/\mathcal{E}}$, and those between accelerations $\mathbf{a}_{P/\mathcal{E}}$ and $\mathbf{a}_{P\in\mathcal{F}/\mathcal{E}}$, and $(d\mathbf{v}_{P\in\mathcal{F}/\mathcal{E}}/dt)_{\mathcal{E}}$. These kinematical formulas will prove to be fundamental to the kinematic analysis of mechanisms and to the study of the effect of a rotating referential (such as Earth) on the dynamic behavior of a material system.

6.1 Coinciding Point

CONSIDER the example of ant A walking toward the center O of a turntable $\mathcal{F}$, itself in rotation about axis Oz of some referential $\mathcal{E}$. See Figure 6.1(a). At any instant, there exists a point attached to $\mathcal{F}$ which coincides with the position A of the ant. We should not expect this point to have the same velocity as that of point A relative to referential $\mathcal{E}$, since the motion of $\mathcal{F}$ is independent of that of A. Hence we must denote this velocity $\mathbf{v}_{A\in\mathcal{F}/\mathcal{E}}$ to ensure that this is the velocity of a point of frame $\mathcal{F}$ rather than that of point A. At instant t, a particular point of $\mathcal{F}$ coincides with the position of point A. At any other time, another point of $\mathcal{F}$ coincides with the position of A. Clearly, velocity $\mathbf{v}_{A\in\mathcal{F}/\mathcal{E}}$ cannot be obtained as $(d\mathbf{r}_{OA}/dt)_{\mathcal{E}} = \mathbf{v}_{A/\mathcal{E}}$. However the difference $\mathbf{v}_{A/\mathcal{E}} - \mathbf{v}_{A\in\mathcal{F}/\mathcal{E}}$ can be interpreted physically, as we shall learn in Section 6.2.

Consider as a second example the vertical disk $\mathcal{F}$ (of center C) which rolls on a horizontal support of a referential $\mathcal{E}$. See Figure 6.1(b). Consider at a particular instant the point of

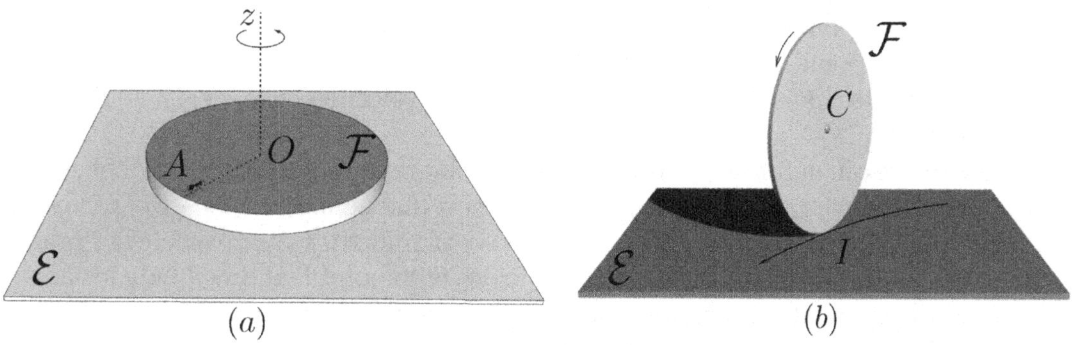

Figure 6.1

contact I of the disk. At point I, there exist two possible ways of defining a velocity relative to $\mathcal{E}$: (i) the velocity of the point I moving along a curve of the horizontal plane, that is, along the locus described by the contact points as the disk rolls, and (ii) the velocity of point $I \in \mathcal{F}$, that is, of the point rigidly attached to $\mathcal{F}$ and coinciding with the contact point. Again, we should expect these velocities to be different, and we denote them as $\mathbf{v}_{I/\mathcal{E}}$ and $\mathbf{v}_{I\in\mathcal{F}/\mathcal{E}}$, respectively. In fact, if the disk rolls without slipping, we expect to have $\mathbf{v}_{I\in\mathcal{F}/\mathcal{E}} = \mathbf{0}$ whereas $\mathbf{v}_{I/\mathcal{E}} = \mathbf{v}_{C/\mathcal{E}} \neq \mathbf{0}$.

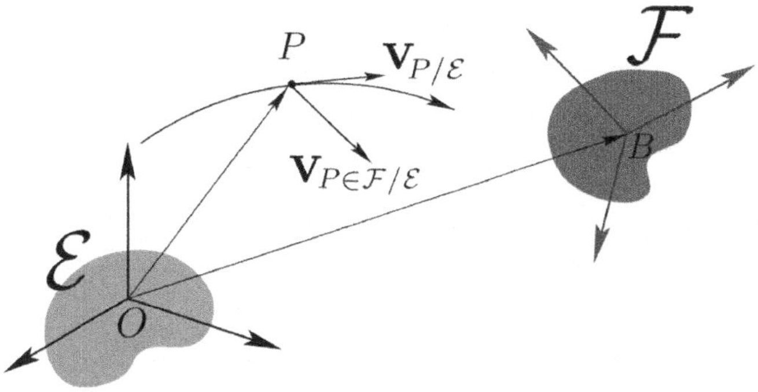

Figure 6.2

More generally, consider two referentials $\mathcal{E}$ and $\mathcal{F}$ in relative motion. Denote by O and B two points attached to $\mathcal{E}$ and $\mathcal{F}$, respectively. See Figure 6.2. The motion of $\mathcal{F}$ relative to $\mathcal{E}$ is specified by the velocity $\mathbf{v}_{B/\mathcal{E}}$ and acceleration $\mathbf{a}_{B/\mathcal{E}}$ of point B, and by its angular velocity $\boldsymbol{\omega}_{\mathcal{F}/\mathcal{E}}$ and angular acceleration $\boldsymbol{\alpha}_{\mathcal{F}/\mathcal{E}}$. Consider a point P in motion relative to both $\mathcal{E}$ and $\mathcal{F}$. Its velocity relative to $\mathcal{E}$ is defined as

$$\mathbf{v}_{P/\mathcal{E}} = \left(\frac{d\mathbf{r}_{OP}}{dt}\right)_{\mathcal{E}}$$

At any given time t, consider the point fixed in $\mathcal{F}$ which coincides at this instant with the position of point P. We denote its velocity relative to $\mathcal{E}$ as $\mathbf{v}_{P\in\mathcal{F}/\mathcal{E}}$. This velocity is in general different from $\mathbf{v}_{P/\mathcal{E}}$, since it is the velocity of a point (instantaneously) attached to $\mathcal{F}$: the only thing $P \in \mathcal{F}$ and point P have in common is their position in space at time t. The velocity of the coinciding point $P \in \mathcal{F}$ can be determined by relating it to another point of $\mathcal{F}$, say B, according to the kinematic screw formula (3.20)

$$\mathbf{v}_{P\in\mathcal{F}/\mathcal{E}} = \mathbf{v}_{B/\mathcal{E}} + \boldsymbol{\omega}_{\mathcal{F}/\mathcal{E}} \times \mathbf{r}_{BP} \tag{6.1}$$

As t varies, the points coinciding with P in $\mathcal{F}$ must occupy different physical positions within $\mathcal{F}$, since point P is in motion relative to $\mathcal{F}$.

In following section, we shall learn how the three velocities, $\mathbf{v}_{P/\mathcal{E}}$, $\mathbf{v}_{P/\mathcal{F}}$ and $\mathbf{v}_{P\in\mathcal{F}/\mathcal{E}}$ relate to each other.

Likewise, we can define $\mathbf{a}_{P\in\mathcal{F}/\mathcal{E}}$ as the acceleration relative to $\mathcal{E}$ of the point of $\mathcal{F}$ coinciding with point P at time t. Again we should not expect that acceleration $\mathbf{a}_{P\in\mathcal{F}/\mathcal{E}}$ can be obtained by time-differentiation of velocity $\mathbf{v}_{P/\mathcal{E}}$ or even of velocity $\mathbf{v}_{P\in\mathcal{F}/\mathcal{E}}$ whenever point P is in motion relative to $\mathcal{F}$: again point $P \in \mathcal{F}$ coincides with point P at time t only instantaneously. However we can relate its acceleration to that of another point attached (at all times) to $\mathcal{F}$, say point B of $\mathcal{F}$, according to formula (5.6)

$$\mathbf{a}_{P\in\mathcal{F}/\mathcal{E}} = \mathbf{a}_{B/\mathcal{E}} + \boldsymbol{\alpha}_{\mathcal{F}/\mathcal{E}} \times \mathbf{r}_{BP} + \boldsymbol{\omega}_{\mathcal{F}/\mathcal{E}} \times (\boldsymbol{\omega}_{\mathcal{F}/\mathcal{E}} \times \mathbf{r}_{BP}). \tag{6.2}$$

As in the case of velocities, we shall learn how the accelerations $\mathbf{a}_{P/\mathcal{E}}$, $\mathbf{a}_{P/\mathcal{F}}$ and $\mathbf{a}_{P\in\mathcal{F}/\mathcal{E}}$ are related to each other.

6.2 Relative Motion Analysis: Velocity

We first aim to relate the velocity of point P in $\mathcal{E}$ to that in $\mathcal{F}$. We start with the equality $\mathbf{r}_{OP} = \mathbf{r}_{OB} + \mathbf{r}_{BP}$ which we differentiate relative to $\mathcal{E}$ to obtain:

$$\mathbf{v}_{P/\mathcal{E}} = \mathbf{v}_{B/\mathcal{E}} + \left(\frac{d}{dt}\mathbf{r}_{BP}\right)_{\mathcal{E}}$$

The derivative of $\mathbf{r}_{BP}$ in $\mathcal{E}$ can be obtained from that in $\mathcal{F}$ according to formula (3.3)

$$\left(\frac{d}{dt}\mathbf{r}_{BP}\right)_{\mathcal{E}} = \left(\frac{d}{dt}\mathbf{r}_{BP}\right)_{\mathcal{F}} + \boldsymbol{\omega}_{\mathcal{F}/\mathcal{E}} \times \mathbf{r}_{BP} = \mathbf{v}_{P/\mathcal{F}} + \boldsymbol{\omega}_{\mathcal{F}/\mathcal{E}} \times \mathbf{r}_{BP}$$

Hence,

$$\mathbf{v}_{P/\mathcal{E}} = \mathbf{v}_{P/\mathcal{F}} + \mathbf{v}_{B/\mathcal{E}} + \boldsymbol{\omega}_{\mathcal{F}/\mathcal{E}} \times \mathbf{r}_{BP}$$

The sum of the last two terms, $\mathbf{v}_{B/\mathcal{E}} + \boldsymbol{\omega}_{\mathcal{F}/\mathcal{E}} \times \mathbf{r}_{BP}$, is then recognized as the velocity $\mathbf{v}_{P\in\mathcal{F}/\mathcal{E}}$ of the point coinciding with P in $\mathcal{F}$ relative to $\mathcal{E}$. We can now state the following result.

Theorem 6.1 — Change of Referential (Velocity). Given two referentials $\mathcal{E}$ and $\mathcal{F}$ in relative motion, the velocity $\mathbf{v}_{P/\mathcal{E}}$ of a particle P relative to $\mathcal{E}$ can be found from its velocity $\mathbf{v}_{P/\mathcal{F}}$ relative to $\mathcal{F}$ according to the formula

$$\mathbf{v}_{P/\mathcal{E}} = \mathbf{v}_{P/\mathcal{F}} + \mathbf{v}_{P\in\mathcal{F}/\mathcal{E}} \tag{6.3}$$

where $\mathbf{v}_{P\in\mathcal{F}/\mathcal{E}}$ is known as the *transport velocity* of P by $\mathcal{F}$ relative to $\mathcal{E}$. The velocities vectors $\mathbf{v}_{P/\mathcal{E}}$ and $\mathbf{v}_{P/\mathcal{F}}$ are commonly called *absolute velocity* and *relative velocity*, respectively.

Remark 1. We see from formula (6.3) that the equality $\mathbf{v}_{P/\mathcal{E}} = \mathbf{v}_{P\in\mathcal{F}/\mathcal{E}}$ holds at all time whenever the relative velocity $\mathbf{v}_{P/\mathcal{F}}$ is zero, that is, when P is a point attached to referential $\mathcal{F}$ at all times. This justifies omitting the notation $P \in \mathcal{F}$ in the expression $\mathbf{v}_{P/\mathcal{E}}$ whenever we are dealing with the velocity of a point P unambiguously attached to $\mathcal{F}$, as opposed to a point considered attached to $\mathcal{F}$ only instantaneously.

Remark 2. We now see that the difference $\mathbf{v}_{A/\mathcal{E}} - \mathbf{v}_{A\in\mathcal{F}/\mathcal{E}}$ in example (a) of Figure 6.1 is in fact given by the relative velocity $\mathbf{v}_{A/\mathcal{F}}$. See Example 6.1 for more detail.

6.3 Relative Motion Analysis: Acceleration

We can derive a similar relationship between the accelerations of point P relative to $\mathcal{E}$ and $\mathcal{F}$. We start by taking the time derivative in $\mathcal{E}$ of equation (6.3) to obtain

$$\mathbf{a}_{P/\mathcal{E}} = \left(\frac{d}{dt}\mathbf{v}_{P/\mathcal{F}}\right)_{\mathcal{E}} + \left(\frac{d}{dt}\mathbf{v}_{P\in\mathcal{F}/\mathcal{E}}\right)_{\mathcal{E}}$$

First we relate the derivative of $\mathbf{v}_{P/\mathcal{F}}$ in $\mathcal{E}$ to that in $\mathcal{F}$ according to formula (3.3):

$$\left(\frac{d}{dt}\mathbf{v}_{P/\mathcal{F}}\right)_{\mathcal{E}} = \left(\frac{d}{dt}\mathbf{v}_{P/\mathcal{F}}\right)_{\mathcal{F}} + \boldsymbol{\omega}_{\mathcal{F}/\mathcal{E}} \times \mathbf{v}_{P/\mathcal{F}} = \mathbf{a}_{P/\mathcal{F}} + \boldsymbol{\omega}_{\mathcal{F}/\mathcal{E}} \times \mathbf{v}_{P/\mathcal{F}}.$$

To find the derivative $(d\mathbf{v}_{P\in\mathcal{F}/\mathcal{E}}/dt)_{\mathcal{E}}$, we differentiate the equation $\mathbf{v}_{P\in\mathcal{F}/\mathcal{E}} = \mathbf{v}_{B/\mathcal{E}} + \boldsymbol{\omega}_{\mathcal{F}/\mathcal{E}} \times \mathbf{r}_{BP}$ term by term to find:

$$\left(\frac{d}{dt}\mathbf{v}_{P\in\mathcal{F}/\mathcal{E}}\right)_{\mathcal{E}} = \mathbf{a}_{B/\mathcal{E}} + \boldsymbol{\alpha}_{\mathcal{F}/\mathcal{E}} \times \mathbf{r}_{BP} + \boldsymbol{\omega}_{\mathcal{F}/\mathcal{E}} \times (\mathbf{v}_{P/\mathcal{F}} + \boldsymbol{\omega}_{\mathcal{F}/\mathcal{E}} \times \mathbf{r}_{BP})$$

where we have used $(d\mathbf{r}_{BP}/dt)_{\mathcal{E}} = \mathbf{v}_{P/\mathcal{F}} + \boldsymbol{\omega}_{\mathcal{F}/\mathcal{E}} \times \mathbf{r}_{BP}$. We then recognize the sum $\mathbf{a}_{B/\mathcal{E}} + \boldsymbol{\alpha}_{\mathcal{F}/\mathcal{E}} \times \mathbf{r}_{BP} + \boldsymbol{\omega}_{\mathcal{F}/\mathcal{E}} \times (\boldsymbol{\omega}_{\mathcal{F}/\mathcal{E}} \times \mathbf{r}_{BP})$ as the acceleration $\mathbf{a}_{P\in\mathcal{F}/\mathcal{E}}$ of the point coinciding with P in $\mathcal{F}$ according to equation (6.2). Hence,

$$\left(\frac{d}{dt}\mathbf{v}_{P\in\mathcal{F}/\mathcal{E}}\right)_{\mathcal{E}} = \mathbf{a}_{P\in\mathcal{F}/\mathcal{E}} + \boldsymbol{\omega}_{\mathcal{F}/\mathcal{E}} \times \mathbf{v}_{P/\mathcal{F}} \tag{6.4}$$

Finally, after regrouping all terms, we find the change of referential formula for acceleration:

Theorem 6.2 — Change of Referential (Acceleration). Given two referentials $\mathcal{E}$ and $\mathcal{F}$ in relative motion, the acceleration $\mathbf{a}_{P/\mathcal{E}}$ of a particle P relative to $\mathcal{E}$ can be found from its acceleration $\mathbf{a}_{P/\mathcal{F}}$ relative to $\mathcal{F}$ according to the formula

$$\mathbf{a}_{P/\mathcal{E}} = \mathbf{a}_{P/\mathcal{F}} + \mathbf{a}_{P\in\mathcal{F}/\mathcal{E}} + 2\boldsymbol{\omega}_{\mathcal{F}/\mathcal{E}} \times \mathbf{v}_{P/\mathcal{F}} \tag{6.5}$$

where

(i) $\mathbf{a}_{P\in\mathcal{F}/\mathcal{E}}$ is referred to as the *transport acceleration* of P by $\mathcal{F}$ relative to $\mathcal{E}$,

(ii) $2\boldsymbol{\omega}_{\mathcal{F}/\mathcal{E}} \times \mathbf{v}_{P/\mathcal{F}}$ is called *Coriolis acceleration* of P.

(iii) the accelerations vectors $\mathbf{a}_{P/\mathcal{E}}$ and $\mathbf{a}_{P/\mathcal{F}}$ are commonly called *absolute acceleration* and *relative acceleration*, respectively.

Remark 3. The derivative (relative to $\mathcal{E}$) of the transport velocity is not equal to the transport acceleration as clearly shown by formula (6.4). Unless of course $\mathbf{v}_{P/\mathcal{F}} = \mathbf{0}$, that is, when P is attached to $\mathcal{F}$ at all times, in which case we have

$$\mathbf{a}_{P\in\mathcal{F}/\mathcal{E}} = \mathbf{a}_{P/\mathcal{E}} = \left(\frac{d}{dt}\mathbf{v}_{P\in\mathcal{F}/\mathcal{E}}\right)_{\mathcal{E}}$$

Remark 4. As will be seen in the examples below, the application of the change of referential formulas requires in general more labor than the direct approach of taking the time derivative of $\mathbf{r}_{OP}$ and $\mathbf{v}_{P/\mathcal{E}}$ to find $\mathbf{v}_{P/\mathcal{E}}$ and $\mathbf{a}_{P/\mathcal{E}}$, respectively.

Remark 5. In practice, formulas (6.3-6.5) are fundamental to problems of dynamics in which the Earth's rotation must be taken into account. See Chapter 16 for examples.

6.4 Special Cases

Here we consider the two special cases of the change of referential formulas (6.3-6.5) corresponding to translational motion and rotational motion.

Translation.

Recall that if $\mathcal{F}$ is in translational motion relative to $\mathcal{E}$, its angular velocity and acceleration are zero at all times: $\boldsymbol{\omega}_{\mathcal{F}/\mathcal{E}} = \mathbf{0}$, and $\boldsymbol{\alpha}_{\mathcal{F}/\mathcal{E}} = \mathbf{0}$. This implies that the transport velocity and acceleration take the same expression irrespective of the motion of point P:

$$\mathbf{v}_{P\in\mathcal{F}/\mathcal{E}} = \mathbf{v}_{B/\mathcal{E}}, \qquad \mathbf{a}_{P\in\mathcal{F}/\mathcal{E}} = \mathbf{a}_{B/\mathcal{E}}$$

Furthermore, the Coriolis acceleration of point P is necessarily zero. With these simplifications, the change of referential formulas (6.3) and (6.5) take the following form

$$\mathbf{v}_{P/\mathcal{E}} = \mathbf{v}_{P/\mathcal{F}} + \mathbf{v}_{B/\mathcal{E}}$$

$$\mathbf{a}_{P/\mathcal{E}} = \mathbf{a}_{P/\mathcal{F}} + \mathbf{a}_{B/\mathcal{E}}$$

Rotation.

If $\mathcal{F}$ is in rotational motion relative to $\mathcal{E}$ about axis $\Delta(O, \hat{\mathbf{e}}_3)$, we may denote the angular velocity and acceleration of $\mathcal{F}$ as $\boldsymbol{\omega}_{\mathcal{F}/\mathcal{E}} = \omega\hat{\mathbf{e}}_3$, and $\boldsymbol{\alpha}_{\mathcal{F}/\mathcal{E}} = \dot{\omega}\hat{\mathbf{e}}_3$. Then the transport velocity and acceleration of a point P take the following expression:

$$\mathbf{v}_{P\in\mathcal{F}/\mathcal{E}} = \omega\hat{\mathbf{e}}_3 \times \mathbf{r}_{HP}, \qquad \mathbf{a}_{P\in\mathcal{F}/\mathcal{E}} = \dot{\omega}\hat{\mathbf{e}}_3 \times \mathbf{r}_{HP} - \omega^2\mathbf{r}_{HP}$$

where H is the projection of P on axis Δ. Then the change of referential formulas (6.3) and (6.5) take the following form

$$\mathbf{v}_{P/\mathcal{E}} = \mathbf{v}_{P/\mathcal{F}} + \omega\hat{\mathbf{e}}_3 \times \mathbf{r}_{HP}$$

$$\mathbf{a}_{P/\mathcal{E}} = \mathbf{a}_{P/\mathcal{F}} + \dot{\omega}\hat{\mathbf{e}}_3 \times \mathbf{r}_{HP} - \omega^2\mathbf{r}_{HP} + 2\omega\hat{\mathbf{e}}_3 \times \mathbf{v}_{P/\mathcal{F}}$$

6.5 Examples

Example 6.1 In the first example of Figure 6.1, find the "absolute" velocity and acceleration of point A from its "relative" velocity and acceleration, given that $\mathbf{r}_{OA} = \rho(t)\hat{\mathbf{f}}_1$ where $\hat{\mathbf{f}}_1$ is a unit vector attached to $\mathcal{F}$. Assume that $\boldsymbol{\omega}_{\mathcal{F}/\mathcal{E}} = \omega(t)\hat{\mathbf{f}}_3$. ■

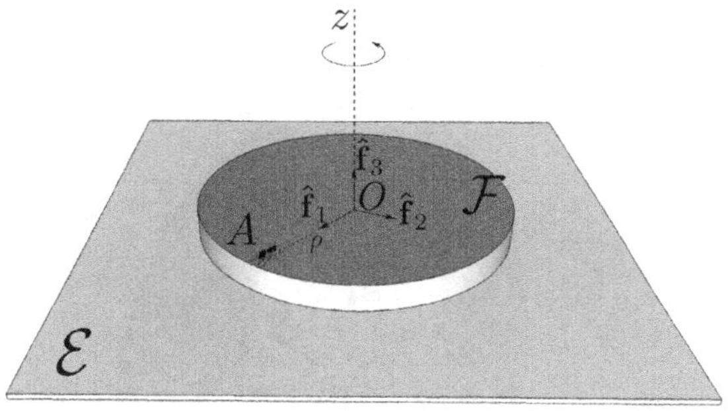

Figure 6.3

The motion of $\mathcal{F}$ relative to $\mathcal{E}$ is a rotation about axis $(O, \hat{\mathbf{f}}_3)$. We denote $\hat{\mathbf{f}}_2 = \hat{\mathbf{f}}_3 \times \hat{\mathbf{f}}_1$. The relative velocity and acceleration of point A are easily found to be

$$\mathbf{v}_{A/\mathcal{F}} = \left(\frac{d}{dt}\mathbf{r}_{OA}\right)_{\mathcal{F}} = \dot{\rho}\,\hat{\mathbf{f}}_1, \qquad \mathbf{a}_{A/\mathcal{F}} = \left(\frac{d}{dt}\mathbf{v}_{A/\mathcal{F}}\right)_{\mathcal{F}} = \ddot{\rho}\,\hat{\mathbf{f}}_1$$

The transport velocity and acceleration are found by considering the coinciding point $A(t) \in \mathcal{F}$ whose motion is instantaneously that of a point in rotation with $\mathcal{F}$ about axis $(O, \hat{\mathbf{f}}_3)$:

$$\begin{aligned}
\mathbf{v}_{A\in\mathcal{F}/\mathcal{E}} &= \boldsymbol{\omega}_{\mathcal{F}/\mathcal{E}} \times \mathbf{r}_{OA} = \omega\hat{\mathbf{f}}_3 \times \rho\hat{\mathbf{f}}_1 = \rho\omega\hat{\mathbf{f}}_2, \\
\mathbf{a}_{A\in\mathcal{F}/\mathcal{E}} &= \boldsymbol{\alpha}_{\mathcal{F}/\mathcal{E}} \times \mathbf{r}_{OA} + \boldsymbol{\omega}_{\mathcal{F}/\mathcal{E}} \times (\boldsymbol{\omega}_{\mathcal{F}/\mathcal{E}} \times \mathbf{r}_{OA}) = \rho\dot{\omega}\hat{\mathbf{f}}_2 - \rho\omega^2\hat{\mathbf{f}}_1
\end{aligned}$$

The Coriolis acceleration of A is given by

$$2\boldsymbol{\omega}_{\mathcal{F}/\mathcal{E}} \times \mathbf{v}_{A/\mathcal{F}} = 2\omega\hat{\mathbf{f}}_3 \times \dot{\rho}\,\hat{\mathbf{f}}_1 = 2\omega\dot{\rho}\hat{\mathbf{f}}_2$$

We can now apply formulas (6.3) and (6.5) to find the absolute velocity and acceleration of A:

$$\mathbf{v}_{A/\mathcal{E}} = \mathbf{v}_{A/\mathcal{F}} + \mathbf{v}_{A\in\mathcal{F}/\mathcal{E}} = \dot{\rho}\,\hat{\mathbf{f}}_1 + \rho\omega\hat{\mathbf{f}}_2$$

$$\mathbf{a}_{A/\mathcal{E}} = \mathbf{a}_{A/\mathcal{F}} + \mathbf{a}_{A\in\mathcal{F}/\mathcal{E}} + 2\boldsymbol{\omega}_{\mathcal{F}/\mathcal{E}} \times \mathbf{v}_{A/\mathcal{F}} = \ddot{\rho}\,\hat{\mathbf{f}}_1 + (\rho\dot{\omega}\hat{\mathbf{f}}_2 - \rho\omega^2\hat{\mathbf{f}}_1) + 2\omega\dot{\rho}\hat{\mathbf{f}}_2$$

or

$$\mathbf{a}_{A/\mathcal{E}} = (\ddot{\rho} - \rho\omega^2)\hat{\mathbf{f}}_1 + (\rho\dot{\omega} + 2\omega\dot{\rho})\hat{\mathbf{f}}_2$$

These results can be obtained much more efficiently by taking two consecutive time-derivatives of vector $\rho(t)\hat{\mathbf{f}}_1$ relative to $\mathcal{E}$, or by recognizing that (ρ, θ) $(\dot{\theta} = \omega)$ are the polar coordinates of A. ∎

Example 6.2 A hoop $\mathcal{H}(O, \hat{\mathbf{u}}, \hat{\mathbf{v}}, \hat{\mathbf{k}})$ of center O is in rotation about axis $(O, \hat{\mathbf{k}})$ of referential $\mathcal{E}(O, \hat{\imath}, \hat{\jmath}, \hat{\mathbf{k}})$. Its orientation is defined by angle $\theta = (\hat{\imath}, \hat{\mathbf{u}}) = (\hat{\jmath}, \hat{\mathbf{v}})$. A sphere of center P can move within the interior of $\mathcal{H}$. Its position is defined by angle $\phi = (\hat{\mathbf{u}}, \mathbf{r}_{OP})$. Denote by R the distance $|OP|$ and by $\hat{\mathbf{x}}$ the unit vector along line OP. See Figure 6.4.

Find the velocity and acceleration of P relative to $\mathcal{H}$. Then find $\mathbf{v}_{P/\mathcal{E}}$ and $\mathbf{a}_{P/\mathcal{E}}$ from the previously found quantities, that is, by using the change of referential formulas. ∎

First we determine the kinematics of point P relative to $\mathcal{H}(O, \hat{\mathbf{u}}, \hat{\mathbf{v}}, \hat{\mathbf{k}})$ (with $\hat{\mathbf{v}} = \hat{\mathbf{k}} \times \hat{\mathbf{u}}$) by the "direct" method of taking the time-derivative (in $\mathcal{H}$) of $\mathbf{r}_{OP} = R\hat{\mathbf{x}}$ (define unit vectors $\hat{\mathbf{x}}$ along line OP and $\hat{\mathbf{z}} = \hat{\mathbf{x}} \times \hat{\mathbf{v}}$).

$$\mathbf{v}_{P/\mathcal{H}} = \left(\frac{d}{dt}\mathbf{r}_{OP}\right)_{\mathcal{H}} = R\dot{\phi}\hat{\mathbf{z}}, \quad \mathbf{a}_{P/\mathcal{H}} = R\ddot{\phi}\hat{\mathbf{z}} - R\dot{\phi}^2\hat{\mathbf{x}}$$

The transport velocity and acceleration are the velocity and acceleration of the coinciding point

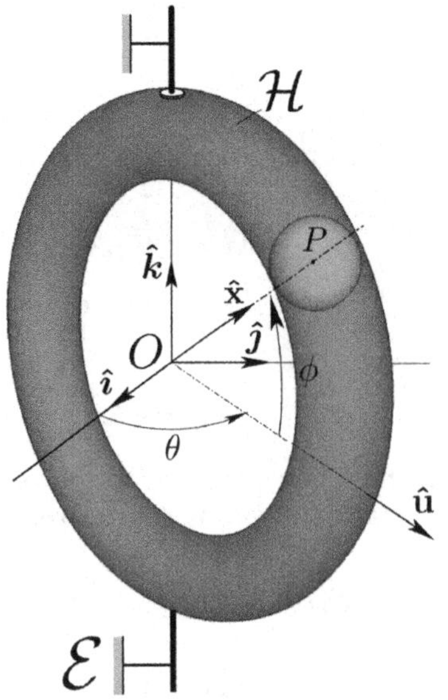

Figure 6.4

$P(t) \in \mathcal{H}$ whose motion is instantaneously that of a point in pure rotation with $\mathcal{H}$ about axis $(O, \hat{\mathbf{k}})$ relative to $\mathcal{E}$:

$$\begin{aligned}
\mathbf{v}_{P\in\mathcal{H}/\mathcal{E}} &= \boldsymbol{\omega}_{\mathcal{H}/\mathcal{E}} \times \mathbf{r}_{OP} = \dot{\theta}\hat{\mathbf{k}} \times R\hat{\mathbf{x}} = R\dot{\theta}\cos\phi\hat{\mathbf{v}}, \\
\mathbf{a}_{P\in\mathcal{H}/\mathcal{E}} &= \boldsymbol{\alpha}_{\mathcal{H}/\mathcal{E}} \times \mathbf{r}_{OP} + \boldsymbol{\omega}_{\mathcal{H}/\mathcal{E}} \times (\boldsymbol{\omega}_{\mathcal{H}/\mathcal{E}} \times \mathbf{r}_{OP}) \\
&= R\ddot{\theta}\cos\phi\hat{\mathbf{v}} - R\dot{\theta}^2\cos\phi\hat{\mathbf{u}}
\end{aligned}$$

The Coriolis acceleration of P is given by $2\boldsymbol{\omega}_{\mathcal{H}/\mathcal{E}} \times \mathbf{v}_{P/\mathcal{H}} = 2\dot{\theta}\hat{\mathbf{k}} \times R\dot{\phi}\hat{\mathbf{z}} = -2R\dot{\theta}\dot{\phi}\sin\phi\hat{\mathbf{v}}$. We can now apply formulas (6.3) and (6.5) between $\mathcal{H}$ and $\mathcal{E}$ to find the velocity and acceleration of P relative to $\mathcal{E}$:

$$\begin{aligned}
\mathbf{v}_{P/\mathcal{E}} &= \mathbf{v}_{P/\mathcal{H}} + \mathbf{v}_{P\in\mathcal{H}/\mathcal{E}} = R\dot{\phi}\hat{\mathbf{z}} + R\dot{\theta}\cos\phi\hat{\mathbf{v}} \\
\mathbf{a}_{P/\mathcal{E}} &= \mathbf{a}_{P/\mathcal{H}} + \mathbf{a}_{P\in\mathcal{H}/\mathcal{E}} + 2\boldsymbol{\omega}_{\mathcal{H}/\mathcal{E}} \times \mathbf{v}_{P/\mathcal{H}} \\
&= (R\ddot{\phi}\hat{\mathbf{z}} - R\dot{\phi}^2\hat{\mathbf{x}}) + (R\ddot{\theta}\cos\phi\hat{\mathbf{v}} - R\dot{\theta}^2\cos\phi\hat{\mathbf{u}}) - 2R\dot{\theta}\dot{\phi}\sin\phi\hat{\mathbf{v}}
\end{aligned}$$

The reader will verify these results by the direct approach of taking the first and second time-derivatives of $\mathbf{r}_{OP}$ relative to $\mathcal{E}$. ■

Example 6.3 Consider the motion $\mathcal{A}/\mathcal{E}$ of Examples 3.8 and 5.5. Find velocity $\mathbf{v}_{Q\in\mathcal{A}/\mathcal{E}}$ and acceleration $\mathbf{a}_{Q\in\mathcal{A}/\mathcal{E}}$ from $\mathbf{v}_{Q/\mathcal{E}}$, $\mathbf{v}_{Q/\mathcal{A}}$, and $\mathbf{a}_{Q/\mathcal{E}}$, $\mathbf{a}_{Q/\mathcal{A}}$, and recover the previous results.

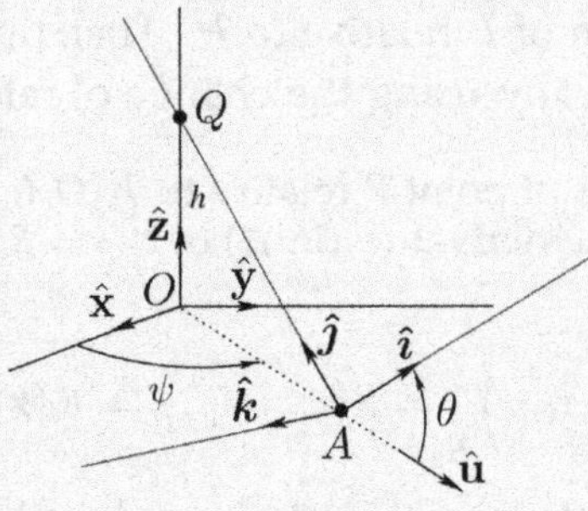

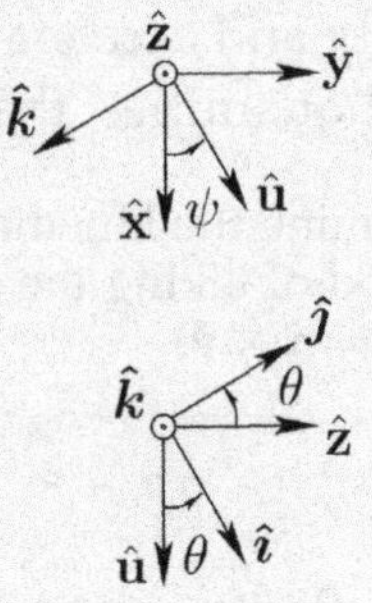

For the determination of $\mathbf{v}_{Q\in\mathcal{A}/\mathcal{E}}$, we apply equation (6.3):

$$\mathbf{v}_{Q\in\mathcal{A}/\mathcal{E}} = \mathbf{v}_{Q/\mathcal{E}} - \mathbf{v}_{Q/\mathcal{A}}$$

with $\mathbf{v}_{Q/\mathcal{E}} = \mathbf{0}$ (recall that Q is fixed in $\mathcal{E}$), and $\mathbf{v}_{Q/\mathcal{A}} = [d(r\hat{\jmath})/dt]_{\mathcal{A}} = \dot{r}\hat{\jmath}$ (denoting $r = |\mathbf{r}_{AQ}| = h/\cos\theta$, $\dot{r} = h\dot{\theta}\sin\theta/\cos^2\theta$). This leads to

$$\mathbf{v}_{Q\in\mathcal{A}/\mathcal{E}} = -\dot{r}\hat{\jmath}$$

We found the same result in Example 3.8. Then for the determination of $\mathbf{a}_{Q\in\mathcal{A}/\mathcal{E}}$, we apply equation (6.5):

$$\mathbf{a}_{Q\in\mathcal{A}/\mathcal{E}} = \mathbf{a}_{Q/\mathcal{E}} - \mathbf{a}_{Q/\mathcal{A}} - 2\boldsymbol{\omega}_{\mathcal{A}/\mathcal{E}} \times \mathbf{v}_{P/\mathcal{A}}$$

with $\mathbf{a}_{Q/\mathcal{E}} = \mathbf{0}$, and $\mathbf{a}_{Q/\mathcal{A}} = \ddot{r}\hat{\jmath}$ and $\boldsymbol{\omega}_{\mathcal{A}/\mathcal{E}} \times \mathbf{v}_{P/\mathcal{A}} = (\dot{\psi}\hat{\mathbf{z}} + \dot{\theta}\hat{\mathbf{k}}) \times (\dot{r}\hat{\jmath}) = \dot{r}(\dot{\psi}\sin\theta\hat{\mathbf{k}} - \dot{\theta}\hat{\imath})$. This leads to

$$\mathbf{a}_{Q\in\mathcal{A}/\mathcal{E}} = -\ddot{r}\hat{\jmath} - 2\dot{r}(\dot{\psi}\sin\theta\hat{\mathbf{k}} - \dot{\theta}\hat{\imath})$$

as we found in Example 5.5. ■

The change of referential formulas (6.3-6.5) are very useful when one wishes to study the effect of Earth's rotation on the motion of a rigid body. The following problem shows how to account for Earth's rotation in the acceleration of a particle P.

Example 6.4 Figure 6.5 shows Earth $\mathcal{E}$ modeled as a rigid body of center C. To account for the rotation of Earth, we define the geocentric referential $\mathcal{F}$ of origin C with three Cartesian axes CX, CY and CZ defined as follows:
(i) axis CZ coincides with axis $(C, \hat{\mathbf{k}})$ of rotation of Earth, that is, the line joining the South pole to the North pole,
(ii) the axes CX, CY of $\mathcal{F}$ points toward "fixed" stars in space.

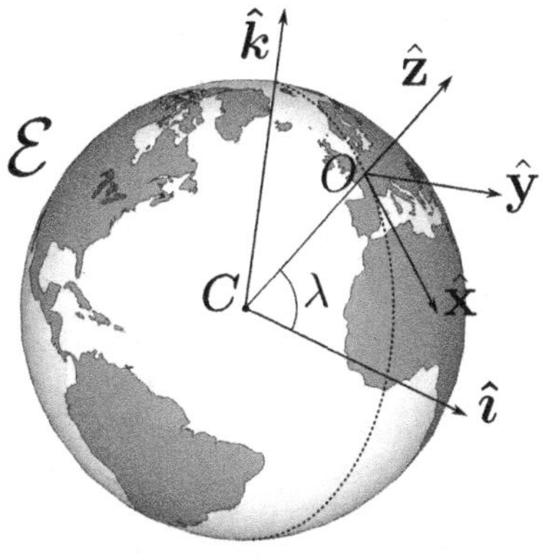

Figure 6.5

Hence, Earth is in rotational motion about geocentric referential $\mathcal{F}$ with angular velocity $\boldsymbol{\omega}_{\mathcal{E}/\mathcal{F}} = \Omega\hat{\mathbf{k}}$ ($\Omega > 0$ is a constant). Consider three Cartesian axes $(O, \hat{\mathbf{x}})$, $(O, \hat{\mathbf{y}})$, $(O, \hat{\mathbf{z}})$ attached to Earth at a particular point O ($|OC| = R$). Axis $(O, \hat{\mathbf{x}})$ points to the South. Axis $(O, \hat{\mathbf{y}})$ points toward the East. Axis $(O, \hat{\mathbf{z}})$ points toward the vertical at O. Point

O is located at latitude λ. Finally, consider a particle P in motion in plane $(O, \hat{\mathbf{x}}, \hat{\mathbf{y}})$: $\mathbf{r}_{OP} = x(t)\hat{\mathbf{x}} + y(t)\hat{\mathbf{y}}$ with $x, y \ll R$.
Find the "absolute" acceleration $\mathbf{a}_{P/\mathcal{F}}$ of point P by determining the "relative" acceleration $\mathbf{a}_{P/\mathcal{E}}$, the transport acceleration $\mathbf{a}_{P\in\mathcal{E}/\mathcal{F}}$ and the Coriolis acceleration $2\Omega\hat{\mathbf{k}} \times \mathbf{v}_{P/\mathcal{E}}$ of P. ■

Referential $\mathcal{E}$ is in rotation about axis $(C, \hat{\mathbf{k}})$ relative to referential $\mathcal{F}$. To find $\mathbf{a}_{P\in\mathcal{E}/\mathcal{F}}$ we need to find

$$\mathbf{a}_{P\in\mathcal{E}/\mathcal{F}} = \Omega\hat{\mathbf{k}} \times (\Omega\hat{\mathbf{k}} \times \mathbf{r}_{CP}) \approx \Omega\hat{\mathbf{k}} \times (\Omega\hat{\mathbf{k}} \times \mathbf{r}_{CO})$$

where we used the approximation $\mathbf{r}_{CP} \approx \mathbf{r}_{CO}$. This gives

$$\mathbf{a}_{P\in\mathcal{E}/\mathcal{F}} = -R\Omega^2 \cos\lambda \hat{\mathbf{\imath}} = -R\Omega^2 \cos\lambda(\cos\lambda\hat{\mathbf{z}} + \sin\lambda\hat{\mathbf{x}})$$

The Coriolis acceleration is given by

$$2\Omega\hat{\mathbf{k}} \times \mathbf{v}_{P/\mathcal{E}} = 2\Omega\hat{\mathbf{k}} \times (\dot{x}\hat{\mathbf{x}} + \dot{y}\hat{\mathbf{y}}) = 2\Omega(\dot{x}\sin\lambda\hat{\mathbf{y}} - \dot{y}\hat{\mathbf{\imath}}) = 2\Omega[\dot{x}\sin\lambda\hat{\mathbf{y}} - \dot{y}(\cos\lambda\hat{\mathbf{z}} + \sin\lambda\hat{\mathbf{x}})]$$

Using $\mathbf{a}_{P/\mathcal{F}} = \mathbf{a}_{P/\mathcal{E}} + \mathbf{a}_{P\in\mathcal{E}/\mathcal{F}} + 2\Omega\hat{\mathbf{k}} \times \mathbf{v}_{P/\mathcal{E}}$ we find

$$\mathbf{a}_{P/\mathcal{F}} = (\ddot{x}\hat{\mathbf{x}} + \ddot{y}\hat{\mathbf{y}}) - R\Omega^2\cos\lambda(\cos\lambda\hat{\mathbf{z}} + \sin\lambda\hat{\mathbf{x}}) + 2\Omega[\dot{x}\sin\lambda\hat{\mathbf{y}} - \dot{y}(\cos\lambda\hat{\mathbf{z}} + \sin\lambda\hat{\mathbf{x}})]$$

■

6.6 Kinematic Loop Formula

We can extend the change of referential formula (6.3) derived in Section 6.2 by assuming that particle P moving relative to body $\mathcal{B}$ (itself in motion relative to body $\mathcal{A}$) is actually rigidly attached to a third body $\mathcal{C}$: hence the problem is to determine the kinematics of $\mathcal{C}$ relative to $\mathcal{A}$ from the knowledge of its kinematics relative to $\mathcal{B}$. More specifically, can the kinematic screw $\{\mathcal{V}_{\mathcal{C}/\mathcal{A}}\}$ be obtained from kinematic screws $\{\mathcal{V}_{\mathcal{C}/\mathcal{B}}\}$ and $\{\mathcal{V}_{\mathcal{B}/\mathcal{A}}\}$? See Figure 6.6.

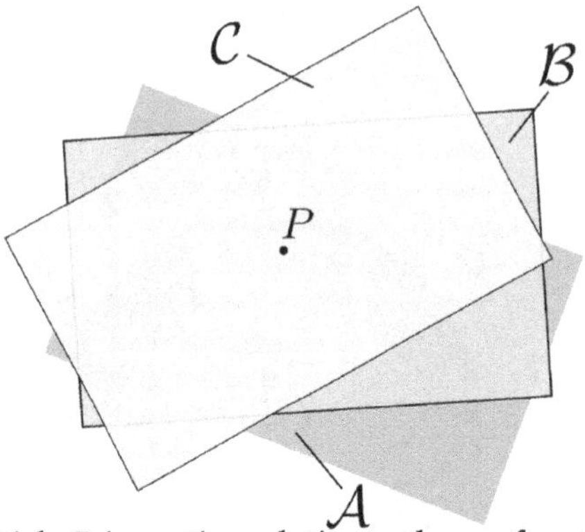

Figure 6.6 – *Particle P in motion relative to three referentials $\mathcal{A}$, $\mathcal{B}$, and $\mathcal{C}$.*

Recall from Section 3.1 that, given three rigid bodies (or referentials) $\mathcal{A}$, $\mathcal{B}$ and $\mathcal{C}$ in relative motion, the angular velocities $\boldsymbol{\omega}_{\mathcal{C}/\mathcal{A}}$, $\boldsymbol{\omega}_{\mathcal{A}/\mathcal{B}}$ and $\boldsymbol{\omega}_{\mathcal{B}/\mathcal{C}}$ satisfy the loop equation

$$\boldsymbol{\omega}_{\mathcal{C}/\mathcal{A}} + \boldsymbol{\omega}_{\mathcal{A}/\mathcal{B}} + \boldsymbol{\omega}_{\mathcal{B}/\mathcal{C}} = \mathbf{0} \tag{6.6}$$

Also recall the change of referential formula (6.3) for an arbitrary particle P in motion relative $\mathcal{A}$, $\mathcal{B}$ or $\mathcal{C}$:

$$\mathbf{v}_{P/\mathcal{A}} = \mathbf{v}_{P/\mathcal{B}} + \mathbf{v}_{P\in\mathcal{B}/\mathcal{A}} \tag{6.7}$$

Now consider the point of body $\mathcal{C}$ coinciding with P: $\mathbf{v}_{P/\mathcal{A}}$ and $\mathbf{v}_{P/\mathcal{B}}$ in (6.3) are now replaced by $\mathbf{v}_{P\in\mathcal{C}/\mathcal{A}}$ and $\mathbf{v}_{P\in\mathcal{C}/\mathcal{B}}$, respectively. Formula (6.3) now becomes

$$\mathbf{v}_{P\in\mathcal{C}/\mathcal{A}} = \mathbf{v}_{P\in\mathcal{C}/\mathcal{B}} + \mathbf{v}_{P\in\mathcal{B}/\mathcal{A}}$$

Since $\mathbf{v}_{P\in\mathcal{C}/\mathcal{B}} = -\mathbf{v}_{P\in\mathcal{B}/\mathcal{C}}$ and $\mathbf{v}_{P\in\mathcal{B}/\mathcal{A}} = -\mathbf{v}_{P\in\mathcal{A}/\mathcal{B}}$, this leads to the following velocity loop equation

$$\mathbf{v}_{P\in\mathcal{C}/\mathcal{A}} + \mathbf{v}_{P\in\mathcal{A}/\mathcal{B}} + \mathbf{v}_{P\in\mathcal{B}/\mathcal{C}} = \mathbf{0} \tag{6.8}$$

Equations (6.6) and (6.8) can be grouped in screw notation to obtain the following fundametal theorem:

Theorem 6.3 — Kinematic Loop Formula. Given three rigid bodies (referentials) $\mathcal{A}$, $\mathcal{B}$ and $\mathcal{C}$ in relative motion, the kinematic screws $\{\mathcal{V}_{\mathcal{C}/\mathcal{A}}\}$, $\{\mathcal{V}_{\mathcal{A}/\mathcal{B}}\}$, and $\{\mathcal{V}_{\mathcal{B}/\mathcal{C}}\}$ add up to zero:

$$\{\mathcal{V}_{\mathcal{C}/\mathcal{A}}\} + \{\mathcal{V}_{\mathcal{A}/\mathcal{B}}\} + \{\mathcal{V}_{\mathcal{B}/\mathcal{C}}\} = \{0\} \tag{6.9}$$

Furthermore, we have

$$\{\mathcal{V}_{\mathcal{A}/\mathcal{B}}\} = -\{\mathcal{V}_{\mathcal{B}/\mathcal{A}}\} \tag{6.10}$$

Equation (6.10) is shown by letting $\mathcal{C} = \mathcal{A}$ in equation (6.9), noting that $\{\mathcal{V}_{\mathcal{A}/\mathcal{A}}\} = \{0\}$.

Remark 6. It is not possible to write an acceleration loop equation, that is, in general we have $\mathbf{a}_{P\in\mathcal{C}/\mathcal{A}} + \mathbf{a}_{P\in\mathcal{A}/\mathcal{B}} + \mathbf{a}_{P\in\mathcal{B}/\mathcal{C}} \neq \mathbf{0}$ due to the presence of Coriolis accelerations.

The kinematic loop formula will prove to be pivotal to the kinematic analysis of mechanisms, as will be seen in Chapter 8. We illustrate its use with the following example.

Example 6.5 Two referentials $\mathcal{A}(A, \mathbf{a}_1, \mathbf{a}_2, \hat{\mathbf{e}}_3)$ and $\mathcal{B}(B, \hat{\mathbf{b}}_1, \hat{\mathbf{b}}_2, \hat{\mathbf{e}}_3)$ are in rotational motion about axis $(A, \hat{\mathbf{e}}_3)$ and $(B, \hat{\mathbf{e}}_3)$, respectively, relative to a referential $\mathcal{E}(O, \hat{\mathbf{e}}_1, \hat{\mathbf{e}}_2, \hat{\mathbf{e}}_3)$. Points A and B are located on axis $(O, \hat{\mathbf{e}}_1)$, with O midpoint of AB. $\mathcal{A}$ rotates at constant angular velocity ω in the counterclockwise direction. $\mathcal{B}$ rotates at constant angular velocity 2ω in the clockwise direction. The axes $(A, \mathbf{a}_1)$ and $(B, \hat{\mathbf{b}}_1)$ both coincide with axis $(O, \hat{\mathbf{e}}_1)$ at $t = 0$. Denote by 2ℓ the distance $|AB|$. See Figure 6.7.

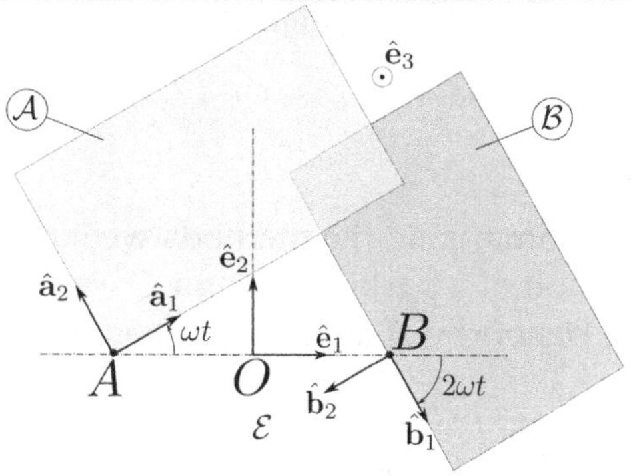

Figure 6.7

a. Find the kinematic screw $\{\mathcal{V}_{\mathcal{B}/\mathcal{A}}\}$ resolved at point A, then at point B.
b. Show that $\mathcal{B}$ is in instantaneous rotation relative to $\mathcal{A}$. Determine the corresponding instantaneous axis of rotation Δ. Describe the surfaces described by Δ during its motion relative to $\mathcal{A}$, then relative to $\mathcal{B}$. Then characterize the motions of $\mathcal{A}$ and $\mathcal{B}$ relative to $\mathcal{E}$. ■

a. We can use the kinematic loop formula to find $\{\mathcal{V}_{\mathcal{B}/\mathcal{A}}\} = \{\mathcal{V}_{\mathcal{B}/\mathcal{E}}\} - \{\mathcal{V}_{\mathcal{A}/\mathcal{E}}\}$ with

$$\{\mathcal{V}_{\mathcal{B}/\mathcal{E}}\} = \begin{Bmatrix} -2\omega\hat{\mathbf{e}}_3 \\ \mathbf{0} \end{Bmatrix}_B, \qquad \{\mathcal{V}_{\mathcal{A}/\mathcal{E}}\} = \begin{Bmatrix} \omega\hat{\mathbf{e}}_3 \\ \mathbf{0} \end{Bmatrix}_A$$

Upon finding $\mathbf{v}_{A\in\mathcal{B}/\mathcal{E}} = -2\omega\hat{\mathbf{e}}_3 \times \mathbf{r}_{BA} = 4\ell\omega\hat{\mathbf{e}}_2$ and $\mathbf{v}_{A\in\mathcal{A}/\mathcal{E}} = \mathbf{0}$, we obtain

$$\{\mathcal{V}_{\mathcal{B}/\mathcal{A}}\} = \begin{Bmatrix} -3\omega\hat{\mathbf{e}}_3 \\ \mathbf{v}_{A\in\mathcal{B}/\mathcal{E}} - \mathbf{v}_{A\in\mathcal{A}/\mathcal{E}} \end{Bmatrix}_A = \begin{Bmatrix} -3\omega\hat{\mathbf{e}}_3 \\ 4\ell\omega\hat{\mathbf{e}}_2 \end{Bmatrix}_A = \begin{Bmatrix} -3\omega\hat{\mathbf{e}}_3 \\ -2\ell\omega\hat{\mathbf{e}}_2 \end{Bmatrix}_B$$

b. To show that $\{\mathcal{V}_{\mathcal{B}/\mathcal{A}}\}$ is a slider, we look for the point I lying in plane $(O, \hat{\mathbf{e}}_1, \hat{\mathbf{e}}_2)$ which satisfies $\mathbf{v}_{I\in\mathcal{B}/\mathcal{A}} = \mathbf{0}$, that is, $3\omega\hat{\mathbf{e}}_3 \times \mathbf{r}_{AI} = 4\ell\omega\hat{\mathbf{e}}_2$. Upon taking the cross-product of this last equation with $\hat{\mathbf{e}}_3$, we find $\mathbf{r}_{AI} = \frac{4\ell}{3}\hat{\mathbf{e}}_1$. This shows that the motion $\mathcal{B}/\mathcal{A}$ is characterized by the instantaneous axis of rotation $\Delta(I, \hat{\mathbf{e}}_3)$ with $\mathbf{r}_{OI} = \frac{\ell}{3}\hat{\mathbf{e}}_1$. We note that Δ is fixed relative to $\mathcal{E}$. When time varies, Δ describes a cylinder centered about $(B, \hat{\mathbf{e}}_3)$ of radius $2\ell/3$ relative to $\mathcal{B}$. Similarly, Δ describes relative to $\mathcal{A}$ a cylinder centered about $(A, \hat{\mathbf{e}}_3)$ of radius $4\ell/3$. As far as their velocity field is concerned, the motions of $\mathcal{A}$ and $\mathcal{B}$ can thus be viewed as the motion of two cylinders in contact along $\Delta(I, \hat{\mathbf{e}}_3)$. The contact is achieved without slipping. See Figure 6.8. ■

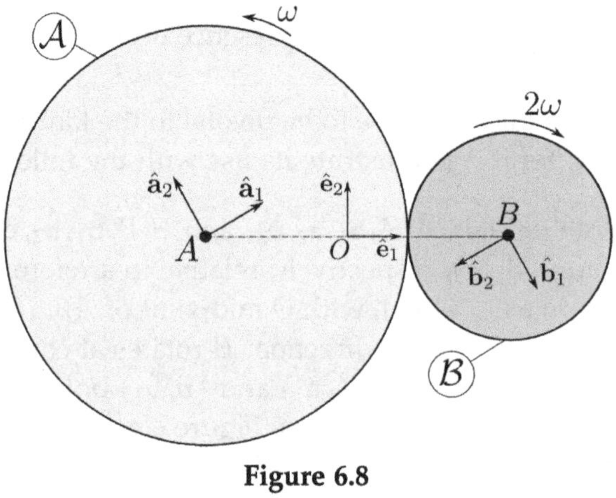

Figure 6.8

6.7 Kinematics: Summary

We end this chapter by summarizing the methods we may apply for the determination of the velocity and acceleration of a particular point Q attached to a rigid body $\mathcal{B}$ in motion relative to referential $\mathcal{A}$. Denote by A a point attached to $\mathcal{A}$ at all times.

Method 1: *Point Q is attached to $\mathcal{B}$ at all times.* Then, the velocity of Q is found most efficiently by first resolving the position vector $\mathbf{r}_{AQ}$ along some unit vectors $\hat{\mathbf{u}}$, $\hat{\mathbf{v}}$, $\hat{\mathbf{w}}$, ... which are not necessarily attached to $\mathcal{A}$ or $\mathcal{B}$:

$$\mathbf{r}_{AQ} = U(t)\hat{\mathbf{u}} + V(t)\hat{\mathbf{v}} + W(t)\hat{\mathbf{w}} + \cdots$$

Then the velocity of Q relative to $\mathcal{A}$ is obtained as

$$\begin{aligned}\mathbf{v}_{Q\in\mathcal{B}/\mathcal{A}} &= \mathbf{v}_{Q/\mathcal{A}} = \left(\frac{d\mathbf{r}_{AQ}}{dt}\right)_{\mathcal{A}} \\ &= \dot{U}\hat{\mathbf{u}} + U\left(\frac{d\hat{\mathbf{u}}}{dt}\right)_{\mathcal{A}} + \dot{V}\hat{\mathbf{v}} + V\left(\frac{d\hat{\mathbf{v}}}{dt}\right)_{\mathcal{A}} + \dot{W}\hat{\mathbf{w}} + W\left(\frac{d\hat{\mathbf{w}}}{dt}\right)_{\mathcal{A}} + \cdots\end{aligned}$$

The time-derivatives $(d\hat{\mathbf{u}}/dt)_{\mathcal{A}}$, $(d\hat{\mathbf{v}}/dt)_{\mathcal{A}}$, $(d\hat{\mathbf{w}}/dt)_{\mathcal{A}}$, ..., are determined by using the concept of angular velocity:

$$\left(\frac{d\hat{\mathbf{u}}}{dt}\right)_{\mathcal{A}} = \boldsymbol{\omega}_{\mathcal{U}/\mathcal{A}} \times \hat{\mathbf{u}}, \qquad \left(\frac{d\hat{\mathbf{v}}}{dt}\right)_{\mathcal{A}} = \boldsymbol{\omega}_{\mathcal{V}/\mathcal{A}} \times \hat{\mathbf{v}}, \quad \cdots$$

where $\mathcal{U}$ (resp. $\mathcal{V}$) is an auxiliary referential relative to which $\hat{\mathbf{u}}$ (resp. $\hat{\mathbf{v}}$) is fixed. The acceleration $\mathbf{a}_{Q\in\mathcal{B}/\mathcal{A}} = \mathbf{a}_{Q/\mathcal{A}}$ of Q is then simply found as $(d\mathbf{v}_{Q/\mathcal{A}}/dt)_{\mathcal{A}}$ by following the process just outlined.

Method 2: *Point Q is not attached to $\mathcal{B}$ at all times.* Then $\mathbf{v}_{Q\in\mathcal{B}/\mathcal{A}}$ is interpreted as the velocity of the point of $\mathcal{B}$ which coincides with point Q. This velocity cannot be obtained as $(d\mathbf{r}_{AQ}/dt)_{\mathcal{A}}$. Instead, it can be obtained by using the kinematic screw $\{\mathcal{V}_{\mathcal{B}/\mathcal{A}}\}$, that is, by relating it to the velocity of another point, say B, attached to $\mathcal{B}$ at all times:

$$\mathbf{v}_{Q\in\mathcal{B}/\mathcal{A}} = \mathbf{v}_{B/\mathcal{A}} + \boldsymbol{\omega}_{\mathcal{B}/\mathcal{A}} \times \mathbf{r}_{BQ}$$

where $\mathbf{v}_{B/\mathcal{A}}$ is a known quantity (typically determined according to Method 1). Likewise $\mathbf{a}_{Q\in\mathcal{B}/\mathcal{A}}$ can be determined from $\mathbf{a}_{B/\mathcal{A}}$ according to

$$\mathbf{a}_{Q\in\mathcal{B}/\mathcal{A}} = \mathbf{a}_{B/\mathcal{A}} + \boldsymbol{\alpha}_{\mathcal{B}/\mathcal{A}} \times \mathbf{r}_{BQ} + \boldsymbol{\omega}_{\mathcal{B}/\mathcal{A}} \times (\boldsymbol{\omega}_{\mathcal{B}/\mathcal{A}} \times \mathbf{r}_{BQ})$$

Note that another way to determine $\mathbf{v}_{Q\in\mathcal{B}/\mathcal{A}}$ is to use formula (6.3):

$$\mathbf{v}_{Q\in\mathcal{B}/\mathcal{A}} = \mathbf{v}_{Q/\mathcal{A}} - \mathbf{v}_{Q/\mathcal{B}}$$

where $\mathbf{v}_{Q/\mathcal{A}}$ and $\mathbf{v}_{Q/\mathcal{B}}$ are determined according to (assuming A is fixed in $\mathcal{A}$ and B is fixed in $\mathcal{B}$ at all times):

$$\mathbf{v}_{Q/\mathcal{A}} = \left(\frac{d\mathbf{r}_{AQ}}{dt}\right)_{\mathcal{A}}, \qquad \mathbf{v}_{Q/\mathcal{B}} = \left(\frac{d\mathbf{r}_{BQ}}{dt}\right)_{\mathcal{B}}$$

where each position vector is differentiated as outlined in Method 1. A similar method can be followed for the acceleration by using formula (6.5):

$$\mathbf{a}_{Q\in\mathcal{B}/\mathcal{A}} = \mathbf{a}_{Q/\mathcal{A}} - \mathbf{a}_{Q/\mathcal{B}} - 2\boldsymbol{\omega}_{\mathcal{B}/\mathcal{A}} \times \mathbf{v}_{Q/\mathcal{B}}$$

Method 3: Assuming that $\mathbf{v}_{Q\in\mathcal{B}/\mathcal{C}}$ is known relative to some referential $\mathcal{C}$ whose motion is also known relative to referentials $\mathcal{A}$ and $\mathcal{B}$, then $\mathbf{v}_{Q\in\mathcal{B}/\mathcal{A}}$ can be obtained by applying formula (6.8):

$$\mathbf{v}_{Q\in\mathcal{B}/\mathcal{A}} = \mathbf{v}_{Q\in\mathcal{B}/\mathcal{C}} + \mathbf{v}_{Q\in\mathcal{C}/\mathcal{A}}$$

where $\mathbf{v}_{Q\in\mathcal{C}/\mathcal{A}}$ is determined from the knowledge of $\{\mathcal{V}_{\mathcal{C}/\mathcal{A}}\}$. Note that no such rule can be expressed for the acceleration. However, application of formula (6.5) gives

$$\mathbf{a}_{Q\in\mathcal{B}/\mathcal{A}} = \mathbf{a}_{Q\in\mathcal{B}/\mathcal{C}} + \mathbf{a}_{Q\in\mathcal{C}/\mathcal{A}} + 2\omega_{\mathcal{C}/\mathcal{A}} \times \mathbf{v}_{Q\in\mathcal{B}/\mathcal{C}}$$

6.8 Problems

Problem 6.1 A slender rod $\mathcal{G}$ is in motion relative to a referential $\mathcal{E}(O, \hat{\mathbf{x}}, \hat{\mathbf{y}}, \hat{\mathbf{z}})$ in the following way:

(i) its endpoints A and B move in a vertical plane $(O, \hat{\mathbf{u}}, \hat{\mathbf{z}})$ which rotates relative to $\mathcal{E}$ about vertical axis $(O, \hat{\mathbf{z}})$ with angular velocity $\dot{\psi}\hat{\mathbf{z}}$,

(ii) point B slides on axis $(O, \hat{\mathbf{z}})$ while point A slides on axis $(O, \hat{\mathbf{u}})$.

The orientation of rod $\mathcal{G}$ relative to referential $\mathcal{F}(O, \hat{\mathbf{u}}, \hat{\mathbf{v}} = \hat{\mathbf{z}} \times \hat{\mathbf{u}}, \hat{\mathbf{z}})$ is defined by angle $\theta(t)$ as shown. A small ring P slides on line AB in such a way that $\mathbf{r}_{PB} = \rho(t)\hat{\boldsymbol{\imath}}$. Denote $\hat{\boldsymbol{\jmath}} = \hat{\mathbf{v}} \times \hat{\boldsymbol{\imath}}$ and $L = |AB|$.

a. Find $\mathbf{v}_{P/\mathcal{F}}$ from the expression of $\mathbf{v}_{P/\mathcal{G}}$. Then find $\mathbf{v}_{P/\mathcal{E}}$ from the expression of $\mathbf{v}_{P/\mathcal{F}}$.

b. Repeat for acceleration of P: find $\mathbf{a}_{P/\mathcal{F}}$ from $\mathbf{a}_{P/\mathcal{G}}$, then find $\mathbf{a}_{P/\mathcal{E}}$ from $\mathbf{a}_{P/\mathcal{F}}$.

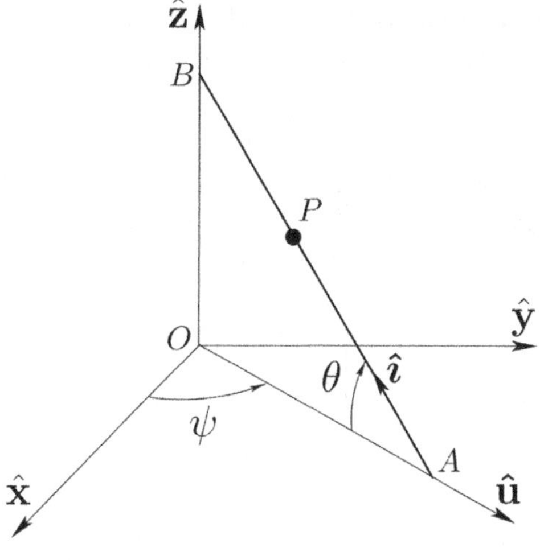

Problem 6.2 A small ring P slides relative to a circular frame $\mathcal{C}$ of center O and radius R at constant speed v. Frame $\mathcal{C}$ rotates about its diameter Oz at constant angular velocity $\omega\hat{\mathbf{e}}_z$ relative to referential $\mathcal{E}$. At time $t = 0$, $\mathcal{C}$ lies in the plane Oxz of $\mathcal{E}$ and P is at point A on axis Ox.

a. Find the velocity and acceleration of P relative to $\mathcal{C}$.

b. Using the quantities found in a) find the velocity and acceleration of P relative to $\mathcal{E}$.

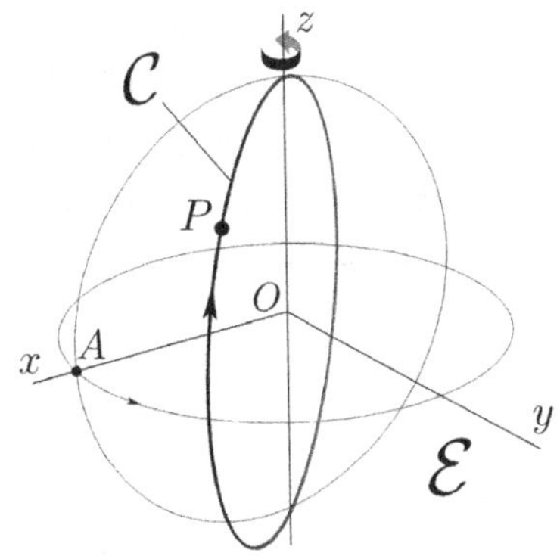

Problem 6.3 An aircraft must travel along a straight path between two positions A and B separated by a distance D. Due to a horizontal wind blowing opposite to the path of the aircraft at a speed w and angle α relative to line AB, the pilot must fly the aircraft at an angle β into the wind. The aircraft flies at constant speed v relative to the air.

a. Find the angle β that the aircraft must make relative to line AB so as to travel along the intended path. Under what condition is the trajectory realizable? Find angle β for $v = 100$ km/h, $D = 500$ km, $\alpha = 30°$ and $w = 50$ km/h.

b. The aircraft must travel from A to B then return to A. Find the corresponding time T_{AB} taken by the aircraft. Compare with the time t_{AB} in the absence of wind. Can T_{AB} ever be smaller than t_{AB}?

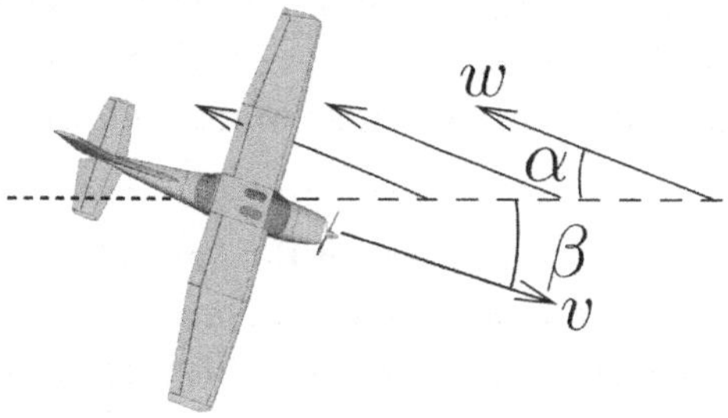

Problem 6.4 A sailboat P travels in a current so that a buoy located at a fixed point O always stays directly abeam to P, that is, the line connecting O and P stays perpendicular to the boat's relative velocity. The boat's

speed in still water is the constant v. The current has a constant velocity $\mathbf{u}$ (relative to the ground). Denote by $\hat{\mathbf{e}}_r$ the unit vector directed from O to P, and by $r(t)$ the radial distance. With axis Ox defined as the fixed line perpendicular to $\mathbf{u}$, $\theta(t)$ is the angle made by line OP with axis Ox.

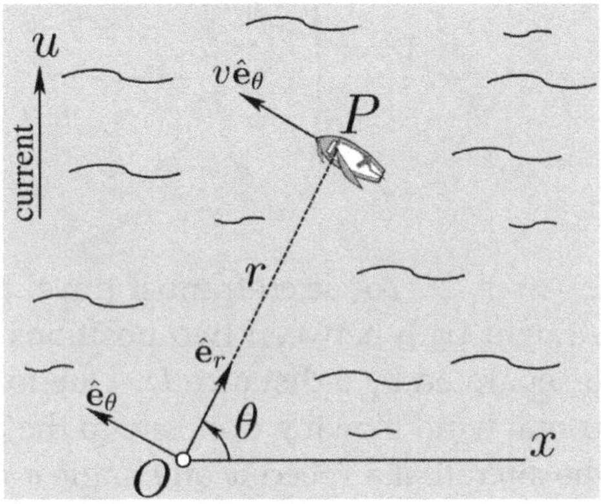

a. Find the absolute velocity of P, that is, measured relative to the ground on the polar basis $(\hat{\mathbf{e}}_r, \hat{\mathbf{e}}_\theta)$.

b. Find the trajectory $r(\theta)$ of P assuming that at time $t = 0$, $\theta = 0$ and $r = r_0$. Characterize this trajectory according to the ratio $e = u/v$. Plot the trajectories of P for $e = 0.5, 1, 2$.

Problem 6.5 An angler attempts to cross a river of width D whose banks are parallel straight lines. The speed v of his boat in calm water is constant. The current velocity relative to the ground is of constant magnitude u and in the direction of the river's banks. The angler has two choices: cross the river in the shortest path, or cross in the minimum time.

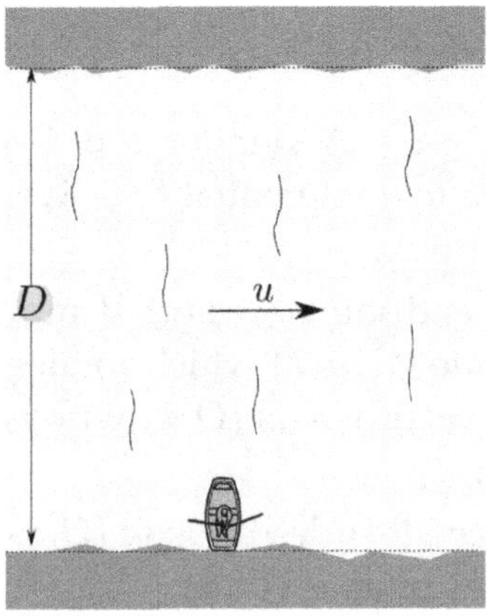

a. Which direction should the angler give his boat so that the shortest path is traveled? Find the duration T_1 of the crossing. (*hint: two cases must be considered: $u > v$ and $u < v$*)
b. Which direction should the boat take for the shortest duration T_2 of the crossing?

Problem 6.6 Four particles A, B, C and D initially located at the corners of a square travel at the same constant speed v along the sides, A toward B, B toward C, C toward D and D toward A as shown. The square is in rectilinear translation relative to a fixed referential $\mathcal{E}$ at constant speed v.
Show that the absolute trajectories of the four particles, that is, viewed by an observer fixed in referential $\mathcal{E}$, intersect at a point I.

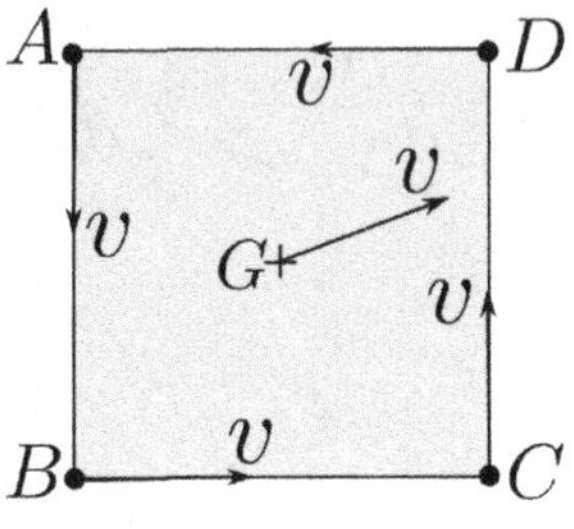

Problem 6.7 Consider the "grasshopper" carousel of Figure 6.9. The system is composed of three interconnected rigid bodies $\mathcal{A}$, $\mathcal{B}$ and $\mathcal{C}$. It is comprised of a central mast $\mathcal{A}(O, \hat{\mathbf{a}}_1, \hat{\mathbf{a}}_2, \hat{\mathbf{a}}_3)$, a system of arms such as $\mathcal{B}(A, \hat{\mathbf{b}}_1, \hat{\mathbf{b}}_2, \hat{\mathbf{b}}_3)$ extending radially from the mast and supporting a passenger-carrying seat $\mathcal{C}(B, \hat{\mathbf{c}}_1, \hat{\mathbf{c}}_2, \hat{\mathbf{c}}_3)$.
1. The mast $\mathcal{A}$ is in rotation with angle ψ about a vertical axis $(O, \hat{\mathbf{e}}_3 = \hat{\mathbf{a}}_3)$ relative to a referential $\mathcal{E}(O, \hat{\mathbf{e}}_1, \hat{\mathbf{e}}_2, \hat{\mathbf{e}}_3)$ attached to the ground.
2. The arm $\mathcal{B}$ can rotate about axis $(A, \hat{\mathbf{a}}_2 = \hat{\mathbf{b}}_2)$ of $\mathcal{A}$ with angle θ relative to $\mathcal{A}$. An actuator (pneumatic jack) mounted between $\mathcal{A}$ and $\mathcal{B}$ is able to create sudden lifting or lowering motions of arm $\mathcal{B}$.

3. The seat $\mathcal{C}$ supported by arm $\mathcal{B}$ can rotate about an axis $(B, \hat{\mathbf{c}}_3 = \hat{\mathbf{b}}_3)$ with angle ϕ relative to arm $\mathcal{B}$. The points A and B are defined by $\mathbf{r}_{OA} = h\hat{\mathbf{e}}_3 + R\hat{\mathbf{a}}_1$ and $\mathbf{r}_{AB} = L\hat{\mathbf{b}}_1$ (h, R, and L are constant).

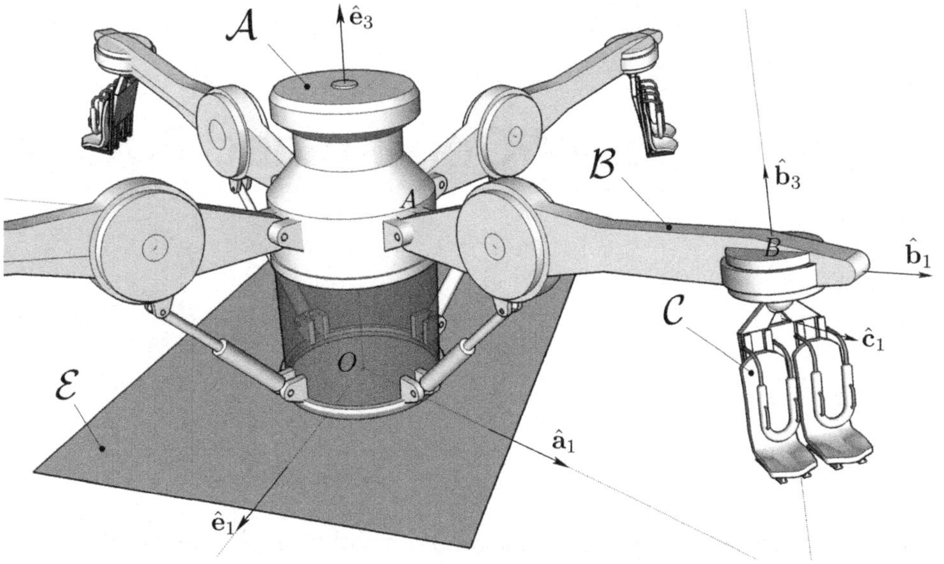

Figure 6.9

a. Find the kinematic screws $\{\mathcal{V}_{\mathcal{C}/\mathcal{B}}\}$, $\{\mathcal{V}_{\mathcal{B}/\mathcal{A}}\}$ and $\{\mathcal{V}_{\mathcal{A}/\mathcal{E}}\}$.
b. Find the kinematic screw $\{\mathcal{V}_{\mathcal{C}/\mathcal{E}}\}$ by using the kinematic loop formula.

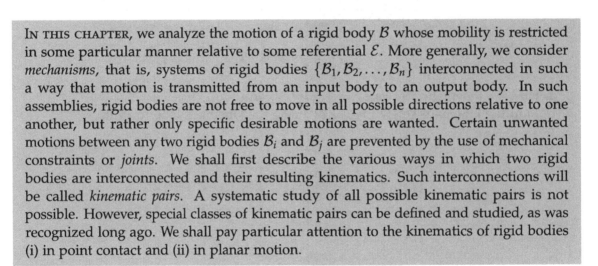

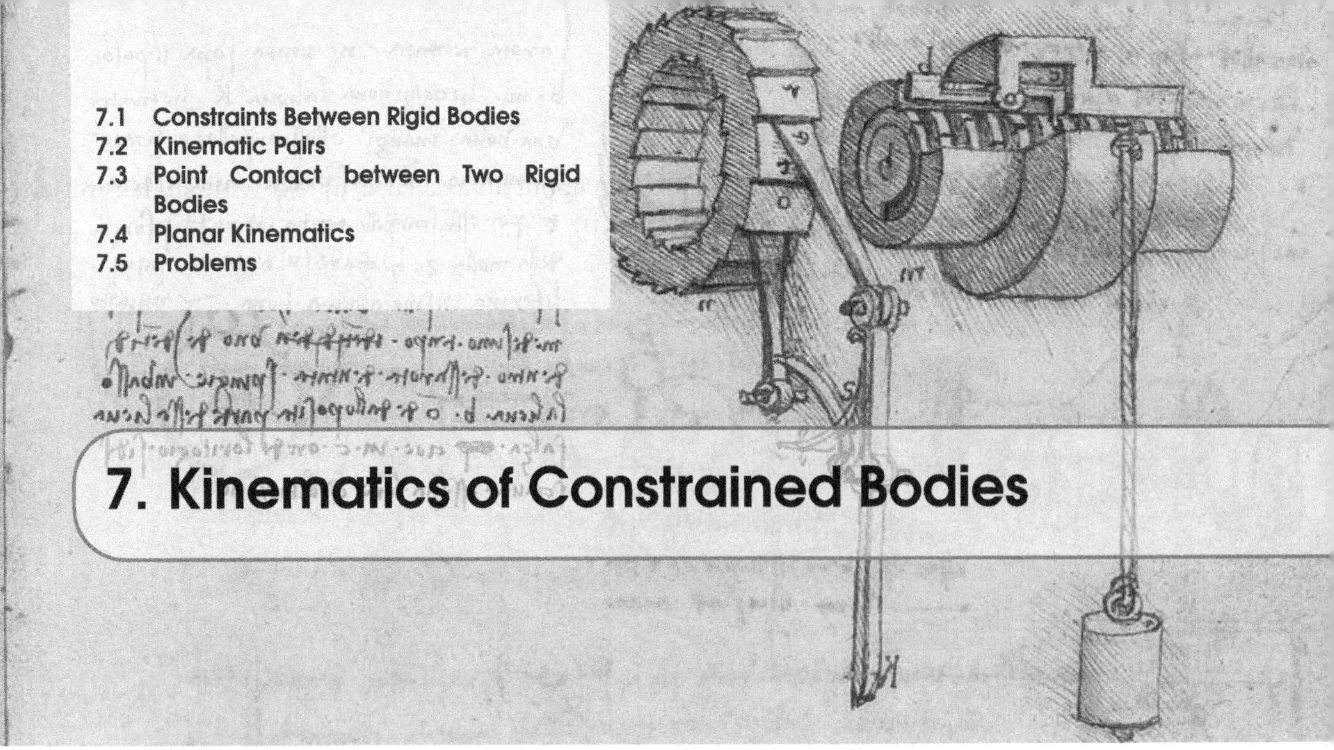

7. Kinematics of Constrained Bodies

IN THIS CHAPTER, we analyze the motion of a rigid body $\mathcal{B}$ whose mobility is restricted in some particular manner relative to some referential $\mathcal{E}$. More generally, we consider *mechanisms*, that is, systems of rigid bodies $\{\mathcal{B}_1, \mathcal{B}_2, \ldots, \mathcal{B}_n\}$ interconnected in such a way that motion is transmitted from an input body to an output body. In such assemblies, rigid bodies are not free to move in all possible directions relative to one another, but rather only specific desirable motions are wanted. Certain unwanted motions between any two rigid bodies $\mathcal{B}_i$ and $\mathcal{B}_j$ are prevented by the use of mechanical constraints or *joints*. We shall first describe the various ways in which two rigid bodies are interconnected and their resulting kinematics. Such interconnections will be called *kinematic pairs*. A systematic study of all possible kinematic pairs is not possible. However, special classes of kinematic pairs can be defined and studied, as was recognized long ago. We shall pay particular attention to the kinematics of rigid bodies (i) in point contact and (ii) in planar motion.

Throughout this chapter, to simplify notations, we denote $\{\mathcal{V}_{j/i}\}$ the kinematic screw of body $\mathcal{B}_j$ relative to body $\mathcal{B}_i$, $\omega_{j/i}$ the corresponding angular velocity, $\mathbf{v}_{P\in j/i}$ the velocity of a point P of $\mathcal{B}_j$ relative to $\mathcal{B}_i$, etc. We may in fact simply denote a system Σ of rigid bodies as a set `{1,2, ..., N}` in motion relative to a referential `0`.

7.1 Constraints Between Rigid Bodies

7.1.1 Geometric versus kinematic constraints

Recall from Chapter 1 that the parametrization of the position of a rigid body $\mathcal{B}_2$ relative to rigid body $\mathcal{B}_1$ can be achieved by parametrizing (i) the position of a particular point O_2 attached to $\mathcal{B}_2$, and (ii) the orientation of a basis $(\hat{\mathbf{x}}_2, \hat{\mathbf{y}}_2, \hat{\mathbf{z}}_2)$ attached to $\mathcal{B}_2$ relative to a basis $(\hat{\mathbf{x}}_1, \hat{\mathbf{y}}_1, \hat{\mathbf{z}}_1)$ attached to $\mathcal{B}_1$. In general, it takes six independent coordinates

$\mathbf{q}(t) = (q_1(t), \ldots, q_6(t))$ to define the unconstrained motion of $\mathcal{B}_2$ relative to $\mathcal{B}_1$. However, if this motion is constrained, there must exist relationships between these coordinates and possibly between their time-derivatives, thereby restricting the mobility of $\mathcal{B}_2$ relative to $\mathcal{B}_1$. Two broad types of constraints can be defined:

Definition 7.1 Constraints which lead to equations of the type

$$f(\mathbf{q}, t) = 0 \tag{7.1}$$

are said to be *holonomic* constraints.

They are also referred to as *geometric constraints* when the variable t is not explicit in (7.1). Geometric constraints typically appear when one or more points of $\mathcal{B}_2$ have a constrained motion relative to $\mathcal{B}_1$. Various methods can be used to find geometric constraint equations as illustrated in Section 7.1.2.

Definition 7.2 Constraints which lead to equations of the type

$$f(\mathbf{q}, \dot{\mathbf{q}}, t) = 0 \tag{7.2}$$

are called *non-holonomic* or *kinematic* constraints.

Remark 1. Constraint equations such as (7.2) are generally linear in the variable $\dot{\mathbf{q}}$, that is, are of the type

$$f_0(\mathbf{q}) + f_1(\mathbf{q})\dot{q}_1 + \cdots + f_6(\mathbf{q})\dot{q}_6 = 0 \tag{7.3}$$

Remark 2. If by integration a non-holonomic constraint can be reduced to a holonomic one, the constraint is called *pseudo-holonomic*.

Remark 3. As will be seen in Section 7.3, non-holonomic constraint equations can be the result of particular motions of $\mathcal{B}_2$ in point or line contact with $\mathcal{B}_1$, such as rolling without slipping or rolling without pivoting.

7.1.2 Examples of Geometric Constraint

Example 7.1 A sphere $\mathcal{B}_1$ (of center C, radius R) is constrained to move in a referential $\mathcal{B}_0(O, \hat{\mathbf{x}}_0, \hat{\mathbf{y}}_0, \hat{\mathbf{z}}_0)$ in such a way as to remain in contact with plane $(O, \hat{\mathbf{x}}_0, \hat{\mathbf{y}}_0)$. After parametrizing the motion of $\mathcal{B}_1$ relative to $\mathcal{B}_0$, find the equation(s) which express the constraint of $\mathcal{B}_1$ in $\mathcal{B}_0$.
Repeat for the case of a disk in contact with plane $(O, \hat{\mathbf{x}}_0, \hat{\mathbf{y}}_0)$ at a point of its rim, then for the case of a cylinder in contact with this plane along one of its generatrices. ■

a. The motion of sphere $\mathcal{B}_1$ in contact with plane $(O, \hat{\mathbf{x}}_0, \hat{\mathbf{y}}_0)$ of referential $\mathcal{B}_0$ can be defined by specifying
- the three Cartesian coordinates (x_C, y_C, z_C) of C: $\mathbf{r}_{OC} = x_C\hat{\mathbf{x}}_0 + y_C\hat{\mathbf{y}}_0 + z_C\hat{\mathbf{z}}_0$,
- the three Euler angles (ψ, θ, ϕ) defining the orientation of a basis $(\hat{\mathbf{x}}_1, \hat{\mathbf{y}}_1, \hat{\mathbf{z}}_1)$ attached to $\mathcal{B}_1$ relative to basis $(\hat{\mathbf{x}}_0, \hat{\mathbf{y}}_0, \hat{\mathbf{z}}_0)$ of $\mathcal{B}_0$.

The geometric constraint of contact at point I simply translates into the equation

$$z_C = R$$

The remaining coordinates $(x_C, y_C, \psi, \theta, \phi)$ are in general independent. The number of degrees of freedom of $\mathcal{B}_1$ relative to $\mathcal{B}_0$ has been decreased by one. Additional constraints can be

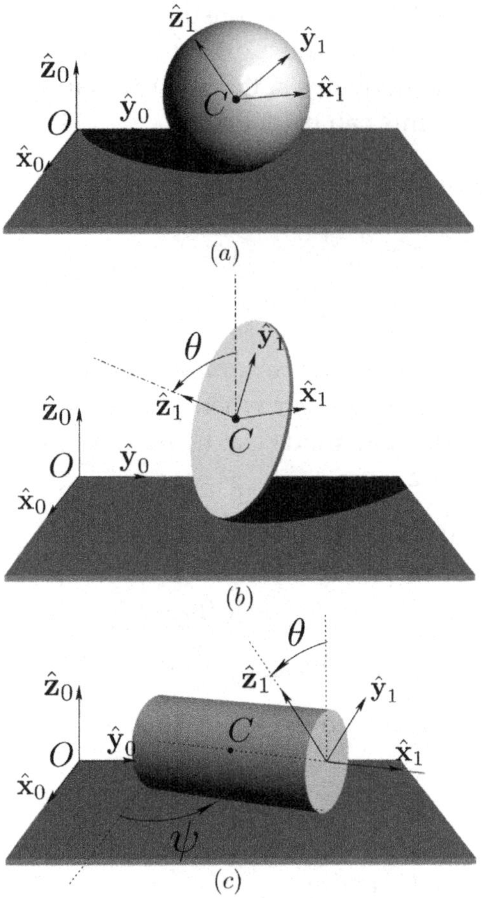

Figure 7.1 – *Examples of geometric constraints.*

introduced by imposing that the sphere does not slip at contact point I, as will be seen in Section 7.3.2.

b. Similarly, for a disk $\mathcal{B}_1$ of radius R in motion on a plane $(O, \hat{\mathbf{x}}_0, \hat{\mathbf{y}}_0)$, the inclination angle θ and the vertical coordinate $z_C = \mathbf{r}_{OC} \cdot \hat{\mathbf{z}}_0$ of its center C are constrained according to the equation

$$z_C = R \sin\theta$$

See Figure 7.1(b). Two additional (Euler) angles (ψ, ϕ) would define the orientation of a basis of unit vectors attached to $\mathcal{B}_1$ relative to $\mathcal{B}_0$. Again the number of degrees of freedom has been decreased by one.

c. Finally, the parametrization of cylinder $\mathcal{B}_1$ relative to $\mathcal{B}_0$ can be done with Cartesian coordinates (x_C, y_C, z_C) of a point C of the axis of $\mathcal{B}_1$ and the Euler angles (ψ, θ, ϕ) to define the orientation of basis $(\hat{\mathbf{x}}_1, \hat{\mathbf{y}}_1, \hat{\mathbf{z}}_1)$ attached to $\mathcal{B}_1$ relative to a basis $(\hat{\mathbf{x}}_0, \hat{\mathbf{y}}_0, \hat{\mathbf{z}}_0)$ of $\mathcal{B}_0$. See Figure 7.1(c). Two constraint equations can be written

$$z_C = R, \qquad \phi = 0$$

If $\hat{\mathbf{x}}_1$ denotes a unit vector of the axis of $\mathcal{B}_1$, then basis $(\hat{\mathbf{x}}_1, \hat{\mathbf{y}}_1, \hat{\mathbf{z}}_1)$ can be defined from basis $(\hat{\mathbf{x}}_0, \hat{\mathbf{y}}_0, \hat{\mathbf{z}}_0)$ by the following sequence of rotations

$$(\hat{\mathbf{x}}_0, \hat{\mathbf{y}}_0, \hat{\mathbf{z}}_0) \xrightarrow{\mathcal{R}_{\psi,\hat{\mathbf{z}}_0}} (\hat{\mathbf{x}}_1, \hat{\mathbf{v}}, \hat{\mathbf{z}}_0) \xrightarrow{\mathcal{R}_{\theta,\hat{\mathbf{x}}_1}} (\hat{\mathbf{x}}_1, \hat{\mathbf{y}}_1, \hat{\mathbf{z}}_1)$$

The number of degrees of freedom of $\mathcal{B}_1$ relative to $\mathcal{B}_0$ is reduced to four. ∎

Example 7.2 A plate $\mathcal{B}_1$ of side length ℓ is constrained to slide on a planar support $\mathcal{B}_0$ along edge AC and on an inclined plane along edge BD. The motion is parametrized with the coordinates x_A and θ, as shown in Figure 7.2. Find the constraint equation between x_A and θ. ■

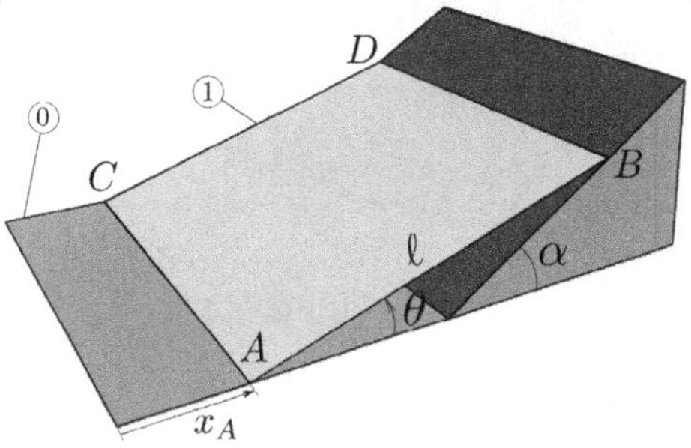

Figure 7.2

Define $(\hat{\mathbf{x}}_0, \hat{\mathbf{y}}_0, \hat{\mathbf{z}}_0)$ attached to the fixed support with $\mathbf{r}_{OA} = x_A \hat{\mathbf{x}}_0$, and unit vectors $(\hat{\mathbf{x}}_1, \hat{\mathbf{y}}_1)$ attached to $\mathcal{B}_1$ with $\mathbf{r}_{AB} = \ell \hat{\mathbf{x}}_1$. See Figure 7.3.

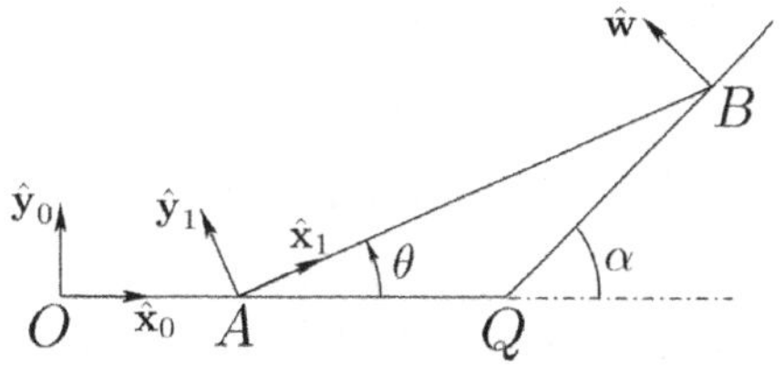

Figure 7.3

The coordinates (x_A, θ) parametrize the motion of $\mathcal{B}_1$: they are not independent, due to the constraint of point B with the inclined wall. This constraint can be stated by imposing that the velocity of point B must be directed along the inclined wall, that is, $\mathbf{v}_B \cdot \hat{\mathbf{w}} = 0$ (with $\hat{\mathbf{w}}$ normal to the inclined wall). With $\mathbf{v}_{B\in 1/0} = \mathbf{v}_{A\in 1/0} + \dot{\theta}\hat{\mathbf{z}} \times \ell\hat{\mathbf{x}}_1 = \dot{x}_A \hat{\mathbf{x}}_0 + \ell\dot{\theta}\hat{\mathbf{y}}_1$, this gives

$$-\dot{x}_A \sin\alpha + \ell\dot{\theta}\cos(\alpha - \theta) = 0$$

This is of course not a true kinematic constraint since it is integrable:

$$x_A \sin\alpha + \ell \sin(\alpha - \theta) = \text{constant}$$

expressing the geometric constraint $|OQ| \sin\alpha = \text{constant}$. ■

Example 7.3 A square plate $\mathcal{B}_1$ of side length a is motion in a referential $\mathcal{B}_0$ in such a way that its lower edge AB slides in the plane Oxy of $\mathcal{B}_0$, and that its upper edge slides along axis Oz normal to plane Oxy. See Figure 7.4.
Parametrize the position of $\mathcal{B}_1$ relative to $\mathcal{B}_0$. Find the possible constraint equations. Then determine the kinematic screw of $\mathcal{B}_1$ relative to $\mathcal{B}_0$. ■

To define the orientation of a basis $(\hat{\mathbf{x}}_1, \hat{\mathbf{y}}_1, \hat{\mathbf{z}}_1)$ of $\mathcal{B}_0$ relative to basis $(\hat{\mathbf{x}}_0, \hat{\mathbf{y}}_0, \hat{\mathbf{z}}_0)$, we first define unit vector $\hat{\mathbf{x}}_1$ along edge AB, such that $\mathbf{r}_{AB} = a\hat{\mathbf{x}}_1$. The orientation of line AB is defined by angle θ as shown in Figure 7.5, and such that $\hat{\mathbf{x}}_1 = -\sin\theta\hat{\mathbf{x}}_0 + \cos\theta\hat{\mathbf{y}}_0$. The position of point A is defined by its Cartesian coordinates (x_A, y_A): $\mathbf{r}_{OA} = x_A\hat{\mathbf{x}}_0 + y_A\hat{\mathbf{y}}_0$.

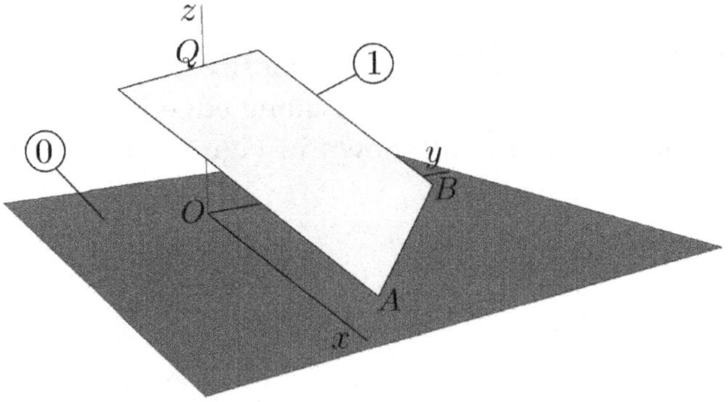

Figure 7.4

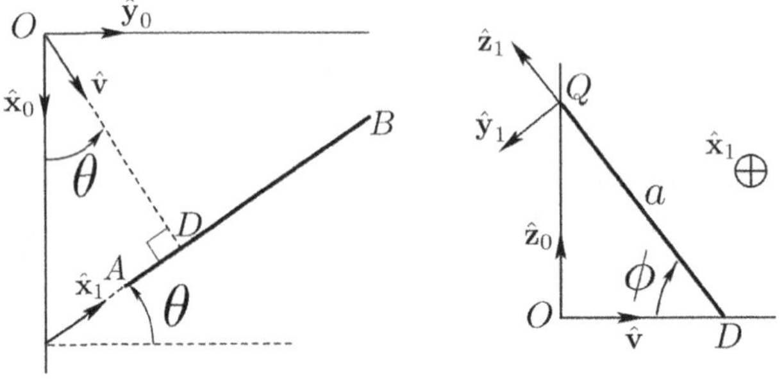

Figure 7.5

We then define point D as the projection of O onto line AB. Finally, the inclination of $\mathcal{B}_1$ is defined by introducing angle ϕ such that the contact point Q of $\mathcal{B}$ with axis Oz is defined by $\mathbf{r}_{DQ} = a\hat{\mathbf{z}}_1 = a(\sin\phi\hat{\mathbf{z}}_0 - \cos\phi\hat{\mathbf{v}})$. Unit vector $\hat{\mathbf{y}}_1 = \hat{\mathbf{z}}_1 \times \hat{\mathbf{x}}_1$ is normal to plate $\mathcal{B}_1$. See Figure 7.5. There exists a constraint equation between the coordinates (x_A, y_A, θ, ϕ): in triangle OAD, we find

$$x_A \cos\theta + y_A \sin\theta = a\cos\phi$$

using $\mathbf{r}_{OD} = a\cos\phi\hat{\mathbf{v}}$. This shows that body $\mathcal{B}_1$ has 3 degrees of freedom. With this parametrization, the kinematic screw of $\mathcal{B}_1$ is given by

$$\{\mathcal{V}_{1/0}\} = \left\{ \begin{array}{c} \dot{\theta}\hat{\mathbf{z}}_0 + \dot{\phi}\hat{\mathbf{x}}_1 \\ \dot{x}_A\hat{\mathbf{x}}_0 + \dot{y}_A\hat{\mathbf{y}}_0 \end{array} \right\}_A$$

■

Example 7.4 — Axial Piston Pump. Figure 7.6 shows a sketch of a variable-displacement axial piston pump. Body $0(O, \hat{\mathbf{x}}_0, \hat{\mathbf{y}}_0, \hat{\mathbf{z}}_0)$ denotes the pump housing. A piston thrust plate is attached to 0 and is inclined with constant angle α. The value of angle α can be adjusted to vary the pump volumetric volume. Body 1 is the rotationally-driven pump barrel: it is rotating relative to 0 about axis $(A, \hat{\mathbf{x}}_0)$. Body 2 is a piston connected to 1 by sliding along axis $(B, \hat{\mathbf{x}}_0)$. Only one piston is shown in the diagram. Piston 2 is in contact at all time with the inclined thrust plate at a point J. A spring (not shown) assures that contact is always realized.
The motion of this mechanism is parametrized by oriented angle $\theta(t) = (\hat{\mathbf{z}}_0, \hat{\mathbf{z}}_1)$. The displacement of the piston relative to the pump barrel is defined by the variable $x(t) = \mathbf{r}_{JB} \cdot \hat{\mathbf{x}}_0$.
Find the relationship between x, θ, and the constants α, $R = \mathbf{r}_{AB} \cdot \hat{\mathbf{z}}_1$, and $d = \mathbf{r}_{OA} \cdot \hat{\mathbf{x}}_0$. ■

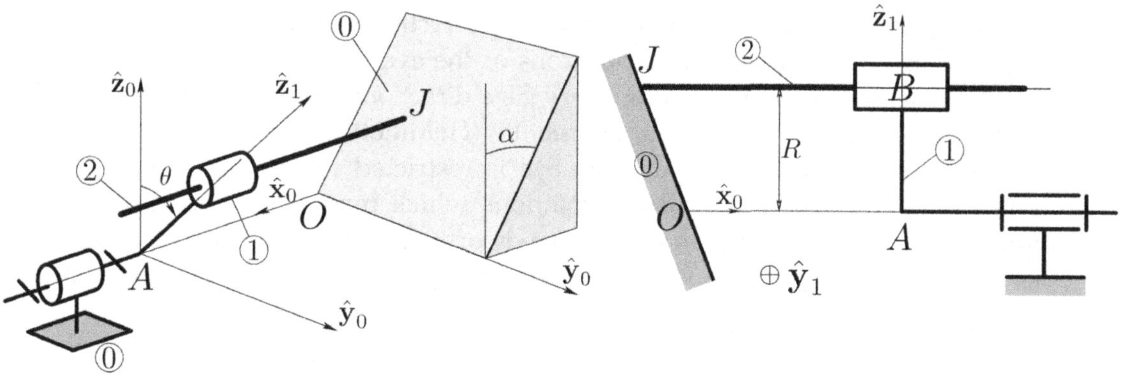

Figure 7.6

To find the input-output law, we need to relate the position of points O, A, B, and J to one another. A possible method is to write the vector loop equation between these points:

$$\mathbf{r}_{OA} + \mathbf{r}_{AB} + \mathbf{r}_{BJ} + \mathbf{r}_{JO} = \mathbf{0}$$

with $\mathbf{r}_{OA} = d\hat{\mathbf{x}}_0$, $\mathbf{r}_{AB} = R\hat{\mathbf{z}}_1$ and $\mathbf{r}_{BJ} = -x\hat{\mathbf{x}}_0$. The expression of $\mathbf{r}_{OJ}$ is found by imposing that point J lies in the plane $(O, \hat{\mathbf{y}}_0, \hat{\mathbf{w}}_0)$ of the thrust plate. Vector $\hat{\mathbf{w}}_0 = \cos\alpha\hat{\mathbf{z}}_0 - \sin\alpha\hat{\mathbf{x}}_0$ is a unit vector of the plane of contact normal to $\hat{\mathbf{y}}_0$. Thus we can write

$$\mathbf{r}_{OJ} = y_J\hat{\mathbf{y}}_0 + w_J\hat{\mathbf{w}}_0$$

We arrive at the following vector equation

$$d\hat{\mathbf{x}}_0 + R\hat{\mathbf{z}}_1 - x\hat{\mathbf{x}}_0 - y_J\hat{\mathbf{y}}_0 - w_J(\cos\alpha\hat{\mathbf{z}}_0 - \sin\alpha\hat{\mathbf{x}}_0) = \mathbf{0}$$

giving 3 scalar equations

$$d - x + w_J\sin\alpha = 0, \quad R\sin\theta - y_J = 0, \quad R\cos\theta - w_J\cos\alpha = 0$$

We then find the input-output law

$$x = d + R\cos\theta\tan\alpha$$

■

Example 7.5 — Listing's law of eye movements. The motion of the eye 1 relative to the head 0 can be considered spherical, that is, a point O of the eye can be considered fixed relative to 0. Hence, it is sufficient to parametrize the orientation of a basis $(\hat{\mathbf{x}}_1, \hat{\mathbf{y}}_1, \hat{\mathbf{z}}_1)$ of 1 relative to a basis $(\hat{\mathbf{x}}_0, \hat{\mathbf{y}}_0, \hat{\mathbf{z}}_0)$ of 0. The plane $(O, \hat{\mathbf{y}}_0, \hat{\mathbf{z}}_0)$ is parallel to the head plane of symmetry with the direction of $\hat{\mathbf{y}}_0$ defined as the frontal gaze direction. When basis $(\hat{\mathbf{x}}_1, \hat{\mathbf{y}}_1, \hat{\mathbf{z}}_1)$ coincides with basis $(\hat{\mathbf{x}}_0, \hat{\mathbf{y}}_0, \hat{\mathbf{z}}_0)$, the eye's position is said to be in its primary position. Unit vector $\hat{\mathbf{y}}_1$ defines the gaze direction: its orientation is defined by two angles α and β which defines the following rotation sequence

$$(\hat{\mathbf{x}}_0, \hat{\mathbf{y}}_0, \hat{\mathbf{z}}_0) \xrightarrow{\mathcal{R}_{(\alpha,\hat{\mathbf{x}}_0)}} (\hat{\mathbf{x}}_2 = \hat{\mathbf{x}}_0, \hat{\mathbf{y}}_2, \hat{\mathbf{z}}_2) \xrightarrow{\mathcal{R}_{(\beta,\hat{\mathbf{z}}_2)}} (\hat{\mathbf{x}}_3, \hat{\mathbf{y}}_3 = \hat{\mathbf{y}}_1, \hat{\mathbf{z}}_3 = \hat{\mathbf{z}}_2)$$

The orientation of the eye is then obtained by the rotation about $\hat{\mathbf{y}}_1$:

$$(\hat{\mathbf{x}}_3, \hat{\mathbf{y}}_3 = \hat{\mathbf{y}}_1, \hat{\mathbf{z}}_3) \xrightarrow{\mathcal{R}_{(\gamma,\hat{\mathbf{y}}_1)}} (\hat{\mathbf{x}}_1, \hat{\mathbf{y}}_1, \hat{\mathbf{z}}_1)$$

From a physiological viewpoint, only the gaze direction vector is of importance. Donders (1847) discovered that the actual positions of the eye are restricted in such a way that there is only one eye orientation for every gaze direction: in other words angle γ must be a function of α and β. Listing and Helmholtz (Helmholtz, 1867) were able to determine which two-dimensional subspace the eye is restricted to. Their result, now known as Listing's law, states that all eye rotations which map $(\hat{\mathbf{x}}_0, \hat{\mathbf{y}}_0, \hat{\mathbf{z}}_0)$ to $(\hat{\mathbf{x}}_1, \hat{\mathbf{y}}_1, \hat{\mathbf{z}}_1)$ are equivalent to a single rotation about an axis orthogonal to the primary gaze direction $\hat{\mathbf{y}}_0$. The goal of this problem is to find how Listing Law leads to a holonomic constraint equation between angles α, β and γ.
Using the quaternion representation of rotations $\mathcal{R}_{\alpha,\hat{\mathbf{x}}_0}$, $\mathcal{R}_{\beta,\hat{\mathbf{z}}_2}$, and $\mathcal{R}_{\gamma,\hat{\mathbf{y}}_1}$, find the axis of the equivalent rotation which maps $(\hat{\mathbf{x}}_0, \hat{\mathbf{y}}_0, \hat{\mathbf{z}}_0)$ to $(\hat{\mathbf{x}}_1, \hat{\mathbf{y}}_1, \hat{\mathbf{z}}_1)$. Then impose that this axis lies in the $(\hat{\mathbf{x}}_0, \hat{\mathbf{z}}_0)$ plane to find a holonomic constraint between α, β and γ. ■

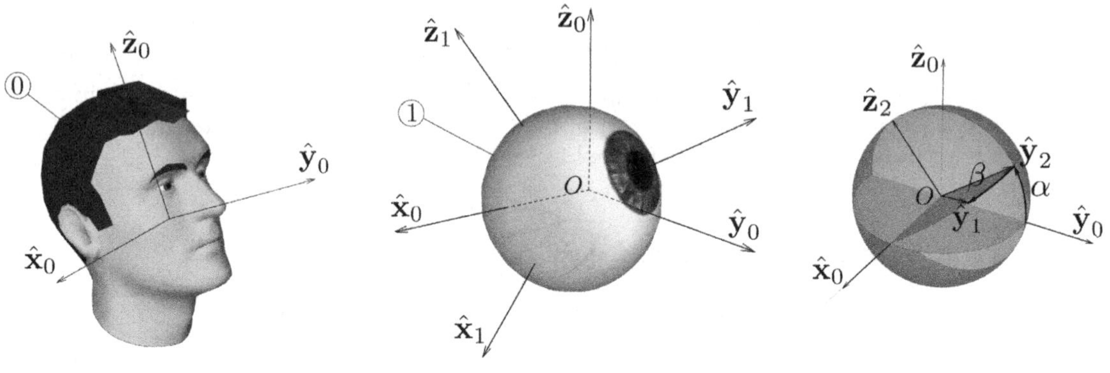

Figure 7.7

The three unit quaternions associated with rotations $\mathcal{R}_{\alpha,\hat{\mathbf{x}}_2}$, $\mathcal{R}_{\beta,\hat{\mathbf{z}}_2}$ and $\mathcal{R}_{\gamma,\hat{\mathbf{y}}_3}$ are (see Section 1.6)

$$Q_\alpha = \cos\frac{\alpha}{2} + \sin\frac{\alpha}{2}\hat{\mathbf{x}}_2, \quad Q_\beta = \cos\frac{\beta}{2} + \sin\frac{\beta}{2}\hat{\mathbf{z}}_2, \quad Q_\gamma = \cos\frac{\gamma}{2} + \sin\frac{\gamma}{2}\hat{\mathbf{y}}_3$$

The equivalent axis/angle rotation corresponds to the product $Q_\gamma Q_\beta Q_\alpha$. First we find the product $Q_\beta Q_\alpha$ according to equation (1.31)

$$Q_\beta Q_\alpha = \cos\frac{\alpha}{2}\cos\frac{\beta}{2} + \cos\frac{\beta}{2}\sin\frac{\alpha}{2}\hat{\mathbf{x}}_2 + \cos\frac{\alpha}{2}\sin\frac{\beta}{2}\hat{\mathbf{z}}_2 + \sin\frac{\alpha}{2}\sin\frac{\beta}{2}\hat{\mathbf{y}}_2$$

Then to find product $Q_\gamma Q_\beta Q_\alpha$ we need to express Q_γ on basis $(\hat{\mathbf{x}}_2, \hat{\mathbf{y}}_2, \hat{\mathbf{z}}_2)$:

$$Q_\gamma = \cos\frac{\gamma}{2} + \sin\frac{\gamma}{2}(\cos\beta\hat{\mathbf{y}}_2 - \sin\beta\hat{\mathbf{x}}_2)$$

The vector part of $Q_\gamma Q_\beta Q_\alpha$ is then given by

$$\text{Vect}(Q) = \cos\frac{\gamma}{2}\text{Vect}(Q_\beta Q_\alpha) + \cos\frac{\alpha}{2}\cos\frac{\beta}{2}\text{Vect}(Q_\gamma) + \text{Vect}(Q_\gamma) \times \text{Vect}(Q_\beta Q_\alpha)$$

This gives $\text{Vect}(Q)$ which defines the direction of the equivalent rotation

$$\text{Vect}(Q) = (s_{\frac{\alpha}{2}}c_{\frac{\beta}{2}}c_{\frac{\gamma}{2}} - c_{\frac{\alpha}{2}}s_{\frac{\beta}{2}}s_{\frac{\gamma}{2}})\hat{\mathbf{x}}_2 + (s_{\frac{\alpha}{2}}s_{\frac{\beta}{2}}c_{\frac{\gamma}{2}} + c_{\frac{\alpha}{2}}c_{\frac{\beta}{2}}s_{\frac{\gamma}{2}})\hat{\mathbf{y}}_2 + (c_{\frac{\alpha}{2}}s_{\frac{\beta}{2}}c_{\frac{\gamma}{2}} - s_{\frac{\alpha}{2}}c_{\frac{\beta}{2}}s_{\frac{\gamma}{2}})\hat{\mathbf{z}}_2$$

According to Listing law we must impose $\text{Vect}(Q) \cdot \hat{\mathbf{y}}_0 = \text{Vect}(Q) \cdot (c_\alpha\hat{\mathbf{y}}_2 - s_\alpha\hat{\mathbf{z}}_2)$: this gives the following holonomic constraint equation

$$\tan\frac{\gamma}{2} = \tan\frac{\alpha}{2}\,\tan\frac{\beta}{2}$$

■

7.2 Kinematic Pairs

MECHANISMS can be considered as "kinematic chains" assembled from elementary kinematic pairs formed by two rigid bodies in direct contact. The analysis of mechanisms hinges on the study of kinematic pairs, and the particular relative motion that they permit between two rigid bodies. There are many possible ways of interconnecting rigid bodies. A systematic description of all kinematic pairs is not feasible, as was discovered by Reuleaux.[1] However it is possible to classify them into two distinct classes depending on the type of contact imposed between the bodies: this leads to *lower kinematic pairs* and *higher kinematic pairs*. Lower pairs occur when the connection is realized through a surface of contact maintained between the two bodies. Higher pairs involve contact between lines or points of the two bodies. While there are many possible higher pairs, only six types of lower pairs are possible. The corresponding joints which define the interconnection in these pairs will be described in Section 7.2.1. These joints form the building block of mechanisms. However, most complex mechanisms involve a combination of lower and higher pairs. A few examples of higher pairs will be given in Section 7.2.2.

7.2.1 Lower kinematic pairs

LOWER kinematic pairs are achieved by direct surface contact. Arbitrary surfaces of contact do not permit relative motion between two bodies. Lower pairs correspond to the following surfaces:

(a) prismatic surfaces (prismatic joint or slider),
(b) surface of revolution (revolute joint or pivot),
(c) helical surface (helical joint or screw),
(d) right-circular cylindrical surface (cylindrical joint or slider-pivot),
(e) spherical surface (spherical joint),
(f) planar surface (planar joint).

These surfaces remain invariant during the motion of one body relative to the other. The resulting pairs are sketched in Figure 7.8. These pairs have important geometric properties.

Each joint realized between bodies $\mathcal{B}_1$ and $\mathcal{B}_2$ can be described in terms of its kinematic screw $\{\mathcal{V}_{2/1}\}$ which, resolved at a particular point O_2, takes the form

$$\{\mathcal{V}_{2/1}\} = \left\{ \begin{array}{c} \boldsymbol{\omega}_{2/1} \\ \\ \mathbf{v}_{O_2\in 2/1} \end{array} \right\} = \left\{ \begin{array}{c} \omega_x\hat{\mathbf{x}} + \omega_y\hat{\mathbf{y}} + \omega_z\hat{\mathbf{z}} \\ \\ v_{O_2x}\hat{\mathbf{x}} + v_{O_2y}\hat{\mathbf{y}} + v_{O_2z}\hat{\mathbf{z}} \end{array} \right\}_{O_2} \tag{7.4}$$

on a particular basis $(\hat{\mathbf{x}}, \hat{\mathbf{y}}, \hat{\mathbf{z}})$ of orthonormal vectors. Since the motion of body $\mathcal{B}_2$ relative to $\mathcal{B}_1$ is constrained, there must exist relationships between the components $(\omega_x, \omega_y, \omega_z, v_{O_2x},$

[1] Reuleaux F., *The Kinematics of Machinery; Outlines of a Theory of Machines*, MacMillan & Co, London (1876).

$v_{O_2y}, v_{O_2z})$. With a judicious choice of point O_2 and basis $(\hat{\mathbf{x}}, \hat{\mathbf{y}}, \hat{\mathbf{z}})$, it is possible to write the kinematic screw in terms of independent components by setting one or more components of the set $\{\omega_x, \omega_y, \omega_z, v_{O_2x}, v_{O_2y}, v_{O_2z}\}$ to zero. In the description of each lower kinematic pair, we give a spatial and planar schematic of the joint, and the corresponding number of degrees of freedom defined as the number of independent components of the set $\{\omega_x, \omega_y, \omega_z, v_{O_2x}, v_{O_2y}, v_{O_2z}\}$. These schematic diagrams are displayed in Figure 7.9. These diagrams will prove useful for the modeling and kinematic analysis of complex mechanisms.

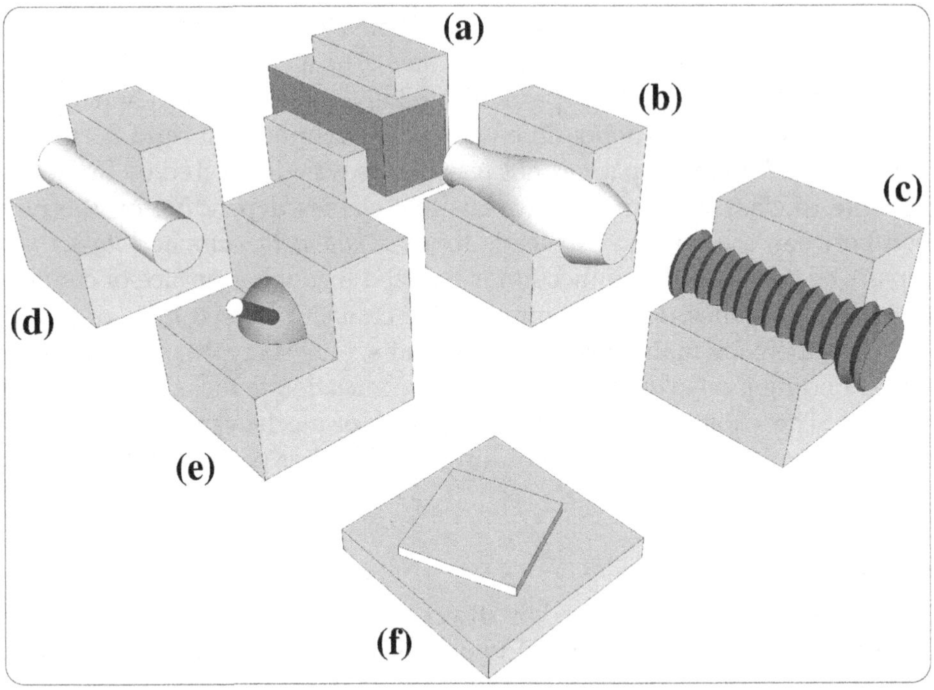

Figure 7.8 – *Lower kinematic pairs.*

Slider.

In a slider shown in Figures 7.8a and 7.9a, a prismatic surface of $\mathcal{B}_2$ slides against an identical prismatic surface of $\mathcal{B}_1$, thus restricting the motion to a rectilinear translation along a direction $\hat{\mathbf{x}}_1 = \hat{\mathbf{x}}_2$ common to $\mathcal{B}_1$ and $\mathcal{B}_2$. We set $(\hat{\mathbf{x}}_1, \hat{\mathbf{y}}_1, \hat{\mathbf{z}}_1) = (\hat{\mathbf{x}}_2, \hat{\mathbf{y}}_2, \hat{\mathbf{z}}_2)$ with $\hat{\mathbf{x}}_1 = \hat{\mathbf{x}}_2$ directed along the direction of the translation. This is a one-degree-of-freedom joint. The kinematic screw of $\mathcal{B}_2$ relative to $\mathcal{B}_1$ takes the form

$$\{\mathcal{V}_{2/1}\} = \left\{ \begin{array}{c} \mathbf{0} \\ v_{O_2x}\hat{\mathbf{x}}_1 \end{array} \right\}_{O_2} = \left\{ \begin{array}{c} \mathbf{0} \\ v_{2/1}\hat{\mathbf{x}}_1 \end{array} \right\}_{\forall P \in 2} \tag{7.5}$$

Pivot.

A pivot or revolute joint shown in Figures 7.8b and 7.9b is a one-degree-of-freedom joint which permits a rotation about an axis $(O_1, \hat{\mathbf{x}}_1) = (O_2, \hat{\mathbf{x}}_2)$ common to $\mathcal{B}_1$ and $\mathcal{B}_2$. Hence, the angular velocity $\boldsymbol{\omega}_{2/1} = \omega_x \hat{\mathbf{x}}_1$ has two vanishing components, and the velocity $\mathbf{v}_{O_2 \in 2/1}$ of point O_2 is zero, as is the velocity of any point on the axis of rotation

$$\{\mathcal{V}_{2/1}\} = \left\{ \begin{array}{c} \omega_x\hat{\mathbf{x}}_1 \\ \mathbf{0} \end{array} \right\}_{O_2} = \left\{ \begin{array}{c} \omega_x\hat{\mathbf{x}}_1 \\ \mathbf{0} \end{array} \right\}_{\forall P \in (O_2, \hat{\mathbf{x}}_2)} \tag{7.6}$$

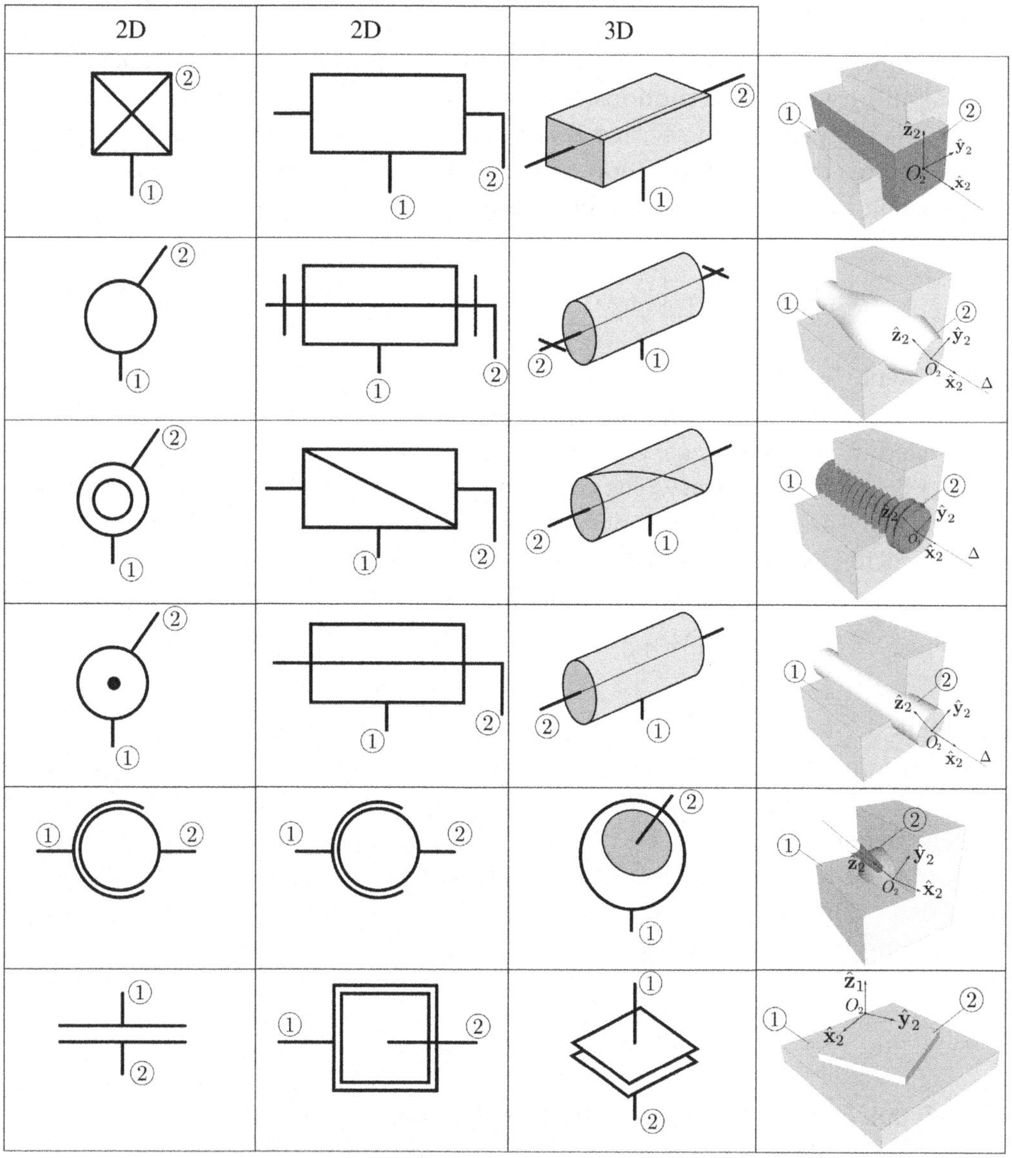

Figure 7.9 – *Schematics of kinematic pairs (joints).*

Slider-Pivot.

A slider-pivot or cylindrical joint shown in Figures 7.8d and 7.9d is a two-degree-of-freedom joint which permits body $\mathcal{B}_2$ to rotate about and translate along an axis $(O_1, \hat{\mathbf{x}}_1)$ of body $\mathcal{B}_1$. We may take $\hat{\mathbf{x}}_1 = \hat{\mathbf{x}}_2$ and point O_2 on axis $(O_1, \hat{\mathbf{x}}_1)$. Hence, both the angular velocity $\boldsymbol{\omega}_{2/1} = \omega_x \hat{\mathbf{x}}_1$ and the velocity $\mathbf{v}_{O_2/1} = v_{O_2x} \hat{\mathbf{x}}_1$ of point O_2 have two vanishing components. The motion $\mathcal{B}_2$ relative to $\mathcal{B}_1$ is helical about axis $(O_1, \hat{\mathbf{x}}_1)$ and all points of axis $(O_2, \hat{\mathbf{x}}_2)$ have the same velocity $v_{O_2x} \hat{\mathbf{x}}_1$:

$$\{\mathcal{V}_{2/1}\} = \left\{ \begin{array}{c} \omega_x \hat{\mathbf{x}}_1 \\ v_{O_2x} \hat{\mathbf{x}}_1 \end{array} \right\}_{O_2} = \left\{ \begin{array}{c} \omega_x \hat{\mathbf{x}}_1 \\ v_{O_2x} \hat{\mathbf{x}}_1 \end{array} \right\}_{\forall P \in (O_2, \hat{\mathbf{x}}_2)} \tag{7.7}$$

Helical Joint.

A *helical joint* or *screw* shown in Figures 7.8c and 7.9c is a slider-pivot joint for which the rotational and translational motions are constrained by the relation $v_{O_2x} = (p/2\pi)\omega_x$. The constant p is the pitch of the screw: it is the distance traveled by point O_2 on axis $(O_1, \hat{\mathbf{x}}_1)$ when $\mathcal{B}_2$ rotates by a full revolution. Thus, this is a one-degree-of-freedom joint, and the corresponding kinematic screw can be written as

$$\{\mathcal{V}_{2/1}\} = \left\{ \begin{array}{c} \omega_x \hat{\mathbf{x}}_1 \\ \frac{p}{2\pi}\omega_x \hat{\mathbf{x}}_1 \end{array} \right\}_{\forall P \in (O_2, \hat{\mathbf{x}}_2)} \tag{7.8}$$

Spherical Joint.

In a *spherical* or *ball-socket* joint shown in Figures 7.8e and 7.9e, a single point O_2 of $\mathcal{B}_2$ remains fixed in $\mathcal{B}_1$: we may set $O_2 = O_1$. The orientation of basis $(\hat{\mathbf{x}}_2, \hat{\mathbf{y}}_2, \hat{\mathbf{z}}_2)$ relative to basis $(\hat{\mathbf{x}}_1, \hat{\mathbf{y}}_1, \hat{\mathbf{z}}_1)$ is however arbitrary. The components $(\omega_x, \omega_y, \omega_z)$ of $\boldsymbol{\omega}_{2/1}$ on basis $(\hat{\mathbf{x}}_1, \hat{\mathbf{y}}_1, \hat{\mathbf{z}}_1)$ (or basis $(\hat{\mathbf{x}}_2, \hat{\mathbf{y}}_2, \hat{\mathbf{z}}_2)$) are independent of each other: a spherical joint is a three-degree-of-freedom joint with corresponding kinematic screw

$$\{\mathcal{V}_{2/1}\} = \left\{ \begin{array}{c} \omega_x \hat{\mathbf{x}}_1 + \omega_y \hat{\mathbf{y}}_1 + \omega_z \hat{\mathbf{z}}_1 \\ \mathbf{0} \end{array} \right\}_{O_2} \tag{7.9}$$

Planar Joint.

In a planar joint shown in Figures 7.8f and 7.9f, a plane $(O_2, \hat{\mathbf{x}}_2, \hat{\mathbf{y}}_2)$ of $\mathcal{B}_2$ coincides with a plane $(O_1, \hat{\mathbf{x}}_1, \hat{\mathbf{y}}_1)$ of $\mathcal{B}_1$. Hence the motion of point O_2 of plane $(O_2, \hat{\mathbf{x}}_2, \hat{\mathbf{y}}_2)$ has two degrees of freedom: $\mathbf{v}_{O_2 \in 2/1} = v_{O_2x}\hat{\mathbf{x}}_1 + v_{O_2y}\hat{\mathbf{y}}_1$. In addition, $\mathcal{B}_2$ is free to rotate about vector $\hat{\mathbf{z}}_1 = \hat{\mathbf{z}}_2$ normal to plane of motion with angular velocity $\boldsymbol{\omega}_{2/1} = \omega_z \hat{\mathbf{z}}_1$. The components $(\omega_z, v_{O_2x}, v_{O_2y})$ are independent: a planar joint is a three-degree-of-freedom joint with corresponding kinematic screw

$$\{\mathcal{V}_{2/1}\} = \left\{ \begin{array}{c} \omega_z \hat{\mathbf{z}}_1 \\ v_{O_2x}\hat{\mathbf{x}}_1 + v_{O_2y}\hat{\mathbf{y}}_1 \end{array} \right\}_{O_2} \tag{7.10}$$

A more detailed study of planar motions will be given in Section 7.4.

Example 7.6 A lower kinematic pair may be created by imposing contact between two toroidal surfaces as displayed in Figure 7.10. After identifying the possible relative motion between the two bodies, parametrize the position of $\mathcal{B}_2$ relative to $\mathcal{B}_1$. We may call the corresponding pair "circular slider". By finding the corresponding kinematic screw, show that this assembly does not define a new kinematic pair. ■

Consider the common midplane of $\mathcal{B}_1$ and $\mathcal{B}_2$ as shown in Figure 7.10: a point O_2 of $\mathcal{B}_2$ can be considered as lying on the midline of $\mathcal{B}_2$. Angle $\theta = (\hat{\mathbf{x}}_1, \mathbf{r}_{O_1O_2})$ defines the position of O_2 relative to $\mathcal{B}_1$. Let $\hat{\mathbf{x}}_2$ be the unit vector such that $\mathbf{r}_{O_1O_2} = R\hat{\mathbf{x}}_2$ (R is a constant). It is readily seen that unit vector $\hat{\mathbf{x}}_2$ is attached to $\mathcal{B}_2$. Then define $\hat{\mathbf{y}}_2 = \hat{\mathbf{z}}_1 \times \hat{\mathbf{x}}_2$. The basis of unit vectors $(\hat{\mathbf{x}}_2, \hat{\mathbf{y}}_2, \hat{\mathbf{z}}_2)$ is attached to $\mathcal{B}_2$. Its orientation relative to $\mathcal{B}_1$ is defined by the same angle θ. Hence, we can write the kinematic screw of $\mathcal{B}_2$ in the following form

$$\{\mathcal{V}_{2/1}\} = \left\{ \begin{array}{c} \dot{\theta}\hat{\mathbf{z}}_1 \\ R\dot{\theta}\hat{\mathbf{y}}_2 \end{array} \right\}_{O_2} = \left\{ \begin{array}{c} \dot{\theta}\hat{\mathbf{z}}_1 \\ \mathbf{0} \end{array} \right\}_{O_1}$$

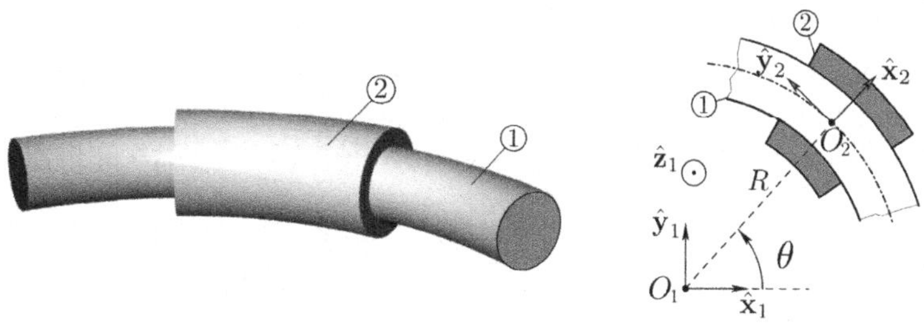

Figure 7.10

In the last expression, we have used $\mathbf{v}_{O_1\in 2/1} = R\dot{\theta}\hat{\mathbf{y}}_2 + \dot{\theta}\hat{\mathbf{z}}_1 \times (-R\hat{\mathbf{x}}_2) = \mathbf{0}$. Hence, this is the kinematic screw of a body in rotation about axis $(O, \hat{\mathbf{z}}_1)$: the kinematic pair is equivalent to a pivot of axis $(O, \hat{\mathbf{z}}_1)$. We conclude that this is not a new lower kinematic pair. ■

7.2.2 Higher kinematic pairs

HIGHER kinematic pairs are characterized by line or point contact, such as would occur in ball or roller bearings, gears, cams, etc. Figure 7.11 shows three examples of higher pairs. Note that higher kinematic pairs, as opposed to lower pairs, often require to be connected with other pairs to be functional.

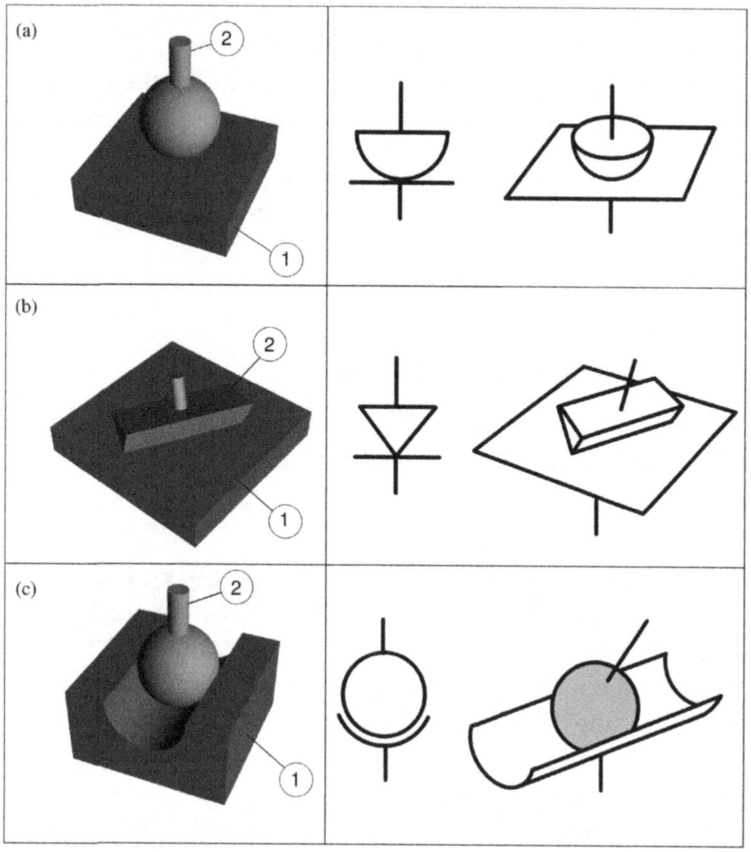

Figure 7.11 – *Examples of higher kinematics pairs.*

Figure 7.11(a) shows a body $\mathcal{B}_2$ bounded by a curved surface in contact with a planar surface of $\mathcal{B}_1$ about a single point O_2 of $\mathcal{B}_2$. Since O_2 is constrained to remain in a plane $(O_1, \hat{\mathbf{x}}_1, \hat{\mathbf{y}}_1)$ of $\mathcal{B}_1$, its velocity takes the form $\mathbf{v}_{O_2 \in 2/1} = v_{O_2 x}\hat{\mathbf{x}}_1 + v_{O_2 y}\hat{\mathbf{y}}_1$. The orientation of $\mathcal{B}_2$ relative to $\mathcal{B}_1$ is free to vary arbitrarily. Assuming the components $(\omega_x, \omega_x, \omega_z, v_{O_2 x}, v_{O_2 y})$ independent, we have a five-degree-of-freedom joint with corresponding kinematic screw

$$\{\mathcal{V}_{2/1}\} = \left\{ \begin{array}{c} \omega_x \hat{\mathbf{x}}_1 + \omega_y \hat{\mathbf{y}}_1 + \omega_z \hat{\mathbf{z}}_1 \\ v_{O_2 x}\hat{\mathbf{x}}_1 + v_{O_2 y}\hat{\mathbf{y}}_1 \end{array} \right\}_{O_2} \tag{7.11}$$

Constraints realized by point contact will be analyzed in more detail in Section 7.4.

Figure 7.11(b) shows a body $\mathcal{B}_2$ constrained to remain in contact with a plane $(O_1, \hat{\mathbf{x}}_1, \hat{\mathbf{y}}_1)$ of $\mathcal{B}_1$ along a line $(O_2, \hat{\mathbf{x}}_2)$ of $\mathcal{B}_2$. This line constraint in turn imposes a constraint on the orientation of a basis of $\mathcal{B}_2$: a basis $(\hat{\mathbf{x}}_2, \hat{\mathbf{y}}_2, \hat{\mathbf{z}}_2)$ of $\mathcal{B}_2$ is obtained by a rotation about $\hat{\mathbf{z}}_1$ normal to the plane of contact followed by a rotation about $\hat{\mathbf{x}}_2$: this leads to $\boldsymbol{\omega}_{2/1} = \omega_x \hat{\mathbf{x}}_2 + \omega_z \hat{\mathbf{z}}_1$, and $\mathbf{v}_{O_2 \in 2/1} = v_{O_2 x}\hat{\mathbf{x}}_1 + v_{O_2 y}\hat{\mathbf{y}}_1$. Assuming the components $(\omega_x, \omega_z, v_{O_2 x}, v_{O_2 y})$ independent, this joint has four degrees of freedom joint whose kinematic screw is given by

$$\{\mathcal{V}_{2/1}\} = \left\{ \begin{array}{c} \omega_x \hat{\mathbf{x}}_2 + \omega_z \hat{\mathbf{z}}_1 \\ v_{O_2 x}\hat{\mathbf{x}}_1 + v_{O_2 y}\hat{\mathbf{y}}_1 \end{array} \right\}_{\forall P \in (O_2, \hat{\mathbf{x}}_2)} \tag{7.12}$$

Finally, Figure 7.11(c) shows a sphere constrained to the interior surface of a cylinder. The two surfaces are in contact along an arc of circle. The center O_2 of the sphere is constrained to move along the axis $(O_1, \hat{\mathbf{x}}_1)$ of the cylinder: this imposes $\mathbf{v}_{O_2/1} = v_{O_2 x}\hat{\mathbf{x}}_1$. The orientation of basis $(\hat{\mathbf{x}}_2, \hat{\mathbf{y}}_2, \hat{\mathbf{z}}_2)$ of the sphere relative to basis $(\hat{\mathbf{x}}_1, \hat{\mathbf{y}}_1, \hat{\mathbf{z}}_1)$ of the cylinder is however arbitrary. This is a four-degree-of-freedom joint with corresponding kinematic screw

$$\{\mathcal{V}_{2/1}\} = \left\{ \begin{array}{c} \omega_x \hat{\mathbf{x}}_1 + \omega_y \hat{\mathbf{y}}_1 + \omega_z \hat{\mathbf{z}}_1 \\ v_{O_2 x}\hat{\mathbf{x}}_1 \end{array} \right\}_{O_2} \tag{7.13}$$

It can be viewed as the combination of a slider and a spherical joint.

7.3 Point Contact between Two Rigid Bodies

Joints resulting from point contact between two surfaces play a special role in countless mechanisms, such as ball bearings, gears, cams, etc.

7.3.1 Assumptions

Consider two rigid bodies $\mathcal{B}_1(O_1, \hat{\mathbf{x}}_1, \hat{\mathbf{y}}_1, \hat{\mathbf{z}}_1)$ and $\mathcal{B}_2(O_2, \hat{\mathbf{x}}_2, \hat{\mathbf{y}}_2, \hat{\mathbf{z}}_2)$ in relative motion and maintained in contact at a point I. Assume that at least one of the surfaces is smooth[2]. At any given time, there exists a point instantaneously attached to $\mathcal{B}_1$ which coincides at I with a point instantaneously attached to $\mathcal{B}_2$. Assume that there exists a tangent plane Π to the surfaces bounding $\mathcal{B}_1$ and $\mathcal{B}_2$ at point I. We denote by $(\hat{\boldsymbol{\tau}}_1, \hat{\boldsymbol{\tau}}_2, \hat{\mathbf{n}}_{12})$ a basis of unit vectors, with $\hat{\mathbf{n}}_{12}$ the unit normal vector to Π pointing from $\mathcal{B}_1$ to $\mathcal{B}_2$. Vectors $(\hat{\boldsymbol{\tau}}_1, \hat{\boldsymbol{\tau}}_2)$ lie in the tangent plane Π. See Figure 7.12.

Of interest is the motion of $\mathcal{B}_2$ relative to $\mathcal{B}_1$. The parametrization of the position of both $\mathcal{B}_1$ and $\mathcal{B}_2$ is typically defined relative to a referential $\mathcal{B}_0$ (relative to which the motions of

[2]If one of the surfaces is not smooth, as is the case of a cone whose vertex is in contact with a smooth surface, then we define Π as the plane tangential to the smooth surface.

$\mathcal{B}_1$ and $\mathcal{B}_2$ are observed). In this case, the kinematics of $\mathcal{B}_2$ relative to $\mathcal{B}_1$ can be related to the kinematics of $\mathcal{B}_2$ and $\mathcal{B}_1$ relative to $\mathcal{B}_0$ by application of formula (6.9):

$$\{\mathcal{V}_{2/1}\} = \left\{ \begin{array}{c} \boldsymbol{\omega}_{2/1} \\ \mathbf{v}_{I\in 2/1} \end{array} \right\} = \{\mathcal{V}_{2/0}\} - \{\mathcal{V}_{1/0}\} = \left\{ \begin{array}{c} \boldsymbol{\omega}_{2/0} - \boldsymbol{\omega}_{1/0} \\ \mathbf{v}_{I\in 2/0} - \mathbf{v}_{I\in 1/0} \end{array} \right\} \tag{7.14}$$

We now describe the physical characterization and properties of the two kinematic quantities $\mathbf{v}_{I\in 2/1}$ and $\boldsymbol{\omega}_{2/1}$.

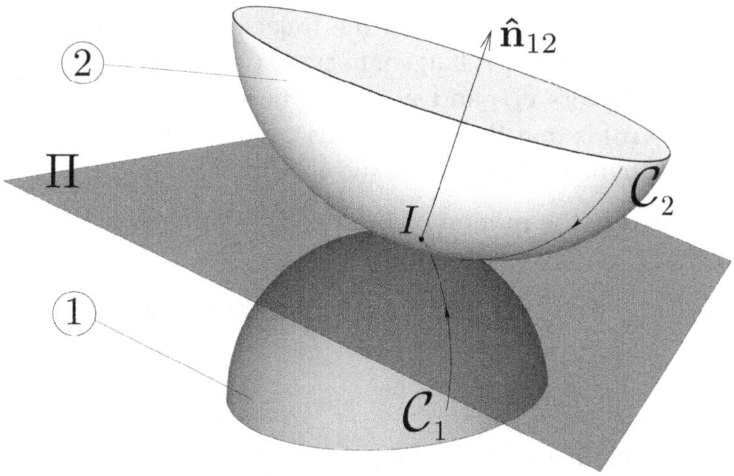

Figure 7.12 – *Two rigid bodies in contact at a point I.*

7.3.2 The slip velocity of a rigid body

Definition 7.3 — Slip velocity. The *slip velocity* of body $\mathcal{B}_2$ relative to body $\mathcal{B}_1$ at contact point I is the instantaneous velocity $\mathbf{v}_{I\in 2/1}$ of contact point I. It characterizes the *slipping* (or *sliding*) motion of $\mathcal{B}_2$ relative to $\mathcal{B}_1$.

For the contact to be maintained, the slip-velocity must remain in tangential plane Π, that is, the component of $\mathbf{v}_{I\in 2/1}$ along unit vector $\hat{\mathbf{n}}_{12}$ must be imposed to zero

$$\mathbf{v}_{I\in 2/1} \cdot \hat{\mathbf{n}}_{12} = \mathbf{v}_{O_2\in 2/1} \cdot \hat{\mathbf{n}}_{12} + \boldsymbol{\omega}_{2/1} \cdot (\mathbf{r}_{O_2 I} \times \hat{\mathbf{n}}_{12}) = 0 \tag{7.15}$$

This provides an equation of the type

$$f_1(\mathbf{q})\dot{q}_1 + f_2(\mathbf{q})\dot{q}_2 + \cdots + f_6(\mathbf{q})\dot{q}_6 = 0$$

where $\mathbf{q} = (q_1, \ldots, q_6)$ represents the six coordinates which define the position of $\mathcal{B}_2$ relative to $\mathcal{B}_1$. Hence the contact of $\mathcal{B}_2$ with $\mathcal{B}_1$ at point I reduces the mobility of $\mathcal{B}_2$ relative to $\mathcal{B}_1$ from six to five. In general, this equation is expected to be integrable and to provide a geometric constraint of the type (7.1).

Often the parametrization of the position $\mathcal{B}_1$ relative to $\mathcal{B}_2$ implicitly takes into account the contact at I. In this case, condition (7.15) will be automatically satisfied. In other cases, equation (7.15) provides a simple way to impose this geometric condition, once the slip-velocity at I has been found. See Section 7.3.5 for practical examples.

There exist two practical ways to determine the slip-velocity at I:

1. It can be related to the motion of point I relative to $\mathcal{B}_1$ and $\mathcal{B}_2$ by application of formula (6.3):

$$\mathbf{v}_{I\in 2/1} = \mathbf{v}_{I/1} - \mathbf{v}_{I/2} \tag{7.16}$$

   where

$$\mathbf{v}_{I/1} = \left(\frac{d\mathbf{r}_{O_1 I}}{dt}\right)_1, \qquad \mathbf{v}_{I/2} = \left(\frac{d\mathbf{r}_{O_2 I}}{dt}\right)_2$$

   As $\mathcal{B}_2$ moves relative to $\mathcal{B}_1$, contact point I describes the trajectory $\mathcal{C}_1$ relative to $\mathcal{B}_1$ inscribed on the surface of $\mathcal{B}_1$ and the trajectory $\mathcal{C}_2$ relative to $\mathcal{B}_2$ inscribed on the surface of $\mathcal{B}_2$. Velocity $\mathbf{v}_{I/1}$ is tangent to curve $\mathcal{C}_1$, while velocity $\mathbf{v}_{I/2}$ is tangent to curve $\mathcal{C}_2$. Since both vectors $\mathbf{v}_{I/1}$ and $\mathbf{v}_{I/2}$ must necessarily lie in plane Π, a consequence of equation (7.16) is that the slip velocity also lies in tangential plane Π, as long as contact is maintained. This justifies the condition $\mathbf{v}_{I\in 2/1} \cdot \hat{\mathbf{n}}_{12} = 0$ of equation (7.15).

2. It can be related to the motion of $\mathcal{B}_1$ and $\mathcal{B}_2$ relative to a referential $\mathcal{B}_0$ according to equation (7.14):

$$\mathbf{v}_{I\in 2/1} = \mathbf{v}_{I\in 2/0} - \mathbf{v}_{I\in 1/0} \tag{7.17}$$

   where

$$\mathbf{v}_{I\in i/0} = \mathbf{v}_{O_i/0} + \boldsymbol{\omega}_{i/0} \times \mathbf{r}_{O_i I}, \qquad i = 1, 2$$

   is the velocity relative to $\mathcal{B}_0$ of the point of body $\mathcal{B}_i$ coinciding with contact point I. Equation (7.17) is especially useful when the motions of $\mathcal{B}_1$ and $\mathcal{B}_2$ are parametrized relative to a referential $\mathcal{B}_0$.

We now states the following definition.

Definition 7.4 — no-slip motion. The motion of $\mathcal{B}_2$ relative to $\mathcal{B}_1$ is said to be without slip at contact point I if the slip-velocity at I is identically zero during a finite time interval:

$$\mathbf{v}_{I\in 2/1} = \mathbf{0} \tag{7.18}$$

Remark 4. If $\mathcal{B}_2$ is in motion relative to $\mathcal{B}_1$ without slipping, then $\mathcal{B}_2$ is in instantaneous rotation relative to $\mathcal{B}_1$ about the axis $\Delta_{2/1}$ passing through I and directed along angular velocity $\boldsymbol{\omega}_{2/1}$ (only as far as velocities are concerned). Hence, axis $\Delta_{2/1}$ is the *instantaneous axis of rotation of $\mathcal{B}_2$ relative to $\mathcal{B}_1$*.

Remark 5. In general, the no-slip condition (7.18) will generate two non-holonomic, non-integrable constraint equations of the type (7.2). The mobility of $\mathcal{B}_2$ relative to $\mathcal{B}_1$ is then reduced to three.

NEVER determine the slip velocity $\mathbf{v}_{I\in 2/1}$ by direct time-differentiation of a position vector $\mathbf{r}_{O_1 I}$ (relative to $\mathcal{B}_1$). The same applies to velocities $\mathbf{v}_{I\in 2/0}$ and $\mathbf{v}_{I\in 1/0}$.

7.3.3 The pivoting and rolling motions of a rigid body

By writing the angular velocity $\boldsymbol{\omega}_{2/1}$ as the sum of tangential and normal components, we can characterize the motion of body $\mathcal{B}_2$ relative to body $\mathcal{B}_1$ in terms of its pivoting and rolling components.

Definition 7.5 — pivoting and rolling motions. At any instant, the angular velocity $\omega_{2/1}$ can be written as the sum of a normal component $\omega^n_{2/1}$ normal and a tangential component $\omega^t_{2/1}$ with respect to tangent plane Π at I :

$$\omega^n_{2/1} = (\omega_{2/1} \cdot \hat{\mathbf{n}}_{12})\hat{\mathbf{n}}_{12}, \qquad \omega^t_{2/1} = \hat{\mathbf{n}}_{12} \times (\omega_{2/1} \times \hat{\mathbf{n}}_{12}) \tag{7.19}$$

The normal component $\omega^n_{2/1}$ characterizes the *pivoting* motion of $\mathcal{B}_2$ on $\mathcal{B}_1$, while tangential component $\omega^t_{2/1}$ characterizes its *rolling* motion. If these two components are non-zero, body $\mathcal{B}_2$ is said to roll and pivot (with or without slipping) relative to body $\mathcal{B}_1$.

7.3.4 The Axodes of a Rigid Body Motion

We have learned in Chapter 5 that, in general, the kinematic screw $\{\mathcal{V}_{2/1}\}$ is characterized at any given time by its instantaneous screw axis $\Delta_{2/1}$ directed along $\omega_{2/1}$ and passing through a point I whose position is given by

$$\mathbf{r}_{O_2I} = \frac{\omega_{2/1} \times \mathbf{v}_{O_2/1}}{\omega^2_{2/1}}$$

as long as $\omega_{2/1} \neq \mathbf{0}$. Viewed by an observer attached to $\mathcal{B}_1$, rigid body $\mathcal{B}_2$ is instantaneously in helical motion about $\Delta_{2/1}$, that is, its velocity field appears to be the sum of rotational velocity field about $\Delta_{2/1}$ and a translational velocity field along $\Delta_{2/1}$: for any point $P \in \mathcal{B}_2$, we have

$$\mathbf{v}_{P\in 2/1} = p_{2/1}\,\omega_{2/1} + \omega_{2/1} \times \mathbf{r}_{IP} \tag{7.20}$$

where the *pitch* $p_{2/1}$ is given by

$$p_{1/2} = \frac{\omega_{2/1} \cdot \mathbf{v}_{Q\in 2/1}}{\omega^2_{2/1}}$$

Recall that all points on $\Delta_{2/1}$ have the same velocity $p_{2/1}\,\omega_{2/1}$. Axis $\Delta_{2/1}$ is attached neither to $\mathcal{B}_1$ nor to $\mathcal{B}_2$. See Figure 7.13.

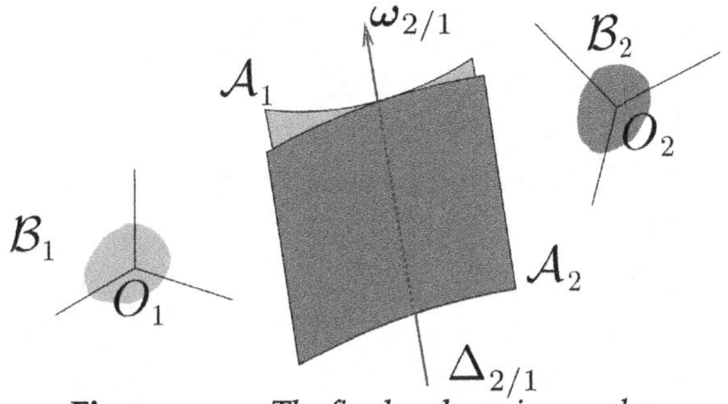

Figure 7.13 – *The fixed and moving axodes.*

Definition 7.6 — Fixed and Moving Axodes. During the motion of body $\mathcal{B}_2$ relative to body $\mathcal{B}_1$, the instantaneous screw axis $\Delta_{2/1}$ generates two ruled surfaces $\mathcal{A}_1$ (relative to $\mathcal{B}_1$) and $\mathcal{A}_2$ (relative to $\mathcal{B}_2$) called *fixed and moving axodes*, respectively. The velocity field of body $\mathcal{B}_2$ relative to $\mathcal{B}_1$ is identical to that of ruled surface $\mathcal{A}_2$ in line contact with ruled surface $\mathcal{A}_1$ along $\Delta_{2/1}$.

Consider a "contact point" I between $\mathcal{A}_2$ and $\mathcal{A}_1$, that is, a particular point of $\Delta_{1/2}$. We can describe the motion of $\mathcal{B}_2$ relative to $\mathcal{B}_1$ equivalently as the motion of axode $\mathcal{A}_2$ in line-contact with axode $\mathcal{A}_1$ in terms of sliding, pivoting and rolling components. More specifically, we can identify

1. a sliding component along $\Delta_{2/1}$ with slip velocity $\mathbf{v}_{I\in 2/1} = p_{2/1}\boldsymbol{\omega}_{2/1}$,
2. a vanishing pivoting component, since $\omega^n_{2/1} = \boldsymbol{\omega}_{1/2} \cdot \hat{\mathbf{n}}_{2/1} = 0$,
3. a rolling component given by $\boldsymbol{\omega}^t_{2/1} = \boldsymbol{\omega}_{2/1}$.

Hence two cases can be distinguished:

1. if $p_{2/1} = 0$ at all time, then $\mathcal{A}_2$ rolls without slipping (and without pivoting) relative to $\mathcal{A}_1$: $\mathcal{A}_2$ is in instantaneous rotation about $\Delta_{2/1}$ (the instantaneous axis of rotation).
2. if $p_{2/1} \neq 0$, then $\mathcal{A}_2$ rolls about and slips along $\Delta_{1/2}$ without pivoting relative to $\mathcal{A}_1$.

7.3.5 Examples

Example 7.7 — **Rolling Motion of a Cylindrical Tube.** A cylinder $\mathcal{B}_1(C, \hat{\mathbf{x}}_1, \hat{\mathbf{y}}_1, \hat{\mathbf{z}}_0)$ whose cross-section is not necessarily circular is in rolling motion on a right circular cylindrical support of a referential $\mathcal{B}_0(O, \hat{\mathbf{x}}_0, \hat{\mathbf{y}}_0, \hat{\mathbf{z}}_0)$. See Figure 7.14. The boundary of $\mathcal{B}_1$ is defined as a closed curve defined as the set of points Q satisfying

$$\mathbf{r}_{CQ}(s) = f(s)\hat{\mathbf{x}}_1 + g(s)\hat{\mathbf{y}}_1$$

where the given functions f and g are periodic in the variable s. The position of $\mathcal{B}_1$ is defined by
-the angle $\phi = (\hat{\mathbf{x}}_0, \hat{\mathbf{x}}_1) = (\hat{\mathbf{y}}_0, \hat{\mathbf{y}}_1)$ defining the orientation of basis $(\hat{\mathbf{x}}_1, \hat{\mathbf{y}}_1, \hat{\mathbf{z}}_1 = \hat{\mathbf{z}}_0)$,
-the angle $\theta = (\hat{\mathbf{x}}_0, \hat{\mathbf{x}}_2) = (\hat{\mathbf{y}}_0, \hat{\mathbf{y}}_2)$ defining the position of contact point I: $\mathbf{r}_{OI} = R\hat{\mathbf{x}}_2$.

a. Find the slip velocity $\mathbf{v}_{I\in 1/0}$ of body $\mathcal{B}_1$ relative to $\mathcal{B}_0$. Deduce a geometric condition which guarantees contact at I. Then find $\mathbf{v}_{C/0}$.

b. Assume that $\mathcal{B}_1$ rolls without slipping on $\mathcal{B}_0$. Find a holonomic constraint. Then consider the case of (i) a circular cylinder $(f, g) = (r\cos s, r\sin s)$, and (ii) of an elliptic cylinder $(f, g) = (a\cos s, b\sin s)$. ■

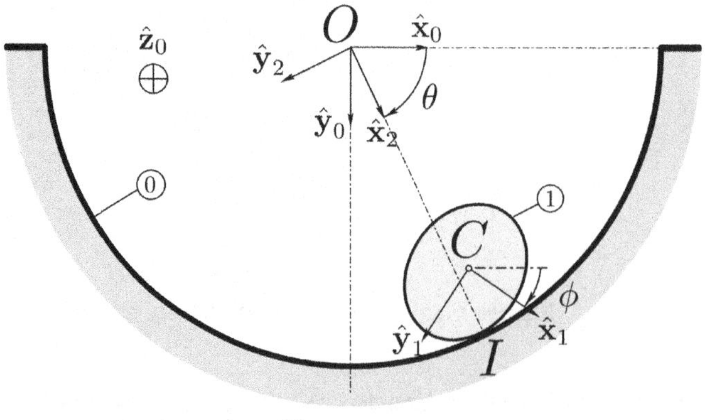

Figure 7.14

a. The contact velocity $\mathbf{v}_{I\in 1/0}$ can be found as follows

$$\mathbf{v}_{I\in 1/0} = \mathbf{v}_{I/0} - \mathbf{v}_{I/1}$$

where velocity $\mathbf{v}_{I/0}$ found as $(d\mathbf{r}_{OI}/dt)_0$

$$\mathbf{v}_{I/0} = \left(\frac{d(R\hat{\mathbf{x}}_2)}{dt}\right)_0 = R\dot{\theta}\hat{\mathbf{y}}_2$$

Likewise, velocity $\mathbf{v}_{I/1}$ is found as the time-derivative of $\mathbf{r}_{CI}$ relative to body $\mathcal{B}_1$. Since the trajectory of I relative to $\mathcal{B}_1$ lies on the boundary of $\mathcal{B}_1$, we can write $\mathbf{r}_{CI} = f(s)\hat{\mathbf{x}}_1 + g(s)\hat{\mathbf{y}}_1$ where scalar $s = s(t)$ parametrizes the position of I. This leads to

$$\mathbf{v}_{I/1} = \left(\frac{d}{dt}(f(s)\hat{\mathbf{x}}_1 + g(s)\hat{\mathbf{y}}_1)\right)_1 = \dot{s}(f'\hat{\mathbf{x}}_1 + g'\hat{\mathbf{y}}_1)$$

with $f' = df/ds$, $g' = dg/ds$. This gives

$$\mathbf{v}_{I\in 1/0} = R\dot{\theta}\hat{\mathbf{y}}_2 - \dot{s}(f'\hat{\mathbf{x}}_1 + g'\hat{\mathbf{y}}_1)$$

The slip-velocity $\mathbf{v}_{I\in 1/0}$ must be tangent at I with contact line for the contact to be realized. We must impose $\mathbf{v}_{I\in 1/0} \cdot \hat{\mathbf{x}}_2 = 0$. This gives the condition

$$\mathbf{v}_{I\in 1/0} \cdot \hat{\mathbf{x}}_2 = -\dot{s}(f'\hat{\mathbf{x}}_1 + g'\hat{\mathbf{y}}_1) \cdot \hat{\mathbf{x}}_2 = -\dot{s}(f'\cos(\theta - \phi) + g'\sin(\theta - \phi)) = 0$$

which can be recast as

$$\tan(\theta - \phi) = G(s) = -\frac{f'(s)}{g'(s)} \tag{1}$$

This relationship enables the determination of the position of I (and hence of C) as a function of $(\theta - \phi)$. From $\mathbf{r}_{OC} = \mathbf{r}_{OI} + \mathbf{r}_{IC} = R\hat{\mathbf{x}}_2 - f\hat{\mathbf{x}}_1 - g\hat{\mathbf{y}}_1$ we obtain

$$\mathbf{v}_{C/0} = R\dot{\theta}\hat{\mathbf{y}}_2 - \dot{s}(f'\hat{\mathbf{x}}_1 + g'\hat{\mathbf{y}}_1) + \dot{\phi}(f\hat{\mathbf{y}}_1 - g\hat{\mathbf{x}}_1)$$

with $G'(s)\dot{s} = (\dot{\theta} - \dot{\phi})/\cos^2(\theta - \phi)$ by differentiation of (1).

b. The no-slip condition is imposed by setting $\mathbf{v}_{I\in 1/0} = \mathbf{0}$:

$$R\dot{\theta} = \dot{s}(-f'\sin(\theta - \phi) + g'\cos(\theta - \phi))$$

This equation imposes a relationship between ϕ and θ. This is an integrable non-holonomic constraint equation: by using (1) we can express θ versus s

$$R(\theta - \theta_0) = \int_{s_0}^{s} (f'^2 + g'^2)^{1/2} ds \tag{2}$$

θ_0 and s_0 are constants of integration. For the circular cylinder, we find from (2) $R\dot{\theta} = r\dot{s}$ and from (1) $\tan(\theta - \phi) = \tan s$ or $\dot{\theta} - \dot{\phi} = \dot{s}$ leading to

$$\phi - \phi_0 = (1 + \frac{R}{r})(\theta - \theta_0)$$

For the elliptic cylinder, (2) gives θ versus s

$$R(\theta - \theta_0) = \int_{s_0}^{s} (a^2 \sin^2 s + b^2 \cos^2 s)^{1/2} ds$$

and (1) gives ϕ versus s. We can also find a quadrature formula giving θ versus ϕ by eliminating s:

$$R(\theta - \theta_0) = \int_{\psi_0}^{\psi} \frac{a^2 b^2}{(a^2 \cos^2 u + b^2 \sin^2 u)^{3/2}} du$$

by defining $\psi = \theta - \phi$ and $\psi_0 = \theta_0 - \phi_0$. In both cases, we recognize that equation (2) expresses the equality of arc length of the two curves (the centrodes) described by I on the boundary of $\mathcal{B}_0$ and $\mathcal{B}_1$. ■

Example 7.8 — Rolling and pivoting of a disk on a horizontal support. A disk $\mathcal{B}_1$ of center C and radius R is constrained to roll, pivot and slip about contact point I relative to horizontal plane $(O, \hat{\mathbf{x}}_0, \hat{\mathbf{y}}_0)$ of a referential $\mathcal{B}_0$. Its position is defined by the coordinates (x, y) of contact point I and by the three Euler angles (ψ, θ, ϕ) as defined by Figure 7.15.

a. Determine the kinematic screw of $\mathcal{B}_1$. Find the pivoting and rolling components of the angular velocity of $\mathcal{B}_1$. Find its angular acceleration.

b. After finding the slip velocity $\mathbf{v}_{I\in 1/0}$, determine the kinematic constraint equations which express the no-slip condition of $\mathcal{B}_1$ relative to $\mathcal{B}_0$. Can $\mathcal{B}_1$ roll without slipping and pivoting? ■

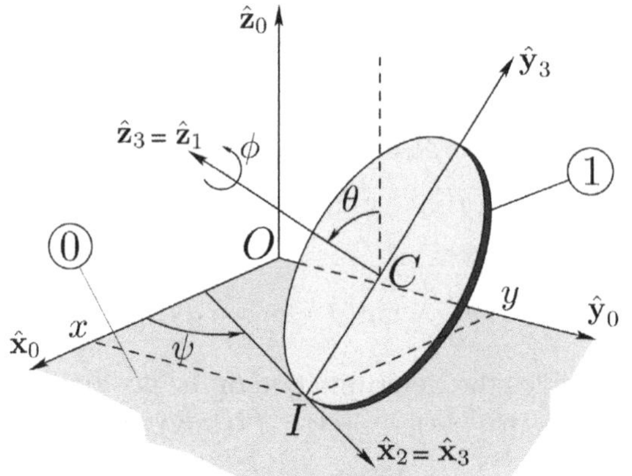

Figure 7.15

a. The parametrization of the position of disk $\mathcal{B}_1(C, \hat{\mathbf{x}}_1, \hat{\mathbf{y}}_1, \hat{\mathbf{z}}_1)$ relative to $\mathcal{B}_0(O, \hat{\mathbf{x}}_0, \hat{\mathbf{y}}_0, \hat{\mathbf{z}}_0)$ is done with the set of coordinates $(x, y, \psi, \theta, \phi)$ defined as follows:
- (x, y) are the Cartesian coordinates of contact point I on the axes $(O, \hat{\mathbf{x}}_0)$ and $(O, \hat{\mathbf{y}}_0)$.
- angle ψ defines the orientation of the line $(I, \hat{\mathbf{x}}_2)$ tangent at the point of contact I to the rim of the disk: $\psi = (\hat{\mathbf{x}}_0, \hat{\mathbf{x}}_2)$. This leads to the transformation

$$(\hat{\mathbf{x}}_0, \hat{\mathbf{y}}_0, \hat{\mathbf{z}}_0) \xrightarrow{\mathcal{R}_{\psi, \hat{\mathbf{z}}_0}} (\hat{\mathbf{x}}_2, \hat{\mathbf{y}}_2, \hat{\mathbf{z}}_2 = \hat{\mathbf{z}}_0)$$

- angle θ defines the orientation of the normal $(I, \hat{\mathbf{z}}_3)$ to disk $\mathcal{B}_1$: $\theta = (\hat{\mathbf{z}}_0, \hat{\mathbf{z}}_3)$. Then, we define $\hat{\mathbf{y}}_3 = \hat{\mathbf{z}}_3 \times \hat{\mathbf{x}}_2$ such that $\mathbf{r}_{IC} = R\hat{\mathbf{y}}_3$. This leads to the transformation

$$(\hat{\mathbf{x}}_2, \hat{\mathbf{y}}_2, \hat{\mathbf{z}}_0) \xrightarrow{\mathcal{R}_{\theta, \hat{\mathbf{x}}_2}} (\hat{\mathbf{x}}_3 = \hat{\mathbf{x}}_2, \hat{\mathbf{y}}_3, \hat{\mathbf{z}}_3)$$

- the basis $(\hat{\mathbf{x}}_1, \hat{\mathbf{y}}_1, \hat{\mathbf{z}}_1 = \hat{\mathbf{z}}_3)$ attached to $\mathcal{B}_1$ is obtained from basis $(\hat{\mathbf{x}}_3 = \hat{\mathbf{x}}_2, \hat{\mathbf{y}}_3, \hat{\mathbf{z}}_3)$ by a rotation of angle $\phi = (\hat{\mathbf{x}}_2, \hat{\mathbf{x}}_1) = (\hat{\mathbf{y}}_3, \hat{\mathbf{y}}_2)$ about $\hat{\mathbf{z}}_3$:

$$(\hat{\mathbf{x}}_2, \hat{\mathbf{y}}_3, \hat{\mathbf{z}}_3) \xrightarrow{\mathcal{R}_{\phi, \hat{\mathbf{z}}_3}} (\hat{\mathbf{x}}_1, \hat{\mathbf{y}}_1, \hat{\mathbf{z}}_1 = \hat{\mathbf{z}}_3)$$

With this parametrization, we find $\boldsymbol{\omega}_{1/0} = \boldsymbol{\omega}_{1/3} + \boldsymbol{\omega}_{3/2} + \boldsymbol{\omega}_{2/0} = \dot{\phi}\hat{\mathbf{z}}_3 + \dot{\theta}\hat{\mathbf{x}}_2 + \dot{\psi}\hat{\mathbf{z}}_0$. To find the pivoting component of $\boldsymbol{\omega}_{1/0}$, we project $\boldsymbol{\omega}_{1/0}$ on the unit normal $\hat{\mathbf{z}}_0$:

$$\boldsymbol{\omega}^n_{1/0} = (\boldsymbol{\omega}_{1/0} \cdot \hat{\mathbf{z}}_0)\hat{\mathbf{z}}_0 = [(\dot{\psi}\hat{\mathbf{z}}_0 + \dot{\theta}\hat{\mathbf{x}}_2 + \dot{\phi}\hat{\mathbf{z}}_3) \cdot \hat{\mathbf{z}}_0]\hat{\mathbf{z}}_0$$

or

$$\boldsymbol{\omega}^n_{1/0} = (\dot{\psi} + \dot{\phi}\cos\theta)\hat{\mathbf{z}}_0$$

The rolling component is then given by $\boldsymbol{\omega}^t_{1/0} = \boldsymbol{\omega}_{1/0} - \boldsymbol{\omega}^n_{1/0}$

$$\boldsymbol{\omega}^t_{1/0} = \dot{\theta}\hat{\mathbf{x}}_2 - \dot{\phi}\sin\theta\hat{\mathbf{y}}_2$$

The angular acceleration of $\mathcal{B}_1$ relative to $\mathcal{B}_0$ can be found as:

$$\boldsymbol{\alpha}_{1/0} = \ddot{\phi}\hat{\mathbf{z}}_3 + \ddot{\theta}\hat{\mathbf{x}}_2 + \ddot{\psi}\hat{\mathbf{z}}_0 + \dot{\phi}(\dot{\theta}\hat{\mathbf{x}}_2 + \dot{\psi}\hat{\mathbf{z}}_0) \times \hat{\mathbf{z}}_3 + \dot{\theta}\dot{\psi}\hat{\mathbf{y}}_2$$

leading to, on basis $(\hat{\mathbf{x}}_3, \hat{\mathbf{y}}_3, \hat{\mathbf{z}}_3)$

$$\boldsymbol{\alpha}_{1/0} = (\ddot{\theta} + \dot{\psi}\dot{\phi}\sin\theta)\hat{\mathbf{x}}_3 + (\ddot{\psi}\sin\theta - \dot{\theta}\dot{\phi} + \dot{\psi}\dot{\theta}\cos\theta)\hat{\mathbf{y}}_3 + (\ddot{\phi} + \ddot{\psi}\cos\theta - \dot{\psi}\dot{\theta}\sin\theta)\hat{\mathbf{z}}_3$$

To write the kinematic screw $\{\mathcal{V}_{1/0}\}$ of $\mathcal{B}_1$, we need to find the velocity of center C by differentiating the position vector $\mathbf{r}_{OC} = x\hat{\mathbf{x}}_0 + y\hat{\mathbf{y}}_0 + R\hat{\mathbf{y}}_3$:

$$\mathbf{v}_{C/0} = \dot{x}\hat{\mathbf{x}}_0 + \dot{y}\hat{\mathbf{y}}_0 + R(\dot{\theta}\hat{\mathbf{x}}_2 + \dot{\psi}\hat{\mathbf{z}}_0) \times \hat{\mathbf{y}}_3 = \dot{x}\hat{\mathbf{x}}_0 + \dot{y}\hat{\mathbf{y}}_0 + R(\dot{\theta}\hat{\mathbf{z}}_3 - \dot{\psi}\cos\theta\hat{\mathbf{x}}_3)$$

This leads to the expression

$$\{\mathcal{V}_{1/0}\} = \begin{Bmatrix} \dot{\phi}\hat{\mathbf{z}}_3 + \dot{\theta}\hat{\mathbf{x}}_2 + \dot{\psi}\hat{\mathbf{z}}_0 \\ \dot{x}\hat{\mathbf{x}}_0 + \dot{y}\hat{\mathbf{y}}_0 + R(\dot{\theta}\hat{\mathbf{z}}_3 - \dot{\psi}\cos\theta\hat{\mathbf{x}}_3) \end{Bmatrix}_C$$

b. To find slip-velocity at I, that is, the velocity of the point of $\mathcal{B}_1$ coinciding with I, we use the kinematic screw formula:

$$\mathbf{v}_{I\in 1/0} = \mathbf{v}_{C\in 1/0} + \boldsymbol{\omega}_{1/0} \times \mathbf{r}_{CI} = \mathbf{v}_{C\in 1/0} + R(\dot{\phi}\hat{\mathbf{x}}_3 - \dot{\theta}\hat{\mathbf{z}}_3 + \dot{\psi}\cos\theta\hat{\mathbf{x}}_3)$$

This gives, after simplifications,

$$\mathbf{v}_{I\in 1/0} = \dot{x}\hat{\mathbf{x}}_0 + \dot{y}\hat{\mathbf{y}}_0 + R\dot{\phi}\hat{\mathbf{x}}_3 \tag{1}$$

Note that the condition $\mathbf{v}_{I\in 1/0} \cdot \hat{\mathbf{z}}_0 = 0$ is satisfied since the parametrization in terms of $(x, y, \psi, \theta, \phi)$ takes into account the condition of contact at I. The expression of the slip-velocity can be used to define the kinematic screw of $\mathcal{B}_1$:

$$\{\mathcal{V}_{1/0}\} = \begin{Bmatrix} \dot{\phi}\hat{\mathbf{z}}_3 + \dot{\theta}\hat{\mathbf{x}}_2 + \dot{\psi}\hat{\mathbf{z}}_0 \\ \dot{x}\hat{\mathbf{x}}_0 + \dot{y}\hat{\mathbf{y}}_0 + R\dot{\phi}\hat{\mathbf{x}}_3 \end{Bmatrix}_I$$

If $\mathcal{B}_1$ rolls and pivots without slipping on $\mathcal{B}_0$, then $\mathbf{v}_{I\in 1/0} = \mathbf{0}$: we project equation (1) on $(\hat{\mathbf{x}}_0, \hat{\mathbf{y}}_0)$ to obtain the following two *non-holonomic constraints* equations

$$\begin{aligned} \dot{x} &= -R\dot{\phi}\cos\psi \\ \dot{y} &= -R\dot{\phi}\sin\psi \end{aligned}$$

These equations are non-integrable. For $\mathcal{B}_1$ to roll without slipping and pivoting, a third non-holonomic equation must be imposed:

$$\dot{\psi} + \dot{\phi}\cos\theta = 0$$

Remark. We could have found $\mathbf{v}_{I\in 1/0}$ as the difference $\mathbf{v}_{I/0} - \mathbf{v}_{I/1}$ with

$$\mathbf{v}_{I/0} = (d\mathbf{r}_{OI}/dt)_0 = \dot{x}\hat{\mathbf{x}}_0 + \dot{y}\hat{\mathbf{y}}_0$$

and

$$\mathbf{v}_{I/1} = (d\mathbf{r}_{CI}/dt)_1 = -R\boldsymbol{\omega}_{3/1} \times \hat{\mathbf{y}}_3 = R\dot{\phi}\hat{\mathbf{z}}_3 \times \hat{\mathbf{y}}_3 = -R\dot{\phi}\hat{\mathbf{x}}_3$$

We recover the same expression.

■

Example 7.9 Figure 7.16 shows two rigid bodies $\mathcal{B}_1$ and $\mathcal{B}_2$ in relative motion in a referential $\mathcal{B}_0$ of origin O and basis $(\hat{\mathbf{x}}_0, \hat{\mathbf{y}}_0, \hat{\mathbf{z}}_0)$. Body $\mathcal{B}_1$ is a truncated cone (of half-angle α) connected to $\mathcal{B}_0$ by a pivot of axis $(A, \hat{\mathbf{u}})$ (the axis of the cone) whose orientation in $\mathcal{B}_0$ is defined by angle α. The angular velocity of body $\mathcal{B}_1$ is $\boldsymbol{\omega}_{1/0} = \omega_1 \hat{\mathbf{u}}$. Body $\mathcal{B}_2$ is a circular platform mounted on a pivot of axis $(O, \hat{\mathbf{z}}_0)$: its angular velocity is $\boldsymbol{\omega}_{2/0} = \omega_2 \hat{\mathbf{z}}_0$. The two bodies are in contact along the line segment IJ. Figure 7.16 represents the plane containing both axes $(A, \hat{\mathbf{u}})$ and $(O, \hat{\mathbf{z}}_0)$. Denote by a the distance $|OA|$.

a. Find the angular velocity $\boldsymbol{\omega}_{2/1}$ of body $\mathcal{B}_2$ relative to body $\mathcal{B}_1$. Decompose $\boldsymbol{\omega}_{2/1}$ into rolling and pivoting components.

b. Express the kinematic screw $\{\mathcal{V}_{2/1}\}$ at a point of your choice.

c. Find the velocity $\mathbf{v}_{Q\in 2/1}$ of any point Q of the contact line OA. Deduce that the instantaneous screw axis $\Delta_{2/1}$ passes through two points in the plane of the figure. What is the corresponding velocity of points of the screw axis? Describe the two axodes generated by the motion of $\Delta_{2/1}$ relative to $\mathcal{B}_1$ and to $\mathcal{B}_2$, then characterize the motion of $\mathcal{B}_2$ relative to $\mathcal{B}_1$ in terms of the relative motion of the axodes. ■

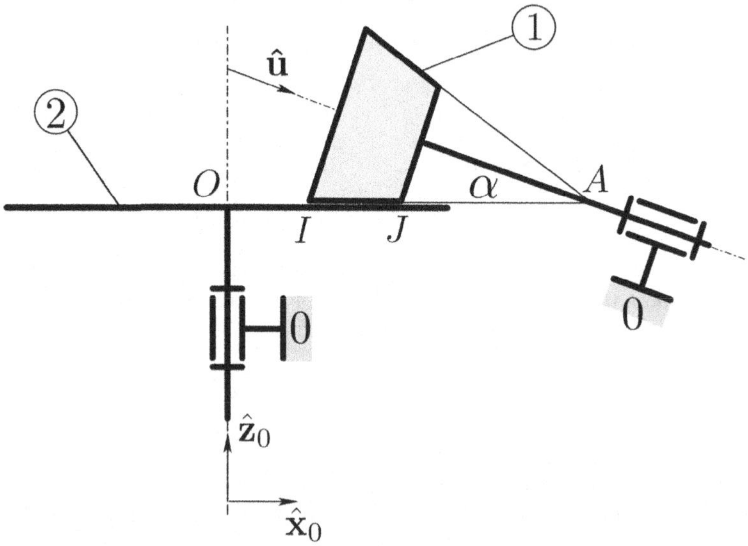

Figure 7.16

a. We obtain $\boldsymbol{\omega}_{2/1}$ by taking the difference between $\boldsymbol{\omega}_{2/0}$ and $\boldsymbol{\omega}_{1/0}$:

$$\boldsymbol{\omega}_{2/1} = \boldsymbol{\omega}_{2/0} - \boldsymbol{\omega}_{1/0} = \omega_2 \hat{\mathbf{z}}_0 - \omega_1 \hat{\mathbf{u}} = (\omega_2 + \omega_1 \sin\alpha)\hat{\mathbf{z}}_0 - \omega_1 \cos\alpha \hat{\mathbf{x}}_0$$

Since the two surfaces in contact (along line IJ) have a common normal along $\hat{\mathbf{z}}_0$, the pivoting component of $\boldsymbol{\omega}_{2/1}$ is $(\omega_2 + \omega_1 \sin\alpha)\hat{\mathbf{z}}_0$ and the rolling component is $-\omega_1 \cos\alpha \hat{\mathbf{x}}_0$.

b. We first define $\hat{\mathbf{y}}_0 = \hat{\mathbf{z}}_0 \times \hat{\mathbf{x}}_0$. We obtain kinematic screw $\{\mathcal{V}_{2/1}\}$ as the difference between $\{\mathcal{V}_{2/0}\}$ and $\{\mathcal{V}_{1/0}\}$:

$$\{\mathcal{V}_{2/1}\} = \{\mathcal{V}_{2/0}\} - \{\mathcal{V}_{1/0}\}$$

Since the joint between $\mathcal{B}_1$ and $\mathcal{B}_0$ is a pivot of axis $(A, \hat{\mathbf{u}})$, we have:

$$\{\mathcal{V}_{1/0}\} = \begin{Bmatrix} \omega_1 \hat{\mathbf{u}} \\ \mathbf{0} \end{Bmatrix}_A$$

Similarly, the joint between $\mathcal{B}_2$ and $\mathcal{B}_0$ is a pivot of axis $(O, \hat{\mathbf{z}}_0)$:

$$\{\mathcal{V}_{2/0}\} = \begin{Bmatrix} \omega_2 \hat{\mathbf{z}}_0 \\ \mathbf{0} \end{Bmatrix}_O$$

This leads to

$$\{\mathcal{V}_{2/1}\} = \begin{Bmatrix} \omega_2 \hat{\mathbf{z}}_0 \\ \mathbf{0} \end{Bmatrix}_O - \begin{Bmatrix} \omega_1 \hat{\mathbf{u}} \\ \mathbf{0} \end{Bmatrix}_A = \begin{Bmatrix} \omega_2 \hat{\mathbf{z}}_0 - \omega_1 \hat{\mathbf{u}} \\ -a\omega_1 \sin\alpha \hat{\mathbf{y}}_0 \end{Bmatrix}_O$$

where we have used $\mathbf{v}_{O\in 1/0} = \omega_1 \hat{\mathbf{u}} \times \mathbf{r}_{AO} = -\omega_1 \hat{\mathbf{u}} \times a\hat{\mathbf{x}}_0 = a\omega_1 \sin\alpha \hat{\mathbf{y}}_0$.

c. First, we define the position of an arbitrary point on line OA as $\mathbf{r}_{OQ} = \lambda \hat{\mathbf{x}}_0$ (λ is arbitrary scalar). We find $\mathbf{v}_{Q\in 2/1}$ by using the kinematic screw found in b):

$$\mathbf{v}_{Q\in 2/1} = \mathbf{v}_{O\in 2/1} + \boldsymbol{\omega}_{2/1} \times \mathbf{r}_{OQ} = -a\omega_1 \sin\alpha \hat{\mathbf{y}}_0 + (\omega_2 \hat{\mathbf{z}}_0 - \omega_1 \hat{\mathbf{u}}) \times \lambda \hat{\mathbf{x}}_0$$

leading to

$$\mathbf{v}_{Q\in 2/1} = [-a\omega_1 \sin\alpha + \lambda(\omega_2 + \omega_1 \sin\alpha)]\hat{\mathbf{y}}_0$$

Note the direction of $\mathbf{v}_{Q\in 2/1}$: it has no component on $\hat{\mathbf{z}}_0$, as expected. We also note that $\mathbf{v}_{Q\in 2/1}$ has a **non zero** value for all points Q of line OA except if scalar λ takes the value

$$\lambda_* = a \frac{\omega_1 \sin\alpha}{\omega_2 + \omega_1 \sin\alpha}$$

We call Q_* the corresponding point: $\mathbf{v}_{Q_* \in 2/1} = \mathbf{0}$ (this point lies between O and A if scalars ω_1 and ω_2 are both positive). The existence of point Q_* indicates that screw axis $\Delta_{2/1}$ is an instantaneous axis of rotation since it passes through Q_*. Note that the corresponding pitch is necessarily zero. Another point of interest is point B defined as the intersection of the rotation axes $(A, \hat{\mathbf{u}})$ and $(O, \hat{\mathbf{z}}_0)$: since B belongs to both axes, we have

$$\mathbf{v}_{B\in 2/1} = \mathbf{v}_{B\in 2/0} - \mathbf{v}_{B\in 1/0} = \mathbf{0}$$

Hence, point B must also belong to axis $\Delta_{2/1}$: we conclude that $\Delta_{2/1}$ is the line BQ_*. This axis is fixed relative to referential 0. Relative to body 2, it generates a cone of axis $(B, \hat{\mathbf{z}}_0)$ and apex B. Similarly, $\Delta_{2/1}$ generates a cone of axis $(B, \hat{\mathbf{u}})$ and apex B. The motion 2/1 (as far as velocities are concerned) is then equivalent to the motion of a cone of $\mathcal{B}_1$ rolling without slipping on a cone of $\mathcal{B}_2$. See Figure 7.17 for a sketch of these two axodes.

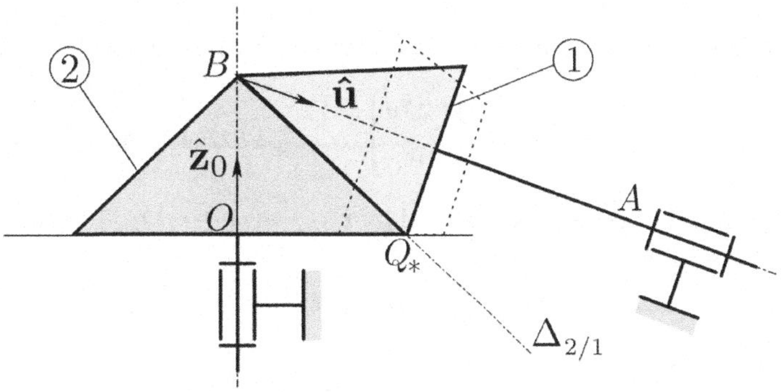

Figure 7.17

■

Example 7.10 — Circular shafts in rolling contact. Two circular shafts 1 and 2 are in uniform rotation in a referential $0(O, \hat{\mathbf{x}}_0, \hat{\mathbf{y}}_0, \hat{\mathbf{z}}_0)$ about perpendicular axes $(O, \hat{\mathbf{y}}_0)$ and $(A, \hat{\mathbf{x}}_0)$. Denote by $\omega_1 \hat{\mathbf{y}}_0$ the angular velocity of shaft 1 and by $\omega_2 \hat{\mathbf{x}}_0$ the angular velocity of shaft 2. The two shafts are in contact at a point I located on axis $(O, \hat{\mathbf{z}}_0)$ at a distance r_1 from O and r_2 from A. See Figure 7.18.

a. Find the kinematic screw of 2 relative to 1. Then find the slip-velocity $\mathbf{v}_{I\in 2/1}$.

b. Find the corresponding screw axis $\Delta_{1/2}$ and the corresponding axodes. Describe the motion in terms of the axodes.

c. Find the condition satisfied by the constants $(r_1, r_2, \omega_1, \omega_2)$ so that the magnitude of the slip-velocity $\mathbf{v}_{I\in 2/1}$ is minimized. Then find the minimum slip velocity. ■

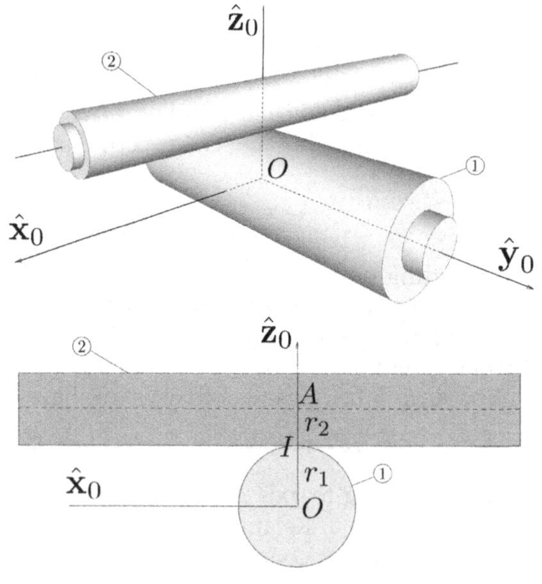

Figure 7.18

a. The kinematic screws of the two shafts relative to referential 0 are given by

$$\{\mathcal{V}_{1/0}\} = \begin{Bmatrix} \omega_1 \hat{\mathbf{y}}_0 \\ \mathbf{0} \end{Bmatrix}_O, \qquad \{\mathcal{V}_{2/0}\} = \begin{Bmatrix} \omega_2 \hat{\mathbf{x}}_0 \\ \mathbf{0} \end{Bmatrix}_A$$

where the position of point A is defined by $\mathbf{r}_{OA} = (r_1 + r_2)\hat{\mathbf{z}}_0$. To find the kinematic screw of 2 relative to 1 we first need to find

$$\mathbf{v}_{O\in 2/0} = \omega_2 \hat{\mathbf{x}}_0 \times \mathbf{r}_{AO} = (r_1 + r_2)\omega_2 \hat{\mathbf{y}}_0$$

Then we can write

$$\{\mathcal{V}_{2/1}\} = \begin{Bmatrix} \omega_2 \hat{\mathbf{x}}_0 - \omega_1 \hat{\mathbf{y}}_0 \\ (r_1 + r_2)\omega_2 \hat{\mathbf{y}}_0 \end{Bmatrix}_O$$

The slip-velocity $\mathbf{v}_{I\in 2/1}$ is then given by

$$\mathbf{v}_{I\in 2/1} = \mathbf{v}_{O\in 2/1} + \boldsymbol{\omega}_{2/1} \times \mathbf{r}_{OI}$$

leading to the expression

$$\mathbf{v}_{I\in 2/1} = -r_1 \omega_1 \hat{\mathbf{x}}_0 + r_2 \omega_2 \hat{\mathbf{y}}_0$$

b. The instantaneous screw axis $\Delta_{2/1}$ is directed along $\omega_{2/1}$ and passes through point J whose position is given by

$$\mathbf{r}_{OJ} = \frac{\omega_{2/1} \times \mathbf{v}_{O\in 2/1}}{\omega_{2/1}^2} = (r_1 + r_2)\frac{\omega_2^2}{\omega_1^2 + \omega_2^2}\hat{\mathbf{z}}_0$$

which shows that point J is located on axis $(O, \hat{\mathbf{z}}_0)$. Hence, axis $\Delta_{2/1}$ is fixed in referential 0. $\Delta_{2/1}$ generates two surfaces relatives to 1 and 2, the so-called axodes $\mathcal{A}_1$ and $\mathcal{A}_2$. To find $\mathcal{A}_1$ on axes $(O, \hat{\mathbf{x}}_1, \hat{\mathbf{y}}_1 = \hat{\mathbf{y}}_0, \hat{\mathbf{z}}_1)$, we state that $\mathcal{A}_1$ is the set of points Q satisfying $\mathbf{r}_{OQ} = \mathbf{r}_{OJ} + \lambda(\hat{\mathbf{x}}_0 - \kappa\hat{\mathbf{y}}_0) = X_1\hat{\mathbf{x}}_1 + Y_1\hat{\mathbf{y}}_1 + Z_1\hat{\mathbf{z}}_1$:

$$X_1 = -\mu \sin\theta_1 + \lambda\cos\theta_1, \quad Y_1 = -\lambda\kappa, \quad Z_1 = \mu\cos\theta_1 - \lambda\sin\theta_1$$

with $\mu = (r_1 + r_2)\omega_2^2/(\omega_1^2 + \omega_2^2)$ and $\kappa = \omega_1/\omega_2$. We can eliminate angle θ_1 to find the Cartesian equation of $\mathcal{A}_1$:

$$(X_1Y_1 + \kappa\mu Z_1)^2 + (Y_1Z_1 + \kappa\mu X_1)^2 = \kappa^2(\mu^2 - Y_1^2/\kappa^2)^2$$

We can find in a similar way the Cartesian equation of $\mathcal{A}_2$ on axes $(A, \hat{\mathbf{x}}_2 = \hat{\mathbf{x}}_0, \hat{\mathbf{y}}_2, \hat{\mathbf{z}}_2)$

$$(X_2Y_2 + \kappa\mu Z_2)^2 + (X_2Z_2 + \kappa\mu Y_2)^2 = \kappa^2(\mu^2\kappa^2 - X_2^2)^2$$

c. Recall that the minimum speed of a rigid body is reached on its instantaneous screw axis. The slip-velocity $\mathbf{v}_{I\in 2/1}$ is minimized if contact point I belongs to the instantaneous screw axis $\Delta_{2/1}$: we must impose $\mathbf{r}_{OI} = \mathbf{r}_{OJ}$. This leads to the condition

$$\frac{r_2}{r_1} = \frac{\omega_1^2}{\omega_2^2} \qquad (1)$$

The corresponding slip velocity can be found as $|p\omega_{2/1}|$ or as $|\mathbf{v}_{I\in 2/1}|$ using condition (1):

$$|\mathbf{v}_{I\in 2/1}| = (r_1(r_1 + r_2))^{1/2}\omega_1$$

■

Example 7.11 — Tapered Roller Bearings. Figure 7.19 shows a tapered roller bearing assembly mounted between a rotating shaft 1 and a fixed housing 0. Such bearings are made of four components: (i) an inner ring or cone attached to rotating shaft 1, (ii) a cup or outer ring attached to the fixed housing 0, (iii) tapered rollers (truncated cones) 3, and (iv) a cage (spacer-retainer) 2 which maintains the rollers equidistant to one another. For simplicity, cage 2 is not shown, and only one roller 3 needs to be considered for the analysis. Figure 7.19 shows a cross section of the assembly which contains the axis $(O, \hat{\mathbf{x}}_0)$ of shaft 1 and the axis $(O, \hat{\mathbf{x}}_3)$ of roller 3. This cross section represents a plane $(O, \hat{\mathbf{x}}_0, \hat{\mathbf{y}}_2)$ which rotates with cage 2 about axis $(O, \hat{\mathbf{x}}_0)$. More specifically, we denote by O the intersection point of the rollers' axes with the shaft axis, and by H the intersection of the roller's contact lines with the inner and outer rings: H is the vertex of the cone formed by the roller. We denote by β the half-angle of this cone, and by α the angle between axis $(O, \hat{\mathbf{x}}_0)$ and axis $(O, \hat{\mathbf{x}}_3)$. Henry Timken patented the tapered roller bearing in 1898.

a. Under what geometric condition is no-slip guaranteed for all points of the roller's contact lines with the inner and outer rings?

b. Assuming this condition satisfied, find the angular velocity $\omega_{2/0}$ of the cage relative to the housing and the angular velocity $\omega_{3/2}$ of the roller relative to the cage as a function of the shaft's angular velocity $\omega_{1/0}$ and angles β and α. ■

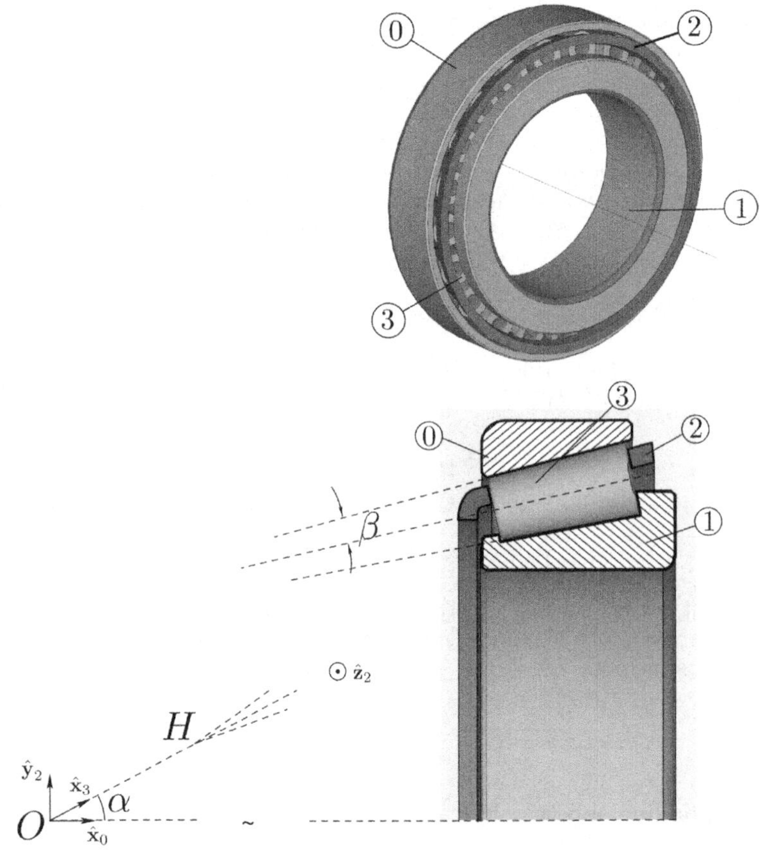

Figure 7.19

a. If the roller's contact lines with the inner and outer rings are no-slip contact lines, then they represent instantaneous axis of rotation $\Delta_{3/1}$ and $\Delta_{3/0}$, respectively. Point H is the intersection of these two axes. See Figure 7.20. Hence at point H we can write

$$\mathbf{v}_{H\in 3/1} = \mathbf{v}_{H\in 3/0} = \mathbf{0}$$

which leads to

$$\mathbf{v}_{H\in 1/0} = \mathbf{v}_{H\in 3/0} - \mathbf{v}_{H\in 3/1} = \mathbf{0}$$

This shows that point H is a point of the axis of rotation $\Delta_{1/0} = (O, \hat{\mathbf{x}}_0)$: point H must be located on axis $(O, \hat{\mathbf{x}}_0)$, and hence H *must coincide with point* O.

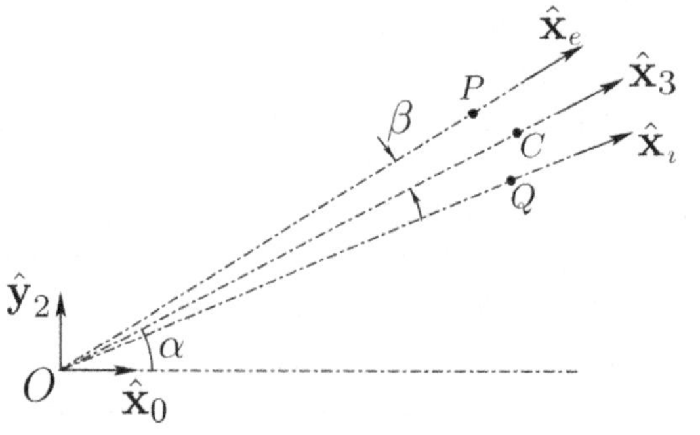

Figure 7.20

b. We sketch Figure 7.21 with point H coinciding with O and we denote by P an arbitrary point of contact line $\Delta_{3/0}(O, \hat{\mathbf{x}}_e)$ of 3 with 0 (roller with exterior ring) and by Q an arbitrary point of contact line $\Delta_{3/1}(O, \hat{\mathbf{x}}_i)$ of 3 with 1 (roller with interior ring). The position of points P and Q is defined by $\mathbf{r}_{OP} = \lambda\hat{\mathbf{x}}_e$ and $\mathbf{r}_{OQ} = \mu\hat{\mathbf{x}}_i$ (μ and λ are arbitrary scalars). Finally, let C denote an arbitrary point of the roller's axis $(O, \hat{\mathbf{x}}_3)$, with $\mathbf{r}_{OC} = c\hat{\mathbf{x}}_3$. Since the cage rotates relative to the housing about axis $(O, \hat{\mathbf{x}}_0)$, its angular velocity can be written as $\boldsymbol{\omega}_{2/0} = \omega_{2/0}\hat{\mathbf{x}}_0$. Similarly, the roller rotates relative to the cage about axis $(O, \hat{\mathbf{x}}_3)$, and its angular velocity can be written as $\boldsymbol{\omega}_{3/2} = \omega_{3/2}\hat{\mathbf{x}}_3$.

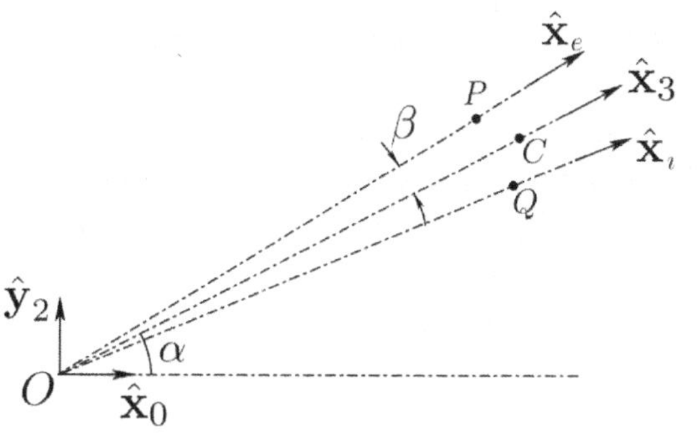

Figure 7.21

The no-slip condition at point P can then be written as $\mathbf{v}_{P\in 3/0} = \mathbf{0}$, with

$$\begin{aligned}\mathbf{v}_{P\in 3/0} &= \mathbf{v}_{C\in 3/0} + \boldsymbol{\omega}_{3/0} \times \mathbf{r}_{CP} = c\sin\alpha\,\omega_{2/0}\hat{\mathbf{z}}_2 + (\omega_{3/2}\hat{\mathbf{x}}_3 + \omega_{2/0}\hat{\mathbf{x}}_0) \times (\lambda\hat{\mathbf{x}}_e - x\hat{\mathbf{x}}_3)\\ &= \lambda(\omega_{2/0}\sin(\alpha+\beta) + \omega_{3/2}\sin\beta)\hat{\mathbf{z}}_2\end{aligned}$$

Hence for all $\lambda \neq 0$, we have

$$\omega_{2/0}\sin(\alpha+\beta) + \omega_{3/2}\sin\beta = 0 \tag{1}$$

The no-slip condition of point Q can be written as $\mathbf{v}_{Q\in 3/0} = \mathbf{v}_{Q\in 1/0}$ with

$$\begin{aligned}\mathbf{v}_{Q\in 3/0} &= \mathbf{v}_{C\in 3/0} + \boldsymbol{\omega}_{3/0} \times \mathbf{r}_{CQ} = c\sin\alpha\,\omega_{2/0}\hat{\mathbf{z}}_2 + (\omega_{3/2}\hat{\mathbf{x}}_3 + \omega_{2/0}\hat{\mathbf{x}}_0) \times (\mu\hat{\mathbf{x}}_i - x\hat{\mathbf{x}}_3)\\ &= \mu(\omega_{2/0}\sin(\alpha-\beta) - \omega_{3/2}\sin\beta)\hat{\mathbf{z}}_2\end{aligned}$$

and

$$\mathbf{v}_{Q\in 1/0} = \omega_{1/0}\hat{\mathbf{x}}_0 \times \mu\hat{\mathbf{x}}_i = \mu\omega_{1/0}\sin(\alpha-\beta)\hat{\mathbf{z}}_2$$

leading to

$$\omega_{2/0}\sin(\alpha-\beta) - \omega_{3/2}\sin\beta = \omega_{1/0}\sin(\alpha-\beta) \tag{2}$$

for all $\mu \neq 0$. Equations (1) and (2) solve for $\omega_{2/0}$ and $\omega_{3/2}$ in terms of $\omega_{1/0}$ and the geometric parameters α and β:

$$\omega_{2/0} = \omega_{1/0}\frac{\sin(\alpha-\beta)}{2\sin\alpha\cos\beta} \qquad \omega_{3/2} = -\omega_{1/0}\frac{\sin(\alpha-\beta)\sin(\alpha+\beta)}{\sin\alpha\sin 2\beta}$$

■

Example 7.12 — Thomson integrator. Many calculating devices, such as planimeters used for area measurement, have been designed based on rigid body kinematics. Figure 7.22 shows a three-dimensional view of a mechanical assembly known as Thomson integrator developed by James Thomson in 1876. The mechanism consists of a disk 1, a sphere 2, and a cylinder 3 in motion relative to a support $0(O, \hat{\mathbf{x}}_0, \hat{\mathbf{y}}_0, \hat{\mathbf{z}}_0)$. The disk of center O can rotate about the axis $(O, \hat{\mathbf{z}}_0)$ which is inclined relative to the vertical. The cylinder 3 is free to rotate about its horizontal axis $(A, \hat{\mathbf{y}}_0)$ which is positioned relative to the disk in such a way that a gap of uniform width is left between the disk and the cylinder. The sphere (of center C) is placed in this gap, and thus remains in contact with both the disk (at point I) and the cylinder (at point J). Contact point I can travel along the horizontal line $(O, \hat{\mathbf{y}}_0)$ parallel to cylinder's axis. A mechanism (not shown) imposes the motion of the sphere along the gap as a function of the rotation of the disk, that is, the quantity $y_C = \mathbf{r}_{OC} \cdot \hat{\mathbf{y}}_0 = y_C(\theta)$ can be prescribed as a function of the rotational angle θ of the disk. The output of the integrator is given by the cylinder's rotational angle ϕ about axis $(A, \hat{\mathbf{y}}_0)$. The geometry is defined by the constants r, R and α as shown in Figure 7.23.

a. By imposing the no-slip condition at contact points I and J, find the angular velocities $\omega_{2/0}$ and $\omega_{3/0} = \dot{\phi}\hat{\mathbf{y}}_0$ in terms of angle θ and coordinate $y_C(\theta)$.

b. Conclude that the mechanism can yield values of integrals of the type $\int y\,dx$. ■

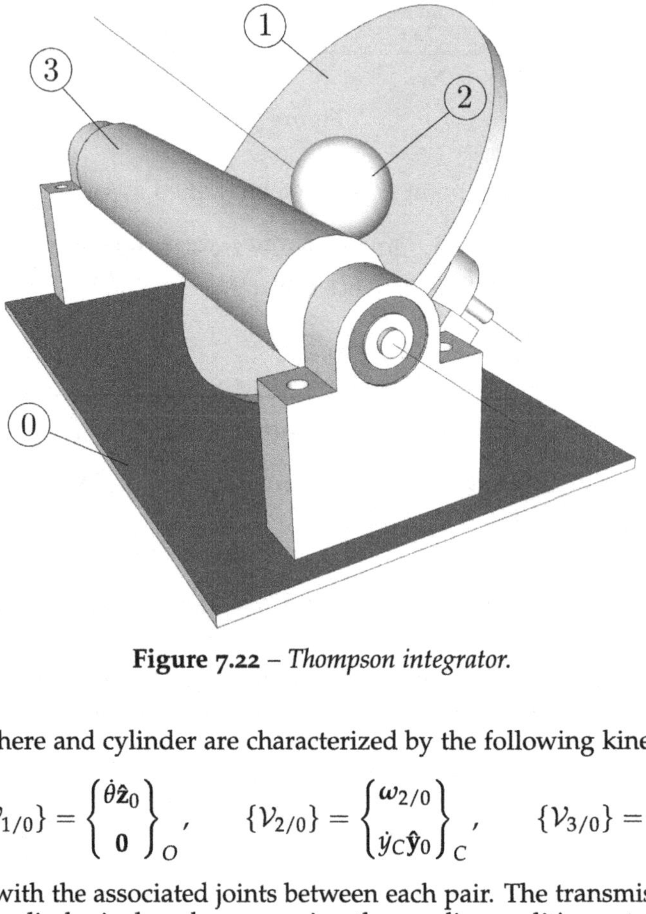

Figure 7.22 – *Thompson integrator.*

a. The disk, sphere and cylinder are characterized by the following kinematic screws

$$\{\mathcal{V}_{1/0}\} = \begin{Bmatrix} \dot{\theta}\hat{\mathbf{z}}_0 \\ \mathbf{0} \end{Bmatrix}_O, \qquad \{\mathcal{V}_{2/0}\} = \begin{Bmatrix} \omega_{2/0} \\ \dot{y}_C\hat{\mathbf{y}}_0 \end{Bmatrix}_C, \qquad \{\mathcal{V}_{3/0}\} = \begin{Bmatrix} \dot{\phi}\hat{\mathbf{y}}_0 \\ \mathbf{0} \end{Bmatrix}_A$$

in accordance with the associated joints between each pair. The transmission of the motion of the disk to the cylinder is done by expressing the no-slip conditions at contact points I and J. At I, we must impose $\mathbf{v}_{I\in 1/0} = \mathbf{v}_{I\in 2/0}$. Using the kinematic screws $\{\mathcal{V}_{1/0}\}$ and $\{\mathcal{V}_{2/0}\}$, we find $\dot{\theta}\hat{\mathbf{z}}_0 \times \mathbf{r}_{OI} = \dot{y}_C\hat{\mathbf{y}}_0 + \omega_{2/0} \times \mathbf{r}_{CI}$. With $\mathbf{r}_{OI} = y_C\hat{\mathbf{y}}_0$, $\mathbf{r}_{CI} = -r\hat{\mathbf{z}}_0$, $\omega_{2/0} = \omega_{2x}\hat{\mathbf{x}}_0 + \omega_{2y}\hat{\mathbf{y}}_0 + \omega_{2z}\hat{\mathbf{z}}_0$, we obtain

$$-y_C\dot{\theta}\hat{\mathbf{x}}_0 = \dot{y}_C\hat{\mathbf{y}}_0 + r(\omega_{2x}\hat{\mathbf{y}}_0 - \omega_{2y}\hat{\mathbf{x}}_0)$$

This gives

$$\omega_{2/0} = -\frac{\dot{y}_C}{r}\hat{\mathbf{x}}_0 + \frac{y_C}{r}\dot{\theta}\hat{\mathbf{y}}_0 + \omega_{2z}\hat{\mathbf{z}}_0$$

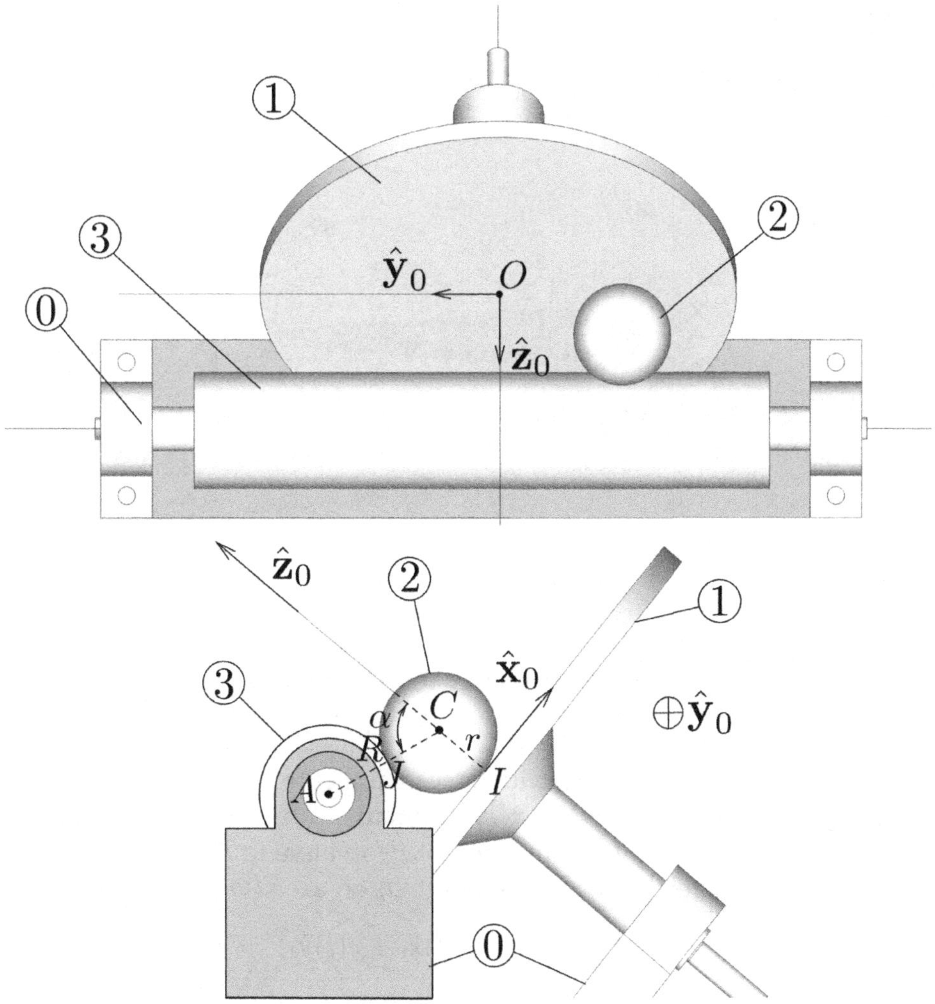

Figure 7.23 – *Top and side views of Thompson integrator.*

where component ω_{2z} is yet to be found. Next we write the no-slip condition at J between the sphere and the cylinder: $\mathbf{v}_{J\in 3/0} = \mathbf{v}_{J\in 2/0}$. This leads to

$$\dot{\phi}\hat{\mathbf{y}}_0 \times \mathbf{r}_{AJ} = \dot{y}_C\hat{\mathbf{y}}_0 + \boldsymbol{\omega}_{2/0} \times \mathbf{r}_{CJ}$$

With $\mathbf{r}_{AJ} = -R\hat{\mathbf{u}}$, $\mathbf{r}_{CJ} = r\hat{\mathbf{u}}$ and the expression of $\boldsymbol{\omega}_{2/0}$ just found, we obtain (defining $\hat{\mathbf{v}} = \hat{\mathbf{y}}_0 \times \hat{\mathbf{u}}$)

$$-R\dot{\phi}\hat{\mathbf{v}} = \dot{y}_C\hat{\mathbf{y}}_0 + (-\dot{y}_C\hat{\mathbf{x}}_0 + y_C\dot{\theta}\hat{\mathbf{y}}_0 + r\omega_{2z}\hat{\mathbf{z}}_0) \times \hat{\mathbf{u}} \tag{1}$$

Equation (1) solves for $\dot{\phi}$ (on $\hat{\mathbf{v}}$) and ω_{2z} (on $\hat{\mathbf{y}}_0$)

$$\dot{\phi} = \frac{y_C}{R}\dot{\theta}, \qquad \omega_{2z} = -\frac{1-\cos\alpha}{r\sin\alpha}\dot{y}_C$$

b. We can write the cylinder's rotational angle ϕ as

$$\phi = \frac{1}{R}\int y_C(\theta)d\theta + \text{const}$$

This shows that the mechanism acts like an integrator. ■

7.4 Planar Kinematics

RIGID bodies in planar motion play an important role in countless technological applications. Their kinematics can be analyzed in a straightforward manner.

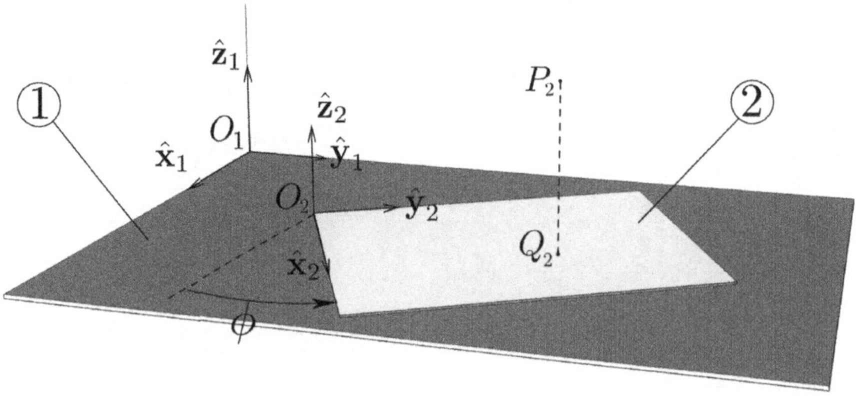

Figure 7.24 – *Planar motion.*

> **Definition 7.7** Rigid body $\mathcal{B}_2$ is in planar motion relative to rigid body $\mathcal{B}_1$ if a plane $(O_2, \hat{\mathbf{x}}_2, \hat{\mathbf{y}}_2)$ of $\mathcal{B}_2$ coincides geometrically with a plane $(O_1, \hat{\mathbf{x}}_1, \hat{\mathbf{y}}_1)$ of $\mathcal{B}_1$ at all times.

Hence, all points attached to $\mathcal{B}_2$ move in planes parallel to plane $(O_1, \hat{\mathbf{x}}_1, \hat{\mathbf{y}}_1)$. The orientation of the normal direction to plane $(O_2, \hat{\mathbf{x}}_2, \hat{\mathbf{y}}_2)$ remains constant, and we can choose $\hat{\mathbf{z}}_2 = \hat{\mathbf{z}}_1$. See Figure 7.24. At any instant, the position of $\mathcal{B}_2$ relative to $\mathcal{B}_1$ is defined by
- the Cartesian coordinates $(x(t), y(t))$ of point O_2 on axes $(O_1, \hat{\mathbf{x}}_1)$ and $(O_1, \hat{\mathbf{y}}_1)$:

$$\mathbf{r}_{O_1O_2} = x(t)\hat{\mathbf{x}}_1 + y(t)\hat{\mathbf{y}}_1$$

- the angle $\phi(t) = (\hat{\mathbf{x}}_1, \hat{\mathbf{x}}_2) = (\hat{\mathbf{y}}_1, \hat{\mathbf{y}}_2)$ defining the orientation of $\mathcal{B}_2$ relative to $\mathcal{B}_1$.

Hence, in general, a rigid body $\mathcal{B}_2$ in planar motion relative to $\mathcal{B}_1$ has three degrees of freedom: the functions $x(t)$, $y(t)$ and $\phi(t)$ are in general independent, and completely specify the motion of $\mathcal{B}_2$. Note that we can view $x \equiv x(\phi)$ and $y \equiv y(\phi)$ as functions of ϕ instead of t, with $\phi \equiv \phi(t)$. The kinematic screw of $\mathcal{B}_2$ relative to $\mathcal{B}_1$ can then be written in terms of coordinates (x, y, ϕ):

$$\{\mathcal{V}_{2/1}\} = \left\{ \begin{array}{c} \boldsymbol{\omega}_{2/1} \\ \mathbf{v}_{O_2\in 2/1} \end{array} \right\} = \left\{ \begin{array}{c} \dot{\phi}\hat{\mathbf{z}}_1 \\ \dot{x}\hat{\mathbf{x}}_1 + \dot{y}\hat{\mathbf{y}}_1 \end{array} \right\}_{O_2} = \dot{\phi} \left\{ \begin{array}{c} \hat{\mathbf{z}}_1 \\ \frac{dx}{d\phi}\hat{\mathbf{x}}_1 + \frac{dy}{d\phi}\hat{\mathbf{y}}_1 \end{array} \right\}_{O_2} \tag{7.21}$$

All points P attached to $\mathcal{B}_2$ which projects onto point Q of plane $(O_2, \hat{\mathbf{x}}_2, \hat{\mathbf{y}}_2)$ have the same velocity: indeed we have

$$\mathbf{v}_{P\in 2/1} = \mathbf{v}_{Q\in 2/1} + \dot{\phi}\hat{\mathbf{z}}_1 \times \mathbf{r}_{QP} = \mathbf{v}_{Q\in 2/1}$$

since position vector $\mathbf{r}_{QP}$ is collinear to $\hat{\mathbf{z}}_1$. This implies that the trajectory of point P can be obtained from that of Q by a translation along $\hat{\mathbf{z}}_1$. Similarly, the acceleration of P is equal to that of Q

$$\mathbf{a}_{P\in 2/1} = \mathbf{a}_{Q\in 2/1} + \ddot{\phi}\hat{\mathbf{z}}_1 \times \mathbf{r}_{QP} + \dot{\phi}\hat{\mathbf{z}}_1 \times (\dot{\phi}\hat{\mathbf{z}}_1 \times \mathbf{r}_{QP}) = \mathbf{a}_{Q\in 2/1}$$

This shows that the analysis of the kinematics of $\mathcal{B}_2$ can be reduced to that of plane $(O_2, \hat{\mathbf{x}}_2, \hat{\mathbf{y}}_2)$.

7.4.1 Instantaneous center of rotation

Theorem 7.1 At any instant, there exists a unique point I_{12} of $\mathcal{B}_2$ of plane $(O_2, \hat{\mathbf{x}}_2, \hat{\mathbf{y}}_2)$, called *instantaneous center of rotation* of $\mathcal{B}_2$ relative to $\mathcal{B}_1$ whose instantaneous velocity relative to $\mathcal{B}_1$ is zero:

$$\mathbf{v}_{I_{12}\in 2/1} = \mathbf{0} \tag{7.22}$$

as long as $\boldsymbol{\omega}_{2/1} \neq \mathbf{0}$.

Proof. To show the existence of I_{12}, we find the set of points satisfying $\mathbf{v}_{P\in 2/1} = 0$, that is,

$$\dot{\phi}\hat{\mathbf{z}}_1 \times \mathbf{r}_{O_2P} = -\mathbf{v}_{O_2\in 2/1}$$

This equation can be solved to give

$$\mathbf{r}_{O_2P} = \frac{1}{\dot{\phi}}\hat{\mathbf{z}}_1 \times \mathbf{v}_{O_2\in 2/1} + \lambda\hat{\mathbf{z}}_1 \tag{7.23}$$

as long as $\dot{\phi} \neq 0$, and where λ is an arbitrary scalar. This set of points is the instantaneous axis of rotation Δ_{12} of $\mathcal{B}_2$ relative to $\mathcal{B}_1$. Point I_{12} in plane $(O_2, \hat{\mathbf{x}}_2, \hat{\mathbf{y}}_2)$ is obtained by setting $\lambda = 0$ in (7.23). ■

Hence, body $\mathcal{B}_2$ appears to be in an instantaneous rotational motion about axis $\Delta_{12}(I_{12}, \hat{\mathbf{z}}_1)$ *as far as its velocity field is concerned*: for any point Q in plane $(O_2, \hat{\mathbf{x}}_2, \hat{\mathbf{y}}_2)$

$$\mathbf{v}_{Q\in 2/1} = \dot{\phi}\hat{\mathbf{z}}_1 \times \mathbf{r}_{I_{12}Q} \tag{7.24}$$

This shows that the line $I_{12}Q$ is perpendicular to velocity $\mathbf{v}_{Q\in 2/1}$. This property provides a method for the construction of I_{12}. If the velocity of two points A and B of body $\mathcal{B}_2$ are known in direction at a particular instant, then point I_{12} is located at the intersection of the two normals based at A and B to velocities $\mathbf{v}_{A\in 2/1}$ and $\mathbf{v}_{B\in 2/1}$, respectively. See Figure 7.25.

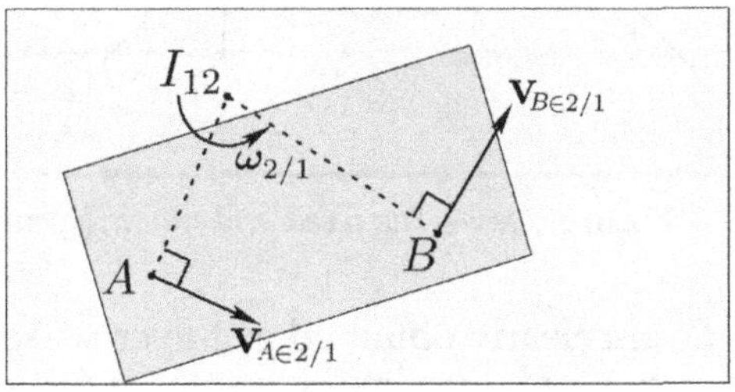

Figure 7.25 – *Construction of the instantaneous center.*

Remark 6. The acceleration field of $\mathcal{B}_2$ is not that of a body in rotation about I_{12}. In fact, the acceleration of $I_{12} \in 2$ is not zero.

Proof. To find the expression of $\mathbf{a}_{I_{12}\in 2/1}$, let us denote $\mathbf{r}_{O_1O_2} = \mathbf{r}(\phi)$ and note that the position of I_{12} according to (7.23) can be rewritten in the form

$$\mathbf{r}_{O_2I_{12}} = \hat{\mathbf{z}}_1 \times \frac{d\mathbf{r}}{d\phi} \tag{7.25}$$

where the derivative $d\mathbf{r}/d\phi$ is performed relative to $\mathcal{B}_1$. Then, the acceleration $\mathbf{a}_{I_{12}\in 2/1}$ is found according to formula relating the accelerations of two points of $\mathcal{B}_2$

$$\mathbf{a}_{I_{12}\in 2/1} = \mathbf{a}_{O_2\in 2/1} + \ddot{\phi}\hat{\mathbf{z}}_1 \times (\hat{\mathbf{z}}_1 \times \frac{d\mathbf{r}}{d\phi}) - \dot{\phi}^2\hat{\mathbf{z}}_1 \times \frac{d\mathbf{r}}{d\phi}$$

with

$$\mathbf{a}_{O_2\in 2/1} = \frac{d}{dt}\left(\dot{\phi}\frac{d\mathbf{r}}{d\phi}\right) = \ddot{\phi}\frac{d\mathbf{r}}{d\phi} + \dot{\phi}^2\frac{d^2\mathbf{r}}{d\phi^2}$$

We can then simplify this expression to obtain

$$\mathbf{a}_{I_{12}\in 2/1} = \dot{\phi}^2\left(\frac{d^2\mathbf{r}}{d\phi^2} - \hat{\mathbf{z}}_1 \times \frac{d\mathbf{r}}{d\phi}\right)$$

which shows that $\mathbf{a}_{I_{12}\in 2/1}$ is not zero even if $\ddot{\phi} = 0$ (in fact, it is not a function of $\ddot{\phi}$!). ■

7.4.2 The fixed and moving centrodes

Definition 7.8 — centrodes. During the planar motion of body $\mathcal{B}_2$ relative to $\mathcal{B}_1$, the instantaneous center of rotation I_{12} describes a curve $\mathcal{C}_1$ in $\mathcal{B}_1$ and a curve $\mathcal{C}_2$ in $\mathcal{B}_2$, known as the *fixed and moving centrodes* of the motion of $\mathcal{B}_2$ relative to $\mathcal{B}_1$.

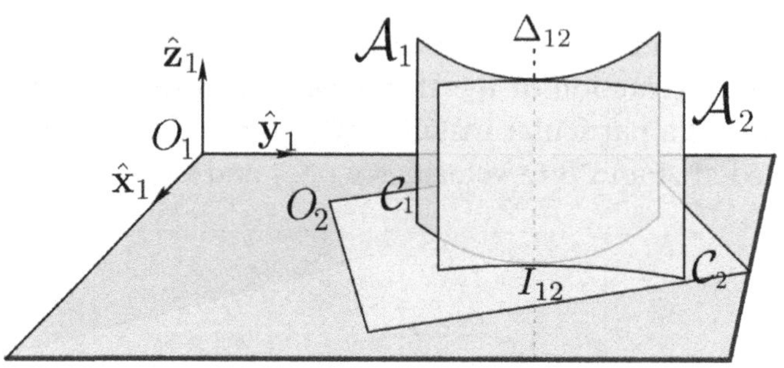

Figure 7.26 – *The fixed and moving centrodes.*

The centrodes $\mathcal{C}_1$ and $\mathcal{C}_2$ are clearly obtained as the cross-sections of the axodes $\mathcal{A}_1$ and $\mathcal{A}_2$, respectively, with plane $(O_1, \hat{\mathbf{x}}_1, \hat{\mathbf{y}}_1)$. See Figure 7.26. We can imagine a point, still denoted I_{12}, whose trajectory relative to $\mathcal{B}_1$ is the fixed centrode $\mathcal{C}_1$. From an observer attached to $\mathcal{B}_2$, the same point moves along the moving centrode $\mathcal{C}_2$. Condition (7.22) is equivalent to

$$\mathbf{v}_{I_{12}/1} = \mathbf{v}_{I_{12}/2}$$

Furthermore, the velocity field of plane $(O_2, \hat{\mathbf{x}}_2, \hat{\mathbf{y}}_2)$ relative to plane $(O_1, \hat{\mathbf{x}}_1, \hat{\mathbf{y}}_1)$ is equivalent to that of centrode $\mathcal{C}_2$ rolling without slipping on centrode $\mathcal{C}_1$.

$V_{I\in 2/1} = V_{I/2} - V_{I/1}$, $V_{I\in 2/1} = 0 \Rightarrow V_{I/2} = V_{I/1}$

The Cartesian equations of $\mathcal{C}_1$ on $(\hat{\mathbf{x}}_1, \hat{\mathbf{y}}_1)$ can be easily be found from equation (7.25). Denoting the Cartesian coordinates of I_{12} as (X_I, Y_I) on $(O_1, \hat{\mathbf{x}}_1, \hat{\mathbf{y}}_1)$, we find

$$\mathbf{r}_{O_1 I_{12}} = X_I \hat{\mathbf{x}}_1 + Y_I \hat{\mathbf{y}}_1 = \mathbf{r} + \hat{\mathbf{z}}_1 \times \frac{d\mathbf{r}}{d\phi}$$

leading to the following parametrization of $\mathcal{C}_1$

$$X_I(\phi) = x(\phi) - \frac{dy}{d\phi}$$
$$Y_I(\phi) = y(\phi) + \frac{dx}{d\phi}$$

Similarly, denoting the coordinates (x_I, y_I) of I_{12} relative to $(O_2, \hat{\mathbf{x}}_2, \hat{\mathbf{y}}_2)$, we find

$$\mathbf{r}_{O_2 I_{12}} = x_I \hat{\mathbf{x}}_2 + y_I \hat{\mathbf{y}}_2 = \hat{\mathbf{z}}_1 \times \frac{d\mathbf{r}}{d\phi} = -\frac{dy}{d\phi}\hat{\mathbf{x}}_1 + \frac{dx}{d\phi}\hat{\mathbf{y}}_1$$

leads to the parametrization

$$x_I(\phi) = \frac{dx}{d\phi}\sin\phi - \frac{dy}{d\phi}\cos\phi$$
$$y_I(\phi) = \frac{dx}{d\phi}\cos\phi + \frac{dy}{d\phi}\sin\phi$$

7.4.3 Kennedy's theorem

CONSIDER three rigid bodies $\mathcal{B}_1$, $\mathcal{B}_2$ and $\mathcal{B}_3$ in relative planar motion. Suppose that at a given time the positions of instantaneous centers of rotation I_{12} and I_{23} are known. See Figure 7.27. Recall from Section 6.6 that kinematic screw $\{\mathcal{V}_{3/1}\}$ can be determined as the sum of screws $\{\mathcal{V}_{2/1}\}$ and $\{\mathcal{V}_{3/2}\}$ according to the kinematic loop formula (6.9). We may then ask whether the position of instantaneous center I_{13} can be found from those of I_{12} and I_{23}.

The equality $\{\mathcal{V}_{3/1}\} = \{\mathcal{V}_{2/1}\} + \{\mathcal{V}_{3/2}\}$ is equivalent to the equations

$$\omega_{3/1} = \omega_{3/2} + \omega_{2/1}$$

and

$$\mathbf{v}_{P\in 3/1} = \mathbf{v}_{P\in 3/2} + \mathbf{v}_{P\in 2/1}$$

for any point P in the three coinciding planes. Choosing P as point I_{13} leads to

$$\mathbf{0} = \mathbf{v}_{I_{13}\in 3/2} + \mathbf{v}_{I_{13}\in 2/1}$$

where we can determine $\mathbf{v}_{I_{13}\in 3/2}$ and $\mathbf{v}_{I_{13}\in 2/1}$ from the centers I_{23} and I_{12}:

$$\mathbf{v}_{I_{13}\in 3/2} = \omega_{3/2} \times \mathbf{r}_{I_{23}I_{13}}, \qquad \mathbf{v}_{I_{13}\in 2/1} = \omega_{2/1} \times \mathbf{r}_{I_{12}I_{13}}$$

These expressions lead to a relationship between the three centers

$$\hat{\mathbf{z}} \times (\omega_{3/2}\mathbf{r}_{I_{23}I_{13}} + \omega_{2/1}\mathbf{r}_{I_{12}I_{13}}) = \mathbf{0}$$

denoting by $\hat{\mathbf{z}} = \hat{\mathbf{z}}_1 = \hat{\mathbf{z}}_2 = \hat{\mathbf{z}}_3$ the common normal to the three planes. This shows that $\mathbf{r}_{I_{23}I_{13}}$ and $\mathbf{r}_{I_{12}I_{13}}$ are collinear.

Theorem 7.2 — Kennedy's Theorem. If three rigid bodies are in relative planar motions, the three instantaneous centers I_{12}, I_{23} and I_{13} are collinear points. Furthermore, the position of I_{13} must satisfy

$$\mathbf{r}_{I_{12}I_{13}} = -\frac{\omega_{3/2}}{\omega_{3/2}+\omega_{2/1}}\mathbf{r}_{I_{12}I_{23}} \tag{7.26}$$

in 3D there exist a common perpendicular to instantaneous axes

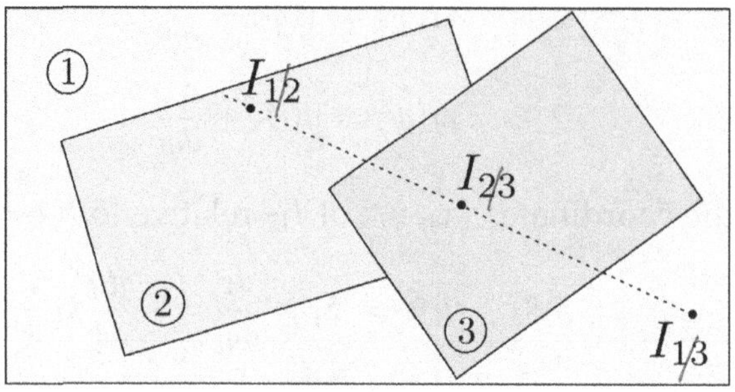

Figure 7.27

Example 7.13 A body $\mathcal{B}_2$ is in planar motion relative to $\mathcal{B}_1(O_1, \hat{\mathbf{x}}_1, \hat{\mathbf{y}}_1)$ in such a way that point O_2 of $\mathcal{B}_2$ slides along axis $(O_1, \hat{\mathbf{x}}_1)$ of $\mathcal{B}_1$ while point A_2 of $\mathcal{B}_2$ slides along axis $(O_1, \hat{\mathbf{y}}_1)$ of $\mathcal{B}_1$. Let $\hat{\mathbf{x}}_2$ be the unit vector such that $\mathbf{r}_{O_2A_2} = \ell\hat{\mathbf{x}}_2$ (ℓ is a constant), and let $\phi(t)$ be the angle which line O_2A_2 makes with axis $(O_1, \hat{\mathbf{x}}_1)$. See Figure 7.28.

a. Determine the kinematic screw of $\mathcal{B}_2$ relative to $\mathcal{B}_1$.

b. Find the position of the instantaneous center of rotation I_{12}. Then determine the corresponding fixed and moving centrodes. Sketch the moving centrodes at various instants. Find the velocity of I_{12} in motion along the fixed centrode, then along the moving centrode. Verify that these two velocities are equal. ■

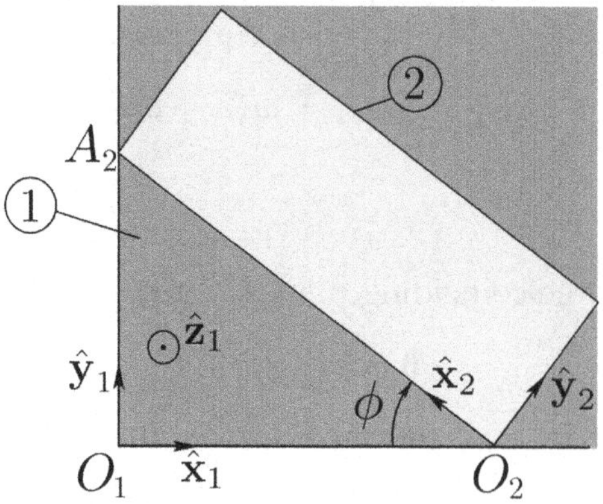

Figure 7.28

a. The kinematic screw of $\mathcal{B}_2$ relative to $\mathcal{B}_1$ is found by determining angular velocity $\omega_{2/1}$ and the velocity of a point of $\mathcal{B}_2$. With the notations of Figure 7.28, we find

$$\{\mathcal{V}_{2/1}\} = \left\{ \begin{array}{c} \omega_{2/1} = -\dot{\phi}\hat{\mathbf{z}}_1 \\ \frac{d}{dt}(\ell\cos\phi\hat{\mathbf{x}}_1) = -\ell\dot{\phi}\sin\phi\hat{\mathbf{x}}_1 \end{array} \right\}_{O_2}$$

b. Given the direction of $\mathbf{v}_{O_2\in 2/1}$ and $\mathbf{v}_{A_2\in 2/1}$, the instantaneous center of rotation I_{12} is located at the intersection of lines $(O_2, \hat{\mathbf{y}}_1)$ and line $(A_2, \hat{\mathbf{x}}_1)$: hence the figure $O_1A_1I_{12}O_2$ forms a rectangle. See Figure 7.29 (left). The Cartesian coordinates of I_{12} on $(O_1, \hat{\mathbf{x}}_1, \hat{\mathbf{y}}_1)$ are easily found to be

$$X_I = \ell\cos\phi, \qquad Y_I = \ell\sin\phi$$

These coordinates define the fixed centrode $\mathcal{C}_1$ of the motion, whose equation is given by $X_I^2 + Y_I^2 = \ell^2$ (by eliminating ϕ): $\mathcal{C}_1$ is the circle of center O_1 and radius ℓ. The fixed centrode must be viewed as a subset of $\mathcal{B}_1$. As $\mathcal{B}_2$ moves relative to $\mathcal{B}_1$, the geometric point I_{12} travels along curve $\mathcal{C}_1$ with velocity $d\mathbf{r}_{O_1I_{12}}/dt$:

$$\mathbf{v}_{I_{12}/1} = \ell\dot{\phi}(-\sin\phi\,\hat{\mathbf{x}}_1 + \cos\phi\,\hat{\mathbf{y}}_1) \tag{1}$$

The moving centrode $\mathcal{C}_2$ is found by determining the coordinates (x_I, y_I) of I_{12} in the Cartesian coordinate system $(O_2, \hat{\mathbf{x}}_2, \hat{\mathbf{y}}_2)$ attached to $\mathcal{B}_2$:

$$\mathbf{r}_{O_2I_{12}} = |\mathbf{r}_{AI}|\,(\cos\phi\hat{\mathbf{y}}_2 + \sin\phi\hat{\mathbf{x}}_2) = \ell\sin\phi(\cos\phi\hat{\mathbf{y}}_2 + \sin\phi\hat{\mathbf{x}}_2)$$

leading to

$$x_I = \frac{\ell}{2}(1 - \cos 2\phi), \qquad y_I = \frac{\ell}{2}\sin 2\phi$$

Elimination of ϕ gives the equation $(x_I - \ell/2)^2 + y_I^2 = \ell^2/4$: $\mathcal{C}_2$ is the circle of center B_2 (midpoint of line segment O_2A_2) and radius $\ell/2$ (passing through points O_2 and A_2). As $\mathcal{B}_2$ moves relative to $\mathcal{B}_1$, $\mathcal{C}_2$ (attached to $\mathcal{B}_2$) rolls without slipping on $\mathcal{C}_1$ (attached to $\mathcal{B}_1$) in "contact" at I_{12}. One can easily verify that the two circles found are tangential at I_{12}.

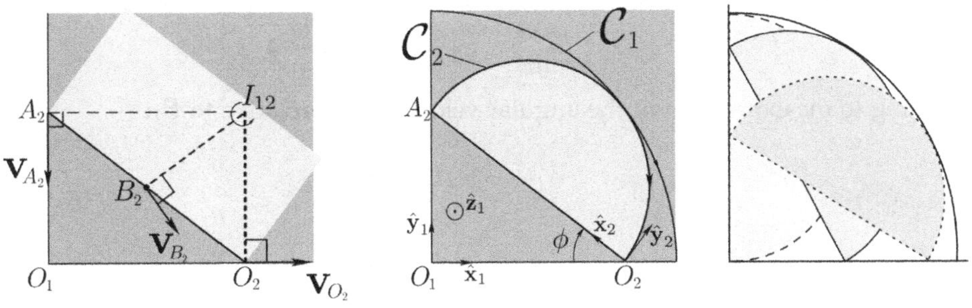

Figure 7.29

Point I_{12} moves along centrode $\mathcal{C}_2$ with velocity $\mathbf{v}_{I_{12}/2}$ obtained by differentiating $\mathbf{r}_{O_2I_{12}}$ relative to $\mathcal{B}_2$:

$$\mathbf{v}_{I_{12}/2} = \ell\dot{\phi}(\cos 2\phi\,\hat{\mathbf{y}}_2 + \sin 2\phi\,\hat{\mathbf{x}}_2) \tag{2}$$

The condition $\mathbf{v}_{I_{12}\in 2/1} = \mathbf{0}$ is equivalent to $\mathbf{v}_{I_{12}/2} = \mathbf{v}_{I_{12}/1}$. This result can easily be verified by comparing equation (1) to equation (2). The two centrodes are shown in Figure 7.29 (center). A few snapshots of the corresponding motion are shown in Figure 7.29 (right). ∎

Example 7.14 Consider a smooth curve $\mathcal{C}$ inscribed in a plane $\mathcal{B}_1(O_1, \hat{\mathbf{x}}_1, \hat{\mathbf{y}}_1)$. A plane $\mathcal{B}_2(O_2, \hat{\mathbf{x}}_2, \hat{\mathbf{y}}_2)$ moves relative to plane $\mathcal{B}_1$ in the following way:
(i) origin O_2 moves along curve $\mathcal{C}$ at constant speed v_0,
(ii) axis $(O_2, \hat{\mathbf{x}}_2)$ is directed along the tangent unit vector $\hat{\mathbf{e}}_t = \hat{\mathbf{x}}_2$ at O_2 to curve $\mathcal{C}$,
(iii) axis $(O_2, \hat{\mathbf{y}}_2)$ is directed along the normal unit vector $\hat{\mathbf{e}}_n$ at O_2 to curve $\mathcal{C}$, pointing toward the center of curvature of $\mathcal{C}$: $\hat{\mathbf{y}}_2 = \hat{\mathbf{e}}_n$. See Figure 7.30.

Find the instantaneous center of rotation associated with the motion of $\mathcal{B}_2$ relative to $\mathcal{B}_1$. Then find the corresponding fixed and moving centrode $\mathcal{C}_1$ and $\mathcal{C}_2$. What is the geometric relationship between curves $\mathcal{C}$ and $\mathcal{C}_1$? ■

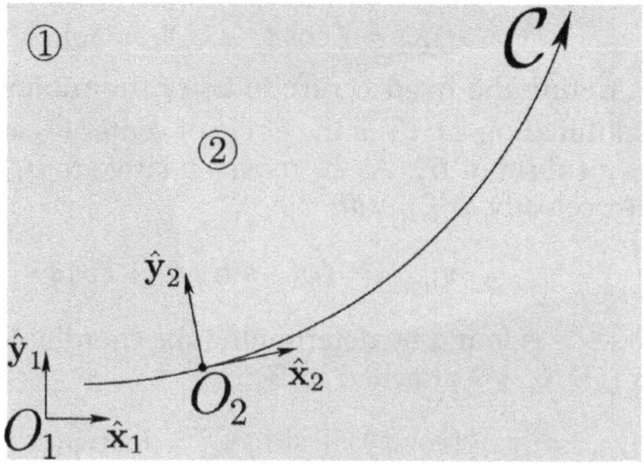

Figure 7.30

The velocity of O_2 is given by

$$\mathbf{v}_{O_2/1} = v_0 \hat{\mathbf{x}}_2, \qquad \frac{d\hat{\mathbf{x}}_2}{dt} = \frac{v_0}{\rho} \hat{\mathbf{y}}_2$$

where ρ is the radius of curvature of curve $\mathcal{C}$ at point O_2. Denote $\hat{\mathbf{z}}_2 = \hat{\mathbf{x}}_2 \times \hat{\mathbf{y}}_2 = \hat{\mathbf{z}}_1$, and $\boldsymbol{\omega}_{2/1} = \omega_{2/1} \hat{\mathbf{z}}_2$:

$$\frac{d\hat{\mathbf{x}}_2}{dt} = \omega_{2/1} \hat{\mathbf{z}} \times \hat{\mathbf{x}}_2 = \frac{v_0}{\rho} \hat{\mathbf{y}}_2$$

leading to the expression of the angular velocity of $\mathcal{B}_2$ relative to $\mathcal{B}_1$:

$$\boldsymbol{\omega}_{2/1} = \frac{v_0}{\rho} \hat{\mathbf{z}}$$

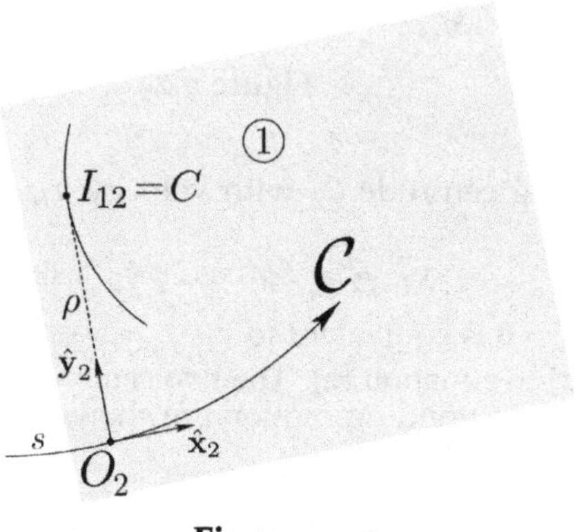

Figure 7.31

The position of instantaneous center of rotation I_{12} can be found from the knowledge of $\mathbf{v}_{O_2/2}$ and $\omega_{2/1}$:

$$\mathbf{r}_{O_2 I_{12}} = \frac{1}{\omega_{2/1}} \hat{\mathbf{z}} \times \mathbf{v}_{O_2/1} = \rho \hat{\mathbf{y}}_2$$

Hence I_{12} is located on axis $(O_2, \hat{\mathbf{y}}_2)$ at a distance ρ from O_2: this shows that I_{12} *coincides with the center of curvature C of curve $\mathcal{C}$ at point O_2.*

The fixed centrode $\mathcal{C}_1$ of the motion is known to be the so-called *evolute* of curve $\mathcal{C}$, that is, *the locus of the center of curvature of* $\mathcal{C}$. The moving centrode $\mathcal{C}_2$ of the motion is the axis $(O_2, \hat{\mathbf{y}}_2)$: as O_2 moves along curve $\mathcal{C}$, the axis $(O_2, \hat{\mathbf{y}}_2)$ rolls without slipping on $\mathcal{C}_1$. Curve $\mathcal{C}$ is an *involute* of $\mathcal{C}_1$: if a string wrapped along $\mathcal{C}_1$ is unwound and is kept taut, the endpoint of the string would describe curve $\mathcal{C}$.

■

7.4.4 Instantaneous Center of Acceleration

RECALL that a body $\mathcal{B}_2$ in planar motion relative to rigid body $\mathcal{B}_1$ admits an instantaneous center of rotation $I \equiv I_{12}$, that is, such that $\mathbf{v}_{P\in 2/1} = \boldsymbol{\omega}_{2/1} \times \mathbf{r}_{IP}$ for any point P and at any given time (as long as $\boldsymbol{\omega}_{2/1} \neq \mathbf{0}$). Also recall that point I describes two curves, the fixed centrode $\mathcal{C}_1$ relative to $\mathcal{B}_1$ and the moving centrode $\mathcal{C}_2$ relative to $\mathcal{B}_2$ and that $\mathcal{C}_2$ rolls without slipping on $\mathcal{C}_1$. See Figure 7.32. Here we wish to show that the motion of $\mathcal{B}_2$ can also be characterized in terms of an *instantaneous center of acceleration.*

First, we express the acceleration of any point P of $\mathcal{B}_2$ in the following way[3]

$$\mathbf{a}_{P/1} = \frac{d}{dt}(\boldsymbol{\omega}_{2/1} \times \mathbf{r}_{IP}) = \boldsymbol{\alpha}_{2/1} \times \mathbf{r}_{IP} + \boldsymbol{\omega}_{2/1} \times (\mathbf{v}_{P/1} - \mathbf{v}_{I/1}) \tag{7.27}$$

In (7.27), $\mathbf{v}_{I/1}$ is the velocity of I along the fixed centrode $\mathcal{C}_1$. Recall that $\mathbf{v}_{I/1}$ is necessarily tangent to $\mathcal{C}_1$ (and $\mathcal{C}_2$) at contact point I. If we define the unit tangent vector $\hat{\boldsymbol{\tau}}$ and unit normal vector $\hat{\mathbf{n}}$ at I, [4] we can then write $\mathbf{v}_{I/1} = v_I \hat{\boldsymbol{\tau}}$. With $\hat{\mathbf{k}} = \hat{\boldsymbol{\tau}} \times \hat{\mathbf{n}}$, we write the angular velocity $\boldsymbol{\omega}_{2/1} = \omega_{2/1}\hat{\mathbf{k}}$ and the angular acceleration $\boldsymbol{\alpha}_{2/1} = \alpha_{2/1}\hat{\mathbf{k}}$. We can now express $\mathbf{a}_{P/1}$ in the form

$$\mathbf{a}_{P/1} = \alpha_{2/1}\hat{\mathbf{k}} \times \mathbf{r}_{IP} - \omega_{2/1}^2 \mathbf{r}_{IP} + \omega_{2/1} v_I \hat{\mathbf{n}} \tag{7.28}$$

where we have used $\boldsymbol{\omega}_{2/1} \times \mathbf{v}_{P/1} = \boldsymbol{\omega}_{2/1} \times (\boldsymbol{\omega}_{2/1} \times \mathbf{r}_{IP}) = -\omega_{2/1}^2 \mathbf{r}_{IP}$.

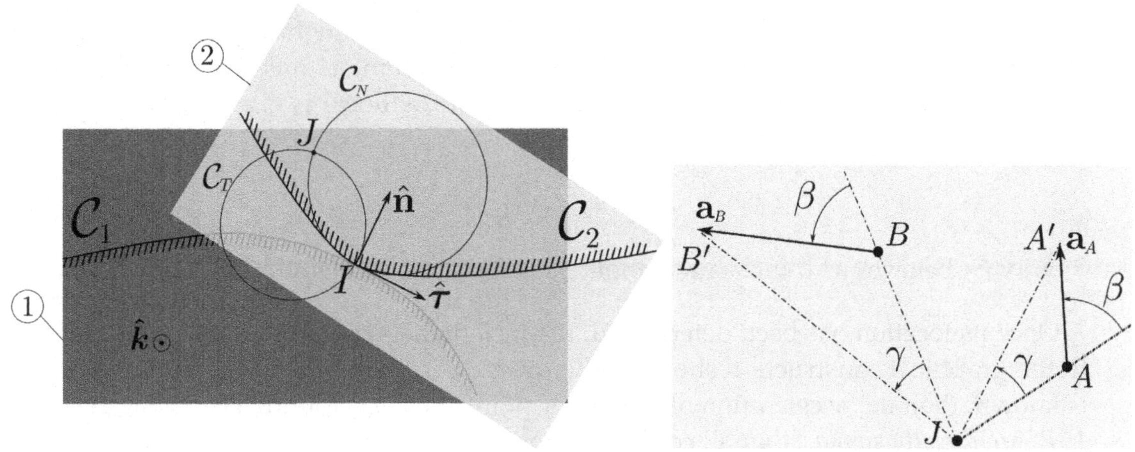

Figure 7.32 – *Center of acceleration* J *and construction of* $\mathbf{a}_B$ *from* $\mathbf{a}_A$.

First, we ask if points of $\mathcal{B}_2$ can be found with *vanishing normal acceleration*: since the tangent direction associated with the path of point P is normal to line IP, such points must satisfy $\mathbf{a}_{P/1} \cdot \mathbf{r}_{IP} = 0$. Using (7.28), we obtain

[3]Do not confuse $\mathbf{v}_{I/1} = \mathbf{v}_{I/2}$ with $\mathbf{v}_{I\in 2/1} = \mathbf{0}$.

[4]The exact direction of unit vectors $\hat{\boldsymbol{\tau}}$ and $\hat{\mathbf{n}}$ is unimportant.

$$-\omega_{2/1}^2 \mathbf{r}_{IP}^2 + \omega_{2/1} v_I \hat{\mathbf{n}} \cdot \mathbf{r}_{IP} = 0$$

Let us define the position of P in terms of its coordinates relative to axes $(I, \hat{\boldsymbol{\tau}})$ and $(I, \hat{\mathbf{n}})$, that is, we define $\mathbf{r}_{IP} = x\hat{\boldsymbol{\tau}} + y\hat{\mathbf{n}}$: then the set of points, denoted $\mathcal{C}_N$, with vanishing normal acceleration is characterized by the equation

$$(x^2 + y^2) - \frac{v_I}{\omega_{2/1}} y = 0 \tag{7.29}$$

This is the circle centered at $(0, \frac{v_I}{2\omega_{2/1}})$ and of radius $r_N = \frac{v_I}{2\omega_{2/1}}$.

Similarly, we can determine the set $\mathcal{C}_T$ of points of body $\mathcal{B}_2$ with *vanishing tangential acceleration*: now we set $\mathbf{a}_{P/2} \times \mathbf{r}_{IP} = \mathbf{0}$. Using (7.28) we obtain

$$(\alpha_{2/1} \hat{\mathbf{k}} \times \mathbf{r}_{IP}) \times \mathbf{r}_{IP} + \omega_{2/1} v_I \hat{\mathbf{n}} \times \mathbf{r}_{IP} = 0$$

or in terms of coordinates (x, y):

$$(x^2 + y^2) + \frac{\omega_{2/1} v_I}{\alpha} x = 0$$

The set $\mathcal{C}_T$ is the circle centered at $(-\frac{\omega_{2/1} v_I}{2\alpha_{2/1}}, 0)$ and of radius $r_T = \frac{\omega_{2/1} v_I}{2\alpha_{2/1}}$. If there exists a point J satisfying $\mathbf{v}_{J \in 2/1} = \mathbf{0}$ it must necessarily lie at the intersection of circles $\mathcal{C}_N$ and $\mathcal{C}_T$: its coordinates (x_J, y_J) must satisfy (7.29) and (7.4.4) leading to $y = -\frac{\omega_{2/1}^2}{\alpha_{2/1}} x$ and the coordinates

$$x_J = -v_I \frac{\omega_{2/1} \alpha_{2/1}}{\omega_{2/1}^4 + \alpha_{2/1}^2}, \qquad y_J = v_I \frac{\omega_{2/1}^3}{\omega_{2/1}^4 + \alpha_{2/1}^2} \tag{7.30}$$

Theorem 7.3 — Instantaneous center of acceleration. At any instant, the motion of body $\mathcal{B}_2$ relative to body $\mathcal{B}_1$ can be characterized by an instantaneous center of acceleration J whose position relative to instantaneous center of rotation I is given by (7.30). Then, the acceleration of any point P of $\mathcal{B}_2$ is given by

$$\mathbf{a}_P = \boldsymbol{\alpha}_{2/1} \times \mathbf{r}_{JP} - \omega_{2/1}^2 \mathbf{r}_{JP} \tag{7.31}$$

Body $\mathcal{B}_2$ behaves as if in rotation about J, as far as its acceleration is concerned.

Once its location has been determined, the instantaneous center of acceleration J can lead to the graphical construction shown in Figure 7.32 (right). If the acceleration of a point A is known, then the acceleration of any other point B can be found. The triangles JAA' and JBB' are *directly similar*, that all corresponding angles in triangles JAA' and JBB' are equal and described in the same rotational sense.

7.5 Problems

Problem 7.1 A rectangular plate 1 of length $2b$ and width $2a$ moves relative to a referential 0 with the following constraints:
- corner point A moves along axis Ox,
- corner point B moves along axis Oy,
- its upper edge slides along axis Oz. Denote by Q the corresponding contact point.

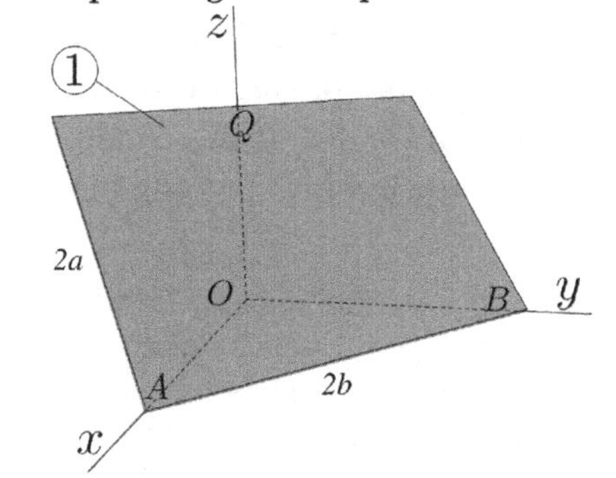

a. Find the kinematic screw $\{\mathcal{V}_{1/0}\}$ resolved at point Q.

b. Find the angular acceleration $\boldsymbol{\alpha}_{1/0}$.

Problem 7.2 Two cones are in motion relative to a referential 0. Cone 2 rotates about axis Oz at constant rate Ω_2. Cone 1 rolls without slipping on cone 2 so that its axis Ox_1 rotates in the horizontal plane Oxy of 0 at constant rate Ω_1 about the vertical axis Oz. Let γ_1 and γ_2 be the vertex half-angle of 1 and 2, respectively.

Find the angular velocity and angular acceleration of cone 1 relative to referential 0. Determine the kinematic screws $\{\mathcal{V}_{1/0}\}$ and $\{\mathcal{V}_{1/2}\}$.

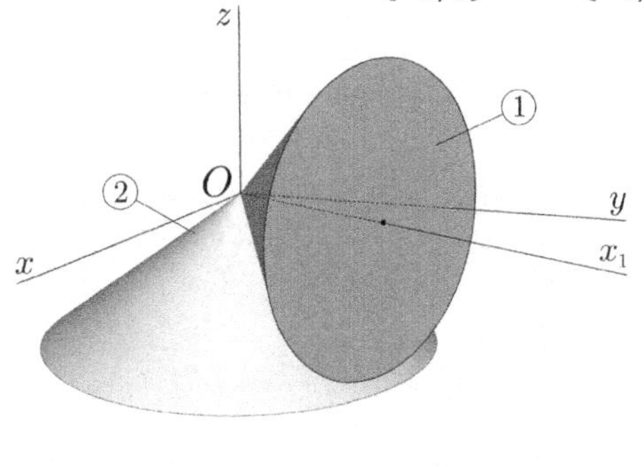

Problem 7.3 A triangular plate 1 of vertices O, A, and B moves in a referential 0 in such a way that
- vertex O remains fixed,
- vertex A is constrained to move in plane Oxz,
- vertex B is constrained to move in plane Oxy.

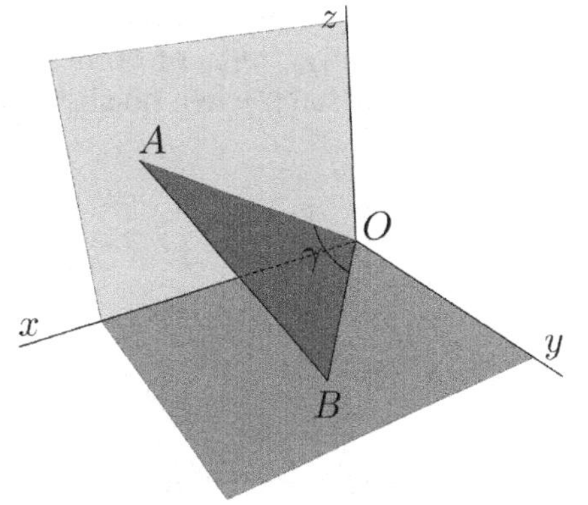

Find the kinematic screw $\{\mathcal{V}_{1/0}\}$ and the corresponding instantaneous screw axis. Assume $|OA| = |OB| = a$, and denote by γ the angle at O.

Problem 7.4 Consider a rigid body 1 consisting of a disk of center C and radius r rigidly connected to a rod AC of length l coinciding with the axis of the disk. Body 1 is set in motion in a referential 0 in such a way that extremity A remains fixed on axis Oz of 0 and that the disk stays in contact with fixed support Oxy. Denote by h the distance from O to A. The angular velocity of plane OAC about the vertical axis Oz is imposed to be Ω.

Determine the angular velocity $\omega_{1/0}$ of the disk in terms of Ω, h, r and l, assuming no-slip at the contact point.

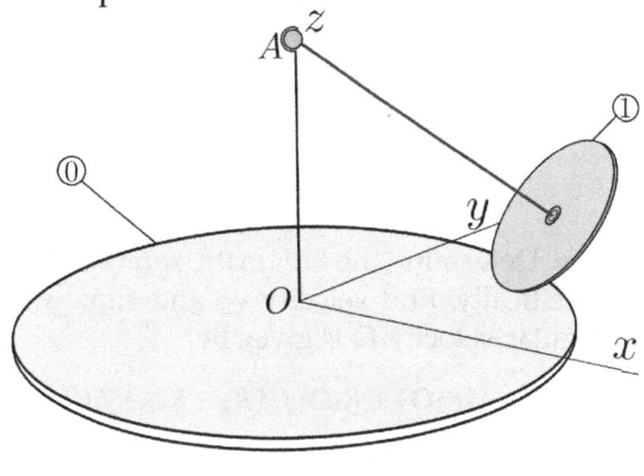

Problem 7.5 In order to facilitate the rotation between two rigid bodies 1 and 2 about the same axis Δ of some referential 0, one can interpose truncated cones 3 between them in such a way that contact is achieved along line segments MN of 1 and IJ of 2.

Determine the geometric condition which guarantees the no-slip condition along both contact lines. Find the relationship between the angular velocities $\omega_{3/0}$, $\omega_{2/0}$, $\omega_{1/0}$ of bodies 3, 2 and 1 relative to referential 0 when no slip is achieved.

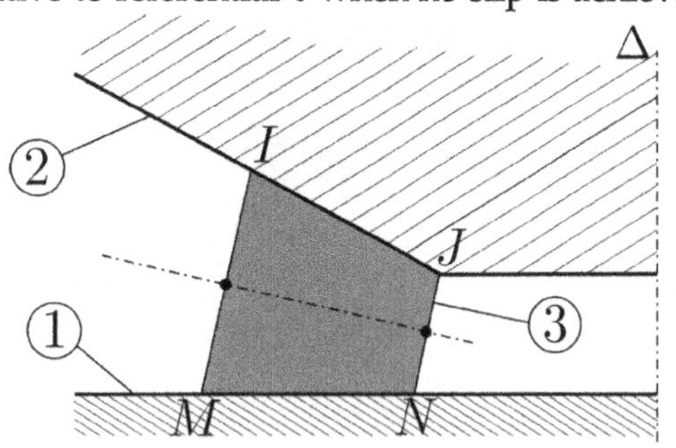

Problem 7.6 We consider the motion of three spheres 1, 2 and 3 in a referential 0 of origin O. Sphere 1 of radius R_1 and center O is rotating about O with a given angular velocity $\mathbf{\Omega}_1(t)$. Sphere 2 of radius $R_2 > R_1$ and center O is also rotating about O with a given angular velocity $\mathbf{\Omega}_2(t)$. Sphere 3 of center C and diameter $(R_2 - R_1)$ is rotating between 1 and 2. Denote by I_1 the contact point between 3 and 1, I_2 the contact point between 3 and 2, $\mathbf{v}_C = \mathbf{v}_{C/0}$ the velocity of C, and by $\mathbf{\Omega} = \omega_{3/0}$ the angular velocity of 3. Assume that no-slip is realized at both contact points I_1 and I_2.

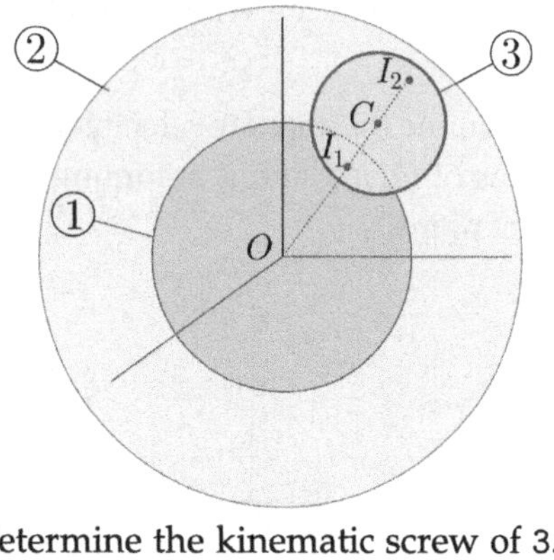

a. Determine the kinematic screw of 3. More specifically, find velocity $\mathbf{v}_C$ and show that the angular velocity $\mathbf{\Omega}$ is given by

$$\mathbf{\Omega} = (R_2\mathbf{\Omega}_2 - R_1\mathbf{\Omega}_1)/(R_2 - R_1) + \lambda(t)\,\mathbf{r}_{OC}$$

where $\lambda(t)$ is an indeterminate function of time. Interpret λ physically. Show that point C can be viewed as rigidly attached to a sphere of center O, radius $(R_1 + R_2)/2$, and rotating with angular velocity $(R_1\mathbf{\Omega}_1 + R_2\mathbf{\Omega}_2)/(R_1 + R_2)$. Find the trajectory of C in the case of constant angular velocities $\mathbf{\Omega}_1$ and $\mathbf{\Omega}_2$.

b. Show that for $\mathbf{\Omega}$ to remain collinear to $\mathbf{r}_{I_1 I_2}$ it is equivalent that $\mathbf{v}_{I_1 \in 1/0} = \mathbf{v}_{I_2 \in 2/0}$.

c. It is possible to determine the function λ if additional kinematic conditions are imposed. Find λ in each of the following three cases: (i) $\mathbf{\Omega}$ and $\mathbf{r}_{I_1 I_2}$ remain perpendicular, (ii) sphere 3 is in pure rolling motion relative to 1 at point I_1, (iii) sphere 3 is in pure rolling motion relative to both 1 and 2.

d. Find the condition to be satisfied between $\mathbf{\Omega}_1$ and $\mathbf{\Omega}_2$ for sphere 3 to be in pure spinning motion relative to 1. If this condition is satisfied, is the sphere in pure spinning motion relative to 2?

Problem 7.7 The Segway Personal Transporter is a two-wheeled, self-balancing electric vehicle. The figure displayed below shows a model of the Segway comprised of three interconnected rigid bodies denoted as 1, 2 and 3 in motion in a referential $0(O, \hat{\mathbf{x}}_0, \hat{\mathbf{y}}_0, \hat{\mathbf{z}}_0)$. Bodies 1 and 2 are the right and left wheels in rotation about axis $(A, \hat{\mathbf{v}})$ of body 3. Wheel 1 of center O_1 and radius R is in contact with the horizontal support $(O, \hat{\mathbf{x}}_0, \hat{\mathbf{y}}_0)$ at point I_1. Wheel 2 of center O_2 and radius R is in contact at point I_2 with its support: $\mathbf{r}_{I_1 O_1} = \mathbf{r}_{I_2 O_2} = R\hat{\mathbf{z}}_0$. Body 3 is the rider/frame/platform assembly relative to which axis $(A, \hat{\mathbf{v}})$ is fixed.

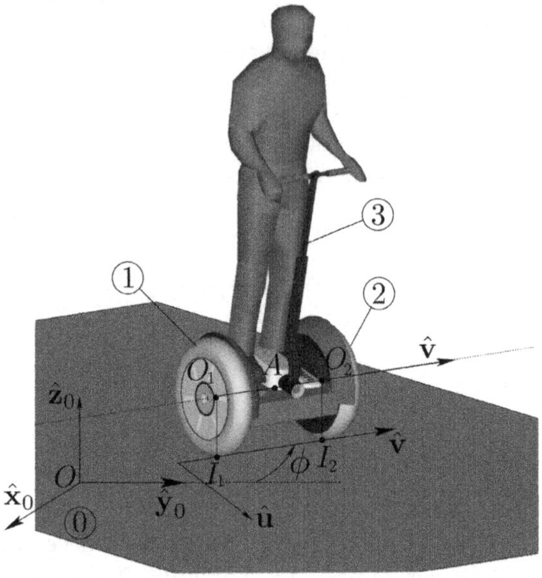

Denote by L the constant length such that $\mathbf{r}_{O_1 A} = \mathbf{r}_{AO_2} = \frac{L}{2}\hat{\mathbf{v}}$. When the Segway takes a turn in the road, the orientation of the wheels' axis is defined by angle $\phi(t) = (\hat{\mathbf{x}}_0, \hat{\mathbf{u}}) = (\hat{\mathbf{y}}_0, \hat{\mathbf{v}})$. The velocity of A is defined by $\mathbf{v}_{A/0} = U(t)\hat{\mathbf{u}} + V(t)\hat{\mathbf{v}}$.

a. Show that the angular velocities of wheels 1 and 2 relative to referential 0 are not independent of each other.

b. Assume that both wheels do not slip relative to plane $(O, \hat{\mathbf{x}}_0, \hat{\mathbf{y}}_0)$. Find the relationships between the quantities U, V, $\dot{\phi}$, $\omega_1 = \boldsymbol{\omega}_{1/0} \cdot \hat{\mathbf{v}}$ and $\omega_2 = \boldsymbol{\omega}_{2/0} \cdot \hat{\mathbf{v}}$. Show that their instantaneous axes of rotation intersect at a point J. Then show that line $(J, \hat{\mathbf{z}}_0)$ must pass through the centers of curvature of the trajectories of O_1 and O_2.

Problem 7.8 Consider the motion of a sphere 3 of radius R and center C constrained between two parallel disks 1 and 2 with non-coinciding verical axes. Disk 1 is in rotation about axis O_1z and angular velocity $\boldsymbol{\omega}_1 = \omega_1 \hat{\mathbf{z}}_0$ relative to a referential 0. Disk 2 is in rotation about axis O_2z and angular velocity $\boldsymbol{\omega}_2 = \omega_2 \hat{\mathbf{z}}_0$ relative to referential 0. Assume that the 3 points O_1, O_2 and C lie in the same horizontal plane. Also assume that sphere 3 does not slip relative to both disks. Denote by I_1 and I_2 the contact points of 3 with disks 1 and 2, $\boldsymbol{\Omega} = \boldsymbol{\omega}_{3/0}$ the angular velocity of sphere 3, and $\mathbf{v}_C = \mathbf{v}_{C/0}$ the velocity of point C.

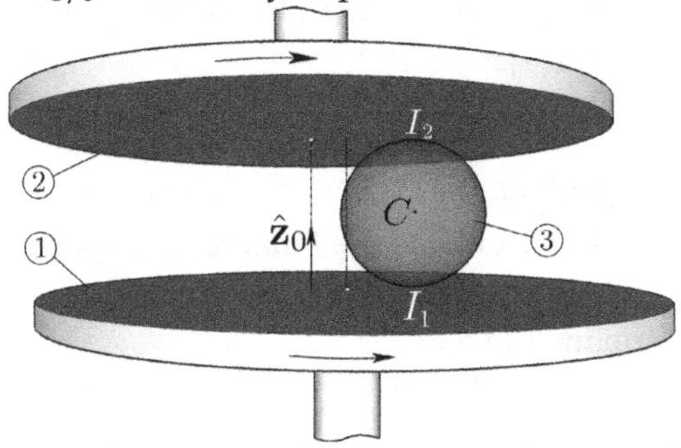

a. Express the no-slip conditions at points I_1 and I_2 in terms of ω_1, ω_2, $\boldsymbol{\Omega}$, $\mathbf{v}_C$, as well as position vectors between the points O_1, O_2, C, I_1 and I_2.

b. Find the velocity of point C in terms of ω_1, ω_2, and the position vectors $\mathbf{r}_{O_1C}$ and $\mathbf{r}_{O_2C}$. Assuming ω_1 and ω_2 constant, show that the trajectory of C is a circle of center O in the midplane defined by $\omega_1 \mathbf{r}_{OO_1} + \omega_2 \mathbf{r}_{OO_2} = \mathbf{0}$. Find the period of C along its trajectory.

c. Show that the angular velocity $\boldsymbol{\Omega}$ is given by

$$\boldsymbol{\Omega} = \frac{1}{2R}(\omega_1 \mathbf{r}_{O_1C} - \omega_2 \mathbf{r}_{O_2C}) + \lambda(t)\, \hat{\mathbf{z}}_0$$

where $\lambda(t)$ is an indeterminate function of time. Interpret λ.

Problem 7.9 The figure shown below is a schematic of a speed reducer/regulator. The purpose of this mechanism is to transmit the rotational motion of a drive shaft 1 to coaxial shaft 2 at a reduced angular velocity about axis $(O, \hat{\mathbf{z}}_0)$. The working principle of this mechanism is based on a number of spherical balls interposed between fixed parts and the rotating shafts. More specifically, each ball is in contact at points I_1 and I_2 with conical surfaces rotating with the shafts 1 and 2, and at points I_3 and I_4 with fixed parts of fixed housing 0. Springs maintain sufficient pressure to prevent slip of the balls at the contact points. For simplicity, a single ball and only part of the conical plates are shown in the figure. We denote by

0: the fixed housing of the mechanism, with basis $(\hat{\mathbf{x}}_0, \hat{\mathbf{y}}_0, \hat{\mathbf{z}}_0)$, with unit vector $\hat{\mathbf{z}}_0$ parallel to the shafts' axes.

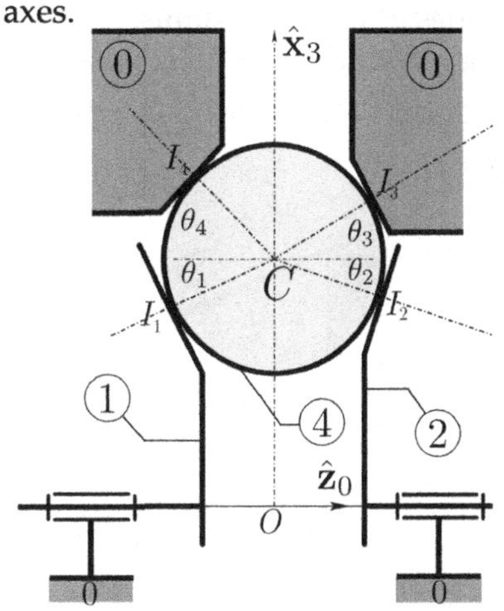

1: the drive shaft, of axis $(O, \hat{\mathbf{z}}_0)$ and of angular velocity $\omega_1 \hat{\mathbf{z}}_0$.

2: the output shaft, of axis $(O, \hat{\mathbf{z}}_0)$, of angular velocity $\omega_2 \hat{\mathbf{z}}_0$.

3: auxiliary referential $(O, \hat{\mathbf{x}}_3, \hat{\mathbf{y}}_3, \hat{\mathbf{z}}_0)$ in rotation relative to 0 about axis $(O, \hat{\mathbf{z}}_0)$, such that $\mathbf{r}_{OC} = R\hat{\mathbf{x}}_3$. The trajectory of point C, center of ball 4, is a circle of center O and radius R.

4: a ball of radius r, and center C, in contact at point I_1 with conical plate 1, at point I_2 with conical plate 2, and at points I_3 and I_4 with fixed conical parts of 0. The position of these contact points is defined by the (constant) angles θ_i, $i = 1, 2, 3, 4$.

a. Find the instantaneous screw axis $\Delta_{4/0}$ associated with kinematic screw $\{\mathcal{V}_{4/0}\}$. Then characterize the motion 4 relative 0. Resolve the kinematic screw $\{\mathcal{V}_{4/0}\}$ at point C in terms of ω_1 and the geometric parameters.

b. Find the input/output law, that is, express the ratio ω_2/ω_1 in terms of parameters R, r and θ_i, $i = 1, 2, 3, 4$.

c. Assume $\theta_1 = \pi/2$, $\theta_2 = \theta_3 = \theta_4 = \theta$, and $R = 2r$. Find the moving and fixed axodes generated by $\Delta_{4/0}$. Likewise, find the moving and fixed axodes generated by the instantaneous screw axes $\Delta_{4/1}$ and $\Delta_{4/2}$.

Problem 7.10 A rod 2 modeled as a line segment O_2A_2 of length l has a planar motion while constrained to remain in contact with a step-like rigid boundary of body 1. Denote by h the height of the step.

a. Determine the kinematic screw of 2 relative to 1. Find the position of the instantaneous center of rotation I_{21}. Then determine the corresponding fixed and moving centrodes. Sketch the moving centrodes at various instants.

b. Repeat for a rod O_2A_2 constrained to be in contact with a circular boundary of radius R of body 1.

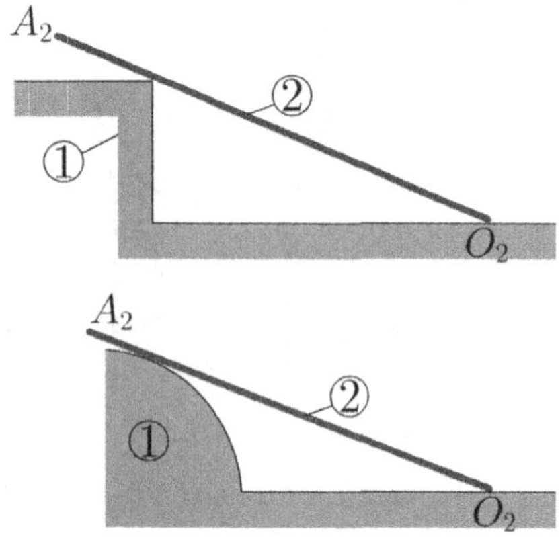

Problem 7.11 A planar motion between to referentials 0 $(O, \hat{\mathbf{x}}_0, \hat{\mathbf{y}}_0, \hat{\mathbf{z}}_0)$ and 1 $(C, \hat{\mathbf{x}}_1, \hat{\mathbf{y}}_1, \hat{\mathbf{z}}_0)$ is constructed in the following manner:
(i) origin C of 1 moves along the circle $\mathcal{C}$ of center O and radius R of 0,
(ii) the lines $(C, \hat{\mathbf{x}}_1)$ and $(C, \hat{\mathbf{y}}_1)$ always pass through the points A and B, respectively, diametrically opposed on circle $\mathcal{C}$.

After parametrizing the motion of 1, find its instantaneous center of rotation and the corresponding fixed and moving centrodes.

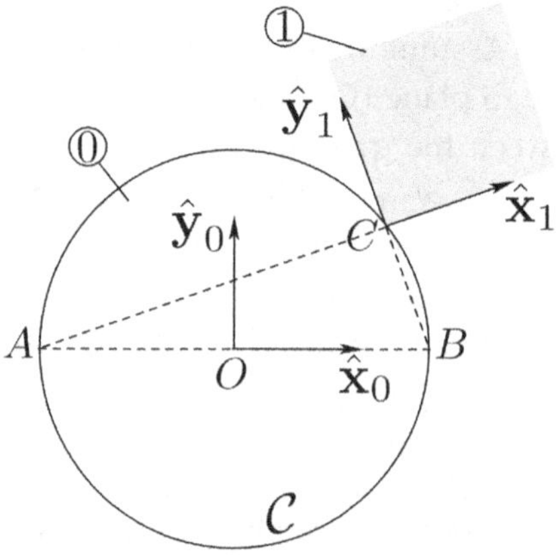

Problem 7.12 Consider in a referential 0 the planar motion of
- a right circular cylinder 1 of radius R, which can roll on a horizontal support Π of 0,
- a straight rod 2 of length $2l$, in contact with the cylinder 1 at point I_{12}, in a plane perpendicular to the axis of the cylinder, and with its end point I_2 in contact with support Π.

Assume that there is slip at all contact points I_1, I_2 and I_{12}.

a. Parametrize the position of both bodies 1 and 2 and determine all possible constraint equations.

b. Determine the kinematic screws of 1 and 2 relative to referential 0 in terms of the coordinates defined in a).

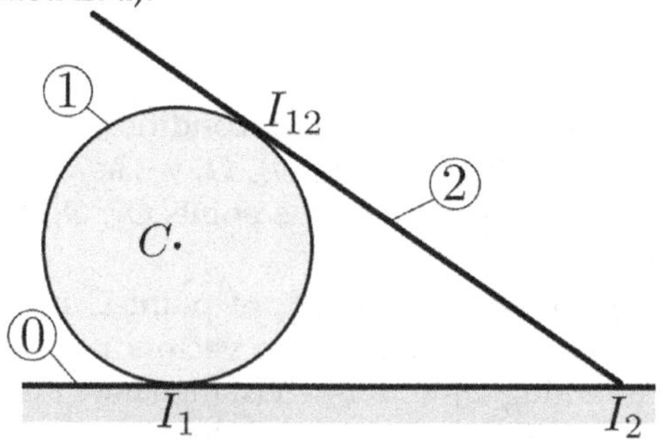

Problem 7.13 A four-wheeled vehicle is in motion on a horizontal plane Oxy of a referential $\mathcal{E}$. The vehicle's frame $\mathcal{F}$ is modeled as a rigid body centered at C and of basis $(\hat{\mathbf{u}}, \hat{\mathbf{v}}, \hat{\mathbf{z}})$ in planar motion relative to $\mathcal{E}$. Connected to this frame are four identical wheels $\mathcal{A}_i$ $(i = 1, 2, 3, 4)$, cylindrical, of axis $(A_i, \hat{\mathbf{y}}_i)$, and radius r. The back wheel axes are fixed: $\hat{\mathbf{y}}_3 = \hat{\mathbf{y}}_4 = \hat{\mathbf{v}}$. The front wheel axes $(A_i, \hat{\mathbf{y}}_i)$, $i = 1, 2$ are free to rotate relative to $\mathcal{F}$ about the vertical axis $(A_i, \hat{\mathbf{z}})$. The vehicle is characterized by wheelbase a and track b: $\mathbf{r}_{A_3A_1} = a\hat{\mathbf{u}}$ and $\mathbf{r}_{A_4A_3} = b\hat{\mathbf{v}}$. The front wheels $\mathcal{A}_1$ and $\mathcal{A}_2$ are in contact with plane Oxy at points I_1 and I_2, respectively, with $\mathbf{r}_{I_1A_1} = \mathbf{r}_{I_2A_2} = r\hat{\mathbf{z}}$.

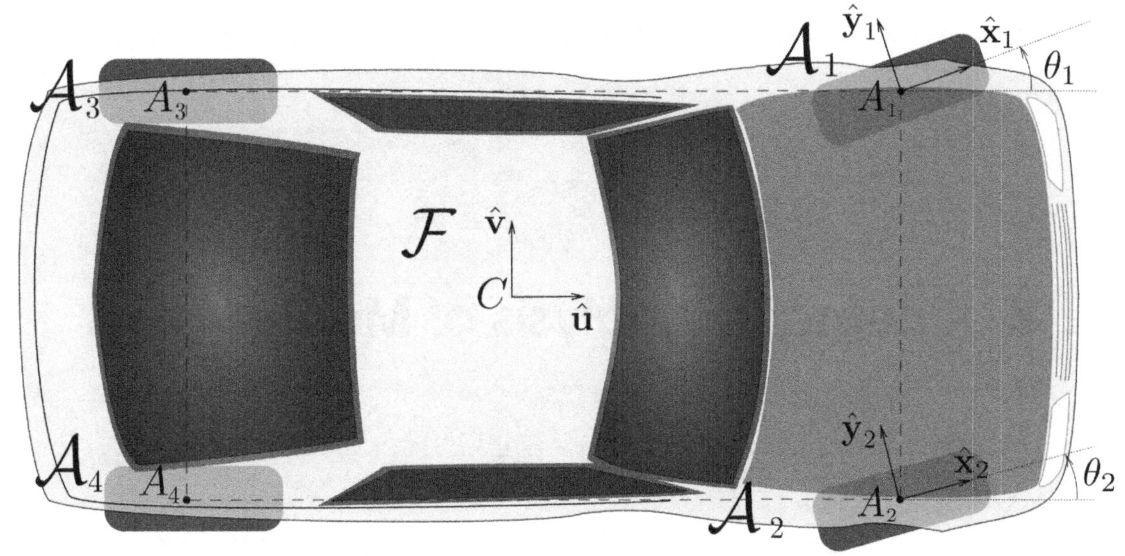

Each wheel $\mathcal{A}_i$ is assumed to roll without slipping at contact point I_i with the horizontal plane. Denote by ω_i the angular velocity $\boldsymbol{\omega}_{\mathcal{A}_i/\mathcal{F}} \cdot \hat{\mathbf{y}}_i$, $\mathbf{v}_C$ the velocity $\mathbf{v}_{C/\mathcal{E}}$ of center C, and Ω the angular velocity $\boldsymbol{\omega}_{\mathcal{F}/\mathcal{E}} \cdot \hat{\mathbf{z}}$.

a. Show that, to guarantee the no-slip conditions, it is necessary that the four axes $(A_i, \hat{\mathbf{y}}_i)$ intersect at some point I. Find the location of I. Deduce that the front wheel steering angles θ_1 and θ_2 are related to each other through the constants a and b.

b. What role does axis $(I, \hat{\mathbf{z}})$ play for rigid body $\mathcal{F}$?

c. Find the angular velocity ω_i of wheel $\mathcal{A}_i$ in terms of $\mathbf{v}_C$ and Ω.

d. Does no-slip at I_i imply no-slip for all contact points of the wheels with the road? Explain and comment.

Problem 7.14 Assume that the Earth $\mathcal{E}$ is a rigid body in motion in the Heliocentric referential of origin S the center of the Sun and whose axes SX and SY point to fixed stars. The axis SZ is normal to the ecliptic plane, defined as the plane which contains the trajectory of center C of $\mathcal{E}$. The motion of $\mathcal{E}$ relative to $\mathcal{H}$ is defined as follows:

- center C has a circular trajectory of radius a centered about S and of constant angular velocity ω,
- the angular velocity of $\mathcal{E}$ relative to $\mathcal{H}$ has constant magnitude Ω and constant direction defined by the obliquity α:

$$\boldsymbol{\omega}_{\mathcal{E}/\mathcal{H}} = \Omega(\cos\alpha\hat{\mathbf{k}} + \sin\alpha\hat{\jmath})$$

a. Define the kinematic screw of $\mathcal{E}$ relative to $\mathcal{H}$.

b. Find the corresponding instantaneous screw axis and the fixed and moving axodes.

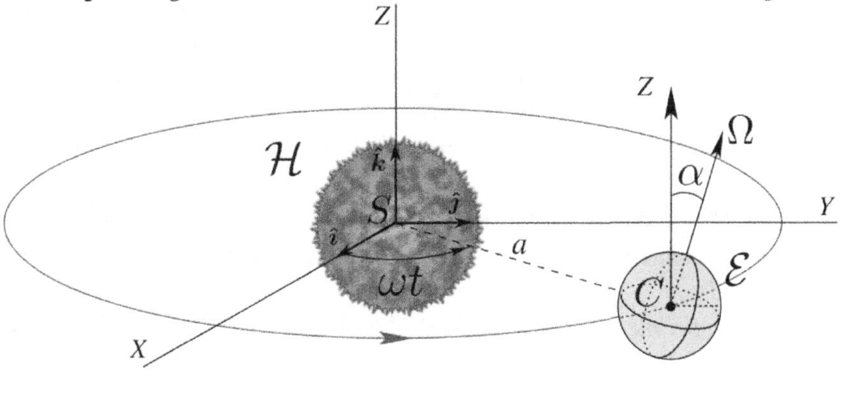

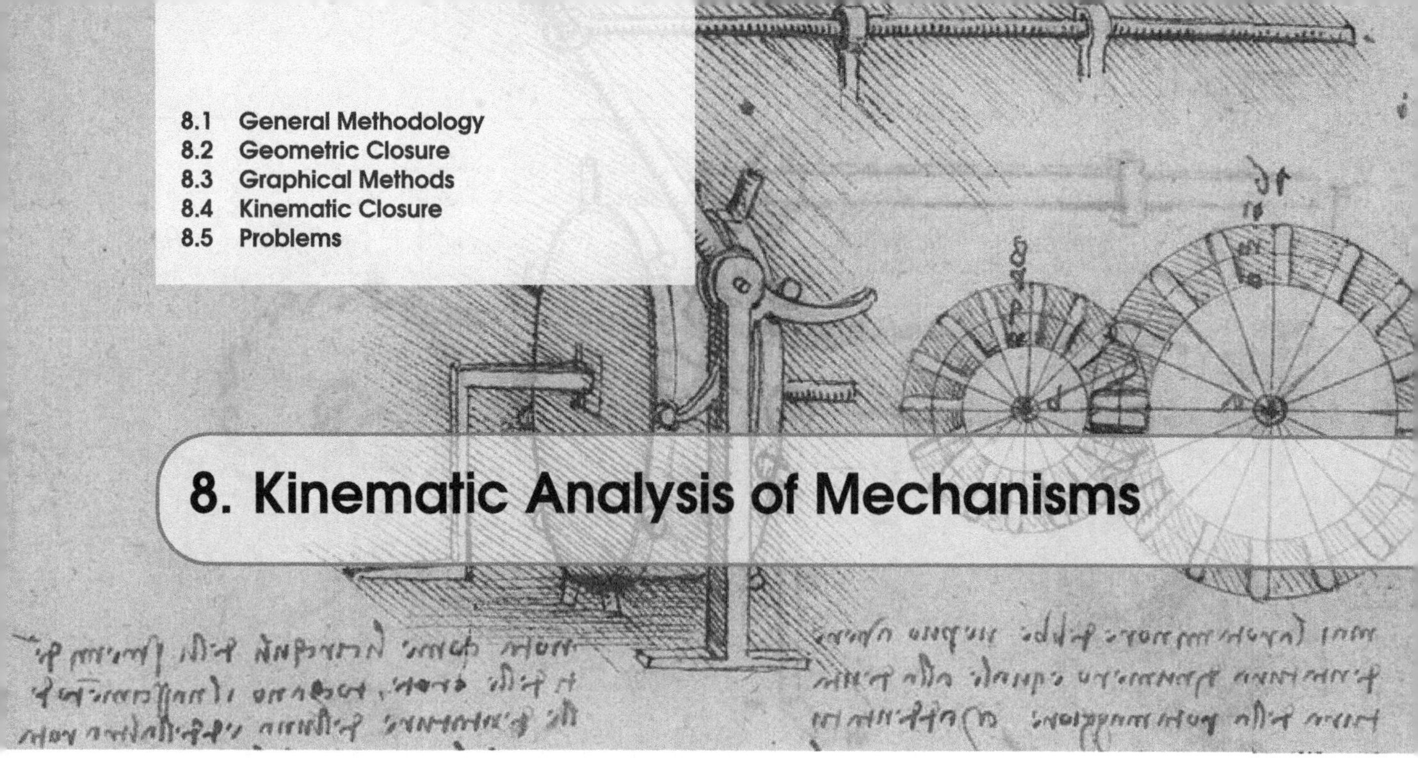

8. Kinematic Analysis of Mechanisms

THIS CHAPTER is devoted to the kinematic analysis of mechanisms, with the goal of determining their kinematic behavior based on simplified models. More specifically, our kinematic analysis may include the determination of

(i) the kinematic screws $\{\mathcal{V}_{i/j}\}$ for all kinematic pairs (i, j) of the mechanism,
(ii) the geometric or kinematic constraint equations,
(iii) the determination of input/output geometric or kinematic laws,
(iv) the trajectory, velocity and acceleration of particular points of the mechanisms.

We shall present three general methods:

1. *method of geometric closure*,
2. *graphical method*, applicable to the analysis of planar mechanism,
3. *method of kinematic closure*, applicable to all mechanisms.

8.1 General Methodology

The kinematic analysis of a mechanism must rely on a well-organized methodology as follows:

1. Given a mechanical system, the first step is to identify the essential rigid bodies $\mathcal{B}_1$, $\mathcal{B}_2$, $\cdots$, $\mathcal{B}_N$, by ignoring all elements (rigid or not) of the systems which do not play any role in the system's kinematic behavior.
2. The next step is to build a *connectivity diagram*, that is, a graph, which gives a pictorial representation of all pairwise relations between the rigid bodies identified in step 1. Two types of mechanisms can be identified from this diagram (See Figure 8.1):
   (a) *open chain mechanisms:* one or more bodies in the mechanism are coupled to only one body.
   (b) *closed chain mechanisms:* each body of the chain is coupled to at least two other bodies.

An open- or closed-chain mechanism may contain one or more loops: one may obtain single-loop or multiple loop chains. In general, in a closed-chain mechanism possessing N bodies interconnected by N_J joints one can identify $\mu = N_J - N + 1$ independent closed loops.

3. The next step is to build a *kinematic diagram* of the mechanism, that is, a simplified model of the system assembled of kinematic pairs (joints) whose schematic was described in Section 7.2. The analysis will rely on a parametrization of the position of each body with a minimal set of coordinates. The mobility or number of degrees of freedom of the mechanism will be determined.
4. Find all geometric constraint equations which may govern the mechanism. This can be done in a systematic way by the method of geometric closure (see Section 8.2).
5. Find all kinematic constraint equations which may govern the mechanism. This can be done in a systematic way by the method of kinematic closure (see Section 8.4).

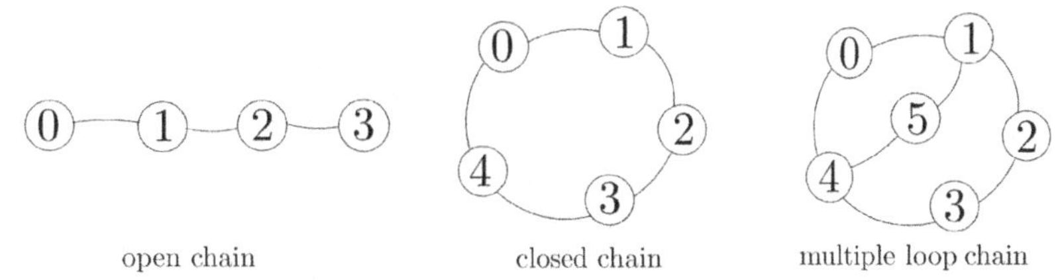

Figure 8.1

8.2 Geometric Closure

The kinematic analysis of mechanisms can often be done by a simple geometric method. If the mechanism is defined in an arbitrary configuration (that is, a configuration not specific to a particular instant), the method consists of finding all geometric relationships governing the mechanism whose position has been parametrized. Then, time-differentiation of these equations will yield all relevant kinematic unknowns. For closed-loop mechanisms, input-output laws can be found systematically by writing vector loop equations, that is, equations of the type

$$\mathbf{r}_{OA_1} + \mathbf{r}_{A_1A_2} + \cdots + \mathbf{r}_{A_{N-1}A_N} + \mathbf{r}_{A_NO} = \mathbf{0} \tag{8.1}$$

where O is a fixed point and the points $A_1, A_2, \cdots, A_N$ are characteristic points of the joints which interconnect pairs of links.

More specifically, the method consists of the following procedure, assuming that a kinematic diagram of the mechanism has been determined.

1. If the configuration of the mechanism is specific to a particular time, then it must be redefined so as to make it valid at all time.
2. Parametrize the position of the mechanism by defining all necessary coordinates.
3. Describe the mechanism by sketching a connectivity diagram, that is, a graph of all pairwise joints between the bodies of the mechanism. Carefully identity the nature of all joints connecting pairs (i, j).

4. Identify *independent* loops and for each loop write the corresponding vector loop equation where each position vector is expressed in terms of coordinates defined in step 2. Otherwise, additional coordinates will need to be defined.
5. Take the time-derivative of these vector loop equations and project them on fixed unit vectors. Identify all kinematic quantities in the newly obtained equations.
6. Repeat step 4 to obtain acceleration information.

The following examples[1] illustrate the method of geometric closure.

Example 8.1 In the configuration shown in Figure 8.2, the slider block 2 is moving at speed v_B and a_B both pointing to the right. Determine the angular velocity of link 1 and the velocity of point A at this instant. ■

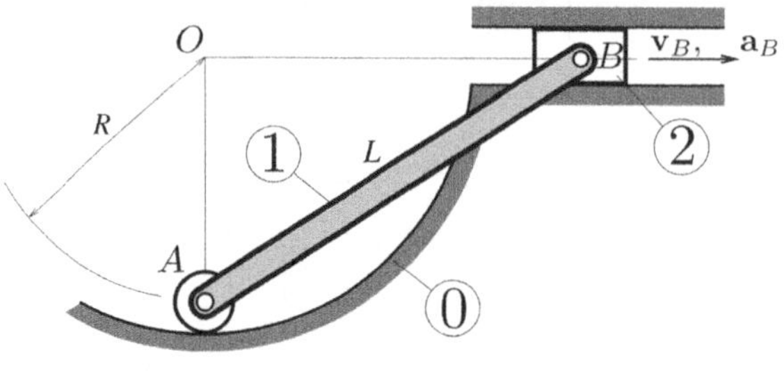

Figure 8.2

We cannot use the configuration of Figure 8.2. Instead we modify it so as to make the position of pin A arbitrary: see Figure 8.3. We then introduce three coordinates to parametrize the system in this configuration:
-angle θ to define the position of A on its circular path (of center O and radius R),
-oriented angle ϕ to define the orientation of line AB, leading to $\omega_1 = \dot{\phi}\hat{\mathbf{k}}$ with the choice of basis $(\hat{\imath}, \hat{\jmath}, \hat{\mathbf{k}})$ shown in Figure 8.3,
-coordinate y_B to define the position of B (in rectilinear motion): $\mathbf{r}_{OB} = y_B\hat{\jmath}$.

The original configuration corresponds to the value $\theta = 0$ and $\phi = \phi_0$ with $\sin\phi_0 = R/L$. We then express the vector loop $\mathbf{r}_{OA} + \mathbf{r}_{AB} + \mathbf{r}_{BO} = \mathbf{0}$ on the chosen unit vectors $(\hat{\imath}, \hat{\jmath})$ in terms of the coordinates (θ, ϕ, y_B) and constants (R, L):

$$R(\cos\theta\hat{\imath} + \sin\theta\hat{\jmath}) + L(-\sin\phi\hat{\imath} + \cos\phi\hat{\jmath}) - y_B\hat{\jmath} = \mathbf{0}$$

leading to two equations

$$R\cos\theta - L\sin\phi = 0, \qquad R\sin\theta + L\cos\phi = y_B \qquad [1-2]$$

Equations [1-2] are valid at all time: we can take their time-derivative to obtain

$$R\dot{\theta}\sin\theta + L\dot{\phi}\cos\phi = 0, \qquad R\dot{\theta}\cos\theta - L\dot{\phi}\sin\phi = \dot{y}_B$$

We now have the expression of the angular velocity of rod 1:

$$\omega_1 = \dot{\phi}\hat{\mathbf{k}} = -\frac{\dot{y}_B}{L}\frac{\sin\theta}{\cos(\theta - \phi)}\hat{\mathbf{k}} \qquad [3]$$

which takes the value

$$\omega_1 = \mathbf{0} \qquad [3']$$

[1]See also Example 7.4 of Chapter 7.

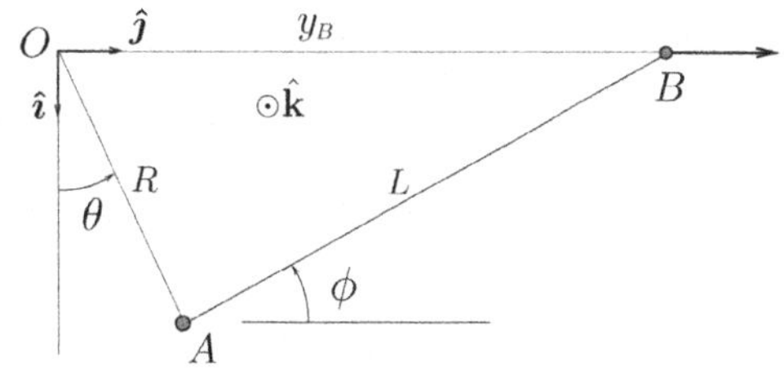

Figure 8.3

when $\theta = 0$. Point A moves along a circular path of center O and radius R at the speed

$$v_A = R\dot{\theta} = \dot{y}_B \frac{\cos\phi}{\cos(\theta - \phi)} \tag{4}$$

The velocity of A is then given by $\mathbf{v}_A = v_B\,\hat{\jmath}$ when $\theta = 0$. ■

Example 8.2 The mechanism shown in Figure 8.4 transforms the rotational motion of body 1 about axis $(O, \hat{\mathbf{x}}_0)$ into the rotational motion of body 3 about a concurrent perpendicular axis $(E, \hat{\mathbf{z}}_0)$. This is achieved by interconnecting the body 2 between bodies 1 and 3. More specifically, body 2 can translate relative to 1 along axis $(B, \hat{\mathbf{x}}_0)$ and can translate relative to 3 along axis $(C, \hat{\mathbf{z}}_0)$. The configuration of the mechanism is defined by the two angles $\theta_1(t)$ and $\theta_3(t)$ and the parameters $l = |DC|$ and $d = |OA|$.

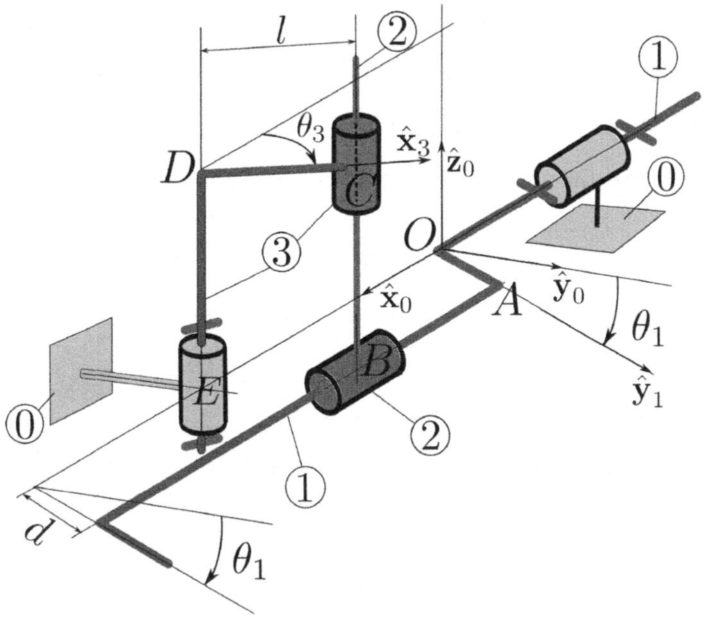

Figure 8.4

Find the input/output relationship between the angular velocities of 1 and 3 by expressing the vector loop equation joining point O to point E. Also find the velocity $\mathbf{v}_{B\in 2/0}$.

Assuming the rotation of body 1 continuous, under what condition can body 3 be in alternating rotation? ■

With the choice of basis $(\hat{\mathbf{x}}_0, \hat{\mathbf{y}}_0, \hat{\mathbf{z}}_0)$ defined in Figure 8.4 we need to introduce the two coordinates ρ and μ in addition to angles θ_1 and θ_3 to parametrize the position of B relative to

A and C: $\mathbf{r}_{AB} = \rho(t)\hat{\mathbf{x}}_0$ and $\mathbf{r}_{BC} = \mu(t)\hat{\mathbf{z}}_0$. We can now write the vector loop equation

$$\mathbf{r}_{OA} + \mathbf{r}_{AB} + \mathbf{r}_{BC} + \mathbf{r}_{CD} + \mathbf{r}_{DE} + \mathbf{r}_{EO} = \mathbf{0} \qquad [1]$$

in terms of coordinates $(\theta_1, \theta_3, \rho, \mu)$ and the constant parameters (l, h, d, e) with $e = |OE|$ and $h = |ED|$. See Figure 8.5.

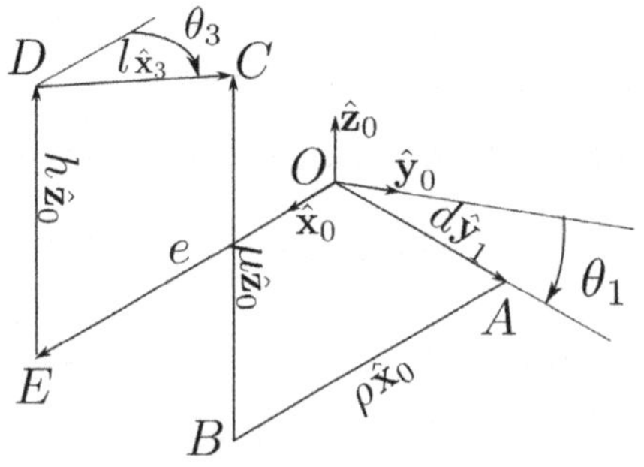

Figure 8.5

Equation [1] is then expressed on basis $(\hat{\mathbf{x}}_0, \hat{\mathbf{y}}_0, \hat{\mathbf{z}}_0)$

$$d(\cos\theta_1\hat{\mathbf{y}}_0 - \sin\theta_1\hat{\mathbf{z}}_0) + \rho(t)\hat{\mathbf{x}}_0 + \mu(t)\hat{\mathbf{z}}_0 + l(\cos\theta_3\hat{\mathbf{x}}_0 - \sin\theta_3\hat{\mathbf{y}}_0) - h\hat{\mathbf{z}}_0 - e\hat{\mathbf{x}}_0 = 0$$

We then arrive at three equations

$$\rho(t) + l\cos\theta_3 - e = 0, \quad d\cos\theta_1 - l\sin\theta_3 = 0, \quad -d\sin\theta_1 + \mu(t) - h = 0 \qquad [2-4]$$

valid at all time. We then differentiate [2-4] w.r.t. to time to obtain

$$\dot{\rho} - l\dot{\theta}_3\sin\theta_3 = 0, \quad -d\dot{\theta}_1\sin\theta_1 - l\dot{\theta}_3\cos\theta_3 = 0, \quad -d\dot{\theta}_1\cos\theta_1 + \dot{\mu} = 0 \qquad [5-7]$$

Equation [6] gives the angular velocity of body 3 in terms of the angular velocity $\omega_1 = -\dot{\theta}_1\hat{\mathbf{x}}_0$ of body 1:

$$\omega_3 = -\dot{\theta}_3\hat{\mathbf{z}}_0, \qquad \dot{\theta}_3 = -\dot{\theta}_1\frac{d}{l}\frac{\sin\theta_1}{\cos\theta_3}$$

with angle θ_3 given by [3]. To find the velocity of B we first find its position vector

$$\mathbf{r}_{OB} = d\hat{\mathbf{y}}_1 + \rho(t)\hat{\mathbf{x}}_0$$

Then we find $\mathbf{v}_B = \mathbf{v}_{B\in 2/0}$ by differentiating $\mathbf{r}_{OB}$:

$$\mathbf{v}_B = \mathbf{v}_{B\in 3/0} = d\dot{\theta}_1(-\sin\theta_1\hat{\mathbf{y}}_0 - \cos\theta_1\hat{\mathbf{z}}_0) + \dot{\rho}\hat{\mathbf{x}}_0$$

which becomes after using [5]

$$\mathbf{v}_B = -d\dot{\theta}_1\big(\sin\theta_1\cot\theta_3\hat{\mathbf{x}}_0 + \sin\theta_1\hat{\mathbf{y}}_0 + \cos\theta_1\hat{\mathbf{z}}_0\big)$$

Equation [3] has a solution if $d \le l$. If in addition $d < l$, then angle θ_3 is bounded

$$|\theta_3| \le \theta_{3,max} \qquad \theta_{3,max} = \sin^{-1}\left(\frac{d}{l}\right)$$

In this case the rotation of body 3 is alternating.

Remark. $\mathbf{v}_B$ can also be found by differentiating $\mathbf{r}_{EB} = h\hat{\mathbf{z}}_0 + l\hat{\mathbf{x}}_3 - \mu\hat{\mathbf{z}}_0$: the same expression is found by using [7].

■

8.3 Graphical Methods

Graphical methods are only suitable for planar mechanisms. These methods hinge on graphical constructions of velocity vectors based on
(i) the concept of the instantaneous centers (IC) of rotation,
(ii) the property of equiprojectivity of the velocity field.
Graphical methods allow for quick and visual solutions, although the constructions must be repeated for each new configuration of the mechanism.

8.3.1 Method of Instantaneous Centers

This method consists of the following procedure:

1. Given a configuration of the system defined at all time or at a particular time, we graphically find the position of the IC of each body of the mechanism. Typically, the direction of the velocities of two points of the same body are used to find the location of the corresponding IC, as shown in Figure 7.25.
2. Once the IC I_k of body $\mathcal{B}_k$ (relative to the fixed referential 0) is found, kinematic input/output relations are found by applying $v_{P\in k/0} = \omega_{k/0}|I_kP|$ for two points P attached (possibly instantaneously) to $\mathcal{B}_k$.
3. Since this method gives velocities (linear or angular) in magnitude, the direction of these quantities is indicated in the graphical construction.
4. If the configuration of the mechanism is general (that is, not specific to a particular instant), then accelerations can be obtained by taking the time-derivative of velocity equations.

The following examples illustrate this procedure.

Example 8.3 In the mechanism shown in Figure 8.6, the plunger 1 is in translation at constant speed $\dot{y} = v_1$. It sets in motion the arm 3 by the use of roller 2 which is pin-connected at its center A to arm 3. The roller rolls without slipping relative to the plunger at contact point I.

By using the method of instantaneous centers, find the angular velocity ω_2 and ω_3 of the roller and arm as a function of v_1 and the geometric parameters. ■

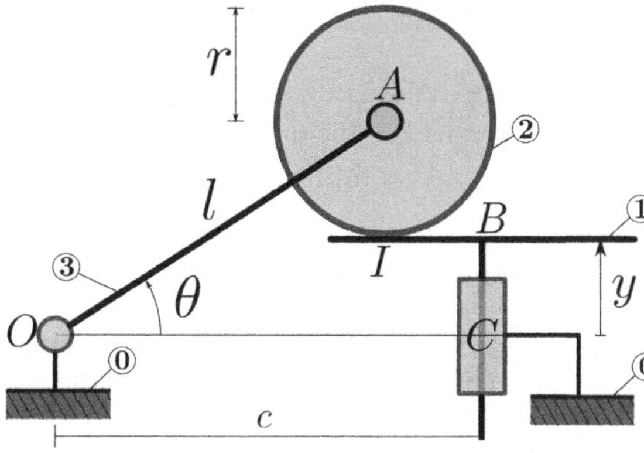

Figure 8.6

The solution hinges on the determination of the IC $I_2 \equiv I_{20}$ of roller 2. It is found by using the knowledge of the direction of $\mathbf{v}_A$ (normal to line OA since point A rotates about O) and of $\mathbf{v}_{I\in 2} = \mathbf{v}_{I\in 1} = \mathbf{v}_B$ (since the roller does not slip relative to the plunger). Hence point I_2 is located at the intersection of line OA (the perpendicular at A to $\mathbf{v}_A$) and the perpendicular at I to $\mathbf{v}_B$. See Figure 8.7 for a construction. Once I_2 is obtained, we can sketch the direction of angular velocity ω_2 (counterclockwise) and that of angular velocity ω_3 (counterclockwise).

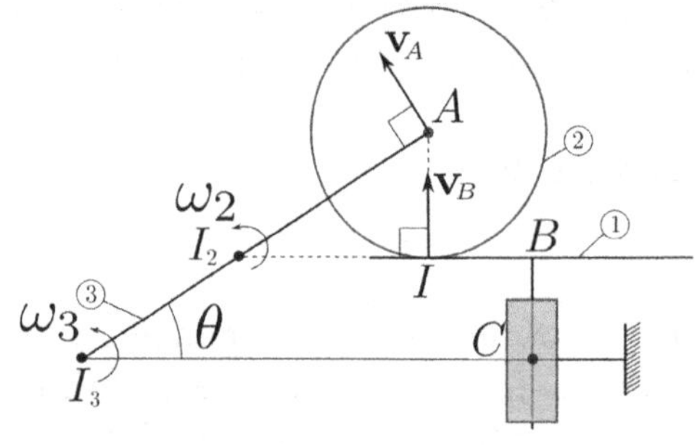

Figure 8.7

The angular speeds are obtained by using the relationship $v_{P\in 2} = \omega_2 |I_2P|$ for $P = I$ and $P = A$:

$$v_1 = \omega_2 |I_2 I|, \qquad v_A = \omega_2 |I_2 A| = \omega_3 |I_3 A| \qquad [1-2]$$

We find the lengths $|I_2 I|$ and $|I_2 A|$ in triangle IAI_2

$$|I_2 I| = r \cot\theta, \qquad |I_2 A| = \frac{r}{\sin\theta} \qquad [3-4]$$

Using [3-4], equations [1-2] give the final result:

$$\omega_2 = \frac{v_1}{r}\tan\theta \ \circlearrowleft, \qquad \omega_3 = \frac{v_1}{l\cos\theta} \ \circlearrowleft$$

■

Example 8.4 Figure 8.8 shows a simple planar mechanism which transforms a continuous rotation into a sinusoidal rotation. Crank-arm 1 is in rotation about O of referential 0. It is connected at pivot A to the rack and pinion system 2–3. The toothed wheel 3 is constrained to be in rotation about point C relative to 0. The motion of the system is parametrized by the angles θ_1, θ_2 and θ_3. Define $R_1 = |OA|$ and $R_3 = |BC|$ where B is the contact point between 2 and 3. Assume no-slip at B, and denote by D the distance between pivots O and C.

By finding the location of instantaneous center I_{20} of 2 relative to referential 0, find the output angular velocity ω_3 versus the input angular velocity ω_1 in terms of the angles θ_1 and θ_2, and the radii R_1 and R_3. Also find the angle θ_2 versus angle θ_1 and the parameters D, R_1 and R_3. ■

Point $I_2 \equiv I_{20}$ is found graphically by finding the direction of the velocities of two points attached to 2: choosing points A and B vector $\mathbf{v}_{A\in 2/0} = \mathbf{v}_{A\in 1/0}$ is normal to line OA, whereas vector $\mathbf{v}_{B\in 2/0} = \mathbf{v}_{B\in 3/0}$ (due to no-slip at B) is normal to line CB. Point I_2 is then located at the intersection of the normal based at A to $\mathbf{v}_{A\in 2/0}$ and the normal based at B to $\mathbf{v}_{B\in 2/0}$. See Figure 8.9. We can then find the ratio ω_3/ω_1 from the location of I_2 by expressing $v_{A\in 2/0}$ and $v_{B\in 2/0}$

$$R_1\omega_1 = \omega_2 |AI_2|, \qquad R_3\omega_3 = \omega_2 |BI_2|$$

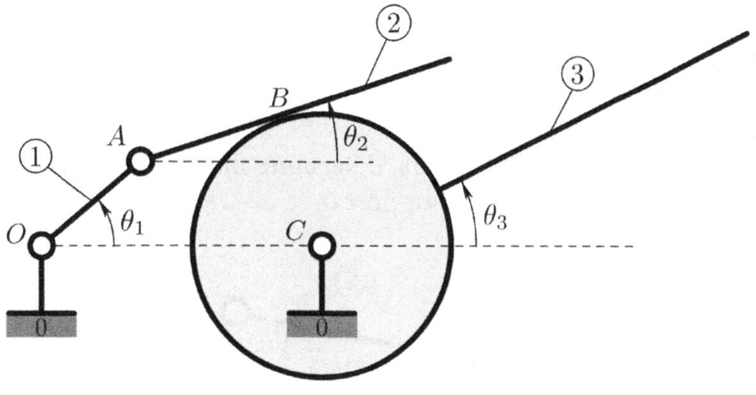

Figure 8.8

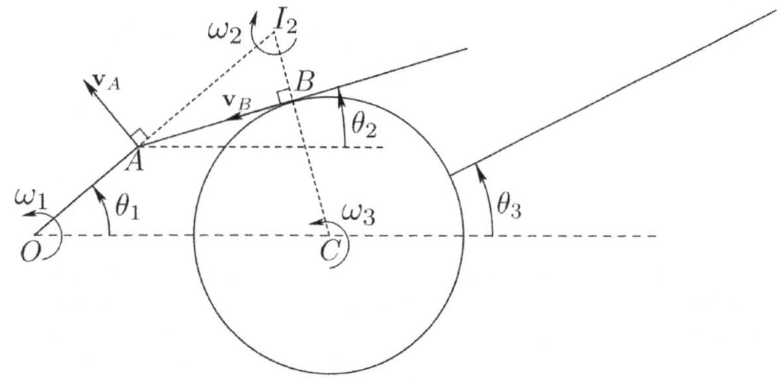

Figure 8.9

leading to

$$\frac{\omega_3}{\omega_1} = \frac{R_1}{R_3} \frac{|BI_2|}{|AI_2|}$$

Consideration of triangle ABI_2 gives $\sin(\theta_1 - \theta_2) = |BI_2|/|AI_2|$. We finally obtain

$$\frac{\omega_3}{\omega_1} = \frac{R_1}{R_3} \sin(\theta_1 - \theta_2)$$

Assuming ω_1 directed in the counterclockwise direction, the directions of ω_2 and ω_3 are shown in Figure 8.9. To express angle θ_2 in terms of angle θ_1 we consider the quadrilateral $OABC$: we can write two equations between angles θ_1, θ_2 and variable $\lambda = |AB|$

$$R_1 \cos\theta_1 + \lambda \cos\theta_2 + R_3 \cos(\pi/2 - \theta_2) = D$$

$$R_1 \sin\theta_1 + \lambda \sin\theta_2 = R_3 \sin(\pi/2 - \theta_2)$$

Eliminating λ gives

$$R_1 \sin(\theta_2 - \theta_1) + R_3 = D \sin\theta_2$$

■

The following example uses the construction of instantaneous centers in conjunction with Kennedy's theorem (see Section 7.4.3).

Example 8.5 — **Four-bar Mechanism.** Three bars are connected into a linkage and are constrained to move in a plane 0 of origin O. Crank 1 of length l_1 pivots about fixed point

O, while crank 3 of length l_3 pivots about fixed point C. The end points A and B are the pivots of coupler bar 2 of length l_2. See Figure 8.10.

Find the location of the six instantaneous centers of rotation I_{ij} which can be formed from the four links 0,1,2,3.

From the knowledge of these centers, determine the relationships between the angular velocities of links 1, 2, 3 relative to support 0. ■

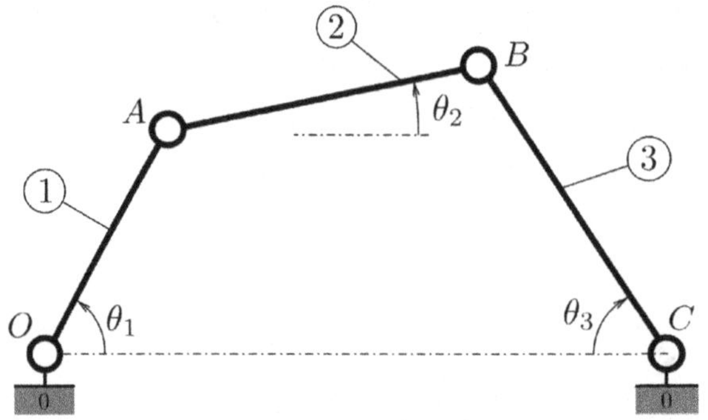

Figure 8.10

First we identify the centers I_{01}, I_{12}, I_{23} and I_{03} to be points O, A, B and C, respectively. To find the positions of the remaining two centers I_{13} and I_{02} we use Kennedy's theorem: point I_{13} must fall on line $I_{12}I_{23}$ but also on line $I_{01}I_{03}$, and hence is the intersection point of these two lines. Similarly, point $I_{02}$is the intersection point of line $I_{01}I_{12}$ and line $I_{03}I_{23}$. See Figure 8.11.

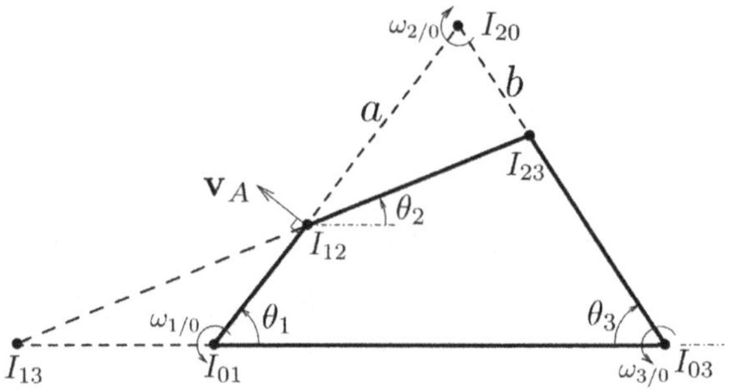

Figure 8.11

We can relate $\omega_{2/0}$ to $\omega_{1/0}$ by determining the magnitude of velocity of point A relative to referential 0 first as a point in rotation about $O \equiv I_{10}$ and then as a point in rotation about I_{02}:

$$v_{A\in 1/0} = |OA|\,\omega_{1/0} = v_{A\in 2/0} = |AI_{02}|\,\omega_{2/0}$$

We have $|OA| = l_1$. The distance $a \equiv |AI_{02}|$ is found by consideration of triangle ABI_{02}:

$$a = l_2 \sin(\theta_3 - \theta_2)/\sin(\theta_3 - \theta_1).$$

This gives

$$\omega_{2/0} = \omega_{1/0} \frac{l_1 \sin(\theta_3 - \theta_1)}{l_2 \sin(\theta_3 - \theta_2)}$$

Similarly, we can relate $\omega_{3/0}$ to $\omega_{2/0}$ by consideration of point B:

$$v_{B\in 3/0} = l_3\,\omega_{3/0} = v_{B\in 2/0} = |BI_{02}|\,\omega_{2/0}$$

with

$$|BI_{02}| \equiv b = l_2 \sin(\theta_1 - \theta_2)/\sin(\theta_3 - \theta_1)$$

This gives

$$\omega_{3/0} = \omega_{1/0} \frac{l_1 \sin(\theta_1 - \theta_2)}{l_3 \sin(\theta_3 - \theta_2)}$$

■

8.3.2 Method of Equiprojectivity

Equiprojectivity is fundamental to rigid body motion: it is a direct consequence of the fact that the distance between any two points A and B must remain constant during the motion. This leads to the property

$$\mathbf{v}_{A\in 2/1} \cdot \mathbf{r}_{AB} = \mathbf{v}_{B\in 2/1} \cdot \mathbf{r}_{AB} \tag{8.2}$$

for any two points A and B. This shows that the velocities $\mathbf{v}_{A\in 2/1}$ and $\mathbf{v}_{B\in 2/1}$ have the same projection on line AB. It also shows that *the velocity of any point of $\mathcal{B}$ can be found from the knowledge of the velocity of one particular point and the direction of another*, as demonstrated in the construction of Figure 8.12. The property of equiprojectivity can be used in practice for the analysis of mechanisms.

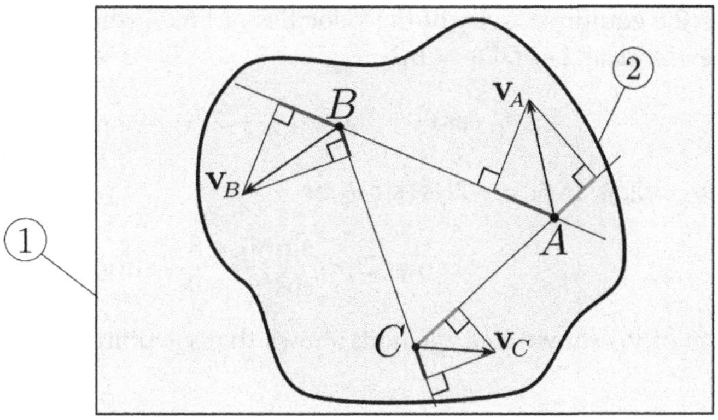

Figure 8.12 – *Equiprojectivity: $\mathbf{v}_{C\in 2/1}$ can be determined from the knowledge of $\mathbf{v}_{A\in 2/1}$ and of the direction of $\mathbf{v}_{B\in 2/1}$*

Example 8.6 Figure 8.13(left) shows a model of a motor-driven toggle press, comprised of a motor crank link 1, connecting rod 2, toggle links 3 and 4, and of punch 5. The two toggle links 3 and 4 are characterized by $|BC| = |BD|$. When link 1 is rotated about O at angular velocity ω_1 in the clockwise direction, the punch 5 translates along the vertical direction. Let $|OA| = l_1$, $|AB| = l_2$, $|BC| = l_3$.

At the configuration shown, find the velocity of D by using the property of equiprojectivity of velocity vectors. ■

We use the equiprojectivity of the velocities of link 2: the projections of $\mathbf{v}_A$ and $\mathbf{v}_B$ on line AB must be identical. Referring to Figure 8.13(right), this implies that $\overline{AA_1} = \overline{BB_1}$ or

$$v_A \cos(\frac{\pi}{2} - \theta_1 - \theta_2) = v_B \cos(\theta_2 + \theta_3)$$

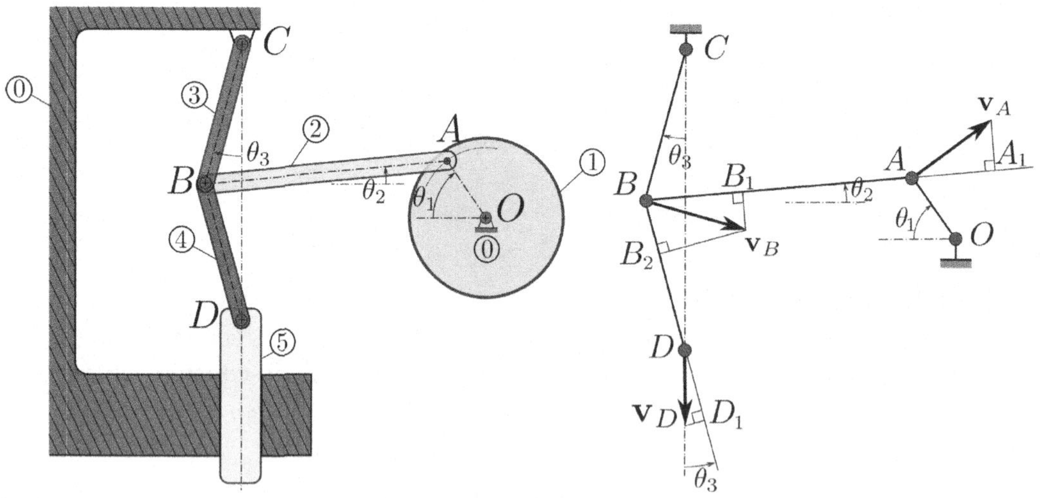

Figure 8.13

with $v_A = l_1\dot{\theta}_1$ (A rotates about O) and $v_B = -l_3\dot{\theta}_3$ (B rotates about C with $\dot{\theta}_3 < 0$). This gives

$$l_3\dot{\theta}_3 = -l_1\dot{\theta}_1 \frac{\sin(\theta_1 + \theta_2)}{\cos(\theta_3 + \theta_2)}$$

Next we use the equiprojectivity of the velocities of link 4: the projections of $\mathbf{v}_B$ and $\mathbf{v}_D$ on line BD must be identical, i.e. $\overline{DD_1} = \overline{BB_2}$:

$$v_D \cos\theta_3 = v_B \cos(\frac{\pi}{2} - 2\theta_3) = v_B \sin 2\theta_3$$

This gives $v_D = 2v_B \sin\theta_3 = -2l_3\dot{\theta}_3 \sin\theta_3$ or

$$v_D = 2l_1\dot{\theta}_1 \frac{\sin(\theta_1 + \theta_2)}{\cos(\theta_3 + \theta_2)} \sin\theta_3$$

The direction of $\mathbf{v}_D$ shown in 8.13(right) shows that $\mathbf{v}_D$ points in the $+\hat{\jmath}$ direction ■

8.4 Kinematic Closure

The method of kinematic closure is very general. It is based on the following procedure:

1. Given a kinematic diagram of the mechanism, describe the mechanism by sketching a connectivity diagram, that is, a graph of all pairwise joints between the bodies of the mechanism. Carefully identity the nature of all joints connecting pairs (i, j).
2. Identify all *independent* closed loops from the connectivity diagram.
3. For each loop found in step 2, derive the kinematic loop equation based on kinematic loop formula (6.9): for each closed loop `i-j-k···-n-p-i`, the closure of the loop can expressed by

$$\{\mathcal{V}_{i/j}\} + \{\mathcal{V}_{j/k}\} + \cdots + \{\mathcal{V}_{n/p}\} + \{\mathcal{V}_{p/i}\} = \{0\} \quad (8.3)$$

In this equation, each kinematic screw $\{\mathcal{V}_{i/j}\}$ is expressed by taking into account the nature of the joint connecting the pair (i, j), without taking into account any connections with other bodies of the mechanism.

4. Project each loop equation (8.3) on an adequate set of unit vectors. This is done by resolving all kinematic screws about the same point A. An adequate point A must be identified. Typically the chosen point plays a key role in the geometry of the loop.
5. Solve for all unknowns. In particular, determine the kinematic input/output law which governs the mechanism. If the configuration of the mechanism is valid at all time, the loop equations can be time-differentiated to obtain acceleration information.

The following examples illustrate the kinematic analysis of mechanisms by the method of kinematic closure.

Example 8.7 — Pin-jointed Four-bar Mechanism. Consider the four-bar mechanism displayed in Figure 8.14. First determine the expression of the kinematic screws $\{\mathcal{V}_{1/0}\}$, $\{\mathcal{V}_{2/1}\}$, $\{\mathcal{V}_{3/2}\}$ $\{\mathcal{V}_{3/0}\}$ by taking into account the nature of the joint connecting each pair (i, j). Then write the kinematic loop equation

$$\{\mathcal{V}_{0/1}\} + \{\mathcal{V}_{1/2}\} + \{\mathcal{V}_{2/3}\} + \{\mathcal{V}_{3/0}\} = 0$$

From this equation, determine the relationships which exist between the angular velocities of 1, 2, and 3 relative to 0. ■

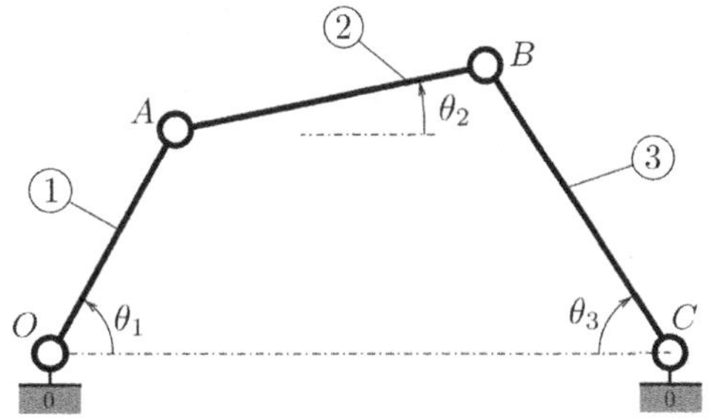

Figure 8.14

First we define the bases of unit vectors $(\hat{\mathbf{u}}_i, \hat{\mathbf{v}}_i, \hat{\mathbf{z}}_i = \hat{\mathbf{z}}_0)$ attached to link i as shown in Figure 8.15.

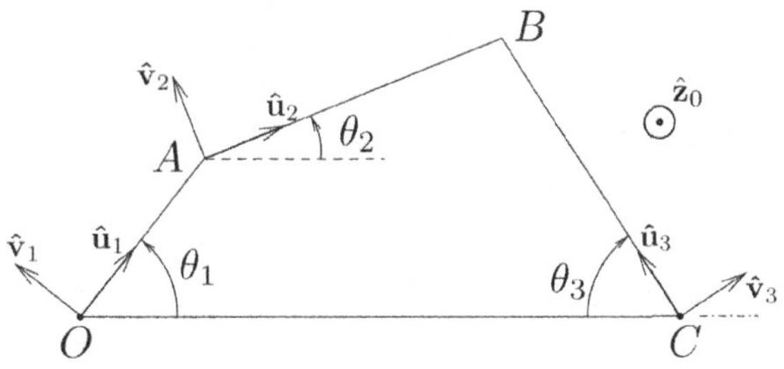

Figure 8.15

Each kinematic screw $\{\mathcal{V}_{1/0}\}$, $\{\mathcal{V}_{2/1}\}$, $\{\mathcal{V}_{3/2}\}$, $\{\mathcal{V}_{3/0}\}$ is representative of a pivot:

$$\{\mathcal{V}_{1/0}\} = \left\{ \begin{matrix} \dot{\theta}_1 \hat{\mathbf{z}}_0 \\ \mathbf{0} \end{matrix} \right\}_O \qquad \{\mathcal{V}_{2/1}\} = \left\{ \begin{matrix} \omega_{2/1} \hat{\mathbf{z}}_0 \\ \mathbf{0} \end{matrix} \right\}_A$$

$$\{\mathcal{V}_{3/2}\} = \left\{ \begin{matrix} \omega_{3/2} \hat{\mathbf{z}}_0 \\ \mathbf{0} \end{matrix} \right\}_B \qquad \{\mathcal{V}_{3/0}\} = \left\{ \begin{matrix} -\dot{\theta}_3 \hat{\mathbf{z}}_0 \\ \mathbf{0} \end{matrix} \right\}_C$$

In the closed loop 0-1-2-3-0 we can write the equation

$$\{\mathcal{V}_{0/1}\} + \{\mathcal{V}_{1/2}\} + \{\mathcal{V}_{2/3}\} + \{\mathcal{V}_{3/0}\} = \{0\}$$

The equality is guaranteed by imposing two equations: first we write the loop equation for the angular velocities

$$-\dot{\theta}_1 - \omega_{2/1} - \omega_{3/2} - \dot{\theta}_3 = 0 \qquad [1]$$

and (resolving each screw at point A)

$$\mathbf{v}_{A\in 0/1} + \mathbf{v}_{A\in 1/2} + \mathbf{v}_{A\in 2/3} + \mathbf{v}_{A\in 3/0} = \mathbf{0}$$

Using the expression of the kinematic screws written above, we find

$$l_1 \dot{\theta}_1 \hat{\mathbf{v}}_1 - l_2 \omega_{3/2} \hat{\mathbf{v}}_2 = \dot{\theta}_3 (l_3 \hat{\mathbf{v}}_3 + l_2 \hat{\mathbf{v}}_2)$$

Then, with $\omega_{2/1} = \omega_{2/0} - \omega_{1/0} = \dot{\theta}_2 - \dot{\theta}_1$, equation [1] gives $\omega_{3/2} = \dot{\theta}_3 - \dot{\theta}_2$. Equation [2] simplifies to

$$l_1 \dot{\theta}_1 \hat{\mathbf{v}}_1 + l_2 \dot{\theta}_2 \hat{\mathbf{v}}_2 = l_3 \dot{\theta}_3 \hat{\mathbf{v}}_3 \qquad [3]$$

We recognize that equation [3] can in fact be obtained by taking the time-derivative of the geometric loop equation:

$$\mathbf{r}_{OC} = \mathbf{r}_{OA} + \mathbf{r}_{AB} + \mathbf{r}_{BO} = l_1 \hat{\mathbf{u}}_1 + l_2 \hat{\mathbf{u}}_2 - l_3 \hat{\mathbf{u}}_3 = \text{Cst}$$

Now we take the scalar product of [3] with unit vector $\hat{\mathbf{u}}_3$ to obtain the relationship between $\dot{\theta}_1$ and $\dot{\theta}_2$:

$$\dot{\theta}_2 = -\dot{\theta}_1 \frac{l_1 \sin(\theta_1 + \theta_3)}{l_2 \sin(\theta_2 + \theta_3)}$$

where we have used $\hat{\mathbf{v}}_1 \cdot \hat{\mathbf{u}}_3 = \sin(\theta_1 + \theta_3)$ and $\hat{\mathbf{v}}_2 \cdot \hat{\mathbf{u}}_3 = \sin(\theta_2 + \theta_3)$. Similarly we obtain $\dot{\theta}_3$ by taking the scalar product of [3] with unit vector $\hat{\mathbf{u}}_2$:

$$\dot{\theta}_3 = \dot{\theta}_1 \frac{l_1 \sin(\theta_2 - \theta_1)}{l_3 \sin(\theta_2 + \theta_3)}$$

■

Example 8.8 — Inverted Crank-Slider. The inverted crank-slider four-bar mechanism shown in Figure 8.16 consists of the three links 1, 2 and 3 constrained to move in a referential 0$(O, \hat{\mathbf{x}}_0, \hat{\mathbf{y}}_0, \hat{\mathbf{z}}_0)$. Links 2 and 3 are connected by a slider in such a way that lines AB and BC remain perpendicular. Denote by $l_0 = |OC|$, $l_1 = |OA|$ and $l_3 = |CB|$.

First determine the expressions of the kinematic screws $\{\mathcal{V}_{1/0}\}$, $\{\mathcal{V}_{2/1}\}$, $\{\mathcal{V}_{3/2}\}$, $\{\mathcal{V}_{3/0}\}$. Then write the kinematic loop equation corresponding to loop 0-1-2-3-0. From this equation, determine the angular velocity $\omega_{3/0}$ and the velocity $\mathbf{v}_{P\in 2/3}$ as a function of $\omega_{1/0}$. ■

First we define the bases of unit vectors $(\hat{\mathbf{u}}_i, \hat{\mathbf{v}}_i, \hat{\mathbf{z}}_i = \hat{\mathbf{z}}_0)$ attached to body i as shown in Figure 8.17. For each pair (0,1) (pivot), (2,1) (pivot), (3,1) (slider) and (3,0) (pivot) the corresponding kinematic screw is written by taking into account the nature of the interconnection and the

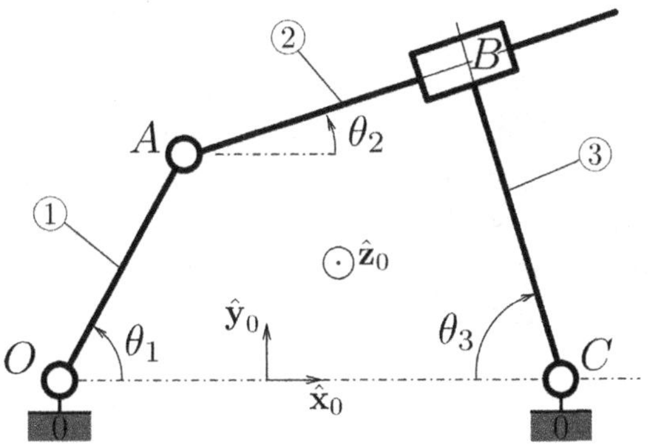

Figure 8.16

parametrization of the system:

$$\{\mathcal{V}_{1/0}\} = \left\{ \begin{matrix} \dot{\theta}_1 \hat{\mathbf{z}}_0 \\ \mathbf{0} \end{matrix} \right\}_O \qquad \{\mathcal{V}_{2/1}\} = \left\{ \begin{matrix} (\dot{\theta}_2 - \dot{\theta}_1)\hat{\mathbf{z}}_0 \\ \mathbf{0} \end{matrix} \right\}_A$$

$$\{\mathcal{V}_{3/2}\} = \left\{ \begin{matrix} \mathbf{0} \\ v_{32}\hat{\mathbf{u}}_2 \end{matrix} \right\} \qquad \{\mathcal{V}_{3/0}\} = \left\{ \begin{matrix} -\dot{\theta}_3 \hat{\mathbf{z}}_0 \\ \mathbf{0} \end{matrix} \right\}_C$$

In the closed loop 0-1-2-3-0, we can write the equation

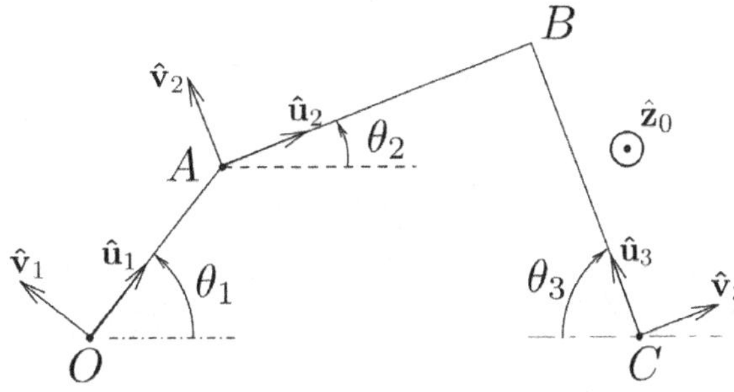

Figure 8.17

$$\{\mathcal{V}_{1/0}\} + \{\mathcal{V}_{2/1}\} + \{\mathcal{V}_{3/2}\} + \{\mathcal{V}_{0/3}\} = 0$$

This screw equality is equivalent to two equations

$$\dot{\theta}_1 + (\dot{\theta}_2 - \dot{\theta}_1) + \dot{\theta}_3 = 0$$

$$\mathbf{v}_{A\in 1/0} + \mathbf{v}_{A\in 2/1} + \mathbf{v}_{A\in 3/2} = \mathbf{v}_{A\in 3/0}$$

leading to

$$\dot{\theta}_3 = -\dot{\theta}_2, \qquad l_1\dot{\theta}_1\hat{\mathbf{v}}_1 + v_{32}\hat{\mathbf{u}}_2 = \dot{\theta}_3(l_0\hat{\mathbf{y}}_0 - l_1\hat{\mathbf{v}}_1)$$

This last equation can be projected onto $(\hat{\mathbf{u}}_2, \hat{\mathbf{v}}_2)$ to obtain:

$$v_{32} = -l_1(\dot{\theta}_3 + \dot{\theta}_1)\sin(\theta_2 - \theta_1) + l_0\dot{\theta}_3 \sin\theta_2$$

$$(l_0 \cos\theta_2 - l_1\cos(\theta_2 - \theta_1))\dot{\theta}_3 = l_1\dot{\theta}_1\cos(\theta_2 - \theta_1)$$

These two equations solve for $v_{32} = \mathbf{v}_{P\in 3/2} \cdot \hat{\mathbf{u}}_2$ and $\dot{\theta}_3$. ■

Example 8.9 — Universal Joint. The universal joint shown in Figure 8.18 is thought to have been invented by the mathematician Gerolamo Cardano in the 16th century. It was first constructed by James Hooke in the 17th century. It is often referred to as Cardan joint or Hooke joint. It is a mechanism used to transmit power between two intersecting shafts which may not necessarily be coinciding. The schematic shown in Figure 8.18 serves as a kinematic model of the universal joint between two rigid bodies 1 and 2 in motion relative to a referential $0(O, \hat{\mathbf{x}}_0, \hat{\mathbf{y}}_0, \hat{\mathbf{z}}_0)$.

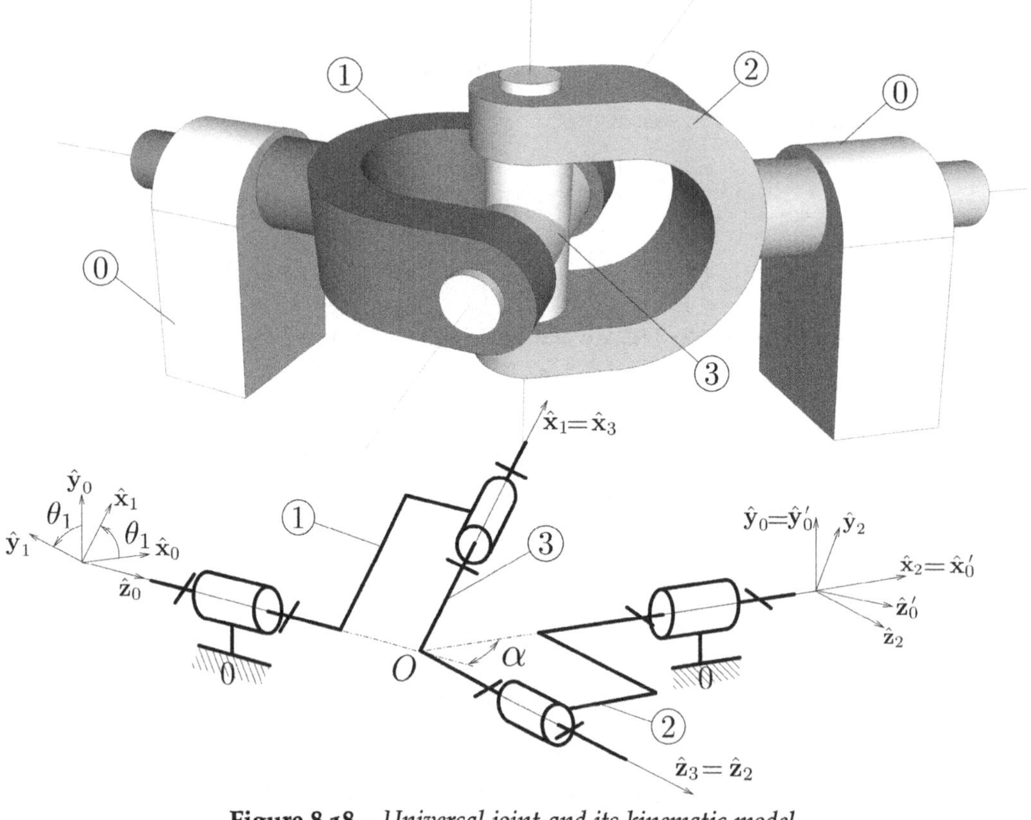

Figure 8.18 – *Universal joint and its kinematic model.*

Rigid body 1 $(O, \hat{\mathbf{x}}_1, \hat{\mathbf{y}}_1, \hat{\mathbf{z}}_0)$ is connected to 0 by a pivot of axis $(O, \hat{\mathbf{z}}_0)$ and is parametrized by the angle $\theta_1 = (\hat{\mathbf{x}}_0, \hat{\mathbf{x}}_1) = (\hat{\mathbf{y}}_0, \hat{\mathbf{y}}_1)$. Denote by $\omega_1 = \dot{\theta}_1$. Rigid body 2 $(O, \hat{\mathbf{x}}_2, \hat{\mathbf{y}}_2, \hat{\mathbf{z}}_2)$ is connected to 0 by a pivot of axis $(O, \hat{\mathbf{x}}_0' = \hat{\mathbf{x}}_2)$ located in plane $(O, \hat{\mathbf{x}}_0, \hat{\mathbf{z}}_0)$ (this plane contains the axis of rotation of both 1 and 2): denote by α the constant angle $(\hat{\mathbf{z}}_0, \hat{\mathbf{x}}_0')$ and by $\omega_{2/0} = \omega_2 \hat{\mathbf{x}}_0'$.

In order to transmit the motion of 1 to 2, a third rigid body 3 $(O, \hat{\mathbf{x}}_3, \hat{\mathbf{y}}_3, \hat{\mathbf{z}}_3)$ is interconnected between 1 and 2 in the following way: 3 is shaped in a cross whose perpendicular branches are connected by pivots to the yokes which terminate the shafts 1 and 2. More specifically, one branch of 3 is connected to 1 by a pivot of axis $(O, \hat{\mathbf{x}}_1)$, while the other branch is connected to 2 by a pivot of axis $(O, \hat{\mathbf{z}}_3)$. One can map the basis $(\hat{\mathbf{x}}_0, \hat{\mathbf{y}}_0, \hat{\mathbf{z}}_0)$ of 0 to the basis $(\hat{\mathbf{x}}_2, \hat{\mathbf{y}}_2, \hat{\mathbf{z}}_2)$ of 2 by the following sequence of rotations

$$(\hat{\mathbf{x}}_0, \hat{\mathbf{y}}_0, \hat{\mathbf{z}}_0) \xrightarrow{\mathcal{R}_{\theta_1, \hat{\mathbf{z}}_0}} (\hat{\mathbf{x}}_1, \hat{\mathbf{y}}_1, \hat{\mathbf{z}}_1 = \hat{\mathbf{z}}_0) \xrightarrow{\mathcal{R}_{\theta_3, \hat{\mathbf{x}}_1}} (\hat{\mathbf{x}}_3 = \hat{\mathbf{x}}_1, \hat{\mathbf{y}}_3, \hat{\mathbf{z}}_3) \xrightarrow{\mathcal{R}_{\theta_2, \hat{\mathbf{z}}_3}} (\hat{\mathbf{x}}_2, \hat{\mathbf{y}}_2, \hat{\mathbf{z}}_3)$$

The angles $(\theta_1, \theta_2, \theta_3)$ play the role of Euler angles to define the orientation of rigid body 2 relative to referential 0.

Find the transmission law ω_2/ω_1 as a function of input angle $\theta_1(t)$ and the geometric constant α. ■

The kinematic screws of 1 and 2 can be written as

$$\{\mathcal{V}_{1/0}\} = \begin{Bmatrix} \omega_1 \hat{\mathbf{z}}_0 \\ \mathbf{0} \end{Bmatrix}_O$$

$$\{\mathcal{V}_{2/0}\} = \begin{Bmatrix} \omega_2 \hat{\mathbf{x}}_2 \\ \mathbf{0} \end{Bmatrix}_O = \{\mathcal{V}_{2/3}\} + \{\mathcal{V}_{3/1}\} + \{\mathcal{V}_{1/0}\} = \begin{Bmatrix} \omega_1 \hat{\mathbf{z}}_0 + \dot{\theta}_3 \hat{\mathbf{x}}_1 + \dot{\theta}_2 \hat{\mathbf{z}}_3 \\ \mathbf{0} \end{Bmatrix}_O$$

Equating $\omega_2 \hat{\mathbf{x}}_2$ to $\omega_1 \hat{\mathbf{z}}_0 + \dot{\theta}_3 \hat{\mathbf{x}}_1 + \dot{\theta}_2 \hat{\mathbf{z}}_3$ we find three scalar equations by projection on $(\hat{\mathbf{x}}_2, \hat{\mathbf{y}}_2, \hat{\mathbf{z}}_3)$:

$$\begin{aligned} \omega_2 &= \omega_1 \sin\theta_2 \sin\theta_3 + \dot{\theta}_3 \cos\theta_2 \\ 0 &= \omega_1 \cos\theta_2 \sin\theta_3 - \dot{\theta}_3 \sin\theta_2 \\ 0 &= \omega_1 \cos\theta_3 + \dot{\theta}_2 \end{aligned}$$

from which we obtain

$$\frac{\omega_2}{\omega_1} = \frac{\sin\theta_3}{\sin\theta_2}$$

We can express the ratio $(\sin\theta_3/\sin\theta_2)$ in terms of angles θ_1 and α by equating $\hat{\mathbf{x}}_2 = \hat{\mathbf{x}}_0' = \cos\alpha \hat{\mathbf{z}}_0 + \sin\alpha \hat{\mathbf{x}}_0$ to $\cos\theta_2 \hat{\mathbf{x}}_1 + \sin\theta_2 \hat{\mathbf{y}}_3$. We obtain by projection on $(\hat{\mathbf{x}}_1, \hat{\mathbf{y}}_3, \hat{\mathbf{z}}_3)$:

$$\begin{aligned} \cos\theta_2 &= \sin\alpha \cos\theta_1 \\ \sin\theta_2 &= \cos\alpha \sin\theta_3 - \sin\alpha \sin\theta_1 \cos\theta_3 \\ 0 &= \cos\alpha \cos\theta_3 + \sin\alpha \sin\theta_1 \sin\theta_3 \end{aligned}$$

which yields $\sin\theta_2 \cos\alpha = (\cos^2\alpha + \sin^2\alpha \sin^2\theta_1) \sin\theta_3$.

Finally the transmission law is found to be

$$\frac{\omega_2}{\omega_1} = \frac{\cos\alpha}{1 - \sin^2\alpha \cos^2\theta_1} \tag{8.4}$$

We observe that, unless $\alpha = 0$ (the two shafts' axes coincide), the ratio ω_2/ω_1 of the shafts angular velocities varies in time: when angle θ_1 varies from 0 to 2π, then ω_2/ω_1 oscillates between the extreme values $\cos\alpha$ and $1/\cos\alpha$. These variations can lead to vibrations which are often unacceptable in practice. This joint is said to be non-homokinetic. Many solutions of homokinetic joints exists: CV (constant-velocity or Rzeppa) joint, Thompson couplings, etc. ■

Example 8.10 — Computer Mouse. An early design of a computer mouse is due to Engelbart (U.S. Pat. 3,541,541). Engelbart invented a mobile manual device which enabled the user to accurately control the position of a cursor on a computer monitor. In its original design, the mouse contained X and Y position wheels of perpendicular axes which would rotate in response to corresponding motion of the mouse on a flat surface. The device was biased to move in the directions corresponding to the rotations of the wheels. To avoid this bias, a better design adopted in most modern-day mechanical computer mice was offered by Opocensky in U.S. Pat. No. 3,987,685 as shown in Figure 8.19. The device includes a control mechanism which comprises a housing 1, a ball 2 coupled with two shafts 3 and 4, and a spring-loaded roller 5. The ball is maintained in a pure rotational motion about the housing while remaining in contact with the surface over which it rides and with the two shafts. These shafts are constrained with the housing by pivot type joints. Their rotations translate into XY motions of the cursor.

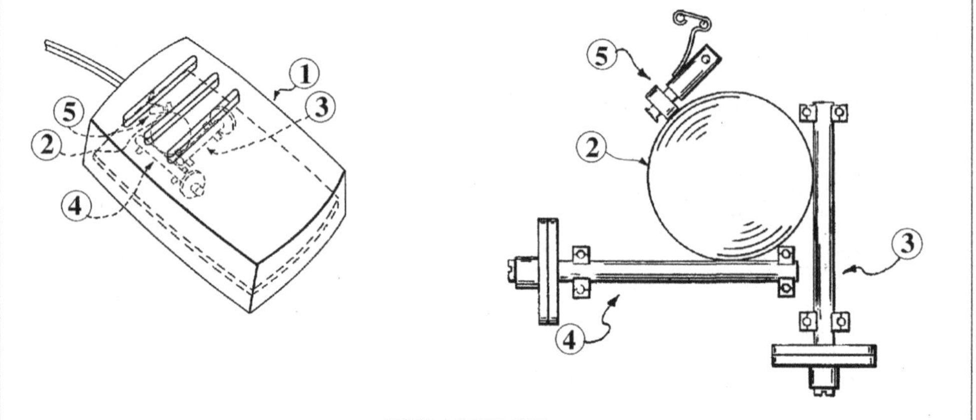

Figure 8.19

A kinematic model of this design is shown in Figure 8.20, comprising the following units:

- a housing 1 which rides on the plane $(O, \hat{\mathbf{x}}_0, \hat{\mathbf{y}}_0)$ (of unit normal $\hat{\mathbf{z}}_0$) of a referential 0. A basis attached to 1 is $(\hat{\mathbf{x}}_1, \hat{\mathbf{y}}_1, \hat{\mathbf{z}}_0)$, whose orientation relative to $(\hat{\mathbf{x}}_0, \hat{\mathbf{y}}_0, \hat{\mathbf{z}}_0)$ is defined by angle $\theta = (\hat{\mathbf{x}}_0, \hat{\mathbf{x}}_1) = (\hat{\mathbf{y}}_0, \hat{\mathbf{y}}_1)$. A point attached to 1 may be taken at C, the center of ball 2. The position of 1 relative to 0 is complete by defining the coordinates (x_C, y_C, R) relative to Cartesian axes $(O, \hat{\mathbf{x}}_0, \hat{\mathbf{y}}_0, \hat{\mathbf{z}}_0)$. The coordinates (x_C, y_C, θ) are "input" variables since they are imposed by the user which manipulates the device.
- a ball 2 of center C and radius R. It is in rotational motion about C relative to 1. Denote by $\omega_{2/1}$ the angular velocity of 2 relative to 1. Ball 2 is in contact with plane $(O, \hat{\mathbf{x}}_0, \hat{\mathbf{y}}_0)$ at point I such that $\mathbf{r}_{IC} = R\hat{\mathbf{z}}_0$.
- a cylindrical shaft 3 of radius r connected to 1 by a pivot of axis $(A, \hat{\mathbf{x}}_1)$ in contact with 2 at a point K such that $\mathbf{r}_{CK} = R\hat{\mathbf{y}}_1$.
- a cylindrical shaft 4 of radius r connected to 1 by a pivot of axis $(A, \hat{\mathbf{y}}_1)$ in contact with 2 at a point J such that $\mathbf{r}_{CJ} = R\hat{\mathbf{x}}_1$.

The shafts 3 and 4 are connected to potentiometers, and their rotations translate into XY displacements on the monitor. Under normal operation the contacts of ball 2 at points I, J and K are achieved without slip.

a. Sketch the connectivity diagram and identify three independent loops.

b. Write the corresponding loop equations and show that all kinematic unknowns can be expressed in terms of the "input" kinematic quantities (x_C, y_C, θ). In particular, show that the "output" angular velocities $\omega_{3/1}$ and $\omega_{4/1}$ are only function of $\dot{x}_C$ and $\dot{y}_C$ and not $\dot{\theta}$.

c. Examine the output motions for particular motions of the mouse. ■

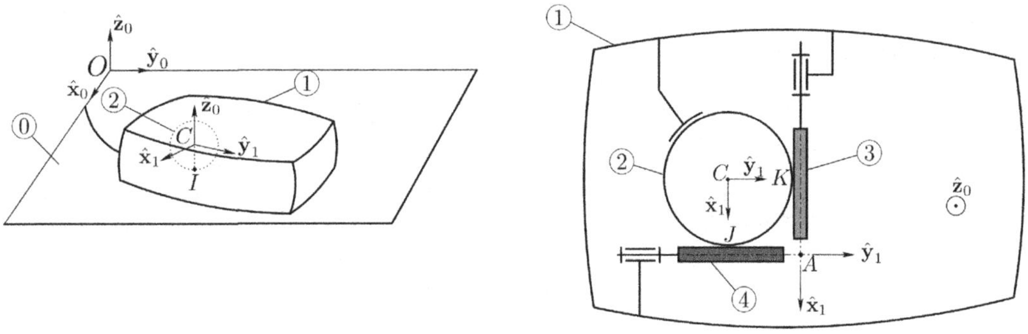

Figure 8.20

a. The connectivity diagram can be sketched as follows:

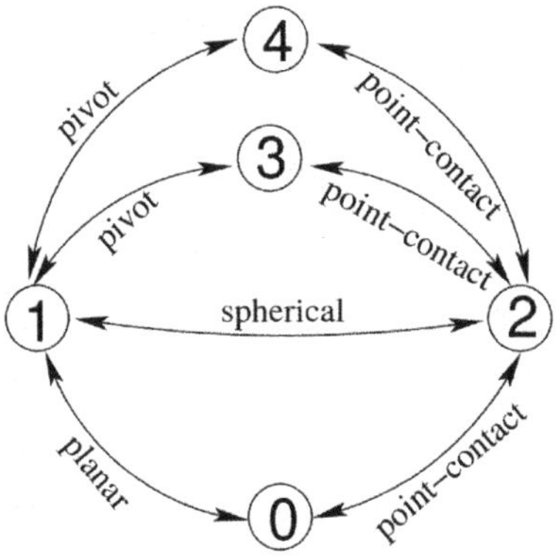

We can identify three independent loops: 0-1-2-0, 1-2-3-1 and 1-2-4-1. The closure of these loops can be stated as

$$\{\mathcal{V}_{1/0}\} + \{\mathcal{V}_{2/1}\} + \{\mathcal{V}_{0/2}\} = 0 \quad (1)$$

$$\{\mathcal{V}_{2/1}\} + \{\mathcal{V}_{3/2}\} + \{\mathcal{V}_{1/3}\} = 0 \quad (2)$$

$$\{\mathcal{V}_{2/1}\} + \{\mathcal{V}_{4/2}\} + \{\mathcal{V}_{1/4}\} = 0 \quad (3)$$

b. We express each of the kinematic screws present in these equations in a manner compatible with the corresponding interconnections.

(i) The pair 0-1 forms a planar joint along plane $(O; \hat{\mathbf{x}}_0, \hat{\mathbf{y}}_0)$: its kinematic screw can be expressed at point C:

$$\{\mathcal{V}_{1/0}\} = \left\{ \begin{array}{c} \dot{\theta}\hat{\mathbf{z}}_0 \\ \dot{x}_C\hat{\mathbf{x}}_0 + \dot{y}_C\hat{\mathbf{y}}_0 \end{array} \right\}_C$$

(ii) The pair 1-2 forms a spherical joint about point C:

$$\{\mathcal{V}_{2/1}\} = \left\{ \begin{array}{c} \omega_{2/1} \\ \mathbf{0} \end{array} \right\}_C$$

(iii) The pair 0-2 is formed by a no-slip sphere-plane contact at I

$$\{\mathcal{V}_{2/0}\} = \begin{Bmatrix} \boldsymbol{\omega}_{2/0} \\ \mathbf{0} \end{Bmatrix}_I$$

(iv) The pair 1-3 forms a pivot about axis $(A; \hat{\mathbf{x}}_1)$:

$$\{\mathcal{V}_{3/1}\} = \begin{Bmatrix} \omega_{3/1}\hat{\mathbf{x}}_1 \\ \mathbf{0} \end{Bmatrix}_A$$

(v) The pair 1-4 forms a pivot about axis $(A; \hat{\mathbf{y}}_1)$:

$$\{\mathcal{V}_{4/1}\} = \begin{Bmatrix} \omega_{4/1}\hat{\mathbf{y}}_1 \\ \mathbf{0} \end{Bmatrix}_A$$

(vi) The pair 2-3 is formed by a no-slip cylinder/sphere point contact at point K:

$$\{\mathcal{V}_{3/2}\} = \begin{Bmatrix} \boldsymbol{\omega}_{3/2} \\ \mathbf{0} \end{Bmatrix}_K$$

we don't know what these are

(vii) The pair 2-4 is formed by a no-slip cylinder/sphere point contact at point J:

$$\{\mathcal{V}_{4/2}\} = \begin{Bmatrix} \boldsymbol{\omega}_{4/2} \\ \mathbf{0} \end{Bmatrix}_J$$

We can now expand on equations (1-3):

$$\dot{\theta}\hat{\mathbf{z}}_0 + \boldsymbol{\omega}_{2/1} - \boldsymbol{\omega}_{2/0} = \mathbf{0}, \quad \dot{x}_C\hat{\mathbf{x}}_0 + \dot{y}_C\hat{\mathbf{y}}_0 - \boldsymbol{\omega}_{2/0} \times \mathbf{r}_{IC} = \mathbf{0}$$

$$\boldsymbol{\omega}_{2/1} + \boldsymbol{\omega}_{3/2} - \omega_{3/1}\hat{\mathbf{x}}_1 = \mathbf{0}, \quad \boldsymbol{\omega}_{3/2} \times \mathbf{r}_{KC} - \omega_{3/1}\hat{\mathbf{x}}_1 \times \mathbf{r}_{AC} = \mathbf{0}$$

$$\boldsymbol{\omega}_{2/1} + \boldsymbol{\omega}_{4/2} - \omega_{4/1}\hat{\mathbf{y}}_1 = \mathbf{0}, \quad \boldsymbol{\omega}_{4/2} \times \mathbf{r}_{JC} - \omega_{4/1}\hat{\mathbf{y}}_1 \times \mathbf{r}_{AC} = \mathbf{0}$$

We can then express angular velocities $\boldsymbol{\omega}_{2/1}$, $\boldsymbol{\omega}_{3/2}$ and $\boldsymbol{\omega}_{4/2}$ in terms of $\dot{\theta}\hat{\mathbf{z}}_0$, $\boldsymbol{\omega}_{2/0}$, $\omega_{3/1}\hat{\mathbf{x}}_1$ and $\omega_{4/1}\hat{\mathbf{y}}_1$:

$$\boldsymbol{\omega}_{2/1} = \boldsymbol{\omega}_{2/0} - \dot{\theta}\hat{\mathbf{z}}_0, \quad \boldsymbol{\omega}_{3/2} = \omega_{3/1}\hat{\mathbf{x}}_1 + \dot{\theta}\hat{\mathbf{z}}_0 - \boldsymbol{\omega}_{2/0} \quad \boldsymbol{\omega}_{4/2} = \omega_{4/1}\hat{\mathbf{y}}_1 + \dot{\theta}\hat{\mathbf{z}}_0 - \boldsymbol{\omega}_{2/0}$$

and substitute these expressions into the velocity loop equations:

$$\dot{x}_C\hat{\mathbf{x}}_0 + \dot{y}_C\hat{\mathbf{y}}_0 - R\boldsymbol{\omega}_{2/0} \times \hat{\mathbf{z}}_0 = \mathbf{0} \tag{4}$$

$$-R(\omega_{3/1}\hat{\mathbf{x}}_1 + \dot{\theta}\hat{\mathbf{z}}_0 - \boldsymbol{\omega}_{2/0}) \times \hat{\mathbf{y}}_1 + (r+R)\omega_{3/1}\hat{\mathbf{x}}_1 \times (\hat{\mathbf{x}}_1 + \hat{\mathbf{y}}_1) = \mathbf{0} \tag{5}$$

$$-R(\omega_{4/1}\hat{\mathbf{y}}_1 + \dot{\theta}\hat{\mathbf{z}}_0 - \boldsymbol{\omega}_{2/0}) \times \hat{\mathbf{x}}_1 + (r+R)\omega_{4/1}\hat{\mathbf{y}}_1 \times (\hat{\mathbf{x}}_1 + \hat{\mathbf{y}}_1) = \mathbf{0} \tag{6}$$

By expressing $\boldsymbol{\omega}_{2/0}$ as $\omega^x_{2/0}\hat{\mathbf{x}}_0 + \omega^y_{2/0}\hat{\mathbf{y}}_0 + \omega^z_{2/0}\hat{\mathbf{z}}_0$, equation (4) gives the components $\omega^x_{2/0}$ and $\omega^y_{2/0}$

$$\omega^x_{2/0} = -\frac{1}{R}\dot{y}_C, \qquad \omega^y_{2/0} = \frac{1}{R}\dot{x}_C$$

Then equation (5) gives $\omega^z_{2/0}$ and $\omega_{3/1}$

$$\omega^z_{2/0} = \dot{\theta}, \qquad R(\omega^x_{2/0}\cos\theta + \omega^y_{2/0}\sin\theta) = -r\omega_{3/1}$$

Substitution of $\omega^x_{2/0}$ and $\omega^y_{2/0}$ finally gives the expression of $\omega_{3/1}$:

$$\omega_{3/1} = \frac{1}{r}(-\dot{x}_C \sin\theta + \dot{y}_C \cos\theta)$$

Proceeding with equation (6) gives the expression of $\omega_{4/1}$

$$\omega_{4/1} = -\frac{1}{r}(\dot{y}_C \sin\theta + \dot{x}_C \cos\theta)$$

The output motions are the angle of rotation θ_3 and θ_4 of the shafts.

c. Two particular cases can be examined:

- if $1/0$ is a rotation about $(C, \hat{\mathbf{z}}_0)$, then $\dot{x}_C = \dot{y}_C = 0$ leading to $\omega_{4/1} = \omega_{3/1} = 0$. The cursor is stationary.

- if $1/0$ is a uniform translation, then θ, $\dot{x}_C$ and $\dot{y}_C$ are constant, leading to constant angular velocities $\omega_{3/1}$ and $\omega_{4/1}$. The motion of the cursor is also a uniform translation. ∎

Example 8.11 — Graham transmission. Figure 8.21 shows a variable speed transmission known as Graham transmission (US Pat. 2,706,916). The drive shaft 1 rotates a carrier which supports three tapered rollers 2. The rollers' axes are inclined so that their outer generatrices remain parallel to the shafts' axes. Each roller ends with a pinion gear which meshes with a ring gear connected to the output shaft 3 coaxial with the drive shaft. A control ring 4 fixed to the main housing 0 encircles and is in contact with the rollers. The angular velocity of the output shaft is controlled by the ring's position which is is adjustable along the axial direction.

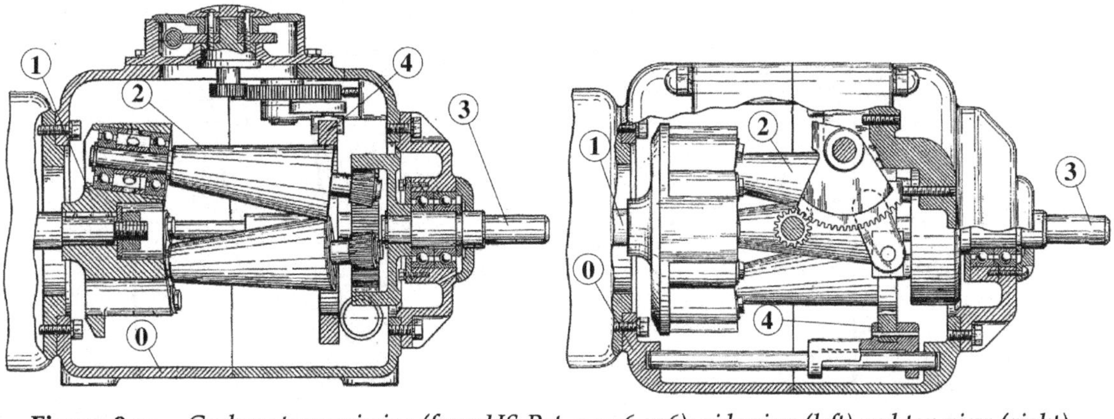

Figure 8.21 – *Graham transmission (from US Pat. 2,706,916): side view (left) and top view (right).*

Figure 8.22 shows a kinematic sketch of Graham transmission where only one roller is displayed. It comprises the following parts:

- 0 $(O, \hat{\mathbf{x}}_0, \hat{\mathbf{y}}_0, \hat{\mathbf{z}}_0)$ represents the transmission housing.

- 1 $(O, \hat{\mathbf{x}}_0, \hat{\mathbf{y}}_1, \hat{\mathbf{z}}_1)$ represents the drive shaft in rotation about axis $(O, \hat{\mathbf{x}}_0)$ relative to 0. The sketch of Figure 8.22 is the plane $(O, \hat{\mathbf{x}}_0, \hat{\mathbf{y}}_1)$ containing the axis AC of roller 2.

- 2 $(O, \hat{\mathbf{x}}_0, \hat{\mathbf{y}}_2, \hat{\mathbf{z}}_2)$ represents one of the three rollers in rotation about axis $(A, \hat{\mathbf{x}}_2)$ relative to body 1. Axis $(A, \hat{\mathbf{x}}_2)$ makes a constant angle α relative to axis $(O, \hat{\mathbf{x}}_0)$. Each roller is in the shape of a truncated cone whose generatrix farthest from axis $(O, \hat{\mathbf{x}}_0)$ is directed along $\hat{\mathbf{x}}_0$ (hence α is also the half-angle of the cone's apex). The pinion gear CD is rigidly attached to the roller and rolls without slipping on the ring gear mounted on the output shaft 3.

- 3 $(O, \hat{\mathbf{x}}_0, \hat{\mathbf{y}}_3, \hat{\mathbf{z}}_3)$ represents the output shaft 3 in rotation about axis $(E, \hat{\mathbf{x}}_0)$ relative to 0.
- 4 represents the control ring whose position during operation is fixed relative to 0. Its position relative to the rollers is defined by parameters μ and λ. Roller 2 rolls without slipping at contact point J relative to 4.

The geometry of the mechanism is defined by the constant parameters R_1, R_2, R_3, μ and λ. We denote the angular velocity of the shafts as $\boldsymbol{\omega}_{1/0} = \omega_1 \hat{\mathbf{x}}_0$ and $\boldsymbol{\omega}_{3/0} = \omega_3 \hat{\mathbf{x}}_0$. One of the goals of this problem is to predict the relationship between ω_1 and ω_3.

a. Sketch the connectivity diagram and identify independent loops. Determine the expression of each kinematic screw $\{\mathcal{V}_{j/i}\}$ for all pairs (i, j) of interconnected rigid bodies.

b. Write the corresponding loop equations and solve for the angular velocities $\boldsymbol{\omega}_{3/0}$ and $\boldsymbol{\omega}_{2/1}$ in terms of the input angular velocity ω_1 and the geometric parameters. Show that angular velocity $\boldsymbol{\omega}_{3/0}$ can vanish for a particular setting of the control ring.

c. Construct the instantaneous screw axes $\Delta_{2/0}$ and $\Delta_{2/3}$ (use simple arguments). Then find a geometric condition for $\boldsymbol{\omega}_{3/0}$ to become zero and recover the condition found in **b** (it will be useful to introduce the distance D measured from point J to the axis OE). ■

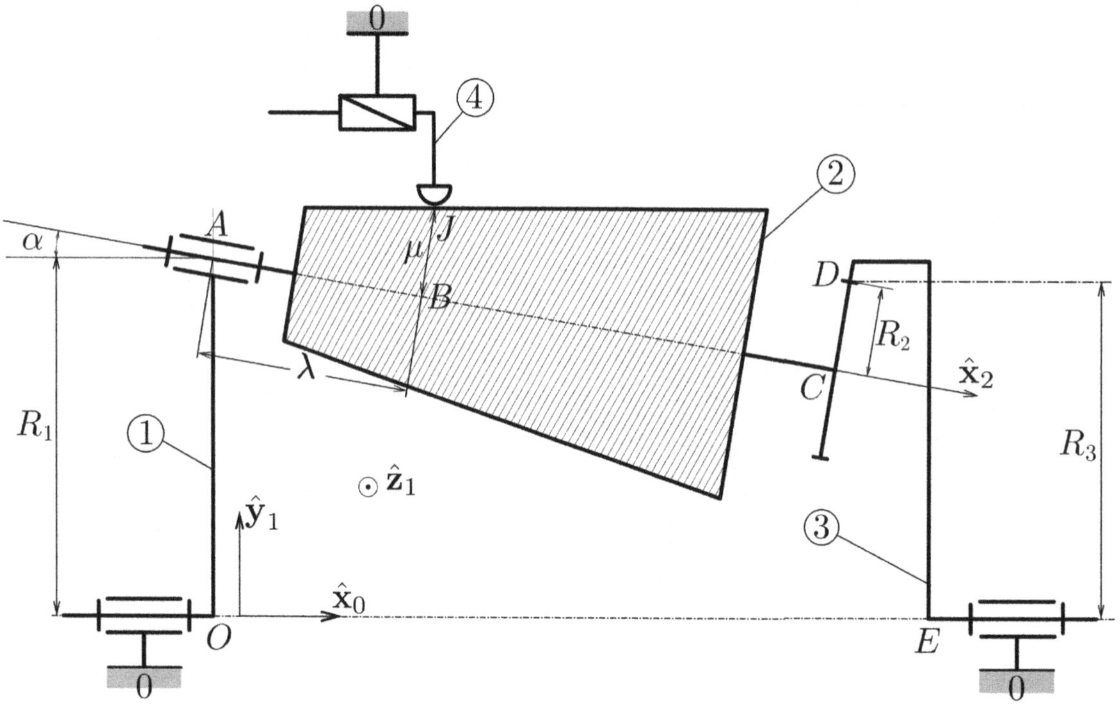

Figure 8.22 – *Graham transmission: kinematic sketch.*

a. The system is comprised of four parts: the fixed housing 0, the input shaft 1, the tapered roller 2, the output shaft 3 (the control ring 4 is fixed). The connectivity diagram is sketched below. We then identify two independent loops from the connectivity diagram : 0-1-2-0 and 0-1-2-3-0. In the connectivity diagram, we find 5 pairs of interconnected bodies: (0,1), (1,2), (2,3), (0,3) and (0,2):

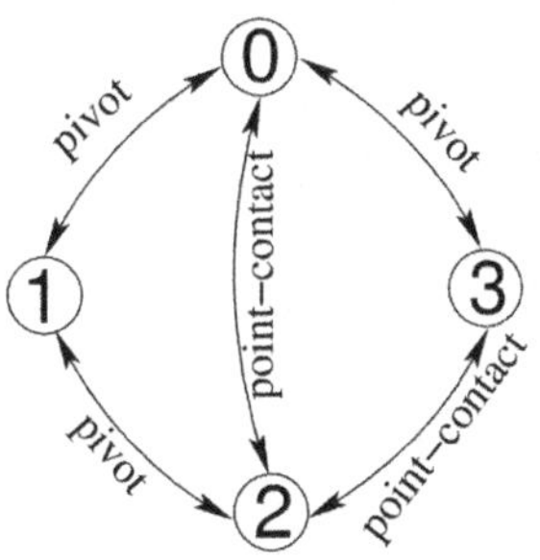

- pair (0,1): the corresponding joint is a pivot of axis $(O, \hat{\mathbf{x}}_0)$

$$\{\mathcal{V}_{1/0}\} = \begin{Bmatrix} \omega_1 \hat{\mathbf{x}}_0 \\ \mathbf{0} \end{Bmatrix}_O$$

- pair (2,1): the corresponding joint is a pivot of axis $(A, \hat{\mathbf{x}}_2)$

$$\{\mathcal{V}_{2/1}\} = \begin{Bmatrix} \omega_{2/1} \hat{\mathbf{x}}_2 \\ \mathbf{0} \end{Bmatrix}_A$$

- pair (3,2): the corresponding joint is a no-slip point contact at D

$$\{\mathcal{V}_{3/2}\} = \begin{Bmatrix} \boldsymbol{\omega}_{3/2} \\ \mathbf{0} \end{Bmatrix}_D$$

- pair (0,3): the corresponding joint is a pivot of axis $(E, \hat{\mathbf{x}}_0)$

$$\{\mathcal{V}_{3/0}\} = \begin{Bmatrix} \omega_3 \hat{\mathbf{x}}_0 \\ \mathbf{0} \end{Bmatrix}_E$$

- pair (0,2): the corresponding joint is a no-slip point contact at J

$$\{\mathcal{V}_{2/0}\} = \begin{Bmatrix} \boldsymbol{\omega}_{2/0} \\ \mathbf{0} \end{Bmatrix}_J$$

b. We start with loop 0-1-2-0: $\{\mathcal{V}_{2/0}\} = \{\mathcal{V}_{2/1}\} + \{\mathcal{V}_{1/0}\}$. This gives

$$\begin{Bmatrix} \boldsymbol{\omega}_{2/0} \\ \mathbf{0} \end{Bmatrix}_J = \begin{Bmatrix} \omega_{2/1} \hat{\mathbf{x}}_2 \\ \mathbf{0} \end{Bmatrix}_A + \begin{Bmatrix} \omega_1 \hat{\mathbf{x}}_0 \\ \mathbf{0} \end{Bmatrix}_O$$

yielding 2 equations (we use point J)

$$\boldsymbol{\omega}_{2/0} = \omega_{2/1} \hat{\mathbf{x}}_2 + \omega_1 \hat{\mathbf{x}}_0, \qquad \mathbf{0} = \omega_{2/1} \hat{\mathbf{x}}_2 \times \mathbf{r}_{AJ} + \omega_1 \hat{\mathbf{x}}_0 \times \mathbf{r}_{OJ}$$

With $\mathbf{r}_{AJ} = \lambda \hat{\mathbf{x}}_2 + \mu \hat{\mathbf{y}}_1'$ (define $\hat{\mathbf{y}}_1' = \hat{\mathbf{z}}_0 \times \hat{\mathbf{x}}_2$) and $\mathbf{r}_{OJ} = (R_1 - \lambda \sin\alpha + \mu \cos\alpha)\hat{\mathbf{y}}_1 + (\lambda \cos\alpha + \mu \sin\alpha)\hat{\mathbf{x}}_0$ we find

$$\mu \omega_{2/1} + (R_1 - \lambda \sin\alpha + \mu \cos\alpha)\omega_1 = 0 \tag{1}$$

We then write the corresponding equation in loop 0-1-2-3-0: $\{\mathcal{V}_{3/0}\} = \{\mathcal{V}_{3/2}\} + \{\mathcal{V}_{2/1}\} + \{\mathcal{V}_{1/0}\}$

$$\begin{Bmatrix} \omega_3 \hat{\mathbf{x}}_0 \\ \mathbf{0} \end{Bmatrix}_E = \begin{Bmatrix} \boldsymbol{\omega}_{3/2} \\ \mathbf{0} \end{Bmatrix}_D + \begin{Bmatrix} \omega_{2/1} \hat{\mathbf{x}}_2 \\ \mathbf{0} \end{Bmatrix}_A + \begin{Bmatrix} \omega_1 \hat{\mathbf{x}}_0 \\ \mathbf{0} \end{Bmatrix}_O$$

yielding 2 equations (we use point D)

$$\omega_3 \hat{\mathbf{x}}_0 = \boldsymbol{\omega}_{3/2} + \omega_{2/1} \hat{\mathbf{x}}_2 + \omega_1 \hat{\mathbf{x}}_0, \qquad \omega_3 \hat{\mathbf{x}}_0 \times \mathbf{r}_{ED} = \omega_{2/1} \hat{\mathbf{x}}_2 \times \mathbf{r}_{AD} + \omega_1 \hat{\mathbf{x}}_0 \times \mathbf{r}_{OD}$$

The last equation gives

$$\omega_3 \hat{\mathbf{x}}_0 \times R_3 \hat{\mathbf{y}}_1 = \omega_{2/1} \hat{\mathbf{x}}_2 \times R_2 \hat{\mathbf{y}}_1' + \omega_1 \hat{\mathbf{x}}_0 \times R_3 \hat{\mathbf{y}}_1$$

or

$$R_3\omega_3 = R_2\omega_{2/1} + R_3\omega_1 \tag{2}$$

We can now use equations (1-2) to solve for ω_3 and $\omega_{2/1}$

$$\omega_3 = \Big(1 - \frac{R_2}{R_3}\frac{R_1 - \lambda\sin\alpha + \mu\cos\alpha}{\mu}\Big)\omega_1, \qquad \omega_{2/1} = -\frac{R_1 - \lambda\sin\alpha + \mu\cos\alpha}{\mu}\omega_1$$

We see that ω_3 can vanish when the parameters $(R_1, R_2, R_3, \lambda, \mu)$ satisfy the equality

$$\frac{R_2}{R_3} = \frac{\mu}{R_1 - \lambda\sin\alpha + \mu\cos\alpha}$$

We note that the quantity $(R_1 - \lambda\sin\alpha + \mu\cos\alpha)$ is in fact the distance D measured from point J to the axis OE: it is a fixed parameter (as the position of J is varied). Hence the position of J which gives $\omega_3 = 0$ can be stated as

$$\mu = \frac{R_2}{R_3}D \tag{3}$$

c. Since $\mathbf{v}_{J\in 2/0} = \mathbf{0}$, the instantaneous screw axis $\Delta_{2/0}$ is an instantaneous axis of rotation passing through point J. Consider the axis $(A, \hat{\mathbf{x}}_2)$ of roller 2: it intersects axis $(O, \hat{\mathbf{x}}_0)$ at point F: at this point we have $\mathbf{v}_{F\in 2/0} = \mathbf{v}_{F\in 2/1} + \mathbf{v}_{F\in 1/0} = \mathbf{0}$. Hence axis $\Delta_{2/0}$ must also pass through point F. Axis $\Delta_{2/0}$ is the line FJ.

Likewise, the condition $\mathbf{v}_{I\in 2/3} = \mathbf{0}$ shows that instantaneous axis of rotation $\Delta_{2/3}$ must pass through point I. At point F we have

$$\mathbf{v}_{F\in 2/3} = \mathbf{v}_{F\in 2/0} + \mathbf{v}_{F\in 0/3} = \mathbf{0}$$

since both velocities $\mathbf{v}_{F\in 2/0}$ and $\mathbf{v}_{F\in 0/3}$ are zero. Hence axis $\Delta_{2/3}$ is the line FI.

Now when angular velocity $\omega_{3/0}$ vanishes (by adjusting position of J) we have the equality

$$\boldsymbol{\omega}_{3/0} = \boldsymbol{\omega}_{3/2} + \boldsymbol{\omega}_{2/0} = \mathbf{0}$$

This shows that the axes $\Delta_{2/0}$ and $\Delta_{2/3}$ must be parallel since their directions are defined by $\boldsymbol{\omega}_{2/0}$ and $\boldsymbol{\omega}_{2/3}$. Given that both axes pass through point F, they must necessarily coincide: we conclude that points J, I and F are aligned. This gives the following construction

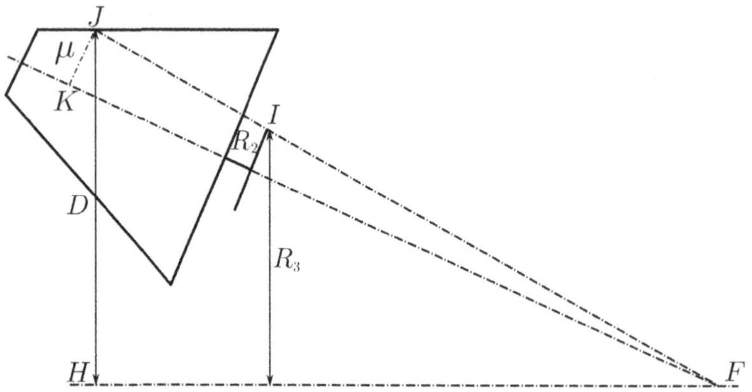

In triangles HJF and KJF we find the following ratios

$$\frac{D}{R_3} = \frac{|JF|}{|IF|}, \qquad \frac{\mu}{R_2} = \frac{|JF|}{|IF|}$$

We recover equation (3).

■

8.5 Problems

Problem 8.1 Three cylinders are in planar motion. Cylinder 1 (of center A, radius r) and cylinder 2 (of center B, radius $r/2$) roll without slipping on a horizontal fixed support 0. Cylinder 3 (of center C, radius $r/4$) rolls without slipping relative to cylinder 1 at contact point I. Center A moves at known speed v_A in the direction shown in the figure.

a. Find the velocities of B and C.

b. Find the instantaneous center I_3 of cylinder 3. Deduce the angular velocities of the three cylinders.

c. Find the slip velocity $\mathbf{v}_{K\in 3/2}$.

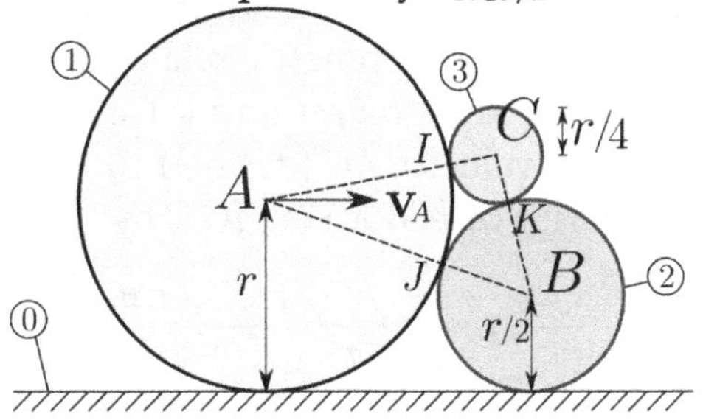

Problem 8.2 A rod 2 is connected to the center A of a wheel 1 of radius r and to a slider 3 at B. The wheel rolls without slipping on a fixed circular support of center O and radius $R+r$. Denote by L the length $|AB|$. The slider moves at constant speed v_B in the direction shown. The orientation of rod 2 is defined by angle ϕ.

a. Construct the location of the instantaneous centers I_1 and I_2 of bodies 1 and 2.

b. Find the velocity $\mathbf{v}_A$ of A, the angular velocities ω_1 and ω_2 of bodies 1 and 2 as a function of ϕ, v_B and the geometric parameters r, R and L.

c. Find the acceleration $\mathbf{a}_A$ of A, the angular accelerations α_1 and α_2 of of bodies 1 and 2 as a function of ϕ, v_B and the geometric parameters r, R and L.

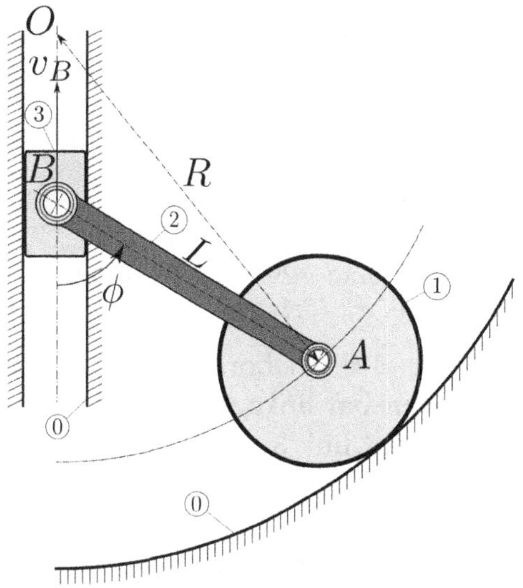

Problem 8.3 A steering mechanism ensures that a vehicle wheels of the same axle are pointing in the desired directions. The arm 1 pivots about O relative to the frame 0. It is actuated by a hydraulic cylinder (not shown). The tie rod 2 connects the arm 1 to the steering arm 3 which pivots about the kingpin C relative to the frame. Only the right-hand side of the mechanism is shown. The configuration of the mechanism is defined by the three angles θ_1, θ_2 and θ_3 and the fixed lengths $l_1 = |OA|$, $l_2 = |AB|$ and $l_3 = |BC|$.

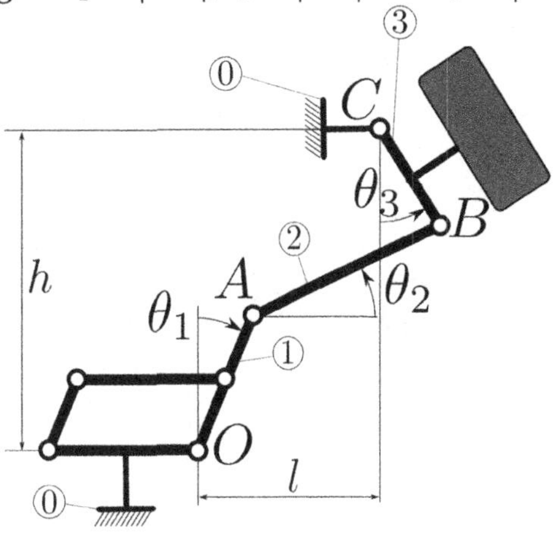

a. Write the geometric vector loop equation between O, A, B and C to find two scalar equations governing θ_1, θ_2 and θ_3.

b. Assume that at $\theta_1 = 0$, we have $\theta_2 = \theta_2^0$ and $\theta_3 = 0$ and that for $\theta_1 \neq 0$, $\theta_2 = \theta_2^0 + \Delta\theta_2$, with $\Delta\theta_2 \ll 1$. Show that angle θ_3 is governed by the equation

$$c_2 \tan^2 \frac{\theta_3}{2} + c_1 \tan \frac{\theta_3}{2} + c_0 = 0$$

Express c_0, c_1 and c_0 in terms of θ_1, and the constants θ_2^0, l_1, l_2 and l_3.

Problem 8.4 A laboratory agitator is based on a four-bar linkage. The drive link 1 and the output link 3 are interconnected by the coupler link 2. Link 1 is in rotation about fixed point O. Link 3 which holds the agitator vessel is in rotation about fixed point C. Denote $l_1 = |OA|$, $l_2 = |AB|$, $l_3 = |BC|$. The constants H and D define the distances between fixed points O and C.

a. Write the geometric loop equation between O, A, B and C to find an equation between angles θ_1, θ_3 and the geometric parameters l_1, l_2, l_3, D and H.

b. From the equation found in a) determine the relationship between $\dot{\theta}_1$ and $\dot{\theta}_3$.

c. Assume that the geometry of the mechanism is such that the angle θ_3 remains small: using the approximation $\sin\theta_3 \approx 0$ and $\cos\theta_3 \approx 1$ show that $\dot{\theta}_3$ is given by

$$\dot{\theta}_3 = \frac{l_1}{l_3}\dot{\theta}_1 \frac{(D - l_3)\sin\theta_1 + H\cos\theta_1}{H + l_1 \sin\theta_1}$$

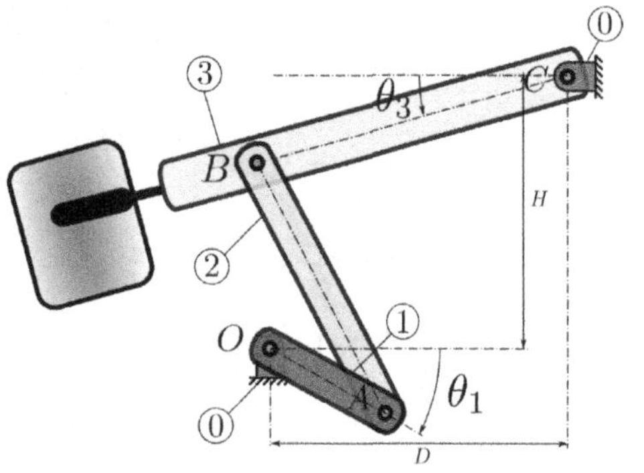

Problem 8.5 A swing-arm quick-return mechanism consists of three rigid bodies in motion relative to a referential 0. Drive link 1 rotates uniformly at angular velocity ω_1 about fixed point C in the counterclockwise direction. It is connected at pin B to slider 2 which is constrained to translate along the slotted arm 3. Arm 3 is constrained to rotate about fixed point A. The orientation of link 1 is defined by angle θ_1 and the geometry is defined by the constant parameters $r = |CB|$ and $l = |AC|$ with $r < l$. We also denote $\lambda(t) = |AB|$.

a. Write the kinematic loop equation ⓪-①-②-⓪ at point B to find the slip velocity $\mathbf{v}_{B\in 2/3}$ and the angular velocity ω_3 of slotted arm 3 (as a function of θ_1, θ_3, r and l and λ).

b. Find two geometric relationships which relate λ and θ_3 to θ_1, r and l. Deduce that the angular velocity ω_3 (defined in the counterclockwise direction) is given by

$$\omega_3 = r\omega_1 \frac{r + l\sin\theta_1}{r^2 + l^2 + 2rl\sin\theta_1}$$

c. From the result of b) conclude that the output motion is a reciprocating motion. Find the ratio r/l so that arm 3 oscillates between the values $\theta_3 = \pm\pi/3$. Plot the corresponding function ω_3/ω_1 vs θ_1 for $0 \leq \theta_1 < 2\pi$ and explain why the mechanism is characterized as "quick-return".

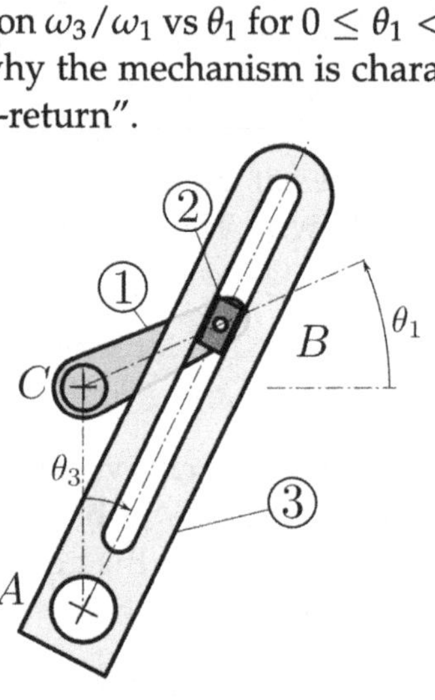

Problem 8.6 In this mechanism, the motion of the hydraulic cylinder/piston assembly 1-2 controls the motion of plunger 5. The

cylinder/piston assembly 1-2 is pinned at point O fixed in referential 0 and at point A with lever 3 itself pinned at B to referential 0. Lever 3 supports a roller 4 of center C. Roller 4 is in contact with the plunger 5. The goal is find the relationship between the plunger's velocity v_5 and the piston's extensional velocity $v_{2/1}$ (measured positively in the directions shown). At any instant, the configuration is defined given by angles θ_1 and θ_3 and by the constant parameters $|BA| = a$ and $|BC| = c$.

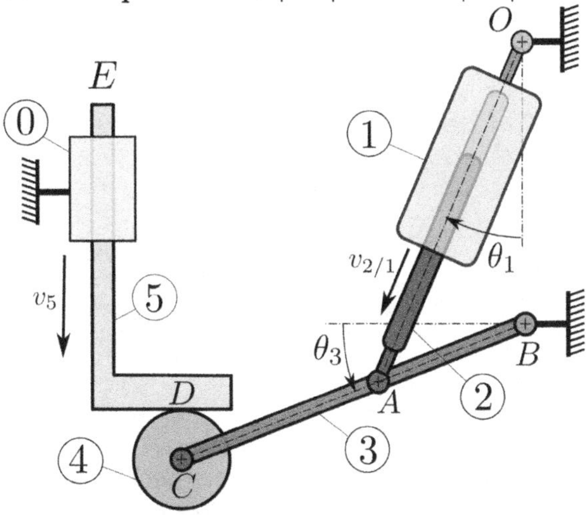

a. From the equation $\mathbf{v}_{C\in 5/0} = \mathbf{v}_{C\in 5/4} + \mathbf{v}_{C\in 4/3} + \mathbf{v}_{C\in 3/0}$, find the relationship between velocity v_5 and angular velocity $\omega_{3/0}$.

b. From the equation $\mathbf{v}_{A\in 3/0} = \mathbf{v}_{A\in 3/2} + \mathbf{v}_{A\in 2/1} + \mathbf{v}_{A\in 1/0}$, find the relationship between velocity $v_{2/1}$ and angular velocity $\omega_{3/0}$.

c. Using the results of a) and b) find the ratio $v_{2/1}/v_5$ in terms of θ_1, θ_3, a and c.

Problem 8.7 In this epicyclic gear train the carrier 1 supports the double satellite gear 2 which is meshed with two ring gears 3 and 4. The geometry is defined by the radii r_1, r_2', r_2''.

a. Identify one (or more) kinematic loop equation(s). Deduce relationship(s) between the angular velocities ω_1, ω_2, ω_3 and ω_4.

b. Assume that ring gear 3 is stationary. Find the ratio ω_1/ω_4 for $r_2'' = 100$ mm, $r_2' = 102.5$ mm, $r_3 = r_1 + r_2' = 210$ mm and $r_4 = r_1 + r_2'' = 215.5$ mm. Comment about the possible use of this mechanism.

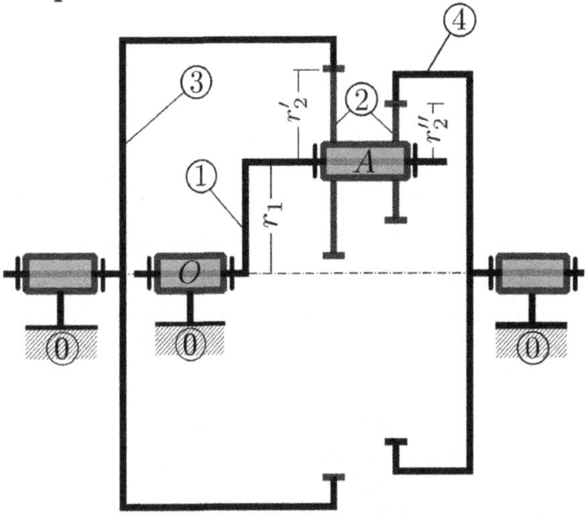

Problem 8.8 The figure displayed below shows a mechanism (assembled and disassembled views) which allows transmission of the rotational motion of a shaft 1 to a shaft 2 whose axis is parallel but not aligned. Each shaft is terminated with a circular flange in which a groove is cut along a diameter. A disk 3 is mounted between the flanges by fitting the tongues of disk 3 inside the flanges' grooves. These two tongues are at right angle to each other. The relative motion between the disk and the shafts is therefore translational. This mechanism is mounted in a referential 0 $(O, \hat{\mathbf{x}}_0, \hat{\mathbf{y}}_0, \hat{\mathbf{z}}_0)$. Denote e the distance between the shafts' axes, $\omega_1 \hat{\mathbf{z}}_0$ the angular velocity of input shaft 1, $\omega_2 \hat{\mathbf{z}}_0$ the angular velocity of output shaft 2. This mechanism is known as the *Oldham coupling* (invented by Irish engineer John Oldham).

a. Describe the motion of disk 3 relative to referential 0.

b. Build a kinematic diagram of this mechanism in referential 0 by using lower kinematic pairs.

c. With the help of this diagram, find the input/output law, that is, ω_2 versus ω_1, and the kinematics of disk 3. Comment.

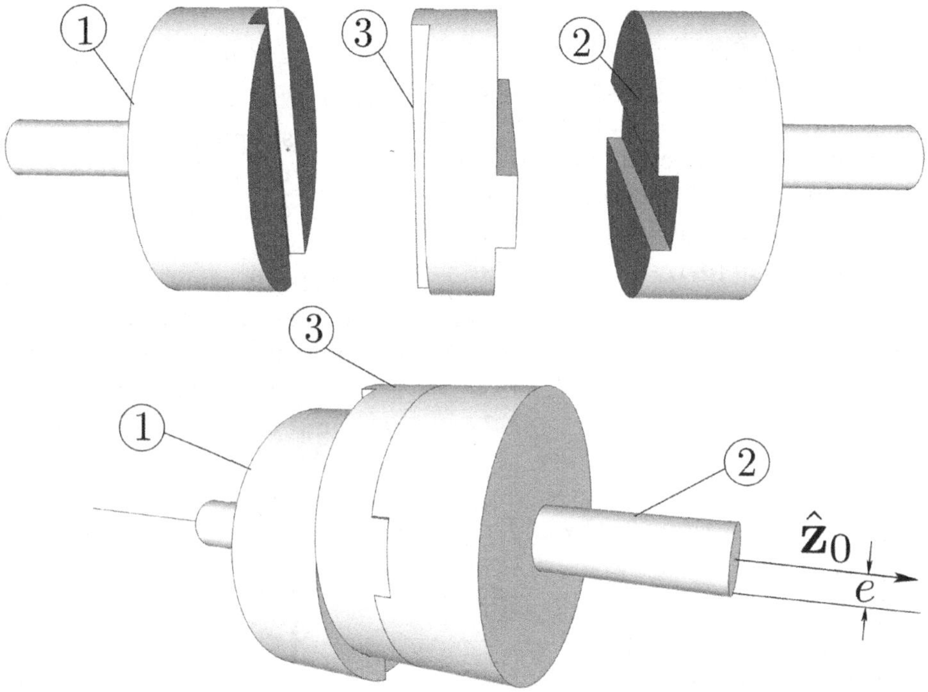

Problem 8.9 Four-wheeled vehicles must be equipped with a differential, a mechanism which allows transmission of rotational motion of the driving shaft to the front wheels at different angular velocities. The figure displayed below shows a model of a differential composed of four rigid bodies 2,3,4,5 assembled in a referential 0 attached to the vehicle's frame:

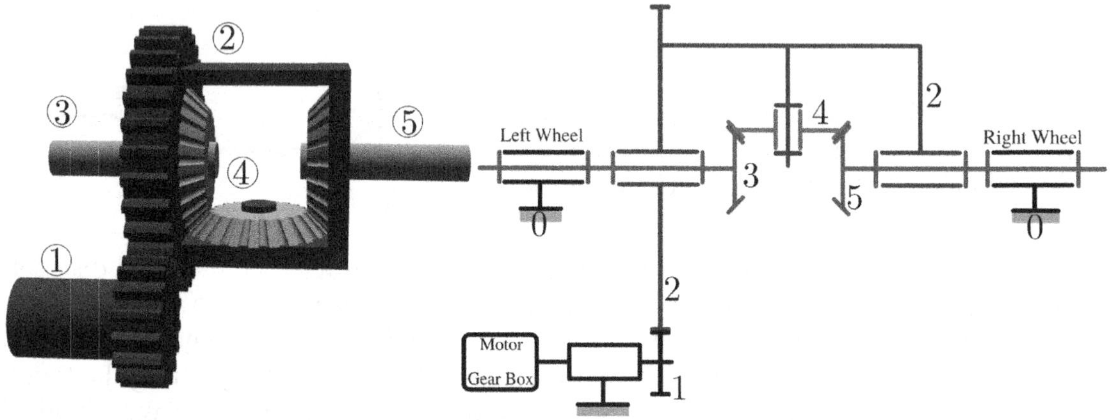

2 is a ring gear/carrier and is in rotation about axis $(O, \hat{\mathbf{x}}_0)$ of 0 ,

3 and 4 are outer gears which are rigidly connected to the shafts driving the left and right wheels,

5 is a satellite gear supported by the carrier 2 and in rotation about axis $(O, \hat{\mathbf{y}}_2)$.

Ring gear 2 is connected to drive-shaft 1 which is terminated by a pinion gear. Denote by R_i the radius of gear i , i=1,2,3,4,5 ($R_3 = R_5$).

Derive the kinematic input/output law, that is, the relationship between the angular velocities $\omega_{3/0}$, $\omega_{4/0}$ and $\omega_{1/0}$.

Problem 8.10 The figure displayed below shows a mechanism which transmits the motion of a body 1 to a body 2 in a referential 0. Body 1 is a disk-shaped roller of center O and radius r which rotates about its axis $(O, \hat{\mathbf{x}}_1)$. Its shaft is mounted on a pivot of axis $(O, \hat{\mathbf{z}}_0)$. Hence the motion of 1 is modeled by two angles θ_1 and ϕ_1. It is in contact at a point I with a cylindrical body 2 of radius R which is free to rotate and translate about its axis $(B, \hat{\mathbf{x}}_0)$. Assume that roller 1 rolls and pivots without slipping on 2 about contact point I.
Find the input/output kinematic relationships of this mechanism, that is, relate the kinematic screw $\{\mathcal{V}_{2/0}\}$ to $\{\mathcal{V}_{1/0}\}$.

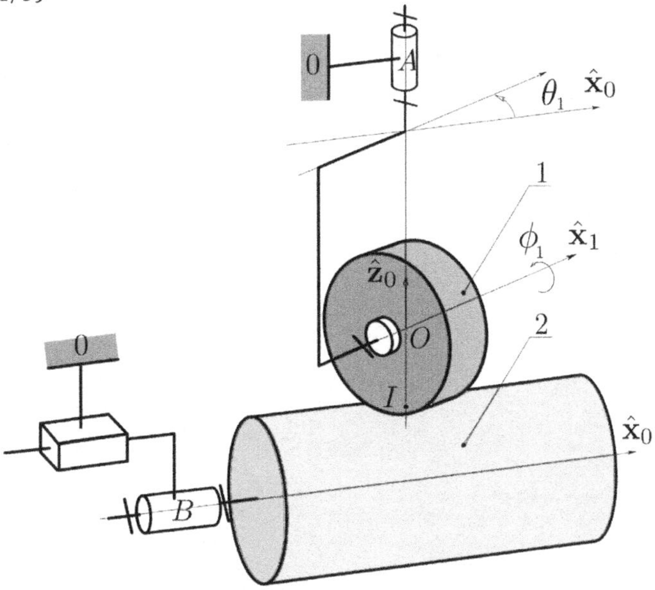

Problem 8.11 A pumpjack (a.k.a. horsehead pump) is used to mechanically pump liquid out of the oil wells. This mechanism converts the uniform rotation of a motor into a vertical reciprocating motion of the pump piston. It comprises four rigid bodies: the crank arm 1, the connecting rod 2, the I-beam 3 (which ends in a curved metal box called *horse head*) and a cable 4 connected to a piston which travels vertically through a stuffing box. During the motion, the cable wraps around the curved part of the horse head without slipping. The configuration of the system is defined by the angles θ_1, θ_2 and θ_3 as shown.

The crank arm rotates at constant angular velocity ω_1. Define $|OA| = L_1$, $|AB| = L_2$, $|BC| = L_3$. The joints at O, A, B and C are pivots. By finding the piston's velocity $\mathbf{v}_{E\in 4}$ in terms of ω_1 we can determine the flow rate of the pump.

a. Find $\mathbf{v}_{E\in 4}$ by a vectorial method in terms of the geometrical parameters θ_1, θ_2, θ_3, L_1, L_2, L_3. Does the piston travel at constant speed? Find $|\mathbf{v}_{E\in 4}|$ for the numerical values $\omega_1 = 0.025$ rev/s, $\theta_1 = 30°$, $L_1 = 5$ m, $L_2 = 14$ m, $L_3 = 7.75$ m, $H = 11.5$ m, $R = 12$ m, $D = R$, $L = 7$ m.

b. Repeat question a) by using a graphical method with the concept of instantaneous center of rotation.

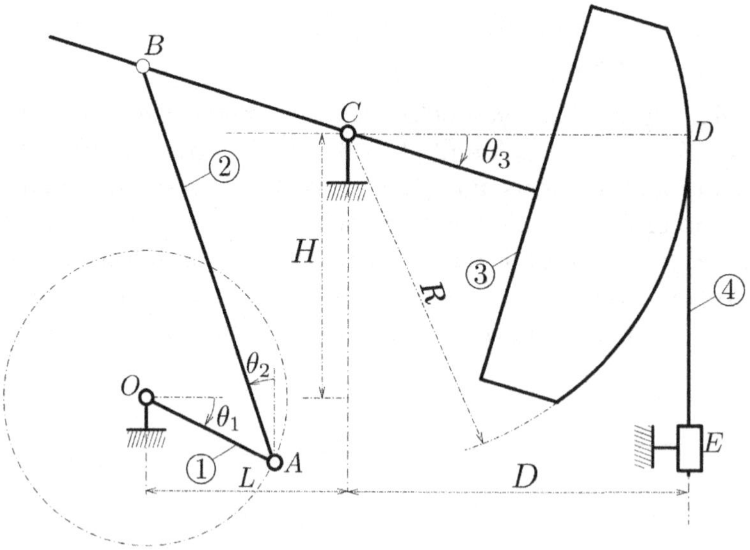
B
C
D
θ_3
②
H
③
R
④
θ_2
O
θ_1
①
L
A
D
E

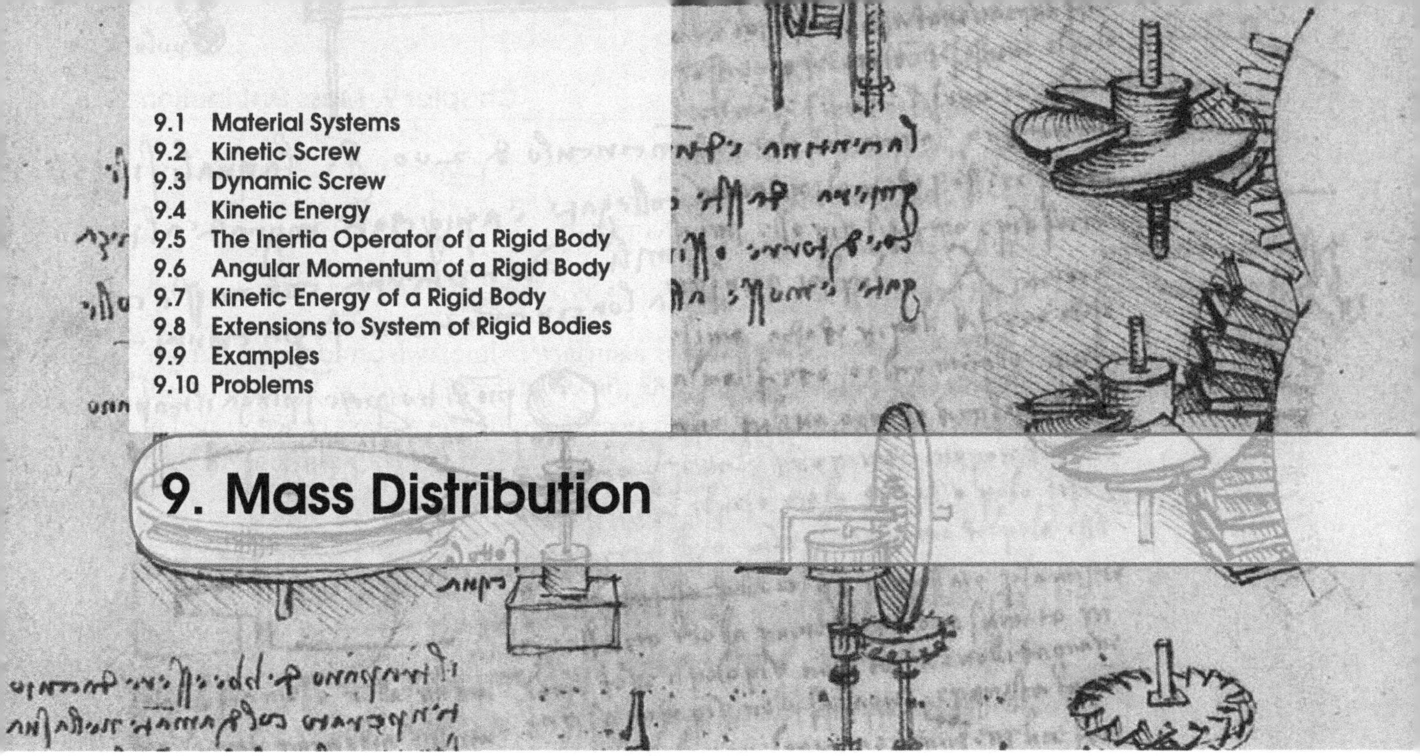

9. Mass Distribution

In this chapter, we are still not concerned with relating the motion of mechanical systems to the causes responsible for such motion. The dynamic behavior of a rigid body depends upon the manner in which mass is distributed over its volume. We introduce the concept of *mass* for an arbitrary continuum. In fact, we shall consider at first arbitrary (deformable) material systems for which much of the notions defined in this chapter are relevant. The standard assumption of classical mechanics is that the system's mass remains constant. After defining the notion of *center of mass*, we tie the concept of mass to such kinematic quantities as the velocity and acceleration fields to define *kinetic* quantities, namely the *linear momentum*, *angular momentum*, *dynamic moment*, and *kinetic energy* of a material system. More specifically, we shall define two vector fields of kinetic nature, leading to two screws: the *kinetic* and *dynamic screws*. The angular momentum is not readily determined for arbitrary material systems. However, for rigid bodies, its determination is straightforward due to the simple (screw) nature of the velocity field. We shall show that the angular momentum and kinetic energy of a rigid body can be calculated from the body's *inertia operator* which quantifies its mass distribution.

9.1 Material Systems

Definition 9.1 A material system Σ is a continuum for which a positive measure m, called *mass measure* (or mass distribution), can be defined at all points P of Σ. It quantifies matter within Σ in a macroscopic manner. It is assumed regular, so that there exists a function $\rho(P)$, called mass density, such that $dm = \rho(P)dV$ for all elementary volume dV of Σ. Furthermore, the mass of system Σ is assumed conserved, that is, for any subset σ

of Σ,

$$m_\sigma = \int_\sigma dm = \text{constant}$$

at all time during the motion of Σ.

If the material system Σ can be approximated as a surface (a line), we can define a surface mass density $\sigma(P)$ (linear mass density $\lambda(P)$) by $dm = \sigma(P)dA \quad (dm = \lambda(P)dl)$ for all surface element dA (line element dl) at P. It is also possible to define a mass concentrated at a point Q of $\mathcal{E}$ by the relationship $dm = m_Q\delta(Q)dV$ where m_Q is the total mass concentrated at Q and $\delta(Q)$ is the Dirac function based at Q.

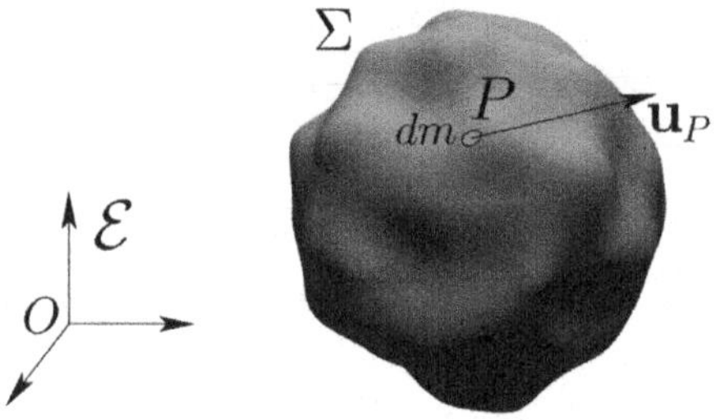

Figure 9.1

A consequence of mass conservation is the following result, which will often be used.

Corollary 9.1 Given a material system Σ in motion relative to referential $\mathcal{E}$, then, for any vector field $P \in \Sigma \mapsto \mathbf{u}_P$, we have

$$\frac{d}{dt}\left[\int_\Sigma \mathbf{u}_P\, dm\right]_\mathcal{E} = \int_\Sigma \left[\frac{d\mathbf{u}_P}{dt}\right]_\mathcal{E} dm \tag{9.1}$$

Proof. We use Reynolds transport theorem for the material time derivative of integrals over a time-varying material volume Σ bounded by the surface $\partial\Sigma$:

$$\frac{d}{dt}\int_\Sigma h\rho dV = \int_\Sigma \frac{\partial}{\partial t}(\rho h)dV + \int_{\partial\Sigma} \rho h \mathbf{v}_P \cdot \hat{\mathbf{n}} dA$$

where h is a scalar field defined on Σ, $\mathbf{v}_P \equiv \mathbf{v}_{P/\mathcal{E}}$ is the velocity of material points of Σ and $\hat{\mathbf{n}}$ is the outward unit normal to $\partial\Sigma$. Upon using the divergence theorem, we find

$$\frac{d}{dt}\int_\Sigma h\rho dV = \int_\Sigma [\frac{\partial}{\partial t}(\rho h) + \nabla \cdot (\rho h \mathbf{v}_P)]dV = \int_\Sigma [\frac{\partial h}{\partial t} + \mathbf{v}_P \cdot \nabla h]dm + \int_\Sigma h[\frac{\partial \rho}{\partial t} + \nabla \cdot (\rho \mathbf{v}_P)]dV$$

In the last equation, the expression $\frac{\partial h}{\partial t} + \mathbf{v}_P \cdot \nabla h$ is the total time derivative of h. Furthermore, the quantity $\frac{\partial \rho}{\partial t} + \nabla \cdot (\rho \mathbf{v}_P)$ vanishes as a consequence of mass conservation (this is known as the continuity equation). Finally, we obtain

$$\frac{d}{dt}\int_\Sigma h dm = \int_\Sigma \frac{dh}{dt} dm$$

This result can then be generalized to vector fields. ■

Next, we introduce the notion of mass center.

Definition 9.2 The *mass center* G of material system Σ is the unique point satisfying

$$\int_{\Sigma} \mathbf{r}_{GP}\, dm = \mathbf{0}$$

Corollary 9.2 The position of G is given by:

$$\mathbf{r}_{QG} = \frac{1}{m} \int_{\Sigma} \mathbf{r}_{QP}\, dm \tag{9.2}$$

where Q is an arbitrary point and m is the total mass of Σ.

If the system is assumed homogeneous, that is, if its mass density ρ is uniform, then its mass center G coincides with the *centroid* of the geometric figure occupied by Σ and its position is often available in tables for commonly found shapes.

If a system Σ of mass m can be regarded as composed of N disjoint parts $\Sigma_1, \ldots, \Sigma_N$, of known mass m_i and mass center G_i $(i = 1, \ldots, N)$, then the mass center of Σ coincides with the mass center of the system of particles $\{G_1, \ldots, G_N\}$ of mass $m_1, \ldots, m_N$ respectively:

$$\mathbf{r}_{OG} = \frac{1}{m}(m_1 \mathbf{r}_{OG_1} + m_2 \mathbf{r}_{OG_2} + \cdots + m_N \mathbf{r}_{OG_N})$$

Also note that if Σ possesses a plane Π of material symmetry, that is, the mass distribution satisfies $\rho(Q) = \rho(P)$ for $Q = \mathrm{Sym}_{\Pi}(P)$ obtained by symmetry with respect to Π, then the mass center G must belong to Π. See Figure 9.2.

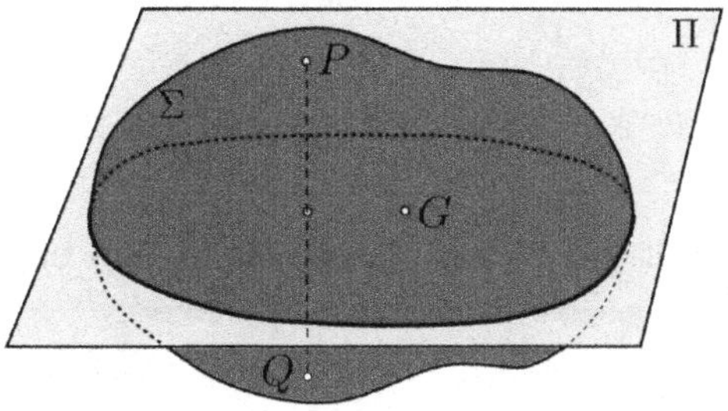

Figure 9.2

Finally recall Pappus' centroid theorems:

1. If a planar curve $\mathcal{C}$ of mass center G and of length L is rotated about an axis Δ which does not intersect $\mathcal{C}$, then the area A of the generated surface is given by $A = 2\pi L\,|GH|$, where H is the projection of G on Δ.
2. If a plane figure of mass center G and area A is rotated about an axis Δ then the volume V of the generated solid body is equal to the product of area A with the distance traveled by G: $V = 2\pi A\,|GH|$.

9.2 Kinetic Screw

Recall from Section 4.8 that, given a vector field $\mathbf{u}_P$ defined over a material system Σ, the vector field defined by

$$A \mapsto \int_\Sigma \mathbf{r}_{AP} \times \mathbf{u}_P \, dm.$$

defines a screw whose resultant is $\int_\Sigma \mathbf{u}_P \, dm$. We can define two screws in this manner by choosing first the velocity then the acceleration fields of Σ relative to a referential $\mathcal{E}$. Keep in mind that system Σ is not necessarily a rigid body.

The first such screw is obtained by choosing $\mathbf{u}_P = \mathbf{v}_{P/\mathcal{E}}$.

Definition 9.3 — Kinetic Screw. The *kinetic screw* of material system Σ is the screw denoted $\{\mathcal{H}_{\Sigma/\mathcal{E}}\}$ corresponding to the vector field $A \mapsto \mathbf{H}_{A,\Sigma/\mathcal{E}} = \int_\Sigma \mathbf{r}_{AP} \times \mathbf{v}_{P/\mathcal{E}} \, dm$. Its resultant, called *linear momentum* of Σ (relative to $\mathcal{E}$), is given by

$$\mathbf{L}_{\Sigma/\mathcal{E}} = \int_\Sigma \mathbf{v}_{P/\mathcal{E}} \, dm. \tag{9.3}$$

Moment $\mathbf{H}_{A,\Sigma/\mathcal{E}}$ is called *angular momentum* of system Σ relative to $\mathcal{E}$ about point A.

We may denote the angular momentum (also known as the *moment of momentum*) simply as $\mathbf{H}_{A,\Sigma}$, or even $\mathbf{H}_A$ when the context permits it.

Theorem 9.1 — Linear Momentum of a Material System. The linear momentum (relative to referential $\mathcal{E}$) of a material system Σ of mass m and mass center G is equal to the linear momentum of a fictitious particle of mass m coinciding with G

$$\int_\Sigma \mathbf{v}_{P/\mathcal{E}} \, dm = m\mathbf{v}_{G/\mathcal{E}} \tag{9.4}$$

Hence, the kinetic screw of Σ can be written in the following form

$$\{\mathcal{H}_{\Sigma/\mathcal{E}}\} = \begin{Bmatrix} m\mathbf{v}_{G/\mathcal{E}} \\ \mathbf{H}_A \end{Bmatrix} \tag{9.5}$$

and the screw property of the angular momentum can be stated in the form

$$\mathbf{H}_A = \mathbf{H}_B + \mathbf{r}_{AB} \times m\mathbf{v}_{G/\mathcal{E}} \tag{9.6}$$

between any two points A and B.

Proof. By definition, we have for any point O fixed in $\mathcal{E}$, $m\mathbf{r}_{OG} = \int_\Sigma \mathbf{r}_{OP} \, dm$, and upon taking the time derivative in $\mathcal{E}$ (using 9.1), we obtain

$$\left(\frac{d}{dt}\int_\Sigma \mathbf{r}_{OP} \, dm\right)_\mathcal{E} = \left(\frac{d}{dt} m\mathbf{r}_{OG}\right)_\mathcal{E} = m\mathbf{v}_{G/\mathcal{E}}$$

recalling that the mass of system Σ is constant. ■

Hence, we have at hand an easy way of determining the linear momentum of a system Σ

from the kinematics of a single particle, the mass center of Σ. The angular momentum of Σ is more difficult to determine for arbitrary material systems. However, for a rigid body $\mathcal{B}$, its determination is straightforward thanks to the screw property of the velocity field $P \in \mathcal{B} \mapsto \mathbf{v}_{P/\mathcal{E}}$. Before we devote our attention to its calculation, we introduce another screw which will play a fundamental role in dynamics.

9.3 Dynamic Screw

Definition 9.4 — Dynamic Screw. The *dynamic screw* of material system Σ relative to referential $\mathcal{E}$ is the screw denoted $\{\mathcal{D}_{\Sigma/\mathcal{E}}\}$ corresponding to the vector field $A \mapsto \mathbf{D}_{A,\Sigma/\mathcal{E}} = \int_\Sigma \mathbf{r}_{AP} \times \mathbf{a}_{P/\mathcal{E}}\, dm$. Its resultant is the vector

$$\int_\Sigma \mathbf{a}_{P/\mathcal{E}}\, dm = m\mathbf{a}_{G/\mathcal{E}} \tag{9.7}$$

Moment $\mathbf{D}_{A,\Sigma/\mathcal{E}}$ is called the *dynamic moment* of Σ relative to $\mathcal{E}$ about point A.

Again, we may denote dynamic moments simply as $\mathbf{D}_{A,\Sigma}$, or even $\mathbf{D}_A$. Dynamic moments about any two points are related by the formula

$$\mathbf{D}_A = \mathbf{D}_B + \mathbf{r}_{AB} \times m\mathbf{a}_{G/\mathcal{E}} \tag{9.8}$$

The dynamic screw plays a fundamental role in the laws of motion of material systems, as will be seen in Chapter 11. Its determination is easily made by relating the dynamic moment to the corresponding angular momentum. This relationship is defined in the following theorem.

Theorem 9.2 The dynamic screw of system Σ is the time-derivative of its kinetic screw:

$$\{\mathcal{D}_{\Sigma/\mathcal{E}}\} = \{\tfrac{d}{dt}\mathcal{H}_{\Sigma/\mathcal{E}}\}_\mathcal{E} \tag{9.9}$$

according to definition (4.16).

Proof. We can relate dynamic moment to angular momentum by taking the time derivative (relative to $\mathcal{E}$) of the expression $\mathbf{H}_A = \int_\Sigma \mathbf{r}_{AP} \times \mathbf{v}_{P/\mathcal{E}}\, dm$ to obtain (using property 9.1)

$$\frac{d}{dt}\mathbf{H}_A = \int_\Sigma \frac{d}{dt}(\mathbf{r}_{AP} \times \mathbf{v}_{P/\mathcal{E}})\, dm = \int_\Sigma (\mathbf{v}_{P/\mathcal{E}} - \mathbf{v}_{A/\mathcal{E}}) \times \mathbf{v}_{P/\mathcal{E}}\, dm + \int_\Sigma \mathbf{r}_{AP} \times \mathbf{a}_{P/\mathcal{E}}\, dm$$

The first integral is recognized to be $m\mathbf{v}_{G/\mathcal{E}} \times \mathbf{v}_{A/\mathcal{E}}$ since $\int_\Sigma \mathbf{v}_{P/\mathcal{E}}\, dm = m\mathbf{v}_{G/\mathcal{E}}$ as obtained by taking the time derivative of $m\mathbf{r}_{OG}$. The second integral is recognized to be the dynamic moment $\mathbf{D}_A$ about point A. Finally, we obtain for any point A (in motion or not) the following formula:

$$\mathbf{D}_A = \left(\frac{d\mathbf{H}_A}{dt}\right)_\mathcal{E} + \mathbf{v}_{A/\mathcal{E}} \times m\mathbf{v}_{G/\mathcal{E}} \tag{9.10}$$

The r.h.s. of (9.10) is precisely the moment of screw $\left\{\frac{d}{dt}\mathcal{H}_{\Sigma/\mathcal{E}}\right\}_{\mathcal{E}}$ about A. It is straightforward to prove the equality of the resultants in (9.9). ■

Whenever applied to a rigid body $\mathcal{B}$, velocity $\mathbf{v}_{A/\mathcal{E}}$ present in (9.10) is to be found as $(d\mathbf{r}_{OA}/dt)_{\mathcal{E}}$ and not to be confused with $\mathbf{v}_{A\in\mathcal{B}/\mathcal{E}}$: point A is not necessarily attached to $\mathcal{B}$.

Remark 1. Formula (9.10) is important in practice: it shows that the dynamic moment are easily found from the corresponding angular momentum.

Remark 2. Note the following special cases of equation (9.10):

1. If point A is fixed relative to $\mathcal{E}$, $\mathbf{v}_{A/\mathcal{E}} = \mathbf{0}$. Then

$$\mathbf{D}_A = \left(\frac{d\mathbf{H}_A}{dt}\right)_{\mathcal{E}} \tag{9.11}$$

2. If A is the mass center G, then $\mathbf{v}_{A/\mathcal{E}} \times m\mathbf{v}_{G/\mathcal{E}} = \mathbf{0}$ leading to

$$\mathbf{D}_G = \left(\frac{d\mathbf{H}_G}{dt}\right)_{\mathcal{E}} \tag{9.12}$$

Remark 3. If we combine equations (9.12) and (9.8) of the dynamic screw, we obtain the relationship

$$\mathbf{D}_A = \left(\frac{d\mathbf{H}_G}{dt}\right)_{\mathcal{E}} + \mathbf{r}_{AG} \times m\mathbf{a}_{G/\mathcal{E}} \tag{9.13}$$

This relationship is very useful since it allows the determination of any dynamic moment from the knowledge of kinematics and kinetics about the mass center G.

9.4 Kinetic Energy

The kinetic energy of particle P of Σ of mass dm relative to $\mathcal{E}$ is defined as $\frac{1}{2}\mathbf{v}^2_{P/\mathcal{E}}\, dm$. This leads to the following definition.

Definition 9.5 The kinetic energy of material system Σ in $\mathcal{E}$ is defined as the scalar quantity

$$\mathbb{K}_{\Sigma/\mathcal{E}} = \frac{1}{2}\int_{\Sigma} \mathbf{v}^2_{P/\mathcal{E}}\, dm \tag{9.14}$$

In general, the determination of the kinetic energy of a material system is not a straightforward task, except in the case of a rigid body or system of rigid bodies, as will be shown in Section 9.7.

The remainder of the chapter is devoted to the kinetics of rigid bodies. Pivotal to the determination of angular momentum and kinetic energy is the notion of inertia operator.

9.5 The Inertia Operator of a Rigid Body

Consider now a *rigid body* $\mathcal{B}$ (of mass center G, and mass m) in motion in a referential $\mathcal{E}$. We show here that the determination of the angular momentum of body $\mathcal{B}$ depends on the mass distribution of $\mathcal{B}$ through the definition of its *inertia operator*.

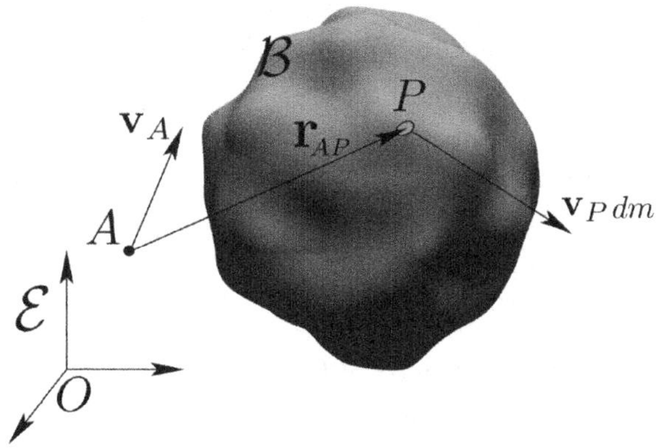

Figure 9.3

Consider an arbitrary point A about which the angular momentum $\mathbf{H}_A = \mathbf{H}_{A,\mathcal{B}/\mathcal{E}}$ is sought. Point A may be in motion relative to $\mathcal{E}$, and is in general not necessarily attached to $\mathcal{B}$. In the expression

$$\mathbf{H}_A = \int_{\mathcal{B}} \mathbf{r}_{AP} \times \mathbf{v}_P\, dm$$

we can relate the velocity of generic point P to that of a particular point attached to $\mathcal{B}$. Denote the chosen point as B. Then

$$\mathbf{v}_P = \mathbf{v}_{B\in\mathcal{B}} + \boldsymbol{\omega}_{\mathcal{B}} \times \mathbf{r}_{BP}$$

We then obtain two integrals. The first integral $\int_{\mathcal{B}} \mathbf{r}_{AP} \times \mathbf{v}_{B\in\mathcal{B}}\, dm$ is readily shown to be $m\mathbf{r}_{AG} \times \mathbf{v}_{B\in\mathcal{B}}$. We then express the second integral by writing $\mathbf{r}_{AP} = \mathbf{r}_{AB} + \mathbf{r}_{BP}$:

$$\int_{\mathcal{B}} (\mathbf{r}_{AB} + \mathbf{r}_{BP}) \times (\boldsymbol{\omega}_{\mathcal{B}} \times \mathbf{r}_{BP})\, dm = \int_{\mathcal{B}} \mathbf{r}_{AB} \times (\boldsymbol{\omega}_{\mathcal{B}} \times \mathbf{r}_{BP})\, dm + \int_{\mathcal{B}} \mathbf{r}_{BP} \times (\boldsymbol{\omega}_{\mathcal{B}} \times \mathbf{r}_{BP})\, dm$$

In this last equation, the first term is simply $m\mathbf{r}_{AB} \times (\boldsymbol{\omega}_{\mathcal{B}} \times \mathbf{r}_{BG})$. We are left with the integral $\int_{\mathcal{B}} \mathbf{r}_{BP} \times (\boldsymbol{\omega}_{\mathcal{B}} \times \mathbf{r}_{BP})\, dm$ which leads us to define the notion of *inertia operator*.

Definition 9.6 — Inertia Operator. The *inertia operator*, denoted $\mathcal{I}_B$, of rigid body $\mathcal{B}$ about point B is the operator defined by

$$\mathbf{V} \xrightarrow{\mathcal{I}_B} \int_{\mathcal{B}} \mathbf{r}_{BP} \times (\mathbf{V} \times \mathbf{r}_{BP})\, dm_P = \mathcal{I}_B(\mathbf{V}) \tag{9.15}$$

Whenever we face system of rigid bodies, we shall use the notation $\mathcal{I}_{B,i}$ for the inertia operator of body $\mathcal{B}_i$.

Theorem 9.3 Operator $\mathcal{I}_B$ is a linear, symmetric operator.

Proof. The linearity of $\mathcal{I}_B$ follows from the properties of the cross-product. Its symmetry is readily shown by writing

$$\mathbf{r}_{BP} \times (\mathbf{V} \times \mathbf{r}_{BP}) = \mathbf{r}_{BP}^2\mathbf{V} - (\mathbf{r}_{BP} \cdot \mathbf{V})\mathbf{r}_{BP}$$

leading to

$$\mathbf{U} \cdot \mathcal{I}_B(\mathbf{V}) = \mathbf{V} \cdot \mathcal{I}_B(\mathbf{U})$$

for any two vectors **U** and **V**. ■

In practice, the determination of $\mathcal{I}_B$ is done by choosing a basis of unit vectors $b(\hat{\mathbf{x}}, \hat{\mathbf{y}}, \hat{\mathbf{z}})$ (not necessarily attached to $\mathcal{B}$). By writing $\mathbf{r}_{BP} = x\hat{\mathbf{x}} + y\hat{\mathbf{y}} + z\hat{\mathbf{z}}$, it is possible to determine the corresponding matrix representation of the inertia operator $\mathcal{I}_B$ on this basis. With the determination of the triple products

$$\begin{aligned}
\mathbf{r}_{BP} \times (\hat{\mathbf{x}} \times \mathbf{r}_{BP}) &= (y^2 + z^2)\hat{\mathbf{x}} - xy\,\hat{\mathbf{y}} - xz\,\hat{\mathbf{z}} \\
\mathbf{r}_{BP} \times (\hat{\mathbf{y}} \times \mathbf{r}_{BP}) &= -xy\,\hat{\mathbf{x}} + (x^2 + z^2)\hat{\mathbf{y}} - yz\,\hat{\mathbf{z}} \\
\mathbf{r}_{BP} \times (\hat{\mathbf{z}} \times \mathbf{r}_{BP}) &= -xz\,\hat{\mathbf{x}} - yz\,\hat{\mathbf{y}} + (x^2 + y^2)\hat{\mathbf{z}}
\end{aligned}$$

the symmetric matrix $[\mathcal{I}_B]_b$, called *inertia matrix* about B on basis $b(\hat{\mathbf{x}}, \hat{\mathbf{y}}, \hat{\mathbf{z}})$ of body $\mathcal{B}$, is found to be:

$$[\mathcal{I}_B]_b = \begin{bmatrix} \int_{\mathcal{B}}(y^2 + z^2)\,dm & -\int_{\mathcal{B}} xy\,dm & -\int_{\mathcal{B}} xz\,dm \\ -\int_{\mathcal{B}} xy\,dm & \int_{\mathcal{B}}(x^2 + z^2)\,dm & -\int_{\mathcal{B}} yz\,dm \\ -\int_{\mathcal{B}} xz\,dm & -\int_{\mathcal{B}} yz\,dm & \int_{\mathcal{B}}(x^2 + y^2)\,dm \end{bmatrix}_b = \begin{bmatrix} I_{Bx} & I_{Bxy} & I_{Bxz} \\ I_{Bxy} & I_{By} & I_{Byz} \\ I_{Bxz} & I_{Byz} & I_{Bz} \end{bmatrix}_b$$

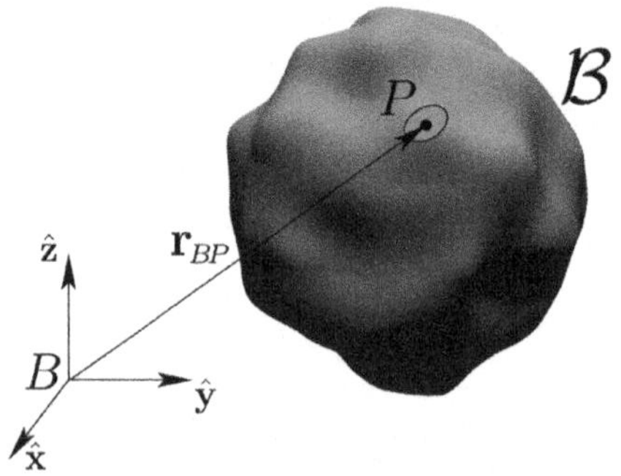

Figure 9.4

Definition 9.7 — Moments and Products of Inertia. The diagonal element I_{Bx}, I_{By} and I_{Bz} of inertia matrix $[\mathcal{I}_B]_b$ are called *moments of inertia* with respect to axis $(B, \hat{\mathbf{x}})$, axis $(B, \hat{\mathbf{y}})$, and axis $(B, \hat{\mathbf{z}})$, respectively. They are given by the inertia operator $\mathcal{I}_B$ according to

$$I_{Bx} = \hat{\mathbf{x}} \cdot \mathcal{I}_B(\hat{\mathbf{x}}), \quad I_{By} = \hat{\mathbf{y}} \cdot \mathcal{I}_B(\hat{\mathbf{y}}), \quad I_{Bz} = \hat{\mathbf{z}} \cdot \mathcal{I}_B(\hat{\mathbf{z}}) \tag{9.16}$$

The off-diagonal terms I_{Bxy}, I_{Bxz}, and I_{Byz}, are called *products of inertia* of $\mathcal{B}$ with respect to rectangular axes $Bxyz$. They are given by the inertia operator $\mathcal{I}_B$ according to

$$\begin{aligned}
I_{Byz} &= \hat{\mathbf{z}} \cdot \mathcal{I}_B(\hat{\mathbf{y}}) = \hat{\mathbf{y}} \cdot \mathcal{I}_B(\hat{\mathbf{z}}) \\
I_{Bxz} &= \hat{\mathbf{x}} \cdot \mathcal{I}_B(\hat{\mathbf{z}}) = \hat{\mathbf{z}} \cdot \mathcal{I}_B(\hat{\mathbf{x}}) \\
I_{Bxy} &= \hat{\mathbf{x}} \cdot \mathcal{I}_B(\hat{\mathbf{y}}) = \hat{\mathbf{y}} \cdot \mathcal{I}_B(\hat{\mathbf{x}})
\end{aligned} \tag{9.17}$$

Remark 4. Moment I_{Bx} is not specific to point B but rather to axis $(B, \hat{\mathbf{x}})$: indeed the integrand $(y^2 + z^2)$ is the squared distance from point P to axis $(B, \hat{\mathbf{x}})$.

Remark 5. The basis $b(\hat{\mathbf{x}}, \hat{\mathbf{y}}, \hat{\mathbf{z}})$ is generally taken as fixed to rigid body $\mathcal{B}$. The corresponding matrix of inertia is then independent of time when $\mathcal{B}$ is in motion relative to referential $\mathcal{E}$. However, the matrix of inertia may still be independent of time for a basis not fixed to $\mathcal{B}$ in special cases of symmetry.

Remark 6. There is no simple physical interpretation of the products of inertia. In fact, they can always be found to vanish with an appropriate choice of axes for the representation of $\mathcal{I}_B$, as shown by the following result.

Theorem 9.4 — Principal Axes of Inertia. For any point B, there always exists a basis $(\hat{\mathbf{x}}_p, \hat{\mathbf{y}}_p, \hat{\mathbf{z}}_p)$, called *principal basis of inertia* at point B, such that the corresponding inertia matrix is diagonal, that is, for which the products of inertia are zero. The corresponding moments of inertia are then called *principal moments of inertia.*

Proof. This result is a consequence of the symmetry of operator $\mathcal{I}_B$. ■

Remark 7. The diagonal elements of the inertia matrix $[\mathcal{I}_B]_b$ on basis $b(\hat{\mathbf{x}}, \hat{\mathbf{y}}, \hat{\mathbf{z}})$ define three moments of inertia about the rectangular axes $Bxyz$. Operator $\mathcal{I}_B$ can actually lead to the determination of any moment of inertia about any axis Δ passing through B. In view of the expressions of moments of inertia I_{Bx}, I_{By} and I_{Bz}, moment of inertia I_Δ is defined as

$$I_\Delta = \int_{\mathcal{B}} \mathbf{r}_{HP}^2 \, dm \tag{9.18}$$

where point H is the projection of $P \in \mathcal{B}$ onto axis Δ. See Figure 9.4. Its determination is given by the following theorem.

Theorem 9.5 — Moment of inertia about an axis Δ. The moment of inertia I_Δ of body $\mathcal{B}$ about an axis Δ passing through B is given by operator $\mathcal{I}_B$ according to

$$I_\Delta = \hat{\mathbf{u}} \cdot \mathcal{I}_B(\hat{\mathbf{u}}) \tag{9.19}$$

where $\hat{\mathbf{u}}$ is a unit vector of Δ.

Proof. The proof hinges on the determination of the squared distance $\mathbf{r}_{HP}^2$:

$$\begin{aligned} \mathbf{r}_{HP}^2 &= \mathbf{r}_{BP}^2 - \mathbf{r}_{BH}^2 = \hat{\mathbf{u}}^2 \mathbf{r}_{BP}^2 - (\mathbf{r}_{BP} \cdot \hat{\mathbf{u}})^2 = \hat{\mathbf{u}} \cdot \left(\mathbf{r}_{BP}^2 \hat{\mathbf{u}} - (\mathbf{r}_{BP} \cdot \hat{\mathbf{u}}) \mathbf{r}_{BP}\right) \\ &= \hat{\mathbf{u}} \cdot (\mathbf{r}_{BP} \times (\hat{\mathbf{u}} \times \mathbf{r}_{BP})) \end{aligned}$$

This result immediately gives (9.19). ■

As a special case, we verify that the moment I_{Bx} can be obtained as $\hat{\mathbf{x}} \cdot \mathcal{I}_B(\hat{\mathbf{x}})$ according to (9.19) by choosing $\hat{\mathbf{u}} = \hat{\mathbf{x}}$.

Finally, we ask if the inertia operators of a given body can be related from one point to another. The answer is provided by the so-called *parallel axis theorem*: it relates the inertia operator $\mathcal{I}_B$ about point B of $\mathcal{B}$ to inertia operator $\mathcal{I}_G$ about mass center G.

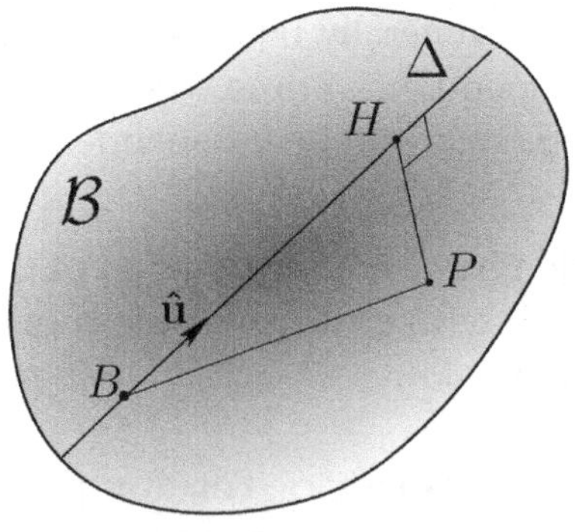

Figure 9.5

Theorem 9.6 — Parallel Axis Theorem. The inertia operator $\mathcal{I}_B$ about point B of body $\mathcal{B}$ can be obtained from inertia operator $\mathcal{I}_G$ about its mass center G according to

$$\mathcal{I}_B(\mathbf{V}) = \mathcal{I}_G(\mathbf{V}) + m\mathbf{r}_{BG} \times (\mathbf{V} \times \mathbf{r}_{BG}) \tag{9.20}$$

for any vector $\mathbf{V}$.

Proof. We start with the definition of $\mathcal{I}_B$ and write vector $\mathbf{r}_{BP}$ as the sum $\mathbf{r}_{BG} + \mathbf{r}_{GP}$:

$$\mathcal{I}_B(\mathbf{V}) = \int_{\mathcal{B}} (\mathbf{r}_{BG} + \mathbf{r}_{GP}) \times (\mathbf{V} \times \mathbf{r}_{BP}) dm = \mathbf{r}_{BG} \times (\mathbf{V} \times \mathbf{r}_{BG}) + \int_{\mathcal{B}} \mathbf{r}_{GP} \times (\mathbf{V} \times \mathbf{r}_{BP}) dm$$

In the last integral, we again write $\mathbf{r}_{BP}$ as the sum $\mathbf{r}_{BG} + \mathbf{r}_{GP}$:

$$\int_{\mathcal{B}} \mathbf{r}_{GP} \times (\mathbf{V} \times \mathbf{r}_{BP}) dm = \int_{\mathcal{B}} \mathbf{r}_{GP} \times (\mathbf{V} \times \mathbf{r}_{BG}) dm + \int_{\mathcal{B}} \mathbf{r}_{GP} \times (\mathbf{V} \times \mathbf{r}_{GP}) dm = \mathcal{I}_G(\mathbf{V})$$

■

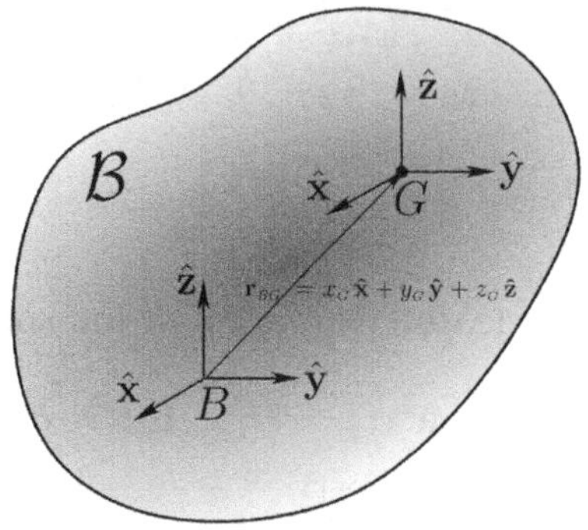

Figure 9.6 – *The Parallel Axis theorem.*

Remark 8. Note that the last term $m\mathbf{r}_{BG} \times (\mathbf{V} \times \mathbf{r}_{BG})$ in equation (9.20) may be viewed as the inertia operator about point B of the "system" defined as particle G of mass m.

Remark 9. The consequence of this result is that knowing the inertia operator about one point B implies the knowledge of the inertia operator about any other point Q:

$$\mathcal{I}_Q(\mathbf{V}) = \mathcal{I}_B(\mathbf{V}) + m\mathbf{r}_{QG} \times (\mathbf{V} \times \mathbf{r}_{QG}) - m\mathbf{r}_{BG} \times (\mathbf{V} \times \mathbf{r}_{BG}) \tag{9.21}$$

Remark 10. By choosing a basis $(\hat{\mathbf{x}}, \hat{\mathbf{y}}, \hat{\mathbf{z}})$, it is possible to relate moments and products of inertia about point B to those about mass center G. See Figure 9.6. For instance the relationship between moment I_{Bx} about axis $(B, \hat{\mathbf{x}})$ and moment I_{Gx} about (parallel) axis $(G, \hat{\mathbf{x}})$ is found to be

$$I_{Bx} = I_{Gx} + m(y_G^2 + z_G^2) \tag{9.22}$$

where $(y_G^2 + z_G^2)$ is seen to be the squared distance between the two axes. Similarly, the products I_{Bxy} and I_{Gxy} are related according to

$$I_{Bxy} = I_{Gxy} - m x_G y_G \tag{9.23}$$

In the form of (9.22-9.23), we can now understand why Theorem 9.6 is referred to as the Parallel Axis theorem.

In practice, it is advantageous to choose a point B and a basis $(\hat{\mathbf{x}}, \hat{\mathbf{y}}, \hat{\mathbf{z}})$ which leads to the simplest determination of the corresponding inertia matrix. One approach consists of exploiting the special characteristics of the rigid body $\mathcal{B}$ at hand, such as material symmetries. Here are three special cases:

Case 1: Body $\mathcal{B}$ admits a plane Π of material symmetry. Then we choose $(B, \hat{\mathbf{x}}, \hat{\mathbf{y}})$ in plane Π and unit vector $\hat{\mathbf{z}}$ normal to Π. See Figure 9.7(a). To any point $P(x, y, z)$ of density $\rho(P)$ corresponds a point $P'(x, y, -z)$ of same density $\rho(P') = \rho(P)$. This leads to the following inertia matrix

$$[\mathcal{I}_B]_b = \begin{bmatrix} I_{Bx} & I_{Bxy} & 0 \\ I_{Bxy} & I_{By} & 0 \\ 0 & 0 & I_{Bz} \end{bmatrix}_b$$

on basis $b(\hat{\mathbf{x}}, \hat{\mathbf{y}}, \hat{\mathbf{z}})$.

Case 2: Body $\mathcal{B}$ is a plate, that is, it can be viewed as a planar figure of negligible thickness. Then we choose $(B, \hat{\mathbf{x}}, \hat{\mathbf{y}})$ as the plane containing $\mathcal{B}$, with $\hat{\mathbf{z}}$ normal to $\mathcal{B}$. See Figure 9.7(b). Points $P \in \mathcal{B}$ are characterized by $\mathbf{r}_{BP} = x\hat{\mathbf{x}} + y\hat{\mathbf{y}}$. This leads to $I_{Bxz} = I_{Byz} = 0$ and $I_{Bz} = I_{Bx} + I_{By}$ and to the following inertia matrix:

$$[\mathcal{I}_B]_b = \begin{bmatrix} I_{Bx} & I_{Bxy} & 0 \\ I_{Bxy} & I_{By} & 0 \\ 0 & 0 & I_{Bx} + I_{By} \end{bmatrix}_b$$

on basis $b(\hat{\mathbf{x}}, \hat{\mathbf{y}}, \hat{\mathbf{z}})$.

Case 3: Body $\mathcal{B}$ admits an axis of revolution $\Delta(B, \hat{\mathbf{z}})$. See Figure 9.7(c). Then the inertia matrix about B is invariant under an arbitrary rotation about axis Δ directed along unit vector $\hat{\mathbf{z}}$. This leads to the following expression

$$[\mathcal{I}_B]_b = \begin{bmatrix} I_{Bx} & 0 & 0 \\ 0 & I_{Bx} & 0 \\ 0 & 0 & I_{Bz} \end{bmatrix}_b$$

on any orthonormal basis $b(-, -, \hat{\mathbf{z}})$ not necessarily attached to $\mathcal{B}$.

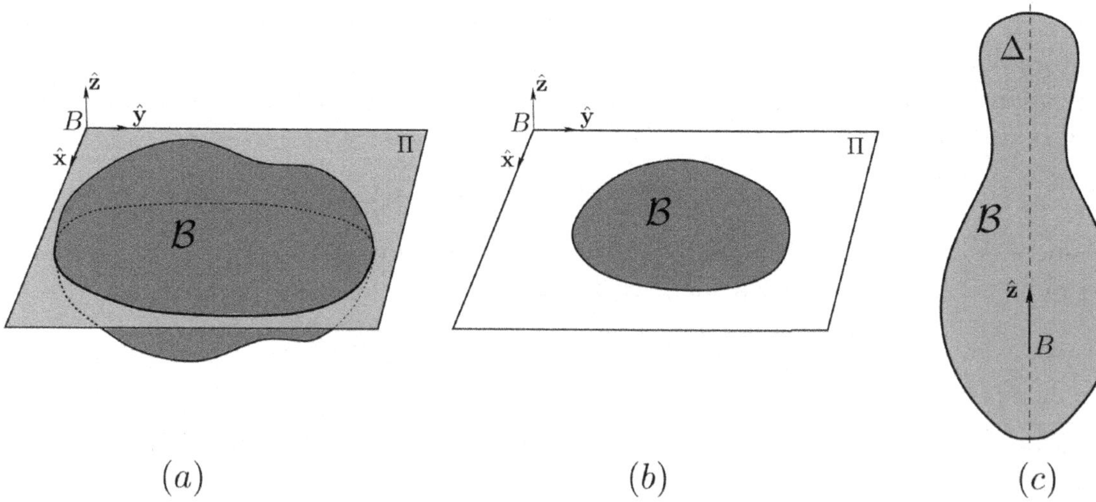

Figure 9.7

The inertia properties of standard shapes are listed in Appendix B. In all cases, a particular set of axes $Bxyz$ is chosen so as to take into account the body's symmetries. The mass density is assumed uniform throughout the body. From this data, we can find moments/products of inertia of more complex bodies by using the extensive property of these quantities:
(i) If rigid body $\mathcal{B}_0 = \mathcal{B}_1 \bigcup \mathcal{B}_2$ is assembled as the union of two bodies $\mathcal{B}_1$ and $\mathcal{B}_2$ without intersection, then

$$I_{Bz,0} = I_{Bz,1} + I_{Bz,2}, \qquad I_{Bxy,0} = I_{Bxy,1} + I_{Bxy,2}$$

(ii) If rigid body $\mathcal{B}_0 = \mathcal{B}_1 \setminus \mathcal{B}_2$ is obtained by removing $\mathcal{B}_2 \subset \mathcal{B}_1$ from body $\mathcal{B}_1$, then

$$I_{Bz,0} = I_{Bz,1} - I_{Bz,2}, \qquad I_{Bxy,0} = I_{Bxy,1} - I_{Bxy,2}$$

This properties is illustrated with the following examples.

Example 9.1 Consider an arbitrary triangle ABC of side lengths a, b and c and mass center G. Show that its moment of inertia about axis Gz is given by

$$I_{Gz} = \frac{m}{36}(a^2 + b^2 + c^2)$$

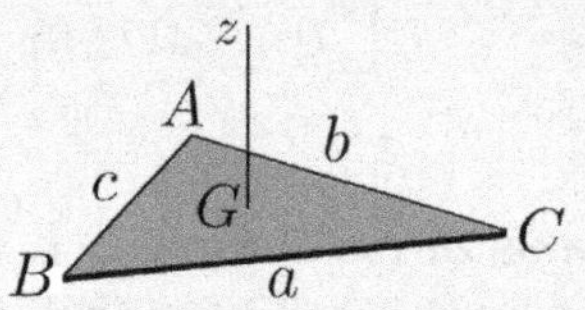

■

We will use a combination of the extensive property of moments of inertia and the Parallel Axis theorem by splitting the triangle into two right-triangular plates of mass center G_1 and G_2 and mass $m_1 = ma_1/a$ and $m_2 = ma_2/a$, respectively. See Figure 9.8. We assume that A can be projected onto side BC to obtain point H. We know the moment of inertia of each right triangle AHB (partition 1) and AHC (partition 2) about H (see Appendix B):

$$I_{Hz,1} = \frac{1}{6}m_1(a_1^2 + h^2), \qquad I_{Hz,2} = \frac{1}{6}m_2(a_2^2 + h^2)$$

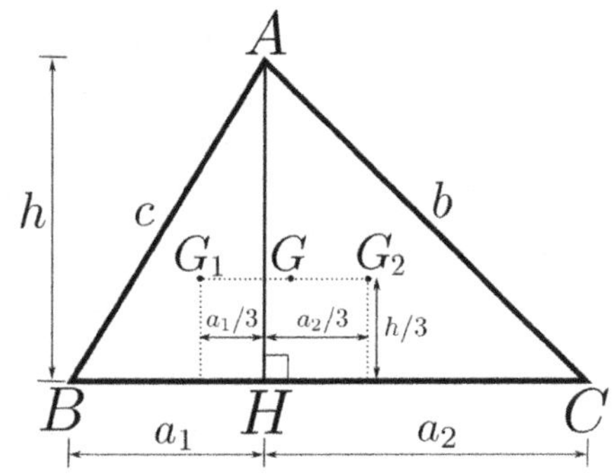

Figure 9.8

Then we use the Parallel Axis theorem to find $I_{G_1z,1}$ and $I_{G_2z,2}$

$$I_{G_1z,1} = I_{Hz,1} - m_1|HG_1|^2 = \frac{1}{6}m_1(a_1^2 + h^2) - \frac{1}{9}m_1(a_1^2 + h^2) = \frac{1}{18}m_1(a_1^2 + h^2) = \frac{1}{18}m_1c^2$$

Similarly $I_{G_2z,2} = \frac{1}{18}m_2b^2$. Next we apply again the Parallel Axis theorem to find $I_{Gz,1}$ and $I_{Gz,2}$ by using

$$|GG_1| = \frac{m_2}{m}|G_1G_2| = \frac{a_2}{3}, \qquad |GG_2| = \frac{m_1}{m}|G_1G_2| = \frac{a_1}{3}$$

leading to

$$I_{Gz,1} = I_{G_1z,1} + \frac{1}{9}m_1a_2^2 = \frac{1}{18}m_1(c^2 + 2a_2^2), \qquad I_{Gz,2} = \frac{1}{18}m_2(b^2 + 2a_1^2)$$

Now we can obtain I_{Gz}:

$$I_{Gz} = I_{Gz,1} + I_{Gz,2} = \frac{1}{18}m_1(c^2 + 2a_2^2) + \frac{1}{18}m_2(b^2 + 2a_1^2)$$

With $m_1 = ma_1/a$ and $m_2 = ma_2/a$ we find

$$I_{Gz} = \frac{m}{18}\frac{a_1c^2 + 2aa_1a_2 + a_2b^2}{a} \qquad [1]$$

Finally we need to express a_1 and a_2 in terms of (a, b, c): in triangle ABC the law of cosines gives (denoting by θ the angle at B)

$$b^2 = c^2 + a^2 - 2ac\cos\theta = c^2 + a^2 - 2aa_1$$

giving

$$a_1 = \frac{c^2 - b^2 + a^2}{2a} \qquad [2]$$

Similarly we find

$$a_2 = \frac{b^2 - c^2 + a^2}{2a} \qquad [3]$$

Finally we substitute (a_1, a_2) of [2-3] into [1]:

$$I_{Gz} = \frac{m}{36a^2}\left(c^2(c^2 - b^2 + a^2) + (c^2 - b^2 + a^2)(b^2 - c^2 + a^2) + b^2(b^2 - c^2 + a^2)\right)$$

After simplifications we find

$$I_{Gz} = \frac{m}{36}(a^2 + b^2 + c^2)$$

■

Example 9.2 Consider the body $\mathcal{B}$ obtained by boring three cylindrical, evenly spaced holes into a cylinder $\mathcal{B}_0$ of axis Oz, radius R and height h. The cylindrical bores $\mathcal{B}_i$ ($i = 1, 2, 3$) have radius r and axis G_iz a distance d from axis Oz. Denote by m the mass and G the mass center of body $\mathcal{B}$.

Show that the inertia matrix of body $\mathcal{B}$ about G has the form

$$[\mathcal{I}_G]_b = \begin{bmatrix} A & 0 & 0 \\ 0 & A & 0 \\ 0 & 0 & C \end{bmatrix}_b$$

on any basis $b(-,-,\hat{\mathbf{z}})$. Then find the moments A and C. ■

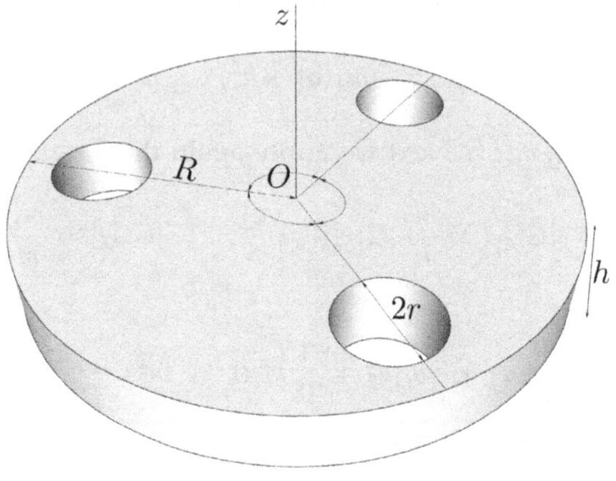

To find the inertia operator $\mathcal{I}_G$ of body $\mathcal{B}$, we must take into account its symmetry. More specifically, the body's mass distribution is invariant under a rotation of angle $\alpha = 2\pi/3$ about axis Oz. This implies that its mass and products of inertia on rectangular axes $Gxyz$ and $GXYZ$ obtained by rotation of angle α about $Oz = OZ$ are identical. See Figure 9.9. This rotation is characterized by the following coordinate transformations:

$$X = x\cos\alpha + y\sin\alpha, \qquad Y = -x\sin\alpha + y\cos\alpha, \qquad Z = z$$

Starting with product of inertia I_{GXY}, we find

$$I_{GXY} = -\int_{\mathcal{B}} XY dm = -\int_{\mathcal{B}} (x\cos\alpha + y\sin\alpha)(-x\sin\alpha + y\cos\alpha) dm = \frac{\sqrt{3}}{4}(I_{Gx} - I_{Gy}) - \frac{1}{2} I_{Gxy}$$

Likewise, for the moments I_{GX} and I_{GY}, we find

$$I_{GX} = \frac{1}{4} I_{Gx} + \frac{3}{4} I_{Gy} - \frac{\sqrt{3}}{2} I_{Gxy}$$

$$I_{GY} = \frac{1}{4} I_{Gy} + \frac{3}{4} I_{Gx} + \frac{\sqrt{3}}{2} I_{Gxy}$$

Upon setting $I_{GXY} = I_{Gxy}$, $I_{GX} = I_{Gx}$ and $I_{GY} = I_{Gy}$, we deduce that

$$I_{Gxy} = 0, \qquad I_{Gx} = I_{Gy} = A$$

Furthermore, the symmetry of the body with respect to plane Gxy, implies that $I_{Gxz} = I_{Gyz} = 0$.

To find the axial moment $C = I_{Gz}$, we use $I_{G_iz,i} = \frac{1}{2} m_1 r^2$ for cylinder $\mathcal{B}_i$ (of mass $m_i = m_1$)

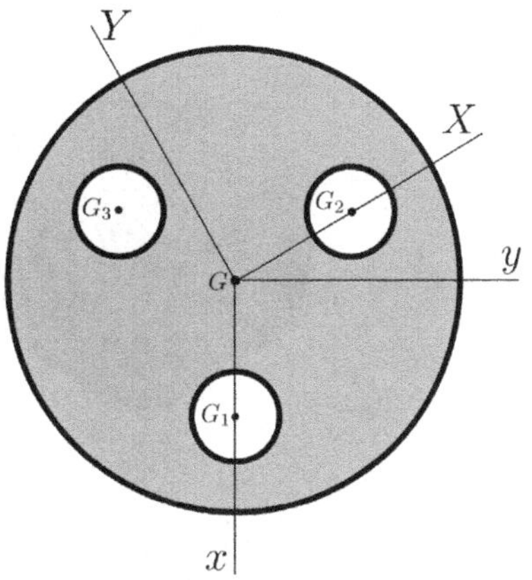

Figure 9.9

leading to $I_{Gz,i} = m_1(r^2/2 + d^2)$. We then impose the equality $I_{Gz} + 3I_{Gz,i} = I_{Gz,0}$ to find

$$C + 3m_1(r^2/2 + d^2) = \tfrac{1}{2} m_0 R^2$$

with $m_0 = m + 3m_1$ and $m_1 = m_0 r^2/R^2$. To find the transverse moment $A = I_{Gx}$, we choose axis Gx to pass through mass center G_1 of cylinder $\mathcal{B}_1$ (as shown in Figure 9.9): then $I_{Gx,1} = I_{G_1x,1} = m_1(r^2/4 + h^2/12)$. For cylinders $\mathcal{B}_2$ and $\mathcal{B}_3$, we find $I_{Gx,2} = I_{Gx,3} = m_1(r^2/4 + h^2/12) + 3m_1 d^2/4$ (using the Parallel Axis Theorem). This gives

$$A + 3m_1(r^2/4 + h^2/12) + 3m_1 d^2/2 = \tfrac{1}{2} m_0 (R^2/4 + h^2/12)$$

■

9.6 Angular Momentum of a Rigid Body

We can now return to the determination of angular momentum $\mathbf{H}_A$ which was started in Section 9.5. Recall that the inertia operator $\mathcal{I}_B$ of body $\mathcal{B}$ about point B is characterized by

$$\mathcal{I}_B(\mathbf{V}) = \int_{\mathcal{B}} \mathbf{r}_{BP} \times (\mathbf{V} \times \mathbf{r}_{BP})\, dm$$

for any vector $\mathbf{V}$. In addition, the velocity field of $\mathcal{B}$ relative to referential $\mathcal{E}$ is entirely described by the kinematic screw $\{\mathcal{V}_{\mathcal{B}/\mathcal{E}}\}$. We found in Section 9.5 that the angular momentum of $\mathcal{B}$ about point A is given by

$$\mathbf{H}_A = m\mathbf{r}_{AG} \times \mathbf{v}_{B\in\mathcal{B}} + m\mathbf{r}_{AB} \times (\boldsymbol{\omega}_{\mathcal{B}} \times \mathbf{r}_{BG}) + \int_{\mathcal{B}} \mathbf{r}_{BP} \times (\boldsymbol{\omega}_{\mathcal{B}} \times \mathbf{r}_{BP})\, dm$$

We now can replace the remaining integral term by $\mathcal{I}_B(\boldsymbol{\omega}_{\mathcal{B}})$. We have thus obtained the most general formula for the determination of the angular momentum of a rigid body.

> Theorem 9.7 — **Angular Momentum of a Rigid Body.** The angular momentum about point A of a rigid body $\mathcal{B}$ of mass m, mass center G, and inertia operator $\mathcal{I}_B$ about point B is given by
>
> $$\mathbf{H}_A = m\mathbf{r}_{AG} \times \mathbf{v}_{B\in\mathcal{B}} + m\mathbf{r}_{AB} \times (\boldsymbol{\omega}_{\mathcal{B}} \times \mathbf{r}_{BG}) + \mathcal{I}_B(\boldsymbol{\omega}_{\mathcal{B}}) \qquad (9.24)$$

Remark 11. In formula (9.24) $\mathbf{v}_{B\in\mathcal{B}}$ may be the velocity of a point attached to $\mathcal{B}$ only instantaneously.

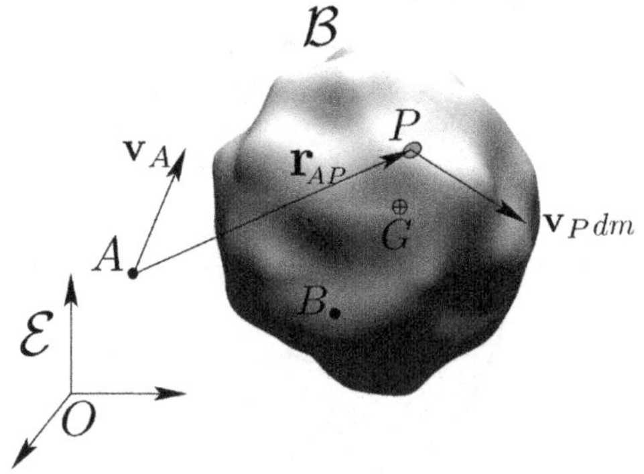

Figure 9.10

Remark 12. The term $\mathcal{I}_B(\boldsymbol{\omega}_{\mathcal{B}})$ in (9.24) is determined in practice by choosing a basis preferably (but not necessarily) attached to $\mathcal{B}$ leading to a matrix representation of operator $\mathcal{I}_B$.

Simplifications can be obtained in formula (9.24) in special cases:

- **Case 1:** $B \equiv G$. Then the second term in (9.24) drops out, and we obtain

$$\mathbf{H}_A = \mathbf{r}_{AG} \times m\mathbf{v}_G + \mathcal{I}_G(\boldsymbol{\omega}_{\mathcal{B}}) \tag{9.25}$$

If we let $A \equiv G$ in this formula, we obtain

$$\mathbf{H}_G = \mathcal{I}_G(\boldsymbol{\omega}_{\mathcal{B}}) \tag{9.26}$$

Note that equation (9.25) can be seen as the property of kinetic screw of $\mathcal{B}$, that is,

$$\mathbf{H}_A = \mathbf{H}_G + \mathbf{r}_{AG} \times m\mathbf{v}_G$$

- **Case 2:** $A \equiv B$. Here again the second term in (9.24) drops out, and we obtain

$$\mathbf{H}_B = \mathbf{r}_{BG} \times m\mathbf{v}_{B\in\mathcal{B}} + \mathcal{I}_B(\boldsymbol{\omega}_{\mathcal{B}}) \tag{9.27}$$

which shows that in general $\mathbf{H}_B \neq \mathcal{I}_B(\boldsymbol{\omega}_{\mathcal{B}})$ unless
(i) B is the mass center G,
(ii) body $\mathcal{B}$ is in rotational motion about point B fixed in both $\mathcal{E}$ and $\mathcal{B}$,
(iii) B is an instantaneous center of rotation (in which case body $\mathcal{B}$ admits an instantaneous axis of rotation).

Finally, recall that the dynamic moment about mass center G is related to angular momentum about G by the equation $\mathbf{D}_G = d\mathbf{H}_G/dt$. It is tempting to then write $\mathbf{D}_G = \frac{d}{dt}(\mathcal{I}_G\boldsymbol{\omega}) = \mathcal{I}_G\boldsymbol{\alpha}$. But this last equality is incorrect.

9.7 Kinetic Energy of a Rigid Body

With the assumptions of Section 9.6, we seek to evaluate the kinetic energy $\mathbb{K}_{\mathcal{B}} = \frac{1}{2}\int_{\mathcal{B}} \mathbf{v}_P^2 dm$ of $\mathcal{B}$ relative to referential $\mathcal{E}$. We can find the velocity of any point P of the body from that of point $B \in \mathcal{B}$:

$$\forall P \in \mathcal{B}, \quad \mathbf{v}_P = \mathbf{v}_{B\in\mathcal{B}} + \boldsymbol{\omega}_{\mathcal{B}} \times \mathbf{r}_{BP}$$

Then, we find

$$\mathbb{K}_\mathcal{B} = \tfrac{1}{2}m\mathbf{v}_{B\in\mathcal{B}}^2 + \mathbf{v}_{B\in\mathcal{B}} \cdot \int_\mathcal{B} \boldsymbol{\omega}_\mathcal{B} \times \mathbf{r}_{BP}\, dm + \tfrac{1}{2}\int_\mathcal{B} (\boldsymbol{\omega}_\mathcal{B} \times \mathbf{r}_{BP})^2\, dm$$

The second term $\int_\mathcal{B} \boldsymbol{\omega}_\mathcal{B} \times \mathbf{r}_{BP}\, dm$ is simply $\boldsymbol{\omega}_\mathcal{B} \times m\mathbf{r}_{BG}$. The third term $\int_\mathcal{B} (\boldsymbol{\omega}_\mathcal{B} \times \mathbf{r}_{BP})^2\, dm$ can be simplified by recalling the identity $(\hat{\mathbf{u}} \times \hat{\mathbf{v}})^2 = \hat{\mathbf{u}} \cdot (\hat{\mathbf{v}} \times (\hat{\mathbf{u}} \times \hat{\mathbf{v}}))$. Hence

$$\int_\mathcal{B} (\boldsymbol{\omega}_\mathcal{B} \times \mathbf{r}_{BP})^2\, dm = \int_\mathcal{B} \boldsymbol{\omega}_\mathcal{B} \cdot (\mathbf{r}_{BP} \times (\boldsymbol{\omega}_\mathcal{B} \times \mathbf{r}_{BP}))\, dm = \boldsymbol{\omega}_\mathcal{B} \cdot \mathcal{I}_\mathcal{B}(\boldsymbol{\omega}_\mathcal{B})$$

We have derived the following result:

$(V_P)^2 = (V_B + \omega \times r_{BM})^2 \qquad K = \tfrac{1}{2}\int V_P^2\, dm$

> **Theorem 9.8 — Kinetic Energy of a Rigid Body.** The kinetic energy of rigid body $\mathcal{B}$ of mass m, mass center G, and inertia operator $\mathcal{I}_\mathcal{B}$ about point B is given by
>
> $V_\mathcal{B} -$
>
> $$\mathbb{K}_\mathcal{B} = \tfrac{1}{2}m\mathbf{v}_{B\in\mathcal{B}}^2 + m\mathbf{v}_{B\in\mathcal{B}} \cdot (\boldsymbol{\omega}_\mathcal{B} \times \mathbf{r}_{BG}) + \tfrac{1}{2}\boldsymbol{\omega}_\mathcal{B} \cdot \mathcal{I}_B(\boldsymbol{\omega}_\mathcal{B}) \qquad (9.28)$$

Simplifications can be obtained in formula (9.28) in two special cases:

- **Case 1:** If point B is fixed in $\mathcal{E}$ at all time, or if B is an instantaneous center of rotation, then $\mathbf{v}_{B\in\mathcal{B}} = \mathbf{0}$ and (9.28) simplifies to

$$\mathbb{K}_\mathcal{B} = \tfrac{1}{2}\boldsymbol{\omega}_\mathcal{B} \cdot \mathcal{I}_B(\boldsymbol{\omega}_\mathcal{B}) \qquad (9.29)$$

- **Case 2:** If point B is chosen to be mass center G, then (9.28) simplifies to

$$\mathbb{K}_\mathcal{B} = \tfrac{1}{2}m\mathbf{v}_G^2 + \tfrac{1}{2}\boldsymbol{\omega}_\mathcal{B} \cdot \mathcal{I}_G(\boldsymbol{\omega}_\mathcal{B}) \qquad (9.30)$$

Finally, we give below a theorem which is useful for the practical determination of the kinetic energy of a rigid body and its time-rate of change:

> **Theorem 9.9** The kinetic energy of a rigid body $\mathcal{B}$ can be obtained from the scalar product between the kinematic screw and the kinetic screw of $\mathcal{B}$ as follows:
>
> $$\mathbb{K}_{\mathcal{B}/\mathcal{E}} = \tfrac{1}{2}\{\mathcal{V}_{\mathcal{B}/\mathcal{E}}\} \cdot \{\mathcal{H}_{\mathcal{B}/\mathcal{E}}\} \qquad (9.31)$$
>
> Similarly, the time-rate of change of $\mathbb{K}_{\mathcal{B}/\mathcal{E}}$ can be found as the scalar product between the kinematic screw and the dynamic screw of $\mathcal{B}$
>
> $$\frac{d}{dt}\mathbb{K}_{\mathcal{B}/\mathcal{E}} = \{\mathcal{V}_{\mathcal{B}/\mathcal{E}}\} \cdot \{\mathcal{D}_{\mathcal{B}/\mathcal{E}}\} \qquad (9.32)$$

Proof. To prove (9.31), we first find the scalar product $\{\mathcal{V}_{\mathcal{B}/\mathcal{E}}\} \cdot \{\mathcal{H}_{\mathcal{B}/\mathcal{E}}\}$ by resolving both screws about mass center G of body $\mathcal{B}$:

$$\{\mathcal{V}_{\mathcal{B}/\mathcal{E}}\} \cdot \{\mathcal{H}_{\mathcal{B}/\mathcal{E}}\} = \boldsymbol{\omega}_\mathcal{B} \cdot \mathbf{H}_G + \mathbf{v}_G \cdot m\mathbf{v}_G$$

With $\mathbf{H}_G = \mathcal{I}_G(\boldsymbol{\omega})$, we recognize $2\mathbb{K}_\mathcal{B}$ given by (9.30). As for (9.32), we take the time-derivative of $\mathbb{K}_{\mathcal{B}}$ to find

$$\frac{d}{dt}\mathbb{K}_{\mathcal{B}/\mathcal{E}} = \int_{\mathcal{B}} \mathbf{v}_P \cdot \mathbf{a}_P dm = \int_{\mathcal{B}} (\mathbf{v}_G + \boldsymbol{\omega}_{\mathcal{B}} \times \mathbf{r}_{GP}) \cdot \mathbf{a}_P dm$$

$$= \mathbf{v}_G \cdot \int_{\mathcal{B}} \mathbf{a}_P dm + \boldsymbol{\omega}_{\mathcal{B}} \cdot \int_{\mathcal{B}} \mathbf{r}_{GP} \times \mathbf{a}_P dm$$

$$= \mathbf{v}_G \cdot m\mathbf{a}_G + \boldsymbol{\omega}_{\mathcal{B}} \cdot \mathbf{D}_G$$

This last expression is recognized as $\{\mathcal{V}_{\mathcal{B}/\mathcal{E}}\} \cdot \{\mathcal{D}_{\mathcal{B}/\mathcal{E}}\}$. ■

9.8 Extensions to System of Rigid Bodies

Unlike kinematic screws, kinetic and dynamic screws can be defined for systems of rigid bodies. This is not surprising since these quantities were defined for arbitrary material systems of constant mass.

Theorem 9.10 The kinetic screw, the dynamic screw and the kinetic energy of a system Σ of N rigid bodies $\{\mathcal{B}_1, \mathcal{B}_2, \dots \mathcal{B}_N\}$ relative to a referential $\mathcal{E}$ are given by

$$\{\mathcal{H}_{\Sigma/\mathcal{E}}\} = \{\mathcal{H}_{\mathcal{B}_1/\mathcal{E}}\} + \{\mathcal{H}_{\mathcal{B}_2/\mathcal{E}}\} + \cdots + \{\mathcal{H}_{\mathcal{B}_N/\mathcal{E}}\} \tag{9.33}$$

$$\{\mathcal{D}_{\Sigma/\mathcal{E}}\} = \{\mathcal{D}_{\mathcal{B}_1/\mathcal{E}}\} + \{\mathcal{D}_{\mathcal{B}_2/\mathcal{E}}\} + \cdots + \{\mathcal{D}_{\mathcal{B}_N/\mathcal{E}}\} \tag{9.34}$$

$$\mathbb{K}_{\Sigma/\mathcal{E}} = \mathbb{K}_{\mathcal{B}_1/\mathcal{E}} + \mathbb{K}_{\mathcal{B}_2/\mathcal{E}} + \cdots + \mathbb{K}_{\mathcal{B}_N/\mathcal{E}} \tag{9.35}$$

Proof. This is simply a consequence of writing the integral $\int_\Sigma \mathbf{r}_{AP} \times \mathbf{u}_P dm$ as the sum $\int_{\mathcal{B}_1} \mathbf{r}_{AP} \times \mathbf{u}_P dm + \int_{\mathcal{B}_2} \mathbf{r}_{AP} \times \mathbf{u}_P dm + \cdots + \int_{\mathcal{B}_N} \mathbf{r}_{AP} \times \mathbf{u}_P dm$. The same applies to the kinetic energy of Σ. ■

9.9 Examples

Example 9.3 A rigid body 1 is constrained to rotate about a fixed axis $(O, \hat{\mathbf{z}}_0)$ of a referential 0. Body 1 is in the shape of a right-triangular plate OAB (of negligible thickness) of uniform mass m, with $\mathbf{r}_{OB} = b\hat{\mathbf{z}}_0$ and $\mathbf{r}_{OA} = a\hat{\mathbf{x}}_1$. See Figure 9.11.

a. Determine the position of the mass center G of 1.

b. Determine the inertia operator $\mathcal{I}_O$ about point O. Then determine the inertia operator $\mathcal{I}_G$ about point G.

c. Determine the kinetic $\{\mathcal{H}_{1/0}\}$ and dynamic $\{\mathcal{D}_{1/0}\}$ screws resolved about point O in terms of a, b, θ and its time-derivatives.

d. Determine the kinetic energy $\mathbb{K}_{1/0}$. ■

a. The position of mass center G is defined by Cartesian coordinates (x_G, z_G) on axes $(O, \hat{\mathbf{x}}_1, \hat{\mathbf{z}}_0)$ attached to body 1. We may use Pappus theorem, given that the volume of a right-circular cone of base radius r and height h is $V = \frac{1}{3}\pi r^2 h$. For instance, the rotation of 1 (of area $A = \frac{1}{2}ab$) about axis $(O, \hat{\mathbf{z}}_0)$ leads to a body of volume $V = \frac{1}{3}\pi a^2 b$: according to Pappus theorem we

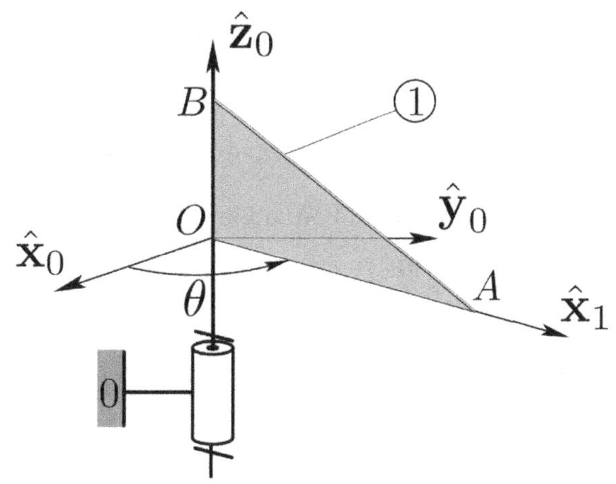

Figure 9.11

have $V = 2\pi x_G A$, giving $x_G = V/(2\pi A) = a/3$. Similarly, we find $z_G = b/3$

$$\mathbf{r}_{OG} = \frac{a}{3}\hat{\mathbf{x}}_1 + \frac{b}{3}\hat{\mathbf{z}}_0$$

b. We may find a representation of $\mathcal{I}_O$ on basis $b_1(\hat{\mathbf{x}}_1, \hat{\mathbf{y}}_1, \hat{\mathbf{z}}_0)$ (with $\hat{\mathbf{y}}_1 = \hat{\mathbf{z}}_0 \times \hat{\mathbf{x}}_1$). On this basis the inertia matrix takes the form

$$[\mathcal{I}_O]_{b_1} = \begin{bmatrix} I_{Ox} & 0 & I_{Oxz} \\ 0 & I_{Oy} & 0 \\ I_{Oxz} & 0 & I_{Oz} \end{bmatrix}_{b_1}$$

Thing plate, in XZ plane

where $I_{Ox} = \int z^2 dm$, $I_{Oz} = \int x^2 dm$, $I_{Oy} = I_{Ox} + I_{Oz}$, and $I_{Oxz} = -\int xz dm$. Here (x, z) represent the Cartesian coordinates of a generic point P of body 1 relative to axes $(O, \hat{\mathbf{x}}_1)$ and $(O, \hat{\mathbf{z}}_0)$.

To find I_{Oz} we consider an element parallel to axis $(O, \hat{\mathbf{z}}_0)$ at a distance x to this axis and of width dx and height $b(1 - x/a)$, and mass $dm = \sigma b(1 - x/a)dx$, denoting by σ the surface mass density ($m = \sigma ab/2$). Then we find

$$I_{Oz} = \int_0^a x^2 dm = \sigma \int_0^a x^2 b(1 - \frac{x}{a})dx = \sigma \frac{ba^3}{12} = \frac{m}{6}a^2$$

By symmetry we find $I_{Ox} = \frac{m}{6}b^2$, and hence $I_{Oy} = \frac{m}{6}(a^2 + b^2)$. Finally we find the product of inertia I_{Oxz} with the following integration

$$I_{Oxz} = -\sigma \int xz\, dxdz = -\sigma \int_0^a x dx \int_0^{b(1-x/a)} z dz = -\frac{m}{12}ab$$

We then find $[\mathcal{I}_G]_{b_1}$ relative to basis $b_1(\hat{\mathbf{x}}_1, \hat{\mathbf{y}}_1, \hat{\mathbf{z}}_0)$ by using the Parallel Axis Theorem

$$[\mathcal{I}_G]_{b_1} = [\mathcal{I}_O]_{b_1} - \begin{bmatrix} \frac{m}{9}b^2 & 0 & -\frac{m}{9}ab \\ 0 & \frac{m}{9}(a^2 + b^2) & 0 \\ -\frac{m}{9}ab & 0 & \frac{m}{9}a^2 \end{bmatrix}_{b_1} = \begin{bmatrix} \frac{m}{18}b^2 & 0 & \frac{m}{36}ab \\ 0 & \frac{m}{18}(a^2 + b^2) & 0 \\ \frac{m}{36}ab & 0 & \frac{m}{18}a^2 \end{bmatrix}_{b_1}$$

c. First we find the angular momentum about O by applying formula (9.24)

$$\mathbf{H}_O = \mathcal{I}_O(\boldsymbol{\omega}) = \dot{\theta}(-I_{Oxz}\hat{\mathbf{x}}_1 + I_{Oz}\hat{\mathbf{z}}_0) = \frac{m}{12}a\dot{\theta}(-b\hat{\mathbf{x}}_1 + 2a\hat{\mathbf{z}}_0)$$

$I_o(\omega) = [\ \ ] [\omega_1\ \omega_2\ \omega_3]$

operator

ang. vel.

This gives the kinetic screw in the following form

$$\{\mathcal{H}_{1/0}\} = \begin{Bmatrix} \frac{m}{3} a\dot{\theta}\hat{\mathbf{y}}_1 \\ \frac{m}{12} a\dot{\theta}(-b\hat{\mathbf{x}}_1 + 2a\hat{\mathbf{z}}_0) \end{Bmatrix}_O$$

Next we find the dynamic moment about about O: we use (9.10) with $A \equiv O$:

$$\mathbf{D}_O = \frac{d\mathbf{H}_O}{dt} = \frac{m}{12} a\ddot{\theta}(-b\hat{\mathbf{x}}_1 + 2a\hat{\mathbf{z}}_0) - \frac{m}{12} ab\dot{\theta}^2\hat{\mathbf{y}}_1$$

leading to

$$\{\mathcal{D}_{1/0}\} = \begin{Bmatrix} \frac{m}{3} a(\ddot{\theta}\hat{\mathbf{y}}_1 - \dot{\theta}^2\hat{\mathbf{x}}_1) \\ \frac{m}{12} a(-b\ddot{\theta}\hat{\mathbf{x}}_1 - b\dot{\theta}^2\hat{\mathbf{y}}_1 + 2a\ddot{\theta}\hat{\mathbf{z}}_0) \end{Bmatrix}_O$$

d. According to formula (9.28) with $B \equiv O$

$$\mathbb{K}_{1/0} = \tfrac{1}{2}\omega \cdot \mathcal{I}_O(\omega) = \frac{m}{6} a^2\dot{\theta}^2$$

■

Example 9.4 Consider the circular disk 1 of Example 7.8. Its mass center is C, its radius R and mass m. It is in motion on a planar support $(O, \hat{\mathbf{x}}_0, \hat{\mathbf{y}}_0)$ of a referential $0(O, \hat{\mathbf{x}}_0, \hat{\mathbf{y}}_0, \hat{\mathbf{z}}_0)$. The unit vectors $(\hat{\mathbf{x}}_3, \hat{\mathbf{y}}_3, \hat{\mathbf{z}}_3)$ shown in Figure 9.12 are defined as follows: (i) the line $(I, \hat{\mathbf{x}}_3)$ is the tangent at the point of contact I to the rim of the disk, (ii) the line $(I, \hat{\mathbf{y}}_3)$ is the line connecting I and C, (iii) the line $(C, \hat{\mathbf{z}}_3)$ is normal to the plane which contains the disk. The orientation of basis $(\hat{\mathbf{x}}_3, \hat{\mathbf{y}}_3, \hat{\mathbf{z}}_3)$ relative to $(\hat{\mathbf{x}}_0, \hat{\mathbf{y}}_0, \hat{\mathbf{z}}_0)$ is defined by the angles $\psi = (\hat{\mathbf{x}}_0, \hat{\mathbf{x}}_3)$ and $\theta = (\hat{\mathbf{z}}_0, \hat{\mathbf{z}}_3)$. Finally, the orientation of a basis of the disk relative to basis $(\hat{\mathbf{x}}_3, \hat{\mathbf{y}}_3, \hat{\mathbf{z}}_3)$ is characterized by the angle ϕ. The rolling and spinning of the disk on plane $(O, \hat{\mathbf{x}}_0, \hat{\mathbf{y}}_0)$ is assumed to take place without slip at point I.

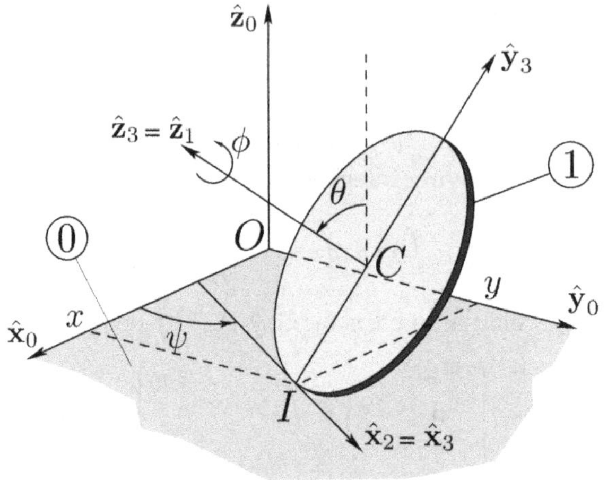

Figure 9.12

a. Using the results of Example 7.8, determine the kinetic screw $\{\mathcal{H}_{1/0}\}$ resolved at point I in terms of components ω_1, ω_2, and ω_3 (and their time-derivatives) of angular velocity

$\boldsymbol{\omega}_{1/0}$ on basis $(\hat{\mathbf{x}}_3, \hat{\mathbf{y}}_3, \hat{\mathbf{z}}_3)$.
b. Repeat the work of question a) for the dynamic screw $\{\mathcal{D}_{1/0}\}$.
c. Determine the kinetic energy $\mathbb{K}_{1/0}$. ■

a. The angles (ψ, θ, ϕ) define the orientation of basis of body 1 relative to 0, giving $\boldsymbol{\omega} \equiv \boldsymbol{\omega}_{1/0} = \dot{\psi}\hat{\mathbf{z}}_0 + \dot{\theta}\hat{\mathbf{x}}_3 + \dot{\phi}\hat{\mathbf{z}}_3$. If we denote by $(\omega_1, \omega_2, \omega_3)$ the components of $\boldsymbol{\omega}$ on basis $b_3(\hat{\mathbf{x}}_3, \hat{\mathbf{y}}_3, \hat{\mathbf{z}}_3)$, we find

$$\omega_1 = \dot{\theta}, \quad \omega_2 = \dot{\psi}\sin\theta, \quad \omega_3 = \dot{\psi}\cos\theta + \dot{\phi}$$

Given the non-holonomic constraints imposed by setting $\mathbf{v}_{I\in 1/0} = \mathbf{0}$, the motion of the disk is entirely specified in terms of three independent angles (ψ, θ, ϕ). The kinematic screw of the disk can then be written at point I as follows

$$\{\mathcal{V}_{1/0}\} = \begin{Bmatrix} \omega_1\hat{\mathbf{x}}_3 + \omega_2\hat{\mathbf{y}}_3 + \omega_3\hat{\mathbf{z}}_3 \\ \mathbf{0} \end{Bmatrix}_I$$

To express the kinetic screw at point I we need the angular momentum about I. We use formula (9.24) with $A \equiv I$ and $B \equiv I$:

$$\mathbf{H}_I = m\mathbf{r}_{IC} \times \mathbf{v}_{I\in 1/0} + \mathcal{I}_I(\boldsymbol{\omega}) = \mathcal{I}_I(\boldsymbol{\omega})$$

where we have taken into account the no-slip condition $\mathbf{v}_{I\in 1/0} = \mathbf{0}$. We need to find the inertia operator about I. We start with the expression of inertia matrix about C on basis $b_3(\hat{\mathbf{x}}_3, \hat{\mathbf{y}}_3, \hat{\mathbf{z}}_3)$

$$[\mathcal{I}_C]_{b_3} = mR^2 \begin{bmatrix} \frac{1}{4} & 0 & 0 \\ 0 & \frac{1}{4} & 0 \\ 0 & 0 & \frac{1}{2} \end{bmatrix}_{b_3}$$

Note that basis b_3 is not attached to the disk. However, the axisymmetry of the disk implies that $I_\Delta = \frac{1}{4}mR^2$ for any line Δ of the plane of the disk passing through C. We can then obtain the inertia matrix about I from that about C from the Parallel Axis Theorem:

$$[\mathcal{I}_I]_{b_3} = mR^2 \begin{bmatrix} \frac{1}{4} & 0 & 0 \\ 0 & \frac{1}{4} & 0 \\ 0 & 0 & \frac{1}{2} \end{bmatrix}_{b_3} + mR^2 \begin{bmatrix} 1 & 0 & 0 \\ 0 & 0 & 0 \\ 0 & 0 & 1 \end{bmatrix}_{b_3} = mR^2 \begin{bmatrix} \frac{5}{4} & 0 & 0 \\ 0 & \frac{1}{4} & 0 \\ 0 & 0 & \frac{3}{2} \end{bmatrix}_{b_3}$$

Now we can determine $\mathbf{H}_I$:

$$\mathbf{H}_I = mR^2 \begin{bmatrix} \frac{5}{4} & 0 & 0 \\ 0 & \frac{1}{4} & 0 \\ 0 & 0 & \frac{3}{2} \end{bmatrix}_{b_3} \begin{bmatrix} \omega_1 \\ \omega_2 \\ \omega_3 \end{bmatrix}_{b_3} = \frac{1}{4}mR^2(5\omega_1\hat{\mathbf{x}}_3 + \omega_2\hat{\mathbf{y}}_3 + 6\omega_3\hat{\mathbf{z}}_3)$$

The kinetic screw can then be expressed in the following form

$$\{\mathcal{H}_{\mathcal{B}/\mathcal{E}}\} = \begin{Bmatrix} mR(\omega_1\hat{\mathbf{z}}_3 - \omega_3\hat{\mathbf{x}}_3) \\ \frac{1}{4}mR^2(5\omega_1\hat{\mathbf{x}}_3 + \omega_2\hat{\mathbf{y}}_3 + 6\omega_3\hat{\mathbf{z}}_3) \end{Bmatrix}_I$$

where the linear momentum of the disk has been found as $m\mathbf{v}_C = m\boldsymbol{\omega} \times \mathbf{r}_{IC}$. An alternative method to find $\mathbf{H}_I$ is to relate it to $\mathbf{H}_C$ by the equation:

$$\mathbf{H}_I = \mathbf{H}_C + \mathbf{r}_{IC} \times m\mathbf{v}_C, \qquad \mathbf{H}_C = \mathcal{I}_C\boldsymbol{\omega} = \frac{1}{4}mR^2(\omega_1\hat{\mathbf{x}}_3 + \omega_2\hat{\mathbf{y}}_3 + 2\omega_3\hat{\mathbf{z}}_3)$$

The same result would be found.
b. Next we need the dynamic moment about I: we use (9.10) with $B \equiv I$

$$\mathbf{D}_I = \frac{d}{dt}\mathbf{H}_I + \mathbf{v}_I \times m\mathbf{v}_C$$

Note that $\mathbf{v}_I = \mathbf{v}_{I/0} \neq \mathbf{v}_{I\in 1/0}$ is not zero, but rather is equal to $\mathbf{v}_I = (d\mathbf{r}_{OI}/dt)_0 = \dot{x}\hat{\mathbf{x}}_0 + \dot{y}\hat{\mathbf{y}}_0$ or according to the no-slip constraint equations

$$\mathbf{v}_I = -R\dot{\phi}\hat{\mathbf{x}}_3 = -R(\omega_3 - \omega_2 \cot\theta)\hat{\mathbf{x}}_3$$

With $\mathbf{v}_C = R(\omega_1\hat{\mathbf{z}}_3 - \omega_3\hat{\mathbf{x}}_3)$ we find

$$\mathbf{v}_I \times m\mathbf{v}_C = mR^2(\omega_1\omega_3 - \omega_1\omega_2\cot\theta)\hat{\mathbf{y}}_3$$

After differentiating $\mathbf{H}_I$ (do not forget to differentiate unit vectors $\hat{\mathbf{x}}_3$, $\hat{\mathbf{y}}_3$ and $\hat{\mathbf{z}}_3$), we find

$$\mathbf{D}_I = \frac{m}{4}R^2[(5\dot{\omega}_1 + 6\omega_2\omega_3 - \omega_2^2\cot\theta)\hat{\mathbf{x}}_3 + (\dot{\omega}_2 + \omega_1\omega_2\cot\theta - 2\omega_1\omega_3)\hat{\mathbf{y}}_3 + (6\dot{\omega}_3 - 4\omega_1\omega_2)\hat{\mathbf{z}}_3]$$

Finally we need $\mathbf{a}_C$:

$$\begin{aligned}\mathbf{a}_C &= R(\dot{\omega}_1\hat{\mathbf{z}}_3 - \dot{\omega}_3\hat{\mathbf{x}}_3) + R\omega_1(\omega_2\hat{\mathbf{x}}_3 - \omega_1\hat{\mathbf{y}}_3) - R\omega_3(\omega_2\cot\theta\hat{\mathbf{y}}_3 - \omega_2\hat{\mathbf{z}}_3)\\ &= R[(-\dot{\omega}_3 + \omega_1\omega_2)\hat{\mathbf{x}}_3 - (\omega_1^2 + \omega_3\omega_2\cot\theta)\hat{\mathbf{y}}_3 + (\dot{\omega}_1 + \omega_2\omega_3)\hat{\mathbf{z}}_3]\end{aligned}$$

An alternative method to find $\mathbf{D}_I$ is to relate it to $\mathbf{D}_C$ by the equation

$$\mathbf{D}_I = \mathbf{D}_C + \mathbf{r}_{IC} \times m\mathbf{a}_C, \qquad \mathbf{D}_C = \frac{d}{dt}\mathbf{H}_C$$

The same result would be found.
c. According to formula (9.28) with $B \equiv I$

$$\mathbb{K} = \tfrac{1}{2}\boldsymbol{\omega}\cdot\mathcal{I}_I(\boldsymbol{\omega}) = \frac{1}{4}mR^2(5\omega_1^2 + \omega_2^2 + 6\omega_3^2)$$

since contact point I plays the role of an instantaneous center of rotation for the disk. ■

Example 9.5 Figure 9.13 shows a rigid body $1(G, \hat{\mathbf{x}}_1, \hat{\mathbf{y}}_1, \hat{\mathbf{z}}_1)$ in motion relative to a referential $0(O, \hat{\mathbf{x}}_0, \hat{\mathbf{y}}_0, \hat{\mathbf{z}}_0)$. Body 1 is an homogeneous cylinder, of mass m, radius R, length $2l$, mass center G, and axis $(G, \hat{\mathbf{x}}_1)$. It is constrained to roll and pivot on the horizontal plane $(O, \hat{\mathbf{x}}_0, \hat{\mathbf{y}}_0)$. The coordinates defining its position relative to 0 are x, y, ψ, and θ such that:

$$\mathbf{r}_{OG} = x\,\hat{\mathbf{x}}_0 + y\,\hat{\mathbf{y}}_0 + R\hat{\mathbf{z}}_0,\ \psi = (\hat{\mathbf{x}}_0, \hat{\mathbf{x}}_1),\ \theta = (\hat{\mathbf{z}}_0, \hat{\mathbf{z}}_1).$$

Determine the kinematic $\{\mathcal{V}_{1/0}\}$, kinetic $\{\mathcal{H}_{1/0}\}$, and dynamic $\{\mathcal{D}_{1/0}\}$ screws of 1 relative to 0 in terms of the chosen coordinates, and their derivatives. Then determine the kinetic energy $\mathbb{K}_{1/0}$. The inertia matrix of 1 about G takes the following form:

$$[\mathcal{I}_G]_b = \begin{bmatrix} \frac{m}{2}R^2 & 0 & 0\\ 0 & \frac{m}{4}R^2 + \frac{m}{3}l^2 & 0\\ 0 & 0 & \frac{m}{4}R^2 + \frac{m}{3}l^2 \end{bmatrix}_b$$

on any orthonormal basis $b(\hat{\mathbf{x}}_1, -, -)$. ■

We first introduce unit vector $\hat{\mathbf{v}} = \hat{\mathbf{z}}_0 \times \hat{\mathbf{x}}_1$ associated with rotation of angle ψ about $\hat{\mathbf{z}}_0$. Then the kinematics of body 1 relative to 0 is defined by $\boldsymbol{\omega} = \dot{\psi}\hat{\mathbf{z}}_0 + \dot{\theta}\hat{\mathbf{x}}_1$ and $\mathbf{v}_G = \dot{x}\hat{\mathbf{x}}_0 + \dot{y}\hat{\mathbf{y}}_0$ leading to the following expression of $\{\mathcal{V}_{1/0}\}$

$$\{\mathcal{V}_{1/0}\} = \left\{ \begin{array}{c} \dot{\psi}\hat{\mathbf{z}}_0 + \dot{\theta}\hat{\mathbf{x}}_1 \\ \dot{x}\hat{\mathbf{x}}_0 + \dot{y}\hat{\mathbf{y}}_0 \end{array} \right\}_G$$

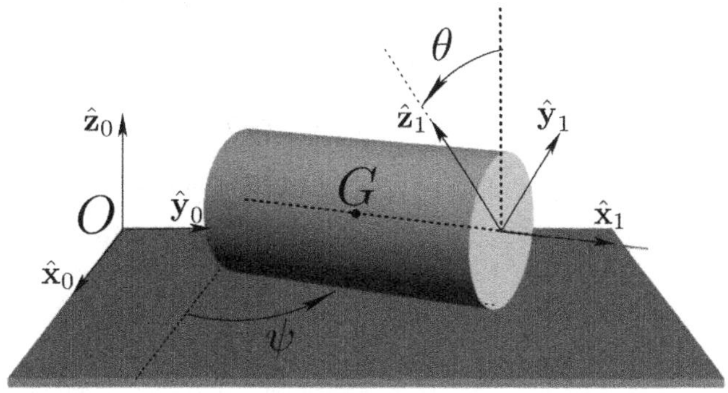

Figure 9.13

The angular momentum about G is found from the expression of $[\mathcal{I}_G]_b$ on basis $b = (\hat{\mathbf{x}}_1, \hat{\mathbf{v}}, \hat{\mathbf{z}}_0)$:

$$\mathbf{H}_G = \mathcal{I}_G(\omega) = m \begin{bmatrix} \frac{R^2}{2} & 0 & 0 \\ 0 & \frac{R^2}{4} + \frac{l^2}{3} & 0 \\ 0 & 0 & \frac{R^2}{4} + \frac{l^2}{3} \end{bmatrix}_b \begin{bmatrix} \dot{\theta} \\ 0 \\ \dot{\psi} \end{bmatrix}_b = \tfrac{m}{2} R^2 \dot{\theta} \hat{\mathbf{x}}_1 + (\tfrac{m}{4} R^2 + \tfrac{m}{3} l^2) \dot{\psi} \hat{\mathbf{z}}_0$$

leading to

$$\{\mathcal{H}_{1/0}\} = \left\{ \begin{array}{c} m(\dot{x}\hat{\mathbf{x}}_0 + \dot{y}\hat{\mathbf{y}}_0) \\ \tfrac{m}{2} R^2 \dot{\theta} \hat{\mathbf{x}}_1 + (\tfrac{m}{4} R^2 + \tfrac{m}{3} l^2) \dot{\psi} \hat{\mathbf{z}}_0 \end{array} \right\}_G$$

The dynamic moment about G is found by taking the time derivative of angular momentum $\mathbf{H}_G$:

$$\mathbf{D}_G = \frac{d}{dt} \mathbf{H}_G = \frac{m}{2} R^2 \ddot{\theta} \hat{\mathbf{x}}_1 + \frac{m}{2} R^2 \dot{\theta} \dot{\psi} \hat{\mathbf{v}} + (\frac{m}{4} R^2 + \frac{m}{3} l^2) \ddot{\psi} \hat{\mathbf{z}}_0$$

leading to

$$\{\mathcal{D}_{1/0}\} = \left\{ \begin{array}{c} m(\ddot{x}\hat{\mathbf{x}}_0 + \ddot{y}\hat{\mathbf{y}}_0) \\ \tfrac{m}{2} R^2 \ddot{\theta} \hat{\mathbf{x}}_1 + \tfrac{m}{2} R^2 \dot{\theta} \dot{\psi} \hat{\mathbf{v}} + (\tfrac{m}{4} R^2 + \tfrac{m}{3} l^2) \ddot{\psi} \hat{\mathbf{z}}_0 \end{array} \right\}_G$$

Finally the kinetic energy $\mathbb{K}_{1/0}$ is found according to

$$\mathbb{K}_{1/0} = \tfrac{1}{2} m \mathbf{v}_G^2 + \omega \cdot \mathcal{I}_G(\omega) = \tfrac{1}{2} m(\dot{x}^2 + \dot{y}^2) + \frac{m}{4} R^2 \dot{\theta}^2 + \frac{m}{2} (\frac{R^2}{4} + \frac{l^2}{3}) \dot{\psi}^2$$

■

Example 9.6 Consider the square plate 1 shown in Figure 9.14. It is assumed homogeneous, of mass m, mass center G, side length $2a$, and basis $(\hat{\mathbf{x}}_1, \hat{\mathbf{y}}_1, \hat{\mathbf{z}}_1)$ ($\hat{\mathbf{x}}_1$ and $\hat{\mathbf{y}}_1$ parallel to the its sides). Its motion relative to a referential $0(O, \hat{\mathbf{x}}_0, \hat{\mathbf{y}}_0, \hat{\mathbf{z}}_0)$ is such that one of its edges is always in contact with the plane $(O, \hat{\mathbf{x}}_0, \hat{\mathbf{y}}_0)$ and stays within a constant distance to origin O. Let A be the midpoint of this edge, and set $\mathbf{r}_{OA} = l\hat{\mathbf{x}}_1$, where l is a constant. Hence, the angles $\psi = (\hat{\mathbf{x}}_0, \hat{\mathbf{x}}_1)$ and $\theta = (\hat{\mathbf{z}}_0, \hat{\mathbf{z}}_1)$ parametrize the motion of body 1 relative to 0.

a. Find the inertia operator $\mathcal{I}_O$ of body 1 about point O.

b. Find its angular momentum $\mathbf{H}_O = \mathbf{H}_{O,1/0}$ about point O.

c. Then find its kinetic energy $\mathbb{K} = \mathbb{K}_{1/0}$. ■

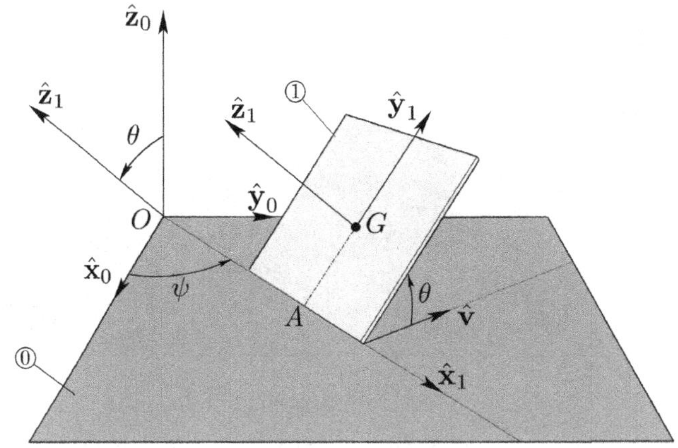

Figure 9.14

a. The inertia matrix of plate 1 about point G is easily determined on basis $b_1(\hat{\mathbf{x}}_1, \hat{\mathbf{y}}_1, \hat{\mathbf{z}}_1)$:

$$[\mathcal{I}_G]_{b_1} = ma^2 \begin{bmatrix} \frac{1}{3} & 0 & 0 \\ 0 & \frac{1}{3} & 0 \\ 0 & 0 & \frac{2}{3} \end{bmatrix}_{b_1}$$

We then find the inertia matrix about point O by using the parallel axis theorem: hence, we express $\mathcal{I}_O$ on the same basis b_1:

$$[\mathcal{I}_O]_{b_1} = [\mathcal{I}_G]_{b_1} + m \begin{bmatrix} a^2 & -al & 0 \\ -al & l^2 & 0 \\ 0 & 0 & a^2 + l^2 \end{bmatrix}_{b_1} = m \begin{bmatrix} \frac{4}{3}a^2 & -al & 0 \\ -al & \frac{1}{3}a^2 + l^2 & 0 \\ 0 & 0 & \frac{5}{3}a^2 + l^2 \end{bmatrix}_{b_1}$$

b. Since point O is fixed relative to the moving plate ($\mathbf{v}_O = \mathbf{v}_{O\in 1} = \mathbf{0}$), the angular momentum about point O can be determined according to $\mathbf{H}_O = \mathcal{I}_O(\boldsymbol{\omega})$ with $\boldsymbol{\omega} \equiv \boldsymbol{\omega}_{1/0} = \dot{\psi}\hat{\mathbf{z}}_0 + \dot{\theta}\hat{\mathbf{x}}_1 = \dot{\psi}\cos\theta\hat{\mathbf{z}}_1 + \dot{\psi}\sin\theta\hat{\mathbf{y}}_1 + \dot{\theta}\hat{\mathbf{x}}_1$. This gives

$$\mathbf{H}_O = m \begin{bmatrix} \frac{4}{3}a^2 & -al & 0 \\ -al & \frac{1}{3}a^2 + l^2 & 0 \\ 0 & 0 & \frac{5}{3}a^2 + l^2 \end{bmatrix}_{\mathbf{b}_1} \begin{bmatrix} \dot{\theta} \\ \dot{\psi}\sin\theta \\ \dot{\psi}\cos\theta \end{bmatrix}_{\mathbf{b}_1}$$

$$= m[a(\frac{4}{3}a\dot{\theta} - l\dot{\psi}\sin\theta)\hat{\mathbf{x}}_1 + (-al\dot{\theta} + (\frac{1}{3}a^2 + l^2)\dot{\psi}\sin\theta)\hat{\mathbf{y}}_1 + (\frac{5}{3}a^2 + l^2)\dot{\psi}\cos\theta\hat{\mathbf{z}}_1]$$

c. Finally, the kinetic energy is found again using the fact that point O is fixed relative to 1:

$$\mathbb{K}_{1/0} = \tfrac{1}{2}\boldsymbol{\omega} \cdot \mathcal{I}_O(\boldsymbol{\omega}) = \tfrac{1}{2}m\Big(\tfrac{4a^2}{3}\dot{\theta}^2 - 2al\dot{\theta}\dot{\psi}\sin\theta + [(\tfrac{a^2}{3} + l^2)\sin^2\theta + (\tfrac{5a^2}{3} + l^2)\cos^2\theta]\dot{\psi}^2\Big)$$

■

Example 9.7 Figure 9.15 shows a model of a three-bladed wind turbine comprised of three interconnected bodies:

- the tower 0 is fixed relative to a referential $(O, \hat{\mathbf{x}}_0, \hat{\mathbf{y}}_0, \hat{\mathbf{z}}_0)$ where $\hat{\mathbf{z}}_0$ is a unit vector directed upward.
- the nacelle $1(O, \hat{\mathbf{x}}_1, \hat{\mathbf{y}}_1, \hat{\mathbf{z}}_0)$ is connected to the tower by a pivot of axis $(O, \hat{\mathbf{z}}_0)$: 1 can rotate about axis $(O, \hat{\mathbf{z}}_0)$ with angle $\theta_1 = (\hat{\mathbf{x}}_0, \hat{\mathbf{x}}_1) = (\hat{\mathbf{y}}_0, \hat{\mathbf{y}}_1)$. The inertia operator of body

1 about O takes the following form

$$[\mathcal{I}_{O,1}]_{b_1} = \begin{bmatrix} A_1 & F_1 & E_1 \\ F_1 & B_1 & D_1 \\ E_1 & D_1 & C_1 \end{bmatrix}_{b_1}$$

on basis $b_1(\hat{\mathbf{x}}_1, \hat{\mathbf{y}}_1, \hat{\mathbf{z}}_0)$.
- the rotor (which includes the blades) $2(G, \hat{\mathbf{x}}_1, \hat{\mathbf{y}}_2, \hat{\mathbf{z}}_2)$ of mass m_2 and mass center G is connected to the nacelle 1 by a pivot of axis $(O, \hat{\mathbf{x}}_1)$. We denote that a the constant such that $\mathbf{r}_{OG} = a\hat{\mathbf{x}}_1$. The inertia operator of body 2 about G takes the following form

$$[\mathcal{I}_{G,2}]_{b_2} = \begin{bmatrix} A_2 & 0 & 0 \\ 0 & B_2 & 0 \\ 0 & 0 & C_2 \end{bmatrix}_{b_2}$$

on basis $b_2(\hat{\mathbf{x}}_1, \hat{\mathbf{y}}_2, \hat{\mathbf{z}}_2)$.

a. Find angular momentum $\mathbf{H}_{O,1/0}$ of body 1 about O and angular momentum $\mathbf{H}_{G,2/0}$ of body 2 about point G.

b. Find component $\hat{\mathbf{z}}_0 \cdot \mathbf{D}_{O,\Sigma/0}$ of the dynamic moment of system $\Sigma = \{1, 2\}$ about O.

c. Find component $\hat{\mathbf{x}}_1 \cdot \mathbf{D}_{G,2/0}$ of the dynamic moment of body 2 about G.

d. Find the kinetic energy of system Σ. ■

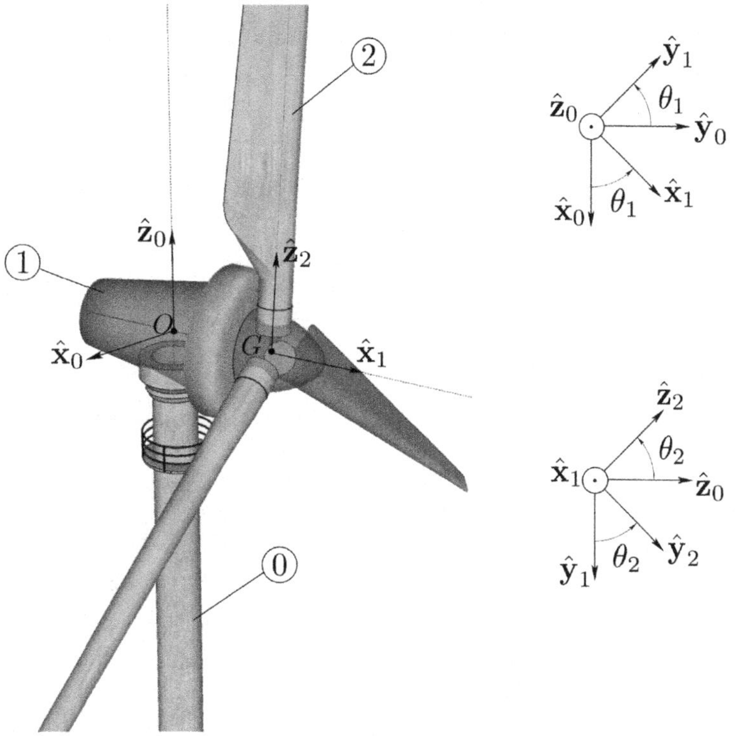

Figure 9.15

a. Since O is a fixed point of body 1 ($\mathbf{v}_{O\in 1/0} = \mathbf{0}$), the angular momentum $\mathbf{H}_{O,1/0}$ is found from the knowledge of inertia operator $\mathcal{I}_{O,1}$ about O and angular velocity $\boldsymbol{\omega}_{1/0} = \dot{\theta}_1 \hat{\mathbf{z}}_0$:

$$\mathbf{H}_{O,1/0} = \mathcal{I}_{O,1}(\boldsymbol{\omega}_{1/0}) = \begin{bmatrix} A_1 & F_1 & E_1 \\ F_1 & B_1 & D_1 \\ E_1 & D_1 & C_1 \end{bmatrix}_{b_1} \begin{bmatrix} 0 \\ 0 \\ \dot{\theta}_1 \end{bmatrix}_{b_1} = \dot{\theta}_1 (E_1 \hat{\mathbf{x}}_1 + D_1 \hat{\mathbf{y}}_1 + C_1 \hat{\mathbf{z}}_0)$$

Similarly for body 2 of angular velocity $\boldsymbol{\omega}_{2/0} = \dot{\theta}_1 \hat{\mathbf{z}}_0 + \dot{\theta}_2 \hat{\mathbf{x}}_1$ and mass center G, we have

$$\mathbf{H}_{G,2/0} = \mathcal{I}_{G,2}(\boldsymbol{\omega}_{2/0}) = \begin{bmatrix} A_2 & 0 & 0 \\ 0 & B_2 & 0 \\ 0 & 0 & C_2 \end{bmatrix}_{b_2} \begin{bmatrix} \dot{\theta}_2 \\ \dot{\theta}_1 \sin\theta_2 \\ \dot{\theta}_1 \cos\theta_2 \end{bmatrix}_{b_2} = A_2 \dot{\theta}_2 \hat{\mathbf{x}}_1 + B_2 \dot{\theta}_1 \sin\theta_2 \hat{\mathbf{y}}_2 + C_2 \dot{\theta}_1 \cos\theta_2 \hat{\mathbf{z}}_2$$

b. We find component $\hat{\mathbf{z}}_0 \cdot \mathbf{D}_{O,\Sigma/0}$ without finding $\mathbf{D}_{O,\Sigma/0}$ as follows:

$$\hat{\mathbf{z}}_0 \cdot \mathbf{D}_{O,\Sigma/0} = \hat{\mathbf{z}}_0 \cdot \frac{d}{dt}(\mathbf{H}_{O,1/0} + \mathbf{H}_{O,2/0}) = \frac{d}{dt}(\hat{\mathbf{z}}_0 \cdot \mathbf{H}_{O,1/0} + \hat{\mathbf{z}}_0 \cdot \mathbf{H}_{O,2/0})$$

with

$$\hat{\mathbf{z}}_0 \cdot \mathbf{H}_{O,1/0} = \hat{\mathbf{z}}_0 \cdot \dot{\theta}_1 (E_1 \hat{\mathbf{x}}_1 + D_1 \hat{\mathbf{y}}_1 + C_1 \hat{\mathbf{z}}_0) = C_1 \dot{\theta}_1$$

and

$$\begin{aligned} \hat{\mathbf{z}}_0 \cdot \mathbf{H}_{O,2/0} &= \hat{\mathbf{z}}_0 \cdot (\mathbf{H}_{G,2/0} + \mathbf{r}_{OG} \times m_2 \mathbf{v}_{G/0}) = \hat{\mathbf{z}}_0 \cdot \dot{\theta}_1 (B_2 \sin\theta_2 \hat{\mathbf{y}}_2 + C_2 \cos\theta_2 \hat{\mathbf{z}}_2) + \hat{\mathbf{z}}_0 \cdot (a \hat{\mathbf{x}}_1 \times m_2 a \dot{\theta}_1 \hat{\mathbf{y}}_1) \\ &= (B_2 \sin^2\theta_2 + C_2 \cos^2\theta_2 + m_2 a^2) \dot{\theta}_1 \end{aligned}$$

This gives the final result:

$$\hat{\mathbf{z}}_0 \cdot \mathbf{D}_{O,\Sigma/0} = \frac{d}{dt}\Big((C_1 + B_2 \sin^2\theta_2 + C_2 \cos^2\theta_2 + m_2 a^2) \dot{\theta}_1 \Big)$$

c. We find the component $\hat{\mathbf{x}}_1 \cdot \mathbf{D}_{G,2/0}$ by using the following steps

$$\hat{\mathbf{x}}_1 \cdot \mathbf{D}_{G,2/0} = \hat{\mathbf{x}}_1 \cdot \frac{d}{dt}\mathbf{H}_{G,2/0} = \frac{d}{dt}(\hat{\mathbf{x}}_1 \cdot \mathbf{H}_{G,2/0}) - \frac{d\hat{\mathbf{x}}_1}{dt} \cdot \mathbf{H}_{G,2/0}$$

with

$$\hat{\mathbf{x}}_1 \cdot \mathbf{H}_{G,2/0} = \hat{\mathbf{x}}_1 \cdot (A_2 \dot{\theta}_2 \hat{\mathbf{x}}_1 + B_2 \dot{\theta}_1 \sin\theta_2 \hat{\mathbf{y}}_2 + C_2 \dot{\theta}_1 \cos\theta_2 \hat{\mathbf{z}}_2) = A_2 \dot{\theta}_2$$

and

$$\frac{d\hat{\mathbf{x}}_1}{dt} \cdot \mathbf{H}_{G,2/0} = \dot{\theta}_1 \hat{\mathbf{y}}_1 \cdot (A_2 \dot{\theta}_2 \hat{\mathbf{x}}_1 + B_2 \dot{\theta}_1 \sin\theta_2 \hat{\mathbf{y}}_2 + C_2 \dot{\theta}_1 \cos\theta_2 \hat{\mathbf{z}}_2) = (B_2 - C_2) \dot{\theta}_1 \cos\theta_2 \sin\theta_2$$

This gives the final result:

$$\hat{\mathbf{x}}_1 \cdot \mathbf{D}_{G,2/0} = A_2 \ddot{\theta}_2 - (B_2 - C_2) \frac{d}{dt}(\dot{\theta}_1 \cos\theta_2 \sin\theta_2)$$

d. We find the kinetic energy of system Σ as follows

$$\begin{aligned} \mathbb{K}_{\Sigma/0} &= \mathbb{K}_{1/0} + \mathbb{K}_{2/0} = \tfrac{1}{2} \boldsymbol{\omega}_{1/0} \cdot \mathcal{I}_{O,1}(\boldsymbol{\omega}_{1/0}) + \tfrac{1}{2} m_2 \mathbf{v}_{G/0}^2 + \tfrac{1}{2} \boldsymbol{\omega}_{2/0} \cdot \mathcal{I}_{G,2}(\boldsymbol{\omega}_{2/0}) \\ &= \tfrac{1}{2} C_1 \dot{\theta}_1^2 + \tfrac{1}{2} m_2 (a \dot{\theta}_1 \hat{\mathbf{y}}_1)^2 + \tfrac{1}{2} \boldsymbol{\omega}_{2/0} \cdot (A_2 \dot{\theta}_2 \hat{\mathbf{x}}_1 + B_2 \dot{\theta}_1 \sin\theta_2 \hat{\mathbf{y}}_2 + C_2 \dot{\theta}_1 \cos\theta_2 \hat{\mathbf{z}}_2) \\ &= \tfrac{1}{2} C_1 \dot{\theta}_1^2 + \tfrac{1}{2} m_2 a^2 \dot{\theta}_1^2 + \tfrac{1}{2} (A_2 \dot{\theta}_2^2 + B_2 \dot{\theta}_1^2 \sin^2\theta_2 + C_2 \dot{\theta}_1^2 \cos^2\theta_2) \\ &= \tfrac{1}{2} (C_1 + m_2 a^2 + B_2 \sin^2\theta_2 + C_2 \cos^2\theta_2) \dot{\theta}_1^2 + \tfrac{1}{2} A_2 \dot{\theta}_2^2 \end{aligned}$$

■

9.10 Problems

Problem 9.1 Consider a rigid body $\mathcal{B}$ of mass center G and mass m in motion relative to a referential $\mathcal{E}$. Consider the *centroidal* referential $\mathcal{E}^*$ defined as the referential relative to which G is fixed and whose orientation is invariant relative to $\mathcal{E}$:

$$\mathbf{v}_{G/\mathcal{E}^*} = 0, \qquad \omega_{\mathcal{E}^*/\mathcal{E}} = \mathbf{0}$$

a. Show that the kinetic and dynamic screws of $\mathcal{B}$ relative to $\mathcal{E}^*$ are couples, that is, the angular momentum $\mathbf{H}_{A,\mathcal{B}/\mathcal{E}^*} = \mathbf{H}^*_{\mathcal{B}}$ and the dynamic moment $\mathbf{D}_{A,\mathcal{B}/\mathcal{E}^*} = \mathbf{D}^*_{\mathcal{B}}$ are independent of the choice of point A.

b. Show that the angular momenta, dynamic moments and kinetic energies of $\mathcal{B}$ relative to $\mathcal{E}$ and $\mathcal{E}^*$ are related according to the equations

$$\mathbf{H}_{A,\mathcal{B}/\mathcal{E}} = \mathbf{H}^*_{\mathcal{B}} + \mathbf{r}_{AG} \times m\mathbf{v}_{G/\mathcal{E}}$$

$$\mathbf{D}_{A,\mathcal{B}/\mathcal{E}} = \mathbf{D}^*_{\mathcal{B}} + \mathbf{r}_{AG} \times m\mathbf{a}_{G/\mathcal{E}}$$

$$\mathbb{K}_{\mathcal{B}/\mathcal{E}} = \mathbb{K}_{\mathcal{B}/\mathcal{E}^*} + \tfrac{1}{2}m\mathbf{v}^2_{G/\mathcal{E}}$$

Problem 9.2 A uniform spherical ball $\mathcal{B}$ of mass m, radius r rolls without slipping in a wedge-shaped guide of angle 2α. Its mass center G is assumed to move at a constant speed v_0.

a. Find the kinetic screw of body $\mathcal{B}$ in terms of v_0, m, and the geometric parameters.

b. Find its kinetic energy.

Problem 9.3 Repeat problem 9.2 for a sphere $\mathcal{B}$ rolling without slipping on the edge of circular groove of radius R and width a. Assume again that its mass center G moves at a constant speed v_0 along its circular trajectory. After parametrizing the motion of $\mathcal{B}$, find expressions of its kinematic screw, kinetic screw, dynamic screw, and kinetic energy.

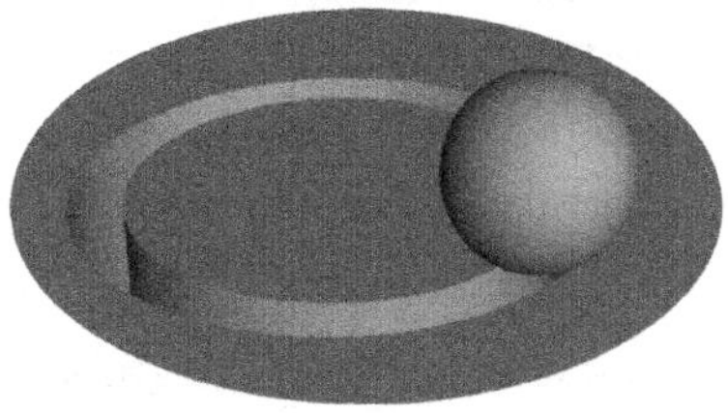

Problem 9.4 A homogeneous rigid sphere $\mathcal{B}$ of center C, mass m, and radius R is in motion in a referential $\mathcal{E}$ in such a way as to remain in contact with horizontal plane Oxy and vertical axis Oz. Denote the corresponding contact points I and J.

After parametrizing the motion of $\mathcal{B}$, determine its kinematic screw, kinetic screw, and the kinetic energy. Simplify these quantities by assuming no-slip at contact points I and J.

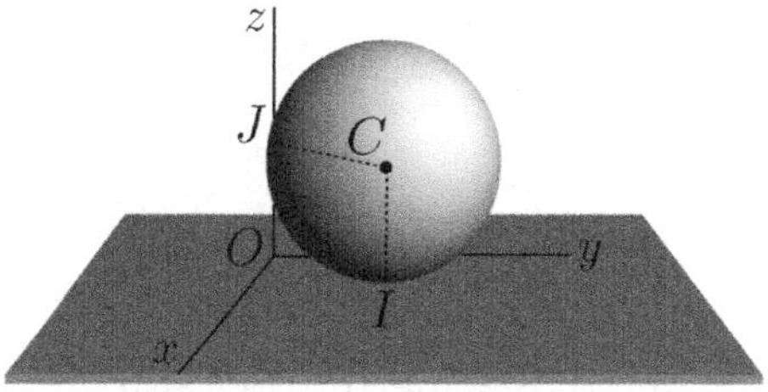

Problem 9.5 A homogeneous sphere 2 of radius r, mass m, center C is in motion inside a cylindrical container 1 of radius R and axis $(O, \hat{\mathbf{z}}_1)$. Ball 2 remains in contact at points I and J of 1.

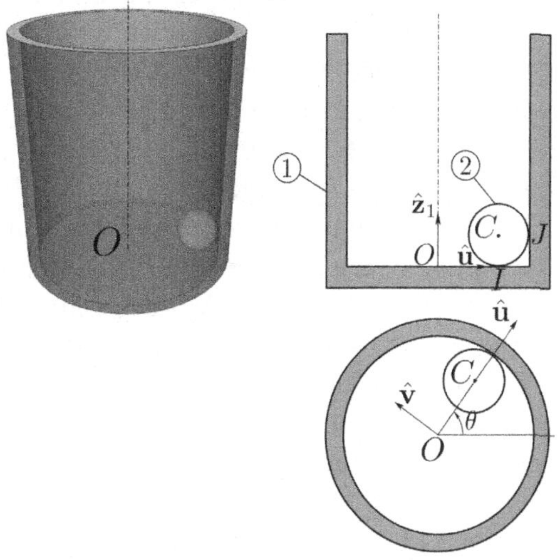

Assume that there is no-slip at both points I and J. The position of point C relative to 1 is defined by angle θ.

Determine the kinetic screw, the dynamic screw and the kinetic energy of 2 relative to 1.

Problem 9.6 A system Σ of three rigid bodies is assembled by joining two square plates (of mass m, and side length $2a$) by a massless rigid rod (of length $2a$). Each plate is free to rotate about the axis of the rod with the same angle θ. The assembly is free to rotate about the axis Oz of a fixed referential $\mathcal{E}$ of rectangular axes $Oxyz$. The mass center O of the system is fixed.

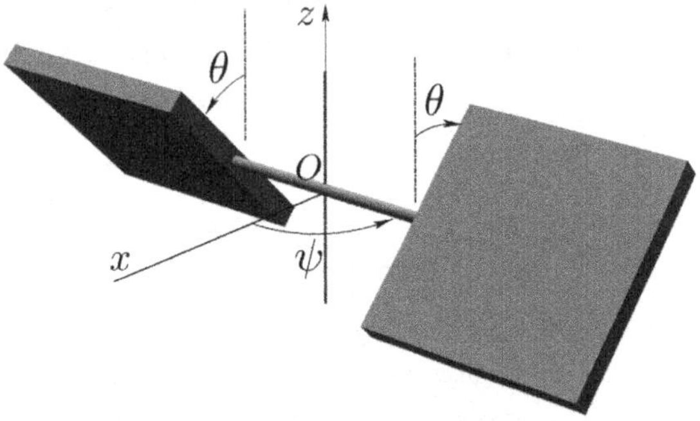

a. Find the inertia operator of Σ about point O.

b. Find the kinetic and dynamic screws of Σ.

c. Find the kinetic energy of Σ.

Problem 9.7 A rigid spherical ball 1 of radius R, and of mass m uniformly distributed on its surface, rolls without slipping on the horizontal support Ox of a referential 0. Its mass center C remains in the vertical plane Oxy. A dog 2 is in motion relative to the ball in such a way that his back feet are located at a point I of the ball, the line IC making an angle α with the vertical. More specifically, the dog walks by making small shuffling steps towards the highest point of the ball so as to maintain angle α constant in time. The dog is modeled as a rigid body of mass center G and mass M such that line IG remains vertical at all times and with $|IG| = h$. We neglect the inertia of the dog's moving parts during his "walk" on the ball.

a. Show that the moment of inertia of the ball about one of its diameters is $\frac{2}{3}mR^2$.

b. Find the angular momentum $\mathbf{H}_{J,\Sigma/0}$ of the system $\Sigma = \{1, 2\}$ about the contact point J. Then find the corresponding dynamic moment $\mathbf{D}_{J,\Sigma/0}$.

c. Find the kinetic energy of the system.

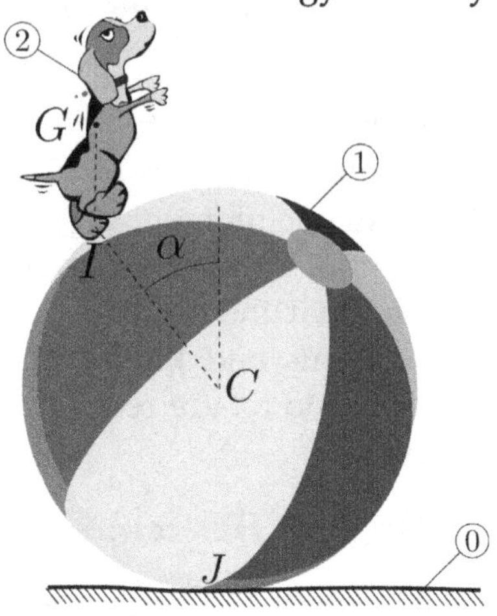

Problem 9.8 A truncated, homogeneous cone $\mathcal{B}$ of mass m rolls without slipping on a horizontal plane Oxy of a referential $\mathcal{E}$ so that its axis Δ intersects plane Oxy at point O. The motion is characterized by angles $\psi(t)$, θ (constant) and ϕ. Its mass center G remains at a constant distance h from O. Its inertia operator about G is characterized by its axial moment of inertia A and its transverse moment of inertia $B = C$.

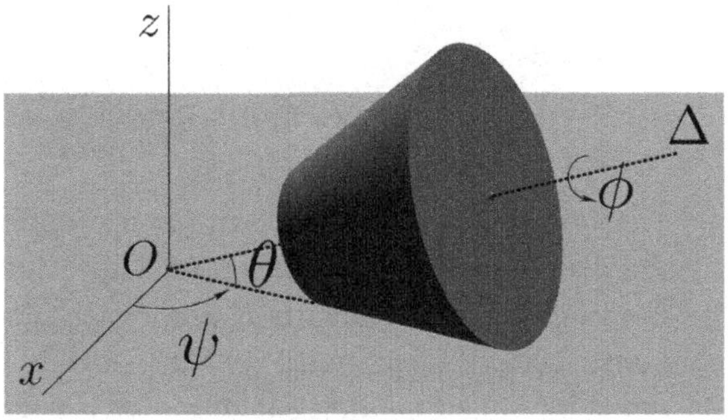

a. Find the kinematic screw of $\mathcal{B}$ by accounting for all constraints.

b. Find its kinetic screw $\{\mathcal{H}_{\mathcal{B}/\mathcal{E}}\}$ resolved about O.

c. Find its dynamic moment about O.

d. Find its kinetic energy.

Problem 9.9 A cube $\mathcal{B}$ of side length a and uniformly distributed mass m is in motion in referential $\mathcal{E}$ of Cartesian axes $Oxyz$ in the following manner: (i) edge AB is constrained to slide in plane Oxy, (ii) cube $\mathcal{B}$ pivots about edge AB.

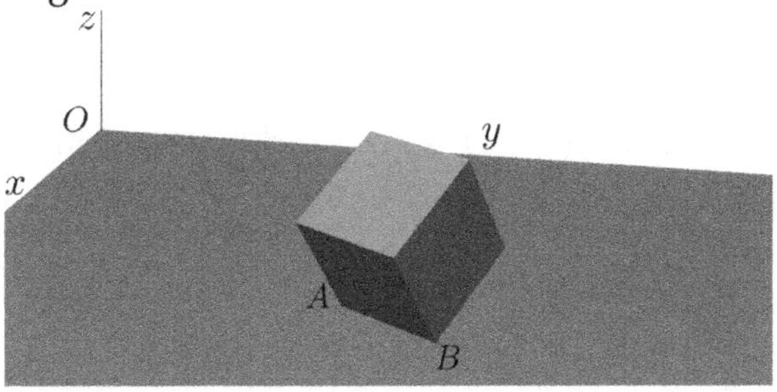

a. Parametrize the position of $\mathcal{B}$ relative to $\mathcal{E}$, then find its kinematic screw.

b. Show that the inertia operator of $\mathcal{B}$ about its mass center G has a spherical symmetry.

c. Find its kinetic screw and kinetic energy.

Problem 9.10 Consider two referentials $\mathcal{E}$ and $\mathcal{F}$ in relative rotation about a common axis $(O, \hat{\mathbf{z}})$. Denote $\omega_{\mathcal{E}/\mathcal{F}} = \Omega\hat{\mathbf{z}}$. It is of interest in some applications to obtain kinetic quantities of a rigid body $\mathcal{B}$ from referential $\mathcal{E}$ (attached to Earth) to referential $\mathcal{F}$ (a referential about which Earth rotates).

a. By using the change of referential formula derived in Section 6.2, find the equation which relate kinetic screw $\{\mathcal{H}_{\mathcal{B}/\mathcal{F}}\}$ to kinetic screw $\{\mathcal{H}_{\mathcal{B}/\mathcal{E}}\}$.

b. Find the equation which allows the determination of kinetic energy $\mathbb{K}_{\mathcal{B}/\mathcal{F}}$ from kinetic energy $\mathbb{K}_{\mathcal{B}/\mathcal{E}}$.

Problem 9.11 Figure 9.16 shows a three-bladed rotor $\mathcal{R}$ of a horizontal axis wind turbine. Its mass center is denoted G, its mass M. The axes $GXYZ$ are attached to the rotor, with corresponding basis $(\hat{\mathbf{x}}_2, \hat{\mathbf{y}}_2, \hat{\mathbf{z}}_2 = \hat{\mathbf{z}}_1)$. This body is motion relative to a referential $\mathcal{E}(O, \hat{\mathbf{x}}_0, \hat{\mathbf{y}}_0, \hat{\mathbf{z}}_0)$ such that $\mathbf{r}_{OG} = a\hat{\mathbf{z}}_1$ (a is a constant).

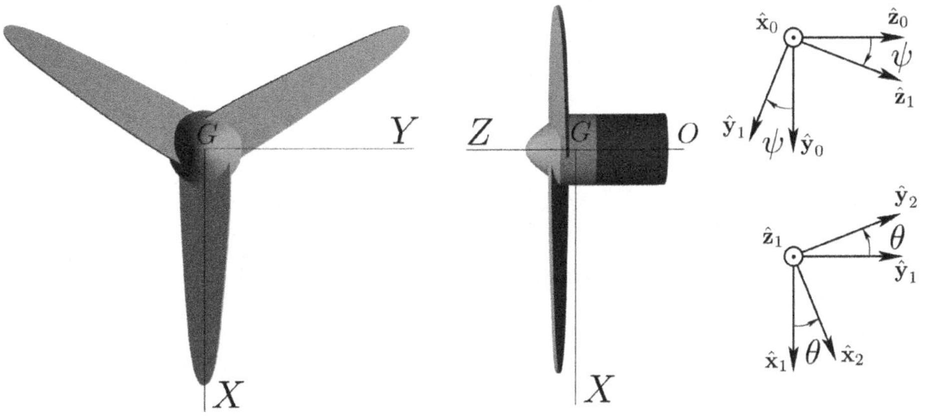

Figure 9.16

a. Assume that the plane GXZ is a plane of material symmetry of the rotor. Shows that this implies that the product of inertia I_{GXY} is then necessarily zero. Then show that the moments of inertia I_{GX} and I_{GY} are equal. The inertia matrix of $\mathcal{R}$ will be denoted as follows

$$[\mathcal{I}_G]_{b_2} = \begin{bmatrix} A & 0 & 0 \\ 0 & A & 0 \\ 0 & 0 & C \end{bmatrix}_{b_2}$$

on basis $b_2(\hat{\mathbf{x}}_2, \hat{\mathbf{y}}_2, \hat{\mathbf{z}}_2)$.

b. Assuming that the motion of $\mathcal{R}$ relative to referential $\mathcal{E}$ is described by the two angles ψ and θ, find its angular momentum $\mathbf{H}_O$ about point O relative to $\mathcal{E}$.

Problem 9.12 A model of a crankshaft $\mathcal{B}$ is shown in Figure 9.17: it is comprised of the rigidly connected, homogeneous bodies 1,2,3,4,5. The identical cylindrical parts 3, 4 and 5 are symmetrically placed about axis $(G, \hat{\mathbf{z}})$ $(\theta = 2\pi/3)$. The following matrices of inertia are given on any basis $b(-,-,\hat{\mathbf{z}})$

$$[\mathcal{I}_{G,1}]_b = \begin{bmatrix} A_1 & 0 & 0 \\ 0 & A_1 & 0 \\ 0 & 0 & 2A_1 \end{bmatrix}_b \qquad [\mathcal{I}_{G,2}] = \begin{bmatrix} A_2 & 0 & 0 \\ 0 & A_2 & 0 \\ 0 & 0 & 2A_2 \end{bmatrix}_b$$

where G is the mass center of $\mathcal{B}$. Each of the cylindrical bodies 3,4,5 admits the following matrix of inertia about their mass center G_k:

$$[\mathcal{I}_{G_k,k}]_b = \begin{bmatrix} I & 0 & 0 \\ 0 & I & 0 \\ 0 & 0 & 2I \end{bmatrix}_b$$

on basis $b(-,-,\hat{\mathbf{z}})$. The geometry of $\mathcal{B}$ is also defined by the constant lengths r, d, and h.

Find the inertia matrix $[\mathcal{I}_{G,\mathcal{B}}]$ of body $\mathcal{B}$ about G on a basis of your choice. Then find its angular momentum $\mathbf{H}_G$ and kinetic energy in a referential $\mathcal{E}$ relative to which $\mathcal{B}$ is in rotation about axis $(G, \hat{\mathbf{z}})$ at angular velocity $\boldsymbol{\omega}_{\mathcal{B}/\mathcal{E}} = \Omega\hat{\mathbf{z}}$.

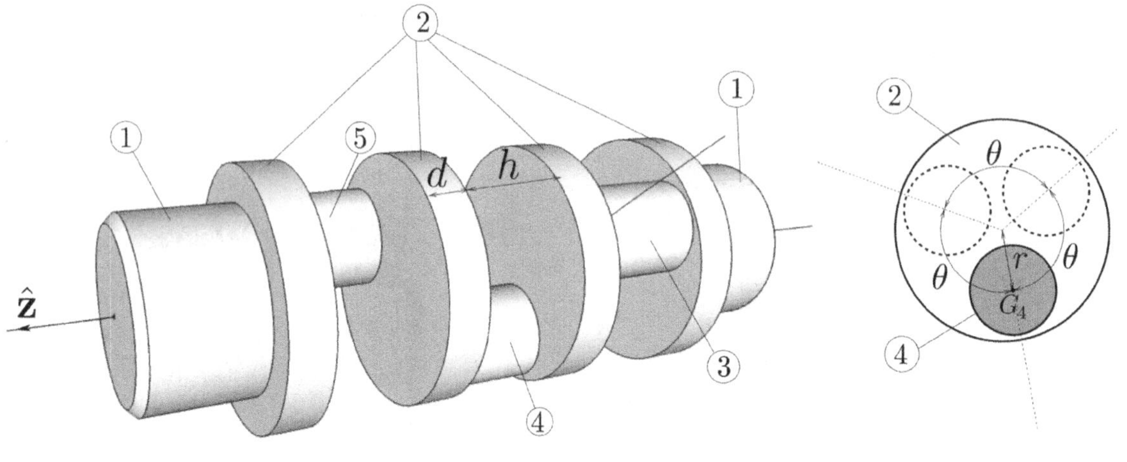

Figure 9.17

Problem 9.13 Figure 9.18 shows a model of a cone crusher designed to crush small granular material which is squeezed between a movable cone and a fixed cone. The diagram shows three bodies:

0 is the main stationary part of the crusher including the fixed cone.

1 represents the drive shaft, which supports an eccentric shaft at A. 1 is in rotation relative to 0 about axis $(O, \hat{\mathbf{z}}_0)$. Its basis $(\hat{\mathbf{x}}_1, \hat{\mathbf{y}}_1)$ is oriented by angle $\theta_1(t)$.

2 is the moving cone supported to 0 by a spherical joint at B. Its motion is driven by the drive shaft 1 through the sleeve at A. Its axis $(B, \hat{\mathbf{z}}_2)$ passes through A. The orientation of its

basis $(\hat{\mathbf{x}}_2, \hat{\mathbf{y}}_2)$ relative to 1 is defined by angle $\theta_2(t)$. We assume that the kinematic no-slip condition along the contact line between 2 and 0 is guaranteed (in reality there is a small gap between 2 and 0 but this gap is filled with small material).

The geometry is defined by the two constant angles α and β.

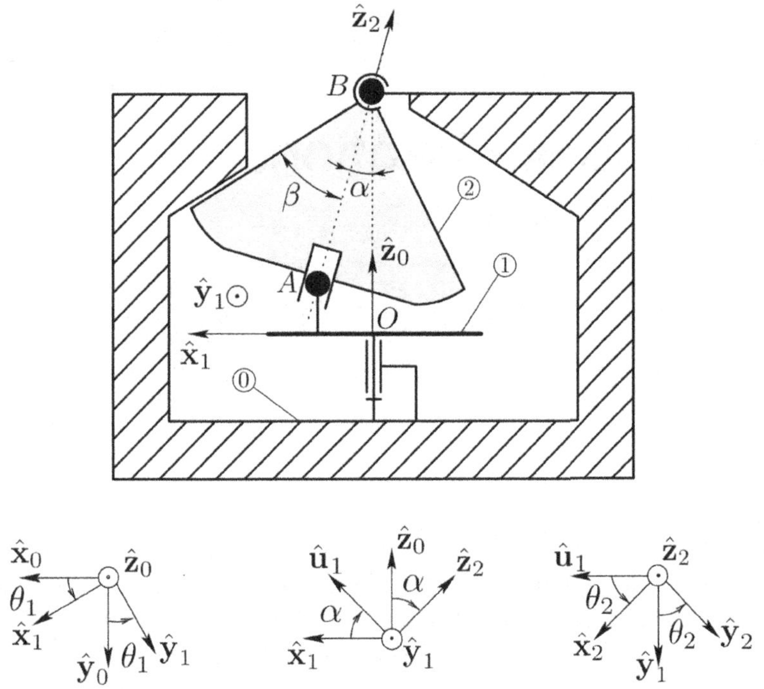

Figure 9.18

a. Show that the no-slip condition between 2 and 0 leads to a condition between $\dot{\theta}_1$ and $\dot{\theta}_2$. Then give an expression of kinematic screw $\{\mathcal{V}_{2/0}\}$.

b. The inertia of 2 about B takes the following form

$$[\mathcal{I}_{B,2}]_{b_2} = \begin{bmatrix} A_2 & 0 & 0 \\ 0 & A_2 & 0 \\ 0 & 0 & C_2 \end{bmatrix}_{b_2}$$

on basis $b_2(\hat{\mathbf{x}}_2, \hat{\mathbf{y}}_2, \hat{\mathbf{z}}_2)$. Find the angular momentum $\mathbf{H}_{B,2/0}$ and the kinetic energy $\mathbb{K}_{2/0}$.

c. Cone 2 is not perfectly axisymmetric and is characterized by an eccentricity modeled as a point mass E of mass m rigidly attached to 2. Its position is given by $\mathbf{r}_{BE} = -h\hat{\mathbf{z}}_2 + x_E\hat{\mathbf{x}}_2$ (h and x_E are constant lengths). The system composed of 2 and eccentricity E is denoted as 3. Find the angular momentum $\mathbf{H}_{B,3/0}$, and kinetic energy $\mathbb{K}_{3/0}$.

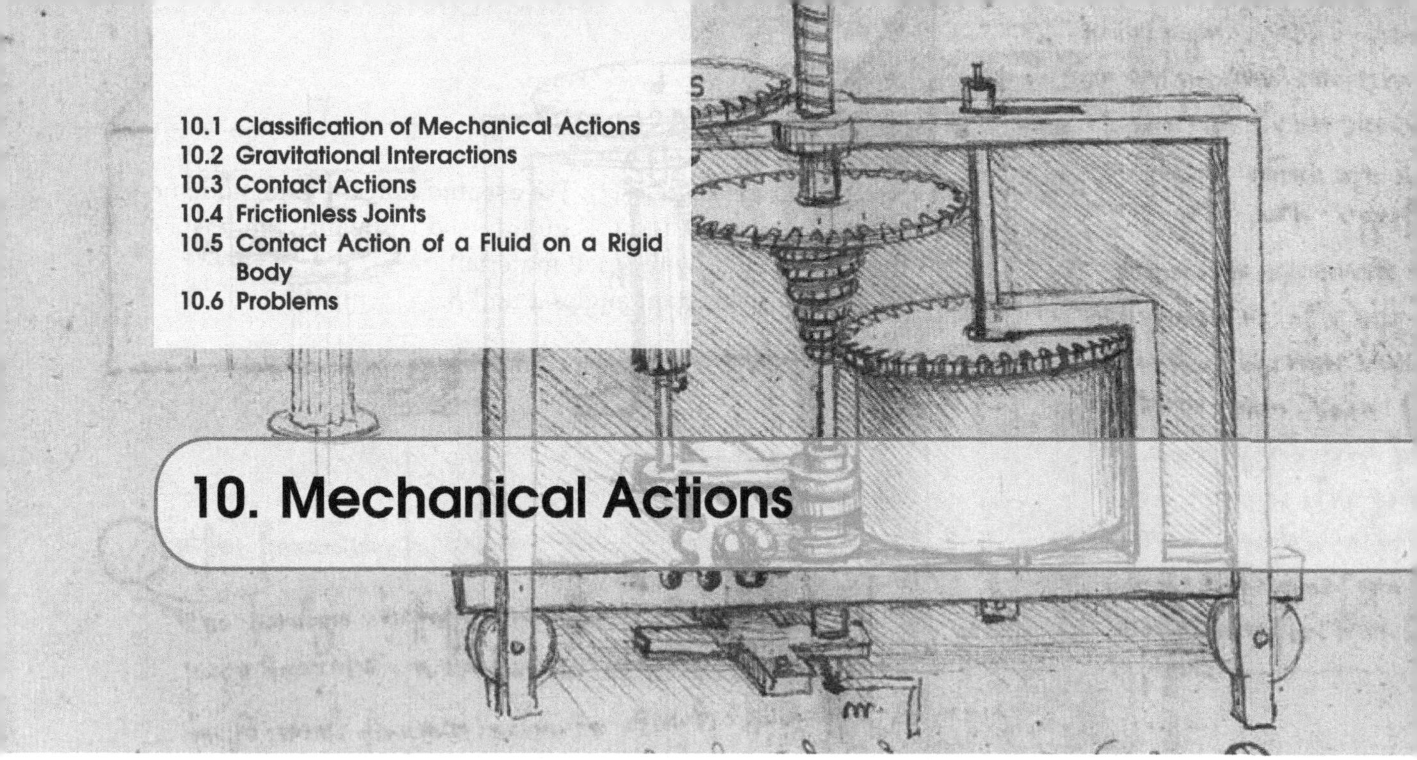

10. Mechanical Actions

IN THIS CHAPTER, we seek to model the mechanical actions exerted on a material system Σ. We define a *mechanical action* as any cause capable of either maintaining a material system in equilibrium, or of modifying its motion or shape. On the simplest level, recall that the action of a force $\mathbf{F}_A$ exerted on a system Σ is properly defined by indicating both the value of vector $\mathbf{F}_A$ and its line of action (or simply a point on this line of action): hence this mechanical action is defined by the bound vector $(A, \mathbf{F}_A)$ or in the language of screws by the slider denoted as

$$\left\{ \begin{matrix} \mathbf{F}_A \\ \mathbf{0} \end{matrix} \right\}_A$$

Screws are useful tools to account for the sum of discrete forces, or for the sum of forces distributed over Σ (or over a subset of Σ). For instance, the action of force $\mathbf{F}_A$ acting through point A and force $\mathbf{F}_B$ acting through point B results in the screw (see Figure 10.1)

$$\left\{ \begin{matrix} \mathbf{F}_A \\ \mathbf{0} \end{matrix} \right\}_A + \left\{ \begin{matrix} \mathbf{F}_B \\ \mathbf{0} \end{matrix} \right\}_B = \left\{ \begin{matrix} \mathbf{F}_A + \mathbf{F}_B \\ \mathbf{F}_A \times \mathbf{r}_{AQ} + \mathbf{F}_B \times \mathbf{r}_{BQ} \end{matrix} \right\}_Q$$

More generally, in the case of distributed forces, we consider two types of actions between material systems Σ_1 and Σ_2: action at-a-distance (such as gravitational actions) exerted at every point within the volume of each systems, and contact actions exerted on all or part of their boundary. From a *local* description of elementary forces modeled as bound vectors (or sliders) acting on infinitesimal elements of volume or surface of Σ_2, we obtain a *global* description of the action of Σ_1 on Σ_2 in term of a screw called *action screw*, and denoted $\{\mathcal{A}_{\Sigma_1 \to \Sigma_2}\}$. The global effect of all mechanical actions exerted on a material system will be defined in terms of the *total external action screw*.

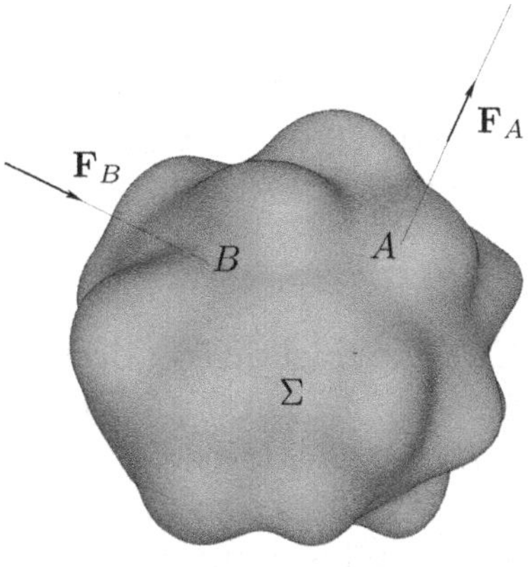

Figure 10.1

10.1 Classification of Mechanical Actions

We denote by Σ a material system (not necessarily a rigid body), by $\overline{\Sigma}$ the *exterior* to Σ, and by $\partial\Sigma$ the boundary of Σ. We classify the mechanical actions exerted on Σ as follows. First we differentiate the internal actions from the external actions exerted on Σ. The mathematical modeling of internal actions is left to a continuum mechanics course. More importantly, their contribution will vanish in the principles and theorems pertaining to the dynamics of systems of rigid bodies. We then classify the external actions exerted on Σ into two groups: actions at-a-distance versus contact actions. For each type we find that these actions can be modeled mathematically in terms of a screw, called *action screw*.

10.1.1 Internal versus External Forces

Given a material system Σ we distinguish between actions which emanate from the exterior $\overline{\Sigma}$ of Σ from those which originate from the interior of Σ. The latter can be viewed as actions exerted on arbitrary subdomains σ of Σ to the interior domain $\Sigma \setminus \sigma$. By consideration of all possible domains σ, it is known in continuum mechanics that these interior actions can be modeled by a second-order tensor, known as the *stress tensor*. As will be seen in Chapter 11, *the contribution of internal actions need not be considered* in the realm of rigid body mechanics. Note that if a material system Σ is defined as the ensemble $\{\mathcal{B}_1, \mathcal{B}_2, \ldots, \mathcal{B}_N\}$ of N rigid bodies, actions internal to Σ also involve any interactions between any two bodies of Σ and will need to be taken into account in certain formulations.

10.1.2 External Actions

The external actions exerted on Σ may be of mechanical, electromagnetic, thermal or chemical origin. We are only concerned with mechanical actions. They can be classified into two groups:

- *actions at-a-distance:* these actions are transmitted from one continuum to another without the need of physical contact between the two. The physical nature of these actions may be gravitational, electrostatic and electromagnetic. They can be modeled by vector fields, more specifically volumetric force fields: at every point of Σ, a local volumetric force can be defined. This rules out the possibility of certain phenomena encountered in some continua which require mechanical actions to be modeled in terms of moments distributed over their domain. Such phenomena are not relevant to rigid body mechanics.

- *contact actions:* these actions arise whenever a material system Σ is in direct physical contact with one or more material systems. Again, we assume that contact actions can be defined by surfacic (or lineic in case of line contact) force fields at all points of boundary $\partial\Sigma$. Again we rule out the existence of fields of moments due to contact.

10.1.3 Action-at-a-distance Screw

Consider a material system $\Sigma_1 \subset \overline{\Sigma}$ which need not be in contact with Σ. See Figure 10.2. System Σ is affected by the presence of Σ_1 in the following way: every infinitesimal volume $dV(P_1)$ located at point P_1 of Σ_1 exerts a force $\mathbf{f}_{\Sigma_1\to\Sigma}(P_1, P)dV(P_1)dV(P)$ on infinitesimal volume $dV(P)$ located at point P of Σ. This force is assumed collinear to position vector $\mathbf{r}_{P_1P}$. The physical origin of this force may be gravitational, electrostatic or electromagnetic. At any point P of Σ one can define a volumetric force field which reflects the overall effect of Σ_1 at P

$$\mathbf{F}^v_{\Sigma_1\to\Sigma}(P) = \int_{\Sigma_1} \mathbf{f}_{\Sigma_1\to\Sigma}(P_1, P)dV(P_1) \tag{10.1}$$

considered a vector bound at P. Hence we model the effect of Σ_1 on Σ by a field of bound vectors $(P, \mathbf{F}^v_{\Sigma_1\to\Sigma}(P))$ (or field of sliders in the language of screws). This rules out certain phenomena whereby the effect of Σ_1 on Σ is only adequately modeled by a *field of screws* characterized locally by both a volumetric force $\mathbf{F}^v_{\Sigma_1\to\Sigma}(P)$ and a volumetric couple $\mathbf{C}_{\Sigma_1\to\Sigma}(P)$ distributed over Σ.

Definition 10.1 — Action-at-a-distance Screw. The global effect of action-at-a-distance forces exerted by material system Σ_1 on material system Σ is modeled by the following screw, called *action-at-a-distance screw*

$$\{\mathcal{A}^v_{\Sigma_1\to\Sigma}\} = \left\{ \begin{array}{c} \mathbf{R}^v_{\Sigma_1\to\Sigma} \\ \\ \mathbf{M}^v_{A,\Sigma_1\to\Sigma} \end{array} \right\} = \left\{ \begin{array}{c} \int_\Sigma \mathbf{F}^v_{\Sigma_1\to\Sigma}(P)dV(P) \\ \\ \int_\Sigma \mathbf{r}_{AP} \times \mathbf{F}^v_{\Sigma_1\to\Sigma}(P)dV(P) \end{array} \right\}_A \tag{10.2}$$

where $\mathbf{F}^v_{\Sigma_1\to\Sigma}(P)$ is the volumetric force field due to Σ_1 at a point P of Σ.

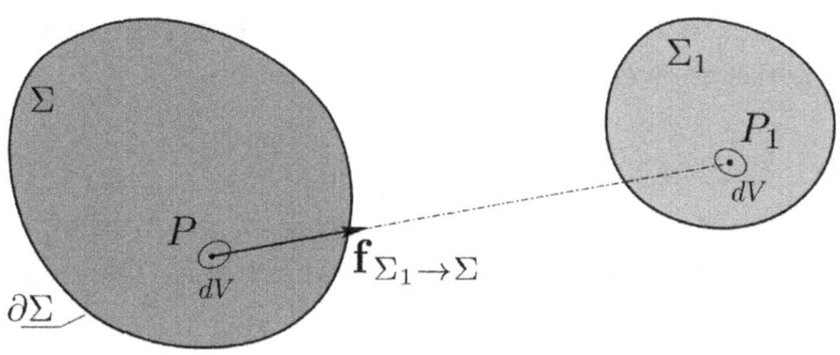

Figure 10.2

Example 1: Gravitational and Electrostatic Actions. When two masses or two electric charges are placed at two locations P_1 and P_2, empirical expressions of the force $\mathbf{f}_{\Sigma_1\to\Sigma}$ caused by P_1 on P_2 are known, leading to various exact and approximate expressions of the corresponding action screw $\{\mathcal{A}_{\Sigma_1\to\Sigma_2}\}$ due to gravitational or electrostatic interactions. In the electrostatic case, the expression of so-called Coulomb force precludes motion of the interacting charges, and hence is of little interest in rigid body dynamics. Gravitational interactions are studied in Section 10.2.

Example 2: Inertial Actions. Whenever a particular referential $\mathcal{E}$ cannot be adequately assumed Newtonian, the laws of motion relative to $\mathcal{E}$ can still be applied by including the effect of inertial forces, the so-called transport and Coriolis forces, which account for the motion of $\mathcal{E}$ relative to some referential assumed Newtonian. In such a case, these inertial forces generate two volumetric force fields over a material system Σ leading to two *inertial action screws* which will be defined in Chapter 16.

10.1.4 Contact Action Screw

Consider now a material system $\Sigma_1 \subset \overline{\Sigma}$ in direct physical contact with Σ as shown in Figure 10.3. However small the surface of contact, one can model the effect of the contact of Σ_1 on Σ by a surface force field $\mathbf{f}^c_{\Sigma_1\to\Sigma}(Q)$ (a force per unit area) defined at all points Q of the boundary $\partial\Sigma_1 \cap \partial\Sigma$. Assuming that unit normal vector $\hat{\mathbf{n}}(Q)$ to surface $\partial\Sigma$ at Q exists, one can then decompose $\mathbf{f}^c_{\Sigma_1\to\Sigma}(Q)$ according to

$$\mathbf{f}^c_{\Sigma_1\to\Sigma}(Q) = N^c_{\Sigma_1\to\Sigma}(Q)\hat{\mathbf{n}}(Q) + \mathbf{T}^c_{\Sigma_1\to\Sigma}(Q)$$

with $\mathbf{T}^c_{\Sigma_1\to\Sigma} \cdot \hat{\mathbf{n}} = 0$. The contributions $N^c_{\Sigma_1\to\Sigma}$ and $\mathbf{T}^c_{\Sigma_1\to\Sigma}$ are called normal surface force density (or contact pressure) and tangential surface force density, respectively.

Definition 10.2 — Action Screw (Contact). The global effect of contact forces exerted by material system Σ_1 in contact with material system Σ is modeled by the following screw, called *contact action screw* and denoted $\{\mathcal{A}^c_{\Sigma_1\to\Sigma}\}$:

$$\{\mathcal{A}^c_{\Sigma_1\to\Sigma}\} = \left\{ \begin{array}{c} \mathbf{R}^c_{\Sigma_1\to\Sigma} \\ \\ \mathbf{M}^c_{A,\Sigma_1\to\Sigma} \end{array} \right\} = \left\{ \begin{array}{c} \int_{\partial\Sigma} \mathbf{f}^c_{\Sigma_1\to\Sigma}(Q)dA(Q) \\ \\ \int_{\partial\Sigma} \mathbf{r}_{AP} \times \mathbf{f}^c_{\Sigma_1\to\Sigma}(Q)dA(Q) \end{array} \right\}_A \tag{10.3}$$

where $\mathbf{f}^c_{\Sigma_1\to\Sigma}(Q)$ is the local force exerted on infinitesimal element of are $dA(Q)$ at Q.

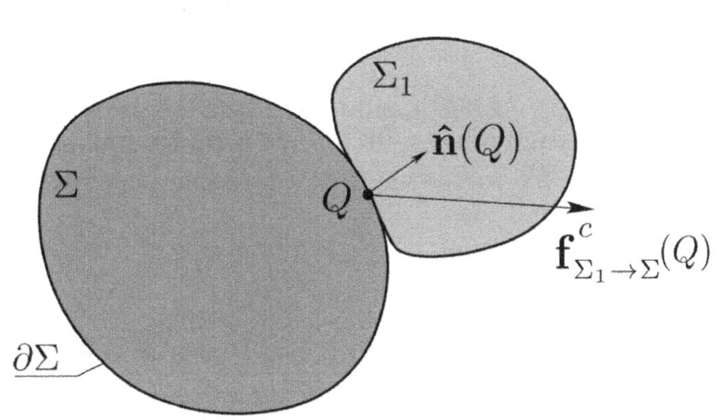

Figure 10.3

Remark 1. Knowledge of the contact action screw $\{\mathcal{A}^c_{\Sigma_1\to\Sigma}\}$ does not in general imply knowledge of the local force field $\mathbf{f}^c_{\Sigma_1\to\Sigma}(Q)$.

Remark 2. Even in a so-called point-contact between Σ_1 and Σ, the contact is actually realized along a small surface. This implies that the contact action screw $\{\mathcal{A}^c_{\Sigma_1\to\Sigma}\}$ is characterized in general by a non-zero moment $\mathbf{M}^c_{I,\Sigma_1\to\Sigma}$ at the point of contact I. See Section 10.3. Nevertheless, many contact actions $\{\mathcal{A}^c_{\Sigma_1\to\Sigma}\}$ are adequately represented by bound vectors $(Q_i, \mathbf{R}^c_{\Sigma_1\to\Sigma})$ at discrete points Q_i of $\partial\Sigma$.

Remark 3. In continuum mechanics, one assumes continuity of stress across the boundary of two material systems in contact. This implies the following condition:

$$\mathbf{f}^c_{\Sigma_1\to\Sigma}(Q) = -\mathbf{f}^c_{\Sigma\to\Sigma_1}(Q) \tag{10.4}$$

at all points $Q \in \partial\Sigma_1 \cap \partial\Sigma$. Hence $\{\mathcal{A}^c_{\Sigma_1\to\Sigma}\} = -\{\mathcal{A}^c_{\Sigma\to\Sigma_1}\}$.

10.1.5 The External Action Screw

By partitioning the exterior $\overline{\Sigma}$ of material system Σ into a finite set of systems $\{\Sigma_1, \Sigma_2, \ldots, \Sigma_N\}$, with $\Sigma_i \cap \Sigma_j = \emptyset$ we can define the *external action screw exerted on* Σ as

$$\{\mathcal{A}_{\overline{\Sigma}\to\Sigma}\} = \sum_{i=1}^{N}\{\mathcal{A}_{\Sigma_i\to\Sigma}\} = \sum_{i=1}^{N}\{\mathcal{A}^v_{\Sigma_i\to\Sigma}\} + \sum_{i=1}^{N}\{\mathcal{A}^c_{\Sigma_i\to\Sigma}\} \tag{10.5}$$

where we have decomposed the action screw of Σ_i on Σ into the sum of action-at-a-distance screw and contact action screws.

10.2 Gravitational Interactions

Gravitational interactions are one of four fundamental action-at-a-distance interactions which are known to occur between particles. At the particle level, they are described by Newton's law of gravitation. We are interested in a macroscopic description of gravitational interactions.

10.2.1 Newton's Law of Gravitation

The success of Newton in predicting the motion of a falling body on Earth or the motion of the planets around the Sun hinges on his *law of universal attraction* which can be stated as follows:

Definition 10.3 Two particles P_1 and P_2 of mass m_1 and m_2, respectively, and at a distance r from each other, attract each other with a force proportional to their mass and inversely proportional to r^2. Hence the force due to P_1 on P_2 can be written as

$$\mathbf{F}^g_{1\to2} = -G\frac{m_1 m_2}{|\mathbf{r}_{P_1P_2}|^3}\mathbf{r}_{P_1P_2} \tag{10.6}$$

where $G = 6.67 \times 10^{-11}\text{N m}^2/\text{kg}^2$ is a universal constant, called *constant of gravitation.*

Note that $\mathbf{F}^g_{2\to1} = -\mathbf{F}^g_{1\to2}$. Every mass particle attracts any other mass particle. However the effect of gravitational forces is only appreciable if at least one of the "particles" has a very large mass. For instance, on Earth's surface we neglect the mutual attraction of bodies in comparison with Earth's gravitational pull. This law is applicable for applications ranging from terrestrial mechanics to celestial mechanics.

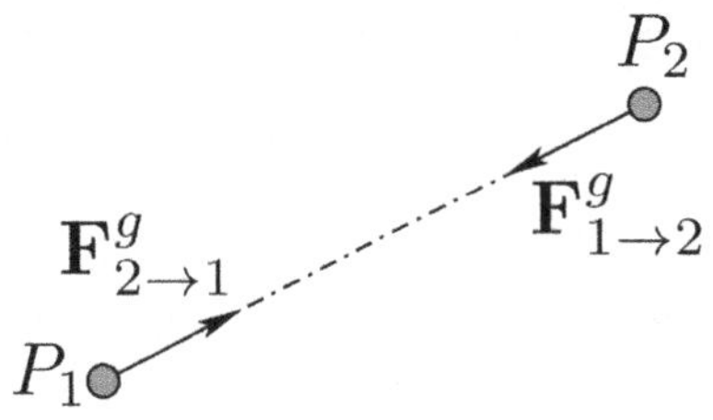

Figure 10.4

10.2.2 Gravitational Field

Definition 10.4 The effect of a discrete or continuous mass distribution Σ_1 on a particle is equivalent to a *gravitational field* $\mathbf{G}_{\Sigma_1}(P)$ at any location P of space, such that, a particle of mass m located at point P at a particular instant would be subjected to the force

$$\mathbf{F}^g_{\Sigma_1 \to P} = m\mathbf{G}_{\Sigma_1}(P) \tag{10.7}$$

For a discrete set of particles $\Sigma_1 = \{P_1, P_2, \cdots P_N\}$ of mass $m_1, m_2, \cdots, m_N$, we find

$$\mathbf{G}_{\Sigma_1}(P) = -G\sum_{i=1}^{N} \frac{m_i \hat{\mathbf{u}}_i}{r_i^2} \tag{10.8}$$

with $r_i = |\mathbf{r}_{P_iP}|$ the distance from P_i to P, and $\hat{\mathbf{u}}_i = \mathbf{r}_{P_iP}/r_i$ the unit vector directed from P_i to P. Hence the gravitational field is obtained by a superposition of individual fields. For a continuous mass system Σ_1, we obtain

$$\mathbf{G}_{\Sigma_1}(P) = -G\int_{\Sigma_1} \frac{\mathbf{r}_{P_1P}}{|\mathbf{r}_{P_1P}|^3} dm(P_1) \tag{10.9}$$

where $dm(P_1) = \rho(P_1)dV$ is an infinitesimal mass of volume dV surrounding P_1. In general, the calculation of this integral is difficult, unless certain assumptions are made as will be done in Section 10.2.3.

The macroscopic gravitational effect of material system Σ_1 on material system Σ can then be modeled in terms of the *gravitational action screw* in following form

$$\{\mathcal{A}^g_{\Sigma_1\to\Sigma}\} = \left\{ \begin{array}{c} \mathbf{R}^g_{\Sigma_1\to\Sigma} \\ \mathbf{M}^g_{A,\Sigma_1\to\Sigma} \end{array} \right\} = \left\{ \begin{array}{c} \int_\Sigma \mathbf{G}_{\Sigma_1}(P)\, dm(P) \\ \int_\Sigma \mathbf{r}_{AP} \times \mathbf{G}_{\Sigma_1}(P)\, dm(P) \end{array} \right\}_A \tag{10.10}$$

For most applications, one considers only the effects of Earth's gravitational forces, that is, one neglects the gravitational effects of all celestial bodies other than that of Earth because such systems are too far, or their mass is too small relative to that of Earth. Furthermore, for applications which take place in domains of small dimensions compared to that of Earth, one may assume that the gravitational field $\mathbf{G}_{\text{Earth}\to\Sigma}(P)$ to be approximately uniform. However, in many applications of celestial mechanics, these assumptions are not adequate and one must then resort to use better approximations of $\mathbf{G}_{\text{Earth}\to\Sigma}(P)$ to obtain useful expressions of $\{\mathcal{A}^g_{\text{Earth}\to\Sigma}\}$.

10.2.3 Gravitational Field of a Body with Spherical Symmetry

Most celestial bodies such as Earth are spherical to a first order of approximation. In addition their mass density can be considered to be only a function of the distance r from their center. Such bodies are said to possess *spherical material symmetry*. Then, by symmetry, the resulting gravitational field at any point is only a function of the radial distance measured from this point to the center of the body. More specifically we can state the following result:

Theorem 10.1 The gravitational field created at a point P by a body Σ_1 of spherical material symmetry, of mass M_1 and center G_1 is given by

$$\mathbf{G}_{\Sigma_1}(P) = -GM_1 \frac{\mathbf{r}_{G_1P}}{|\mathbf{r}_{G_1P}|^3} \tag{10.11}$$

if point P is exterior to Σ_1. Hence, the gravitational field of a body with spherical material symmetry is equivalent to the gravitational field produced by a point mass located at center G_1 of mass M_1.

Proof. The proof is provided by the divergence theorem for the flux of gravitational field $\mathbf{G}_{\Sigma_1}(P)$ across a surface $\partial\Omega$ enclosing a domain Ω

$$\int_{\partial\Omega} \mathbf{G}_{\Sigma_1} \cdot \hat{\mathbf{n}} dA = \int_{\Omega} \nabla \cdot \mathbf{G}_{\Sigma_1} dV = -4\pi G \int_{\Omega} \rho dV$$

where $\hat{\mathbf{n}}$ being the outward unit normal to surface $\partial\Omega$. Recall that $\nabla \cdot \mathbf{G}_{\Sigma_1} = -4\pi G\rho(P)$ where ρ is the local mass density. Let us choose for $\partial\Omega$ the sphere of center G_1 and radius r. Due to the spherical symmetry we expect $\mathbf{G}_{\Sigma_1}$ to be of the form $\mathbf{G}_{\Sigma_1}(P) = g(r)\hat{\mathbf{e}}_r$ for all P on $\partial\Omega$, where $\hat{\mathbf{e}}_r = \hat{\mathbf{n}}$ is unit radial vector at P. This leads to $\int_{\partial\Omega} \mathbf{G}_{\Sigma_1}(P) \cdot \hat{\mathbf{e}}_r dA = 4\pi r^2 g(r)$. With $\int_{\Omega} \rho dV = M_1$, we obtain $g(r) = -GM_1/r^2$. Note that the same approach allows for the determination of field $\mathbf{G}_{\Sigma_1}$ at a point P of the interior of Σ_1. ■

The Gravitational Field of Earth: We can treat the Earth as a body of spherical material symmetry of center C and radius R: the difference between the equatorial radius R_E and the polar radius R_P leads to the value 1/300 of the ratio $(R_E - R_P)/R_E$. Then, the gravitation field at a point P located at altitude z above the Earth's surface (see Figure 10.5) is given by (with $r = R + z$)

$$\mathbf{G}_E(P) = -G\frac{M_E}{(R+z)^2}\hat{\mathbf{e}}_r \tag{10.12}$$

where M_E is Earth's mass, and $\hat{\mathbf{e}}_r$ is the unit vector directed from C to P. If $z \ll R$, we can approximate $1/(R+z)^2$ as $(1 - 2z/R)/R^2$ to first order, and we obtain

$$\mathbf{G}_E(P) \approx -g_0(1 - \frac{2z}{R})\hat{\mathbf{e}}_r \tag{10.13}$$

with

$$g_0 = \frac{GM_E}{R^2} \tag{10.14}$$

the gravitational field at ground level. Hence it is seen that the magnitude of Earth's gravitational field decreases with altitude, though the variation is very weak: with $R = 6400$

km, we find a decrease of 1% at elevation $z = 32$ km. Its direction also varies weakly: two points on the surface of the Earth whose corresponding unit vectors $\hat{\mathbf{e}}_r$ make an angle of one degree are separated by a distance of 110 km. Hence, we see that, *for most terrestrial applications, we may treat the gravitational field as a constant vector in magnitude and direction*

$$\mathbf{G}_E(P) = -g_0 \hat{\mathbf{e}}_r \tag{10.15}$$

With $M_E = 6 \times 10^{24}$ kg, we find $g_0 \approx 9.81$ m/s^2. In this case, the gravitational action screw $\{\mathcal{A}^g_{\text{Earth}\to\Sigma}\}$ takes the form

$$\{\mathcal{A}^g_{\text{Earth}\to\Sigma}\} = \begin{Bmatrix} \int_\Sigma \mathbf{g}\, dm(P) \\ \int_\Sigma \mathbf{r}_{AP} \times \mathbf{g}\, dm(P) \end{Bmatrix}_A = \begin{Bmatrix} M\mathbf{g} \\ \mathbf{0} \end{Bmatrix}_G \tag{10.16}$$

where M denotes the total mass of Σ, and G denotes the mass center of Σ.

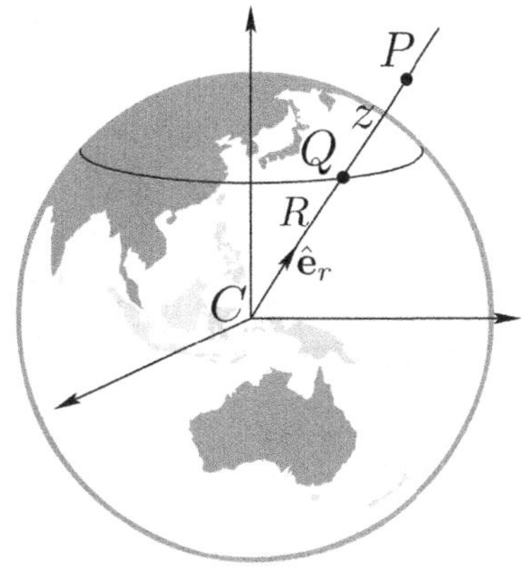

Figure 10.5

In following problem a correction term is obtained for the expression (10.16) of the gravitational action screw due to a body with spherical material symmetry on a "small" body.

Example 10.1 — Small body approximation. Consider the gravitational effect of Earth $\mathcal{E}$ (of mass M, and mass center C) possessing spherical material symmetry on a satellite $\mathcal{S}$ (of mass m, and mass center G) considered small in relation to its distance to Earth. See Figure 10.6.

Show that the resulting gravitational action screw $\{\mathcal{A}^g_{\mathcal{E}\to\mathcal{S}}\}$ is given by

$$\{\mathcal{A}^g_{\mathcal{E}\to\mathcal{S}}\} = -\frac{GMm}{\rho^2} \begin{Bmatrix} \hat{\mathbf{x}} - \frac{3}{2m\rho^2}[(2I_{Gx} - I_{Gy} - I_{Gz})\hat{\mathbf{x}} - 2I_{Gxy}\hat{\mathbf{y}} - 2I_{Gxz}\hat{\mathbf{z}}] \\ \frac{3}{m\rho}(I_{Gxz}\hat{\mathbf{y}} - I_{Gxy}\hat{\mathbf{z}}) \end{Bmatrix}_G$$

where unit vector $\hat{\mathbf{x}}$ is defined by $\mathbf{r}_{CG} = \rho\hat{\mathbf{x}}$, and where $(\hat{\mathbf{x}}, \hat{\mathbf{y}}, \hat{\mathbf{z}})$ forms a right-handed basis. The scalars $I_{Gx} = \hat{\mathbf{x}} \cdot \mathcal{I}_G(\hat{\mathbf{x}})$, $I_{Gy} = \hat{\mathbf{y}} \cdot \mathcal{I}_G(\hat{\mathbf{y}})$, and $I_{Gz} = \hat{\mathbf{z}} \cdot \mathcal{I}_G(\hat{\mathbf{z}})$ are moments of inertia about mass center G. The scalars $I_{Gxy} = \hat{\mathbf{x}} \cdot \mathcal{I}_G(\hat{\mathbf{y}})$, $I_{Gxz} = \hat{\mathbf{x}} \cdot \mathcal{I}_G(\hat{\mathbf{z}})$ are the corresponding products of inertia. (To derive this result, assume that $\mathbf{r} \equiv \mathbf{r}_{GP}$ is much smaller in magnitude than $\rho = |\mathbf{r}_{CG}|$ for any point P of $\mathcal{S}$, and expand the expression $(1+2\hat{\mathbf{x}}\cdot\mathbf{r}/\rho+\mathbf{r}^2/\rho^2)^{-3/2}$ up to second-order in powers of $|\mathbf{r}|/\rho \ll 1$). ■

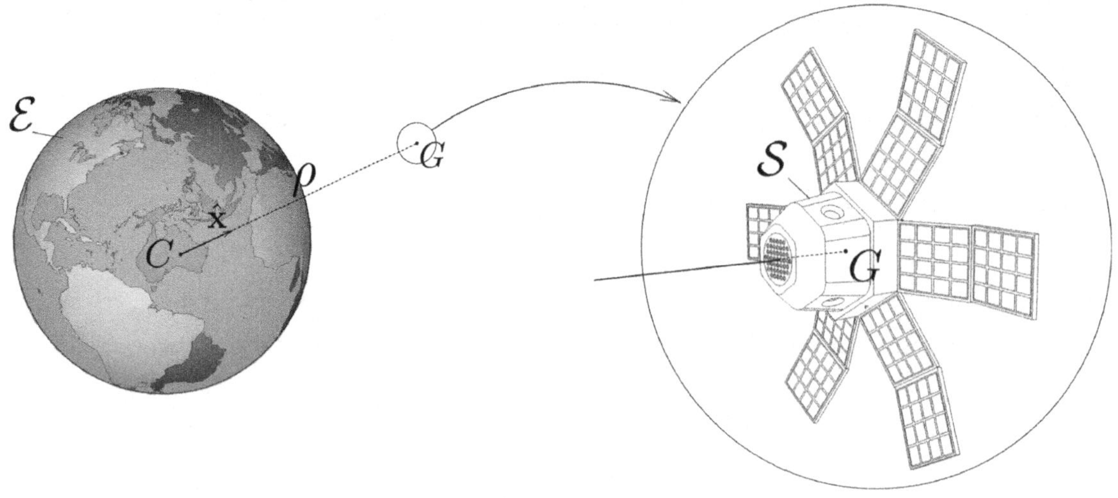

Figure 10.6

We first find the general expression of the resultant of the action screw by using $\mathbf{G}_{\mathcal{E}}(P) = -GM(\rho\hat{\mathbf{x}}+\mathbf{r})/|\rho\hat{\mathbf{x}}+\mathbf{r}|^3$ and denoting $\mathbf{r} = \mathbf{r}_{GP}$:

$$\mathbf{R}^g_{\mathcal{E}\to\mathcal{S}} = -GM\int_{\mathcal{S}} \frac{\rho\hat{\mathbf{x}}+\mathbf{r}}{(\rho^2+2\rho\hat{\mathbf{x}}\cdot\mathbf{r}+\mathbf{r}^2)^{3/2}}dm = -\frac{GM}{\rho^2}\int_{\mathcal{S}} \frac{\hat{\mathbf{x}}+\frac{\mathbf{r}}{\rho}}{(1+2\hat{\mathbf{x}}\cdot\frac{\mathbf{r}}{\rho}+\frac{\mathbf{r}^2}{\rho^2})^{3/2}}dm$$

Assuming $|\mathbf{r}/\rho| \ll 1$, we then expand $(1+2\hat{\mathbf{x}}\cdot\frac{\mathbf{r}}{\rho}+\frac{\mathbf{r}^2}{\rho^2})^{-3/2}$ to second order:

$$\left(1+2\hat{\mathbf{x}}\cdot\frac{\mathbf{r}}{\rho}+\frac{\mathbf{r}^2}{\rho^2}\right)^{-3/2} = 1-3\hat{\mathbf{x}}\cdot\frac{\mathbf{r}}{\rho}-\frac{3}{2}\frac{\mathbf{r}^2}{\rho^2}+\frac{15}{2}(\hat{\mathbf{x}}\cdot\frac{\mathbf{r}}{\rho})^2+\cdots$$

leading to

$$\mathbf{R}^g_{\mathcal{E}\to\mathcal{S}} = -\frac{GmM}{\rho^2}\hat{\mathbf{x}}+\frac{3GM}{2\rho^4}\int_{\mathcal{S}}[(\mathbf{r}^2-5(\hat{\mathbf{x}}\cdot\mathbf{r})^2)\hat{\mathbf{x}}+2(\hat{\mathbf{x}}\cdot\mathbf{r})\mathbf{r}]dm\cdots$$

where we have used the fact that $\int_{\mathcal{S}}\mathbf{r}\,dm = \mathbf{0}$. Each of the integrals in the brackets (the second-order terms) can be expressed in terms of the inertia characteristics of $\mathcal{S}$ about its mass center: by writing $\mathbf{r} = x\hat{\mathbf{x}}+y\hat{\mathbf{y}}+z\hat{\mathbf{z}}$ we find

$$\int_{\mathcal{S}}[(\mathbf{r}^2-5(\hat{\mathbf{x}}\cdot\mathbf{r})^2)\hat{\mathbf{x}}+2(\hat{\mathbf{x}}\cdot\mathbf{r})\mathbf{r}]dm = \int_{\mathcal{S}}[(y^2+z^2-2x^2)\hat{\mathbf{x}}+2xy\hat{\mathbf{y}}+2xz\hat{\mathbf{z}}]dm$$

This gives the final expression

$$\mathbf{R}^g_{\mathcal{E}\to\mathcal{S}} = -\frac{GmM}{\rho^2}\hat{\mathbf{x}}+\frac{3GM}{2\rho^4}\left[(2I_{Gx}-I_{Gy}-I_{Gz})\hat{\mathbf{x}}-2I_{Gxy}\hat{\mathbf{y}}-2I_{Gxz}\hat{\mathbf{z}}\right]+\cdots$$

Note that, as expected, the second-order term vanishes for a body $\mathcal{S}$ of spherical material symmetry, that is, when $I_{Gx} = I_{Gy} = I_{Gz}$ and $I_{Gxy} = I_{Gxz} = 0$. To find the moment about mass center G, we first write

$$\mathbf{M}^g_{G,\mathcal{E}\to\mathcal{S}} = \int_{\mathcal{S}}\mathbf{r}\times\mathbf{G}_{\mathcal{E}}(P)dm = -GM\int_{\mathcal{S}}\mathbf{r}\times(\rho\hat{\mathbf{x}}+\mathbf{r})(\rho^2+2\rho\hat{\mathbf{x}}\cdot\mathbf{r}+\mathbf{r}^2)^{-3/2}dm$$

We then expand to leading order of $|\mathbf{r}|/\rho$:

$$\mathbf{M}^{g}_{G,\mathcal{E}\to\mathcal{S}} = -\frac{GM}{\rho^2}\int_{\mathcal{S}} \mathbf{r}\times\hat{\mathbf{x}}(1-3\hat{\mathbf{x}}\cdot\frac{\mathbf{r}}{\rho}+\cdots)dm = \frac{3GM}{\rho^3}\int_{\mathcal{B}} \mathbf{r}\times\hat{\mathbf{x}}(\hat{\mathbf{x}}\cdot\mathbf{r})dm+\cdots$$

With $\int_{\mathcal{S}} \mathbf{r}\times\hat{\mathbf{x}}(\hat{\mathbf{x}}\cdot\mathbf{r})dm = \int_{\mathcal{S}} x(-y\hat{\mathbf{z}}+z\hat{\mathbf{y}})dm = (I_{Gxy}\hat{\mathbf{z}} - I_{Gxz}\hat{\mathbf{y}})$, we find the final results. ∎

10.2.4 Weight of a Particle and Gravitational Acceleration

Consider in a referential $\mathcal{E}$ a plumb line experiment whereby a particle P of mass m is suspended by a string attached at a point Q fixed in $\mathcal{E}$. See Figure 10.7 (left). If P is at rest in $\mathcal{E}$, we call *vertical* in $\mathcal{E}$ the direction taken by the plumb line.

Definition 10.5 The *weight* $\mathbf{W}$ of particle P in referential $\mathcal{E}$ is the force which balances the tension in the string of a plumb line experiment (in the absence of any other external perturbing influence). Then, the *gravitational acceleration* at the location of P in $\mathcal{E}$ is the vector field $\mathbf{g}(P)$ defined by

$$\mathbf{W} = m\mathbf{g}(P) \qquad (10.17)$$

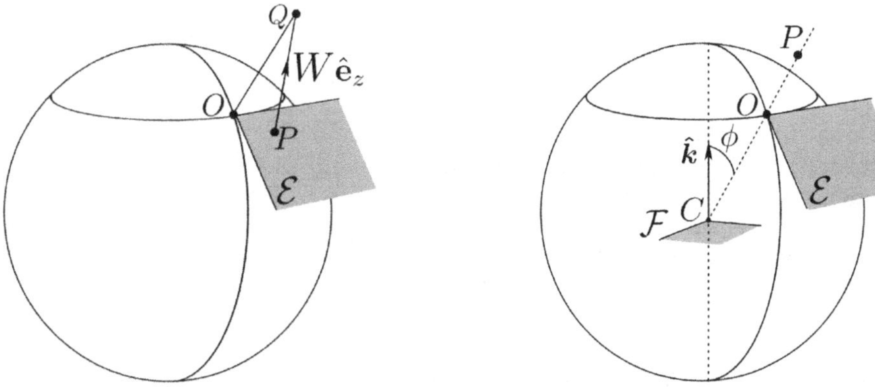

Figure 10.7

Hence, the weight of a particle and the corresponding gravitational acceleration depend on the local value of the gravitational field $\mathbf{G}$ created by one or more celestial bodies and on the transport acceleration of referential $\mathcal{E}$ relative to a (Newtonian) referential $\mathcal{F}$ relative to which it is in motion:

$$\mathbf{g}(P) = \mathbf{G}(P) - \mathbf{a}_{P\in\mathcal{E}/\mathcal{F}} \qquad (10.18)$$

The same particle of mass m will have a different weight whether the plumb line experiment is done on Earth, on the Moon, in the space station, or in an elevator in acceleration.

In terrestrial applications, $\mathbf{g}$ is mostly a function of Earth's gravity field $\mathbf{G} = \mathbf{G}_E$ (which is mostly a function of elevation) and to a much lesser extent a function of Earth's rotation (thus dependent of latitude). The latter effect is obtained by evaluating $\mathbf{a}_{P\in\mathcal{E}/\mathcal{F}}$ relative to the geocentric referential $\mathcal{F}$. The following problem quantifies the effect of Earth's rotation.

Example 10.2 Consider the plumb line experiment done in the terrestrial referential $\mathcal{E}$ attached to Earth at a colatitude ϕ. Apply Newton's second law relative to the geocentric referential $\mathcal{F}$ about which a terrestrial referential $\mathcal{E}$ rotates with angular velocity $\boldsymbol{\omega}_{\mathcal{E}/\mathcal{F}} = \omega_E \hat{\mathbf{k}}$, that is, solve equation

$$-mg_0\hat{\mathbf{e}}_r + W\hat{\mathbf{e}}_z = m\mathbf{a}_{P/\mathcal{F}}$$

to find the weight W of a particle P of mass m, and the angle θ taken by the vertical $\hat{\mathbf{e}}_z$. Use the expression $\mathbf{a}_{P/\mathcal{F}} = \omega_E\hat{\mathbf{k}} \times (\omega_E\hat{\mathbf{k}} \times \mathbf{r}_{CP}) \approx \omega_E^2\mathbf{r}_{OQ}$. See Figure 10.8 for the definitions of unit vectors $\hat{\mathbf{k}}, \hat{\mathbf{e}}_z, \hat{\mathbf{e}}_r$. ■

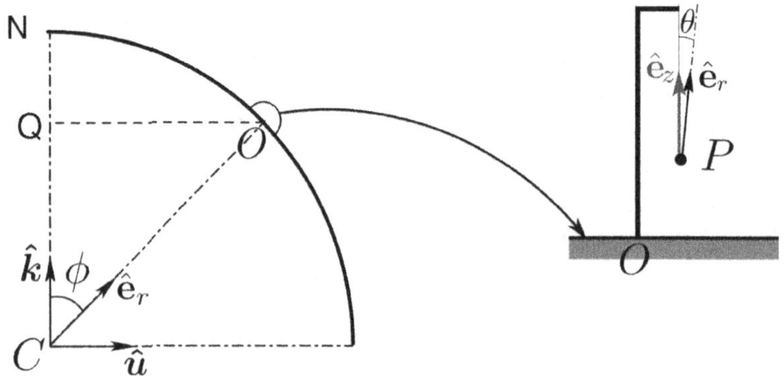

Figure 10.8

We treat the Earth as a body of spherical material symmetry, and neglecting the effect of altitude ($z = 0$), we approximate gravitational field as $\mathbf{G}_E(P) = -g_0\hat{\mathbf{e}}_r$ with $g_0 = GM_E/R^2$. We denote by $\hat{\mathbf{e}}_z$ the unit vector along the string from P to the attachment point Q, by $\hat{\mathbf{e}}_r$ the unit vector directed from Earth's center C to P or to any point "nearby" such as origin O. The string tension is given by $W\hat{\mathbf{e}}_z$, denoting by W the weight of particle P in $\mathcal{E}$. If we account for the rotation of the Earth, the equilibrium of P is now governed by the equation

$$m\mathbf{a}_{P/\mathcal{F}} = -mg_0\hat{\mathbf{e}}_r + W\hat{\mathbf{e}}_z$$

where $\mathcal{F}$ is the so-called geocentric referential defined by Earth's axis of rotation SN, with two additional axes pointing to "fixed" stars, and about which referential $\mathcal{E}$ (Earth) has angular velocity $\boldsymbol{\omega}_{\mathcal{E}/\mathcal{F}} = \omega_E\hat{\mathbf{k}}$, with $\omega = 2\pi$ rad/day. $\hat{\mathbf{k}}$ is the unit vector directed from the south pole S to the north pole N. The change of referential formula for acceleration gives us

$$\begin{aligned}\mathbf{a}_{P/\mathcal{F}} &= \mathbf{a}_{P/\mathcal{E}} + \mathbf{a}_{P\in\mathcal{E}/\mathcal{F}} + 2\boldsymbol{\omega}_{\mathcal{E}/\mathcal{F}} \times \mathbf{v}_{P/\mathcal{E}} = \mathbf{a}_{P\in\mathcal{E}/\mathcal{F}} \approx \omega_E\hat{\mathbf{k}} \times (\omega_E\hat{\mathbf{k}} \times \mathbf{r}_{CP}) \\ &= -R\omega_E^2 \sin\phi\, \hat{\mathbf{u}}\end{aligned}$$

since P is fixed in $\mathcal{E}$, and the motion of $\mathcal{E}$ relative to $\mathcal{F}$ is a uniform rotation about axis $(C, \hat{\mathbf{k}})$. Unit vector $\hat{\mathbf{u}}$ is defined as the vector perpendicular to $\hat{\mathbf{k}}$ lying in the plane containing axis $(C, \hat{\mathbf{k}})$ and point P. Hence the equilibrium equation of P becomes

$$-mg_0\hat{\mathbf{e}}_r + W\hat{\mathbf{e}}_z + mR\omega_E^2 \sin\phi\, \hat{\mathbf{u}} = \mathbf{0}$$

Let us define the ratio ϵ of accelerations by

$$\epsilon = R\omega_E^2/g_0$$

With $R = 6400$ km, $\omega_E = \frac{2\pi}{24\times3600}$ rad/s, and $g_0 = 9.8$ m/s^2, we obtain a very small value

$\epsilon = 0.0034$. Now from the vectorial equation

$$-\hat{\mathbf{e}}_r + \frac{W}{mg_0}\hat{\mathbf{e}}_z + \epsilon \sin\phi \, \hat{\mathbf{u}} = \mathbf{0} \tag{1}$$

we can determine the direction of the vertical $\hat{\mathbf{e}}_z$ and the weight W in referential $\mathcal{E}$: denote by θ the angle $(\hat{\mathbf{e}}_r, \hat{\mathbf{e}}_z)$. To eliminate W from equation (1), take the cross-product with $\hat{\mathbf{e}}_z$ to obtain

$$\tan\theta = \epsilon \frac{\sin\phi\cos\phi}{1 - \epsilon \sin^2\phi}$$

Since $\epsilon \ll 1$, the angle θ is small and can be obtained from

$$\theta = \epsilon \sin\phi \cos\phi.$$

To obtain the weight W and the corresponding gravitational acceleration g in $\mathcal{E}$, take the scalar product of equation (1) with $\hat{\mathbf{e}}_r$

$$W = mg, \qquad g = g_0(1 - \epsilon \sin^2\phi).$$

The maximum angle θ leading to the minimum gravitational acceleration is obtained at colatitude $\phi = \pi/4$:

$$\theta_{\max} = 0.0017, \qquad g_{\min} = 0.997\, g_0.$$

These results show that considering $\mathcal{E}$ as a Newtonian referential for a body at rest is a valid approximation: the error incurred by neglecting the Earth's rotation is very small. ■

A more detailed description of the gravitational acceleration $\mathbf{g}(P)$ at a point P of the surface of the Earth can be given by including the effect of the gravitational field generated by both the Moon $\mathbf{G}_M$ and the Sun $\mathbf{G}_S$, and by accounting for the transport acceleration relative to a heliocentric referential $\mathcal{F}$:

$$\mathbf{g}(P) = \mathbf{G}_E(P) + \mathbf{G}_M(P) + \mathbf{G}_S(P) - \mathbf{a}_{P\in\mathcal{E}/\mathcal{F}}$$

where the transport acceleration $\mathbf{a}_{P\in\mathcal{E}/\mathcal{F}}$ includes the acceleration $\mathbf{a}_{C/\mathcal{F}}$ of the mass center of the Earth around the Sun, in addition to the term $-\omega_E^2 \mathbf{r}_{QP}$ accounting for the rotation of the Earth about its axis

$$\mathbf{a}_{P\in\mathcal{E}/\mathcal{F}} = -\omega_E^2 \mathbf{r}_{QP} + \mathbf{a}_{C/\mathcal{F}}$$

where point Q is the projection of P on the Earth's axis of rotation. To find $\mathbf{a}_{C/\mathcal{F}}$ we apply Newton's law for the motion of C relative to referential $\mathcal{F}$

$$M\mathbf{a}_{C/\mathcal{F}} = M(\mathbf{G}_M(C) + \mathbf{G}_S(C))$$

under the gravitational attraction of the Moon and the Earth.

Definition 10.6 The terrestrial gravitational acceleration can be expressed in the form

$$\mathbf{g}(P) = \mathbf{G}_E(P) + (\mathbf{G}_M(P) - \mathbf{G}_M(C)) + (\mathbf{G}_S(P) - \mathbf{G}_S(C)) + \omega_E^2 \mathbf{r}_{QP} \tag{10.19}$$

where G_M and G_S are the gravitational fields generated by the Moon and the Sun, respectively. The differential terms $\mathbf{G}_M(P) - \mathbf{G}_M(C)$ and $\mathbf{G}_S(P) - \mathbf{G}_S(C)$ are called tidal accelerations.

Remark 4. The contributions of the tidal accelerations to $\mathbf{g}(P)$ are responsible for the tidal phenomena of the Earth's oceans, and for other celestial phenomena.

The following problem attempts to give an explanation of the ocean's tides.

Example 10.3 Consider the system Earth-Moon shown in Figure 10.9. The plane of the figure is assumed to be the equatorial plane of Earth containing the mass center M of the Moon. Both bodies are assumed spherical and of homogeneous mass. The lines CM intersects Earth's surface at points P_1 and P_2. Find the tidal accelerations $\mathbf{G}_M(P) - \mathbf{G}_M(C)$ at these two diametrically opposed points to show that two effects of opposed directions and equal magnitude are obtained, thus explaining the bulging of the oceans at these locations (high tides). Assume that the distance $D_M = |CM|$ is much larger than Earth radius R. How many daily high tides are obtained? Where are low tides obtained?

To assess the strength of the Moon's tidal acceleration relative to that of the Sun, evaluate the ratio $|\mathbf{G}_M(P_1) - \mathbf{G}_M(C)|/|\mathbf{G}_S(P_1) - \mathbf{G}_S(C)|$. Use $D_M/D_S = 2.5 \times 10^{-3}$ and $m_M/m_S = 3.65 \times 10^{-8}$. ■

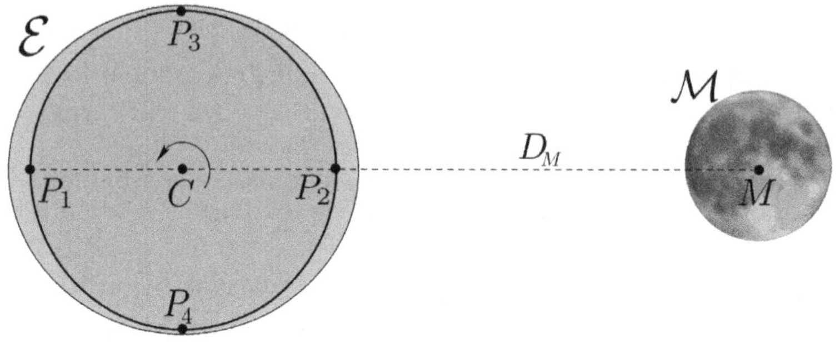

Figure 10.9

Denote by $\hat{\mathbf{u}}$ the unit vector $\mathbf{r}_{CM}/|\mathbf{r}_{CM}|$. Assuming that the Moon is spherical and homogeneous, its gravitational field at points P_1, P_2 and C are given by (denoting m_M the mass of the Moon)

$$\mathbf{G}_M(P_1) = \frac{Gm_M}{(D_M + R)^2}\hat{\mathbf{u}}, \quad \mathbf{G}_M(P_2) = \frac{Gm_M}{(D_M - R)^2}\hat{\mathbf{u}}, \quad \mathbf{G}_M(C) = \frac{Gm_M}{D_M^2}\hat{\mathbf{u}}$$

This leads to the expressions

$$\begin{aligned}\mathbf{G}_M(P_1) - \mathbf{G}_M(C) &= \left(\frac{Gm_M}{(D_M + R)^2} - \frac{Gm_M}{D_M^2}\right)\hat{\mathbf{u}} = \frac{Gm_M}{D_M^2}\left((1 - 2\frac{R}{D_M} + \cdots) - 1\right)\hat{\mathbf{u}}\\ &= -\frac{2Gm_M R}{D_M^3}\hat{\mathbf{u}}\end{aligned}$$

$$\begin{aligned}\mathbf{G}_M(P_2) - \mathbf{G}_M(C) &= \left(\frac{Gm_M}{(D_M - R)^2} - \frac{Gm_M}{D_M^2}\right)\hat{\mathbf{u}} = \frac{Gm_M}{D_M^2}\left((1 + 2\frac{R}{D_M} + \cdots) - 1\right)\hat{\mathbf{u}}\\ &= \frac{2Gm_M R}{D_M^3}\hat{\mathbf{u}}\end{aligned}$$

where we have used the fact that $R/D_M \ll 1$. We have thus obtained two opposed tidal accelerations of equal magnitude at P_1 and P_2. This explains the rising of Earth's ocean surface.

Tidal phenomena vary in time due to the Earth's rotation about its axis. Assuming the Moon stationary relative to a geocentric referential, a given meridian will reach the position P_1P_2 twice a day, thus leading to two high tides per day. In reality, the Moon has a period of 27 days around the Earth, leading to high tides every 12h25min. Low tides are obtained at the locations of a meridian which is perpendicular to line P_1P_2.

We can replace the role played by the Moon by that of the Sun:

$$\mathbf{G}_S(P_1) - \mathbf{G}_S(C) = -\frac{2Gm_S R}{D_S^3}\hat{\mathbf{u}}, \qquad \mathbf{G}_S(P_2) - \mathbf{G}_S(C) = \frac{2Gm_S R}{D_S^3}\hat{\mathbf{u}}$$

We obtain the ratio of tidal accelerations

$$\frac{|\mathbf{G}_M(P_1) - \mathbf{G}_M(C)|}{|\mathbf{G}_S(P_1) - \mathbf{G}_S(C)|} = \frac{m_M}{m_S}\frac{D_S^3}{D_M^3} \approx 2.3$$

This shows that the Moon's tidal force is stronger than that of the Sun by a factor of 2.3. These two effects are superimposed when the Sun and Moon become aligned with Earth: this happens about twice a month, at the new and full moons, leading to a maximum range between low and high tides. ∎

10.3 Contact Actions

Whenever there exist constraints between rigid bodies, such as encountered in a "point-contact" or any other joint, the application of the fundamental laws of dynamics is generally not sufficient to arrive at a closed set of equations: there exist more unknowns than equations, due to the fact that each *contact action screw* associated with such constraints generally leads to six additional unknown scalar quantities. This situation is not unexpected since it arises even in the case of a particle constrained to move along a rigid support. To resolve this indetermination, constitutive laws must be introduced, in order to describe the behavior of moving rigid bodies in contact with one another. Such laws may provide additional equations to fully resolve the indetermination.

Consider two rigid bodies $\mathcal{B}_1$ and $\mathcal{B}_2$ in relative motion in a referential $\mathcal{E}$. Assume that at least one of the bodies possesses a smooth surface. Rigid bodies $\mathcal{B}_1$ and $\mathcal{B}_2$ are assumed to be in contact at all time at a single point I. At any given time, a point I of $\mathcal{B}_1$ coincides with a point I of $\mathcal{B}_2$. Denote by Π the common tangent plane to the bounding surfaces of $\mathcal{B}_1$ and $\mathcal{B}_2$ at point I. If one of the surfaces is not smooth (as in the case of a cone in contact at its apex with a smooth surface), then we define Π as the plane tangential to the smooth surface at I. Denote by $\hat{\mathbf{n}}_{12}$ the unit normal vector to Π pointing from $\mathcal{B}_1$ to $\mathcal{B}_2$. See Figure 10.10.

In general, point-contact between two rigid bodies is associated with a *contact action screw* $\{\mathcal{A}^c_{\mathcal{B}_1\to\mathcal{B}_2}\}$ which may be resolved in the following way

$$\{\mathcal{A}^c_{\mathcal{B}_1\to\mathcal{B}_2}\} = \left\{ \begin{array}{l} \mathbf{R}^c_{1\to 2} = N_{1\to 2}\hat{\mathbf{n}}_{12} + \mathbf{F}_{1\to 2} \\ \mathbf{M}^c_{I,1\to 2} = M_{In}\hat{\mathbf{n}}_{12} + \mathbf{M}_{It} \end{array} \right\} \tag{10.20}$$

Remark 5. Component $N_{1\to 2}$ is called the *normal reaction force* at I. It must satisfy the inequality $N_{1\to 2} \geq 0$ at all times if the point-contact is *unilateral*, that is, if the rigid bodies are free to lose contact with each other under the action of other applied forces. If the equations of motion predict that at some time t^*, $N_{1\to 2} = 0$ and subsequently $N_{1\to 2} < 0$ for $t > t^*$, then the contact at I is lost and $\{\mathcal{A}^c_{\mathcal{B}_1\to\mathcal{B}_2}\} = \{0\}$ for $t > t^*$.

Remark 6. The vector $\mathbf{F}_{1\to 2}$ is the *tangential reaction force* or *frictional force* at I and it is a measure of *resistance to the sliding motion* of $\mathcal{B}_2$ relative to $\mathcal{B}_1$.

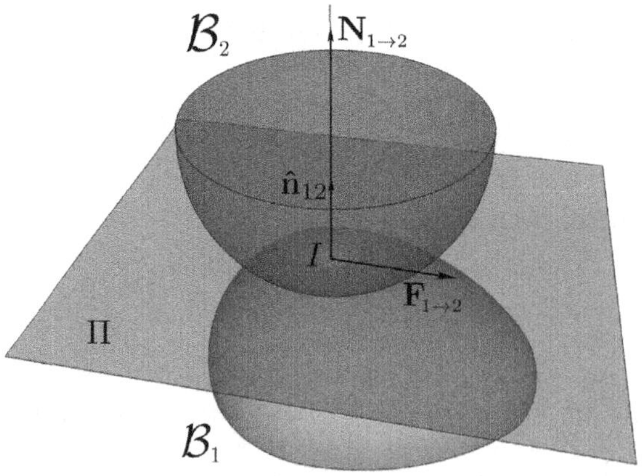

Figure 10.10

Remark 7. The components $M_{In} = \hat{\mathbf{n}}_{12} \cdot \mathbf{M}^c_{I,1\to 2}$ and $\mathbf{M}_{It} = \mathbf{M}^c_{I,1\to 2} - M_{In}\hat{\mathbf{n}}_{12}$ of the moment at point I are measures of the *resistance to the pivoting and rolling motions*, respectively, of $\mathcal{B}_2$ relative to $\mathcal{B}_1$. In general $\mathbf{M}^c_{I,1\to 2}$ should not be expected to be zero, since the contact, although modeled as a point-contact, is in reality occurring over a small area surrounding point I.

Hence, in general, point-contact between two rigid bodies results in six additional unknowns. Problems of rigid body mechanics which involve contact actions will inevitably be unyielding unless simplifying assumptions on the structure of the contact action screw $\{\mathcal{A}^c_{\mathcal{B}_1\to\mathcal{B}_2}\}$ are introduced.

The most drastic simplification amounts to neglecting friction: it is often the only simplification which makes the solution of problems tractable.

10.3.1 Frictionless Contact between two Rigid Bodies

Definition 10.7 The contact at point I is said to be frictionless if the resultant vector $\mathbf{R}^c_{1\to 2}$ is assumed normal to surfaces in contact and bound at the point of contact, that is,

$$\mathbf{F}_{1\to 2} = \mathbf{0} \quad \text{and} \quad \mathbf{M}^c_{I,1\to 2} = \mathbf{0} \tag{10.21}$$

Hence the contact action screw $\{\mathcal{A}^c_{\mathcal{B}_1\to\mathcal{B}_2}\}$ takes the form of a slider

$$\{\mathcal{A}^c_{\mathcal{B}_1\to\mathcal{B}_2}\} = \left\{ \begin{matrix} N_{1\to 2}\hat{\mathbf{n}}_{12} \\ \mathbf{0} \end{matrix} \right\}_I \tag{10.22}$$

As will be seen in Section 10.3.4, frictionless contact can be generalized to line or surface contact. Furthermore, the dynamic analysis of systems of interconnected rigid bodies can often be made soluble (within the realms of rigid body mechanics) by assuming that the interconnecting joints between rigid bodies are frictionless. Frictionless joints are described in Section 10.4.

10.3.2 Coulomb Laws of Sliding Friction

If friction must be taken into account, then we must rely on phenomenological laws governing the sliding motion of body $\mathcal{B}_2$ relative to body $\mathcal{B}_1$ under dry contact conditions, that is, in the absence of lubrication. It is necessary to distinguish two kinematic cases whether there is slip or not.

Definition 10.8 — Coulomb Laws (dry friction). The contact between bodies $\mathcal{B}_1$ and $\mathcal{B}_2$ is characterized by two dimensionless coefficients μ_s and μ_k, called *coefficients of static and kinetic friction*. These coefficients characterize the reaction force $\mathbf{R}^c_{1\to 2}$ in the following manner:

- **Case 1:** if $\mathcal{B}_2$ slips relative to $\mathcal{B}_1$, that is, $\mathbf{v}_{I\in 2/1} \neq 0$, then

$$|\mathbf{F}_{1\to 2}| = \mu_k |N_{1\to 2}|, \tag{10.23}$$

  and the frictional force $\mathbf{F}_{1\to 2}$ must be collinear and opposed to the slip velocity $\mathbf{v}_{I\in 2/1}$:

$$\mathbf{F}_{1\to 2} \times \mathbf{v}_{I\in 2/1} = \mathbf{0} \quad \text{and} \quad \mathbf{F}_{1\to 2} \cdot \mathbf{v}_{I\in 2/1} < 0 \tag{10.24}$$

  or more simply

$$\mathbf{F}_{1\to 2} = -\mu_k |N_{12}| \frac{\mathbf{v}_{I\in 2/1}}{|\mathbf{v}_{I\in 2/1}|} \tag{10.25}$$

- **Case 2:** if $\mathcal{B}_2$ rolls and pivots without slipping relative to $\mathcal{B}_1$ about I, i.e. $\mathbf{v}_{I\in 2/1} = \mathbf{0}$, then the inequality

$$|\mathbf{F}_{1\to 2}| \leq \mu_s |N_{1\to 2}| \tag{10.26}$$

  must be satisfied.

Remark 8. We can define a unique angle ϕ by the relation $\tan\phi = \mu_s$: the inequality (10.26) can be stated as

$$\frac{|\mathbf{F}_{1\to 2}|}{|N_{1\to 2}|} \leq \tan\phi$$

which shows that the contact force $\mathbf{R}^c_{1\to 2}$ must lie inside the cone (known as the friction cone) of axis $(I, \hat{\mathbf{n}}_{12})$ and half-angle ϕ. Angle ϕ is the maximum inclination reached by the reaction force $\mathbf{R}^c_{1\to 2}$ relative to the normal direction $\hat{\mathbf{n}}_{12}$. See Figure 10.11 (left).

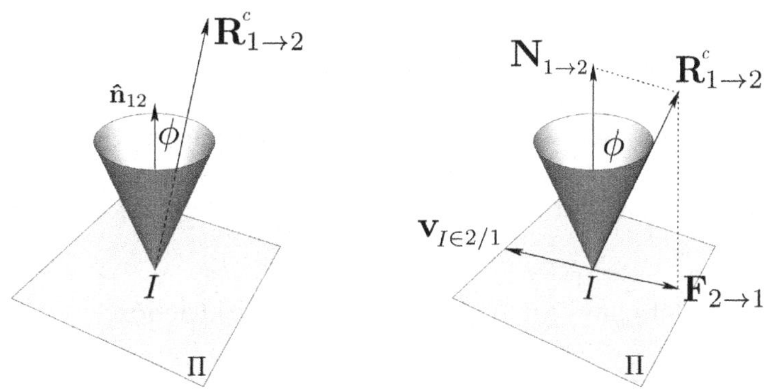

Figure 10.11

Remark 9. Coulomb laws, as stated above, are valid as long as $\mathcal{B}_1$ and $\mathcal{B}_2$ remain in contact: for unilateral constraints, one must guarantee that $N_{1\to 2} > 0$.

Remark 10. In the two cases stated above, two additional scalar equations are provided. These two additional scalar equations are generally sufficient to resolve the indetermination in the case of a *single* point of contact.

Remark 11. It is known that the coefficients of friction depends on the nature of the surface in contact (such as the type of materials, the state of roughness and lubrication of the surfaces) and on the magnitude of the slip velocity $|\mathbf{v}_{I\in 2/1}|$. Various empirical laws can be found in the literature. It can be shown that $\mu_k < \mu_s$. However, one often assumes $\mu_k = \mu_s$. See Figure 10.11 (right).

Remark 12. In cases of multiple points of contact, these laws may not resolve the indetermination created by additional unknown components of the reaction forces.

Remark 13. It was pointed out by Painlevé [1] that in general the normal reaction $N_{1\to 2}$ is a function of the coefficient of kinetic friction in addition to the variables which define the position and velocity of the rigid bodies. In case of slip between the bodies, whether at the start of the motion or not, some situations may arise, whereby either no motion or multiple motions may be possible with given initial conditions. This is typical of ill-posed problems and it shows that Coulomb laws must be used with care. This will be illustrated in Chapter 11.

10.3.3 Rolling and Spinning Friction

In general, the moment at I is negligible as compared to the effect of sliding friction, and one often assumes $\mathbf{M}^c_{I,1\to 2} = \mathbf{0}$. When this assumption is too crude and leads to erroneous (and unacceptable) results, one can use additional laws to account for friction of the rolling and spinning motions. Denote $\omega_n \equiv \boldsymbol{\omega}_{2/1} \cdot \hat{\mathbf{n}}_{12}$ and $\boldsymbol{\omega}_t \equiv \boldsymbol{\omega}_{2/1} - \omega_n \hat{\mathbf{n}}_{12}$ the spinning and rolling components of the angular velocity. We can state the following laws for rolling friction:

Definition 10.9 — Rolling Friction.

- if $\boldsymbol{\omega}_t = \mathbf{0}$ (no rolling motion), then

$$|\mathbf{M}_{It}| \leq k|N_{1\to 2}|$$

- if $\boldsymbol{\omega}_t \neq 0$, then

$$|\mathbf{M}_{It}| = k|N_{1\to 2}|, \qquad \mathbf{M}_{It} \cdot \boldsymbol{\omega}_t < 0, \qquad \mathbf{M}_{It} \times \boldsymbol{\omega}_t = \mathbf{0}$$

  Coefficient k (which has the dimension of a length) is called *coefficient of rolling friction.*

Similarly, we can state laws for pivoting (or spinning) friction:

Definition 10.10 — Pivoting Friction.

- if $\omega_n = 0$ (no pivoting motion), then

$$|M_{In}| \leq h|N_{1\to 2}|$$

[1] P. Painlevé, *Leçon sur le frottement*, Hermann, Paris, 1895.

- if $\omega_n \neq 0$, then

$$|M_{In}| = h|N_{1\to 2}|, \qquad M_{In}\omega_n < 0.$$

Coefficient h (which has the dimension of a length) is called *coefficient of pivoting friction.*

10.3.4 Rigid bodies in line- or surface-contact

In the case of rigid bodies $\mathcal{B}_1$ and $\mathcal{B}_2$ in contact about a line or a surface $\partial\mathcal{B}_1 \cap \partial\mathcal{B}_2$, friction laws are more difficult to formulate. We may assume that at every point $Q \in \partial\mathcal{B}_1 \cap \partial\mathcal{B}_2$ of the surface or line of contact the local force density field $\mathbf{f}^c_{1\to 2}(Q)$ satisfies Coulomb laws of sliding friction. However it may not always be possible to derive a closed-form expression of the global effect of these contact forces due to body $\mathcal{B}_1$ on body $\mathcal{B}_2$. In case of relative slip at point Q, if the direction of the local slip velocity is known, then the local friction force may be determined in both direction and magnitude. Derivation of closed-form expression of $\{\mathcal{A}^c_{\mathcal{B}_1\to\mathcal{B}_2}\}$ is then possible as shown in the following example.

Example 10.4 Consider the system disk-braking pad of an automobile's wheel. Body $\mathcal{B}_2$ represents the brake disk rigidly connected to the rotating wheel. To stop the wheel, a braking pad $\mathcal{B}_1$ is forced to press against the surface of the disk. The pad is modeled as a disk sector of center O, angle 2θ and radii R_1 and R_2. At a given instant, it is assumed that $\mathcal{B}_1$ exerts on $\mathcal{B}_2$ a uniform pressure p over the entire surface of contact. The contacting surfaces are characterized by a kinetic friction coefficient μ. Find the expression of the contact action screw $\{\mathcal{A}^c_{\mathcal{B}_1\to\mathcal{B}_2}\}$ at this instant as a function of pressure p, μ and the geometric parameters. ■

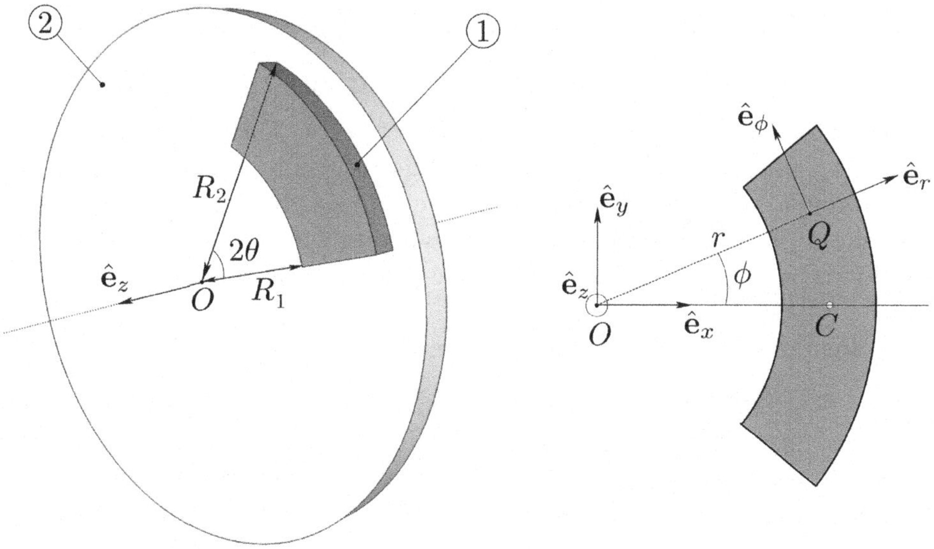

Denote the position of contact point Q by its polar coordinates (r, ϕ). At a given instant the velocity of point Q is given by $\mathbf{v}_{Q\in 2/1} = r\omega_{2/1}\hat{\mathbf{e}}_\phi$, assuming that $\omega_{2/1} = \omega_{1/2}\hat{\mathbf{e}}_z$. The local friction force will be collinear and opposed to the $\mathbf{v}_{Q\in 2/1}$, and its magnitude is μp. The contact force $d\mathbf{R}^c_{1\to 2}$ acting on area $dA = rdrd\phi$ is composed of a normal contribution $-pdA\,\hat{\mathbf{e}}_z$ and a tangential contribution $-\mu p dA \hat{\mathbf{e}}_\phi$:

$$d\mathbf{R}^c_{1\to 2} = -p(\hat{\mathbf{e}}_z + \mu\, \hat{\mathbf{e}}_\phi)dA$$

This gives the resultant force

$$\mathbf{R}^c_{1\to 2} = -\int_{R_1}^{R_2}\int_{-\theta}^{\theta} p(\hat{\mathbf{e}}_z + \mu\hat{\mathbf{e}}_\phi) r dr d\phi = -\frac{p}{2}(R_2^2 - R_1^2)(2\theta\,\hat{\mathbf{e}}_z + 2\mu\sin\theta\,\hat{\mathbf{e}}_y)$$

The total moment about O of these contact forces is given by

$$\mathbf{M}^c_{O,1\to 2} = -\int_{R_1}^{R_2}\int_{-\theta}^{\theta} r\hat{\mathbf{e}}_r \times p(\hat{\mathbf{e}}_z + \mu\hat{\mathbf{e}}_\phi) r dr d\phi = -\frac{p}{3}(R_2^3 - R_1^3)(2\mu\theta\hat{\mathbf{e}}_z - 2\sin\theta\hat{\mathbf{e}}_y)$$

The moment about the geometric center C of $\mathcal{B}_1$ is then found to be

$$\mathbf{M}^c_{C,1\to 2} = \mathbf{M}^c_{O,1\to 2} + \mathbf{R}^c_{1\to 2} \times \mathbf{r}_{OC} = \frac{2}{3}\mu\theta p(R_2^3 - R_1^3)\left(-1 + \frac{\sin^2\theta}{\theta^2}\right)\hat{\mathbf{e}}_z$$

check if these are a slider (do dot product) (invariant)

using $|OC| = (2/3)[(R_2^3 - R_1^3)/(R_2^2 - R_1^2)]\frac{\sin\theta}{\theta}$. This gives the final expression of $\{\mathcal{A}^c_{\mathcal{B}_1\to\mathcal{B}_2}\}$

$$\{\mathcal{A}^c_{\mathcal{B}_1\to\mathcal{B}_2}\} = \begin{Bmatrix} -\frac{p}{2}(R_2^2 - R_1^2)(2\theta\,\hat{\mathbf{e}}_z + 2\mu\sin\theta\,\hat{\mathbf{e}}_y) \\ \frac{2}{3}\mu\theta p(R_2^3 - R_1^3)\left(-1 + \frac{\sin^2\theta}{\theta^2}\right)\hat{\mathbf{e}}_z \end{Bmatrix}_C$$

■

It is apparent that a closed-form expression of $\{\mathcal{A}^c_{\mathcal{B}_1\to\mathcal{B}_2}\}$ of Example 10.4 was feasible thanks for the fact that both the normal force $N_{1\to 2}$ and the slip-velocity were known. But in general, this is not expected, and this makes the expression of $\{\mathcal{A}^c_{\mathcal{B}_1\to\mathcal{B}_2}\}$ very difficult to obtain. If, however, the contact is assumed frictionless, that is, if $\mu_k = \mu_s = 0$ is assumed, then the local contact force (per unit area or unit length) $\mathbf{f}^c_{1\to 2}(Q)$ must satisfy:

$$\mathbf{f}^c_{1\to 2}(Q) = N_{1\to 2}(Q)\hat{\mathbf{n}}_{12}(Q) \tag{10.27}$$

where $\hat{\mathbf{n}}_{12}$ is the local unit normal at the contact point. The contribution of the tangential force density is then neglected. This local assumption does result in some significant simplifications for the global effect of contact forces: the contact action screw $\{\mathcal{A}^c_{\mathcal{B}_1\to\mathcal{B}_2}\}$ will in general have fewer than six unknown resultant and moment components. This assumption is in general sufficient to resolve the indetermination generally encountered in multibody dynamics.

This is illustrated with the following example.

Example 10.5 Consider the case displayed in Figure 10.12 of two bodies $\mathcal{B}_1$ and $\mathcal{B}_2$ constrained in such a way that two coinciding axisymmetric surfaces are in relative rotation about a common axis $\Delta(O, \hat{\mathbf{x}})$. Assume that the contact is frictionless. Show that the moment of the contact forces about any point O of Δ must satisfy

$$\hat{\mathbf{x}} \cdot \mathbf{M}^c_{O,1\to 2} = 0$$

with $\hat{\mathbf{x}}$ a unit vector along Δ. ■

Define unit vectors $(\hat{\mathbf{u}}, \hat{\mathbf{v}} = \hat{\mathbf{x}} \times \hat{\mathbf{u}})$ with $\hat{\mathbf{u}}$ normal to $\hat{\mathbf{x}}$ and in the cross-sectional plane containing Δ and contact point Q. The contact being frictionless, the local contact force (per unit area) is

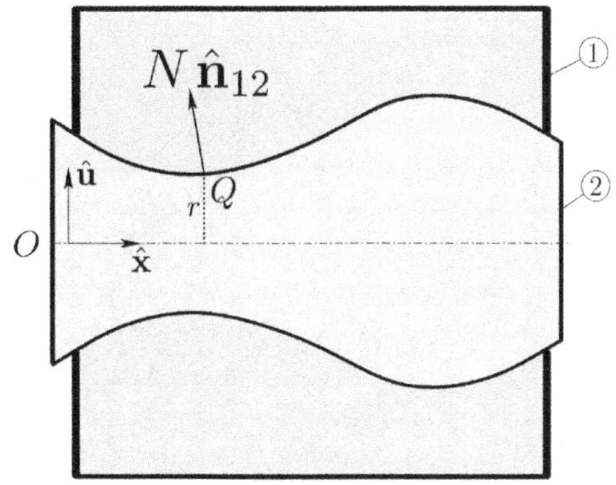

Figure 10.12

directed along the unit normal $\hat{\mathbf{n}}_{12}$ to the surface $\mathcal{S} = \partial \mathcal{B}_1 \cap \partial \mathcal{B}_2$:

$$\mathbf{f}^c_{1\to 2}(Q) = N_{12}(Q)\hat{\mathbf{n}}_{12}$$ *we cannot predict direction of force in this case*

for all contact points Q. Then the resultant moment at any point O of the axis of rotation takes the expression

$$\mathbf{M}^c_{O,1\to 2} = \int_{\mathcal{S}} \mathbf{r}_{OQ} \times N_{12}(Q)\hat{\mathbf{n}}_{12}dA$$

normal to picture plane

leading to

$$\hat{\mathbf{x}} \cdot \mathbf{M}^c_{O,1\to 2} = \int_{\mathcal{S}} (\hat{\mathbf{x}} \times \mathbf{r}_{OQ}) \cdot N_{12}\hat{\mathbf{n}}_{12}dA = \int_{\mathcal{S}} (\hat{\mathbf{v}} \cdot \hat{\mathbf{n}}_{12})N_{12}rdA = 0$$
$\hat{\mathbf{v}} \perp \hat{\mathbf{n}}$

All other components of the action screw $\{\mathcal{A}^c_{1\to 2}\}$ are expected to be non-zero:

$$\mathbf{R}^c_{1\to 2} = R_x\hat{\mathbf{x}} + R_u\hat{\mathbf{u}} + R_v\hat{\mathbf{v}}, \quad \mathbf{M}^c_{O,1\to 2} = M_{Ou}\hat{\mathbf{u}} + M_{Ov}\hat{\mathbf{v}}$$

at any point O of the axis of rotation. ∎

In Section 10.4, we show similar properties for the kinematic lower pairs of rigid bodies described in Chapter 7. Furthermore, we will see in Chapter 12 how to determine the specificity of frictionless contact action screws in a systematic way by using energy arguments.

10.4 Frictionless Joints

The contact action screw which results from the connection of two rigid bodies $\mathcal{B}_1$ and $\mathcal{B}_2$ by a frictionless joint can be simplified due to the fact that the local contact force is directed along the local unit normal vector $\hat{\mathbf{n}}_{12}$ to the surfaces in contact

$$\mathbf{f}^c_{1\to 2}(Q) = N_{1\to 2}(Q)\hat{\mathbf{n}}_{12}(Q) \tag{10.28}$$

at all points Q of the contacting surfaces. We list below the expressions of the action screw $\{\mathcal{A}^c_{1\to 2}\}$ for the six lower kinematic pairs described in Chapter 7.

Frictionless Pivot

Recall that a pivot is a one-degree-of-freedom joint which permits a rotation about a common axis $\Delta \equiv (O_1, \hat{\mathbf{z}}_1) = (O_2, \hat{\mathbf{z}}_2)$ of $\mathcal{B}_1$ and $\mathcal{B}_2$. The corresponding kinematic screw is given by

$$\{\mathcal{V}_{2/1}\} = \left\{ \begin{array}{c} \boldsymbol{\omega}_{2/1} = \omega_z\hat{\mathbf{z}}_1 \\ \mathbf{0} \end{array} \right\}_{A \in \Delta} \tag{10.29}$$

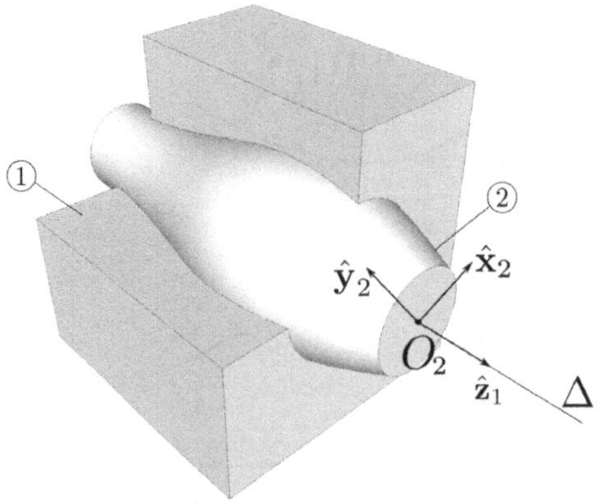

Figure 10.13

Then, assuming frictionless contact, the corresponding action contact screw $\{\mathcal{A}^c_{1\to 2}\}$ satisfies

$$\mathbf{M}^c_{A,1\to 2} \cdot \hat{\mathbf{z}}_1 = 0 \tag{10.30}$$

for any point A of axis Δ as was shown in Example 10.5. All other components of the action screw are in general non-zero:

$$\{\mathcal{A}^c_{1\to 2}\} = \left\{ \begin{array}{c} R_x\hat{\mathbf{x}}_1 + R_y\hat{\mathbf{y}}_1 + R_z\hat{\mathbf{z}}_1 \\ M_{Ax}\hat{\mathbf{x}}_1 + M_{Ay}\hat{\mathbf{y}}_1 \end{array} \right\}_{A\in\Delta}$$

Remark 14. Note that the kinematic $\{\mathcal{V}_{2/1}\}$ and the action $\{\mathcal{A}^c_{1\to 2}\}$ screws satisfy the property (see Section 4.7)

$$\{\mathcal{V}_{2/1}\} \cdot \{\mathcal{A}^c_{1\to 2}\} = \omega_z \hat{\mathbf{z}}_1 \cdot \mathbf{M}^c_{A,1\to 2} + \mathbf{R}^c_{1\to 2} \cdot \mathbf{v}_{A\in 2/1} = 0$$

where point A is an arbitrary point of axis Δ. This equation simply states that the power generated by the contact forces vanishes, as will be shown in Chapter 12.

Frictionless Slider

In a slider, a prismatic surface of $\mathcal{B}_2$ coincides with a prismatic surface of $\mathcal{B}_1$ thus restricting the motion to a rectilinear translation along a direction $\hat{\mathbf{x}}_1 = \hat{\mathbf{x}}_2$ common to $\mathcal{B}_1$ and $\mathcal{B}_2$.

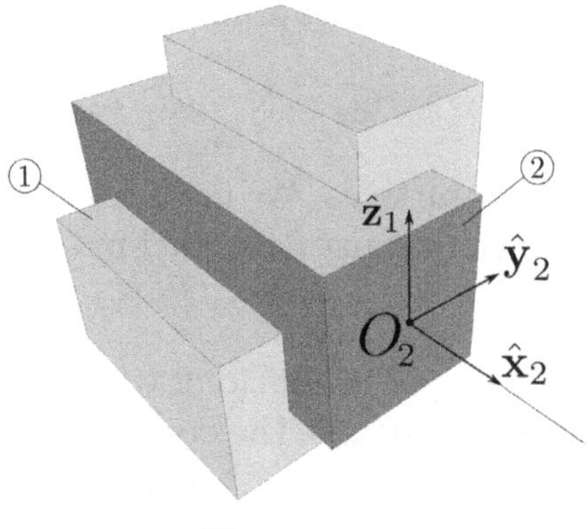

Figure 10.14

This is a one-degree-of-freedom joint, characterized by the following kinematic screw

$$\{\mathcal{V}_{2/1}\} = \left\{ \begin{array}{c} \mathbf{0} \\ v_{2x}\hat{\mathbf{x}}_1 \end{array} \right\} \tag{10.31}$$

Then, assuming frictionless contact, the corresponding contact action screw $\{\mathcal{A}^c_{1\to 2}\}$ satisfies

$$\mathbf{R}^c_{1\to 2}\cdot\hat{\mathbf{x}}_1 = 0 \tag{10.32}$$

All other components of the action screw are non-zero:

$$\{\mathcal{A}^c_{1\to 2}\} = \left\{ \begin{array}{c} R_y\hat{\mathbf{y}}_1 + R_z\hat{\mathbf{z}}_1 \\ M_{Ax}\hat{\mathbf{x}}_1 + M_{Ay}\hat{\mathbf{y}}_1 + M_{Az}\hat{\mathbf{z}}_1 \end{array} \right\}_A$$

Again one can verify again that $\{\mathcal{V}_{2/1}\}\cdot\{\mathcal{A}^c_{1\to 2}\} = 0$.

Frictionless Slider-Pivot

A slider-pivot is a two-degree-of-freedom joint which permits both a rotation about and a translation along an axis $\Delta(O_1, \hat{\mathbf{z}}_1)$.

$$\{\mathcal{V}_{2/1}\} = \left\{ \begin{array}{c} \omega_z\hat{\mathbf{z}}_1 \\ v_{2z}\hat{\mathbf{z}}_1 \end{array} \right\}_{A\in\Delta} \tag{10.33}$$

Then, assuming frictionless contact, the corresponding contact action screw $\{\mathcal{A}^c_{1\to 2}\}$ satisfies

$$\mathbf{R}^c_{1\to 2}\cdot\hat{\mathbf{z}}_1 = 0, \qquad \mathbf{M}^c_{A,1\to 2}\cdot\hat{\mathbf{z}}_1 = 0 \tag{10.34}$$

for all points A of axis Δ. All other components of the action screw are non-zero

$$\{\mathcal{A}^c_{1\to 2}\} = \left\{ \begin{array}{c} R_x\hat{\mathbf{x}}_1 + R_y\hat{\mathbf{y}}_1 \\ M_{Ax}\hat{\mathbf{x}}_1 + M_{Ay}\hat{\mathbf{y}}_1 \end{array} \right\}_{A\in\Delta}$$

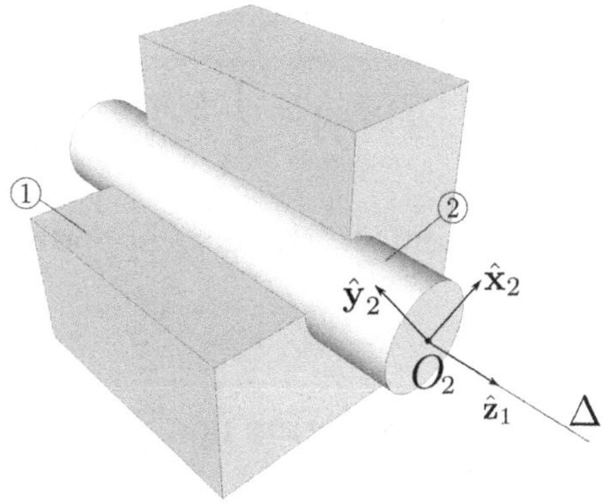

Figure 10.15

Frictionless Helical Joint

A *helical joint* is a slider-pivot joint in which the rotational about and translational motion along axis $\Delta(O_1, \hat{\mathbf{z}}_1)$ are constrained to each other by the relation $v_{2z} = (p/2\pi)\omega_z$ (where p is a constant). Thus, this is a one-degree-of-freedom joint, and the corresponding kinematic screw can be written as

$$\{\mathcal{V}_{2/1}\} = \left\{ \begin{array}{c} \omega_z \hat{\mathbf{z}}_1 \\ \frac{p}{2\pi}\omega_z \hat{\mathbf{z}}_1 \end{array} \right\}_{A\in\Delta} \tag{10.35}$$

Then, assuming frictionless contact, the corresponding contact action screw $\{\mathcal{A}^c_{1\to 2}\}$ satisfies

$$\frac{p}{2\pi}\mathbf{R}^c_{1\to 2} \cdot \hat{\mathbf{z}}_1 + \mathbf{M}^c_{A,1\to 2} \cdot \hat{\mathbf{z}}_1 = 0 \tag{10.36}$$

for any point A of axis Δ. This can be found by imposing $\{\mathcal{V}_{2/1}\} \cdot \{\mathcal{A}^c_{1\to 2}\} = 0$.

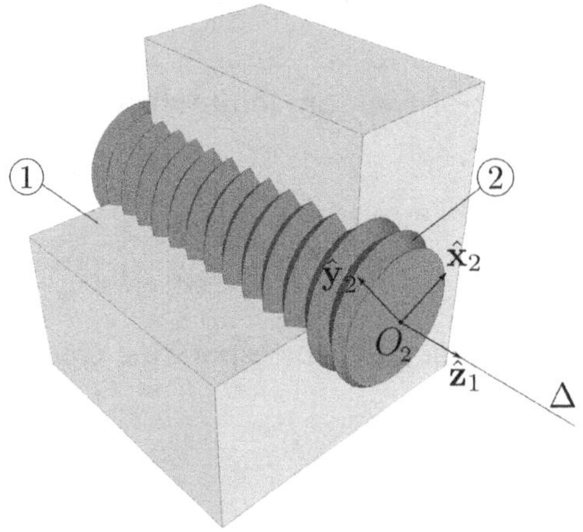

Figure 10.16

Frictionless Spherical Joint

In a spherical joint, a single point O_2 of $\mathcal{B}_2$ remains fixed relative to $\mathcal{B}_1$. This is a three-degree-of-freedom joint with corresponding kinematic screw

$$\{\mathcal{V}_{2/1}\} = \left\{ \begin{array}{c} \boldsymbol{\omega}_{2/1} \\ \mathbf{0} \end{array} \right\}_{O_2} \tag{10.37}$$

Then, assuming frictionless contact, the corresponding contact action screw $\{\mathcal{A}^c_{1\to 2}\}$ satisfies

$$\mathbf{M}^c_{O_2,1\to 2} = \mathbf{0} \tag{10.38}$$

All other components of the action screw are non-zero:

$$\{\mathcal{A}^c_{1\to 2}\} = \left\{ \begin{array}{c} R_x\hat{\mathbf{x}}_2 + R_y\hat{\mathbf{y}}_2 + R_z\hat{\mathbf{z}}_2 \\ \mathbf{0} \end{array} \right\}_{O_2}$$

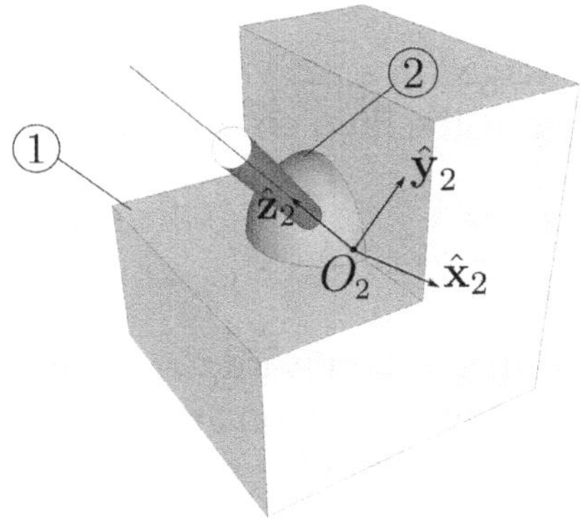

Figure 10.17

Frictionless Planar Joint

In a planar joint between $\mathcal{B}_1$ and $\mathcal{B}_2$, a plane $(O_2, \hat{x}_2, \hat{y}_2)$ of $\mathcal{B}_2$ coincides with a plane $(O_1, \hat{x}_1, \hat{y}_1)$ of $\mathcal{B}_1$. A planar joint is a three-degree-of-freedom joint with corresponding kinematic screw

$$\{\mathcal{V}_{2/1}\} = \left\{ \begin{array}{c} \omega_z \hat{z}_1 \\ v_{O_2 x} \hat{x}_1 + v_{O_2 y} \hat{y}_1 \end{array} \right\}_{O_2} \tag{10.39}$$

The corresponding contact action screw $\{\mathcal{A}^c_{1\to 2}\}$, assuming frictionless contact, satisfies

$$\mathbf{R}^c_{1\to 2} \cdot \hat{x}_1 = 0, \qquad \mathbf{R}^c_{1\to 2} \cdot \hat{y}_1 = 0, \qquad \mathbf{M}^c_{A,1\to 2} \cdot \hat{z}_1 = \mathbf{0} \tag{10.40}$$

about any point A. All other components of the action screw are non-zero:

$$\{\mathcal{A}^c_{1\to 2}\} = \left\{ \begin{array}{c} R_z \hat{z}_1 \\ M_{Ax} \hat{x}_2 + M_{Ay} \hat{y}_2 \end{array} \right\}_A$$

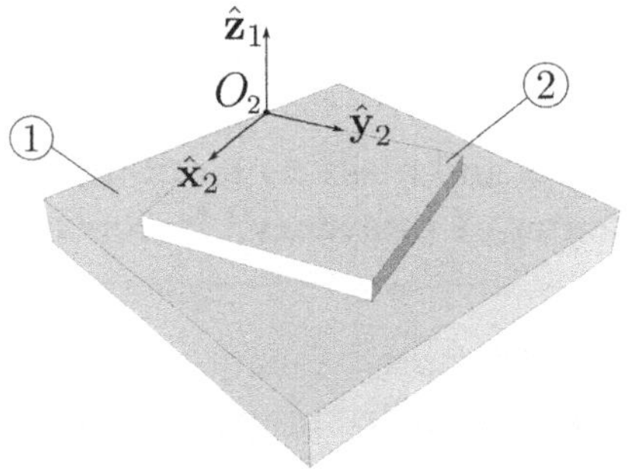

Figure 10.18

Remark 15. It is possible to give the expression of the action screw $\{\mathcal{A}^c_{1\to 2}\}$ for frictionless higher kinematic pairs by imposing the condition $\{\mathcal{V}_{2/1}\} \cdot \{\mathcal{A}^c_{1\to 2}\} = 0$.

dot product between screws $\left\{ \begin{array}{c} x \\ 0 \end{array} \right\}_A \cdot \left\{ \begin{array}{c} 0 \\ x \end{array} \right\}_A$

10.5 Contact Action of a Fluid on a Rigid Body

Power $P = \vec{v} \cdot \vec{F}$

In this section, we describe the effect of fluid forces on a rigid body in terms of action screws.

velocity   force

10.5.1 Case 1: Static Case

Consider a rigid body $\mathcal{B}$ immerged in a fluid of density ρ_f and a constant gravitational field. Then the action screw caused by the fluid on $\mathcal{B}$ can be expressed as

$$\{\mathcal{A}_{fluid \to \mathcal{B}}\} = \left\{ \begin{array}{c} -\int_{\partial\mathcal{B}} p\hat{\mathbf{n}} dA \\ -\int_{\partial\mathcal{B}} \mathbf{r}_{AQ} \times p\hat{\mathbf{n}} dA \end{array} \right\}_A$$

Here unit vector $\hat{\mathbf{n}}$ represents the unit outward normal to $\mathcal{B}$. To find the integrals $\int_{\partial\mathcal{B}} p\hat{\mathbf{n}} dA$ and $\int_{\partial\mathcal{B}} \mathbf{r}_{AQ} \times p\hat{\mathbf{n}} dA$, we replace the region occupied by $\mathcal{B}$ by a region of fluid. This body of fluid (still denoted $\mathcal{B}$) is in equilibrium under the effect of gravity and the forces of pressure due to the outside fluid:

$$\int_{\mathcal{B}} \rho_f \mathbf{g} dV - \int_{\partial\mathcal{B}} p\hat{\mathbf{n}} dA = 0, \quad \int_{\mathcal{B}} \mathbf{r}_{AQ} \times \rho_f \mathbf{g} dV - \int_{\partial\mathcal{B}} \mathbf{r}_{AQ} \times p\hat{\mathbf{n}} dA = 0$$

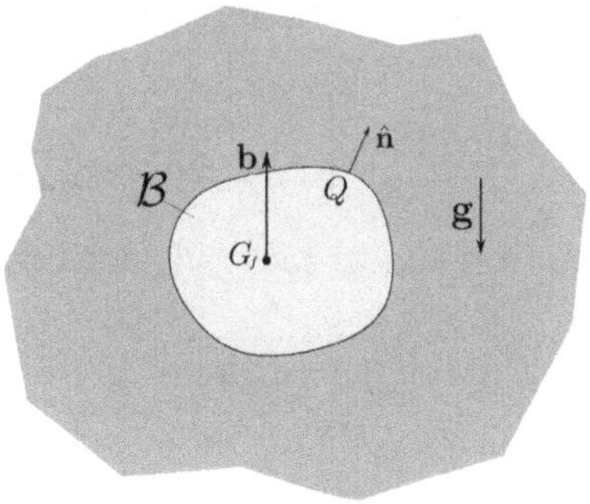

Figure 10.19

This leads us to conclude that:

1. The resultant force, called buoyancy force, is given by $\mathbf{b} = -\int_{\partial\mathcal{B}} p\hat{\mathbf{n}} dA = -\int_{\mathcal{B}} \rho_f \mathbf{g} dV = -m_f \mathbf{g}$.
2. The resultant moment about A is given by $-\int_{\partial\mathcal{B}} \mathbf{r}_{AQ} \times p\hat{\mathbf{n}} dA = -\int_{\mathcal{B}} \mathbf{r}_{AQ} \times \rho_f \mathbf{g} dV = \mathbf{r}_{AG_f} \times \mathbf{b}$.

Here m_f and G_f are the mass and mass center of the displaced region of fluid occupied by $\mathcal{B}$. Point G_f is called **center of buoyancy**. In conclusion, we can state the following theorem:

Theorem 10.2 — Archimedes Principle. A stationary rigid body $\mathcal{B}$ immerged in a fluid at rest is subject to an upward force, called buoyancy force $\mathbf{b} = -m_f \mathbf{g}$, applied at the center of buoyancy G_f:

$$\{\mathcal{A}_{fluid \to \mathcal{B}}\} = \left\{ \begin{array}{c} -m_f \mathbf{g} \\ \mathbf{0} \end{array} \right\}_{G_f}$$

where m_f and G_f are the mass and mass center of the displaced region of fluid occupied by $\mathcal{B}$.

Note that for sufficiently slow motions of $\mathcal{B}$, this result remains valid. The effect of frictional forces would need to be superimposed to the buoyancy effects.

10.5.2 Case 2: Effect of Fluid of a Rigid Body in Motion

The effect of a viscous, incompressible fluid on a moving rigid body $\mathcal{B}$ immersed in this fluid is considerably more complex to evaluate. This effect must now be quantified at the local level by both normal and tangential forces as follows (as in the previous section, $\hat{\mathbf{n}}$ represents the unit outward normal to $\mathcal{B}$)

$$d\mathbf{F}_{fluid\to\mathcal{B}} = -p\hat{\mathbf{n}}dA + \mathbf{T}\hat{\mathbf{n}}dA \tag{10.41}$$

Here $\mathbf{T} = \mu(\nabla\mathbf{u} + \nabla\mathbf{u}^t)$ the viscous stress tensor for an incompressible flow, $\mathbf{u}$ is the flow velocity, p is the pressure and μ is the fluid dynamic viscosity. The global effect of the fluid on body $\mathcal{B}$ is quantified by the action screw $\{\mathcal{A}_{fluid\to\mathcal{B}}\}$ given by

$$\{\mathcal{A}_{fluid\to\mathcal{B}}\} = \left\{ \begin{array}{c} \int_{\partial\mathcal{B}}(-p\hat{\mathbf{n}} + \mathbf{T}\hat{\mathbf{n}})dA \\ \int_{\partial\mathcal{B}} \mathbf{r}_{AQ} \times (-p\hat{\mathbf{n}} + \mathbf{T}\hat{\mathbf{n}})dA \end{array} \right\}_A$$

If the motion of the fluid is known, then the computation of the action screw is reduced to the integration of the fluid pressure and stresses on the body surface. Alternative integral expressions more suitable for experimental measurements or numerical evaluation, have also been derived [2]. Except for rigid body motions at very low speed, there is no realistic problem for which the fluid pressure and velocity fields can be determined without the use of sophisticated extensive CFD computations.

On the other hand, dimensional analysis shows that the forces and moments acting on rigid bodies moving through fluids can be expressed in the form

$$F = \frac{1}{2}\rho_f V_a^2 A C_F, \qquad M = \frac{1}{2}\rho_f V_a^2 L A C_M \tag{10.42}$$

where V_a is a characteristic speed of the body relative to the fluid, L and A are characteristic length and area of the body, and (C_F, C_M) are dimensionless coefficients. These expressions can be used to define the aerodynamic action screw exerted on the vehicle by the surrounding atmosphere. Here, we are most interested in fixed-wing aircraft, although the description which follows is relevant to other applications of aerodynamic flight.

The effects of aerodynamical loads on aircraft $\mathcal{B}$ of mass center G, as shown in Figure 10.20, can be described as follows. First, a set of "body" rectangular axes $(G, \hat{\mathbf{x}}_b, \hat{\mathbf{y}}_b, \hat{\mathbf{z}}_b)$ attached to the aircraft is defined, where $(G, \hat{\mathbf{x}}_b, \hat{\mathbf{z}}_b)$ lies in the aircraft plane of symmetry, $\hat{\mathbf{x}}_b$ pointing along the longitudinal axis toward the nose of the aircraft, and $\hat{\mathbf{z}}_b$ pointing toward the aircraft belly ($\hat{\mathbf{y}}_b$ then points toward the right wing, or starboard). A second set of rectangular axes $(G, \hat{\mathbf{x}}_w, \hat{\mathbf{y}}_w, \hat{\mathbf{z}}_w)$, known as "wind" or "aerodynamic" coordinate axes, is defined such that unit vector $\hat{\mathbf{x}}_w$ points in the direction of velocity $\mathbf{v}_{G/fluid} \equiv V_a\hat{\mathbf{x}}_w$ of the mass center relative to the air mass. The two sets of axes are obtained by two consecutive rotations of angle β (angle of slideslip) and α (angle of attack) which map $\hat{\mathbf{x}}_w$ to $\hat{\mathbf{x}}_b$:

$$(\hat{\mathbf{x}}_w, \hat{\mathbf{y}}_w, \hat{\mathbf{z}}_w) \xrightarrow{\mathcal{R}_{\beta,\hat{\mathbf{z}}_w}} (\hat{\mathbf{x}}_s, \hat{\mathbf{y}}_b, \hat{\mathbf{z}}_w) \xrightarrow{\mathcal{R}_{\alpha,\hat{\mathbf{y}}_b}} (\hat{\mathbf{x}}_b, \hat{\mathbf{y}}_b, \hat{\mathbf{z}}_b)$$

In a symmetric flight, the angle of slideslip is zero and the velocity vector $\mathbf{v}_{G/fluid}$ lies in the plane of symmetry.

[2] M. S. Howe, "On the force and moment on a body in an incompressible fluid, with application to rigid bodies and bubbles at high and low Reynolds number", *Q. J. Mech. Appl. Math.*, 48, pp. 401-426 (1995)

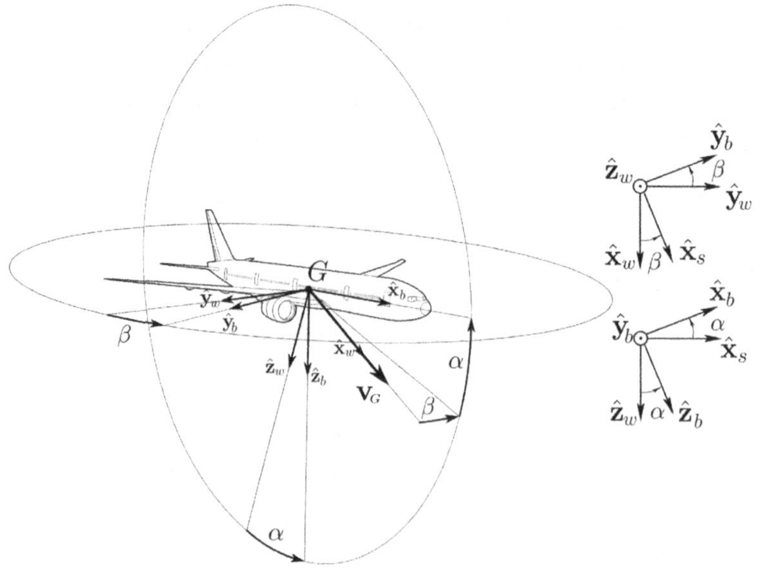

Figure 10.20 – *Aerodynamic and body coordinate systems.*

Since the aerodynamic forces occur due to the direction of the fluid flow relative to the body, the aerodynamic rectangular axes are used to express the aerodynamic forces:

$$\mathbf{F}_{fluid\to\mathcal{B}} = \tfrac{1}{2}\rho_f V_a^2 A \left(-C_{Fx}\hat{\mathbf{x}}_w - C_{Fy}\hat{\mathbf{y}}_w + C_{Fz}\hat{\mathbf{z}}_w\right) \tag{10.43}$$

where A is the wing area, $C_{Fx} > 0$ is the drag coefficient, $C_{Fz} > 0$ is the lift coefficient, and C_{Fy} is slideslip coefficient. These dimensionless coefficients are generally dependent on the Reynolds and Mach numbers, the angles of attack and sideslip, and linear and angular velocity components of the body.

The aerodynamic moment about G acting on an aircraft is resolved on the body rectangular axes

$$\mathbf{M}_{G,fluid\to\mathcal{B}} = \tfrac{1}{2}\rho_f V_a^2 LA \left(C_{Mx}\hat{\mathbf{x}}_b + C_{My}\hat{\mathbf{y}}_b + C_{Mz}\hat{\mathbf{z}}_b\right) \tag{10.44}$$

where L is a characteristic aerodynamic chord, C_{Mx} is the rolling coefficient, C_{My} is the pitching coefficient, and C_{My} is the yawing coefficient.

10.6 Problems

Problem 10.1 All planets assume the shape of oblate spheroid due to their rotation. This shape is characterized by a flattening ratio $f = (R_E - R_P)/R_E$, defined as the ratio of the equatorial-polar radius difference $(R_E - R_P)$ to the equatorial radius R_E. The goal of this problem is to derive an expression for the gravitational field $\mathbf{G}_\Sigma$ created by such a body Σ of mass center O, mass M, equatorial plane Oxy, and polar axis Oz. With reference to the figure, first show that $\mathbf{G}_\Sigma(P)$ at a point P of position $\mathbf{r} \equiv \mathbf{r}_{OP} = r\hat{\mathbf{e}}_r$ is given by

$$\mathbf{G}_\Sigma(P) = -\frac{G}{r^2}\hat{\mathbf{e}}_r \int_\Sigma \left[1 - \frac{3}{2r^2}(\mathbf{s}^2 - 5(\mathbf{s}\cdot\hat{\mathbf{e}}_r)^2)\right] dm + \frac{3G}{r^4}\int_\Sigma (\mathbf{s}\cdot\hat{\mathbf{e}}_r)\mathbf{s}\, dm$$

assuming that the distance $r \equiv |\mathbf{r}_{OP}|$ from P to O is much larger than the distance $|\mathbf{s}|$ from any point Q of Σ to O (use the expansion $(1+x)^{-3/2} = 1 - 3x/2 + 15x^2/8 + \cdots$. Then find the expression

$$\mathbf{G}_\Sigma(P) = -\frac{GM}{r^2}\hat{\mathbf{e}}_r + \frac{3G}{2r^4}(A - C)\left[(1 - 3\sin^2\phi)\hat{\mathbf{e}}_r + 2\sin\phi\cos\phi\hat{\mathbf{e}}_\phi\right]$$

in terms of the coordinates (r, ϕ) of point P, and of the equatorial and polar moments of inertia $A = I_{Ox} = I_{Oy}$ and $C = I_{Oz}$. Deduce that the gravitational field can be expressed in terms of potential $\mathbb{U}$, that is

$$\mathbf{G}_\Sigma(P) = -\nabla\mathbb{U}, \qquad \mathbb{U} = -\frac{GM}{r} + \frac{G}{2r^3}(C - A)(3\sin^2\phi - 1)$$

with $\nabla = -\hat{\mathbf{e}}_r\partial/\partial r - \hat{\mathbf{e}}_\phi\partial/r\partial\phi$. Assuming that the free surface of Σ is a surface of equipotential, show that the flattening ratio f takes the expression

$$f = \frac{3}{2}\frac{(C - A)}{MR_E^2}$$

(f can range from the value 1/300 for Earth to the value 1/10 for Saturn).

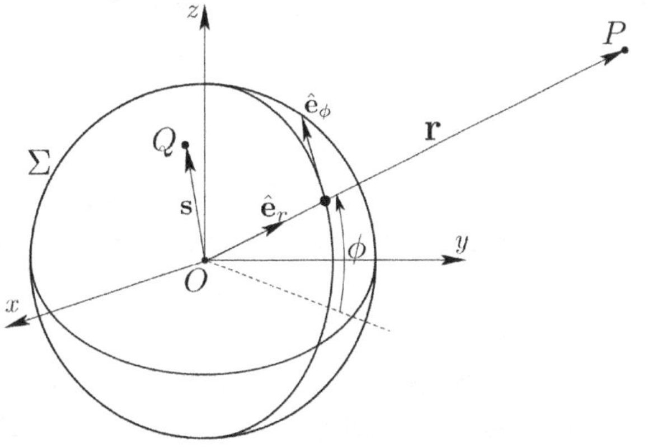

Problem 10.2 Consider the small-body approximation of Example 10.1. Show that the gravitational effect of Earth $\mathcal{E}$ (of mass M, and mass center C) modeled as a spherical body with material symmetry on a satellite $\mathcal{S}$ (of mass m, and mass center G can be approximated as

$$\{\mathcal{A}^g_{\mathcal{E}\to\mathcal{S}}\} = -\frac{GMm}{\rho^2}\left\{\begin{array}{c}\hat{\mathbf{x}} \\ \frac{3}{m\rho}\left[(B - C)c_y c_z\hat{\mathbf{x}}_s + (C - A)c_x c_z\hat{\mathbf{y}}_s + (A - B)c_x c_y\hat{\mathbf{z}}_s\right]\end{array}\right\}_G$$

where $(\hat{\mathbf{x}}_s, \hat{\mathbf{y}}_s, \hat{\mathbf{z}}_s)$ is a principal basis of inertia of $\mathcal{S}$, (A, B, C) the corresponding principal moments of inertia, and (c_x, c_y, c_z) are the direction cosines of $\hat{\mathbf{x}} = \mathbf{r}_{CG}/\rho$ $(\rho = |CG|)$ on $(\hat{\mathbf{x}}_s, \hat{\mathbf{y}}_s, \hat{\mathbf{z}}_s)$: $\hat{\mathbf{x}} = c_x \hat{\mathbf{x}}_s + c_y \hat{\mathbf{y}}_s + c_z \hat{\mathbf{z}}_s$. To derive this result, assume that $\mathbf{r} \equiv \mathbf{r}_{GP}$ is much smaller in magnitude than ρ for any point P of $\mathcal{S}$.

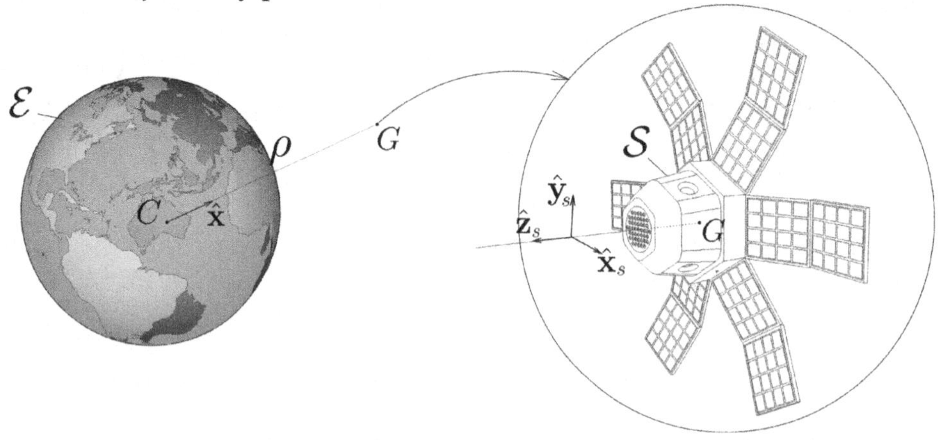

Problem 10.3 When a body such as a satellite or comet comes too close to a large celestial body, it may be pulled apart and disintegrate under the effects of tidal forces. The goal of this problem is to derive the expression of the so-called *Roche limit*, that is, the orbital distance beyond which a body without tensile strength will begin to come apart. The figure displayed below shows a spherical body $\mathcal{B}$ of center B and of constant mass density ρ_B orbiting around a spherical body $\mathcal{A}$ of center A, and constant mass density ρ_A. The two mass centers A and B are separated by distance D.

Find the gravitational acceleration $\mathbf{g}(P)$ at a point P in the interior of $\mathcal{B}$ located for simplicity on line AB, by accounting for the tidal acceleration due to body $\mathcal{A}$ in addition to the gravitational field created by body $\mathcal{B}$. The rotational effect of body $\mathcal{B}$ will be neglected.

Show that $\mathbf{g}(P)$ becomes zero when distance D reaches the value

$$D_R = R_A \left(2 \frac{\rho_A}{\rho_B} \right)^{\frac{1}{3}}$$

where R_A is the radius of body $\mathcal{A}$. On July 7, 1992, the comet Shoemaker-Levy 9 is known to have broken apart in 21 pieces due to tidal forces caused by its motion toward Jupiter.

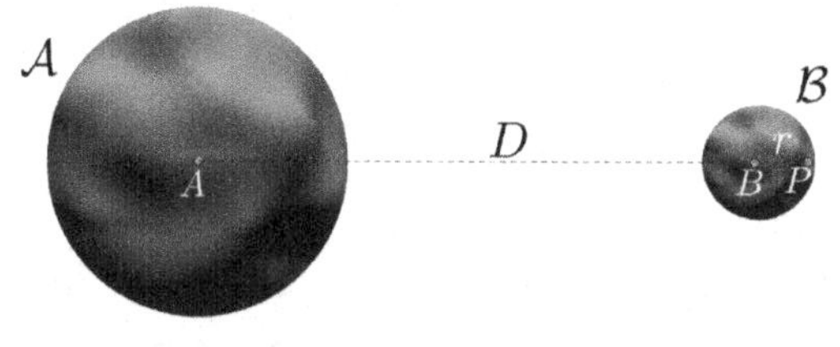

Problem 10.4 Two bodies $\mathcal{B}_1$ and $\mathcal{B}_2$ are in relative rotation about the same axis Δ. Body $\mathcal{B}_1$ is being pressed against $\mathcal{B}_2$ by an axial force P as shown, so that two conical surfaces characterized by kinetic friction coefficient μ remain in contact. Find the contact action screw $\{\mathcal{A}^c_{\mathcal{B}_1 \to \mathcal{B}_2}\}$ in terms of P, μ and the geometrical parameters r_1, r_2 and θ.

Deduce that the maximum torque which can be transmitted from $\mathcal{B}_1$ to $\mathcal{B}_2$ without relative slip between the two contacting surfaces is given by

$$\mathcal{C}_{\max} = \frac{2\mu P}{3\sin\theta}\frac{r_2^3 - r_1^3}{r_2^2 - r_1^2}$$

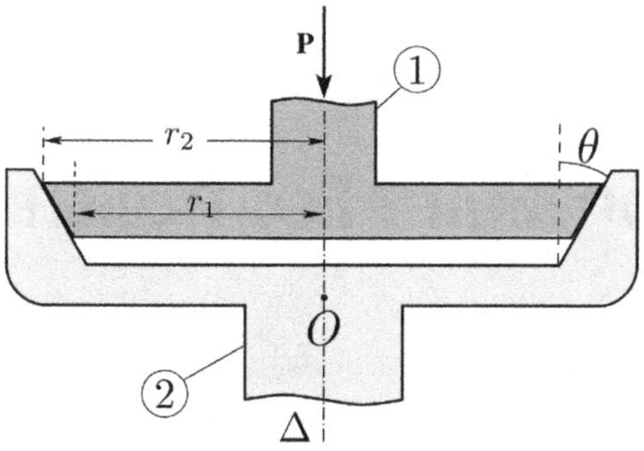

Problem 10.5 Consider the kinematic pair formed by the contact of two toroidal surfaces of bodies $\mathcal{B}_1$ and $\mathcal{B}_2$. Assume that the contact is frictionless, that is, the surface force density is directed along the local unit normal to the surface of contact.

Show that the resulting contact action screw $\{\mathcal{A}^c_{\mathcal{B}_1\to\mathcal{B}_2}\}$ satisfies

$$\hat{\mathbf{z}} \cdot \mathbf{M}^c_{O,1\to 2} = 0$$

where point O is the common center of the tori.

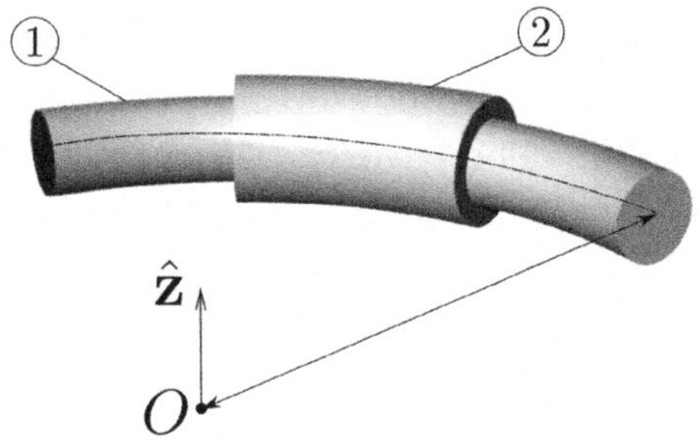

Problem 10.6 Consider a homogeneous rigid body $\mathcal{B}$ of mass center G and mass m in motion relative to a referential $\mathcal{E}$. The ambient fluid exerts on $\mathcal{B}$ a local force normal to its surface $\partial\mathcal{B}$ and proportional to the square of the speed of the local element of area dA:

$$d\mathbf{F}_{\text{fluid}\to\mathcal{B}}(Q) = -\frac{\kappa}{2}\mathbf{v}_Q^2\,\hat{\mathbf{n}}(Q)\,dA$$

where κ is a constant and where $\hat{\mathbf{n}}$ is the unit outward normal at a point Q of $\partial\mathcal{B}$. Show that the resulting contact action screw due to the fluid on body $\mathcal{B}$ is given by

$$\{\mathcal{A}^c_{\text{fluid}\to\mathcal{B}}\} = \kappa V \begin{Bmatrix} \boldsymbol{\omega}\times\mathbf{v}_G \\ \frac{1}{m}\boldsymbol{\omega}\times\mathbf{H}_G \end{Bmatrix}_G$$

where V, $\boldsymbol{\omega}$, $\mathbf{v}_G$ and $\mathbf{H}_G$ are the volume of body $\mathcal{B}$, its angular velocity, the velocity of its mass center G, and its angular momentum about G relative to referential $\mathcal{E}$.

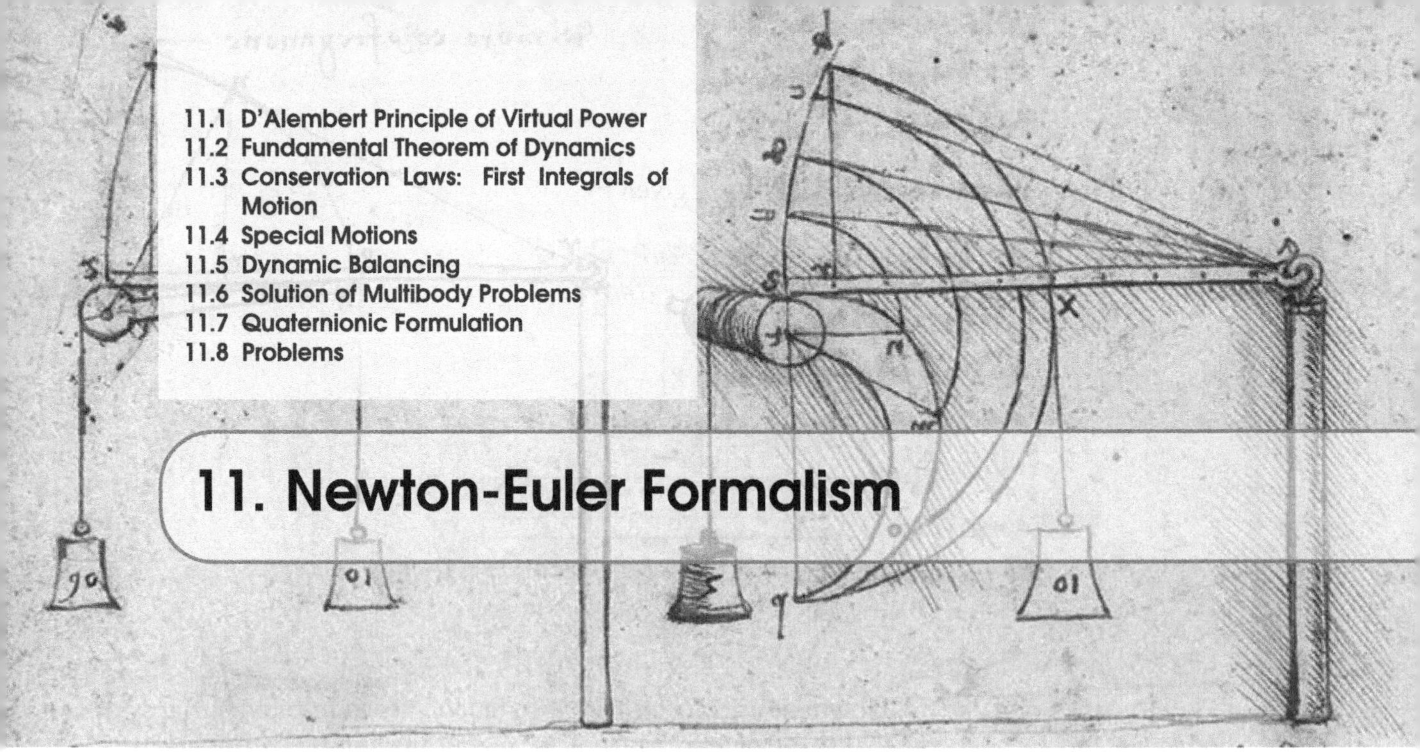

11. Newton-Euler Formalism

THIS CHAPTER is devoted to Newton-Euler formulation of principles which govern the motion of rigid bodies. We start by stating *D'Alembert Principle of Virtual Power* which is applicable to all material systems. To provide some insight into this principle, we consider the case of systems of particles whose motions are governed by Newton's second law. In order to eliminate the virtual power of internal forces, we identify a particular class of virtual velocity field. This principle represents the keystone of engineering dynamics, from which all theorems will be derived:

1. the Fundamental Theorem of Dynamics (Chapter 11),
2. the Kinetic Energy Theorem (Chapter 12),
3. Lagrange equations (Chapter 13),
4. Gibbs-Appell and Kane equations (Chapter 14).

In this chapter, we derive the principal result of vectorial dynamics, the *Fundamental Theorem of Dynamics* (FTD): it relates the rate of change of linear momentum and angular momentum of a material system to the externally applied forces and moments. After illustrating the use of this theorem on a few examples, we examine the conditions which lead to conservation of linear or angular momentum. We then study special types of motions of rigid bodies: rotational and Euler-Poinsot motions. We also examine the problem of dynamic balancing of rigid bodies in rotational motion. Finally, we provide guidelines for the solution of multibody problems.

11.1 D'Alembert Principle of Virtual Power

Before stating the principle of virtual power for arbitrary material systems, we first consider the case of systems of particles. The motion of each particle is assumed to be governed by Newton's laws which can be stated as follows:

1. Newton First Law: There exists at least one referential $\mathcal{E}$, referred to as *Newtonian*,

relative to which any particle P is either at rest or in uniform rectilinear motion in the absence of unbalanced forces acting on P.

2. Newton Second Law: Relative a Newtonian referential $\mathcal{E}$, the acceleration of a particle P is proportional to the resultant force $\mathbf{F}$ exerted on P, and inversely proportional to the mass m of P.

3. Newton Third law: For every action, there is an equal and opposite reaction. More specifically, if $\mathbf{F}_{1\to 2}$ is the force exerted by particle P_1 on particle P_2, then particle P_2 exerts a force $\mathbf{F}_{2\to 1}$ opposed to $\mathbf{F}_{1\to 2}$ and collinear to the line joining P_1 and P_2 (Principle of action and reaction).

We first derive D'Alembert Principle of Virtual Power. This principle states that the virtual powers of all internal, external and inertial forces acting on a system of particles is equal to zero. A special form of this principle can be obtained by choosing the virtual velocity field in a special class which causes the virtual power of internal forces to vanish.

We then state the generalization of this principle to *arbitrary material systems* from which all theorems of dynamics can be proven. This includes the *Fundamental Theorem of Dynamics* central to this chapter, and other methods introduced in subsequent chapters. This theorem is very general: it is applicable to all material systems, deformable or not, whose mass is conserved. In particular, it can be applied to systems of rigid bodies.

11.1.1 Preliminaries: System of Particles

Consider a system Σ of N particles $P_1, P_2, \ldots, P_N$ of mass $m_1, m_2, \ldots, m_N$. Newton's second law states that the motion of each particle can be predicted relative to a Newtonian referential $\mathcal{E}$ according to the equation

$$\mathbf{F}_i = m_i \mathbf{a}_{P_i/\mathcal{E}} \qquad (11.1)$$

where the force $\mathbf{F}_i$ exerted on P_i can be written as the sum $\mathbf{F}_{\overline{\Sigma}\to i} + \sum_j \mathbf{F}_{j\to i}$ of an external force $\mathbf{F}_{\overline{\Sigma}\to i}$ and internal forces $\mathbf{F}_{j\to i}$ caused by the particles of the system. Consider now a vector field $\mathbf{v}_P^*$ defined over $\mathcal{E}$. We then multiply equation (11.1) by $\mathbf{v}_{P_i}^*$ and sum over the set of particles to obtain

ext. forces coming from $\overline{\Sigma}$ to particle 1

$$\underbrace{\sum_{i=1}^{N} \mathbf{v}_{P_i}^* \cdot \mathbf{F}_{\overline{\Sigma}\to i}}_{\substack{\text{virtual power of} \\ \text{external forces}}} + \underbrace{\sum_{i=1}^{N}\sum_{j=1}^{N} \mathbf{v}_{P_i}^* \cdot \mathbf{F}_{j\to i}}_{\substack{\text{virtual power of} \\ \text{internal forces}}} + \underbrace{\sum_{i=1}^{N} \mathbf{v}_{P_i}^* \cdot (-m_i \mathbf{a}_{P_i/\mathcal{E}})}_{\substack{\text{virtual power of} \\ \text{inertial forces}}} = 0 \qquad (11.2)$$

The arbitrary vector field $P \mapsto \mathbf{v}_P^*$ is referred to as a *virtual velocity field*. Each term of (11.2) is referred to as a *virtual power*. Conversely, if equation (11.2) holds for all vector fields $\mathbf{v}_P^*$, then equation (11.1) is obtained for $i = 1, \ldots, N$.

We then ask whether particular virtual velocity fields can be found *so as to cancel out the virtual power of all internal forces*. First, we can simplify this power by taking into account Newton third law $\mathbf{F}_{j\to i} + \mathbf{F}_{i\to j} = \mathbf{0}$:

$$\sum_{i=1}^{N}\sum_{j=1}^{N} \mathbf{v}_{P_i}^* \cdot \mathbf{F}_{j\to i} = \sum_{i=1}^{N}\sum_{j=1}^{i} (\mathbf{v}_{P_i}^* \cdot \mathbf{F}_{j\to i} + \mathbf{v}_{P_j}^* \cdot \mathbf{F}_{i\to j}) = \sum_{i=1}^{N}\sum_{j=1}^{i} (\mathbf{v}_{P_j}^* - \mathbf{v}_{P_i}^*) \cdot \mathbf{F}_{i\to j}$$

rigidifying means it satisfies a screw $v_Q^* = v_P^* + V^* \times r_{PQ}$

The goal is then to find a field $P \mapsto \mathbf{v}_P^*$ such that every term $(\mathbf{v}_{P_j}^* - \mathbf{v}_{P_i}^*) \cdot \mathbf{F}_{i\to j}$ drops out. Recall that force $\mathbf{F}_{i\to j}$ is collinear to position vector $\mathbf{r}_{P_iP_j}$. Hence we obtain $(\mathbf{v}_{P_j}^* - \mathbf{v}_{P_i}^*) \cdot \mathbf{F}_{i\to j} = 0$ if vector $(\mathbf{v}_{P_j}^* - \mathbf{v}_{P_i}^*)$ is normal to vector $\mathbf{r}_{P_iP_j}$ for all possible position of particles P_i and P_j. This is in fact the property satisfied by equiprojective vector fields, that is, vector fields satisfying $\mathbf{v}_Q^* = \mathbf{v}_P^* + \mathbf{V}^* \times \mathbf{r}_{PQ}$ at any two points P and Q: field $P \mapsto \mathbf{v}_P^*$ defines a screw $\{\mathcal{V}^*\}$. We refer to such fields as *rigidifying virtual velocity fields*, since they can be viewed as the velocity fields of virtual rigid bodies. We conclude with the following result:

Theorem 11.1 — D'Alembert Principle of Virtual Power. At any given time, the virtual power of external and inertial forces acting on system Σ relative to a Newtonian referential $\mathcal{E}$ vanishes:

$$\underbrace{\sum_{i=1}^{N} \mathbf{v}_{P_i}^* \cdot \mathbf{F}_{\overline{\Sigma}\to i}}_{\text{virtual power of external forces}} + \underbrace{\sum_{i=1}^{N} \mathbf{v}_{P_i}^* \cdot (-m_i \mathbf{a}_{P_i/\mathcal{E}})}_{\text{virtual power of inertial forces}} = 0 \tag{11.3}$$

for all rigidifying virtual velocities fields $\mathbf{v}^*$, that is, satisfying $\mathbf{v}_Q^* = \mathbf{v}_P^* + \mathbf{V}^* \times \mathbf{r}_{PQ}$.

11.1.2 Generalization to Arbitrary Material Systems

We now generalize D'Alembert Principle of Virtual Power for arbitrary material system Σ of constant mass, in motion under the action of external gravitational forces $\mathbf{F}^g_{\overline{\Sigma}\to\Sigma}(P)$ $(P \in \Sigma)$ (other action-at-a-distance forces could be included) and contact forces $\mathbf{f}^c_{\overline{\Sigma}\to\Sigma}(Q)$ $(Q \in \partial\Sigma)$. See Figure 11.1. The principle can be stated as follows:

Theorem 11.2 — D'Alembert principle of virtual power. There exists at least one referential $\mathcal{E}$, referred to as a *Newtonian* referential, such that, for any material system Σ of constant mass, the virtual power of all external (gravitational and contact) forces and inertial forces acting on system Σ relative to $\mathcal{E}$ is equal to zero at all time:

$$\underbrace{\int_\Sigma \mathbf{v}_P^* \cdot \mathbf{F}^g_{\overline{\Sigma}\to\Sigma}(P)\, dV(P) + \int_{\partial\Sigma} \mathbf{v}_Q^* \cdot \mathbf{f}^c_{\overline{\Sigma}\to\Sigma}(Q)\, dA(Q)}_{\text{virtual power of external forces}} +$$

$$\underbrace{\int_\Sigma \mathbf{v}_P^* \cdot (-\mathbf{a}_{P/\mathcal{E}})\, dm(P)}_{\text{virtual power of inertial forces}} = 0 \tag{11.4}$$

for all rigidifying virtual velocity fields, that is, vector fields satisfying

$$\mathbf{v}_{P'}^* = \mathbf{v}_P^* + \mathbf{V}^* \times \mathbf{r}_{PP'}.$$

Remark 1. Recall from Section 11.1.1 that the "rigidifying" assumption of virtual velocity fields is fundamental to eliminate the contribution of internal forces. In continuum mechanics, this assumption is removed: arbitrary virtual velocity fields are considered in (11.4) and the internal forces (stresses) are taken into account.

Remark 2. The theorems of dynamics which will be presented in this and the following

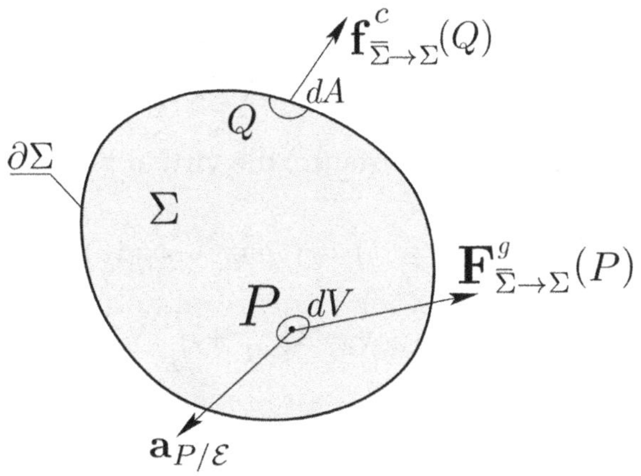

Figure 11.1

chapters will be derived by choosing particular rigidifying virtual velocity fields (screws) in (11.4).

11.1.3 Corollary: action and reaction screws

The following properties can be proved from D'Alembert Principle of Virtual Power:

- Given two interacting disjoint material systems of constant mass Σ_1 and Σ_2, i.e. such that $\Sigma_1 \cap \Sigma_2 = \emptyset$, then

$$\{\mathcal{A}_{\Sigma_2\to\Sigma_1}\} + \{\mathcal{A}_{\Sigma_1\to\Sigma_2}\} = \{0\} \tag{11.5}$$

- Given three mutually disjoint material systems of constant mass Σ_1, Σ_2 and Σ_3, then

$$\{\mathcal{A}_{\Sigma_1\cup\Sigma_2\to\Sigma_3}\} = \{\mathcal{A}_{\Sigma_1\to\Sigma_3}\} + \{\mathcal{A}_{\Sigma_2\to\Sigma_3}\} \tag{11.6}$$

$$\{\mathcal{A}_{\Sigma_1\to\Sigma_2\cup\Sigma_3}\} = \{\mathcal{A}_{\Sigma_1\to\Sigma_2}\} + \{\mathcal{A}_{\Sigma_1\to\Sigma_3}\} \tag{11.7}$$

These equations can be viewed as generalizations of Newton's third law for material systems.

11.2 Fundamental Theorem of Dynamics

The Fundamental Theorem of Dynamics (FTD) is the central result of the Newton-Euler formalism. As its derivation will show, the FTD has the widest range of applicability:
- it applies to all material systems with constant mass, and in particular to systems of one or more rigid bodies,
- it yields all equations (six scalar equations at most) needed to predict the motion of a system, if the external actions are prescribed.
- other theorems will prove to be more specialized and will not yield as much information (equations) as the FTD.

11.2.1 Derivation

The derivation is simple: it does not require the choice of a particular virtual velocity field $P \mapsto \mathbf{v}^*_P$. We denote $\{\mathcal{V}^*\}$ the corresponding screw associated with this field:

$$\{\mathcal{V}^*\} = \left\{ \begin{array}{c} \mathbf{V}^* \\ \mathbf{v}^*_P \end{array} \right\}$$

Next, we simplify each virtual power term by using the relationship

$$\mathbf{v}_P^* = \mathbf{v}_A^* + \mathbf{V}^* \times \mathbf{r}_{AP}$$

where A is an arbitrary point. For instance, the virtual power of the gravitational actions becomes:

$$\begin{aligned}
\int_\Sigma \mathbf{v}_P^* \cdot \mathbf{F}^g_{\overline{\Sigma}\to\Sigma}(P)\, dV(P) &= \int_\Sigma (\mathbf{v}_A^* + \mathbf{V}^* \times \mathbf{r}_{AP}) \cdot \mathbf{F}^g_{\overline{\Sigma}\to\Sigma}(P)\, dV(P) \\
&= \mathbf{v}_A^* \cdot \mathbf{R}^g_{\overline{\Sigma}\to\Sigma} + \int_\Sigma (\mathbf{V}^* \times \mathbf{r}_{AP}) \cdot \mathbf{F}^g_{\overline{\Sigma}\to\Sigma}(P)\, dV(P) \\
&= \mathbf{v}_A^* \cdot \mathbf{R}^g_{\overline{\Sigma}\to\Sigma} + \mathbf{V}^* \cdot \int_\Sigma (\mathbf{F}^g_{\overline{\Sigma}\to\Sigma}(P) \times \mathbf{r}_{AP})\, dV(P) \\
&= \mathbf{v}_A^* \cdot \mathbf{R}^g_{\overline{\Sigma}\to\Sigma} + \mathbf{V}^* \cdot \mathbf{M}^g_{A,\overline{\Sigma}\to\Sigma}
\end{aligned}$$

We now recognize the last expression as the scalar product between arbitrary screw $\{\mathcal{V}^*\}$ and gravitational action screw $\{\mathcal{A}^g_{\overline{\Sigma}\to\Sigma}\}$ and hence is independent of the choice of point A. Thus we have found:

$$\int_\Sigma \mathbf{v}_P^* \cdot \mathbf{F}^g_{\overline{\Sigma}\to\Sigma}(P)\, dV(P) = \{\mathcal{V}^*\} \cdot \{\mathcal{A}^g_{\overline{\Sigma}\to\Sigma}\} \tag{11.8}$$

It is readily verified that the virtual powers of the contact and inertial forces are given by

$$\int_{\partial\Sigma} \mathbf{v}_P^* \cdot \mathbf{f}^c_{\overline{\Sigma}\to\Sigma}(Q)\, dA(P) = \{\mathcal{V}^*\} \cdot \{\mathcal{A}^c_{\overline{\Sigma}\to\Sigma}\} \tag{11.9}$$

$$\int_\Sigma \mathbf{v}_P^* \cdot (-\mathbf{a}_{P/\mathcal{E}})\, dm(P) = -\{\mathcal{V}^*\} \cdot \{\mathcal{D}_{\Sigma/\mathcal{E}}\} \tag{11.10}$$

Now using (11.8-11.10) leads to the following form of D'Alembert principle:

$$\{\mathcal{V}^*\} \cdot \{\mathcal{A}_{\overline{\Sigma}\to\Sigma}\} = \{\mathcal{V}^*\} \cdot \{\mathcal{D}_{\Sigma/\mathcal{E}}\} \tag{11.11}$$

where we have used

$$\{\mathcal{A}^g_{\overline{\Sigma}\to\Sigma}\} + \{\mathcal{A}^c_{\overline{\Sigma}\to\Sigma}\} = \{\mathcal{A}_{\overline{\Sigma}\to\Sigma}\}$$

Since this equation is true for all screws $\{\mathcal{V}^*\}$ we arrive at the FTD by using the following Lemma: If $\{\mathcal{V}^*\} \cdot \{\mathcal{U}\} = \{0\}$ is true for all $\{\mathcal{V}^*\}$, then $\{\mathcal{U}\} = \{0\}$.

Theorem 11.3 — **Fundamental Theorem of Dynamics.** In a Newtonian referential $\mathcal{E}$, the external action screw exerted on a material system Σ of constant mass m and mass center G is equal to the dynamic screw of Σ relative to $\mathcal{E}$:

$$\{\mathcal{D}_{\Sigma/\mathcal{E}}\} = \{\mathcal{A}_{\overline{\Sigma}\to\Sigma}\} \tag{11.12}$$

or, equivalently

$$m\mathbf{a}_{G/\mathcal{E}} = \mathbf{F}_{\overline{\Sigma}\to\Sigma} \tag{11.13}$$

$$\mathbf{D}_{A,\Sigma/\mathcal{E}} = \mathbf{M}_{A,\overline{\Sigma}\to\Sigma} \tag{11.14}$$

where A is an arbitrary point, $\mathbf{F}_{\overline{\Sigma}\to\Sigma}$ is the total external resultant force, and $\mathbf{M}_{A,\overline{\Sigma}\to\Sigma}$ is the total external moment about A acting of Σ.

Some fundamental remarks are in order regarding the FTD:

Remark 3. In (11.13-11.14) we have written the alternate form of the FTD by equating the resultants and the moments (about an arbitrary point A) of the action and dynamic screws. The corresponding two vector equations are traditionally referred to as *Euler's first and second principles*.

Remark 4. The FTD provides at most six independent scalar equations. In particular, the moment equation $\mathbf{D}_{B,\Sigma/\mathcal{E}} = \mathbf{M}_{B,\overline{\Sigma}\to\Sigma}$ written about another point B provides three equations which are of course linear combinations of the previously found six equations.

Remark 5. The FTD can be applied to any material systems, and in particular to a system of (interconnected) rigid bodies $\Sigma = \{\mathcal{B}_1, \mathcal{B}_2, \ldots, \mathcal{B}_N\}$. In this case, the FTD can be applied to each rigid body $\mathcal{B}_i$, to the entire set Σ, or to a subset of Σ consisting of any combination of rigid bodies. For instance, if the FTD is applied to system Σ, the interactions between the rigid bodies of Σ drop out of the equations (the internal action and reaction screws cancel out): the FTD is then stated as

$$\begin{aligned} m_1 \mathbf{a}_{G_1/\mathcal{E}} + \cdots + m_N \mathbf{a}_{G_N/\mathcal{E}} &= \mathbf{F}_{\overline{\Sigma}\to\mathcal{B}_1} + \cdots + \mathbf{F}_{\overline{\Sigma}\to\mathcal{B}_N} \\ \mathbf{D}_{A,\mathcal{B}_1/\mathcal{E}} + \cdots + \mathbf{D}_{A,\mathcal{B}_N/\mathcal{E}} &= \mathbf{M}_{A,\overline{\Sigma}\to\mathcal{B}_1} + \cdots + \mathbf{M}_{A,\overline{\Sigma}\to\mathcal{B}_N} \end{aligned} \tag{11.15}$$

Remark 6. In the moment equation $\mathbf{D}_{A,\Sigma/\mathcal{E}} = \mathbf{M}_{A,\overline{\Sigma}\to\Sigma}$ the dynamic moment is determined in practice from the angular momentum of the system: recall the identity

$$\{\mathcal{D}_{\Sigma/\mathcal{E}}\} = \left\{\frac{d}{dt}\mathcal{H}_{\Sigma/\mathcal{E}}\right\}_{\mathcal{E}} \tag{11.16}$$

Keep in mind that point A is an arbitrary point. In particular, when the dynamic moment $\mathbf{D}_A$ of a rigid body is related to its angular momentum $\mathbf{H}_A$, point A is not necessarily attached to this rigid body. Finally, note that at mass center G of Σ we have

$$\mathbf{D}_{G,\Sigma/\mathcal{E}} = \frac{d}{dt}\mathbf{H}_{G,\Sigma/\mathcal{E}} = \mathbf{M}_{G,\overline{\Sigma}\to\Sigma} \tag{11.17}$$

Kinetic screw is time der. of dynamic.

Refer to Chapter 9 for other ways to determine the dynamic moment $\mathbf{D}_{A,\Sigma/\mathcal{E}}$.

Remark 7. Suppose that the position of a system Σ of N rigid bodies relative to a Newtonian referential $\mathcal{E}$ is defined by M coordinates $\mathbf{q} \equiv (q_1, q_2, ..., q_M)$. Application of the FTD leads to scalar equations of the type $f(\ddot{\mathbf{q}}, \dot{\mathbf{q}}, \mathbf{q}, t) = 0$, that is, non-linear second-order o.d.e.'s. These equations also involve known (prescribed) as well as unknown forces and moments. We call *equation of motion of system* Σ an equation of the type $f(\ddot{\mathbf{q}}, \dot{\mathbf{q}}, \mathbf{q}, t) = 0$ which does not involve any unknown force or moment. We call *first integral of motion of system* Σ an equation of the type $F(\dot{\mathbf{q}}, \mathbf{q}, t) =$ constant which can be obtained by integration of an equation of motion of Σ. If M first integrals of motion can be found, then the motion is entirely known analytically, since the unknown coordinates $\mathbf{q}$ can be obtained by simple quadratures from the first integrals.

Remark 8. Existence and uniqueness: given initial conditions $\mathbf{q} = \mathbf{q}_0$ and $\dot{\mathbf{q}} = \dot{\mathbf{q}}_0$ at time $t = t_0$, a unique solution $\mathbf{q}(t, \mathbf{q}_0, \dot{\mathbf{q}}_0)$ of the equations of motion must exist under general conditions of continuity of $\partial f/\partial q_i$ and $\partial f/\partial \dot{q}_i$.

11.2.2 Class of Newtonian Referentials

Let us assume that a Newtonian referential $\mathcal{E}$ exists. Under which condition will a referential $\mathcal{F}$ in motion relative to $\mathcal{E}$ also qualify as a Newtonian referential? Consider an arbitrary P of a material system Σ. According to the change of referential formula (6.5), we can write

$$\mathbf{a}_{P/\mathcal{E}} = \mathbf{a}_{P/\mathcal{F}} + \mathbf{a}_{P\in\mathcal{F}/\mathcal{E}} + 2\boldsymbol{\omega}_{\mathcal{F}/\mathcal{E}} \times \mathbf{v}_{P/\mathcal{F}}$$

for any point P. The transport and Coriolis accelerations drop out if referential $\mathcal{F}$ is in uniform rectilinear translation relative to $\mathcal{E}$

$$\mathbf{a}_{P/\mathcal{F}} = \mathbf{a}_{P/\mathcal{E}},$$

In this case, equation (11.4) still holds, and $\mathcal{F}$ is also a Newtonian referential.

Theorem 11.4 All Newtonian referentials are in uniform, rectilinear translation relative to one another.

In classical mechanics, we require that postulated physical laws such as D'Alembert Principle of Virtual Power remain invariant under Galilean transformations, that is, transformations mapping a referential into another referential translating at constant velocity.

11.2.3 Approximate Newtonian Referentials

The choice of referential $\mathcal{E}$ in the application of the FTD depends on the particular problem at hand. No experiment has ever been devised to prove the existence of a Newtonian referential. However, comparisons between experimental measurements and application of the FTD can indicate the extent to which a given referential can safely be assumed Newtonian. For most studies, the use of a Terrestrial referential leads to negligible errors and such a referential is an acceptable approximation of a Newtonian referential. Nevertheless, for systems evolving on a large scale (such as satellites in orbit around the Earth) or evolving over long time interval (such as Foucault pendulum) or systems evolving at very high speed (such as high speed gyroscopes), it is more appropriate to apply the FTD relative to the Geocentric referential $\mathcal{G}$, and hence accounting for Earth's rotation. In more extreme cases such as in the motion of interplanetary probes, it is more appropriate to use the Heliocentric referential. In Chapter 16, we shall learn how the FTD extends to a non-Newtonian referential.

These three referentials are pictured on Figure 11.2:

1. The **Heliocentric referential** $\mathcal{H}$ is defined by the mass center S of the Sun, and by three axes SX, SY and SZ pointing toward points in space which remain "fixed" relative to S. More specifically, the axes SX and SY can be chosen into the plane, referred to as the *ecliptic* which contains the trajectory of center C of the Earth.
2. The **Geocentric referential** $\mathcal{G}$ is defined by the mass center C of the Earth, and by axes CX, CY and CZ which remain parallel to the axes SX, SY, SZ of $\mathcal{H}$. Hence $\mathcal{G}$ is in translation relative to $\mathcal{H}$, that is, $\boldsymbol{\omega}_{\mathcal{G}/\mathcal{H}} = \mathbf{0}$, and its motion is specified by the acceleration $\mathbf{a}_{C/\mathcal{H}}$ of center C. Its motion accounts for the orbital motion of Earth around the Sun. This orbit is elliptical with eccentricity $e = 0.017$, and can be considered quasicircular of radius $R = 149,600,000$ km, and period $T = 1$ year $= 365.256$ days. By assuming the motion of C uniform, we readily find that the magnitude of $\mathbf{a}_{C/\mathcal{H}}$ is approximately $a_C = 5.94 \times 10^{-3}$ m/s^2. In reality, the distance

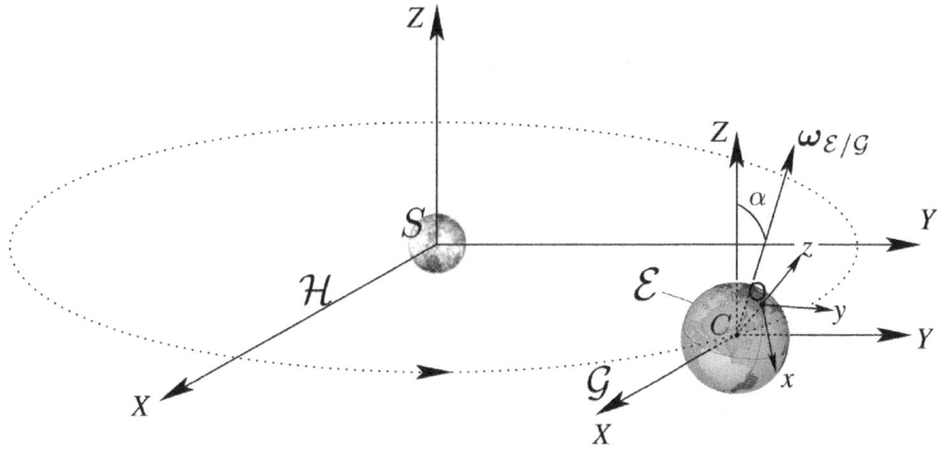

Figure 11.2

from C to S varies from 147.17×10^6 km (early in January) to 153.18×10^6 km (end of July) and the speed of C (relative to $\mathcal{H}$) varies from 31 km/s to 28 km/s. Given the small value of a_C, the non-Newtonian character of $\mathcal{G}$ can be considered quite weak for most applications.

3. The **Terrestrial or Laboratory referential** $\mathcal{E}$ attached to Earth with origin O taken at some fixed point of the surface of the Earth, axes Ox, Oy and Oz pointing southward, eastward, and upward, respectively. The motion of $\mathcal{E}$ relative to $\mathcal{G}$ is a rotation about the axis passing through the south and north poles, with angular velocity $\omega_{\mathcal{E}/\mathcal{G}} = \omega_{\mathcal{E}/\mathcal{H}}$ of magnitude $2\pi/(24 \times 3600) = 7.27 \times 10^{-5}$ rad/s, and directed along the axis of rotation from the south to the north poles. The direction of $\omega_{\mathcal{E}/\mathcal{G}}$ is sensibly constant relative to the axis SZ normal to the ecliptic, making an angle $\alpha = 23^o27'$ [1]. Experiments show that $\mathcal{E}$ can be reasonably assumed Newtonian, as long as the extent and length of the motion are sufficiently small. We will assess the non-Newtonian character of referential $\mathcal{E}$ relative to referential $\mathcal{G}$ in Chapter 16.

11.2.4 Examples

In this section, we solve a few example problems to illustrate the use of the FTD. Whenever faced with a problem involving a single body in motion, these steps should be followed:

1. Parametrize the position of body $\mathcal{B}$ relative to Newtonian referential $\mathcal{E}$, introduce all coordinates, corresponding unit vectors and rotation diagrams.
2. Determine the kinematic screw $\{\mathcal{V}_{\mathcal{B}/\mathcal{E}}\}$ and identify all geometric or kinematic constraints.
3. Given a description of the mass distribution of the body, find the kinetic screw $\{\mathcal{H}_{\mathcal{B}/\mathcal{E}}\}$.
4. Identify all contributions to the external action screw $\{\mathcal{A}_{\overline{\mathcal{B}}\to\mathcal{B}}\}$ exerted on the body.
5. Apply the FTD. Two possible solutions can be devised: (i) If all unknown are sought, then all 6 equations extracted from the FTD are needed, thus requiring all elements of the dynamic and action screws. (ii) If only specific limited information is required, then the FTD will be applied carefully by figuring out how to extract this information without full knowledge of the dynamic/action screws.

[1]The axis of rotation of the Earth is not strictly constant relative to referential $\mathcal{G}$, but rather describes a cone of vertex C and axis CZ over a period of about 26,000 years.

Example 11.1 A homogeneous, spherical ball 1 of mass m and radius r is thrown on a horizontal straight support Ox of a Newtonian referential 0. Its mass center G has initial velocity $\mathbf{v}_0 = v_0\hat{\mathbf{e}}_x$ ($v_0 > 0$) and its initial angular velocity is $\boldsymbol{\omega} = \omega_0\hat{\mathbf{e}}_z$ ($\omega_0 > 0$). The contact is characterized by the coefficient of kinetic friction μ. Rolling friction is neglected. See Figure 11.3.

a. Show that the ball initially slips until time t_1 given by

$$t_1 = \frac{2}{7\mu g}(v_0 + r\omega_0)$$

What happens at time $t = t_1$? Does the sphere move forward or backward?

b. Find the velocity of G and the ball's angular velocity at time $t \geq t_1$. Describe the motion of the ball. ■

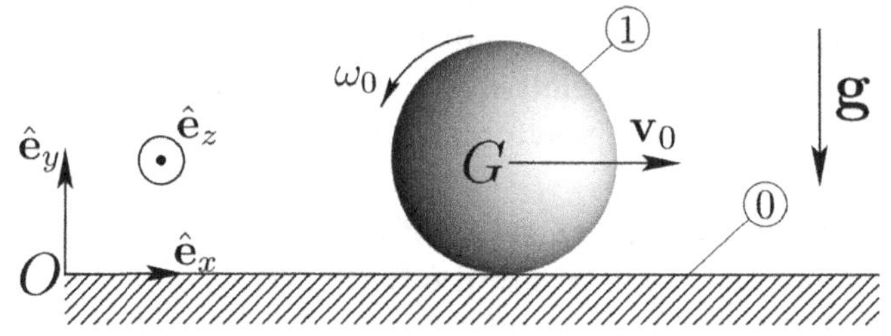

Figure 11.3

a. The kinematics of the ball relative to referential $0(O, \hat{\mathbf{e}}_x, \hat{\mathbf{e}}_y, \hat{\mathbf{e}}_z)$ is entirely specified by the velocity $\mathbf{v}_G = v(t)\hat{\mathbf{e}}_x$ of its mass center, and by its angular velocity $\boldsymbol{\omega} = \omega(t)\hat{\mathbf{e}}_z$. Its slip velocity is given by

$$\mathbf{v}_{I\in 1/0} = \mathbf{v}_G + \boldsymbol{\omega} \times \mathbf{r}_{GI} = (v + r\omega)\hat{\mathbf{e}}_x \qquad (1)$$

At time $t = 0$, the slip velocity takes the expression $\mathbf{v}_{I\in 1/0} = (v_0 + r\omega_0)\hat{\mathbf{e}}_x$. Since $(v_0 + r\omega_0) \neq 0$, the sphere initially slips, and we can assume that the initial phase of motion is also characterized by slipping. The external forces acting on the ball are: (i) the gravitational force $m\mathbf{g}$ applied at mass center G, and (ii) the reaction force $\mathbf{R} = F\hat{\mathbf{e}}_x + N\hat{\mathbf{e}}_y$ applied at the contact point I, neglecting rolling friction:

$$\{\mathcal{A}_{\bar{1}\to 1}\} = \left\{ \begin{array}{c} -mg\hat{\mathbf{e}}_y \\ \mathbf{0} \end{array} \right\}_G + \left\{ \begin{array}{c} F\hat{\mathbf{e}}_x + N\hat{\mathbf{e}}_y \\ \mathbf{0} \end{array} \right\}_I$$

Application of the FTD $\{\mathcal{A}_{\bar{1}\to 1}\} = \{\mathcal{D}_{1/0}\}$ gives:
(i) the resultant equation $m\mathbf{a}_{G/0} = m\mathbf{g} + \mathbf{R}$, or by projection on $(\hat{\mathbf{e}}_x, \hat{\mathbf{e}}_y)$,

$$m\dot{v} = F, \qquad N = mg \qquad (2-3)$$

(ii) the moment equation about mass center G, $\mathbf{D}_G = \mathbf{M}_{G,\bar{1}\to 1} = \mathbf{r}_{GI} \times \mathbf{R} = rF\hat{\mathbf{e}}_z$, leading to, with $\mathbf{D}_G = (d\mathbf{H}_G/dt) = \frac{2}{5}mr^2\dot{\omega}\hat{\mathbf{e}}_z$:

$$\frac{2}{5}mr^2\dot{\omega} = rF \qquad (4)$$

We have obtained 3 equations solving for 4 unknowns v, ω, F and N. We need one more equation. It is given by Coulomb law: $|F| = \mu N$, the friction force $F\hat{\mathbf{e}}_x$ being always opposed to the slip velocity $\mathbf{v}_{I\in 1/0}$: $F\hat{\mathbf{e}}_x \cdot \mathbf{v}_{I\in 1/0} < 0$. Since initially $(v_0 + r\omega_0) > 0$, the slip velocity has the direction of $+\hat{\mathbf{e}}_x$, as long as the ball slips. This shows that $F < 0$: $|F| = -F = \mu N = \mu mg$. Now we solve equations (2-4):

$$\dot{\omega} = -\tfrac{5}{2}\mu\frac{g}{r}, \qquad \dot{v} = -\mu g$$

showing that both v and ω are (linearly) decreasing functions of time. Eventually the slip velocity will vanish. We obtain by integration

$$\omega = \omega_0 - \tfrac{5}{2}\mu\frac{g}{r}t, \qquad v = v_0 - \mu g t$$

leading to the slip velocity

$$\mathbf{v}_{I\in 1/0} = (v_0 + r\omega_0 - \tfrac{7}{2}\mu g t)\hat{\mathbf{e}}_x.$$

The slip ceases at time

$$t_1 = \frac{2}{7\mu g}(v_0 + r\omega_0)$$

Time t_1 corresponds the start of the no-slip phase of motion of the ball: once it stops slipping, it continues to roll without slipping. At time $t = t_1$, G takes the velocity

$$v_1 = v_0 - \mu g t_1 = \tfrac{1}{7}(5v_0 - 2r\omega_0)$$

and the ball has the angular velocity

$$\omega_1 = \omega_0 - \tfrac{5}{2}\mu\frac{g}{r}t_1 = \tfrac{1}{7r}(2r\omega_0 - 5v_0)$$

This shows that at time t_1
- if $v_0 > \frac{2}{5}r\omega_0$, the ball rolls forward: $v_1 > 0$ and $\omega_1 < 0$.
- if $v_0 = \frac{2}{5}r\omega_0$, the ball stops: $v_1 = 0$, $\omega_1 = 0$.
- if $v_0 < \frac{2}{5}r\omega_0$, the ball rolls backward: $v_1 < 0$ and $\omega_1 > 0$.

Remark. We could have applied the moment equation about I instead of G and found: $\mathbf{D}_I = \mathbf{M}_I = \mathbf{0}$, leading to $d\mathbf{H}_I/dt + \mathbf{v}_I \times \mathbf{v}_G = \mathbf{0}$. With $\mathbf{v}_I = \mathbf{v}_G = v\hat{\mathbf{e}}_x$, we find that $d\mathbf{H}_I/dt = \mathbf{0}$: *the angular momentum about I is conserved*. With $\mathbf{H}_I = \mathbf{H}_G + m\mathbf{v}_G \times \mathbf{r}_{GI} = mr(\frac{2}{5}r\omega - v)\hat{\mathbf{e}}_z$, we find

$$\tfrac{2}{5}r\omega - v = \tfrac{2}{5}r\omega_0 - v_0$$

The same results are recovered.

b. For $t \geq t_1$, the ball rolls without slipping: $\mathbf{v}_{I\in 1/0} = \mathbf{0}$. The translational and rotational motion of $\mathcal{S}$ are now coupled:

$$v = -r\omega, \qquad t \geq t_1 \tag{5}$$

The motion is still governed by the equations (2-4). Now with equation (5), we find

$$F = m\dot{v} = -mr\dot{\omega} = \tfrac{2}{5}mr\dot{\omega}$$

implying that $\dot{\omega} = 0$, that is,

$$\omega = \omega_1, \qquad t \geq t_1.$$

Then we find that

$$v = v_1, \qquad t \geq t_1$$

and

$$F = 0.$$

The friction force vanishes during the no-slip phase of the sphere which evolves with constant linear and angular velocity! Note that the condition $|F| < \mu_k N$ is satisfied by the reaction force. These results can be made more realistic by adding the effect of rolling friction.

Remark. The friction force $F\hat{\mathbf{e}}_x$ is not necessarily opposed to $\mathbf{v}_G$: assume that the initial conditions are such that $(v_0 + r\omega_0) < 0$ (with sufficiently strong forward spin $\omega_0 < 0$). Then the slip velocity is directed along $(-\hat{\mathbf{e}}_x)$: the friction force is directed along $(+\hat{\mathbf{e}}_x)$, that is, $F > 0$.

■

Example 11.2 A spherical ball 1 of uniform mass m and radius r is released without initial speed on a support Ox inclined with the horizontal with angle α. The contact is characterized by the coefficient of static and kinetic friction $\mu_s \approx \mu_k = \mu$.

Part 1: We neglect rolling friction. Immediately upon its release, the ball may begin to roll with or without slipping depending on the value of angle α.

1a. Assume that the ball begins to roll without slipping. Describe its motion. In particular, find the reaction force of the support on the ball. Conclude that such a motion is possible only if

$$\mu \geq \tfrac{2}{7} \tan \alpha.$$

Can it slip at a later time?

1b. Assume now $\mu < \frac{2}{7} \tan \alpha$, so that the ball begins to slip immediately upon its release. Find the velocity $\mathbf{v}_G$ of its mass center G and its angular velocity $\boldsymbol{\omega}$. Describe its motion. Can it eventually stop slipping?

Part 2: We now account for rolling friction. Denote by k the coefficient of rolling friction. Assume that $\frac{k}{r} \ll \mu$. Examine under which conditions

2a. the ball rolls without slipping,

2b. the ball slips without rolling,

2c. the ball rolls and slips. ■

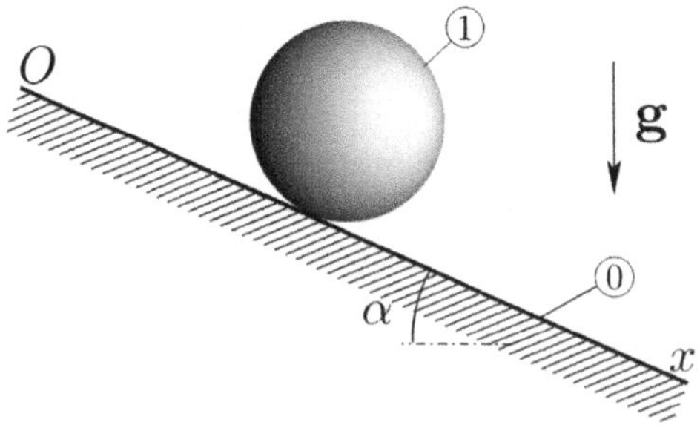

Figure 11.4

1a. The ball's kinematics in referential $0(O, \hat{\mathbf{e}}_x, \hat{\mathbf{e}}_y, \hat{\mathbf{e}}_z)$ is entirely specified by the velocity $\mathbf{v}_G = v_G(t)\hat{\mathbf{e}}_x$, and by its the angular velocity $\boldsymbol{\omega} = \omega(t)\hat{\mathbf{e}}_z$. Then its slip velocity is given by

$$\mathbf{v}_{I\in 1/0} = \mathbf{v}_G + \boldsymbol{\omega} \times \mathbf{r}_{GI} = (v_G + r\omega)\hat{\mathbf{e}}_x$$

If the ball rolls without slipping, then $v_G + r\omega = 0$, and by differentiation w.r.t. time we find

$$\dot{v}_G + r\dot{\omega} = 0 \tag{1}$$

The external forces acting on 1 are (i) the gravitational force $m\mathbf{g}$ applied at mass center G, (ii) the reaction force $\mathbf{R} = F\hat{\mathbf{e}}_x + N\hat{\mathbf{e}}_y$ applied at the contact point I, assuming sliding friction only.

Application of the FTD $\{\mathcal{A}_{\bar{1}\to 1}\} = \{\mathcal{D}_{1/0}\}$ gives:
(i) the resultant equation $m\mathbf{a}_G = m\mathbf{g} + \mathbf{R}$, or by projection on $(\hat{\mathbf{e}}_x, \hat{\mathbf{e}}_y)$

$$m\dot{v}_G = F + mg \sin \alpha \tag{2}$$

$$N - mg \cos \alpha = 0 \tag{3}$$

(ii) the moment equation $\mathbf{D}_G = \mathbf{M}_G$ about point G:

$$\tfrac{2}{5} mr^2 \dot{\omega} = rF \tag{4}$$

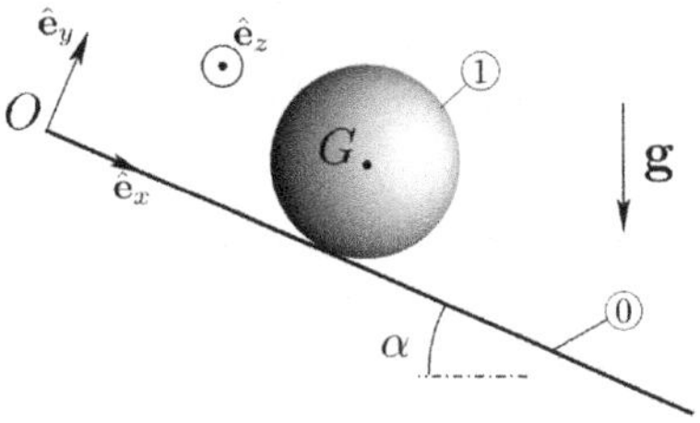

We have obtained 4 equations (1-4) solving for 4 unknowns v_G, ω, F and N. These equations are easily solved:

$$\dot{v}_G = \tfrac{5}{7} g \sin\alpha, \quad \dot{\omega} = -\tfrac{5}{7}\frac{g}{r}\sin\alpha, \quad F = -\frac{2}{7} mg \sin\alpha, \quad N = mg\cos\alpha$$

This shows that the motion is uniformly accelerated in both translation and rotation. Since $v_G = 0$ and $\omega = 0$ at time $t = 0$, we obtain by integration

$$v_G(t) = \frac{5}{7}(g\sin\alpha)t, \qquad \omega(t) = -\frac{5}{7}(\frac{g}{r}\sin\alpha)t.$$

which shows that the motion is independent of the coefficient of friction μ. The no-slip motion of the ball is valid as long as $|F| \leq \mu N$. This gives the *time-independent condition between μ and $\tan\alpha$*:

$$\mu \geq \frac{2}{7}\tan\alpha \tag{5}$$

Since F and N remain constant during the motion, the no-slip motion must continue indefinitely.

1b. If $\mu < \frac{2}{7}\tan\alpha$, the ball must begin to roll and slip. We must have $\mathbf{v}_{I\in 1/0} = (v_G + r\omega)\hat{\mathbf{e}}_x \neq \mathbf{0}$ for $t > 0$. Even though we expect $v_G > 0$ and $\omega < 0$ for $t > 0$, we assume that the quantity $(v_G + r\omega)$ is positive, that is, we assume that the slip velocity has the direction of $\hat{\mathbf{e}}_x$, as long as the ball slips. In this case, for the friction force $F\hat{\mathbf{e}}_x$ to oppose the slip velocity $\mathbf{v}_{I\in 1/0}$, we must have, according to Coulomb law, $|F| = -F = \mu N$.

Equations (2-4) are now replaced by

$$N = mg\cos\alpha, \quad m\dot{v}_G = mg(\sin\alpha - \mu\cos\alpha), \quad \tfrac{2}{5}mr^2\dot{\omega} = -\mu r N = -\mu mgr\cos\alpha$$

leading by integration to

$$v_G(t) = g(\sin\alpha - \mu\cos\alpha)t, \qquad \omega(t) = -\tfrac{5}{2r}\mu g t\cos\alpha$$

Once again the motion is uniformly accelerated in both translation and rotation. But in this case the motion depends on the friction coefficient. We must check *a posteriori* the direction of the slip velocity. We find the expression

$$\mathbf{v}_{I\in 1/0} = (v_G + r\omega)\hat{\mathbf{e}}_x = g(\sin\alpha - \tfrac{7}{2}\mu\cos\alpha)t$$

Given the condition $\mu < \frac{2}{7}\tan\alpha$, our assumption that the slip-velocity is directed along $(+\hat{\mathbf{e}}_x)$ was correct. Furthermore, *the slip velocity increases monotonically: the ball rolls and slips indefinitely.*

2. If we account for rolling friction, then the contact action screw $\{\mathcal{A}^c_{0\to 1}\}$ now takes the form

$$\{\mathcal{A}^c_{\mathcal{E}\to\mathcal{S}}\} = \left\{ \begin{array}{c} N\hat{\mathbf{e}}_y + F\hat{\mathbf{e}}_x \\ M_I\hat{\mathbf{e}}_z \end{array} \right\}_I$$

where according to the laws of rolling friction:
(i) if $\boldsymbol{\omega} = \mathbf{0}$ (no rolling), then $|M_I| \leq kN$, (ii) if $\boldsymbol{\omega} = \omega\hat{\mathbf{e}}_z \neq \mathbf{0}$, then $|M_I| = kN, \quad M_I\omega < 0$,
Equations (2-4) are now replaced by

$$N = mg\cos\alpha, \qquad m\dot{v}_G = F + mg\sin\alpha, \qquad \frac{2}{5}mr^2\dot{\omega} = rF + M_I$$

The analysis then depends upon whether the ball rolls and/or slips.

2a. The ball rolls without slipping. Hence $\omega \neq 0$ and $v_G + r\omega = 0$ and $|M_I| = kN$ with $M_I\omega < 0$. We then find

$$F = -\tfrac{2}{7}mg\sin\alpha - \tfrac{5}{7r}M_I, \qquad N = mg\cos\alpha, \qquad |M_I| = kN, \qquad M_I\omega < 0$$

Since $\omega = 0$ at $t = 0$, the sign of ω must be that taken by $\dot{\omega}$, that is, the sign of $(rT + M_I) = \frac{2}{7}(M_I - mgr\sin\alpha)$. In fact, just as in Part I (no rolling friction), the equations of motion show that $\dot{\omega}$ = constant, leading to $\omega = \dot{\omega}t$. The condition $M_I\omega < 0$ is equivalent to $M_I(M_I - mgr\sin\alpha) < 0$ which implies that

$$0 < M_I < mgr\sin\alpha$$

Now we can set $|M_I| = M_I = kN = kmg\cos\alpha$. This then implies the *condition of rolling without slipping*

$$\frac{k}{r} < \tan\alpha$$

We still have to verify that $|F| < \mu N$ for no-slip to be guaranteed: we find the condition $\tan\alpha < \frac{7}{2}\mu - \frac{5}{2}\frac{k}{r}$. Finally we conclude that the ball *rolls without slipping as long as the condition*

$$\frac{k}{r} < \tan\alpha < \tfrac{7}{2}\mu - \tfrac{5}{2}\frac{k}{r} \tag{6}$$

is satisfied. It is readily verified that *this no-slip rolling motion must continue indefinitely*.

2b. The ball slips without rolling. Now we assume $\omega = 0$ for $t \geq 0$ and the inequality $|M_I| \leq kN$ must be satisfied. We can solve for M_I and N from the equations

$$N = mg\cos\alpha, \quad m\dot{v}_G = F + mg\sin\alpha, \quad rF + M_I = 0, \quad |F| = \mu mg\cos\alpha$$

which implies that $|M_I| = r\mu mg\cos\alpha$ and the condition $\frac{k}{r} \geq \mu$ which is *not physically possible: the ball cannot slip without rolling*.

2c. The ball rolls and slips. This implies that the conditions of case 1 are not satisfied. Let us assume that

$$\tan\alpha > \tfrac{7}{2}\mu - \tfrac{5}{2}\frac{k}{r}$$

Now we must impose $|F| = \mu N$ and $|M_I| = kN$ with $F(v_G + r\omega) < 0$ and $M_I\omega < 0$. We proceed as in case 1b, rolling friction being a small perturbation of sliding friction. Hence we assume that for $t > 0$, $v_G > 0$, $\omega < 0$ and $v_G + r\omega > 0$. We will verify *a posteriori* that these assumptions are correct. Then, this imposes $M_I > 0$ and $F < 0$:

$$M_I = kmg\cos\alpha, \qquad F = -\mu mg\cos\alpha$$

leading to

$$m\dot{v}_G = mg(\sin\alpha - \mu\cos\alpha), \qquad \tfrac{2}{5}mr^2\dot{\omega} = mg(k\cos\alpha - \mu r\cos\alpha)$$

To impose $v_G > 0$ and $\omega < 0$ we must have $\tan\alpha > \mu$ and $k/r < \mu$: both conditions are satisfied. We can now determine the rate of change of the slip velocity

$$\dot{v}_G + r\dot{\omega} = g\cos\alpha(\tan\alpha - \tfrac{7}{2}\mu + \tfrac{5}{2}\frac{k}{r})$$

We now verify that $v_G + r\omega > 0$. We conclude that *the ball rolls and slips if the condition*

$$\tan\alpha > \tfrac{7}{2}\mu - \tfrac{5}{2}\frac{k}{r} \tag{7}$$

is satisfied.

Finally the case $\tan\alpha \leq \frac{k}{r}$ must be considered: it is easy to verify that in this case the ball remains fixed. ■

Example 11.3 Consider rigid body 1 of Example 9.3. It is constrained to rotate about a vertical fixed axis $(O, \hat{\mathbf{z}}_0)$ of a referential 0. Body 1 is in the shape of a right-triangular plate OAB (of negligible thickness) of uniformly distributed mass m, with $\mathbf{r}_{OB} = b\hat{\mathbf{z}}_0$ and $\mathbf{r}_{OA} = a\hat{\mathbf{x}}_1$. See Figure 11.5.

The pivot connecting 0 and 1 is assumed frictionless. A motor $\mathcal{M}$ is mounted between 0 and 1 and its action on 1 is equivalent to a constant couple $C\hat{\mathbf{z}}_0$. In addition, the ambient fluid exerts a viscous force $d\mathbf{F}(P) = -\mu \mathbf{v}_{P/0} dA$ on an element of area dA surrounding a point P of the plate, where μ is a positive constant.

a. After finding the kinematic, kinetic and dynamic screws of the plate, determine the external action screw $\{\mathcal{A}_{\bar{1}\to 1}\}$ exerted on the plate.

b. Apply the FTD to find the equation of motion and the unknown contact action screw $\{\mathcal{A}^c_{0\to 1}\}$ transmitted through the frictionless pivot. Can a steady regime of rotation be established? ■

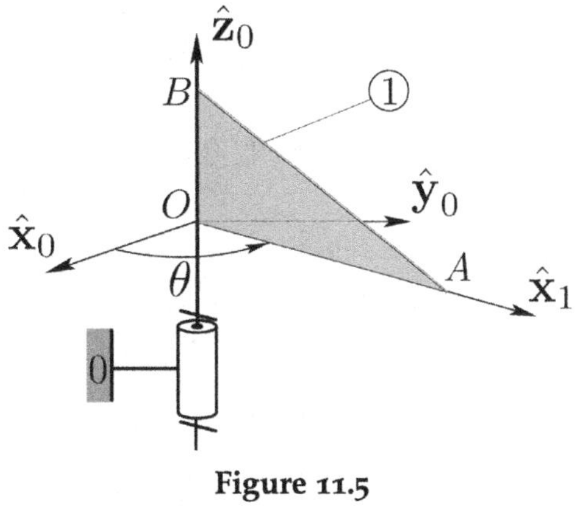

Figure 11.5

a. The kinematic and kinetic screws of the plate take the form (see Example 9.3 for details):

$$\{\mathcal{V}_{1/0}\} = \begin{Bmatrix} \dot{\theta}\hat{\mathbf{z}}_0 \\ \mathbf{0} \end{Bmatrix}_O \quad \{\mathcal{H}_{1/0}\} = \begin{Bmatrix} \frac{m}{3} a\dot{\theta}\hat{\mathbf{y}}_1 \\ \frac{m}{12} a\dot{\theta}(-b\hat{\mathbf{x}}_1 + 2a\hat{\mathbf{z}}_0) \end{Bmatrix}_O$$

from which we obtain the expression of its dynamic screw

$$\{\mathcal{D}_{1/0}\} = \begin{Bmatrix} \frac{m}{3} a(\ddot{\theta}\hat{\mathbf{y}}_1 - \dot{\theta}^2\hat{\mathbf{x}}_1) \\ \frac{m}{12} a(-b\ddot{\theta}\hat{\mathbf{x}}_1 - b\dot{\theta}^2\hat{\mathbf{y}}_1 + 2a\ddot{\theta}\hat{\mathbf{z}}_0) \end{Bmatrix}_O$$

The external action screw $\{\mathcal{A}_{\bar{1}\to 1}\}$ exerted on body 1 is the sum $\{\mathcal{A}^g_{\text{Earth}\to 1}\} + \{\mathcal{A}^c_{0\to 1}\} + \{\mathcal{A}_{\text{fluid}\to 1}\} + \{\mathcal{A}_{\mathcal{M}\to 1}\}$

$$\{\mathcal{A}_{\bar{1}\to 1}\} = \begin{Bmatrix} -mg\hat{\mathbf{z}}_0 \\ \mathbf{0} \end{Bmatrix}_G + \begin{Bmatrix} P\hat{\mathbf{x}}_1 + Q\hat{\mathbf{y}}_1 + R\hat{\mathbf{z}}_0 \\ M\hat{\mathbf{x}}_1 + N\hat{\mathbf{y}}_1 \end{Bmatrix}_O + \begin{Bmatrix} \mathbf{0} \\ C\hat{\mathbf{z}}_0 \end{Bmatrix} + \{\mathcal{A}_{\text{fluid}\to 1}\}$$

We have taken into account the frictionless nature of the joint between body 1 and its support 0: $\mathbf{M}^c_{O,0\to 1} \cdot \hat{\mathbf{z}}_0 = 0$. We need to determine $\{\mathcal{A}_{\text{fluid}\to 1}\}$ by integration of the local surface force field:

$$\{\mathcal{A}_{\text{fluid}\to 1}\} = -\begin{Bmatrix} \int \mu \mathbf{v}_{P\in 1/0} dA \\ \int \mathbf{r}_{OP} \times \mu \mathbf{v}_{P\in 1/0} dA \end{Bmatrix}_O$$

It is then readily recognized that this last expression is related to the kinetic screw $\{\mathcal{H}_{1/0}\}$

according to

$$\{\mathcal{A}_{\text{fluid}\to 1}\} = -\frac{\mu ab}{2m}\{\mathcal{H}_{1/0}\} = -\frac{1}{2}\mu ab \left\{ \begin{array}{c} \frac{1}{3}a\dot{\theta}\hat{\mathbf{y}}_1 \\ \frac{1}{12}a\dot{\theta}(-b\hat{\mathbf{x}}_1 + 2a\hat{\mathbf{z}}_0) \end{array} \right\}_O$$

Now application of the FTD $\{\mathcal{D}_{1/0}\} = \{\mathcal{A}_{\bar{1}\to 1}\}$ by resolving all screws about point O (indeed we need to take into account $\mathbf{M}^c_{O,0\to 1}\cdot\hat{\mathbf{z}}_0 = 0$) leads to

$$\frac{m}{3}a(\ddot{\theta}\hat{\mathbf{y}}_1 - \dot{\theta}^2\hat{\mathbf{x}}_1) = -mg\hat{\mathbf{z}}_0 + \mathbf{R}^c_{0\to 1} - \frac{1}{6}\mu a^2 b\dot{\theta}\hat{\mathbf{y}}_1$$

$$\frac{m}{12}a(-b\ddot{\theta}\hat{\mathbf{x}}_1 - b\dot{\theta}^2\hat{\mathbf{y}}_1 + 2a\ddot{\theta}\hat{\mathbf{z}}_0) = -\mathbf{r}_{OG}\times mg\hat{\mathbf{z}}_0 + \mathbf{M}^c_{O,0\to 1} - \frac{1}{24}\mu a^2 b\dot{\theta}(-b\hat{\mathbf{x}}_1 + 2a\hat{\mathbf{z}}_0) + C\hat{\mathbf{z}}_0$$

This gives:
- the resultant $\mathbf{R}^c_{0\to 1} = P\hat{\mathbf{x}}_1 + Q\hat{\mathbf{y}}_1 + R\hat{\mathbf{z}}_0$ of the contact forces transmitted through the pivot

$$P = -\frac{m}{3}a\dot{\theta}^2, \qquad Q = \frac{m}{3}a\ddot{\theta} + \frac{1}{6}\mu a^2 b\dot{\theta}, \qquad R = mg$$

- the moment $\mathbf{M}^c_{O,0\to 1} = M\hat{\mathbf{x}}_1 + N\hat{\mathbf{y}}_1$ about O of these forces

$$M = -\frac{m}{12}ab\ddot{\theta} - \frac{1}{24}\mu a^2 b^2\dot{\theta}, \qquad N = -\frac{1}{3}mga - \frac{m}{12}ab\dot{\theta}^2$$

- the equation of motion

$$\frac{m}{6}a^2\ddot{\theta} + \frac{1}{12}\mu a^3 b\,\dot{\theta} = C$$

This last equation shows that a steady regime can be established at angular speed

$$\omega = \frac{12C}{\mu a^3 b}$$

Note that even in a steady regime, there is a non-zero resultant reaction force and a resultant moment: the rigid plate is not balanced dynamically. See Section 11.5 on the method to achieve dynamic balancing. ∎

Example 11.4 A circular disk 1 of center C, radius R and uniform mass is in motion on a planar horizontal support $(O, \hat{\mathbf{x}}_0, \hat{\mathbf{y}}_0)$ in a referential 0 $(O, \hat{\mathbf{x}}_0, \hat{\mathbf{y}}_0, \hat{\mathbf{z}}_0)$. See Figure 11.6. A basis $b_3(\hat{\mathbf{x}}_3, \hat{\mathbf{y}}_3, \hat{\mathbf{z}}_3)$ is defined as follows:
- the line $(I, \hat{\mathbf{x}}_3)$ is the tangent at the point of contact I to the edge of the disk.
- the line $(I, \hat{\mathbf{y}}_3)$ is the line connecting I and C.
- the line $(C, \hat{\mathbf{z}}_3)$ is normal to the plane of the disk.

Basis $b_1(\hat{\mathbf{x}}_1, \hat{\mathbf{y}}_1, \hat{\mathbf{z}}_1 = \hat{\mathbf{z}}_3)$ attached to the disk is obtained from basis $b_0(\hat{\mathbf{x}}_0, \hat{\mathbf{y}}_0, \hat{\mathbf{z}}_0)$ by the following sequence of rotations

$$(\hat{\mathbf{x}}_0, \hat{\mathbf{y}}_0, \hat{\mathbf{z}}_0) \xrightarrow{\mathcal{R}_{\psi,\hat{\mathbf{z}}_0}} (\hat{\mathbf{x}}_2, \hat{\mathbf{y}}_2, \hat{\mathbf{z}}_2 = \hat{\mathbf{z}}_0) \xrightarrow{\mathcal{R}_{\theta,\hat{\mathbf{x}}_2}} (\hat{\mathbf{x}}_3 = \hat{\mathbf{x}}_2, \hat{\mathbf{y}}_3, \hat{\mathbf{z}}_3) \xrightarrow{\mathcal{R}_{\phi,\hat{\mathbf{z}}_3}} (\hat{\mathbf{x}}_1, \hat{\mathbf{y}}_1, \hat{\mathbf{z}}_1 = \hat{\mathbf{z}}_3)$$

Assume that the initial conditions are such that the disk initially rolls without slipping on the horizontal plane. It is then physically acceptable to assume that the disk will not slip subsequently. Neglect rolling and pivoting friction can be neglected.

a. Derive the equations of motions governing the coordinates x, y, ψ, θ, ϕ. Then find the unknown reaction force of the support on the disk.

b. Show that the disk can have a "straight-ahead" motion during which it remains vertical and rolls at constant angular velocity $\dot{\phi}_0$. Under which condition is such a motion stable?

c. Show that the disk can have a "spinning motion" about one of its stationary, vertical diameter at constant angular velocity $\dot{\psi}_0$. Under which condition is such a motion stable? ■

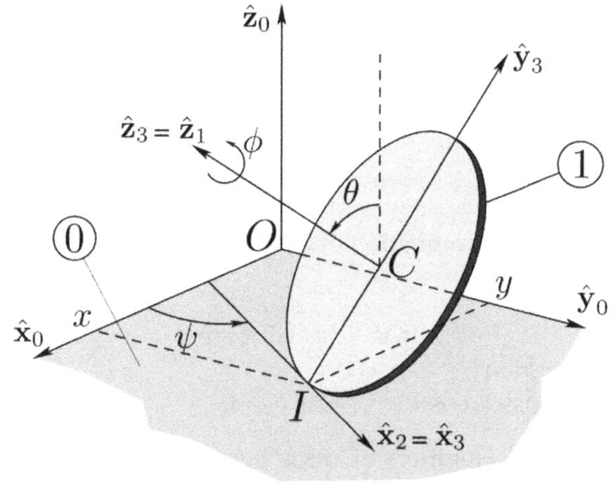

Figure 11.6

a. With the notations of Figure 11.6, we find the following kinematic screw of the disk relative to referential 0

$$\{\mathcal{V}_{1/0}\} = \left\{ \begin{matrix} \dot{\phi}\hat{\mathbf{z}}_3 + \dot{\theta}\hat{\mathbf{x}}_2 + \dot{\psi}\hat{\mathbf{z}}_0 \\ \mathbf{0} \end{matrix} \right\}_I = \left\{ \begin{matrix} \dot{\phi}\hat{\mathbf{z}}_3 + \dot{\theta}\hat{\mathbf{x}}_2 + \dot{\psi}\hat{\mathbf{z}}_0 \\ R\dot{\theta}\hat{\mathbf{z}}_3 - R(\dot{\phi} + \dot{\psi}\cos\theta)\hat{\mathbf{x}}_3 \end{matrix} \right\}_C$$

accounting for the no-slip condition at I. Next we write the external action screw exerted on the disk

$$\{\mathcal{A}_{\bar{1}\to 1}\} = \left\{ \begin{matrix} N\hat{\mathbf{z}}_0 + \mathbf{F} \\ \mathbf{0} \end{matrix} \right\}_I + \left\{ \begin{matrix} -mg\hat{\mathbf{z}}_0 \\ \mathbf{0} \end{matrix} \right\}_C, \qquad \text{with } \mathbf{F}\cdot\hat{\mathbf{z}}_0 = 0, \qquad N > 0,$$

where the friction force $\mathbf{F}$ lies in the horizontal plane, and must satisfy $|\mathbf{F}| \le \mu_k N$ (μ_k is the coefficient of static friction). We have neglected spinning and rolling friction.

There are eight unknowns in this problem: x, y, ψ, θ, ϕ, N, $\mathbf{F}$. The first two equations are given by the non-holonomic constraint equations (no-slip at I)

$$\dot{x} = -R\dot{\phi}\cos\psi \qquad (1)$$
$$\dot{y} = -R\dot{\phi}\sin\psi \qquad (2)$$

Application of the FTD to the disk gives $\{\mathcal{D}_{1/0}\} = \{\mathcal{A}_{\bar{1}\to 1}\}$ leads to six scalar equations:
(i) the resultant equation would allow the determination of N and $\mathbf{F}$ once acceleration $\mathbf{a}_C$ is found

$$\mathbf{F} + (N - mg)\hat{\mathbf{z}}_0 = m\mathbf{a}_C \qquad (3)$$

(ii) the moment equation $\mathbf{D}_I = \mathbf{M}_{I,\bar{1}\to 1}$ about point I eliminates the contribution of the reaction force $N\hat{\mathbf{z}}_0 + \mathbf{F}$ and results in three *equations of motion* governing ψ, θ and ϕ which in turn would determine the motion of center C and $\mathbf{a}_C$ through the use of (1-2).
The moment equation about I gives

$$\mathbf{D}_I = \frac{d}{dt}\mathbf{H}_I + \mathbf{v}_I \times m\mathbf{v}_C = \mathbf{r}_{IC} \times (-mg\hat{\mathbf{z}}_0) = -mgR\cos\theta\hat{\mathbf{x}}_3$$

Note that $\mathbf{v}_I = \mathbf{v}_{I/0}$ is not equal to $\mathbf{v}_{I\in 1/0}$ but rather

$$\mathbf{v}_I = \frac{d}{dt}\mathbf{r}_{OI} = \dot{x}\hat{\mathbf{x}}_0 + \dot{y}\hat{\mathbf{y}}_0 = -R\dot{\phi}\hat{\mathbf{x}}_3$$

To find $\mathbf{D}_I$, we need to find the angular momentum about I:

$$\mathbf{H}_I = \mathcal{I}_I(\boldsymbol{\omega}_{1/0}),$$

since $\mathbf{v}_{I\in 1/0} = \mathbf{0}$. After finding operator $\mathcal{I}_I$ using the parallel axis theorem, we find

$$\mathbf{H}_I = \tfrac{1}{4}mR^2\left(5\dot{\theta}\hat{\mathbf{x}}_3 + \dot{\psi}\sin\theta\hat{\mathbf{y}}_3 + 6(\dot{\phi} + \dot{\psi}\cos\theta)\hat{\mathbf{z}}_3\right)$$

leading to

$$\mathbf{D}_I = \tfrac{1}{4}mR^2\Big((5\ddot{\theta} + 6\dot{\psi}\dot{\phi}\sin\theta + 5\dot{\psi}^2\cos\theta\sin\theta)\hat{\mathbf{x}}_3 + (\ddot{\psi}\sin\theta - 2\dot{\theta}\dot{\phi})\hat{\mathbf{y}}_3 + (6\ddot{\phi} + 6\ddot{\psi}\cos\theta - 10\dot{\psi}\dot{\theta}\sin\theta)\hat{\mathbf{z}}_3\Big)$$

For more detail on the determination of dynamic moment $\mathbf{D}_I$, see Example 9.5. We then obtain the equations of motion:

$$5\ddot{\theta} + 6\dot{\psi}\dot{\phi}\sin\theta + 5\dot{\psi}^2\cos\theta\sin\theta = -\tfrac{4g}{R}\cos\theta \qquad (4)$$
$$\ddot{\psi}\sin\theta - 2\dot{\theta}\dot{\phi} = 0 \qquad (5)$$
$$\ddot{\phi} + \ddot{\psi}\cos\theta - \tfrac{5}{3}\dot{\psi}\dot{\theta}\sin\theta = 0 \qquad (6)$$

We then obtain the acceleration of mass center C by taking the time-derivative of $\mathbf{v}_C = R\dot{\theta}\hat{\mathbf{z}}_3 - R(\dot{\phi} + \dot{\psi}\cos\theta)\hat{\mathbf{x}}_3$ to obtain

$$\mathbf{a}_C = R(2\dot{\psi}\dot{\theta}\sin\theta - \ddot{\phi} - \ddot{\psi}\cos\theta)\hat{\mathbf{x}}_3 + R(\dot{\psi}^2\cos^2\theta + \dot{\psi}\dot{\phi}\cos\theta - \dot{\theta}^2)\hat{\mathbf{y}}_3 + R(\ddot{\theta} + \dot{\psi}^2\cos\theta\sin\theta + \dot{\psi}\dot{\phi}\sin\theta)\hat{\mathbf{z}}_3$$

We can then find the contact resultant force $\mathbf{F} + N\hat{\mathbf{z}}_0 = mg(\hat{\mathbf{z}}_0 + m\mathbf{a}_C)$ according to (3). Note that the no-slip assumption remains valid as long as $|\mathbf{F}| \le \mu_k N$. If this condition is satisfied at $t = 0$, it is likely satisfied for all $t > 0$.

b. It is easy to show that the motion characterized by

$$\theta = \frac{\pi}{2}, \qquad \psi = \psi_0 = \text{constant}, \qquad \dot{\phi} = \dot{\phi}_0 = \text{constant}$$

is a solution of equations (4-6). It represents a vertical disk rolling "straight-ahead" with constant (rolling) angular velocity $\dot{\phi}_0$. See Figure 11.7(left). It is physically plausible that if $\dot{\phi}_0$ is sufficiently large, this motion of the disk is stable to small perturbations: the small deviations from this steady motion will stay bounded. To show this, we study the fate of the small perturbations $\epsilon(t) = \pi/2 - \theta$ by linearizing the equations of motion (4-6): from (5) we find to leading order

$$\ddot{\psi} = -2\dot{\phi}_0\dot{\epsilon},$$

which leads to, after integration, $\dot{\psi} = -2\dot{\phi}_0\epsilon$ for small deviations from the vertical. From (4), we can obtain the linearized equation

$$5\ddot{\epsilon} + \left(12\dot{\phi}_0^2 - \frac{4g}{R}\right)\epsilon = 0$$

which gives the evolution of the small perturbations of the trajectory of C from the straight path. It is then straightforward to obtain the stability condition of the "straight-ahead" motion:

$$\dot{\phi}_0^2 > \frac{g}{3R}$$

c. Another possible motion of the disk, solution of equations (4-6), is given by

$$\theta = \frac{\pi}{2}, \qquad \psi = \psi_0 + \dot{\psi}_0 t, \qquad \phi = \phi_0$$

where ψ_0, $\dot{\psi}_0$ and ϕ_0 are constant. See Figure 11.7(right). This represents the "spinning" motion of the disk about one of its stationary vertical diameter with constant spinning angular velocity $\dot{\psi}_0$. Once again, we can obtain linear equations for the small perturbations $(\phi, \epsilon = \frac{\pi}{2} - \theta)$:

$$\dot{\phi} = -\tfrac{5}{3}\dot{\psi}_0 \epsilon,$$

and

$$\ddot{\epsilon} + \left(\dot{\psi}_0^2 - \frac{4g}{5R}\right)\epsilon = 0$$

leading to the stability condition of the "spinning motion":

$$\dot{\psi}_0^2 > \tfrac{4}{5}\frac{g}{R}.$$

■

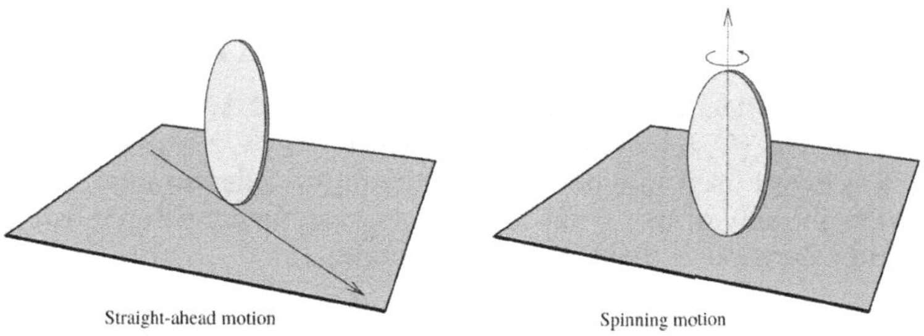

Figure 11.7

Example 11.5 A disk 1 of mass center G, mass m, and radius r is in motion on the horizontal plane $\Pi(O, \hat{\mathbf{x}}_0, \hat{\mathbf{y}}_0)$ of referential 0 in such a way that the *unconstrained* extremity O of its massless axle OG remains fixed in the plane Π. See Figure 11.8.

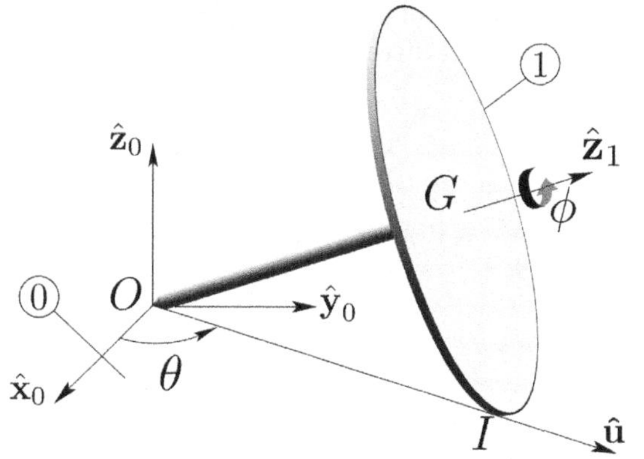

Figure 11.8

Hence, the center G travels along a horizontal circle. We assume that there is sufficient friction between the disk and its support to prevent slipping at both O and I. The motion is then described by the two variable angles $\theta(t)$ and $\phi(t)$ which define the rotation about axis $(O, \hat{\mathbf{z}}_0)$ and the rotation about axis $(O, \hat{\mathbf{z}}_1)$, respectively. The length of axle OG is r.

a. Find the expression of kinematic screw $\{\mathcal{V}_{1/0}\}$ and of angular momentum $\mathbf{H}_O$.

b. Denote by $\mathbf{R}_O = N_O\hat{\mathbf{z}}_0 + F_{Ou}\hat{\mathbf{u}} + F_{Ov}\hat{\mathbf{v}}$ and $\mathbf{R}_I = N_I\hat{\mathbf{z}}_0 + F_{Iu}\hat{\mathbf{u}} + F_{Iv}\hat{\mathbf{v}}$ the reaction forces of the support on body 1 at point O and point I, respectively. Apply the FTD to show that $\dot{\theta}$ is constant and to find the components N_O, N_I, F_{Ou}, F_{Ov}, F_{Iu} and F_{Iv} of the reaction forces.

c. What is the value $\dot{\theta}_1$ which $\dot{\theta}$ must not exceed if the slip of body 1 is to be avoided? (call μ the coefficient of static friction).

d. Using the expressions of N_O and N_I, find the value $\dot{\theta}_2$ which $\dot{\theta}$ must not exceed if the tipping of body 1 about I is to be avoided. ■

a. First introduce angle $\theta = (\hat{\mathbf{x}}_0, \hat{\mathbf{u}}) = (\hat{\mathbf{y}}_0, \hat{\mathbf{v}})$ which defines the orientation of plane $(O, \hat{\mathbf{u}}, \hat{\mathbf{z}}_0)$ containing points O, I and G.Then introduce two unit vectors $\hat{\mathbf{z}}_1$ and $\hat{\mathbf{w}}$ in plane $(O, \hat{\mathbf{u}}, \hat{\mathbf{z}}_0)$ such that

$$\mathbf{r}_{OG} = r\hat{\mathbf{z}}_1, \qquad \mathbf{r}_{IG} = r\hat{\mathbf{w}}$$

Unit vector $\hat{\mathbf{z}}_1$ is attached to disk 1. The angle $\beta = (\hat{\mathbf{u}}, \hat{\mathbf{z}}_1)$ is the constant $\pi/4$. A rotation of angle ϕ about axis $(O, \hat{\mathbf{z}}_1)$ would define a basis $b_1(\hat{\mathbf{x}}_1, \hat{\mathbf{y}}_1, \hat{\mathbf{z}}_1)$ attached to body 1. Note however that basis b_1 is not used in what follows due to the axisymmetry of the system w.r.t. $(O, \hat{\mathbf{z}}_1)$. We also note in view of $\mathbf{r}_{OG} = r\hat{\mathbf{z}}_1$ that point O can be considered as rigidly attached to body 1 (the rigid extension of disk). Hence we obtain

$$\{\mathcal{V}_{1/0}\} = \left\{ \begin{array}{c} \dot{\theta}\hat{\mathbf{z}}_0 + \dot{\phi}\hat{\mathbf{z}}_1 \\ \mathbf{0} \end{array} \right\}_O$$

Then, the no-slip condition gives $\mathbf{v}_{I\in 1/0} = \boldsymbol{\omega}_{1/0} \times \mathbf{r}_{OI} = (\dot{\theta}\hat{\mathbf{z}}_0 + \dot{\phi}\hat{\mathbf{z}}_1) \times \sqrt{2}r\hat{\mathbf{u}} = \sqrt{2}r(\dot{\theta} + \sin\beta\dot{\phi})\hat{\mathbf{v}} = \mathbf{0}$ leading to the constraint:

$$\dot{\phi} = -\sqrt{2}\dot{\theta} \tag{1}$$

Then we obtain

$$\boldsymbol{\omega}_{1/0} = -\dot{\theta}\hat{\mathbf{u}}, \qquad \mathbf{v}_G = \frac{r}{\sqrt{2}}\dot{\theta}\hat{\mathbf{v}}$$

Note that body 1 admits as instantaneous axis of rotation the line OI since $\mathbf{v}_{O\in 1/0} = \mathbf{v}_{I\in 1/0} = \mathbf{0}$. This shows that $\boldsymbol{\omega}_{1/0}$ is indeed directed along unit vector $\hat{\mathbf{u}}$. With the following expression of

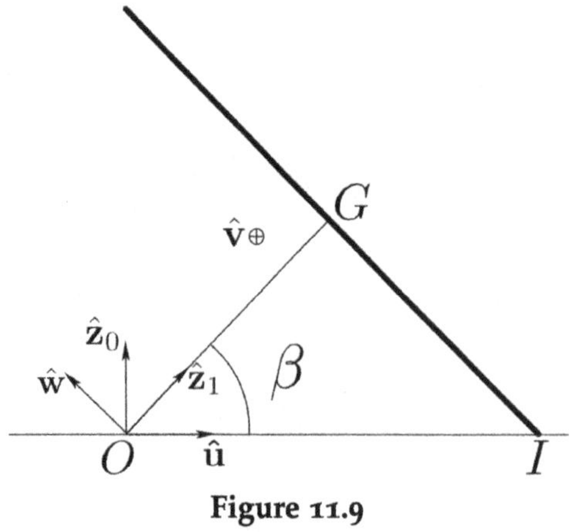

Figure 11.9

the inertia matrix about point G

$$[\mathcal{I}_G]_b = mr^2 \begin{bmatrix} \frac{1}{4} & 0 & 0 \\ 0 & \frac{1}{4} & 0 \\ 0 & 0 & \frac{1}{2} \end{bmatrix}_b$$

on basis $b(\hat{\mathbf{v}}, \hat{\mathbf{w}}, \hat{\mathbf{z}}_1)$, we obtain the angular momentum of body 1 about point G:

$$\mathbf{H}_G = \mathcal{I}_G(\boldsymbol{\omega}_{1/0}) = \frac{1}{4\sqrt{2}} mr^2\dot{\theta}(\hat{\mathbf{w}} - 2\hat{\mathbf{z}}_1)$$

then about point O:

$$\mathbf{H}_O = \mathbf{H}_G + \frac{1}{\sqrt{2}} mr^2\dot{\theta}\hat{\mathbf{v}} \times (-r\hat{\mathbf{z}}_1) = \frac{1}{4\sqrt{2}} mr^2\dot{\theta}(5\hat{\mathbf{w}} - 2\hat{\mathbf{z}}_1)$$

One could also have used $\mathbf{H}_O = \mathcal{I}_O(\boldsymbol{\omega}_{1/0})$ since point O is a fixed point of the body ($\mathcal{I}_O$ is found from $\mathcal{I}_C$ by applying the Parallel Axis theorem).
b. The total external action screw $\{\mathcal{A}_{\bar{1}\to 1}\}$ exerted on body 1 is given by the sum

$$\left\{ \begin{matrix} N_O\hat{\mathbf{z}}_0 + F_{Ou}\hat{\mathbf{u}} + F_{Ov}\hat{\mathbf{v}} \\ \mathbf{0} \end{matrix} \right\}_O + \left\{ \begin{matrix} N_I\hat{\mathbf{z}}_0 + F_{Iu}\hat{\mathbf{u}} + F_{Iv}\hat{\mathbf{v}} \\ \mathbf{0} \end{matrix} \right\}_I + \left\{ \begin{matrix} -mg\hat{\mathbf{z}}_0 \\ \mathbf{0} \end{matrix} \right\}_G$$

where (i) we are accounting for the contact forces at both points O and I, (ii) rolling and spinning friction is neglected, (iii) the contact resultant forces have been decomposed into the sum of normal and tangential components. There is no possible way of eliminating both unknown contact forces $\mathbf{R}_O$ and $\mathbf{R}_I$ by applying a dynamic moment equation $\mathbf{D}_Q = \mathbf{M}_{Q,\bar{1}\to 1}$ about a particular point Q. So we choose point Q to be O since it leads to the simplest evaluation of the dynamic moment: we find

$$\mathbf{D}_O = \frac{d}{dt}\mathbf{H}_O = \frac{1}{4\sqrt{2}} mr^2\ddot{\theta}(5\hat{\mathbf{w}} - 2\hat{\mathbf{z}}_1) - \tfrac{7}{8} mr^2\dot{\theta}^2\hat{\mathbf{v}}$$

where we have used $d\hat{\mathbf{z}}_1/dt = \frac{1}{\sqrt{2}}\dot{\theta}\hat{\mathbf{v}}$ and $d\hat{\mathbf{w}}/dt = -\frac{1}{\sqrt{2}}\dot{\theta}\hat{\mathbf{v}}$. We also obtain

$$\mathbf{M}_{O,\bar{1}\to 1} = (\tfrac{1}{\sqrt{2}} mgr - \sqrt{2}rN_I)\hat{\mathbf{v}} + \sqrt{2}rF_{Iv}\hat{\mathbf{z}}_0$$

By projection on $(\hat{\mathbf{u}}, \hat{\mathbf{v}}, \hat{\mathbf{z}}_0)$ we obtain three scalar equations

$$-\tfrac{7}{8} mr^2\dot{\theta}^2 = \tfrac{1}{\sqrt{2}} mgr - \sqrt{2}rN_I \tag{2}$$

$$-\tfrac{7}{8} mr^2\ddot{\theta} = 0 \tag{3}$$

$$-\tfrac{3}{8} mr^2\ddot{\theta} = \sqrt{2}rF_{Iv} \tag{4}$$

which shows that:
(i) angular velocity $\dot{\theta}$ =constant from equation (3): the rotation of 1 about axis $(O, \hat{\mathbf{z}}_0)$ evolves at constant rate.
(ii) $F_{Iv} = 0$ from equation (4) using $\ddot{\theta} = 0$.

We then write the resultant equation $m\mathbf{a}_G = \mathbf{R}_O + \mathbf{R}_I - mg\hat{\mathbf{z}}_0$ on $(\hat{\mathbf{u}}, \hat{\mathbf{v}}, \hat{\mathbf{z}}_0)$, using $\mathbf{a}_G = \frac{1}{\sqrt{2}} r\dot{\theta} d\hat{\mathbf{v}}/dt = -\frac{1}{\sqrt{2}} r\dot{\theta}^2\hat{\mathbf{u}}$. We find

$$F_{Ov} + F_{Iv} = 0$$
$$N_O + N_I = mg$$
$$-\tfrac{1}{\sqrt{2}} mr\dot{\theta}^2 = F_{Ou} + F_{Iu}$$

which shows that $F_{Ov} = 0$. However *we arrive at an indetermination: only the sum $F_{Ou} + F_{Iu}$ can be determined, and not the individual values of the friction forces of I and O*. Indeed we have six equations from the application of the FTD for seven unknowns: θ, $\mathbf{R}_O$, $\mathbf{R}_I$.

c. The no-slip motion of 1 relative to support Π occurs as long as

$$|\mathbf{F}_O| < \mu N_O, \qquad \text{and} \qquad |\mathbf{F}_I| < \mu N_I$$

An upper bound for $\dot\theta$ can be found in the following way. Assume the inequalities satisfied: then they imply that

$$|\mathbf{F}_O + \mathbf{F}_I| \leq |\mathbf{F}_O| + |\mathbf{F}_I| \leq \mu(N_O + N_I)$$

But with $|\mathbf{F}_O + \mathbf{F}_I| = \frac{1}{\sqrt{2}} mr\dot\theta^2$ and $(N_O + N_I) = mg$, this inequality becomes

$$\frac{1}{\sqrt{2}} mr\dot\theta^2 \leq \mu mg$$

or

$$\dot\theta^2 \leq \dot\theta_1^2 = \sqrt{2}\frac{\mu g}{r}. \tag{11.18}$$

This would appear to be only a necessary condition.

Assume that the value taken for $\dot\theta$ leads to impending slip (at both O and I): then $|\mathbf{F}_O| = \mu N_O$ and $|\mathbf{F}_I| = \mu N_I$. However both F_{Ou} and F_{Iu} must be of the same sign: this follows from the fact that the $\mathbf{v}_{O\in 1/0} \cdot \hat{\mathbf{u}} = \mathbf{v}_{I\in 1/0} \cdot \hat{\mathbf{u}}$. So at impending slip we can write $|F_{Ou} + F_{Ov}| = |F_{Ou}| + |F_{Ov}| = \mu(N_O + N_I)$: this leads to $\dot\theta = \dot\theta_1$.

d. We need to find the normal reaction at point O:

$$N_O = mg - N_I = \tfrac{1}{2} mg - \frac{7}{8\sqrt{2}} mr\dot\theta^2$$

Setting $N_O = 0$ yields the maximum value of $\dot\theta$ above which contact at O is lost (tipping would then follow):

$$\dot\theta_2^2 = \frac{4\sqrt{2}}{7}\frac{g}{r}$$

Note that this result presupposes that the system does not slip. So it is valid as long as $\dot\theta_2^2 < \dot\theta_1^2$, i.e. $\mu > \frac{4}{7}$. If $\mu < \frac{4}{7}$, then sliding occurs before tipping about point I. ■

It was mentioned in Section 10.3.2 that Coulomb laws can lead to ill-posed problems: non-physical situations may arise whereby either no solution or multiple solutions are found from the Fundamental Theorem of Dynamics and the application of these friction laws. This is illustrated in the following example. See also problem 11.6.

Example 11.6 A right-circular cylinder 1 of uniformly distributed mass m and mass center G is set on a rough inclined plane 0 on one of its bases. The contact is characterized by coefficient of kinetic friction μ. The cylinder is given an initial translational motion so that it begins to slip downward along a line Ox of steepest incline: the velocity of its mass center $\mathbf{v}_G$ is initially $\mathbf{v}_0$ while its angular velocity ω is zero. The geometry of cylinder 1 is defined by its radius r and its height $2h$. Its moment of inertia about an axis passing through G and perpendicular to its axis Gz is $J = mk^2$.

Study the motion of the cylinder as a function of friction coefficient μ. In particular show that if the condition $\mu > \frac{k^2}{rh} + \frac{r}{h}$ is satisfied, no motion compatible with Coulomb friction is possible. ■

We first define basis $(\hat{\mathbf{x}}_0, \hat{\mathbf{y}}_0, \hat{\mathbf{z}}_0)$ attached to referential 0 with $(\hat{\mathbf{x}}_0, \hat{\mathbf{z}}_0)$ in the plane of motion containing mass center G. If we assume that the subsequent motion of body 1 is a translation along axis $(O, \hat{\mathbf{x}}_0)$, then application of the FTD shows that the following equations must be

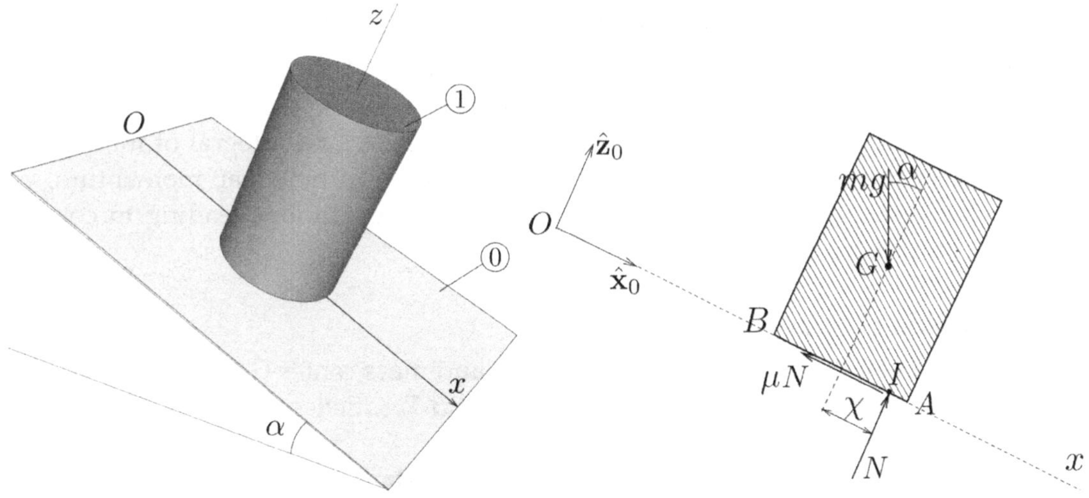

Figure 11.10

satisfied

$$m\dot{v}_G = mg\sin\alpha - \mu N \qquad (1)$$
$$0 = N - mg\cos\alpha \qquad (2)$$
$$mk^2\dot{\omega} = -\chi N + \mu h N = 0 \qquad (3)$$

where we have modeled the contact actions as

$$\{\mathcal{A}^c_{0\to1}\} = \left\{ \begin{array}{c} N\hat{\mathbf{z}}_0 - \mu N\hat{\mathbf{x}}_0 \\ \mathbf{0} \end{array} \right\}_I$$

dot product between moment and resultant is always 0 for any point on BA, ⇒ there is a point I where moment is 0

in accordance with Coulomb laws. The location of point I is defined by distance χ measured from I to axis Gz. See Figure 11.10(right). Equation (3) gives $\chi = \mu h$. Since point I must be located between the points A and B of the contact surface, we must impose $\chi < r$, leading to the condition $\mu < \frac{r}{h}$. When $\mu \to \frac{r}{h}$, the cylinder is about to tip about point A.

For $\mu > \frac{r}{h}$, the cylinder must tip about point A and we must modify equations (1-3) since immediately after release the cylinder possesses a non-zero angular acceleration $\dot{\omega}$ (with $\omega = 0$ and $\chi = r$). Application of the FTD now gives

$$m(a_A + h\dot{\omega}) = mg\sin\alpha - \mu N \qquad (4)$$
$$mr\dot{\omega} = N - mg\cos\alpha \qquad (5)$$
$$mk^2\dot{\omega} = -rN + \mu h N \qquad (6)$$

where we have used $\mathbf{a}_G = \mathbf{a}_A + \dot{\omega}\hat{\mathbf{y}}_0 \times \mathbf{r}_{AG} = (a_A + h\dot{\omega})\hat{\mathbf{x}}_0 + r\dot{\omega}\hat{\mathbf{z}}_0$. We can solve equations (5-6) to find the normal reaction

$$N = \frac{k^2}{k^2 + (r - \mu h)r} mg\cos\alpha$$

Since the contact is unilateral, we must impose $N > 0$: this leads to the condition $\mu < \frac{k^2}{rh} + \frac{r}{h}$. Hence the cylinder slips and tips about A if the condition $\frac{r}{h} < \mu < \frac{k^2}{rh} + \frac{r}{h}$ is satisfied.

Finally for $\mu > \frac{k^2}{rh} + \frac{r}{h}$, no solution compatible with the equations of motion and the friction laws can be found! ■

11.3 Conservation Laws: First Integrals of Motion

Recall that a material system Σ is governed by *a first integral of motion* if it satisfies an equation of the type $F(\dot{\mathbf{q}}, \mathbf{q}, t) =$ constant where $\mathbf{q}$ represents some set of coordinates associated with the motion of Σ relative to a (Newtonian) referential. A first integral of motion typically corresponds to a *conservation law*, such as conservation of linear momentum, angular momentum, energy, etc. Here, we examine general conditions leading to conservation of linear or angular momentum.

11.3.1 Conservation of Linear Momentum

Let Σ be a material system of constant mass m and mass center G.

- **Case 1:** If the total resultant force acting on Σ satisfies $\mathbf{F}_{\overline{\Sigma}\to\Sigma} = \mathbf{0}$ at all time, then $m\mathbf{a}_{G/\mathcal{E}} = \mathbf{0}$ which implies
$$m\mathbf{v}_{G/\mathcal{E}} = \textbf{constant} \tag{11.19}$$
This states the *conservation of the linear momentum of* Σ *relative to* $\mathcal{E}$ (3 first integrals of motion).
- **Case 2:** If the total resultant force acting on Σ satisfies $\hat{\mathbf{u}} \cdot \mathbf{F}_{\overline{\Sigma}\to\Sigma} = 0$ at all time, given a unit vector $\hat{\mathbf{u}}$ constant in $\mathcal{E}$, then we have
$$\hat{\mathbf{u}} \cdot m\mathbf{v}_{G/\mathcal{E}} = \text{constant} \tag{11.20}$$
This states the *conservation of linear momentum of* Σ *relative to* $\mathcal{E}$ *in the direction* $\hat{\mathbf{u}}$ (one first integral of motion).

The following example illustrate conservation of linear momentum.

Example 11.7 A pendulum is assembled by connecting a body 2 of mass center B and mass m to a slider 1 of mass center A and mass M. Slider 1 can translate without friction along the direction Ox of a referential 0 assumed Newtonian. Body 2 can rotate freely about a frictionless pivot at A relative to the slider. The motion of the system occurs in a vertical plane. The slider can be set in a initial position either sufficiently far from a vertical backstop or in contact with it. The pendulum is initially displaced at some angle $-\pi/2 \leq \theta_0 < 0$, defining positive angle θ in the anticlockwise direction. The system slider/pendulum is then released without initial speed.

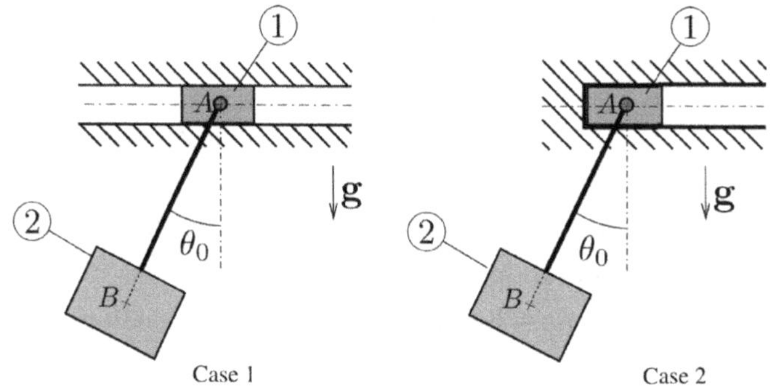

Figure 11.11

Its position at any time t is defined by the coordinate $x(t)$ of A measured along axis Ox and by the angle $\theta(t)$. Denote by l the distance AB and by $J = mk^2$ the moment of inertia of pendulum 2 about its axis of rotation.

a. Case 1. The slider is set in a initial position sufficiently far from the backstop. Find the relationship between $\dot{x}$ and $\dot{\theta}$. Describe the motion of the system. Describe the motion of the mass center G of the system. Along which curve does point B evolve? Find the period of the small amplitude oscillations of the system.

b. Case 2. The slider is now set initially in contact with the backstop. Find the relationship between $\dot{x}$ and $\dot{\theta}$. Show that initially the slider remains in contact with the backstop. When does this contact cease? Show that after contact ceases, the slider never comes back to the backstop. Carefully describe the motion of the system. ■

a. Define the fixed unit vectors $(\hat{\mathbf{e}}_x, \hat{\mathbf{e}}_y, \hat{\mathbf{e}}_z)$ with $\hat{\mathbf{e}}_x$ along horizontal axis Ox, $\hat{\mathbf{e}}_z$ vertical downward, and $\hat{\mathbf{e}}_y = \hat{\mathbf{e}}_z \times \hat{\mathbf{e}}_x$ perpendicular to the plane of motion. See Figure 11.12. The position of the system is defined by coordinate $x(t)$ of A along axis Ox and by the oriented angle $\theta(t)$ which line AB makes with the vertical. Introduce unit vector $\hat{\mathbf{u}}$ along line AB directed from A to B, and $\hat{\mathbf{v}} = \hat{\mathbf{e}}_y \times \hat{\mathbf{u}}$. The position vectors of A and B are then given by

$$\mathbf{r}_{OA} = x\hat{\mathbf{e}}_x, \qquad \mathbf{r}_{OB} = x\hat{\mathbf{e}}_x + l\hat{\mathbf{u}}.$$

Then the velocities of A and B are given by

$$\mathbf{v}_A = \dot{x}\,\hat{\mathbf{e}}_x, \qquad \mathbf{v}_B = \dot{x}\,\hat{\mathbf{e}}_x + l\dot{\theta}\hat{\mathbf{v}}.$$

At time $t = 0$, we have $\theta = \theta_0$, and $\dot{x} = 0$ and $\dot{\theta} = 0$ since the system is released without initial velocity. Denote by Σ the system slider/pendulum and by G its mass center. The external

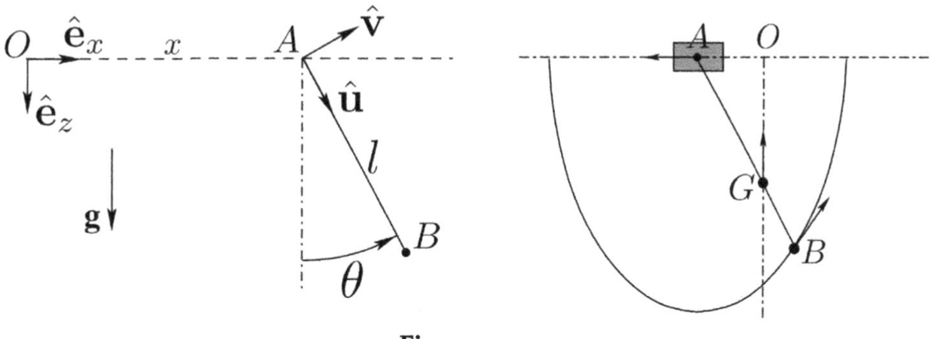

Figure 11.12

forces acting on Σ are the gravitational forces $M\mathbf{g}$ and $m\mathbf{g}$, and the reaction force $N\hat{\mathbf{e}}_z$ directed along $\hat{\mathbf{e}}_z$ in the absence of friction. Hence, the resultant force $\mathbf{F}_{\overline{\Sigma}\to\Sigma}$ on Σ satisfies $\mathbf{F}_{\overline{\Sigma}\to\Sigma} \cdot \hat{\mathbf{e}}_x = 0$. This implies that $(m + M)\mathbf{a}_G \cdot \hat{\mathbf{e}}_x = 0$ and by integration that ($\hat{\mathbf{e}}_x$ is a constant unit vector)

$$(m + M)\mathbf{v}_G \cdot \hat{\mathbf{e}}_x = \text{constant} = 0$$

The constant of integration vanishes since the initial velocity of the system is zero. Hence, *there is conservation of the linear momentum of Σ on axis Ox.* With $(M + m)\mathbf{v}_G = M\mathbf{v}_A + m\mathbf{v}_B$, we obtain

$$(M\mathbf{v}_A + m\mathbf{v}_B) \cdot \hat{\mathbf{e}}_x = (M + m)\dot{x} + ml\dot{\theta}\cos\theta = 0 \tag{1}$$

This equation shows that the sign of $\dot{x}$ (which gives the direction taken by the slider) is the sign of $(-\dot{\theta}\cos\theta)$. Since we expect the angle θ to remain in the interval $-\pi/2 < \theta < \pi/2$, we have $\text{sign}(\dot{x}) = -\text{sign}(\dot{\theta})$: *if the pendulum rotates in the clockwise direction ($\dot{\theta} < 0$), then the slider moves forward ($\dot{x} > 0$). Conversely, if it rotates in the counterclockwise direction ($\dot{\theta} > 0$), then the* *slider moves backward* ($\dot{x} < 0$).

The mass center G of the system moves along a vertical line since from equation (1) $\mathbf{v}_G \cdot \hat{\mathbf{e}}_x = 0$: we get by integration $\mathbf{r}_{OG} \cdot \hat{\mathbf{e}}_x =$ constant. The position of B is given by $\mathbf{r}_{OB} = (x + l\sin\theta)\hat{\mathbf{e}}_x + l\cos\theta\hat{\mathbf{e}}_z$, where $x = -\frac{m}{m+M} l\sin\theta$ by integration of (1) assuming $x = 0$ when $\theta = 0$. The coordinates of B are then given by

$$x_B = \frac{M}{M+m} l\sin\theta, \qquad z_B = l\cos\theta$$

Eliminating θ gives the Cartesian equation of the trajectory of B:

$$\left(\frac{x_B}{l(1+\frac{m}{M})}\right)^2 + \left(\frac{z_B}{l}\right)^2 = 1$$

This equation is that of an ellipse.

To find the period of small oscillations, we need a second equation: we apply the moment equation for pendulum 2 about point A:

$$\hat{\mathbf{e}}_y \cdot \mathbf{D}_{A,2/0} = \hat{\mathbf{e}}_y \cdot \mathbf{M}_{A,\bar{2}\to 2} = \hat{\mathbf{e}}_y \cdot (\mathbf{r}_{AB} \times mg\hat{\mathbf{e}}_z) = -mgl\sin\theta$$

with $\mathbf{D}_{A,2/0} = d\mathbf{H}_{A,2/0}/dt + \mathbf{v}_A \times m\mathbf{v}_G$ and $\mathbf{H}_{A,2/0} \cdot \hat{\mathbf{e}}_y = J\dot{\theta} + \hat{\mathbf{e}}_y \cdot (m\mathbf{r}_{AB} \times \mathbf{v}_A) = J\dot{\theta} + ml\dot{x}\cos\theta$. This gives our second equation of motion

$$J\ddot{\theta} + ml\ddot{x}\cos\theta = -mgl\sin\theta \tag{2}$$

Assuming that the initial angle θ_0 is small, the angle θ and its derivative $\dot{\theta}$ remain small at all time. Using the approximations $\sin\theta \approx \theta$ and $\cos\theta \approx 1$, we obtain a linear approximation of this equation

$$\left(k^2 - \frac{m}{m+M} l^2\right)\ddot{\theta} + gl\theta = 0$$

The period of the oscillations of the system is then

$$T = 2\pi\sqrt{\frac{gl}{k^2 - \frac{m}{m+M} l^2}}$$

Note that k is necessarily larger that $l\sqrt{\frac{m}{m+M}}$.

b. Case 2. If the slider is initially in contact with the backstop, we can expect an initial phase during which it remains in contact with the backstop: indeed as the angle increases from the initial value $\theta_0 < 0$, the slider has a tendency to move backward. Hence, we can assume that there exists an initial phase during which $\dot{x} = 0$ and the external force exerted to system Σ is augmented by a horizontal reaction $R\hat{\mathbf{x}}$ due to the backstop. As long as $R > 0$, contact is maintained. If $R(t) = 0$ at some time t_1, then the slider ceases to be in contact with the backstop. During the first phase, the motion of Σ along the x-axis is governed by the equation

$$R = (m+M)\mathbf{a}_G \cdot \hat{\mathbf{e}}_x = \frac{d}{dt}[(m+M)\dot{x} + ml\dot{\theta}\cos\theta] = ml(\ddot{\theta}\cos\theta - \dot{\theta}^2\sin\theta)$$

We can predict the sign of R without having to find the angular acceleration $\ddot{\theta}$ and the angular velocity $\dot{\theta}$ as a function of θ. Indeed the angular acceleration $\ddot{\theta}$ is positive ($\dot{\theta}$ increases) in the range $\theta_0 \le \theta < 0$, becomes zero for $\theta = 0$, and is negative for $\theta > 0$. Hence $\text{sign}(\ddot{\theta}) = -\text{sign}(\sin\theta)$. This shows that

$$\begin{cases} R > 0, & \theta_0 \le \theta < 0 \\ R = 0, & \theta = 0 \\ R < 0, & \theta > 0 \end{cases}$$

Hence the slider ceases to be in contact with the backstop the moment the pendulum crosses the vertical.

The instant t_1 at which this occurs is of course a function of the initial angle θ_0. In the second phase ($t \geq t_1$), once contact with the backstop ceases, we are in a similar situation as in case 1: there is conservation of linear momentum of Σ along axis Ox. In this case, however, *the linear momentum of Σ along axis Ox is not zero* since

$$(m+M)\mathbf{v}_G \cdot \hat{\mathbf{e}}_x = \text{constant} = m\mathbf{v}_B(t_1) \cdot \hat{\mathbf{e}}_x = ml\dot{\theta}_1$$

where the constant of the motion is obtained at time $t = t_1$: $\dot{\theta} = \dot{\theta}_1$ and $\dot{x} = 0$. Hence in the second phase, *the mass center of Σ moves uniformly in the direction of axis Ox.* Furthermore, the slider's velocity $\dot{x}$ is given by

$$\dot{x} = \frac{m}{M+m} l(\dot{\theta}_1 - \dot{\theta}\cos\theta)$$

We expect in phase 2 that $\dot{\theta} \leq \dot{\theta}_1$ and that $\dot{\theta} = \dot{\theta}_1 > 0$ at $\theta = 0$. This shows that the slider velocity remains positive and becomes zero whenever the pendulum crosses the vertical with a positive velocity. Hence *the slider always moves forward in a non-uniform way in the x-direction, coming to a stop whenever the pendulum crosses the vertical in the forward direction.* It never comes back toward the backstop. The situation is thus quite different from that of case 1. ■

In the next section, we examine conditions for which angular momentum is conserved.

11.3.2 Conservation of Angular Momentum

- **Case 1:** If the total external moment about A satisfies $\mathbf{M}_{A,\bar{\Sigma}\to\Sigma} = \mathbf{0}$ at all time, where A is a fixed point of $\mathcal{E}$ or the mass center G of system Σ, then this implies $\mathbf{D}_{A,\Sigma/\mathcal{E}} = \mathbf{0}$, leading to

$$\mathbf{H}_{A,\Sigma/\mathcal{E}} = \mathbf{constant} \tag{11.21}$$

This states the *conservation of the angular momentum about A of Σ relative to $\mathcal{E}$* (3 first integrals of motion).

- **Case 2:** If the total external moment about fixed point A satisfies $\hat{\mathbf{u}} \cdot \mathbf{M}_{A,\bar{\Sigma}\to\Sigma} = 0$, given a constant vector $\hat{\mathbf{u}}$ of $\mathcal{E}$, then we have

$$\hat{\mathbf{u}} \cdot \mathbf{H}_{A,\Sigma/\mathcal{E}} = \text{constant} \tag{11.22}$$

This states the *conservation of the angular momentum about A of Σ relative to $\mathcal{E}$ in the direction* $\hat{\mathbf{u}}$ (one first integral of motion). Note that if $\hat{\mathbf{u}}$ is not a constant vector, then in general the condition $\hat{\mathbf{u}} \cdot \mathbf{M}_{A,\bar{\Sigma}\to\Sigma} = 0$ does *not* imply that $\hat{\mathbf{u}} \cdot \mathbf{H}_{A,\Sigma/\mathcal{E}} = \text{constant}$.

The following examples illustrate conservation of angular momentum.

Example 11.8 Consider a system Σ of two rigid bodies 1 and 2. Body 1 (of moment of inertia J_1 about Δ) is free to rotate without friction about a vertical axis Δ of referential 0. A uniform disk 2 (of mass m_2 and moment of inertia J_2 about Δ) is constrained to 1 by a frictionless helical joint of axis Δ and constant pitch p (when body 2 rotates by angle 2π about Δ, it translates by a distance p relative to body 1). The system is initially at rest. Upon release, body 2 travels downward until it reaches the end of the screw at a distance h from its initial position. At this point the two bodies are locked together. See Figure 11.13.

a. Find the angular velocities $\omega_{1/0}$ and $\omega_{2/0}$ of the two bodies just before body 2 hits the end of the screw, in terms of parameters h, m_2, J_1 and J_2.

b. Find the same quantities after body 2 hits the end of the screw. ■

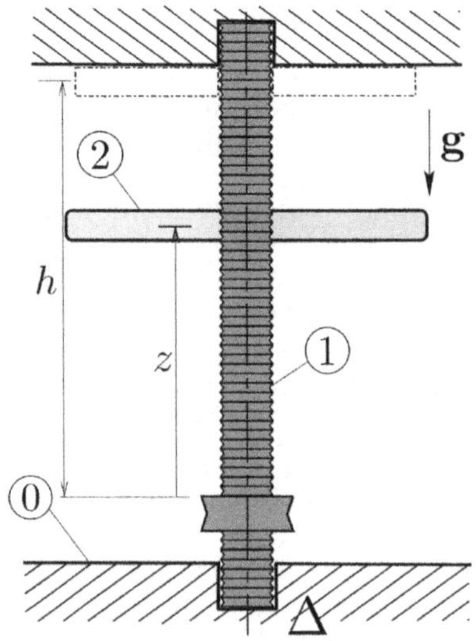

Figure 11.13

a. Denote axis $\Delta = (O, \hat{\mathbf{z}}_0)$, $\hat{\mathbf{z}}_0$ being directed upward. First consider the kinematics of the problem. The release of body 2 sets both 1 and 2 in rotation about Δ. Denote $\boldsymbol{\omega}_{1/0} = \omega_1 \hat{\mathbf{z}}_0$ and $\boldsymbol{\omega}_{2/0} = \omega_2 \hat{\mathbf{z}}_0$. The helical joint between 2 and 1 and the pivot joint between 1 and 0 impose the following kinematic screws

$$\{\mathcal{V}_{2/1}\} = \left\{ \begin{array}{c} (\omega_2 - \omega_1)\hat{\mathbf{z}}_0 \\ \frac{p}{2\pi}(\omega_2 - \omega_1)\hat{\mathbf{z}}_0 \end{array} \right\}_{G_2}, \qquad \{\mathcal{V}_{1/0}\} = \left\{ \begin{array}{c} \omega_1 \hat{\mathbf{z}}_0 \\ \mathbf{0} \end{array} \right\}_{P \in \Delta},$$

where G_2 is the mass center of body 2 (located on axis Δ). This leads to

$$\mathbf{v}_{G_2/0} = \mathbf{v}_{G_2 \in 2/1} + \mathbf{v}_{G_2 \in 1/0} = \frac{p}{2\pi}(\omega_2 - \omega_1)\hat{\mathbf{z}}_0 \tag{1}$$

Consider the external actions exerted on system Σ: the gravitational forces $\{\mathcal{A}_{\text{Earth}\to\Sigma}\}^g$ and the contact actions $\{\mathcal{A}^c_{0\to 1}\}$ acting through pivot: both actions have zero moment about axis Δ, that is, $\hat{\mathbf{z}}_0 \cdot \mathbf{M}_{O,\overline{\Sigma}\to\Sigma} = 0$. This leads to $\hat{\mathbf{z}}_0 \cdot (\mathbf{H}_{O,1/0} + \mathbf{H}_{O,2/0}) = 0$, or

$$J_1 \omega_1 + J_2 \omega_2 = 0. \tag{2}$$

Then consider the external actions exerted on body 2: the gravitational forces $\{\mathcal{A}^g_{\text{Earth}\to 2}\}$ and the contact actions $\{\mathcal{A}^c_{1\to 2}\}$. Since the helical joint is frictionless, we have

$$\frac{p}{2\pi}\mathbf{R}^c_{1\to 2} \cdot \hat{\mathbf{z}}_0 + \mathbf{M}^c_{O,1\to 2} \cdot \hat{\mathbf{z}}_0 = 0 \tag{3}$$

To account for this relationship, we first write the FTD applied to body 2

$$-m_2 g \hat{\mathbf{z}}_0 + \mathbf{R}^c_{1\to 2} = m_2 \mathbf{a}_{G_2/0}, \qquad \mathbf{M}^c_{O,1\to 2} = \mathbf{D}_{O,2/0} \tag{4-5}$$

Equation (3) then leads to

$$\frac{p}{2\pi}\left(m_2 g + m_2 \frac{p}{2\pi}(\dot{\omega}_2 - \dot{\omega}_1)\right) + J_2 \dot{\omega}_2 = 0$$

This last equation can be integrated to give

$$\frac{p}{2\pi} m_2 g t + m_2 (\frac{p}{2\pi})^2 (\omega_2 - \omega_1) + J_2 \omega_2 = 0$$

using $\omega_1 = \omega_2 = 0$ at $t = 0$. Using equation (1) we can find the time t_* taken by G_2 to travel distance h:

$$h = \left(\frac{p}{2\pi}\right)^2 (1 + J_2/J_1) \frac{m_2 g t_*^2/2}{m_2(\frac{p}{2\pi})^2(1 + J_2/J_1) + J_2}$$

leading to final value of angular velocity ω_2

$$\omega_{2,*}^2 = \frac{1}{1 + J_2/J_1} \frac{2m_2 gh}{m_2(\frac{p}{2\pi})^2(1 + J_2/J_1) + J_2}$$

b. After body 2 hits the end of the screw, both bodies 1 and 2 rotate about Δ at the same angular velocity $\omega_1 = \omega_2 = \omega_{**}$. The angular momentum of the system is still conserved $J_1\omega_1 + J_2\omega_2 = 0$. Hence $\omega_{**} = 0$.

■

Example 11.9 Figure 11.14 shows a spherical shell 1 (of mass center G, mass m_1, and radius R) in contact with a rough horizontal plane $(O, \hat{\mathbf{x}}_0, \hat{\mathbf{y}}_0)$ of a referential 0 assumed Newtonian. A cylinder 2 (mass m_2, radius R) is connected in the interior of 1 by a pivot whose axis coincides with the diameter $(G, \hat{\mathbf{y}}_0)$ of 1. The mass centers of 2 coincides with point G. At $t = 0$, body 1 is immobile, while body 2 is given an initial angular velocity $\boldsymbol{\omega}_{2/0} = \omega_0 \hat{\mathbf{y}}_0$ with $\omega_0 > 0$. The effect of friction on the connection between 1 and 2 induces the constant couple $-\mathcal{C}\hat{\mathbf{y}}_0$ so as to oppose the rotation of 2 relative to 1. Denote by I_1 and I_2 the moments of inertia of bodies 1 and 2 about axis $(G, \hat{\mathbf{y}}_0)$.

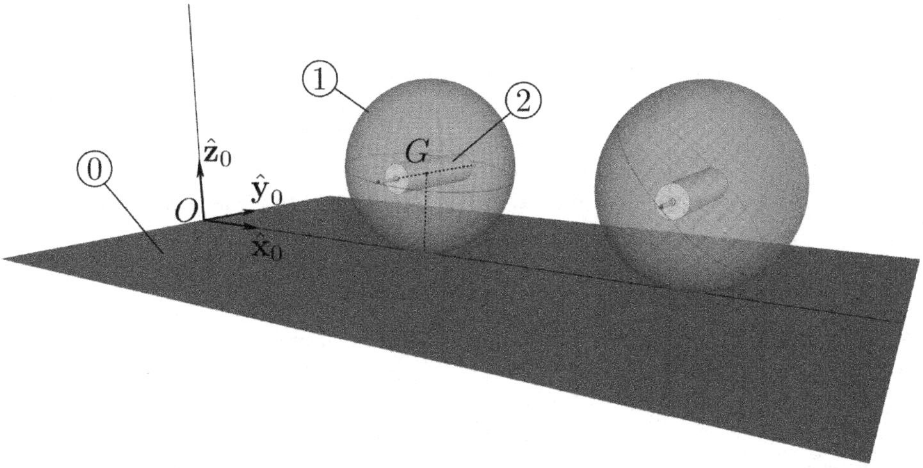

Figure 11.14

a. Sphere 1 is observed to roll forward along line $(O, \hat{\mathbf{x}}_0)$. Why? Assuming rolling without slipping of 1, find an equation which relates angular velocity $\boldsymbol{\omega}_{1/0} = \omega_1 \hat{\mathbf{y}}_0$ to angular velocity $\boldsymbol{\omega}_{2/0} = \omega_2 \hat{\mathbf{y}}_0$.
b. Find another equation which gives ω_2 versus time. Using these two equations, find ω_2 and ω_1 versus time, and deduce the time T taken for the relative rotation between 2 and 1 to cease. Describe the motion of the system for $t > T$. ■

a. This can be explained by conservation of angular momentum. To find out exactly how this takes place, we write the expression of external action screw exerted on the system Σ ={1,2}:

$$\{\mathcal{A}_{\overline{\Sigma}\to\Sigma}\} = \left\{ \begin{matrix} \mathbf{R}_I \\ \mathbf{0} \end{matrix} \right\}_I + \left\{ \begin{matrix} -(m_1 + m_2)g\hat{\mathbf{z}}_0 \\ \mathbf{0} \end{matrix} \right\}_G = \left\{ \begin{matrix} \mathbf{R}_I - (m_1 + m_2)g\hat{\mathbf{z}}_0 \\ \mathbf{0} \end{matrix} \right\}_I$$

This shows that $\mathbf{M}_{I,\bar{\Sigma}\to\Sigma} = \mathbf{0}$ implying that $\mathbf{D}_{I,\Sigma/0} = \mathbf{0}$. Now the dynamic moment of system Σ about I is found to be

$$\begin{aligned} \mathbf{D}_{I,\Sigma/0} &= \frac{d}{dt}(\mathbf{H}_{I,1/0} + \mathbf{H}_{I,2/0}) + \mathbf{v}_{I/0} \times m_1\mathbf{v}_{G/0} + \mathbf{v}_{I/0} \times m_2\mathbf{v}_{G/0} \\ &= \frac{d}{dt}(\mathbf{H}_{I,1/0} + \mathbf{H}_{I,2/0}) \end{aligned}$$

where we have used $\mathbf{v}_{I/0} = \mathbf{v}_{G/0}$. *This leads to conservation of angular momentum* $\mathbf{H}_{I,1/0} + \mathbf{H}_{I,2/0}$: we find

$$\mathbf{H}_{I,1/0} = (I_1 + m_1R^2)\omega_1\hat{\mathbf{y}}_0, \quad \mathbf{H}_{I,2/0} = (I_2\omega_2 + m_2R^2\omega_1)\hat{\mathbf{y}}_0$$

where these expressions can be obtained by using $\mathbf{H}_{I,i/0} = \mathbf{H}_{C,i/0} + \mathbf{r}_{IG} \times m_i\mathbf{v}_{G/0}$ with $\mathbf{v}_{G/0} = R\omega_1\hat{\mathbf{x}}_0$ (by accounting for no-slip condition at I). Hence we obtain, using $\omega_1 = 0$ and $\omega_2 = \omega_0$ at $t = 0$:

$$(I_1 + MR^2)\omega_1 + I_2\omega_2 = \text{constant} = I_2\omega_0$$

leading to

$$(I_1 + MR^2)\omega_1 = I_2(\omega_0 - \omega_2)$$

where we have denoted $M = m_1 + m_2$.

We expect that $\omega_2(t) < \omega_0$ due to slowing effect of the frictional couple between 1 and 2. This shows that $\omega_1 > 0$: the sphere rolls forward along axis $(O, \hat{\mathbf{x}}_0)$.

b. To find a second equation, we write the dynamic moment equation which gives the rate of change of angular momentum $\mathbf{H}_{G,2/0}$ of body 2 about G:

$$\frac{d}{dt}\mathbf{H}_{G,2/0} = \mathbf{M}^c_{G,1\to 2} + \mathbf{M}^g_{G,\bar{2}\to 2} = -C\hat{\mathbf{y}}_0$$

leading to $I_2\dot{\omega}_2 = -C$ which can be integrated to give

$$\omega_2(t) = \omega_0 - \frac{Ct}{I_2}, \qquad \omega_1 = \frac{Ct}{I_1 + MR^2}$$

At time $t = T$, the relative motion of 2 has stopped so that $\omega_2 = \omega_1$: this gives time T

$$T = \frac{\omega_0}{C}\frac{I_2(I_1 + MR^2)}{I_1 + I_2 + MR^2}$$

Note that if $I_2 \ll I_1$, we find $T \approx 0$ as expected. For $t > T$, the sphere rolls uniformly at constant angular velocity $\omega_2(T)$.

■

The following example shows that in some circumstances the angular momentum of a rigid body relative to a particular Newtonian referential can be conserved along a direction which is *not fixed* relative to this referential.

Example 11.10 Two bodies 1 and 2 are in motion relative to a referential 0 attached to Earth. Bodies 1 and 2 are connected by a frictionless pivot of axis $(G_2, \hat{\mathbf{z}}_2)$, where G_2 is the mass center of body 2. Assume that body 2 is an axisymmetric rigid body about $(G_2, \hat{\mathbf{z}}_2)$. Assume that on a basis $b_2(\hat{\mathbf{x}}_2, \hat{\mathbf{y}}_2, \hat{\mathbf{z}}_2)$ attached to 2, the inertia operator of 2 takes the form

$$[\mathcal{I}_{G_2,2}]_{b_2} = \begin{bmatrix} A_2 & 0 & 0 \\ 0 & A_2 & 0 \\ 0 & 0 & C_2 \end{bmatrix}_{b_2}$$

The motion of body 1 relative to referential 0 is *arbitrary*. Assume that there are no other mechanical actions exerted on body 2 other than Earth's gravity. Show that the angular momentum of 2 about G_2 is conserved along axis $\hat{\mathbf{z}}_2$:

$$\hat{\mathbf{z}}_2 \cdot \mathbf{H}_{G_2,2/0} = \text{constant}$$

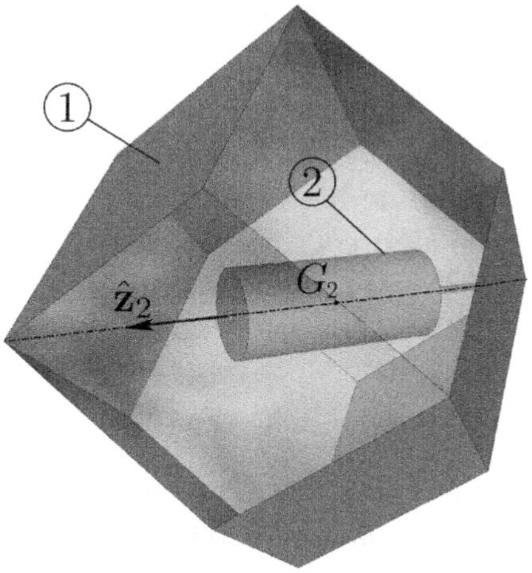

Figure 11.15

Since G_2 is the mass center of body 2, we have $\mathbf{M}^g_{G_2,\bar{2}\to 2} = \mathbf{0}$. The frictionless pivot implies $\hat{\mathbf{z}}_2 \cdot \mathbf{M}_{G_2,\bar{2}\to 2} = \mathbf{0}$. This leads to

$$\hat{\mathbf{z}}_2 \cdot \frac{d}{dt}\mathbf{H}_{G_2,2/0} = 0$$

This can be written in the following form

$$\frac{d}{dt}[\hat{\mathbf{z}}_2 \cdot \mathbf{H}_{G_2,2/0}] - \mathbf{H}_{G_2,2/0} \cdot \frac{d\hat{\mathbf{z}}_2}{dt} = 0$$

To evaluate the expression $\mathbf{H}_{G_2,2/0} \cdot d\hat{\mathbf{z}}_2/dt$ we first express angular velocity $\boldsymbol{\omega}_{2/0}$ on basis $b_2(\hat{\mathbf{x}}_2, \hat{\mathbf{y}}_2, \hat{\mathbf{z}}_2)$:

$$\boldsymbol{\omega}_{2/0} = p_2\hat{\mathbf{x}}_2 + q_2\hat{\mathbf{y}}_2 + r_2\hat{\mathbf{z}}_2$$

Then we have

$$\frac{d\hat{\mathbf{z}}_2}{dt} = \boldsymbol{\omega}_{2/0} \times \hat{\mathbf{z}}_2 = (p_2\hat{\mathbf{x}}_2 + q_2\hat{\mathbf{y}}_2 + r_2\hat{\mathbf{z}}_2) \times \hat{\mathbf{z}}_2 = -p_2\hat{\mathbf{y}}_2 + q_2\hat{\mathbf{x}}_2$$

and

$$\mathbf{H}_{G_2,2/0} = \mathcal{I}_{G_2,2}(\boldsymbol{\omega}_{2/0}) = A_2p_2\hat{\mathbf{x}}_2 + A_2q_2\hat{\mathbf{y}}_2 + C_2r_2\hat{\mathbf{z}}_2$$

This shows that

$$\mathbf{H}_{G_2,2/0} \cdot \frac{d\hat{\mathbf{z}}_2}{dt} = (A_2p_2\hat{\mathbf{x}}_2 + A_2q_2\hat{\mathbf{y}}_2 + C_2r_2\hat{\mathbf{z}}_2) \cdot (-p_2\hat{\mathbf{y}}_2 + q_2\hat{\mathbf{x}}_2) = 0$$

leading to

$$\frac{d}{dt}[\hat{\mathbf{z}}_2 \cdot \mathbf{H}_{G_2,2/0}] = 0$$

or

$$\hat{\mathbf{z}}_2 \cdot \mathbf{H}_{G_2,2/0} = \text{constant}$$

This shows that *the angular momentum about G_2 of body 2 relative to 0 in the direction $\hat{\mathbf{z}}_2$ is conserved.* ■

11.4 Special Motions

We examine in this section two special types of rigid body motion: (i) rotational motions, (ii) Euler-Poinsot motions.

11.4.1 Rigid Body in Rotation about a Fixed Axis

Countless technological applications involve rigid bodies in pure rotational motion. Consider a rigid body 1 connected to some Newtonian referential 0 by a *frictionless pivot* of axis $(O, \hat{\mathbf{z}}_0)$ fixed relative to $\mathcal{E}$. See Figure 11.16. Assume that $\mathcal{B}$ has mass m, mass center G and inertia operator $\mathcal{I}_O$ about O. We assume that point G is not necessarily located on axis of rotation $(O, \hat{\mathbf{z}}_0)$, and define its position by

$$\mathbf{r}_{OG} = e\,\hat{\mathbf{x}}_1$$

by a choice of origin O, e being a constant. The basis of unit vectors $b_1(\hat{\mathbf{x}}_1, \hat{\mathbf{y}}_1, \hat{\mathbf{z}}_0)$ is attached to body 1 and its orientation relative to basis $(\hat{\mathbf{x}}_0, \hat{\mathbf{y}}_0, \hat{\mathbf{z}}_0)$ is defined by oriented angle $\theta = (\hat{\mathbf{x}}_0, \hat{\mathbf{x}}_1) = (\hat{\mathbf{y}}_0, \hat{\mathbf{y}}_1)$. We assume that the inertia operator $\mathcal{I}_O$ takes the following form in basis b_1:

$$[\mathcal{I}_O]_{b_1} = \begin{bmatrix} I_{Ox} & I_{Oxy} & I_{Oxz} \\ I_{Oxy} & I_{Oy} & I_{Oyz} \\ I_{Oxz} & I_{Oyz} & I_{Oz} \end{bmatrix}_{b_1}$$

The kinematic screw of the body takes the simple form

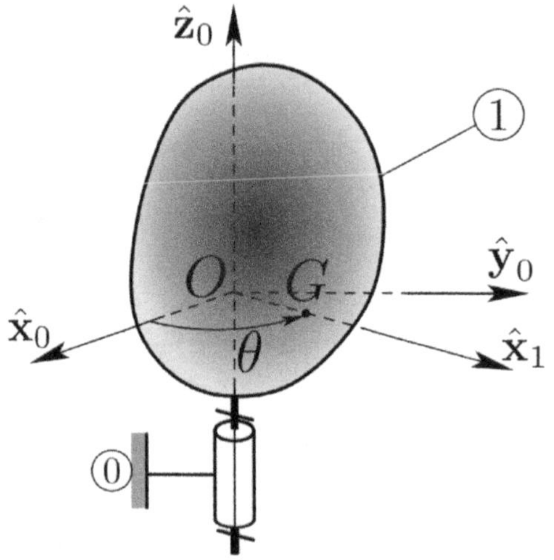

Figure 11.16

$$\{\mathcal{V}_{1/0}\} = \begin{Bmatrix} \dot{\theta}\hat{\mathbf{z}}_0 \\ \\ e\dot{\theta}\hat{\mathbf{y}}_1 \end{Bmatrix}_G$$

Furthermore, we assume that, in addition to the contact actions $\{\mathcal{A}^c_{0\to1}\}$ transmitted by the pivot connection, the external efforts exerted on the body also include a known applied action $\{\mathcal{A}_{\mathcal{O}\to1}\}$ (such as the action of a motor, of gravity, or of aerodynamic forces, ...):

$$\{\mathcal{A}_{\bar{1}\to1}\} = \{\mathcal{A}^c_{0\to1}\} + \{\mathcal{A}_{\mathcal{O}\to1}\} = \left\{\begin{array}{c} R_x\hat{\mathbf{x}}_1 + R_y\hat{\mathbf{y}}_1 + R_z\hat{\mathbf{z}}_0 \\ \\ M_x\hat{\mathbf{x}}_1 + M_y\hat{\mathbf{y}}_1 \end{array}\right\}_O + \left\{\begin{array}{c} F_x\hat{\mathbf{x}}_1 + F_y\hat{\mathbf{y}}_1 + F_z\hat{\mathbf{z}}_0 \\ \\ N_x\hat{\mathbf{x}}_1 + N_y\hat{\mathbf{y}}_1 + N_z\hat{\mathbf{z}}_0 \end{array}\right\}_O$$

Now application of the FTD, $\{\mathcal{D}_{1/0}\} = \{\mathcal{A}_{\bar{1}\to1}\}$, to body 1 gives

$$\left\{\begin{array}{c} m\mathbf{a}_G \\ \\ \mathbf{D}_O \end{array}\right\} = \left\{\begin{array}{c} R_x\hat{\mathbf{x}}_1 + R_y\hat{\mathbf{y}}_1 + R_z\hat{\mathbf{z}}_0 \\ M_x\hat{\mathbf{x}}_1 + M_y\hat{\mathbf{y}}_1 \end{array}\right\}_O + \left\{\begin{array}{c} F_x\hat{\mathbf{x}}_1 + F_y\hat{\mathbf{y}}_1 + F_z\hat{\mathbf{z}}_0 \\ \\ N_x\hat{\mathbf{x}}_1 + N_y\hat{\mathbf{y}}_1 + N_z\hat{\mathbf{z}}_0 \end{array}\right\}_O$$

With the acceleration of G, the dynamic moment about O and the angular momentum given by $\mathbf{a}_G = e(\ddot{\theta}\hat{\mathbf{y}}_1 - \dot{\theta}^2\hat{\mathbf{x}}_1)$, $\mathbf{D}_O = d\mathbf{H}_O/dt$, $\mathbf{H}_O = \mathcal{I}_O(\boldsymbol{\omega})$, respectively, we find the following expression of the dynamic screw of body 1

$$\{\mathcal{D}_{1/0}\} = \left\{\begin{array}{c} me(\ddot{\theta}\hat{\mathbf{y}}_1 - \dot{\theta}^2\hat{\mathbf{x}}_1) \\ \\ (I_{Oxz}\ddot{\theta} - I_{Oyz}\dot{\theta}^2)\hat{\mathbf{x}}_1 + (I_{Oxz}\dot{\theta}^2 + I_{Oyz}\ddot{\theta})\hat{\mathbf{y}}_1 + I_{Oz}\ddot{\theta}\hat{\mathbf{z}}_0 \end{array}\right\}_O$$

Finally we obtain the following system of six equations

$$\left\{\begin{array}{l} -me\dot{\theta}^2 = R_x + F_x \\ me\ddot{\theta} = R_y + F_y \\ 0 = R_z + F_z \end{array}\right. \qquad \left\{\begin{array}{l} I_{Oxz}\ddot{\theta} - I_{Oyz}\dot{\theta}^2 = M_x + N_x \\ I_{Oxz}\dot{\theta}^2 + I_{Oyz}\ddot{\theta} = M_y + N_y \\ I_{Oz}\ddot{\theta} = N_z \end{array}\right.$$

These equations would allow the determination of angle $\theta(t)$ and unknown contact forces and moments $(R_x, R_y, R_z, M_x, M_y)$ resulting from the action of known forces and moments $(F_x, F_y, F_z, N_x, N_y, N_z)$. In particular, these equations show that inertial terms involving $\dot{\theta}^2$ and to a much lesser extent $\ddot{\theta}$ can lead to significant high values of (R_x, M_x, M_y): it is possible to cancel these effects by *dynamic balancing* as will be shown in Section 11.5.

11.4.2 Euler-Poinsot Motion

Definition 11.1 A rigid body $\mathcal{B}$ is said have an Euler-Poinsot motion[a] relative to Newtonian referential $\mathcal{E}$ if the following conditions are satisfied:

1. A point O of $\mathcal{B}$ remains fixed in $\mathcal{E}$ at all time.
2. The external action screw $\{\mathcal{A}_{\bar{\mathcal{B}}\to\mathcal{B}}\}$ satisfies $\mathbf{M}_{O,\bar{\mathcal{B}}\to\mathcal{B}} = \mathbf{0}$, thereby implying conservation of angular momentum of $\mathcal{B}$ about O: $\mathbf{H}_{O,\mathcal{B}/\mathcal{E}} = \mathbf{H}_0$, $\mathbf{H}_0$ being a constant vector determined by the body's initial angular velocity.

[a] Louis Poinsot, *Théorie nouvelle de la rotation des corps*, Paris, Bachelier, 1834.

Examples of Euler-Poinsot motions can be given:

(i) The free motion of a rigid body is amenable to a Euler-Poinsot motion: indeed, if $\{\mathcal{A}_{\bar{\mathcal{B}}\to\mathcal{B}}\} = \{0\}$, then angular momentum $\mathbf{H}_{G,\mathcal{B}/\mathcal{E}}$ about mass center G is a constant vector. Then the rotational motion of $\mathcal{B}$ has the property of an Euler-Poinsot motion.

(ii) A rigid body under the sole effect of a gravitational field which can be assumed constant over the extent of the body (such as the case of a small celestial body) is also amenable to a Euler-Poinsot motion since, in this case, $\mathbf{M}_{G,\overline{\mathcal{B}}\to\mathcal{B}} = \mathbf{M}^g_{G,\overline{\mathcal{B}}\to\mathcal{B}} = \mathbf{0}$ and thus implying a constant angular momentum $\mathbf{H}_{G,\mathcal{B}/\mathcal{E}}$. Since the mass center G of $\mathcal{B}$ is in motion, the gravitational field is generally a function of time. But at any given instant, this field can be considered constant over space if the body is sufficiently "small".

In order to study the properties of a rigid body $\mathcal{B}$ in Euler-Poinsot (rotational) motion, we consider its principal basis $b_p(\hat{\mathbf{x}}_p, \hat{\mathbf{y}}_p, \hat{\mathbf{z}}_p)$ and the corresponding principal moments A, B, and C, that is, the inertia operator of $\mathcal{B}$ about point O takes the form

$$[\mathcal{I}_O]_{b_p} = \begin{bmatrix} A & 0 & 0 \\ 0 & B & 0 \\ 0 & 0 & C \end{bmatrix}_{b_p}$$

assuming that A, B and C non-zero and not all equal. Denote $\boldsymbol{\omega} = \boldsymbol{\omega}_{\mathcal{B}/\mathcal{E}}$.

We can write the angular velocity of $\mathcal{B}$ in the form $\boldsymbol{\omega} = p\hat{\mathbf{x}}_p + q\hat{\mathbf{y}}_p + r\hat{\mathbf{z}}_p$, and the components (p, q, r) satisfy the first integral of motion

$$Ap\hat{\mathbf{x}}_p + Bq\hat{\mathbf{y}}_p + Cr\hat{\mathbf{z}}_p = \mathbf{H}_0 \tag{11.23}$$

It turns out that more quantitative information can be derived from the equations of motion derived by projecting equation $\mathbf{D}_O = \mathbf{0}$ on principal basis $(\hat{\mathbf{x}}_p, \hat{\mathbf{y}}_p, \hat{\mathbf{z}}_p)$ to obtain the set of o.d.e.'s

$$A\dot{p} + (C - B)qr = 0 \tag{11.24}$$
$$B\dot{q} + (A - C)pr = 0 \tag{11.25}$$
$$C\dot{r} + (B - A)pq = 0 \tag{11.26}$$

Three cases must then be considered.

Case 1: $A = B = C \neq 0$. This case corresponds to spherical (isotropic) inertia about O. In this case, we have $\mathbf{H}_O = A\boldsymbol{\omega} = \mathbf{C}_0$ implying that the angular velocity $\boldsymbol{\omega}$ remains constant.

Case 2: $A = B, C \neq 0$. In this case, body $\mathcal{B}$ admits the line $(O, \hat{\mathbf{z}}_p)$ as axis of material revolution. Let us denote by k the scalar $(C - A)/A$. The governing equations can then be written as

$$\dot{p} + kqr = 0 \tag{11.27}$$
$$\dot{q} - kpr = 0 \tag{11.28}$$
$$\dot{r} = 0 \tag{11.29}$$

which shows that $r = r_0 =$ constant. Components $p(t)$ and $q(t)$ can be obtained by introducing complex variable $z = p + iq$ ($i^2 = -1$). Then equations (11.27-11.28) lead to equation $\dot{z} = ikr_0 z$ whose solution is $z = z_0 \exp(ikr_0 t) = \omega_0 \exp(ikr_0 t + i\phi_0)$:

$$p = \omega_0 \cos(kr_0 t + \phi_0), \qquad q = \omega_0 \sin(kr_0 t + \phi_0) \tag{11.30}$$

where the constants of integration (r_0, ω_0, ϕ_0) are determined from the initial conditions. This equation shows that the vector $p\hat{\mathbf{x}}_p + q\hat{\mathbf{y}}_p$ rotates in plane $(O, \hat{\mathbf{x}}_p, \hat{\mathbf{y}}_p)$ at constant angular rate kr_0. Furthermore the magnitude of $\boldsymbol{\omega}$ remains constant:

$$\frac{d}{dt}(p^2 + q^2 + r^2) = 2p(-kqr) + 2q(kpr) + 2r\dot{r} = 0$$

Now recall that axis $(O, \boldsymbol{\omega})$ is the instantaneous axis of rotation of $\mathcal{B}$. Also recall that the locus described by this axis relative to $\mathcal{B}$ is known as the *moving axode* $\mathcal{A}_\mathcal{B}$. It is clearly seen that $\mathcal{A}_\mathcal{B}$ is the cone of revolution of axis $(O, \hat{\mathbf{z}}_p)$ and of vertex half-angle α given by $\tan\alpha = \omega_0/r_0$ (assuming ω_0 and r_0 both positive).

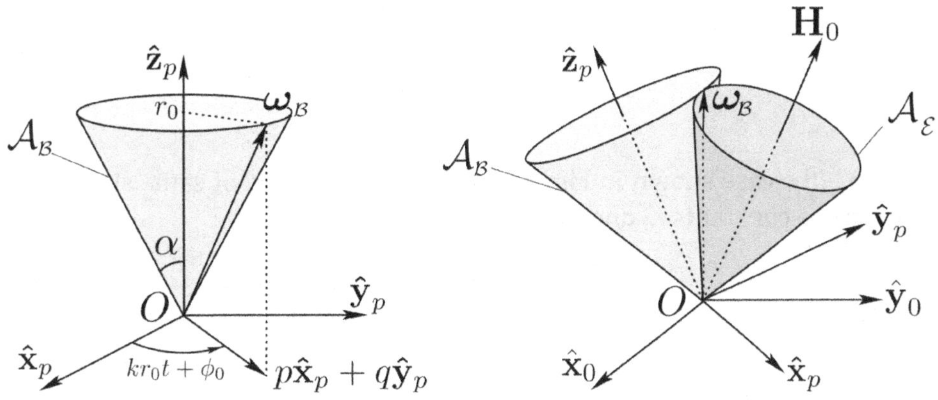

Figure 11.17 – *Fixed and moving axodes of the Euler-Poinsot motion ($A = B$).*

Likewise, axis $(O, \boldsymbol{\omega})$ describes a locus relative to $\mathcal{E}$ known as the *fixed axode*. Recall that angular momentum $\mathbf{H}_O = Ap\hat{\mathbf{x}}_p + Bq\hat{\mathbf{y}}_p + Cr\hat{\mathbf{z}}_p$ is a constant vector $\mathbf{H}_0$ relative to $\mathcal{E}$. Since component r is constant, $\mathbf{H}_0$ and unit vector $\hat{\mathbf{z}}_p$ form a constant angle β given by $\tan\beta = A\omega_0/Cr_0$. This implies that the angle between $\mathbf{H}_0$ and angular velocity $\boldsymbol{\omega}$ is necessarily constant. The fixed axode $\mathcal{A}_\mathcal{E}$ is then the cone of revolution of axis $(O, \mathbf{H}_0)$ and of vertex half-angle $|\beta - \alpha|$. Furthermore, we know from general kinematic considerations (see Section 7.3.4) of rigid bodies that *the motion of $\mathcal{B}$ relative to $\mathcal{E}$ can be interpreted at the rolling motion without slipping of moving axode $\mathcal{A}_\mathcal{B}$ on fixed axode $\mathcal{A}_\mathcal{E}$*. Figure 11.17 shows the fixed and moving axodes for the case $A > C$.

One can now relate the motion of $\mathcal{B}$ to the Euler angles (ψ, θ, ϕ) where the angle θ is defined relative to axis $(O, \mathbf{H}_0)$, that is, unit vector $\hat{\mathbf{z}}_0$ is chosen so that $\mathbf{H}_0 = H_0\hat{\mathbf{z}}_0$ with $H_0 > 0$. Then equation (11.23) becomes, with $\boldsymbol{\omega} = \dot{\psi}\hat{\mathbf{z}}_0 + \dot{\theta}\hat{\mathbf{u}} + \dot{\phi}\hat{\mathbf{z}}_p$:

$$A(\dot{\psi}\sin\theta\hat{\mathbf{w}} + \dot{\theta}\hat{\mathbf{u}}) + C(\dot{\phi} + \dot{\psi}\cos\theta)\hat{\mathbf{z}}_p = H_0\hat{\mathbf{z}}_0 \tag{11.31}$$

with $\hat{\mathbf{w}} = \hat{\mathbf{z}}_p \times \hat{\mathbf{u}}$. See Figure 11.18. First projection on unit vector $\hat{\mathbf{u}}$ shows that $\dot{\theta} = 0$, thus $\theta = \theta_0 = \text{constant} = \beta$. Assume that $0 < \theta_0 < \pi/2$. Then projection on $\hat{\mathbf{w}}$ and $\hat{\mathbf{z}}_p$ show that $\dot{\psi} = \text{constant} = \dot{\psi}_0$ and $\dot{\phi} = \text{constant} = \dot{\phi}_0$ with

$$\dot{\psi}_0 = \frac{H_0}{A}, \qquad \dot{\phi}_0 = (\frac{A}{C} - 1)\dot{\psi}_0\cos\theta_0$$

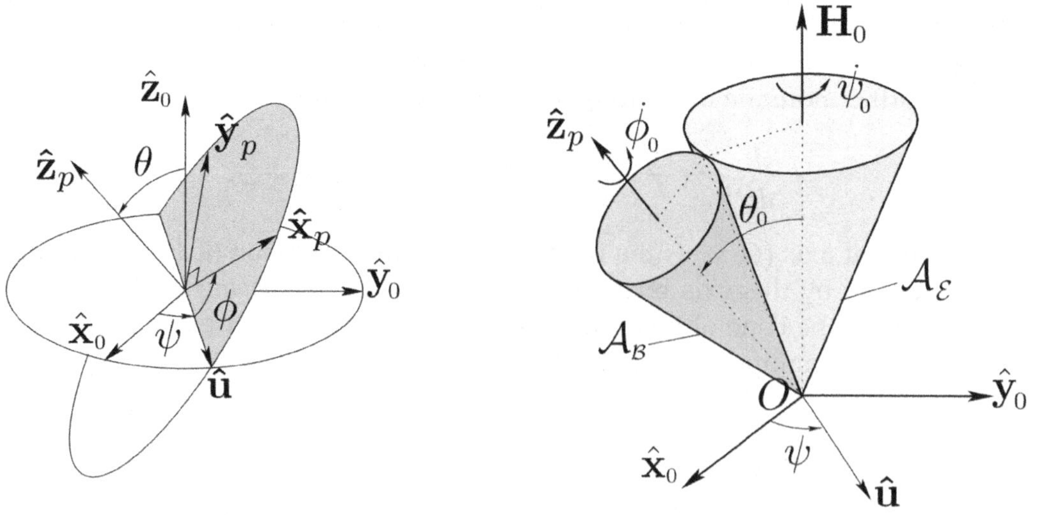

Figure 11.18

For $A > C$ (the case shown in Figure 11.18), $\dot{\psi}_0$ and $\dot{\phi}_0$ are of same sign. We can relate $\dot{\psi}_0$ and $\dot{\phi}_0$ from the constants r_0 and ω_0:

$$\omega_0 = \dot{\psi}_0 \sin\theta_0, \qquad kr_0 = \dot{\phi}_0$$

which yields

$$\begin{aligned} p &= \dot{\psi}_0 \sin\theta_0 \cos(\dot{\phi}_0 t + \phi_0) \\ q &= \dot{\psi}_0 \sin\theta_0 \sin(\dot{\phi}_0 t + \phi_0) \\ r &= \dot{\psi}_0 \cos\theta_0 + \dot{\phi}_0 \end{aligned}$$

Two special cases which are excluded from the previous analysis must be studied:

- Special Case 1: if axes $(O, \hat{\mathbf{z}}_p)$ and $(O, \mathbf{H}_0)$ coincides at all times (in this case Euler angles are not defined). Then equation (11.23) necessarily implies $p = q = 0$ and $r = H_0/C$, which shows that $\mathcal{B}$ rotates uniformly about stationary axis $(O, \hat{\mathbf{z}}_p)$

- Special Case 2: if axes $(O, \hat{\mathbf{z}}_p)$ and $(O, \mathbf{H}_0)$ remain perpendicular to one another, then in this case angle $\theta_0 = \pi/2$ and $\hat{\mathbf{z}}_0 = \hat{\mathbf{w}}$. Equation (11.31) becomes $A\dot{\psi}\hat{\mathbf{w}} + C\dot{\phi}\hat{\mathbf{z}}_p = H_0\hat{\mathbf{w}}$ and yields

$$\dot{\psi}_0 = \frac{H_0}{A}, \qquad \dot{\phi}_0 = 0$$

which shows that $\mathcal{B}$ rotates uniformly about a stationary principal axis $(O, \hat{\mathbf{z}}_0) \equiv (O, \hat{\mathbf{w}})$ which lies in plane $(O, \hat{\mathbf{x}}_p, \hat{\mathbf{y}}_p)$.

Case 3: $A \neq B \neq C \neq 0$. Two first integrals of motion can be derived from (11.24-11.26). The first is obtained by premultiplying (11.24) by p, (11.25) by q and (11.26) by r: we then obtain

$$Ap\dot{p} + Bq\dot{q} + Cr\dot{r} = 0$$

which can be integrated to give $Ap^2 + Bq^2 + Cr^2 = \text{constant} = 2K_0$. (The constant K_0 is of course the kinetic energy of $\mathcal{B}$ which is conserved during the motion. See Chapter 12.)

Another scalar first integral of motion is obtained from (11.23): the magnitude of angular momentum $\mathbf{H}_0$ remains constant during the motion, that is, $A^2r^2 + B^2q^2 + C^2r^2 = H_0^2$.

We can now replace the system of equations (11.24-11.26) by

$$Ap^2 + Bq^2 + Cr^2 = 2K_0 \tag{11.32}$$
$$A^2r^2 + B^2q^2 + C^2r^2 = H_0^2 \tag{11.33}$$
$$C\dot{r} + (B - A)pq = 0 \tag{11.34}$$

The first two equations allow p^2 and q^2 to be expressed as linear functions of r^2. Then the third equation can be expressed as a separable first-order o.d.e. of the type $\dot{r} = \pm\sqrt{R(r)}$. Hence the functions $(p(t), q(t), r(t))$ can readily be obtained as functions of time. The Euler angles (ψ, θ, ϕ) are then obtained by (numerical) integrations of the equations

$$\begin{aligned}\dot{\psi} &= (p\sin\phi + q\cos\phi)/\sin\theta \\ \dot{\theta} &= p\cos\phi - q\sin\phi \\ \dot{\phi} &= r - \cot\theta(p\sin\phi + q\cos\phi)\end{aligned}$$

which are valid as long as $\sin\theta \neq 0$.

A particular solution of (11.24-11.26) can be considered: assume that at $t = 0$, $\boldsymbol{\omega}$ is directed along a principal direction, say $\hat{\mathbf{z}}_p$. Then $p(0) = p_0 = 0$, $q(0) = q_0 = 0$ and $r(0) = r_0 \neq 0$. It is straightforward to show that the solution of the equations of motion is given by

$$p(t) = 0, \qquad q(t) = 0, \qquad r(t) = r_0$$

Since $\mathbf{H}_0 = Cr(t)\hat{\mathbf{z}}_p(t) = Cr_0\hat{\mathbf{z}}_p(0)$, this shows that the direction of principal vector $\hat{\mathbf{z}}_p$ remains fixed in $\mathcal{E}$, and that the body rotates uniformly about this axis. We may then ask whether this motion is stable. It can be shown, by linearization, that small perturbations are governed by the equations

$$\ddot{p} + \frac{(C-A)(C-B)}{AB}r_0^2\, p = 0, \qquad \ddot{q} + \frac{(C-A)(C-B)}{AB}r_0^2\, q = 0$$

which shows that the motion is stable if the axial moment of inertia C is either the smallest or the largest of the 3 principal moments, that is, if the condition $(C - A)(C - B) > 0$ is satisfied. What happens if $(C - A)(C - B) < 0$? Then the rotation about axis $(O, \hat{\mathbf{z}}_p)$ is not stable. A small disturbance along the other axes causes the object to "flip" periodically. The corresponding effect is often named after Soviet cosmonaut Vladimir Dzhanibekov, who noted the phenomenon during the 1985 Soyuz T-13 mission. This is also referred to as the "Tennis Racket Theorem"[2] after the unexpected behavior of a tennis racket flipped into the air. Essentially, this theorem states that rotation of a rigid body (in Euler-Poinsot motion for which $A < C < B$) about its first and third principal axes (associated with A and B) is stable, while rotation about its second principal axis (or intermediate axis, associated with C) is unstable.

[2] M. S. Ashbaugh, C. C. Chicone and R. H. Cushman, "The Twisting Tennis Racket", *Journal of Dynamics and Differential Equations*, 3, 1991 pp. 67–85.

11.5 Dynamic Balancing

Recall from Section 11.4.1 that the rotational motion of a rigid body about a fixed axis $(O, \hat{\mathbf{z}}_0)$ is governed by the equation

$$\begin{aligned} -me\dot{\theta}^2 &= R_x + F_x \\ me\ddot{\theta} &= R_y + F_y \\ 0 &= R_z + F_z \\ I_{Oxz}\ddot{\theta} - I_{Oyz}\dot{\theta}^2 &= M_x + N_x \\ I_{Oxz}\dot{\theta}^2 + I_{Oyz}\ddot{\theta} &= M_y + N_y \\ I_{Oz}\ddot{\theta} &= N_z \end{aligned}$$

These equations show that the inertial terms involving $\dot{\theta}^2$ can have a significant effect on the forces and moments exerted on the supporting bearings. For fast-rotating bodies, these inertial effects can lead to significant vibrations, noise, wear and possibly failure. It is important to minimize them. This can be achieved by a process known as *dynamic balancing*.

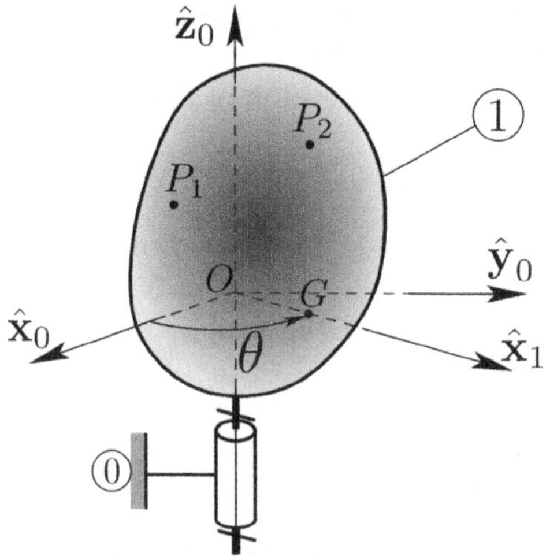

Figure 11.19

Theorem 11.5 A body in rotation at constant angular velocity about a fixed axis is said to be *balanced* if the bearings which support its shaft are not subject to inertial effects. The body is said to be *statically balanced* if the effects of inertial forces vanish. The body is said to be *dynamically balanced* if it is statically balanced and the effects of inertial moments vanish. Dynamic balancing is guaranteed if the conditions

$$e = 0 \quad \text{and} \quad I_{Oxz} = I_{Oyz} = 0 \tag{11.35}$$

are satisfied.

Remark 9. The condition of static balancing $e = 0$ states that mass center G must be located on the axis of rotation.

Remark 10. The condition of dynamic balancing $I_{Oxz} = I_{Oyz} = 0$ states that the axis of rotation $(O, \hat{\mathbf{z}}_0)$ is a principal axis of rotation.

Hence, to guarantee the dynamic balancing of a rigid body one must alter its mass distribution, typically by adding or removing a pair of concentrated masses (m_1, m_2) at locations (P_1, P_2) fixed relative to body 1: the body is then replaced by the rigid system $\Sigma \equiv \{1, (P_1, m_1), (P_2, m_2)\}$. The masses m_1 and m_2 and the locations of P_1 and P_2 are determined by imposing conditions (11.35) for system Σ. Denote by $\mathbf{r}_{OP_i} = x_i\hat{\mathbf{x}}_1 + y_i\hat{\mathbf{y}}_1 + z_i\hat{\mathbf{z}}_0$. Then, the mass center G_Σ and the products D_Σ, E_Σ are given by

$$(m + m_1 + m_2)\mathbf{r}_{OG_\Sigma} = m\mathbf{r}_{OG} + m_1\mathbf{r}_{OP_1} + m_2\mathbf{r}_{OP_2}$$

$$I_{Oyz,\Sigma} = I_{Oyz} - m_1 y_1 z_1 - m_2 y_2 z_2$$

$$I_{Oxz,\Sigma} = I_{Oxz} - m_1 x_1 z_1 - m_2 x_2 z_2$$

Then the conditions of dynamic balancing are satisfied by the equations

$$\begin{aligned} & me + m_1 x_1 + m_2 x_2 = 0 \\ & m_1 y_1 + m_2 y_2 = 0 \\ & I_{Oyz} - m_1 y_1 z_1 - m_2 y_2 z_2 = 0 \\ & I_{Oxz} - m_1 x_1 z_1 - m_2 x_2 z_2 = 0 \end{aligned} \tag{11.36}$$

This gives four equations to solve for eight unknowns $(m_1, m_2, x_1, y_1, z_1, x_2, y_2, z_2)$: infinitely many solutions are possible.

Remark 11. The addition (or removal) of a single mass does not allow dynamic balancing.

In practice, constraints are placed on the locations P_1 and P_2 of the point masses, as is the case for the dynamic balancing of car tire/wheel assemblies. For instance, both points are placed at the same (prescribed) distance R from the axis of rotation and in two parallel planes $z_1 = 0$ and $z_2 = H$. Introducing the polar angles ϕ_1 and ϕ_2, the coordinates of P_1 and P_2 are now

$$\mathbf{r}_{OP_1} = R(\cos\phi_1\hat{\mathbf{x}}_1 + \sin\phi_1\hat{\mathbf{y}}_1), \qquad \mathbf{r}_{OP_2} = R(\cos\phi_2\hat{\mathbf{x}}_1 + \sin\phi_2\hat{\mathbf{y}}_1) + H\hat{\mathbf{z}}_0$$

Then, the four unknowns $(m_1, m_2, \phi_1, \phi_2)$ are found by solving the following four equations:

$$\begin{aligned} & me + m_1 R\cos\phi_1 + m_2 R\cos\phi_2 = 0 \\ & m_1 \sin\phi_1 + m_2 \sin\phi_2 = 0 \\ & I_{Oxz} - m_2 HR\cos\phi_2 = 0 \\ & I_{Oyz} - m_2 HR\sin\phi_2 = 0 \end{aligned}$$

A unique solution is then found.

11.6 Solution of Multibody Problems

When faced with a multibody dynamics problem, the solution will seem daunting unless a methodical approach is adopted. Given a system Σ of N interconnected rigid bodies $\mathcal{B}_1$, $\mathcal{B}_2$, ..., $\mathcal{B}_N$, the first step consists in sketching a diagram showing all interconnections and to list all unknowns. These unknowns are typically of two types: (i) unknown motion variables $q_1(t), q_2(t), \ldots, q_M(t)$ which define the position of system Σ relative to a Newtonian referential $\mathcal{E}$, (ii) unknown internal contact action screws $\{\mathcal{A}^c_{\mathcal{B}_j \to \mathcal{B}_i}\}$ or external action screws

$\{\mathcal{A}^c_{\overline{\Sigma}\to\Sigma}\}$. The various interconnections will typically be modeled by frictionless joints. It is vital to identify the specificities of all joints which can be later exploited for the solution. The next step is to identify which of the unknowns listed above are asked to be solved for.

At this point, two strategies can be employed:

1. STRATEGY BASED ON LINEAR MOMENTUM. This strategy consists in identifying a subset Σ_h of Σ and a direction (unit vector) $\hat{\mathbf{u}}$ toward the application of equation (11.13) (Euler's first principle) to obtain

$$\mathbf{F}_{\overline{\Sigma}_h\to\Sigma_h}\cdot\hat{\mathbf{u}} = m_h\mathbf{a}_{G_h/\mathcal{E}}\cdot\hat{\mathbf{u}} \tag{11.37}$$

where G_h and m_h are the mass center and mass of system Σ_h. Typically, system Σ_h is chosen so as to make one or more particular forces *internal* to Σ_h. Unit vector $\hat{\mathbf{u}}$ is chosen normal to particular forces *external* to Σ_h. It may then happen that $\mathbf{F}_{\overline{\Sigma}_h\to\Sigma_h}\cdot\hat{\mathbf{u}} = 0$, that is, the resultant external force acting on Σ_h has a vanishing component along $\hat{\mathbf{u}}$. Then, *if unit vector* $\hat{\mathbf{u}}$ *is fixed in* $\mathcal{E}$, equation (11.37) necessarily leads to

$$m_h\mathbf{v}_{G_h/\mathcal{E}}\cdot\hat{\mathbf{u}} = (m_1\mathbf{v}_{G_1/\mathcal{E}} + m_2\mathbf{v}_{G_2/\mathcal{E}} + \cdots)\cdot\hat{\mathbf{u}} = \text{Constant} \tag{11.38}$$

where bodies 1,2,... belong to system Σ_h. Equation (11.38) expresses the *conservation of the linear momentum of system* Σ_h *along direction* $\hat{\mathbf{u}}$.

2. STRATEGY BASED ON ANGULAR MOMENTUM. This strategy consists in identifying a subset Σ_k of Σ, a point Q and a direction $\hat{\mathbf{z}}$ toward the application of (11.14) (Euler's second principle) to obtain

$$\mathbf{M}_{Q,\overline{\Sigma}_k\to\Sigma_k}\cdot\hat{\mathbf{z}} = \mathbf{D}_{Q,\Sigma_k/\mathcal{E}}\cdot\hat{\mathbf{z}} \tag{11.39}$$

Again, system Σ_k is chosen so as to make particular action *internal* to Σ_k. Point Q and direction $\hat{\mathbf{z}}$ are chosen so as to make certain external moments $\mathbf{M}_{Q,\overline{\Sigma}_k\to\Sigma_k}\cdot\hat{\mathbf{z}}$ vanish, for instance by exploiting the frictionless nature of particular joints. It may then happen that $\mathbf{M}_{Q,\overline{\Sigma}_k\to\Sigma_k}\cdot\hat{\mathbf{z}} = 0$, that is, the resultant external moment about Q acting on Σ_k is vanishing along $\hat{\mathbf{z}}$. Then, *if both* Q *and* $\hat{\mathbf{z}}$ *are fixed in* $\mathcal{E}$, equation (11.39) necessarily leads to

$$\mathbf{H}_{Q,\Sigma_k}\cdot\hat{\mathbf{z}} = \mathbf{H}_{Q,1}\cdot\hat{\mathbf{z}} + \mathbf{H}_{Q,2}\cdot\hat{\mathbf{z}} + \cdots = \text{Constant} \tag{11.40}$$

where bodies 1,2,... belong to system Σ_k. Equation (11.40) expresses the *conservation of the angular momentum of system* Σ_k *about axis* Qz.

The following examples illustrate this strategy.

Example 11.11 Consider the planar motion of the system consisting of
- a right circular cylinder 1 of radius R, mass m_1, mass center G_1 which can roll on a horizontal support Oxy of a referential 0,
- a plate 2 of side length $2l$, mass m_2, mass center G_2 in contact with the disk and the horizontal plane. Assume that G_1 and G_2 move in the same vertical plane Oxy, so as to treat this problem as that of a planar motion. See Figure 11.20.

Assume that all surfaces of contact are smooth so that slip occurs at all contact lines.

Find the equations of motion bodies 1 and 2 relative to 0. Can first integrals of motion be found?

Recall that $I_{G_1z} = \frac{1}{2}m_1R^2$ for the cylinder and $I_{G_2z} = \frac{1}{3}m_2l^2$ for the plate. ■

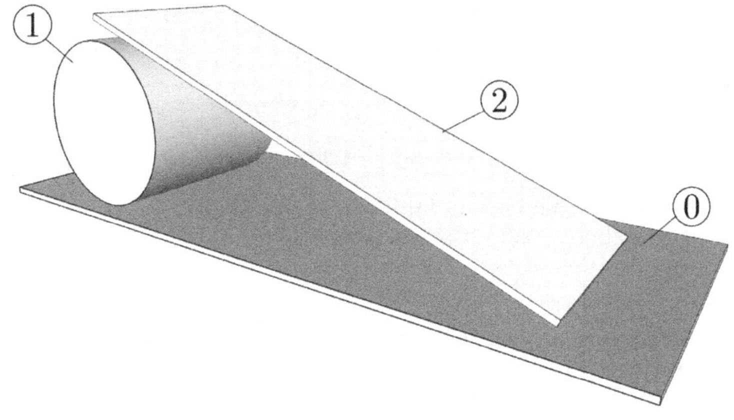

Figure 11.20

With the parmetrization (x_1, x_2, θ, ϕ) shown in Figure 11.21, we find the following kinematic screws

$$\{\mathcal{V}_{1/0}\} = \left\{ \begin{array}{c} -\dot{\phi}\hat{\mathbf{z}}_0 \\ \dot{x}_1\hat{\mathbf{x}}_0 \end{array} \right\}_{G_1}, \qquad \{\mathcal{V}_{2/0}\} = \left\{ \begin{array}{c} -\dot{\theta}\hat{\mathbf{z}}_0 \\ \dot{x}_2\hat{\mathbf{x}}_0 + l\dot{\theta}\hat{\mathbf{y}}_2 \end{array} \right\}_{G_2}$$

with the following geometric constraint (in triangle $I_1 I_2 G_1$)

$$x_1 - x_2 = R\cot\beta, \qquad \beta = \frac{\pi}{4} - \frac{\theta}{2} \tag{1}$$

Assume slip at points I_1, I_2 and I_{12} and that all contacts are frictionless. Then, the external

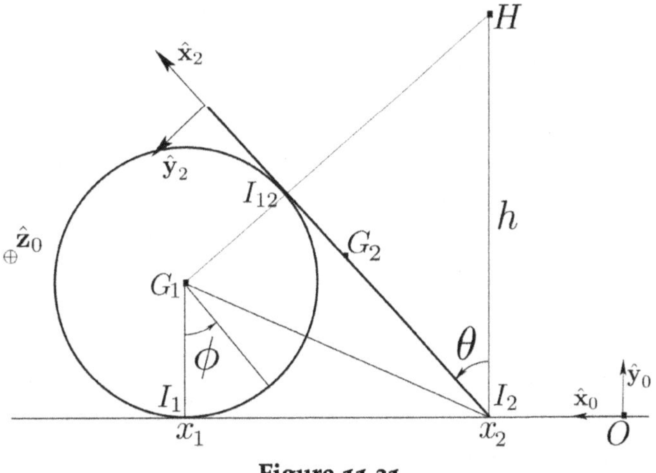

Figure 11.21

action screws are identified as follows:

$$\{\mathcal{A}_{\bar{1}\to 1}\} = \left\{ \begin{array}{c} N_1\hat{\mathbf{y}}_0 \\ \mathbf{0} \end{array} \right\}_{I_1} + \left\{ \begin{array}{c} N_{12}\hat{\mathbf{y}}_2 \\ \mathbf{0} \end{array} \right\}_{I_{12}} + \left\{ \begin{array}{c} -m_1 g\hat{\mathbf{y}}_0 \\ \mathbf{0} \end{array} \right\}_{G_1}$$

$$\{\mathcal{A}_{\bar{2}\to 2}\} = \left\{ \begin{array}{c} N_2\hat{\mathbf{y}}_0 \\ \mathbf{0} \end{array} \right\}_{I_2} + \left\{ \begin{array}{c} -N_{12}\hat{\mathbf{y}}_2 \\ \mathbf{0} \end{array} \right\}_{I_{12}} + \left\{ \begin{array}{c} -m_2 g\hat{\mathbf{y}}_0 \\ \mathbf{0} \end{array} \right\}_{G_2}$$

There are seven unknowns in this problem: x_1, x_2, ϕ, θ, N_1, N_2 and N_{12}. In addition to constraint equation (1), application of the FTD for the planar motions of 1 and 2 would lead to

six additional scalar equations. *We seek three equations governing the coordinates x_1 (or x_2), ϕ, θ in such a way as to avoid coupling with unknowns N_1, N_2 and N_{12} (the normal reactions).*
We can identify the following equations:
1. Apply (11.13) to system $\Sigma = \{1,2\}$ along $\hat{\mathbf{x}}_0$ to find

$$(m_1 \mathbf{a}_{G_1/0} + m_2 \mathbf{a}_{G_2/0}) \cdot \hat{\mathbf{x}}_0 = 0 \tag{2}$$

since there are no external horizontal forces acting on the system.
2. Apply (11.14) to body 1 about mass center G_1 to find

$$\mathbf{D}_{G_1,1/0} = \mathbf{0} \tag{3}$$

since all lines of action of the external forces acting on 1 pass through mass center G_1.
3. Finally, apply (11.14) to body 2 about point H to find

$$\mathbf{D}_{H,2/0} = \mathbf{r}_{G_2H} \times m_2 g \hat{\mathbf{y}}_0 = -m_2 g l \sin\theta \hat{\mathbf{z}}_0 \tag{4}$$

since the lines of action of the external reaction forces on 2 pass through point H shown in Figure 11.21.

Equation (2) implies *conservation of linear momentum of system Σ along direction $\hat{\mathbf{x}}_0$*: $(m_1 \mathbf{v}_{G_1/0} + m_2 \mathbf{v}_{G_2/0}) \cdot \hat{\mathbf{x}}_0 =$ constant leading to

$$m_1 \dot{x}_1 + m_2(\dot{x}_2 + l\dot{\theta}\cos\theta) = \text{constant} \tag{2'}$$

Equation (3) implies *conservation of angular momentum of 1 about point G_1*: $\mathbf{H}_{G_1,1/0} =$ constant leading to

$$\dot{\phi} = \text{constant} \tag{3'}$$

As for equation (4), we need to find the dynamic moment of body 2 about point H:

$$\mathbf{D}_{H,2/0} = \frac{d}{dt}\mathbf{H}_{G_2,2/0} + \mathbf{r}_{HG_2} \times m_2 \mathbf{a}_{G_2/0}$$

with

$$\mathbf{H}_{G_2,2/0} = -\tfrac{1}{3} m_2 l^2 \dot{\theta} \hat{\mathbf{z}}_0, \quad \mathbf{r}_{G_2H} = -l\hat{\mathbf{x}}_2 + h\hat{\mathbf{y}}_0, \quad h = R\frac{\cot\beta}{\cos\theta}, \quad \mathbf{a}_{G_2/0} = \ddot{x}_2 \hat{\mathbf{x}}_0 + l\ddot{\theta}\hat{\mathbf{y}}_2 - l\dot{\theta}^2 \hat{\mathbf{x}}_2$$

This gives the equation of motion

$$(\frac{4}{3}l^2 - hl\cos\theta)\ddot{\theta} + hl\dot{\theta}^2 \sin\theta - (h - l\cos\theta)\ddot{x}_2 = gl\sin\theta \tag{4'}$$

■

Example 11.12 We consider in this problem the motion of a system Σ which includes a sphere 2 connected to a rigid hoop 1 of small rectangular cross-section, and in point-contact with a horizontal plane $\Pi(O, \hat{\mathbf{x}}_0, \hat{\mathbf{y}}_0)$ fixed in a Newtonian referential 0. More specifically, body 1 of center G, radius r, and negligible mass, rolls without slipping on plane Π in such a way as to remain vertical. Denote by $(G, \hat{\mathbf{v}})$ the axis of body 1. The unit vector $\hat{\mathbf{z}}$ shown in Figure 11.22 is directed along a particular diameter AB of 1. Denote by I the contact point of 1 with Π, and by (x, y, r) the Cartesian coordinates of point G relative to the Cartesian axes $(O, \hat{\mathbf{x}}_0)$, $(O, \hat{\mathbf{y}}_0)$, $(O, \hat{\mathbf{z}}_0)$. See Figure 11.22.

The orientation of body 1 relative to 0 is defined by the following angles:
- θ defines the orientation of the vertical plane containing 1 relative to 0,
- ψ defines the orientation of diameter AB relative to the vertical plane containing 1.

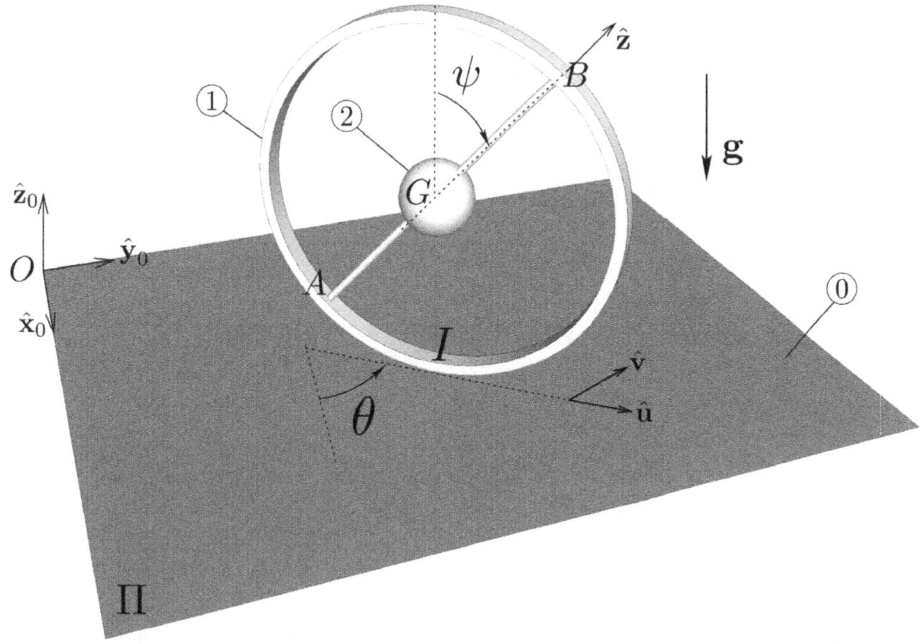

Figure 11.22

Sphere 2, of mass center G, of homogeneous mass m is mounted on the diameter AB of 1 through a frictionless pivot: it is free to rotate about diameter AB. Denote by ϕ the angle of rotation of body 2 relative to body 1 measured about axis $(G, \hat{\mathbf{z}})$. Denote by J the moment of inertia of body 2 about one of its diameter.

a. Find the kinematic screws of bodies 1 and 2 relative to 0. Find the equations which express the no-slip condition of body 1 at point I. Find the acceleration of point G.

b. Assume that the contact at I is realized with sliding friction, neglecting spinning and rolling friction, that is, the corresponding action screw takes the form

$$\{\mathcal{A}^c_{\Pi\to 1}\} = \begin{Bmatrix} \mathbf{R}_I \\ \Gamma\hat{\mathbf{u}} \end{Bmatrix}_I$$

where the (unknown) couple $\Gamma\hat{\mathbf{u}}$ accounts for the fact that body 1 is maintained vertical. Find the three equations which allow for the determination of angles (θ, ϕ, ψ).

c. Find the unknown reaction $\mathbf{R}_I$ and couple Γ.

d. What would be the consequence of not accounting for couple Γ? Explain how one would find the components of the contact action screw $\{\mathcal{A}^c_{1\to 2}\}$. ■

a. The kinematics of 1 and 2 relative to 0 are characterized by

$$\{\mathcal{V}_{1/0}\} = \begin{Bmatrix} \dot{\theta}\hat{\mathbf{z}}_0 + \dot{\psi}\hat{\mathbf{v}} \\ \dot{x}\hat{\mathbf{x}}_0 + \dot{y}\hat{\mathbf{y}}_0 \end{Bmatrix}_G \qquad \{\mathcal{V}_{2/0}\} = \{\mathcal{V}_{2/1}\} + \{\mathcal{V}_{1/0}\} = \begin{Bmatrix} \dot{\phi}\hat{\mathbf{z}} \\ \mathbf{0} \end{Bmatrix}_G + \{\mathcal{V}_{1/0}\}$$

where we have used $\mathbf{v}_{G/0} = \frac{d}{dt}(x\hat{\mathbf{x}}_0 + y\hat{\mathbf{y}}_0 + r\hat{\mathbf{z}}_0)$. The no-slip condition at I can be stated as

$\mathbf{v}_{I\in 1/0} = \mathbf{v}_{G/0} + \boldsymbol{\omega}_{1/0} \times \mathbf{r}_{GI} = \mathbf{0}$, giving the equations

$$\dot{x}\hat{\mathbf{x}}_0 + \dot{y}\hat{\mathbf{y}}_0 - r\dot{\psi}\hat{\mathbf{u}} = \mathbf{0} \Longrightarrow \begin{cases} \dot{x} = r\dot{\psi}\cos\theta \\ \dot{y} = r\dot{\psi}\sin\theta \end{cases} \qquad (1-2)$$

The acceleration of G is obtained by differentiating $\mathbf{v}_{G/0} = r\dot{\psi}\hat{\mathbf{u}}$: $\mathbf{a}_{G/0} = r\ddot{\psi}\hat{\mathbf{u}} + r\dot{\psi}\dot{\theta}\hat{\mathbf{v}}$

b. The interactions of system Σ can be summarized in Figure 11.23.

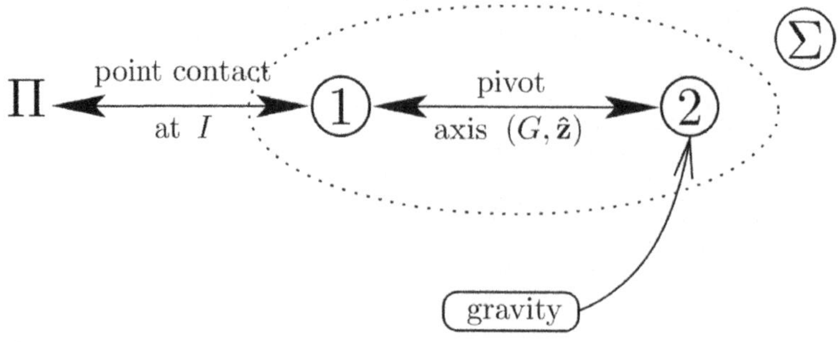

Figure 11.23

To find three equations of motion governing the evolution of angles (θ, ψ, ϕ), that is, equations which do involve any coupling with the unknowns $\mathbf{R}_I$, Γ and $\{\mathcal{A}^c_{1\to 2}\}$ we use the specificities of the two contact action screws $\{\mathcal{A}^c_{\Pi\to 1}\}$ and $\{\mathcal{A}^c_{1\to 2}\}$:

1. First we can exploit the fact that $\mathbf{M}^c_{G,1\to 2} \cdot \hat{\mathbf{z}} = 0$ (the pivot connection between 1 and 2 is frictionless) by writing $\mathbf{D}_{G,2/0} \cdot \hat{\mathbf{z}} = \mathbf{M}_{G,\bar{2}\to 2} \cdot \hat{\mathbf{z}} = \mathbf{M}^g_{G,\bar{2}\to 2} \cdot \hat{\mathbf{z}} = 0$. This does not immediately yield the first-integral of motion $\mathbf{H}_{G,2/0} =$ constant (expressing the conservation of angular momentum of body 2 about G along direction $\hat{\mathbf{z}}$) since unit vector $\hat{\mathbf{z}}$ is not constant.
2. Second, we take advantage of the fact that contact action screw $\{\mathcal{A}^c_{\Pi\to 1}\}$ satisfies the conditions $\mathbf{M}_{I,\Pi\to 1} \cdot \hat{\mathbf{v}} = \mathbf{M}_{I,\Pi\to 1} \cdot \hat{\mathbf{z}}_0 = 0$. This does not however lead to the equations $\mathbf{D}_{I,1/0} \cdot \hat{\mathbf{v}} = \mathbf{D}_{I,1/0} \cdot \hat{\mathbf{z}}_0 = 0$: body 1 is also subjected to the action of body 2 and $\mathbf{M}_{I,2\to 1} \neq 0$. Instead we must make the action $\{\mathcal{A}^c_{1\to 2}\}$ "internal" by consideration of system Σ which is subjected to

$$\{\mathcal{A}_{\bar{\Sigma}\to\Sigma}\} = \begin{Bmatrix} \mathbf{R}_I \\ \Gamma\hat{\mathbf{u}} \end{Bmatrix}_I + \begin{Bmatrix} -mg\hat{\mathbf{z}}_0 \\ \mathbf{0} \end{Bmatrix}_G$$

So if we apply $\mathbf{D}_{I,\Sigma/0} = \mathbf{M}_{I,\bar{\Sigma}\to\Sigma}$ we eliminate the contribution of $\{\mathcal{A}^c_{1\to 2}\}$:

$$\mathbf{D}_{I,\Sigma/0} = \mathbf{D}_{I,2/0} = \Gamma\hat{\mathbf{u}} + \mathbf{r}_{IG} \times m\mathbf{g} = \Gamma\hat{\mathbf{u}}$$

which gives us two additional equations:

$$\mathbf{D}_{I,2/0} \cdot \hat{\mathbf{z}}_0 = \mathbf{D}_{I,2/0} \cdot \hat{\mathbf{v}} = 0$$

Now recall that

$$\mathbf{D}_{I,2/0} = \frac{d}{dt}\mathbf{H}_{I,2/0} + \mathbf{v}_{I/0} \times m\mathbf{v}_{G/0} = \frac{d}{dt}\mathbf{H}_{I,2/0}$$

since $\mathbf{v}_{I/0} = \mathbf{v}_{G/0}$. Finally we have:

$$\mathbf{H}_{I,2/0} \cdot \hat{\mathbf{z}}_0 = \text{constant}, \qquad \hat{\mathbf{v}} \cdot \frac{d}{dt}\mathbf{H}_{I,2/0} = 0$$

The first of these results shows that the angular momentum about I of body 2 along direction $\hat{\mathbf{z}}_0$ is conserved.

We can now write the equations of motion governing angles (θ, ϕ, ψ). First, we write

$\hat{\mathbf{z}} \cdot \frac{d}{dt}\mathbf{H}_{G,2/0} = \frac{d}{dt}(\mathbf{H}_{G,2/0} \cdot \hat{\mathbf{z}}) - \mathbf{H}_{G,2/0} \cdot \frac{d\hat{\mathbf{z}}}{dt} = 0$. With $\omega_{2/0} = \dot{\theta}\hat{\mathbf{z}}_0 + \dot{\psi}\hat{\mathbf{v}} + \dot{\phi}\hat{\mathbf{z}}$, we find $\mathbf{H}_{G,2/0} = J(\dot{\theta}\hat{\mathbf{z}}_0 + \dot{\psi}\hat{\mathbf{v}} + \dot{\phi}\hat{\mathbf{z}})$. Also we have $\frac{d\hat{\mathbf{z}}}{dt} = (\dot{\theta}\hat{\mathbf{z}}_0 + \dot{\psi}\hat{\mathbf{v}}) \times \hat{\mathbf{z}} = \dot{\theta}\sin\psi\hat{\mathbf{v}} + \dot{\psi}\hat{\mathbf{w}}$ (defining unit vector $\hat{\mathbf{v}} \times \hat{\mathbf{z}} = \hat{\mathbf{w}}$). Therefore, we can write:

$$\begin{aligned}
\hat{\mathbf{z}} \cdot \frac{d}{dt}\mathbf{H}_{G,2/0} &= J\frac{d}{dt}(\dot{\theta}\cos\psi + \dot{\phi}) - J(\dot{\theta}\hat{\mathbf{z}}_0 + \dot{\psi}\hat{\mathbf{v}} + \dot{\phi}\hat{\mathbf{z}}) \cdot (\dot{\theta}\sin\psi\hat{\mathbf{v}} + \dot{\psi}\hat{\mathbf{w}}) \\
&= J\frac{d}{dt}(\dot{\theta}\cos\psi + \dot{\phi}) = 0
\end{aligned}$$

leading to the first-integral of motion

$$\dot{\theta}\cos\psi + \dot{\phi} = \text{constant} \tag{3}$$

So after all, the angular momentum of body 2 about G is conserved along direction $\hat{\mathbf{z}}$.

To find angular momentum $\mathbf{H}_{I,2/0}$ we write

$$\mathbf{H}_{I,2/0} = \mathbf{H}_{G,2/0} + \mathbf{r}_{IG} \times m\mathbf{v}_{G/0} = \mathbf{H}_{G,2/0} + mr^2\dot{\psi}\hat{\mathbf{v}}$$

So the equation $\mathbf{H}_{I,2/0} \cdot \hat{\mathbf{z}}_0 =$ constant gives us the first-integral

$$\dot{\theta} + \dot{\phi}\cos\psi = \text{constant} \tag{4}$$

Finally we can write

$$\hat{\mathbf{v}} \cdot \frac{d}{dt}\mathbf{H}_{I,2/0} = \frac{d}{dt}(\hat{\mathbf{v}} \cdot \mathbf{H}_{I,2/0}) + \dot{\theta}\hat{\mathbf{u}} \cdot \mathbf{H}_{I,2/0} = 0$$

which gives

$$(mr^2 + J)\ddot{\psi} + J\dot{\theta}\dot{\phi}\sin\psi = 0 \tag{5}$$

c. To find reaction force $\mathbf{R}_I$ we apply (11.13) to system Σ: $\mathbf{R}_{\overline{\Sigma}\to\Sigma} = m\mathbf{a}_{G/0}$: this gives

$$\mathbf{R}_I = mg\hat{\mathbf{z}}_0 + mr(\ddot{\psi}\hat{\mathbf{u}} + \dot{\psi}\dot{\theta}\hat{\mathbf{v}}) \tag{6}$$

To find couple Γ, we apply (11.13) to body 2: $\mathbf{D}_{I,2/0} = \Gamma\hat{\mathbf{u}}$ (see question **b**): with

$$\mathbf{D}_{I,2/0} \cdot \hat{\mathbf{u}} = \frac{d}{dt}(\hat{\mathbf{u}} \cdot \mathbf{H}_{I,2/0}) - \dot{\theta}\hat{\mathbf{v}} \cdot \mathbf{H}_{I,2/0}$$

we find

$$\Gamma = J\frac{d}{dt}(\dot{\phi}\sin\psi) - (J + mr^2)\dot{\theta}\dot{\psi} \tag{7}$$

d. Let us assume that the contact action at I is modeled as

$$\{\mathcal{A}^c_{\text{II}\to 1}\} = \begin{Bmatrix} \mathbf{R}_I \\ \mathbf{0} \end{Bmatrix}_I$$

We can list the problem's unknowns: $(x, y, \theta, \psi, \phi)$ (5 unknowns), $\{\mathcal{A}^c_{\text{II}\to 1}\}$ (3 unknowns) and $\{\mathcal{A}^c_{1\to 2}\}$ (5 unknowns) for a total of 13 (scalar) unknowns. The equations governing the problem are: the no-slip condition at I (2 equations), the FTD applied to body 2 (6 equations) and the FTD applied to body 1 (6 equations). Thus we have 14 equations governing 13 unknowns. The problem has no solution unless we assume a non-zero couple $\Gamma\hat{\mathbf{u}}$ at I. In reality, the contact at I is not a point contact but rather a "cylinder-on-plane" contact: a couple $\Gamma\hat{\mathbf{u}}$ is necessary to prevent the rotation about axis $(I, \hat{\mathbf{u}})$. ∎

Example 11.13 A motorcycle and its rider are modeled as a system Σ of four interconnected rigid bodies denoted as 1, 2, 3 and 4:

- Body 1 represents the motorcycle frame, the engine, and the rider: the driver is assumed stationary relative to the frame, hence is considered as a rigid part of the frame. The mass of body 1 is m_1, its mass center is G_1 and a basis attached to 1 is $b_1(\hat{\mathbf{x}}_1, \hat{\mathbf{y}}_1, \hat{\mathbf{z}}_1)$. The midplane $(G_1, \hat{\mathbf{x}}_1, \hat{\mathbf{z}}_1)$ is a plane of material symmetry. Hence the inertia operator of body 1 about G_1 has the following matrix representation

$$[\mathcal{I}_{G_1,1}]_{b_1} = \begin{bmatrix} I_1 & 0 & E_1 \\ 0 & J_1 & 0 \\ E_1 & 0 & K_1 \end{bmatrix}_{b_1}$$

- Body 2 represents the fork/handlebar assembly. Its mass is negligible. The motion of 2 relative to 1 is irrelevant in this problem. Hence 2 is assumed fixed relative to 1.

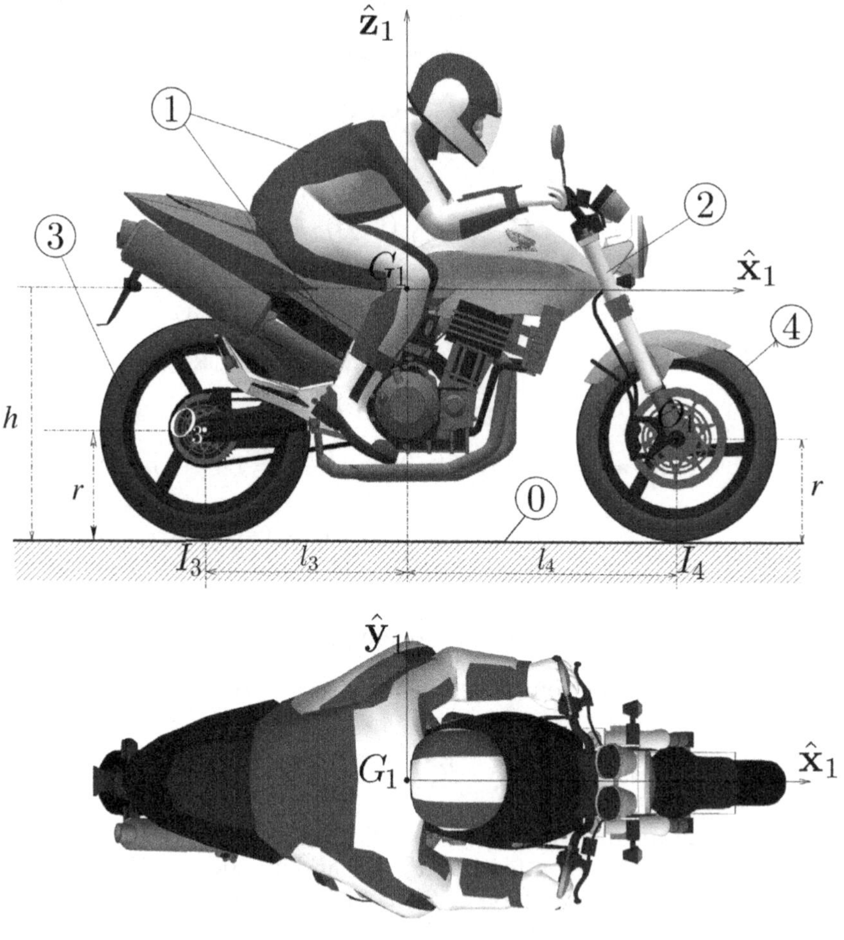

Figure 11.24

- Body 3 represents the back wheel: it is connected to body 1 by a frictionless pivot of axis $(O_3, \hat{\mathbf{y}}_1)$, its mass center is O_3, its mass is m_3, a basis attached to 2 is $b_3(\hat{\mathbf{x}}_3, \hat{\mathbf{y}}_1, \hat{\mathbf{z}}_3)$ whose orientation relative to 1 is defined by angle $\theta_3 = (\hat{\mathbf{x}}_1, \hat{\mathbf{x}}_3) = (\hat{\mathbf{y}}_1, \hat{\mathbf{y}}_3)$. It is assumed axisymmetric w.r.t. axis $(O_3, \hat{\mathbf{y}}_1)$: its inertia operator about point O_3 has the following representation on basis b_3

$$[\mathcal{I}_{O_3,3}]_{b_3} = \begin{bmatrix} I_3 & 0 & 0 \\ 0 & J_3 & 0 \\ 0 & 0 & J_3 \end{bmatrix}_{b_3}$$

In addition to the contact forces between 1 and 3 transmitted through the pivot, the engine drives the rotation of 3 by exerting a couple $\Gamma\hat{\mathbf{y}}_1$ (Γ being a positive constant).

- Body 4 represents the front wheel: it is connected to the fork by a frictionless pivot of axis $(O_4, \hat{\mathbf{y}}_1)$, its mass center is O_4, its mass is m_4, a basis attached to 4 is $b_4(\hat{\mathbf{x}}_4, \hat{\mathbf{y}}_1, \hat{\mathbf{z}}_4)$ whose orientation relative to 1 is defined by angle $\theta_4 = (\hat{\mathbf{x}}_1, \hat{\mathbf{x}}_4) = (\hat{\mathbf{z}}_1, \hat{\mathbf{z}}_4)$. It is assumed axisymmetric w.r.t. axis $(O_4, \hat{\mathbf{y}}_1)$: its inertia operator about point O_4 has the following representation on basis b_4

$$[\mathcal{I}_{O_4,4}]_{b_4} = \begin{bmatrix} I_4 & 0 & 0 \\ 0 & J_4 & 0 \\ 0 & 0 & J_4 \end{bmatrix}_{b_4}$$

Note that points O_3 and O_4 remain stationary in the midplane $(G_1, \hat{\mathbf{x}}_1, \hat{\mathbf{z}}_1)$. The geometry is characterized by the constant lengths h, l_3, l_4 and r as shown in Figure 11.24.

The frame/rider 1 is assumed in rectilinear motion relative to some Newtonian referential 0 $(O, \hat{\mathbf{x}}_0, \hat{\mathbf{y}}_0, \hat{\mathbf{z}}_0)$ attached to a straight horizontal road defined by direction $(O, \hat{\mathbf{x}}_0)$. Axis $(O, \hat{\mathbf{z}}_0)$ defines the vertical directed upward. Hence, we have $\hat{\mathbf{x}}_0 = \hat{\mathbf{x}}_1$, $\hat{\mathbf{y}}_0 = \hat{\mathbf{y}}_1$, $\hat{\mathbf{z}}_0 = \hat{\mathbf{z}}_1$ at all time. The front and back wheels are in contact with horizontal support $(O, \hat{\mathbf{x}}_0)$ at points I_3 and I_4, respectively. Assume that the wheels do not slip relative to the road. The contacts are characterized by coefficient of static friction μ. Neglect rolling friction. We define Cartesian coordinate $x(t) = \mathbf{r}_{OG_1} \cdot \hat{\mathbf{x}}_0$ of G_1 relative to axis $(O, \hat{\mathbf{x}}_0)$.

a. Determine the kinematic screws of 1, 3 and 4 relative to 0.

b. Sketch a diagram showing the various interconnections within system Σ and the internal/external actions exerted on Σ. Find the expression of the action screws $\{\mathcal{A}_{\bar{\Sigma}\to\Sigma}\}$, $\{\mathcal{A}_{\bar{3}\to 3}\}$ and $\{\mathcal{A}_{\bar{4}\to 4}\}$.

c. Derive from the Fundamental Theorem of Dynamics the 5 scalar equations which govern the acceleration $\ddot{x}$ and the reaction forces $\mathbf{R}_3$ and $\mathbf{R}_4$ of the road on the wheels. Then solve for acceleration $\ddot{x}$ in terms of couple Γ and the geometric/inertia parameters.

d. Under which condition governing couple Γ will the motorcycle tip without slipping about point I_3? ■

a. Since the system frame/rider 1 is in rectilinear motion along $(O, \hat{\mathbf{x}}_0)$ we can write

$$\{\mathcal{V}_{1/0}\} = \begin{Bmatrix} \mathbf{0} \\ \dot{x}\hat{\mathbf{x}}_0 \end{Bmatrix}_{G_1}$$

We can then express the kinematic screw of wheel 3 and 4 by taking into account the no-slip conditions at contact points I_3 and I_3:

$$\{\mathcal{V}_{3/0}\} = \begin{Bmatrix} \dot{\theta}_3\hat{\mathbf{y}}_0 \\ \mathbf{0} \end{Bmatrix}_{I_3}, \qquad \{\mathcal{V}_{4/0}\} = \begin{Bmatrix} \dot{\theta}_4\hat{\mathbf{y}}_0 \\ \mathbf{0} \end{Bmatrix}_{I_4}$$

Since the center points O_3 and O_4 are fixed relative to 1 we have

$$\mathbf{v}_{O_3/0} = \dot{x}\hat{\mathbf{x}}_0 = \dot{\theta}_3\hat{\mathbf{y}}_0 \times \mathbf{r}_{I_3O_3} = \dot{\theta}_3\hat{\mathbf{y}}_0 \times r\hat{\mathbf{z}}_0 = r\dot{\theta}_3\hat{\mathbf{x}}_0 = \mathbf{v}_{O_4/0} = r\dot{\theta}_4\hat{\mathbf{x}}_0$$

This gives

$$\dot{\theta}_3 = \dot{\theta}_4 = \frac{\dot{x}}{r} \tag{1-2}$$

b. The sketch showing the interconnections within system Σ is shown in Figure 11.25. The

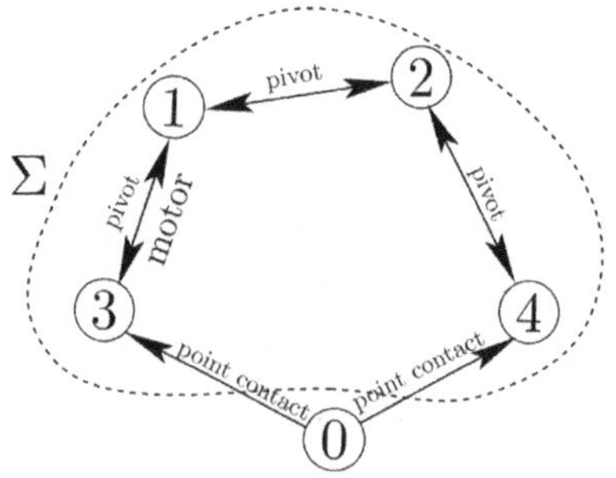

Figure 11.25

expression of the action screws $\{\mathcal{A}_{\bar{\Sigma}\to\Sigma}\}$ is given by

$$\{\mathcal{A}_{\bar{\Sigma}\to\Sigma}\} = \{\mathcal{A}^g_{\text{Earth}\to\Sigma}\} + \{\mathcal{A}^c_{0\to 3}\} + \{\mathcal{A}^c_{0\to 4}\}$$

$$= \begin{Bmatrix} -m_1 g\hat{\mathbf{z}}_0 \\ \mathbf{0} \end{Bmatrix}_{G_1} + \begin{Bmatrix} -m_3 g\hat{\mathbf{z}}_0 \\ \mathbf{0} \end{Bmatrix}_{O_3} + \begin{Bmatrix} -m_4 g\hat{\mathbf{z}}_0 \\ \mathbf{0} \end{Bmatrix}_{O_4} + \begin{Bmatrix} N_3\hat{\mathbf{z}}_0 + F_3\hat{\mathbf{x}}_0 \\ \mathbf{0} \end{Bmatrix}_{I_3} + \begin{Bmatrix} N_4\hat{\mathbf{z}}_0 + F_4\hat{\mathbf{x}}_0 \\ \mathbf{0} \end{Bmatrix}_{I_4}$$

The action screw $\{\mathcal{A}_{\bar{3}\to 3}\}$ is described by

$$\{\mathcal{A}_{\bar{3}\to 3}\} = \begin{Bmatrix} -m_3 g\hat{\mathbf{z}}_0 \\ \mathbf{0} \end{Bmatrix}_{O_3} + \begin{Bmatrix} N_3\hat{\mathbf{z}}_0 + F_3\hat{\mathbf{x}}_0 \\ \mathbf{0} \end{Bmatrix}_{I_3} + \{\mathcal{A}^c_{1\to 3}\}$$

where the action screw $\{\mathcal{A}^c_{1\to 3}\}$ satisfies $\mathbf{M}^c_{O_3,1\to 3} \cdot \hat{\mathbf{y}}_0 = \Gamma$. Finally action screw $\{\mathcal{A}_{\bar{4}\to 4}\}$ is described by

$$\{\mathcal{A}_{\bar{4}\to 4}\} = \begin{Bmatrix} -m_4 g\hat{\mathbf{z}}_0 \\ \mathbf{0} \end{Bmatrix}_{O_4} + \begin{Bmatrix} N_4\hat{\mathbf{z}}_0 + F_4\hat{\mathbf{x}}_0 \\ \mathbf{0} \end{Bmatrix}_{I_4} + \{\mathcal{A}^c_{2\to 4}\}$$

where the action screw $\{\mathcal{A}^c_{2\to 4}\}$ satisfies $\mathbf{M}^c_{O_4,2\to 4} \cdot \hat{\mathbf{y}}_0 = 0$.

c. We can first take into account the condition $\mathbf{M}^c_{O_4,2\to 4} \cdot \hat{\mathbf{y}}_0 = 0$ and apply the following dynamic moment equation for the front wheel about O_4

$$\mathbf{D}_{O_4,4/0} \cdot \hat{\mathbf{y}}_0 = \frac{d}{dt}(\mathbf{H}_{O_4,4/0} \cdot \hat{\mathbf{y}}_0) = \mathbf{M}_{O_4,\bar{4}\to 4} \cdot \hat{\mathbf{y}}_0 = -rF_4 \tag{3}$$

Next we take into account the condition $\mathbf{M}^c_{O_3,1\to 3} \cdot \hat{\mathbf{y}}_0 = \Gamma$ and apply the following dynamic moment equation for the back wheel about O_3

$$\mathbf{D}_{O_3,3/0} \cdot \hat{\mathbf{y}}_0 = \frac{d}{dt}(\mathbf{H}_{O_3,3/0} \cdot \hat{\mathbf{y}}_0) = \mathbf{M}_{O_3,2\to 4} \cdot \hat{\mathbf{y}}_0 = \Gamma - rF_3 \tag{4}$$

Finally we apply the FTD for system Σ to obtain three additional equations

$$(m_1 + m_3 + m_4)\ddot{x} = F_3 + F_4 \tag{5}$$

$$0 = N_3 + N_4 - (m_1 + m_3 + m_4)g \tag{6}$$

$$\begin{aligned} \mathbf{D}_{I_3,\Sigma/0} \cdot \hat{\mathbf{y}}_0 &= -\mathbf{r}_{I_3G_1} \times m_1 g\hat{\mathbf{z}}_0 - \mathbf{r}_{I_3O_4} \times m_4 g\hat{\mathbf{z}}_0 + \mathbf{r}_{I_3I_4} \times (N_4\hat{\mathbf{z}}_0 + F_4\hat{\mathbf{x}}_0) \\ &= m_3 g l_3 + m_4 g(l_3 + l_4) - (l_3 + l_4)N_4 \end{aligned} \tag{7}$$

It remains to find the dynamic moments of equations (3), (4) and (7):

$$\mathbf{D}_{O_4,4/0}\cdot\hat{\mathbf{y}}_0 = \frac{d}{dt}(I_4\dot{\theta}_4) = I_4\ddot{\theta}_4, \qquad \mathbf{D}_{O_3,3/0}\cdot\hat{\mathbf{y}}_0 = \frac{d}{dt}(I_3\dot{\theta}_3) = I_3\ddot{\theta}_3$$

$$\mathbf{D}_{I_3,\Sigma/0}\cdot\hat{\mathbf{y}}_0 = (I_3\ddot{\theta}_3 + m_3 r\ddot{x}) + (I_4\ddot{\theta}_4 + m_4 r\ddot{x}) + m_1 h\ddot{x}$$

Equations (3), (4) and (7) now take the form

$$I_4\ddot{\theta}_4 = -rF_4 \tag{3'}$$

$$I_3\ddot{\theta}_3 = \Gamma - rF_3 \tag{4'}$$

$$I_3\ddot{\theta}_3 + I_4\ddot{\theta}_4 + [(m_3+m_4)r + m_1 h]\ddot{x} = m_3 g l_3 + m_4 g(l_3+l_4) - (l_3+l_4)N_4 \tag{7'}$$

This gives seven equations to solve for seven unknowns $(\ddot{x}, \ddot{\theta}_3, \ddot{\theta}_4, N_3, N_4, F_3, F_4)$. We can solve for unknown $\ddot{x}$:

$$\ddot{x} = \frac{r\Gamma}{I_3 + I_4 + Mr^2} \tag{8}$$

denoting $M = m_1 + m_3 + m_4$.

d. To find the condition governing couple Γ which causes the motorcycle to tip about point I_3, we need to find normal reaction force N_4 and impose $N_4 \geq 0$: we obtain from equation (7′)

$$(I_3 + I_4 + Mr^2 + m_1(h-r)r)\frac{\ddot{x}}{r} \leq (m_3 l_3 + m_4(l_3+l_4))g$$

Then using (8) we find

$$\Gamma \leq \Gamma_{1,max} = \frac{m_3 l_3 + m_4(l_3+l_4)}{1 + \frac{m_1(h-r)r}{I_3+I_4+Mr^2}} g$$

An additional condition must be imposed to prevent the motorcycle to slip: $F_3 \leq \mu N_3$ (with $N_4 = 0$). This gives

$$\Gamma \leq \Gamma_{2,max} = \mu \frac{Mgr}{1 - \frac{I_3}{I_3+I_4+Mr^2}}$$

■

Example 11.14 The goal of this problem is to study the behavior of a gyroscopic instrument mounted on aircraft, known as attitude indicator or artificial horizon, and which provides a vertical reference irrespective of the position or motion of its support. Its working principle is based on conservation of angular momentum: its axis of rotation remains fixed relative to a Newtonian referential in the absence of perturbative effects. The system Σ is comprised of three bodies mounted in a case $\mathcal{S}(O, \hat{\mathbf{x}}_0, \hat{\mathbf{y}}_0, \hat{\mathbf{z}}_0)$ attached to the stationary or moving support (the aircraft):

-the outer gimbal $1(O, \hat{\mathbf{x}}_1, \hat{\mathbf{y}}_1, \hat{\mathbf{z}}_0)$ is mounted to the case by pivots of axis $(O, \hat{\mathbf{z}}_0)$. Its mass center is located on axis $(O, \hat{\mathbf{z}}_0)$. Denote by L its moment of inertia about its axis of rotation.

-the inner gimbal $2(O, \hat{\mathbf{x}}_1, \hat{\mathbf{y}}_2, \hat{\mathbf{z}}_2)$ mounted to the outer gimbal 1 by pivots of axis $(O, \hat{\mathbf{x}}_1)$. Its mass center is O and its inertia matrix about O is assumed of the form (its inertia operator about O has spherical symmetry)

$$[\mathcal{I}_{O,2}]_{b_2} = \begin{bmatrix} K & 0 & 0 \\ 0 & K & 0 \\ 0 & 0 & K \end{bmatrix}_{(\hat{\mathbf{x}}_1, \hat{\mathbf{y}}_2, \hat{\mathbf{z}}_2)}$$

-the rotor $3(O, \hat{\mathbf{x}}_3, \hat{\mathbf{y}}_3, \hat{\mathbf{z}}_2)$ mounted to the inner gimbal 2 by pivots of axis $(O, \hat{\mathbf{z}}_2)$. Its mass is M, its mass center G is located on axis $(O, \hat{\mathbf{z}}_2)$ with $\mathbf{r}_{OG} = a\hat{\mathbf{z}}_2$ $(a > 0)$, and its inertia matrix about O relative to axes $(O, \hat{\mathbf{x}}_3, \hat{\mathbf{y}}_3, \hat{\mathbf{z}}_2)$ is given by

$$[\mathcal{I}_{O,3}]_{b_3} = \begin{bmatrix} A & 0 & 0 \\ 0 & A & 0 \\ 0 & 0 & C \end{bmatrix}_{(\hat{\mathbf{x}}_3, \hat{\mathbf{y}}_3, \hat{\mathbf{z}}_2)}$$

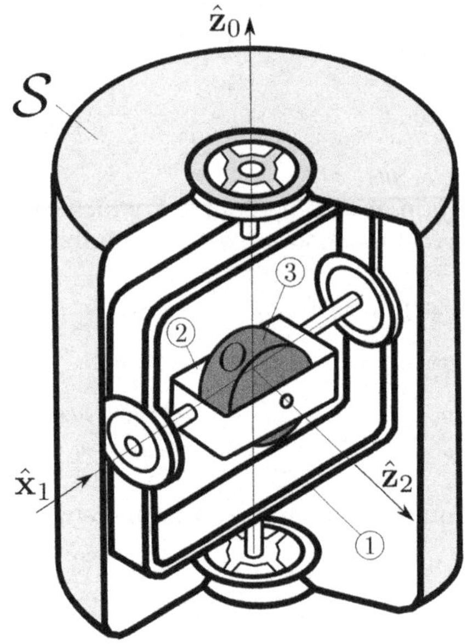

Figure 11.26

The system has three degrees of freedom described by the angles ψ, θ, ϕ and the corresponding transformations:

$$(\hat{\mathbf{x}}_0, \hat{\mathbf{y}}_0, \hat{\mathbf{z}}_0) \xrightarrow{\mathcal{R}_{\psi, \hat{\mathbf{z}}_0}} (\hat{\mathbf{x}}_1, \hat{\mathbf{y}}_1, \hat{\mathbf{z}}_0) \xrightarrow{\mathcal{R}_{\theta, \hat{\mathbf{x}}_1}} (\hat{\mathbf{x}}_1, \hat{\mathbf{y}}_2, \hat{\mathbf{z}}_2) \xrightarrow{\mathcal{R}_{\phi, \hat{\mathbf{z}}_2}} (\hat{\mathbf{x}}_3, \hat{\mathbf{y}}_3, \hat{\mathbf{z}}_2)$$

The rotation of the rotor relative to the inner gimbal is maintained uniform thanks to a small motor $\mathcal{M}$ of negligible mass resulting in the time relationship

$$\phi = \omega t, \qquad \omega = Cst$$

The action of the motor on the rotor is represented by the screw

$$\{\mathcal{A}_{\mathcal{M}\to 3}\} = \begin{Bmatrix} \mathbf{0} \\ \Gamma\hat{\mathbf{z}}_2 \end{Bmatrix}$$

All joints are assumed frictionless. In this study, the vehicle is assumed fixed relative to Earth assumed Newtonian. The vertical directed downward is defined by unit vector $\hat{\mathbf{x}}_0$ and the gravitational acceleration is given by $\mathbf{g} = g\hat{\mathbf{x}}_0$.

a. Apply the Fundamental Theorem of Dynamics to find three equations: two equations of motion (governing angles ψ and θ) and one equation giving couple Γ.
b. Find the values of angles (ψ, θ) which correspond to stationary position of the axis $(O, \hat{\mathbf{z}}_2)$ of the rotor. Which position of the rotor's axis corresponds to the values $\psi = -\pi/2$ and $\theta = \pi/2$?
c. Define the variables $\alpha = \psi + \pi/2$ and $\beta = \theta - \pi/2$. Linearize the two o.d.e.'s governing α and β. Find the characteristic equation corresponding to these equations and deduce the condition of stability of the position defined by$\psi = -\pi/2$ and $\theta = \pi/2$. Derive the minimal value of angular velocity ω guaranteeing stability as a function of the parameters (L, K, A, C, M, a, g). Find the numerical value of ω_{min} for $A = 400$ g.cm^2, $C = 900$ g.cm^2, $L = 2000$ g.cm^2, $K = 1600$ g.cm^2, $a = 4$ cm, $M = 200$ g and $g = 9.81$ m/s^2. ■

a. We first sketch a diagram showing the connections within system Σ and with the exterior as shown in Figure 11.27.

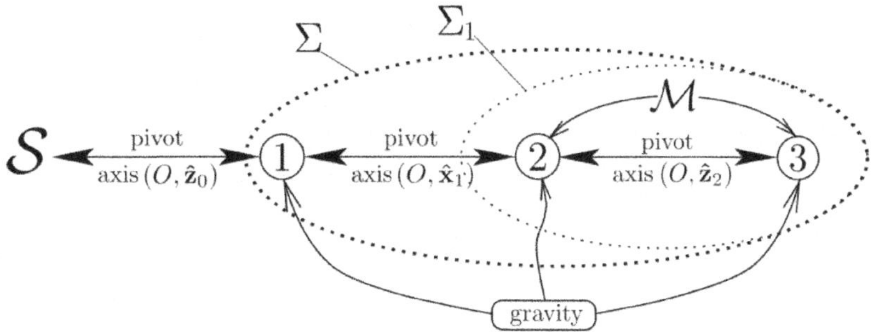

Figure 11.27

The equations of motion are found by taking into account the conditions expressing the frictionless character of the three joints $\mathcal{S} \leftrightarrow 1$, $1 \leftrightarrow 2$ and $2 \leftrightarrow 3$:

$$\hat{\mathbf{z}}_2 \cdot \mathbf{M}^c_{O,2\to3} = 0, \quad \hat{\mathbf{x}}_1 \cdot \mathbf{M}^c_{O,1\to2} = 0, \quad \hat{\mathbf{z}}_0 \cdot \mathbf{M}^c_{O,\mathcal{S}\to1} = 0$$

The first equation is obtained by consideration of rotor 3: to eliminate the reaction forces due to inner gimbal 2, we find the dynamic moment equation about O along $\hat{\mathbf{z}}_2$:

$$\hat{\mathbf{z}}_2 \cdot \frac{d}{dt}\mathbf{H}_{O,3/0} = \hat{\mathbf{z}}_2 \cdot \mathbf{M}^c_{O,\bar{3}\to3} = \hat{\mathbf{z}}_2 \cdot (\Gamma\hat{\mathbf{z}}_2 + \mathbf{r}_{OG} \times M\mathbf{g} + \mathbf{M}^c_{O,2\to3})$$

with angular momentum $\mathbf{H}_{O,3/0}$ given by

$$\mathbf{H}_{O,3/0} = \mathcal{I}_{O,3}(\boldsymbol{\omega}_{3/0}) = A\dot{\theta}\hat{\mathbf{x}}_1 + A\dot{\psi}\sin\theta\hat{\mathbf{y}}_2 + C(\dot{\phi} + \dot{\psi}\cos\theta)\hat{\mathbf{z}}_2$$

We have used the expression $\boldsymbol{\omega}_{3/0} = \dot{\psi}\hat{\mathbf{z}}_0 + \dot{\theta}\hat{\mathbf{x}}_1 + \dot{\phi}\hat{\mathbf{z}}_2$ of angular velocity of body 3, and we have taken advantage of the invariance of matrix $[\mathcal{I}_{O,3}]$ by rotation about $\hat{\mathbf{z}}_2$. We then obtain $\hat{\mathbf{z}}_2 \cdot \frac{d}{dt}\mathbf{H}_{O,3/0}$ as follows:

$$\begin{aligned}
\hat{\mathbf{z}}_2 \cdot \frac{d}{dt}\mathbf{H}_{O,3/0} &= \frac{d}{dt}(\hat{\mathbf{z}}_2 \cdot \mathbf{H}_{O,3/0}) - \frac{d\hat{\mathbf{z}}_2}{dt} \cdot \mathbf{H}_{O,3/0} = \frac{d}{dt}(C(\dot{\phi} + \dot{\psi}\cos\theta)) - (\dot{\psi}\hat{\mathbf{z}}_0 + \dot{\theta}\hat{\mathbf{x}}_1) \times \hat{\mathbf{z}}_2 \cdot \mathbf{H}_{O,3/0} \\
&= \frac{d}{dt}(C(\dot{\phi} + \dot{\psi}\cos\theta)) - (\dot{\psi}\sin\theta\hat{\mathbf{x}}_1 - \dot{\theta}\hat{\mathbf{y}}_2) \cdot \mathbf{H}_{O,3/0} \\
&= \frac{d}{dt}(C(\dot{\phi} + \dot{\psi}\cos\theta)) - (A\dot{\theta}\dot{\psi}\sin\theta - A\dot{\theta}\dot{\psi}\sin\theta) \\
&= C(\ddot{\psi}\cos\theta - \dot{\psi}\dot{\theta}\sin\theta)
\end{aligned}$$

Finally, we obtain the equation governing couple Γ:

$$\Gamma = C(\ddot{\psi}\cos\theta - \dot{\psi}\dot{\theta}\sin\theta) \tag{1}$$

The second equation is obtained by taking into account the property $\hat{\mathbf{x}}_1 \cdot \mathbf{M}^c_{O,1\to 2} = 0$: to make sure that the reaction forces due to the rotor are excluded, we make them internal by finding the dynamic moment equation about O for the system $\Sigma_1 = \{2, 3\}$ along $\hat{\mathbf{x}}_1$:

$$\hat{\mathbf{x}}_1 \cdot \frac{d}{dt}\mathbf{H}_{O,\Sigma_1/0} = \hat{\mathbf{x}}_1 \cdot \mathbf{M}^c_{O,\overline{\Sigma}_1\to\Sigma_1} = \hat{\mathbf{x}}_1 \cdot (\mathbf{r}_{OG} \times M\mathbf{g} + \mathbf{M}^c_{O,1\to 2})$$

with angular momentum $\mathbf{H}_{O,\Sigma_1/0}$ given by

$$\mathbf{H}_{O,2/0} + \mathbf{H}_{O,3/0} = K\boldsymbol{\omega}_{2/0} + \mathcal{I}_{O,3}(\boldsymbol{\omega}_{3/0}) = K\dot{\psi}\hat{\mathbf{z}}_0 + (A+K)\dot{\theta}\hat{\mathbf{x}}_1 + A\dot{\psi}\sin\theta\hat{\mathbf{y}}_2 + C(\dot{\phi} + \dot{\psi}\cos\theta)\hat{\mathbf{z}}_2$$

This leads to

$$\hat{\mathbf{x}}_1 \cdot \frac{d}{dt}\mathbf{H}_{O,\Sigma_1/0} = (A+K)\ddot{\theta} - \dot{\psi}\hat{\mathbf{y}}_1 \cdot \mathbf{H}_{O,\Sigma_1/0} = (A+K)\ddot{\theta} - (A-C)\dot{\psi}^2\sin\theta\cos\theta + C\omega\dot{\psi}\sin\theta$$

This gives the equation of motion for angle θ:

$$(A+K)\ddot{\theta} - (A-C)\dot{\psi}^2\sin\theta\cos\theta + C\omega\dot{\psi}\sin\theta = Mga\sin\psi\cos\theta \tag{2}$$

Finally, the third equation is obtained by taking into account $\hat{\mathbf{z}}_0 \cdot \mathbf{M}^c_{O,\mathcal{S}\to 1} = 0$ (since the pivot joining $\mathcal{S}$ and outer gimbal 2 is frictionless): we must find the dynamic moment equation for system Σ along $\hat{\mathbf{z}}_0$, thereby making all reaction forces between 1 and 2 and between 2 and 3 internal

$$\hat{\mathbf{z}}_0 \cdot \frac{d}{dt}\mathbf{H}_{O,\Sigma/0} = \hat{\mathbf{z}}_0 \cdot \mathbf{M}^c_{O,\overline{\Sigma}\to\Sigma} = \hat{\mathbf{z}}_0 \cdot (\mathbf{r}_{OG} \times M\mathbf{g} + \mathbf{M}^c_{O,\mathcal{S}\to 1})$$

with angular momentum $\hat{\mathbf{z}}_0 \cdot \mathbf{H}_{O,\Sigma_1/0}$ given by

$$\begin{aligned}\hat{\mathbf{z}}_0 \cdot (\mathbf{H}_{O,1/0} + \mathbf{H}_{O,2/0} + \mathbf{H}_{O,3/0}) &= L\dot{\psi} + \hat{\mathbf{z}}_0 \cdot (K\boldsymbol{\omega}_{2/0} + \mathcal{I}_{O,3}\boldsymbol{\omega}_{3/0}) \\ &= (L+K)\dot{\psi} + A\dot{\psi}\sin^2\theta + C(\dot{\phi} + \dot{\psi}\cos\theta)\cos\theta\end{aligned}$$

This gives the equation of motion for angle ψ:

$$(L+K)\ddot{\psi} + \frac{d}{dt}[(A\sin^2\theta + C\cos^2\theta)\dot{\psi} + C\omega\cos\theta] = Mga\sin\theta\cos\psi \tag{3}$$

b. The equilibrium positions of axis $(O, \hat{\mathbf{z}}_2)$ are obtained by setting $\dot{\psi} = \dot{\theta} = 0$ in (2-3): this gives the positions $(\psi, \theta) = (0, 0)$ ($\hat{\mathbf{z}}_2 = \hat{\mathbf{z}}_0$), $(\psi, \theta) = (\pi/2, \pi/2)$ ($\hat{\mathbf{z}}_2 = \hat{\mathbf{x}}_0$), and $(\psi, \theta) = (-\pi/2, \pi/2)$ ($\hat{\mathbf{z}}_2 = -\hat{\mathbf{x}}_0$). For the values $\psi = -\pi/2$ and $\theta = \pi/2$, the axis $(O, \hat{\mathbf{z}}_2)$ is vertical with mass center G located directly above O. This position is unstable when $\omega = 0$.

c. With the change of variables $\alpha = \psi + \pi/2$ and $\beta = \theta - \pi/2$, equations (2-3) become

$$(A+K)\ddot{\beta} + (A-C)\dot{\alpha}^2\sin\beta\cos\beta + C\omega\dot{\alpha}\cos\beta = Mga\cos\alpha\sin\beta$$

$$(L+K)\ddot{\alpha} + \frac{d}{dt}[(A\cos^2\beta + C\sin^2\beta)\dot{\alpha} - C\omega\sin\beta] = Mga\cos\beta\sin\alpha$$

After linearization, we obtain

$$(A+K)\ddot{\beta} + C\omega\dot{\alpha} = Mga\beta \tag{2'}$$

$$(A+L+K)\ddot{\alpha} - C\omega\dot{\beta} = Mga\alpha \tag{3'}$$

To find the characteristic equation we look for solutions of the type

$$\begin{bmatrix}\alpha\\ \beta\end{bmatrix} = e^{\Omega t}\begin{bmatrix}\alpha_0\\ \beta_0\end{bmatrix}$$

Substitution in (2′-3′) gives

$$\begin{bmatrix} (A+L+K)\Omega^2 - Mga & -C\omega\Omega \\ C\omega\Omega & (A+K)\Omega^2 - Mga \end{bmatrix} \begin{bmatrix} \alpha_0 \\ \beta_0 \end{bmatrix} = \begin{bmatrix} 0 \\ 0 \end{bmatrix}$$

To obtain non-trivial solutions, we need to impose that the determinant of the homogeneous linear system be zero:

$$[(A+L+K)\Omega^2 - Mga][(A+K)\Omega^2 - Mga] + C^2\omega^2\Omega^2 = 0$$

This is a quadratic equation in Ω^2: for stability we need to obtain two negative roots Ω_1^2 and Ω_2^2 (this would make both Ω_1 and Ω_2 imaginary numbers). Therefore, we need to impose that the product of the roots is positive (which is satisfied) and that the sum of the root is negative. This last condition is equivalent to

$$C^2\omega^2 > Mga(L + 2A + 2K) \tag{4}$$

Hence the vertical position of axis $(O, \hat{\mathbf{z}}_2)$ is stabilized if the rotor's angular velocity exceed the minimum value given by (4) (this is known as *gyroscopic stabilization*: See Chapter 15). For the given numerical values, we find $\omega_{min} = 12.1$ rev/s. ∎

11.7 Quaternionic Formulation

In some applications, the definition of orientation (or attitude) in terms of Euler or Bryant angles leads to indeterminations in certain configurations. We have learned in Chapter 1 that the use of quaternions to represent rigid body orientation can resolve this problem. It is thus of interest to derive a quaternionic formulation of the rotational equations of motion.

Consider a rigid body $\mathcal{B}$ in motion in a Newtonian referential $\mathcal{E}$. Consider the unit quaternion $Q(t)$ associated with the rotation which maps a basis $b_E(\hat{\mathbf{e}}_1, \hat{\mathbf{e}}_2, \hat{\mathbf{e}}_3)$ of $\mathcal{E}$ to a basis $b_B(\hat{\mathbf{b}}_1, \hat{\mathbf{b}}_2, \hat{\mathbf{b}}_3)$ of body $\mathcal{B}$. A vector $\mathbf{V}_0$ fixed in $\mathcal{E}$ is mapped into a vector $\mathbf{V}$ fixed in $\mathcal{B}$ according to the quaternion relationship

$$\mathbf{V}(t) = Q(t)\mathbf{V}_0\overline{Q}(t) \tag{11.41}$$

Using this relationship, we proved in Section 3.4 that the quaternion $\Omega_E = 0 + \Omega_1\hat{\mathbf{e}}_1 + \Omega_2\hat{\mathbf{e}}_2 + \Omega_3\hat{\mathbf{e}}_3$ associated with the body's angular velocity $\omega_{\mathcal{B}/\mathcal{E}}$ on basis $(\hat{\mathbf{e}}_1, \hat{\mathbf{e}}_2, \hat{\mathbf{e}}_2)$ of $\mathcal{E}$ can be determined in terms of Q and its derivative (relative to $\mathcal{E}$) according to

$$\Omega_E = 2\dot{Q}\overline{Q} \tag{11.42}$$

This gives the equation on basis $(\hat{\mathbf{e}}_1, \hat{\mathbf{e}}_2, \hat{\mathbf{e}}_2)$

$$\dot{Q} = \frac{1}{2}\Omega_E Q = \frac{1}{2}(0 + \Omega_1\hat{\mathbf{e}}_1 + \Omega_2\hat{\mathbf{e}}_2 + \Omega_3\hat{\mathbf{e}}_3)(Q_0 + Q_1\hat{\mathbf{e}}_1 + Q_2\hat{\mathbf{e}}_2 + Q_3\hat{\mathbf{e}}_3) \tag{11.43}$$

or, equivalently, in matrix form (using the multiplication rule 1.31)

$$\begin{bmatrix} \dot{Q}_0 \\ \dot{Q}_1 \\ \dot{Q}_2 \\ \dot{Q}_3 \end{bmatrix} = \frac{1}{2} \begin{bmatrix} 0 & -\Omega_1 & -\Omega_2 & -\Omega_3 \\ \Omega_1 & 0 & -\Omega_3 & \Omega_2 \\ \Omega_2 & \Omega_3 & 0 & -\Omega_1 \\ \Omega_3 & -\Omega_2 & \Omega_1 & 0 \end{bmatrix} \begin{bmatrix} Q_0 \\ Q_1 \\ Q_2 \\ Q_3 \end{bmatrix} \tag{11.44}$$

In practice, it is more convenient to work on the body's basis $(\hat{\mathbf{b}}_1, \hat{\mathbf{b}}_2, \hat{\mathbf{b}}_3)$: denote by $\Omega_B = 0 + \omega_1\hat{\mathbf{b}}_1 + \omega_2\hat{\mathbf{b}}_2 + \omega_3\hat{\mathbf{b}}_3$ the corresponding quaternion associated with $\omega_{\mathcal{B}/\mathcal{E}}$. Ω_B can be obtained from Ω_E by using the transformation

$$\Omega_B = \overline{Q}\Omega_E Q = 2\overline{Q}\dot{Q} \tag{11.45}$$

leading to

$$\dot{Q} = \frac{1}{2}Q\Omega_B = \frac{1}{2}(q_0 + q_1\hat{\mathbf{b}}_1 + q_2\hat{\mathbf{b}}_2 + q_3\hat{\mathbf{b}}_3)(0 + \omega_1\hat{\mathbf{b}}_1 + \omega_2\hat{\mathbf{b}}_2 + \omega_3\hat{\mathbf{b}}_3)$$

or, equivalently, in matrix form

$$\begin{bmatrix} \dot{q}_0 \\ \dot{q}_1 \\ \dot{q}_2 \\ \dot{q}_3 \end{bmatrix} = \frac{1}{2} \begin{bmatrix} 0 & -\omega_1 & -\omega_2 & -\omega_3 \\ \omega_1 & 0 & \omega_3 & -\omega_2 \\ \omega_2 & -\omega_3 & 0 & \omega_1 \\ \omega_3 & \omega_2 & -\omega_1 & 0 \end{bmatrix} \begin{bmatrix} q_0 \\ q_1 \\ q_2 \\ q_3 \end{bmatrix} \tag{11.46}$$

If basis b_B is a principal basis for inertia operator $\mathcal{I}_G$, the moment equation of $\mathcal{B}$ about its mass center G can be written in the form

$$\left(\frac{d}{dt}\mathcal{I}_G(\omega)\right)_E = \left(\frac{d}{dt}\mathcal{I}_G(\omega)\right)_B + \omega \times \mathcal{I}_G(\omega) = \mathbf{M}_{G,\overline{\mathcal{B}}\to\mathcal{B}} \tag{11.47}$$

leading to Euler equations:

$$\begin{aligned} I_1\dot{\omega}_1 &= (I_2 - I_3)\omega_2\omega_3 + M_{G1} \\ I_2\dot{\omega}_2 &= (I_3 - I_1)\omega_1\omega_3 + M_{G2} \\ I_3\dot{\omega}_3 &= (I_1 - I_2)\omega_1\omega_2 + M_{G3} \end{aligned} \tag{11.48}$$

denoting I_1, I_2, I_3 the principal moments of inertia w.r.t. axes $(G, \hat{\mathbf{b}}_1)$, $(G, \hat{\mathbf{b}}_2)$, and $(G, \hat{\mathbf{b}}_3)$, respectively, and (M_{G1}, M_{G2}, M_{G3}) the components of external moment $\mathbf{M}_{G,\overline{\mathcal{B}}\to\mathcal{B}}$ on basis b_B. Equations (11.46) and (11.48) form a closed set of equations govering the orientation of body $\mathcal{B}$.

Remark 12. Initial value of $Q = q_0 + q_1\hat{\mathbf{b}}_1 + q_2\hat{\mathbf{b}}_2 + q_3\hat{\mathbf{b}}_3$ must be given such that $q_0^2 + q_1^2 + q_2^2 + q_3^2 = 1$. Then, the solution of (11.46) yields a unit quaternion. In practice, numerical errors during time-integration may not yield of unit quaternion. Quaternion Q must be normalized whenever the error exceeds a threshold.

Remark 13. Integration of equations (11.46-11.48) yields the attitude of body $\mathcal{B}$ in the moving axes. Recall that the rotation $\mathcal{R}_{EB}$ which maps basis $(\hat{\mathbf{e}}_1, \hat{\mathbf{e}}_2, \hat{\mathbf{e}}_2)$ to basis $(\hat{\mathbf{b}}_1, \hat{\mathbf{b}}_2, \hat{\mathbf{b}}_3)$ can be represented in terms of Q as follows (see equation 1.33):

$$[\mathcal{R}_{EB}]_E = [\mathcal{R}_{EB}]_B = \begin{bmatrix} 2q_0^2 + 2q_1^2 - 1 & 2(q_1q_2 - q_0q_3) & 2(q_1q_3 + q_0q_2) \\ 2(q_1q_2 + q_0q_3) & 2q_0^2 + 2q_2^2 - 1 & 2(q_2q_3 - q_0q_1) \\ 2(q_1q_3 - q_0q_2) & 2(q_2q_3 + q_0q_1) & 2q_0^2 + 2q_3^2 - 1 \end{bmatrix}$$

This expression can yield the components of any vector on the fixed basis from those on the moving basis (See Section 1.3).

11.8 Problems

Problem 11.1 A spherical body $\mathcal{B}$ of mass m moves along a horizontal support Ox. The contact is characterized by coefficient of kinetic friction μ and coefficient of rolling friction k. The initial condition corresponds to a forward motion of its mass center G at speed v_0 and backspin at angular speed ω_0.

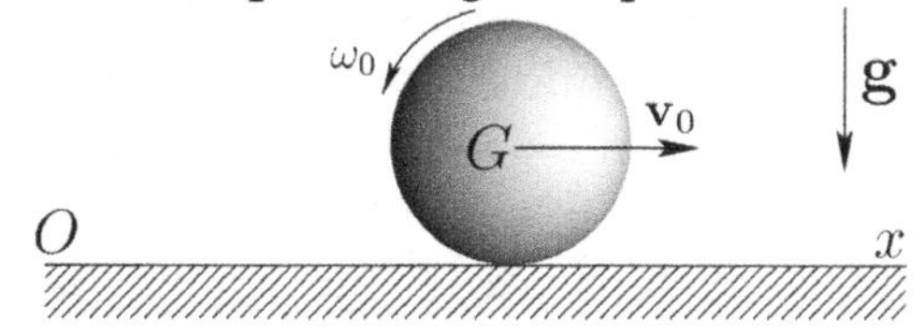

Analyze the motion of $\mathcal{B}$.

Problem 11.2 A cube of homogeneous density, mass m, side $2a$ is placed without initial speed on a rough inclined plane Oxy. The contact between the face of the cube in contact and the plane is characterized by the coefficient of static and kinetic friction coefficient $\mu_s = \mu_k = \mu$. Denote by α the angle of inclination of Ox with the horizontal. Find under which conditions on the parameters μ and α the impending situations occur upon release of the cube without initial speed:

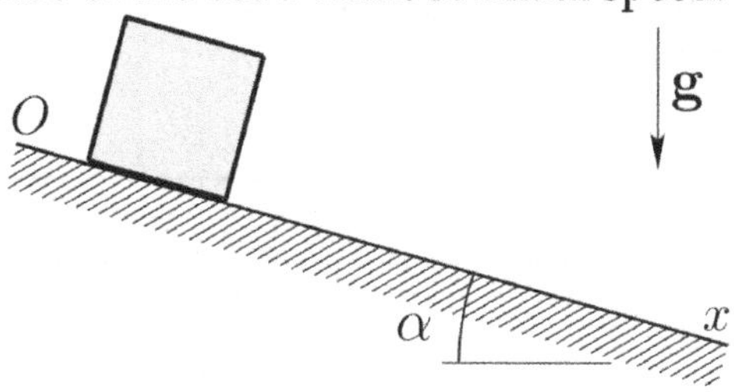

a. the cube stays at rest.

b. the cube slips without tipping.

c. the cube tips about its lower edge without slipping.

d. the cube slips and tips.

Sketch the domain of realizability of each case in the parameter plane $(\mu, \tan\alpha)$.

Problem 11.3 A rod AB of mass m, mass center G, and length $2l$ is set against a vertical wall Oy, with one of its extremity A coinciding with the corner O of the horizontal support Ox. A small perturbation destroys this unstable equilibrium, and the rod rotates about O and may lose contact with the corner O. Assume that the contact with Ox is frictionless. The inclination of the rod with the horizontal is described by angle θ. The position of A is defined by the coordinate x_A on axis Ox.

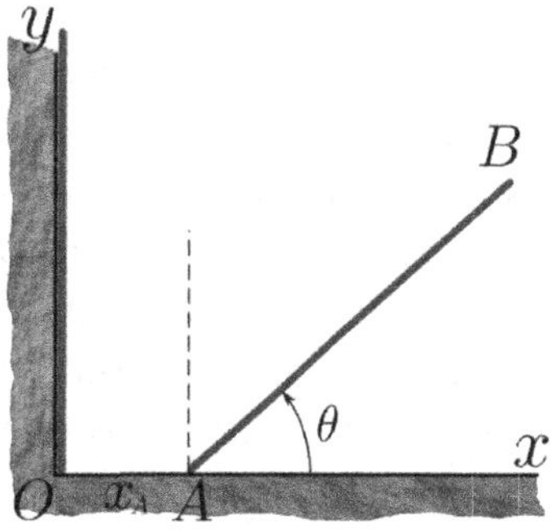

a. Show that the motion of the rod is first a rotation about point O until the angle θ reaches the value θ_1. At this point, the extremity A must leave the vertical wall Oy. Find the expression of θ_1.

b. Study the motion of the rod for $\theta < \theta_1$ by finding the equation of motion which governs angle θ. To solve this equation, make the change of variable $u = \dot{\theta}^2$ and find an o.d.e. governing u as a function of θ. Then solve this equation to find the angular velocity $\dot{\theta}$ as a function of θ, g and l.

c. Show that once point A takes off from the wall, it cannot move back toward the wall nor can it lose contact with support Ox.

Problem 11.4 A system is comprised of two rigid bodies, a frame 1 (of mass m_1, mass center G_1) and a homogeneous cylinder 2 (of mass m_2, mass center G_2, radius r) connected to frame 1 by a frictionless pivot. The frame 1 is connected to a fixed support 0 by a frictionless pivot of axis Ox. The mass centers G_1 and G_2 are located in the same vertical plane at a distance l_1 and l_2, respectively, from axis Ox. The moment of inertia of body 1 about axis Ox is denoted as I_1.

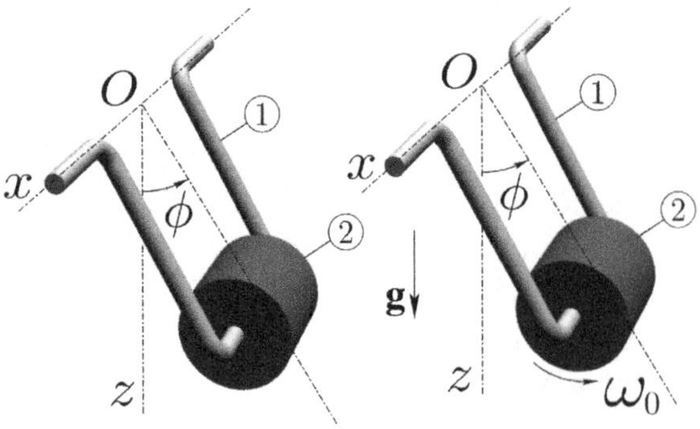

In the first experiment, the rotation of cylinder 2 is blocked, so that the assembly makes small amplitude oscillations about the vertical axis Oz as a single rigid body. In the second experiment, the rotation of the disk is free: the frame 1 is released without initial speed making a small angle ϕ_0 with the vertical, while the cylinder rotates with initial angular velocity ω_0.

Find the periods T_1 and T_2 of the small amplitude oscillations of the system in both experiments. Compare T_1 and T_2. Does the rotation of cylinder 2 have any influence on the period?

Problem 11.5 Consider a system of two identical slender rods 1 and 2 moving in a vertical plane. Both rods have same mass of m, and same length of $2l$. Their endpoints are connected by massless inextensible strings of identical length l_0. Rod 1 is free to rotate without friction about its center O. The system is initially at rest in the position shown. The string at A is then cut.

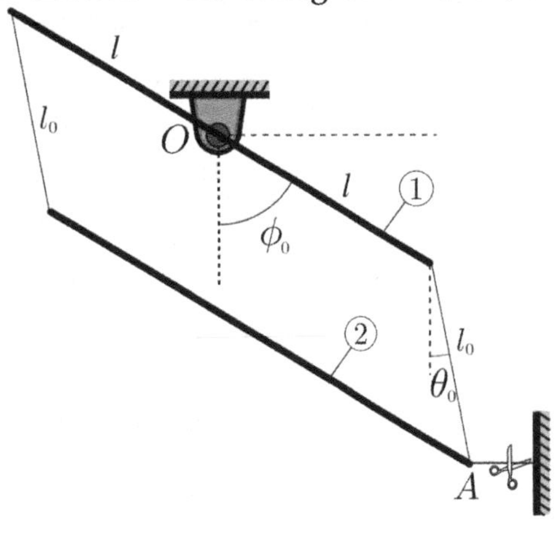

a. Derive the equations of motion of the system by finding the angular accelerations $\ddot{\phi}$ and $\ddot{\theta}$ at an arbitrary time. In particular, show that the mass center of rod 2 moves as a particle connected to O by a massless inextensible string of length l_0.

b. Find the tensions in the strings.

Problem 11.6 Consider the pendulum of example 11.7. It is assembled by connecting a body 2 of mass center B and mass m to a body 1 of mass center A and mass M. We examine the effect of friction on the motion of the system. More specifically, the contact between body 1 and its guide is characterized by coefficient of kinetic friction μ. Body 2 can rotate freely about a frictionless pivot at A relative to body 1. The motion of the system occurs in a vertical plane. The position of the system at any time t is defined by the coordinate $x(t)$ of A measured along axis Ox and by the angle $\theta(t)$ defined positively in the anticlockwise direction. The system is given initial conditions $(x_0, \theta_0, \dot{x}_0, \dot{\theta}_0)$ (with $0 < \theta_0 < \pi/2$). Denote by l the distance AB, by $J = m\kappa l^2$ the moment of inertia of pendulum 2 about its axis of rotation, and by δ the ratio $m/(m+M)$.

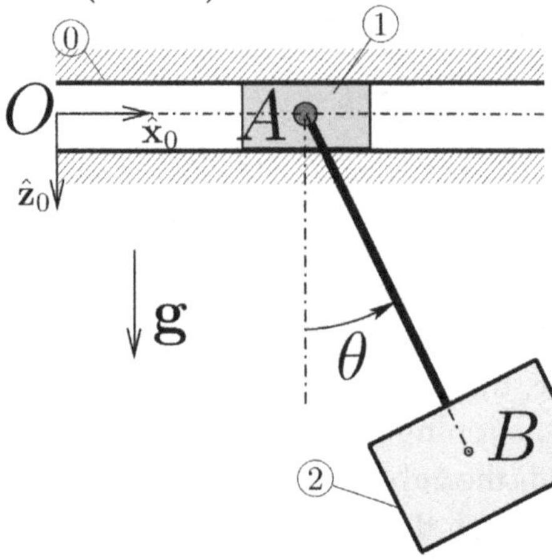

a. Denote by $\mathbf{R} = R_x\hat{\mathbf{x}}_0 + R_z\hat{\mathbf{z}}_0$. According to Coulomb law $R_x = -\epsilon\mu R_z$ with $\epsilon = \pm 1$. The actual value chosen for ϵ depends on the sign of R_z and $\dot{x}$. Show in all cases the quantity $\epsilon\dot{x}R_z$ is always positive.

b. Find the three equations which solve

for the unknowns (x, θ, R_x, R_z). After using $R_x = -\epsilon\mu R_z$, express R_z as a function of ϵ and θ, $\dot{\theta}$ and the parameters κ and δ.

c. Assuming $\kappa > \delta$ and that the friction coefficient μ is sufficiently large so as to satisfy the condition

$$\frac{\kappa}{\delta} - 1 + \sin^2\theta_0 - \mu \sin\theta_0 \cos\theta_0 < 0$$

Show that
(i) if $\dot{x}_0 > 0$, no motion compatible with Coulomb laws is possible.
(ii) if $\dot{x}_0 < 0$, two possible motions are possible (starting with the same initial conditions!).

Problem 11.7 The figure displayed below shows an experiment displayed in many science museums: a ball set in motion on a rotating turntable can display many surprising motions. The object of this problem is to examine a few properties of these motions. Consider a horizontal turntable $\mathcal{D}$ constrained to rotate *uniformly* about a vertical axis $(O, \hat{\mathbf{e}}_z)$ fixed in some Newtonian referential $\mathcal{E}$. A spherical rigid body $\mathcal{S}$ of radius r, of mass m is constrained to move without slipping on top of $\mathcal{D}$. We denote by mk^2r^2 the moment of inertia of $\mathcal{S}$ about one of its diameters, by I the contact point between $\mathcal{S}$ and $\mathcal{D}$, by $\omega\hat{\mathbf{e}}_z$ the *prescribed* constant angular velocity of platform $\mathcal{D}$, by $\mathbf{\Omega}$ the unknown angular velocity of $\mathcal{S}$, and by $\mathbf{v}_C$ the velocity of its mass center C. $\mathbf{\Omega}$ and $\mathbf{v}_C$ are defined relative to $\mathcal{E}$. We neglect rolling and spinning friction. The initial position vector and velocity of C and the initial angular velocity of $\mathcal{S}$ are denoted by $\mathbf{r}_0 = \mathbf{r}_{OC_0}$, $\mathbf{v}_0$ and $\mathbf{\Omega}_0$, respectively.

a. Derive the three vectorial equations expressing the no-slip condition at contact point I and the Fundamental Theorem of Dynamics applied to $\mathcal{S}$. Verify that there are as many unknowns as equations.

b. Show that the spin component of the angular velocity of $\mathcal{S}$ remains constant, and that the velocity of point C satisfies

$$\frac{d\mathbf{v}_C}{dt} = \frac{k^2}{1+k^2}\omega\hat{\mathbf{e}}_z \times \mathbf{v}_C.$$

From this equation, prove that C moves *uniformly* along a circular path relative to referential $\mathcal{E}$. Find the radius of this circular path, the corresponding angular velocity and the position of its center. Show that the friction force acting on $\mathcal{S}$ stays constant in magnitude.

c. Show that if C is set without initial velocity ($\mathbf{v}_0 = \mathbf{0}$), then C remains fixed relative to $\mathcal{E}$. Find the condition satisfied by the initial angular velocity $\mathbf{\Omega}_0$. Find the friction force. Comment.

d. The motion of the turntable $\mathcal{D}$ is produced by a motor mounted between $\mathcal{E}$ and $\mathcal{D}$. Show that the couple C developed by this motor must be given by

$$C = \frac{k^2}{2(1+k^2)}\omega\frac{d}{dt}\mathbf{r}_{OC}^2.$$

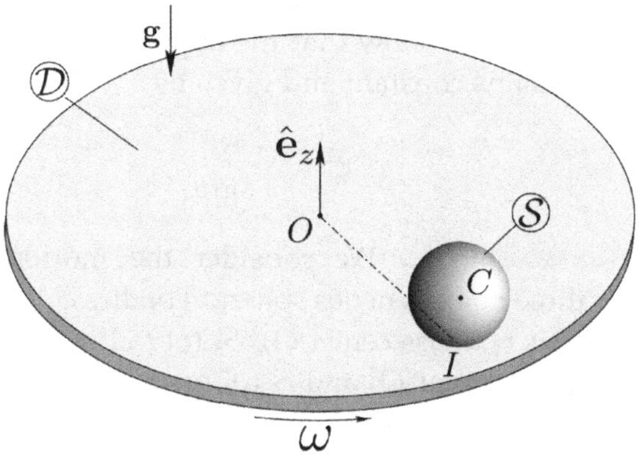

Problem 11.8 A heavy, uniform disk $1(G, \hat{\imath}, \hat{\jmath}, \hat{\mathbf{k}})$ of mass m, and radius r rolls on a horizontal table $(O, \hat{\mathbf{x}}, \hat{\mathbf{y}})$ of a referential $0(O, \hat{\mathbf{x}}, \hat{\mathbf{y}}, \hat{\mathbf{z}})$ in such as way that
(i) its mass center G remains stationary in 0,
(ii) the point of rolling contact I moves along a circle of center O.

The orientation of body 1 relative to referential 0 is defined in terms of the three angles (ψ, θ, ϕ) according the following sequence of rotations:

$$(\hat{\mathbf{x}},\hat{\mathbf{y}},\hat{\mathbf{z}}) \xrightarrow{\mathcal{R}_{\psi,\hat{\mathbf{z}}}} (\hat{\mathbf{u}},\hat{\mathbf{v}},\hat{\mathbf{z}}) \xrightarrow{\mathcal{R}_{\theta,\hat{\mathbf{u}}}} (\hat{\mathbf{u}},\hat{\mathbf{w}},\hat{\mathbf{k}}) \xrightarrow{\mathcal{R}_{\phi,\hat{\mathbf{k}}}} (\hat{\boldsymbol{\imath}},\hat{\boldsymbol{\jmath}},\hat{\mathbf{k}})$$

The body is under the sole effect of gravity and contact forces, neglecting rolling and pivoting friction. Recall that the inertia operator of body 1 about G is given by $I_{Gz} = \hat{\mathbf{k}} \cdot \mathcal{I}_G(\hat{\mathbf{k}}) = \frac{1}{2}mr^2$ and $I_{Gx} = I_{Gy} = \hat{\boldsymbol{\imath}} \cdot \mathcal{I}_G(\hat{\boldsymbol{\imath}}) = \hat{\boldsymbol{\jmath}} \cdot \mathcal{I}_G(\hat{\boldsymbol{\jmath}}) = \frac{1}{4}mr^2$.

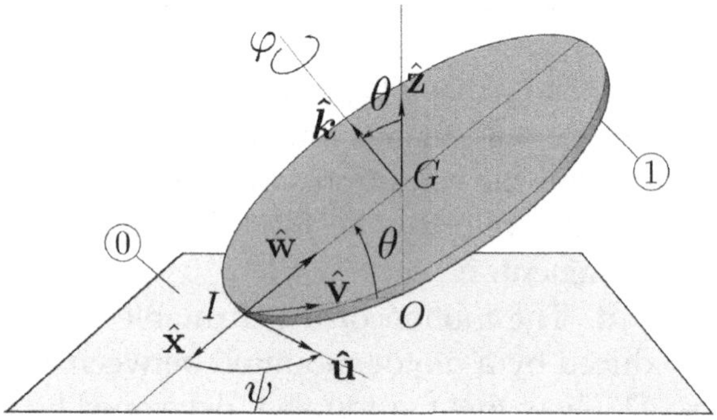

a. By accounting for all constraints, find the kinematic screw of body 1. Conclude that the body has a single degree of freedom (use angle ψ).

b. Apply the Fundamental Theorem of Dynamics to show that the angular velocity $\dot{\psi}$ remains constant and given by

$$\dot{\psi}^2 = \frac{4g}{r\sin\theta}$$

Problem 11.9 We consider the motion of three homogeneous spherical bodies $\mathcal{S}_1$ (of radius r_1, mass center O), $\mathcal{S}_2$ (of radius $r_2 > r_1$, mass center O) and $\mathcal{S}$ (of mass center C, diameter $r_2 - r_1$) in a referential $\mathcal{E}$ of origin O. $\mathcal{S}_1$ and $\mathcal{S}_2$ are free to rotate about O in $\mathcal{E}$ without friction.

$\mathcal{S}$ is constrained to move between $\mathcal{S}_1$ and $\mathcal{S}_2$ without slipping. Denote by I_1 the contact point between $\mathcal{S}$ and $\mathcal{S}_1$, I_2 the contact point between $\mathcal{S}$ and $\mathcal{S}_2$, $\mathbf{v}_C$ the velocity of C in $\mathcal{E}$, and by $\boldsymbol{\Omega}$, $\boldsymbol{\Omega}_1$ and $\boldsymbol{\Omega}_2$ the angular velocity of $\mathcal{S}$, $\mathcal{S}_1$, and $\mathcal{S}_2$, respectively, relative to $\mathcal{E}$. Neglect rolling and spinning friction. Denote by J_1, J_2 and J the inertia moments of $\mathcal{S}_1$, $\mathcal{S}_2$ and $\mathcal{S}$ about one of their diameters.

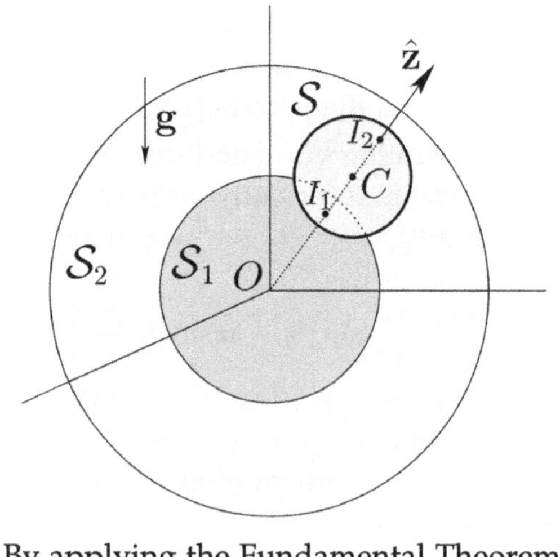

By applying the Fundamental Theorem of Dynamics, derive the equations governing $\boldsymbol{\Omega}$, $\boldsymbol{\Omega}_1$, $\boldsymbol{\Omega}_2$ and $\mathbf{v}_C$. Can first integrals be found?

Problem 11.10 A rigid rectangular frame $BCC'B'$ of negligible mass can rotate about a vertical axis Δ. Each of its sides AB, BC, etc., is of same length a. The pivots at A and D are frictionless. Two identical right-circular homogeneous cylinders of radius r, height h and mass m are mounted on the sides BC and $B'C'$ of the frame, about which they can rotate without friction. Their mass centers coincide with the centers of the bars.

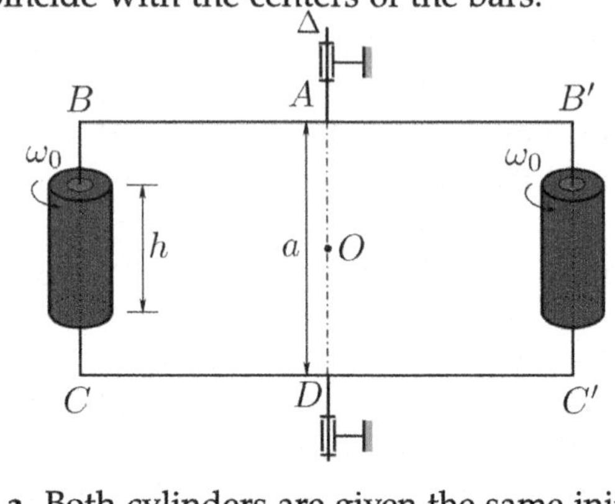

a. Both cylinders are given the same initial angular velocity ω_0, the frame being initially at rest. At a later time, a mechanism attached to the frame, of negligible mass, suddenly stops the rotation of one of the cylinders. Find the angular velocity ω_1 taken then by the frame in terms of a, h, r, ω_0, m.

b. The frame now turning at angular velocity ω_1 with one of the cylinders immobilized, the second cylinder still rotating is suddenly put to a sudden complete stop relative to the frame. Find the angular velocity ω_2 taken then by the frame in terms of a, h, r, ω_0, m.

Problem 11.11 A disk $\mathcal{D}$ of mass m, radius r, and mass center C is rolling without slipping on the interior of a rough circular support of radius R and center O. Pinned at point C is a rod $\mathcal{R}$ of length $2l$ and mass m, free to oscillate about the axis of the disk. The connection at C is frictionless. The motions occur is the plane of the figure.

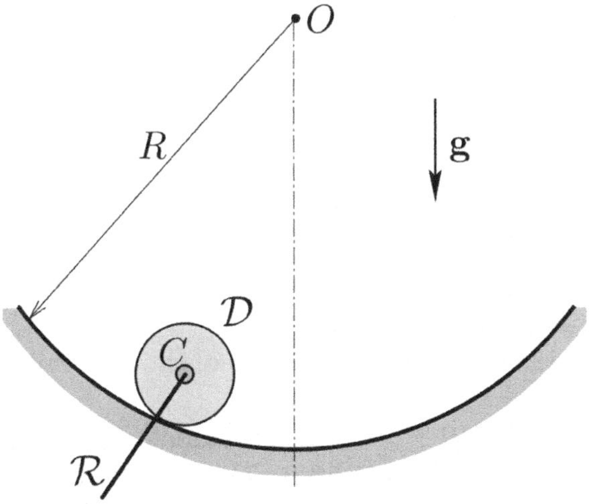

a. Parametrize the motion of the system. Find the velocity of the mass centers of $\mathcal{D}$ and $\mathcal{R}$.

b. Find the equations which govern the motion of the system.

c. Assuming that the motion of the disk and of the rod are of small amplitude, find the period of small oscillations of the system.

Problem 11.12 An axisymmetric body 2 of mass center O is free to rotate about its axis $(O, \hat{\mathbf{x}}_1)$ relative to a frame 1. The joint between 1 and 2 is frictionless. Frame 1, assumed massless, is itself connected to a fixed support 0 by frictionless pivots of axis $(O, \hat{\mathbf{z}}_0)$ directed along the vertical. The inertia matrix of body 2 about O on any basis $b(\hat{\mathbf{x}}_1, -, -)$ is given by

$$[\mathcal{I}_O]_b = \begin{bmatrix} C & 0 & 0 \\ 0 & A & 0 \\ 0 & 0 & A \end{bmatrix}_b$$

The position of the system is defined by the angles θ and ϕ. At $t = 0$, the system is given angular velocities $\dot{\theta}_0$ and $\dot{\phi}_0$.

a. Show that the angular velocities $\dot{\theta}$ and $\dot{\phi}$ remain constant during the motion if no external forces and moments are acting of the systems other than those due to gravity and the contact at the pivots.

b. Find the moment $\mathbf{M}^c_{O,1\to 2}$ due to contact forces between 1 and 2. If $\dot{\theta}_0 \neq 0$ and if $\dot{\phi}_0$ is very large, what do you conclude as far as the construction of the joints between 1 and 2?

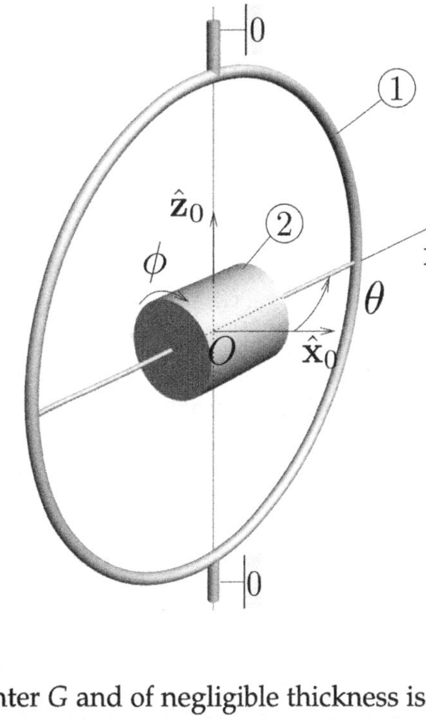

Problem 11.13 A long plank 1 of mass m, mass center G and of negligible thickness is placed without initial speed on top of two counter-rotating cylindrical rollers 2 and 3 of radius R centered at A and B. The rollers are driven at the same constant angular velocity ω, and their axes are parallel and located in the same horizontal plane as shown in Figure 11.28.

The plank is observed to oscillate along the horizontal direction without losing contact with the rollers. The position of G is defined by coordinate $x(t)$: assume that, at $t = 0$, $x(0) = x_0$ with $0 < x_0 < L$. Denote by μ the coefficient of kinetic friction between the rollers and the plank, and by L the distance $|OA| = |OB|$ (O is the midpoint of line segment AB).

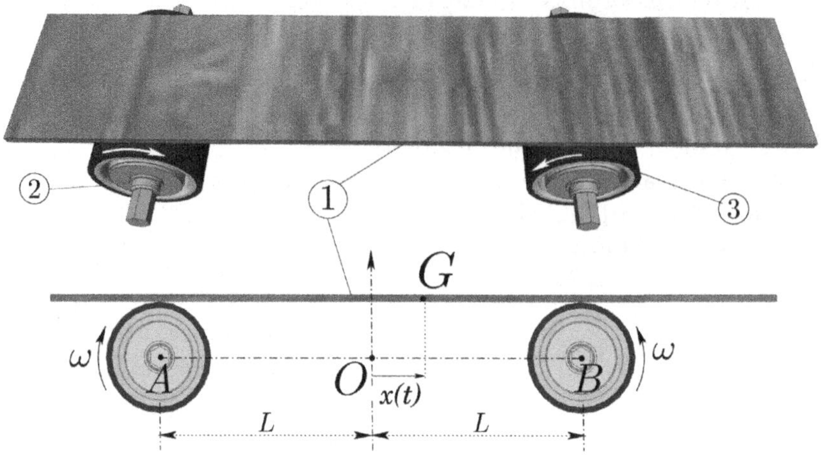

Figure 11.28

a. At $t = 0$, the plank necessarily slips relative to the rollers. Find the slip velocities of the plank relative to the rollers in terms of $x(t)$ and ω.

b. Find the equation of motion of the plank and the reaction forces of the rollers on the plank.

c. Show that the plank oscillates and find the period T of these oscillations Show that the amplitude x_0 must satisfy a condition for these oscillations to occur. Describe the motion of the plank if this condition is not satisfied.

Problem 11.14 The goal of this problem is to perform a dynamic analysis of the Segway in planar motion. The Segway and its rider shown in Figure 11.29 below are modeled as a system $\Sigma = \{1, 2, 3, 4\}$ of four interconnected rigid bodies in motion in a Newtonian referential $0(O, \hat{\mathbf{x}}_0, \hat{\mathbf{y}}_0, \hat{\mathbf{z}}_0)$. The axis $(O, \hat{\mathbf{z}}_0)$ represents the vertical directed upward.

- Body $1(O, \hat{\mathbf{x}}_1, \hat{\mathbf{y}}_1 = \hat{\mathbf{y}}_3, \hat{\mathbf{z}}_1)$ is the right wheel in rotation about axis $(A, \hat{\mathbf{y}}_3)$ of body 3. Its parametrization is done by angle $\theta_1(t) = (\hat{\mathbf{x}}_3, \hat{\mathbf{x}}_1) = (\hat{\mathbf{z}}_3, \hat{\mathbf{z}}_1)$ relative to body 3. It is in contact with the horizontal road $(O, \hat{\mathbf{x}}_0, \hat{\mathbf{y}}_0)$ at point I_1 and is assumed to roll without slipping ($\mathbf{r}_{I_1O_1} = R\hat{\mathbf{z}}_0$). Its mass center is O_1, its mass $M_1 = M$ and its inertia operator about O_1 takes the form

$$[\mathcal{I}_{O_1,1}]_{b_1} = \begin{bmatrix} I & 0 & 0 \\ 0 & J & 0 \\ 0 & 0 & K \end{bmatrix}_{b_1}$$

on basis $b_1(\hat{\mathbf{x}}_1, \hat{\mathbf{y}}_1, \hat{\mathbf{z}}_1)$.

- Body $2(O, \hat{\mathbf{x}}_2, \hat{\mathbf{y}}_2 = \hat{\mathbf{y}}_3, \hat{\mathbf{z}}_2)$ is the left wheel in rotation about axis $(A, \hat{\mathbf{y}}_3)$ of body 3. Its parametrization is done by angle $\theta_2(t) = (\hat{\mathbf{x}}_3, \hat{\mathbf{x}}_2) = (\hat{\mathbf{z}}_3, \hat{\mathbf{z}}_2)$ relative to body 3. It is in contact with the horizontal road at point I_2 and is assumed to roll without slipping ($\mathbf{r}_{I_2O_2} = R\hat{\mathbf{z}}_0$). Its

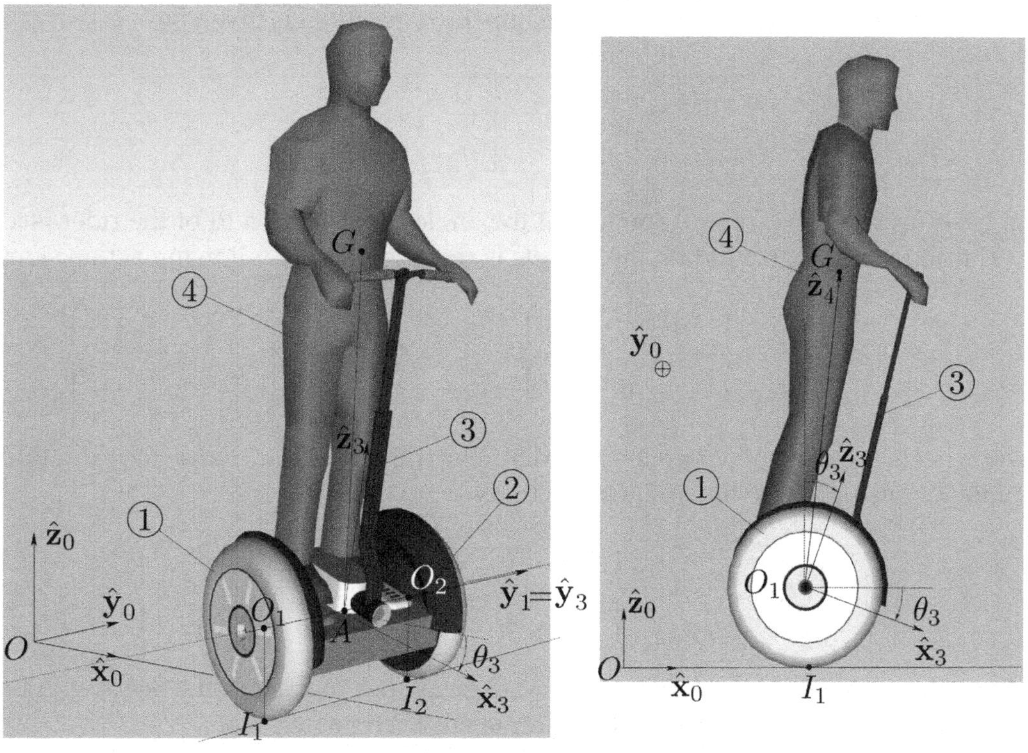

Figure 11.29

mass center is O_2, its mass $M_2 = M$ and its inertia operator about O_2 takes the form

$$[\mathcal{I}_{O_2,2}]_{b_2} = \begin{bmatrix} I & 0 & 0 \\ 0 & J & 0 \\ 0 & 0 & K \end{bmatrix}_{b_2}$$

on basis $b_2(\hat{\mathbf{x}}_2, \hat{\mathbf{y}}_2 = \hat{\mathbf{y}}_3, \hat{\mathbf{z}}_2)$

- Body $3(A, \hat{\mathbf{x}}_3, \hat{\mathbf{y}}_3, \hat{\mathbf{z}}_3)$ is the frame/platform/handlebar assembly. The axis $(A, \hat{\mathbf{y}}_3)$ represents the axis of rotation of the wheels. Axis $(A, \hat{\mathbf{z}}_3)$ is normal to the platform and takes the direction of the handlebar which can be inclined by the rider relative to the vertical. Point A is assumed to be in translation relative to referential 0 along direction $\hat{\mathbf{x}}_0$ so that $\hat{\mathbf{y}}_3 = \hat{\mathbf{y}}_1 = \hat{\mathbf{y}}_2 = \hat{\mathbf{y}}_0$ at all times. The position of A is defined by $\mathbf{r}_{OA} = x_A(t)\hat{\mathbf{x}}_0 + R\hat{\mathbf{z}}_0$. The orientation of basis $b_3(\hat{\mathbf{x}}_3, \hat{\mathbf{y}}_3 = \hat{\mathbf{y}}_0, \hat{\mathbf{z}}_3)$ relative to basis $(\hat{\mathbf{x}}_0, \hat{\mathbf{y}}_0, \hat{\mathbf{z}}_0)$ is defined by angle $\theta_3(t) = (\hat{\mathbf{x}}_0, \hat{\mathbf{x}}_3) = (\hat{\mathbf{z}}_0, \hat{\mathbf{z}}_3)$. A control system aims at maintaining the value of angle θ_3 as close to zero as possible. Its mass is M_3, its mass center is point A: we set $\mathbf{r}_{O_1A} = \mathbf{r}_{AO_2} = \frac{L}{2}\hat{\mathbf{y}}_3$. Its inertia operator about A takes the form

$$[\mathcal{I}_{A,3}]_{b_3} = \begin{bmatrix} A_3 & 0 & 0 \\ 0 & B_3 & 0 \\ 0 & 0 & C_3 \end{bmatrix}_{b_3}$$

- Body $4(G, \hat{\mathbf{x}}_4, \hat{\mathbf{y}}_4 = \hat{\mathbf{y}}_3, \hat{\mathbf{z}}_4)$ represents the driver standing on the platform and holding the handlebar. Its motion relative to the frame 3 is assumed to be a rotation about axis $(A, \hat{\mathbf{y}}_3)$ with angle $\theta_4 = (\hat{\mathbf{x}}_3, \hat{\mathbf{x}}_4) = (\hat{\mathbf{z}}_3, \hat{\mathbf{z}}_4)$. Its mass center is G whose position is given by

$\mathbf{r}_{AG} = H\hat{\mathbf{z}}_4$. Its mass is M_4 and its inertia operator about G is given by

$$[\mathcal{I}_{G,4}]_{b_4} = \begin{bmatrix} A_4 & 0 & 0 \\ 0 & B_4 & 0 \\ 0 & 0 & C_4 \end{bmatrix}_{b_4}$$

on basis $b_4(\hat{\mathbf{x}}_4, \hat{\mathbf{y}}_4 = \hat{\mathbf{y}}_3, \hat{\mathbf{z}}_4)$. Assume that the angle of inclination θ_4 of the rider is a constant.

The action of the ground on the wheels is modeled by the following action screws:

$$\{\mathcal{A}_{0\to1}\}^c = \left\{ \begin{array}{c} X_1\hat{\mathbf{x}}_0 + Z_1\hat{\mathbf{z}}_0 \\ \mathbf{0} \end{array} \right\}_{I_1} \qquad \{\mathcal{A}_{0\to2}\}^c = \left\{ \begin{array}{c} X_2\hat{\mathbf{x}}_0 + Z_2\hat{\mathbf{z}}_0 \\ \mathbf{0} \end{array} \right\}_{I_2}$$

The wheels are driven by two independent electric motors $\mathcal{M}_{13}$ and $\mathcal{M}_{23}$ mounted on the frame 3 which provide the following actions

$$\{\mathcal{A}_{\mathcal{M}_{13}\to1}\} = \left\{ \begin{array}{c} \mathbf{0} \\ C_1\hat{\mathbf{y}}_3 \end{array} \right\} \qquad \{\mathcal{A}_{\mathcal{M}_{23}\to2}\} = \left\{ \begin{array}{c} \mathbf{0} \\ C_2\hat{\mathbf{y}}_3 \end{array} \right\}$$

where the couple must satisfy $C_1 = C_2 = \mathcal{C}$ for planar motion of the Segway. Assume that the joints between the wheels and the frame are frictionless pivots.

a. By applying the Fundamental Theorem of Dynamics show that the following two equations can be obtained between the unknowns x_A and θ_3 in terms of the driving couple $\mathcal{C}$:

$$(M_4H^2 + B_3 + B_4)\ddot{\theta}_3 + M_4H\ddot{x}_A\cos(\theta_3 + \theta_4) = M_4Hg\sin(\theta_3 + \theta_4) - 2\mathcal{C}$$

$$(M_3 + M_4 + 2M)\ddot{x}_A + M_4H\ddot{\theta}_3\cos(\theta_4 + \theta_3) - M_4H\dot{\theta}_3^2\sin(\theta_4 + \theta_3) = -2\frac{J}{R^2}\ddot{x}_A + 2\frac{\mathcal{C}}{R}$$

b. Find the contact action screw $\{\mathcal{A}^c_{3\to4}\}$.

Problem 11.15 We consider in this problem the motion of a satellite $\mathcal{S}$ of mass m and mass center G under the effect of Earth's gravitation. See Figure 11.30. The Earth is assumed spherical and of center C. Denote by $\mathcal{F}(C, \hat{\imath}, \hat{\jmath}, \hat{\mathbf{k}})$ a Geocentric referential such that the plane $(C, \hat{\imath}, \hat{\jmath})$ contains the circular path of G centered about C and of radius R. Assumed that the angular speed ω_0 of G is the constant given by

$$\omega_0 = \frac{GM}{R^3}$$

where G is the gravitational constant and M is the Earth's mass. The Earth's gravitational forces on $\mathcal{S}$ give rise to the resultant moment

$$\mathbf{M}_{G,\mathcal{E}\to\mathcal{S}} = 3\omega_0^2\,\hat{\mathbf{u}} \times \mathcal{I}_G(\hat{\mathbf{u}})$$

where $\hat{\mathbf{u}} = \frac{\mathbf{r}_{CG}}{|CG|}$ and $\mathcal{I}_G$ is the inertia operator of $\mathcal{S}$ about G. Let $\mathcal{R}(G, \hat{\mathbf{u}}, \hat{\mathbf{v}}, \hat{\mathbf{k}})$ be the orbiting referential, with $\hat{\mathbf{v}} = \hat{\mathbf{k}} \times \hat{\mathbf{u}}$.

a. Show that the angular velocity $\omega = \omega_{\mathcal{S}/\mathcal{F}}$ is governed by the following equation

$$\mathcal{I}_G(\boldsymbol{\alpha}) + \boldsymbol{\omega} \times \mathcal{I}_G(\boldsymbol{\omega}) = 3\omega_0^2\hat{\mathbf{u}} \times \mathcal{I}_G(\hat{\mathbf{u}}) \qquad (1)$$

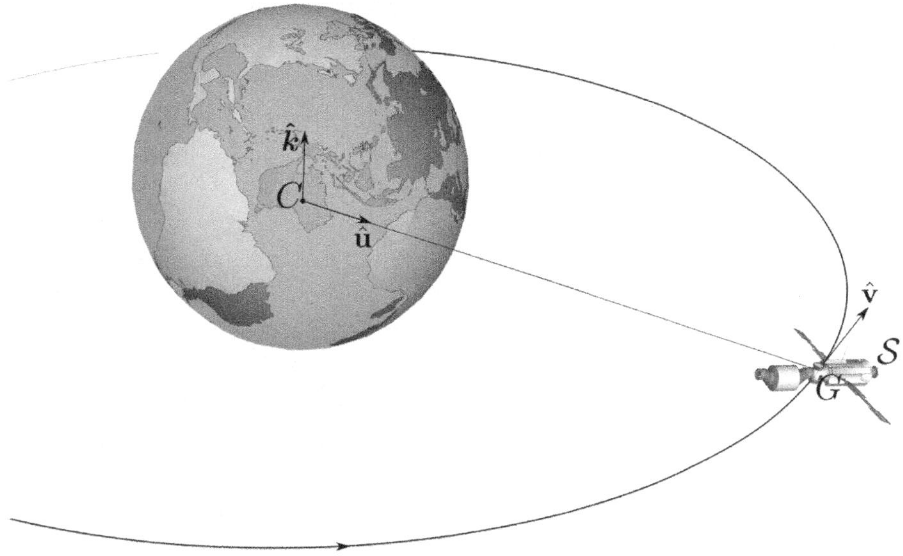

Figure 11.30

where $\boldsymbol{\alpha} = (d\boldsymbol{\omega}/dt)_{\mathcal{F}}$.

b. Show that the equilibrium positions of $\mathcal{S}$ relative to the orbiting referential $\mathcal{R}$ are the solutions of the equation

$$\hat{\mathbf{k}} \times \mathcal{I}_G(\hat{\mathbf{k}}) - 3\hat{\mathbf{u}} \times \mathcal{I}_G(\hat{\mathbf{u}}) = \mathbf{0}$$

Show that, if the principal moments of inertia (A, B, C) of $\mathcal{S}$ are distinct, then the only equilibrium positions of $\mathcal{S}$ relative to $\mathcal{R}$ are such that $(\hat{\mathbf{u}}, \hat{\mathbf{v}}, \hat{\mathbf{k}})$ is a principal basis of inertia for $\mathcal{I}_G$. How many equilibrium configurations can be found?

c. Let $(\hat{\mathbf{x}}, \hat{\mathbf{y}}, \hat{\mathbf{z}})$ be a principal basis for $\mathcal{I}_G$. Denote by (p, q, r) and (u_x, u_y, u_z) the components of $\boldsymbol{\omega}$ and $\hat{\mathbf{u}}$, respectively, on basis $(\hat{\mathbf{x}}, \hat{\mathbf{y}}, \hat{\mathbf{z}})$. Denote by (ψ, θ, ϕ) the angles which define the orientation of basis $(\hat{\mathbf{x}}, \hat{\mathbf{y}}, \hat{\mathbf{z}})$ relative to $(\hat{\mathbf{u}}, \hat{\mathbf{v}}, \hat{\mathbf{k}})$ according to the following transformations

$$(\hat{\mathbf{v}}, \hat{\mathbf{k}}, \hat{\mathbf{u}}) \xrightarrow{\mathcal{R}_{\psi,\hat{\mathbf{u}}}} (\hat{\mathbf{v}}_1, \hat{\mathbf{k}}_1, \hat{\mathbf{u}}) \xrightarrow{\mathcal{R}_{\theta,\hat{\mathbf{v}}_1}} (\hat{\mathbf{v}}_1, \hat{\mathbf{w}}, \hat{\mathbf{z}}) \xrightarrow{\mathcal{R}_{\phi,\hat{\mathbf{z}}}} (\hat{\mathbf{x}}, \hat{\mathbf{y}}, \hat{\mathbf{z}})$$

Express (p, q, r) and (u_x, u_y, u_z) in terms of (ψ, θ, ϕ). To study the stability of the relative equilibrium position $(\psi, \theta, \phi) = (\pi, \pi/2, \pi/2)$, consider the small perturbations $(\psi_*, \theta_*, \phi_*) = (\psi - \pi, \theta - \pi/2, \phi - \pi/2)$ about this position: determine from (1) the linearized equations which govern $(\psi_*, \theta_*, \phi_*)$ and show that necessary conditions for stability are given by

$$B - A > 0, \qquad (C - B)(C - A) > 0$$

where A, B,and C are the principal moments of inertia about axes $(G, \hat{\mathbf{x}})$, $(G, \hat{\mathbf{y}})$ and $(G, \hat{\mathbf{z}})$, respectively.

Problem 11.16 The goal of this problem is to study the effect of the rotating airplane propeller on the motion of an airplane during a flat turn maneuver, that is, a turn of the airplane without banking its wings. Figure 11.31 shows the airplane 1 $(G_1, \hat{\mathbf{x}}_1, \hat{\mathbf{y}}_1, \hat{\mathbf{z}}_0)$ in motion in a horizontal plane $(O, \hat{\mathbf{x}}_0, \hat{\mathbf{y}}_0)$ of a Newtonian referential $0(O, \hat{\mathbf{x}}_0, \hat{\mathbf{y}}_0, \hat{\mathbf{z}}_0)$. The airplane's orientation is defined by angle ψ about unit vector $\hat{\mathbf{z}}_0$. The propeller $2(G_2, \hat{\mathbf{x}}_1, \hat{\mathbf{y}}_2, \hat{\mathbf{z}}_2)$ of mass center G_2 is in rotation about axis $(G_2, \hat{\mathbf{x}}_1)$ at angular velocity $\omega_{2/1} = \dot{\phi}\hat{\mathbf{x}}_1$. The orientation of basis $b_2(\hat{\mathbf{x}}_1, \hat{\mathbf{y}}_2, \hat{\mathbf{z}}_2)$ is defined by:

$$b_0(\hat{\mathbf{x}}_0, \hat{\mathbf{y}}_0, \hat{\mathbf{z}}_0) \xrightarrow{\mathcal{R}_{\psi,\hat{\mathbf{z}}_0}} b_1(\hat{\mathbf{x}}_1, \hat{\mathbf{y}}_1, \hat{\mathbf{z}}_0) \xrightarrow{\mathcal{R}_{\phi,\hat{\mathbf{x}}_1}} b_2(\hat{\mathbf{x}}_1, \hat{\mathbf{y}}_2, \hat{\mathbf{z}}_2)$$

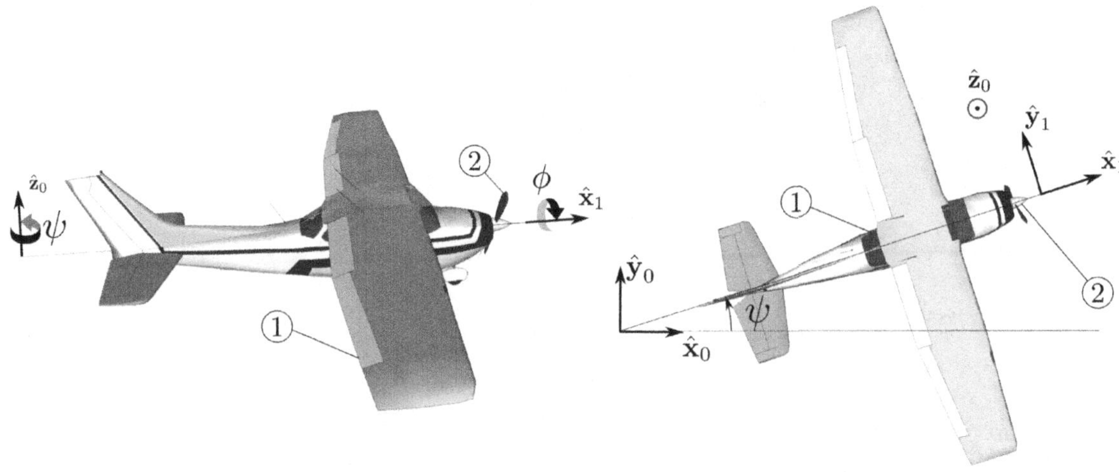

Figure 11.31

The inertia operator of the propeller about G_2 is represented by

$$[\mathcal{I}_{G_2,2}]_{b_2} = \begin{bmatrix} A_2 & 0 & 0 \\ 0 & B_2 & 0 \\ 0 & 0 & C_2 \end{bmatrix}_{b_2}$$

Assume that $\dot{\psi}$ and $\dot{\phi}$ are constant, with $|\dot{\psi}| \ll \dot{\phi}$. For simplicity we assume that $\{\mathcal{A}_{\bar{2}\to 2}\} = \{\mathcal{A}_{1\to 2}\}$ and we denote $\mathbf{M}_{G_2,1\to 2} = L_1\hat{\mathbf{x}}_1 + M_1\hat{\mathbf{y}}_1 + N_1\hat{\mathbf{z}}_0$.

a. Find the dynamic moment $\mathbf{D}_{G_2,2/0} = \frac{d}{dt}\mathbf{H}_{G_2,2/0}$.

b. Assuming that $B_2 = C_2$, find the components L_1, M_1, N_1 of $\mathbf{M}_{G_2,1\to 2}$ as a function of $\dot{\psi}$, $\dot{\phi}$ and the moment of inertia (A_2, B_2). Deduce the qualitative effects of the propeller's rotation on the motion of the airplane.

c. Assuming that $B_2 \neq C_2$, show that an additional oscillatory term at the frequency $2\dot{\phi}$ is superimposed to the constant term $\mathbf{M}_{G_2,1\to 2}$ found in b). Discuss the corresponding effects on the airplane.

Problem 11.17 We consider in this problem the possible motions of a billiard ball $\mathcal{B}$ on the horizontal plane $\Pi(O, \hat{\mathbf{x}}_0, \hat{\mathbf{y}}_0)$ of a referential $\mathcal{E}(O, \hat{\mathbf{x}}_0, \hat{\mathbf{y}}_0, \hat{\mathbf{z}}_0)$ (assumed Newtonian). Body $\mathcal{B}$ is assumed to be a solid sphere of homogeneous density, of mass m, of radius r, and mass center G. Denote by $\mathbf{v}_G = \mathbf{v}_{G/\mathcal{E}}$ the velocity of G at time t, $\mathbf{v}_0 = \mathbf{v}_G(t_0)$ the initial velocity of G at time $t = t_0$, $\omega = \omega_{\mathcal{B}/\mathcal{E}}$ the angular velocity of $\mathcal{B}$ at time t, and $\omega_0 = \omega(t_0)$ its initial angular velocity at $t = t_0$. We assume that the contact actions satisfy Coulomb Laws, that is,

$$\{\mathcal{A}^c_{\Pi\to\mathcal{B}}\} = \begin{Bmatrix} \mathbf{F} + N\hat{\mathbf{z}}_0 \\ \\ \mathbf{0} \end{Bmatrix}_I$$

where I is the contact point of $\mathcal{B}$ with Π. Hence we neglect rolling and pivoting friction. The coefficients of static and kinetic friction between $\mathcal{B}$ and Π are denoted as $\mu_s = \mu_k = \mu$. The goal of this problem is to study the motion of $\mathcal{B}$.

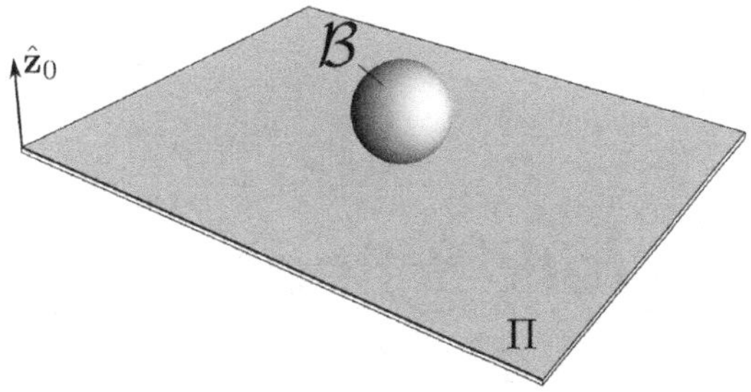

Figure 11.32

a. Show that the angular momentum $\mathbf{H}_I$ of $\mathcal{B}$ about point I remains constant during the motion. Then show that the angular velocity and the slip velocity of $\mathcal{B}$ satisfy

$$\omega = \omega_0 + \frac{5}{2r}\hat{\mathbf{z}}_0 \times (\mathbf{v}_0 - \mathbf{v}_G)$$

and

$$\mathbf{v}_{I\in\mathcal{B}} = \frac{7}{2}\mathbf{v}_G + r\hat{\mathbf{z}}_0 \times \omega_0 - \frac{5}{2}\mathbf{v}_0$$

b. Assume that at $t = t_0$ the ball slips relative to plane Π, that is, $\mathbf{v}_{I\in\mathcal{B}}(t_0) \neq \mathbf{0}$. Thus we assume that there exists a time interval $[t_0, t_1)$ such that the slip velocity $\mathbf{v}_{I\in\mathcal{S}}(t) \neq \mathbf{0}$. Show that the slip velocity keeps a constant direction $\hat{\mathbf{u}}_0$ in $\mathcal{E}$ during the slip phase of the ball $\mathcal{S}$, defined by

$$\mathbf{v}_{I\in\mathcal{S}}(t_0) = s_0\hat{\mathbf{u}}_0, \qquad s_0 = -|\mathbf{v}_{I\in\mathcal{B}}(t_0)|.$$

Show that the trajectory of center G is the parabola given by the equation:

$$\mathbf{r}_{G_0G} = \frac{\mu g}{2}(t - t_0)^2\hat{\mathbf{u}}_0 + (t - t_0)\mathbf{v}_0$$

where G_0 denotes the initial position of G, unless $\hat{\mathbf{u}}_0$ and $\mathbf{v}_0$ are collinear. Show that the slip phase of $\mathcal{B}$ will last until time $t = t_1$ given by

$$t_1 = t_0 - \frac{2s_0}{7\mu g}.$$

c. The slip velocity must remain zero for $t > t_1$, that is, the ball must roll without slipping on plane Π for $t > t_1$. Predict the motion of body $\mathcal{B}$ during this phase of motion.

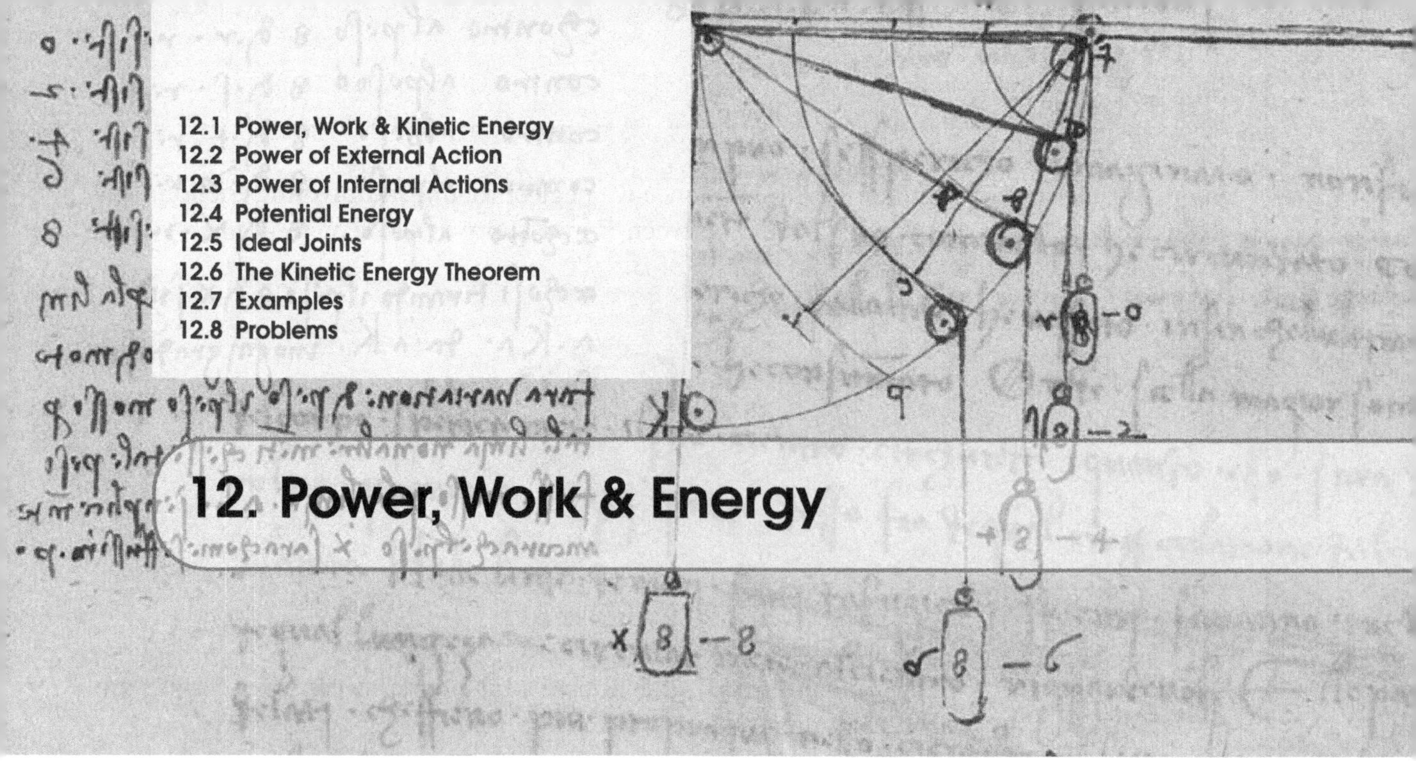

12. Power, Work & Energy

THE NOTIONS of power, work and energy play a fundamental role in mechanics. After reviewing these concepts for forces acting on particles, we extend them to the case of mechanical actions exerted on rigid bodies. We can then relate power and kinetic energy by a straightforward application of D'Alembert Principle of Virtual Power. We obtain a theorem of great practical importance, known as the Kinetic Energy Theorem (KET). The KET provides a single scalar equation, and, contrary to the Fundamental Theorem of Dynamics of the Newton-Euler formalism, requires the contribution of internal interactions between rigid bodies.

12.1 Power, Work & Kinetic Energy

RECALL that the *power* $\mathbb{P}$ generated by force $\mathbf{F}$ acting on particle P relative to referential $\mathcal{E}(O, \hat{\mathbf{e}}_x, \hat{\mathbf{e}}_y, \hat{\mathbf{e}}_z)$ is defined as the scalar product $\mathbf{F} \cdot \mathbf{v}_{P/\mathcal{E}}$. The integral defined by

$$\mathcal{W}_{t_1}^{t_2} = \int_{t_1}^{t_2} \mathbb{P} dt = \int_{P_1}^{P_2} (F_x dx + F_y dy + F_z dz) \tag{12.1}$$

is the *work* done by force $\mathbf{F} = F_x \hat{\mathbf{e}}_x + F_y \hat{\mathbf{e}}_y + F_z \hat{\mathbf{e}}_z$ during the interval of time $t_1 \leq t \leq t_2$.

Remark 1. In general the work done by a force along the trajectory of particle P between two instants t_1 and $t_2 > t_1$ is a function of the actual path taken by P between the starting and ending positions P_1 and P_2.

The work done by a time-independent force $\mathbf{F}$ is only a function of the initial and final positions of a particle P in $\mathcal{E}$ whenever there exists a scalar field $\mathbb{U}(P)$, called *potential energy* such that

$$\mathcal{W}_{t_1}^{t_2} = \int_{P_1}^{P_2} \mathbf{F}_P \cdot d\mathbf{r}_{OP} = \mathbb{U}(P_1) - \mathbb{U}(P_2) \tag{12.2}$$

In this case, force $\mathbf{F}$ is said to be *conservative*, and that it *derives from potential* $\mathbb{U}$. If it exists, potential $\mathbb{U}$ is defined by

$$\mathbf{F} = -\nabla\mathbb{U} = -\frac{\partial\mathbb{U}}{\partial x}\hat{\mathbf{e}}_x - \frac{\partial\mathbb{U}}{\partial y}\hat{\mathbf{e}}_y - \frac{\partial\mathbb{U}}{\partial z}\hat{\mathbf{e}}_z \tag{12.3}$$

Now consider a particle P of mass m moving in a Newtonian referential $\mathcal{E}$ under the effect of a resultant force $\mathbf{F}$. Then according to Newton's second law we have

$$m\mathbf{a}_{P/\mathcal{E}} = \mathbf{F}$$

Upon taking the scalar product of this equation with velocity $\mathbf{v}_{P/\mathcal{E}}$ and integrating from instant $t = t_1$ to $t = t_2$ we obtain

$$\int_{t_1}^{t_2} m\mathbf{a}_{P/\mathcal{E}} \cdot \mathbf{v}_{P/\mathcal{E}}dt = \int_{t_1}^{t_2} \mathbf{F} \cdot \mathbf{v}_{P/\mathcal{E}}dt$$

We recognize in this last equation that:

1. the integral $\int_{t_1}^{t_2} m\mathbf{a}_{P/\mathcal{E}} \cdot \mathbf{v}_{P/\mathcal{E}}dt = \frac{1}{2}m\mathbf{v}^2_{P/\mathcal{E}}(t_2) - \frac{1}{2}m\mathbf{v}^2_{P/\mathcal{E}}(t_1)$ is the variation of the kinetic energy of P between the two instants.
2. the integral $\int_{t_1}^{t_2} \mathbf{F} \cdot \mathbf{v}_{P/\mathcal{E}}dt$ is the work done by force $\mathbf{F}$ along the motion of P from $t = t_1$ to $t = t_2$ in $\mathcal{E}$.

Then we can write the following equation

$$\frac{1}{2}m\mathbf{v}^2_{P/\mathcal{E}}(t_2) - \frac{1}{2}m\mathbf{v}^2_{P/\mathcal{E}}(t_1) = \mathcal{W}_{t_1}^{t_2} \tag{12.4}$$

known as the *Work-Energy Theorem*: The work done by the resultant force $\mathbf{F}$ during the motion of P from $t = t_1$ to $t = t_2$ in a Newtonian referential $\mathcal{E}$ is equal to the change of the particle's kinetic energy.

The instantaneous version of this theorem, known as the *Kinetic Energy Theorem* can be stated as follows:

$$\frac{d\mathbb{K}}{dt} = \mathbb{P} \tag{12.5}$$

Hence, the time rate of change of kinetic energy $\mathbb{K}$ of particle P is equal to the power $\mathbb{P} = \mathbf{F} \cdot \mathbf{v}_{P/\mathcal{E}}$ generated by resultant force $\mathbf{F}$ acting on P in Newtonian referential $\mathcal{E}$.

Consider now a system Σ of N particles $P_1, P_2, \ldots, P_N$ of mass $m_1, m_2, \ldots, m_N$, respectively, in motion in a *Newtonian* referential $\mathcal{E}$. The forces acting on each particle P_i are comprised of the external force $\mathbf{F}_{\overline{\Sigma}\to i}$ and a sum of internal forces $\sum_{j=1}^{N}\mathbf{F}_{j\to i}$ due to the other particles of Σ. The power generated by external force $\mathbf{F}_{\overline{\Sigma}\to i}$ acting on particle P_i relative to referential $\mathcal{E}$ is given by $\mathbb{P}_{\overline{\Sigma}\to i/\mathcal{E}} = \mathbf{v}_{P_i/\mathcal{E}} \cdot \mathbf{F}_{\overline{\Sigma}\to i}$. The power generated by the resultant external forces $\mathbf{F}_{\overline{\Sigma}\to\Sigma} = \sum_{i=1}^{N}\mathbf{F}_{\overline{\Sigma}\to i}$ acting on Σ relative to $\mathcal{E}$ can be defined as the sum

$$\mathbb{P}_{\overline{\Sigma}\to\Sigma/\mathcal{E}} = \sum_{i=1}^{N} \mathbf{v}_{P_i/\mathcal{E}} \cdot \mathbf{F}_{\overline{\Sigma}\to i} = \sum_{i=1}^{N} \mathbb{P}_{\overline{\Sigma}\to i/\mathcal{E}} \tag{12.6}$$

Similarly the power generated by the sum of all internal forces $\mathbf{F}_{i\to j}$ can be determined according to

$$\sum_{i=1}^{N}\sum_{j=1}^{N} \mathbf{v}_{P_i/\mathcal{E}} \cdot \mathbf{F}_{j\to i}$$

Despite the law of action and reaction, this power does not, in general, vanish. Consider the terms due to a pair of interacting forces $\mathbf{F}_{i\to j} = F_{ij}\,\hat{\mathbf{e}}_{ij} = -\mathbf{F}_{j\to i}$ between particles P_i and P_j directed along $\mathbf{r}_{P_iP_j} = r_{ij}\,\hat{\mathbf{e}}_{ij}$:

$$\mathbf{F}_{j\to i} \cdot \mathbf{v}_{P_i/\mathcal{E}} + \mathbf{F}_{i\to j} \cdot \mathbf{v}_{P_j/\mathcal{E}} = \mathbf{F}_{i\to j} \cdot (\mathbf{v}_{P_j/\mathcal{E}} - \mathbf{v}_{P_i/\mathcal{E}}) = F_{ij}\hat{\mathbf{e}}_{ij} \cdot \frac{d}{dt} r_{ij}\hat{\mathbf{e}}_{ij} = F_{ij}\frac{dr_{ij}}{dt}$$

where we have used the fact that unit vector $\hat{\mathbf{e}}_{ij}$ satisfies $\hat{\mathbf{e}}_{ij} \cdot \frac{d}{dt}\hat{\mathbf{e}}_{ij} = 0$.

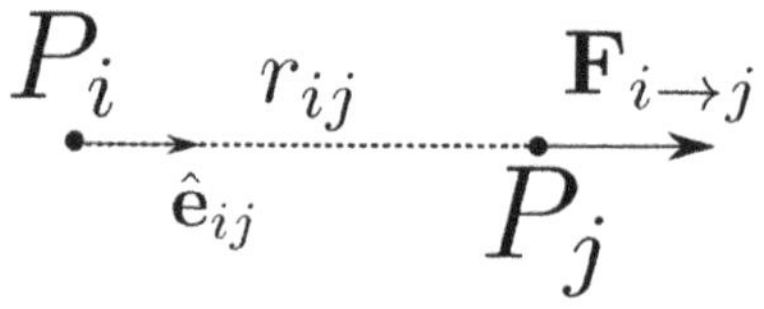

Figure 12.1

Hence, when viewed pairwise, the internal power is only a function of the time rate of change of the relative distance between the particles of Σ, and, consequently, is not a function of the chosen referential $\mathcal{E}$: we denote this internal power between particles P_i and P_j as $\mathbb{P}_{i\leftrightarrow j}$. Then the power generated by all internal forces can be written as

$$\sum_{1\le i<j\le N} \mathbb{P}_{i\leftrightarrow j} \tag{12.7}$$

Next we sum the N equations derived by the Kinetic Energy Theorem applied to each particle (relative to referential $\mathcal{E}$) to find

$$\frac{d}{dt}\mathbb{K}_{\Sigma/\mathcal{E}} = \sum_{i=1}^{N} \mathbf{F}_i \cdot \mathbf{v}_{P_i/\mathcal{E}}$$

We then decompose $\mathbf{F}_i$ in terms of external and internal forces. The power generated by all (internal and external) forces can be written as the sum:

$$\sum_{i=1}^{N} \mathbf{F}_i \cdot \mathbf{v}_{P_i/\mathcal{E}} = \mathbb{P}_{\overline{\Sigma}\to\Sigma/\mathcal{E}} + \sum_{1\le i<j\le N} \mathbb{P}_{i\leftrightarrow j}$$

Theorem 12.1 — **Kinetic Energy Theorem (KET).** The time rate of change of the kinetic energy of system Σ in motion in a Newtonian referential is equal to the power generated by the external and internal forces acting on Σ

$$\frac{d}{dt}\mathbb{K}_{\Sigma/\mathcal{E}} = \mathbb{P}_{\overline{\Sigma}\to\Sigma/\mathcal{E}} + \sum_{1\le i<j\le N} \mathbb{P}_{i\leftrightarrow j} \tag{12.8}$$

Recall that internal forces do not come into play in the Euler-Newton formulation due to the law of action and reaction. This represents a fundamental difference with the KET.

Next, we generalize these results for systems of rigid bodies.

12.2 Power of External Action

Recall that the power generated by a force $\mathbf{F}$ acting on a particle P moving at velocity $\mathbf{v}_{P/\mathcal{E}}$ relative to a referential $\mathcal{E}$ is defined as the scalar $\mathbf{F} \cdot \mathbf{v}_{P/\mathcal{E}}$. Let Σ_1 and Σ_2 be two material systems in mutual interaction under the effect of gravitational (or other action at-a-distance) forces $\mathbf{F}^g_{1\to 2}(P_2)$ ($P_2 \in \Sigma_2$) and contact forces $\mathbf{f}^c_{1\to 2}(Q_2)$ ($Q_2 \in \partial\Sigma_1 \cap \partial\Sigma_2$) resulting in the action screws $\{\mathcal{A}^g_{\Sigma_1\to\Sigma_2}\}$ and $\{\mathcal{A}^c_{\Sigma_1\to\Sigma_2}\}$. See Figure 12.2.

Definition 12.1 The powers generated by the mechanical actions $\{\mathcal{A}^g_{\Sigma_1\to\Sigma_2}\}$ and $\{\mathcal{A}^c_{\Sigma_1\to\Sigma_2}\}$ during the motion of Σ_2 relative to a referential $\mathcal{E}$, are defined, at any given time, by

$$\mathbb{P}^g_{\Sigma_1\to\Sigma_2/\mathcal{E}} = \int_{\Sigma_2} \mathbf{F}^g_{1\to 2}(P_2) \cdot \mathbf{v}_{P_2/\mathcal{E}} dV \quad (12.9)$$

$$\mathbb{P}^c_{\Sigma_1\to\Sigma_2/\mathcal{E}} = \int_{\partial\Sigma_1\cap\partial\Sigma_2} \mathbf{f}^c_{1\to 2}(Q_2) \cdot \mathbf{v}_{Q_2/\mathcal{E}}\, dA \quad (12.10)$$

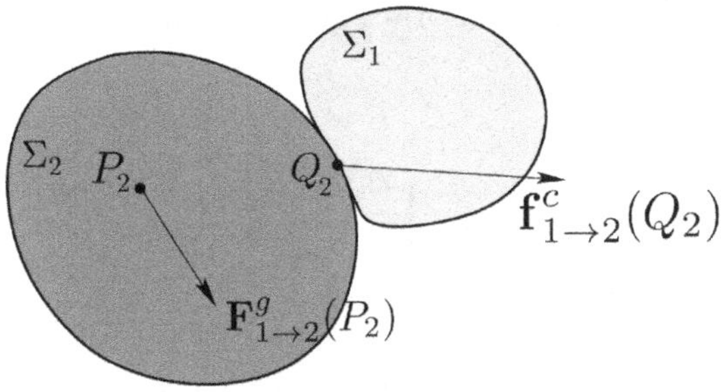

Figure 12.2

It is not possible in general to express these integrals in terms of the actions screws $\{\mathcal{A}^g_{\Sigma_1\to\Sigma_2}\}$ and $\{\mathcal{A}^c_{\Sigma_1\to\Sigma_2}\}$, unless Σ_2 is a rigid body. Assume that Σ_2 is a rigid body denoted as $\mathcal{B}$. Then the power generated by the forces exerted by Σ_1 on rigid body $\mathcal{B}$ relative to a referential $\mathcal{E}$ can be expressed in terms of the corresponding action screw by taking advantage of the screw property of the velocity field $P \in \mathcal{B} \mapsto \mathbf{v}_{\mathcal{B}/\mathcal{E}}$ as the scalar product between the action and kinematic screws:

Theorem 12.2 The power generated by the external actions exerted on rigid body $\mathcal{B}$ relative to referential $\mathcal{E}$ can be found as the scalar product between the action screw and the kinematic screw of $\mathcal{B}$:

$$\mathbb{P}^g_{\Sigma_1\to\mathcal{B}/\mathcal{E}} = \{\mathcal{A}^g_{\Sigma_1\to\mathcal{B}}\} \cdot \{\mathcal{V}_{\mathcal{B}/\mathcal{E}}\} = \mathbf{R}^g_{\Sigma_1\to\mathcal{B}} \cdot \mathbf{v}_{A\in\mathcal{B}/\mathcal{E}} + \mathbf{M}^g_{A,\Sigma_1\to\mathcal{B}} \cdot \boldsymbol{\omega}_{\mathcal{B}/\mathcal{E}} \quad (12.11)$$

where $\mathbf{R}^g_{\Sigma_1\to\mathcal{B}}$ and $\mathbf{M}^g_{A,\Sigma_1\to\mathcal{B}}$ are the resultant and moment about arbitrary point A of action screw $\{\mathcal{A}^g_{\Sigma_1\to\mathcal{B}}\}$. Likewise, we have for the contact action

$$\mathbb{P}^c_{\Sigma_1\to\mathcal{B}/\mathcal{E}} = \{\mathcal{A}^c_{\Sigma_1\to\mathcal{B}}\} \cdot \{\mathcal{V}_{\mathcal{B}/\mathcal{E}}\} = \mathbf{R}^c_{\Sigma_1\to\mathcal{B}} \cdot \mathbf{v}_{A\in\mathcal{B}/\mathcal{E}} + \mathbf{M}^c_{A,\Sigma_1\to\mathcal{B}} \cdot \boldsymbol{\omega}_{\mathcal{B}/\mathcal{E}} \quad (12.12)$$

Proof. The expression of the virtual power defined as the integral $\int_{\mathcal{B}} \mathbf{v}^*_P \cdot \mathbf{F}^g_{\Sigma_1\to\mathcal{B}}(P)dV$ in terms of the virtual velocity $P \mapsto \mathbf{v}^*_P$ (which defines a screw $\{\mathcal{V}^*\}$) was derived for the derivation of the FTD. See section 11.2.1. It was found to be given by $\{\mathcal{V}^*\} \cdot \{\mathcal{A}^g_{\Sigma_1 \to \mathcal{B}}\}$. Here the virtual velocity $P \mapsto \mathbf{v}^*_P$ is replaced by the velocity field $P \in \mathcal{B} \mapsto \mathbf{v}_P$ of rigid body $\mathcal{B}$. Hence, the volume integral of equation (12.9) which defines the expression of power can be written in terms of the scalar product $\{\mathcal{A}^g_{\Sigma_1 \to \mathcal{B}}\} \cdot \{\mathcal{V}_{\mathcal{B}/\mathcal{E}}\}$. ■

The formalism of screws enables us to express the power $\mathbb{P}_{\Sigma_1 \to \mathcal{B}/\mathcal{E}}$ in a manner identical to the case of particles. More importantly, formulas (12.11) and (12.12) offer practical ways of determining expressions of powers generated by mechanical actions as demonstrated by the following examples.

Example 12.1 Consider rigid body 1 of Example 11.3. It is constrained to rotate about a vertical fixed axis $(O, \hat{\mathbf{z}}_0)$ of a referential 0. The pivot connecting 0 and 1 is assumed frictionless. A motor $\mathcal{M}$ is mounted between 0 and 1 and its action on 1 is a constant couple $C\hat{\mathbf{z}}_0$. In addition, the ambient fluid exerts a viscous force $d\mathbf{F}(P) = -\mu \mathbf{v}_{P/0} dA$ on an element of area dA surrounding a point P of the plate, where μ is a positive constant.

Determine the power generated by each contribution of the external action screw $\{\mathcal{A}_{\bar{1} \to 1}\}$ exerted on body 1. ■

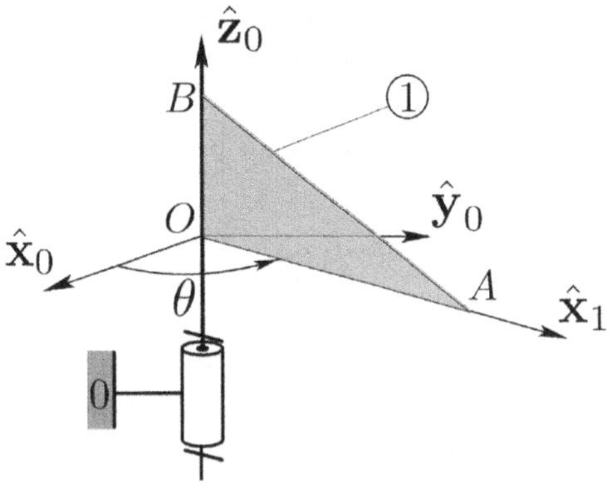

Figure 12.3

The power generated by action screw $\{\mathcal{A}_{\bar{1} \to 1}\}$ exerted on body 1 can be determined for each of the actions $\{\mathcal{A}^g_{\text{Earth} \to 1}\}$, $\{\mathcal{A}^c_{0 \to 1}\}$, $\{\mathcal{A}_{\text{fluid} \to 1}\}$ and $\{\mathcal{A}_{\mathcal{M} \to 1}\}$ by applying formulas (12.11) and (12.12) using the expression

$$\{\mathcal{V}_{1/0}\} = \begin{Bmatrix} \dot{\theta}\hat{\mathbf{z}}_0 \\ \mathbf{0} \end{Bmatrix}_O = \begin{Bmatrix} \dot{\theta}\hat{\mathbf{z}}_0 \\ \frac{1}{3} a\dot{\theta}\hat{\mathbf{y}}_1 \end{Bmatrix}_G$$

of the kinematic screw of body 1. We obtain

$$\mathbb{P}^g_{\text{Earth} \to 1/0} = \{\mathcal{A}^g_{\text{Earth} \to 1}\} \cdot \{\mathcal{V}_{1/0}\} = \begin{Bmatrix} -mg\hat{\mathbf{z}}_0 \\ \mathbf{0} \end{Bmatrix}_G \cdot \begin{Bmatrix} \dot{\theta}\hat{\mathbf{z}}_0 \\ \frac{1}{3} a\dot{\theta}\hat{\mathbf{y}}_1 \end{Bmatrix}_G$$

$$= -mg\hat{\mathbf{z}}_0 \cdot \frac{1}{3} a\dot{\theta}\hat{\mathbf{y}}_1 = 0$$

$$\mathbb{P}^c_{0\to 1/0} = \{\mathcal{A}^c_{0\to 1}\}\cdot\{\mathcal{V}_{1/0}\} = \underbrace{\begin{Bmatrix} \mathbf{R}^c_{0\to 1} \\ \mathbf{M}^c_{O,0\to 1} \end{Bmatrix}\cdot\begin{Bmatrix} \dot\theta\hat{\mathbf{z}}_0 \\ \mathbf{0} \end{Bmatrix}_O}_{\mathbf{M}^c_{O,0\to 1}\cdot\hat{\mathbf{z}}_0=0} = \mathbf{M}^c_{O,0\to 1}\cdot\dot\theta\hat{\mathbf{z}}_0 = 0$$

(taking into account that the pivot connection is frictionless)

$$\mathbb{P}_{\text{fluid}\to 1/0} = \{\mathcal{A}_{\text{fluid}\to 1}\}^c\cdot\{\mathcal{V}_{1/0}\} = -\frac{1}{2}\mu ab\begin{Bmatrix} \frac{1}{3}a\dot\theta\hat{\mathbf{y}}_1 \\ \frac{1}{12}a\dot\theta(-b\hat{\mathbf{x}}_1 + 2a\hat{\mathbf{z}}_0) \end{Bmatrix}_O\cdot\begin{Bmatrix} \dot\theta\hat{\mathbf{z}}_0 \\ \mathbf{0} \end{Bmatrix}_O = -\frac{1}{12}\mu a^3 b\dot\theta^2$$

and finally

$$\mathbb{P}_{\mathcal{M}\to 1/0} = \{\mathcal{A}_{\mathcal{M}\to 1}\}^c\cdot\{\mathcal{V}_{1/0}\} = \begin{Bmatrix} \mathbf{0} \\ C\hat{\mathbf{z}}_0 \end{Bmatrix}\cdot\begin{Bmatrix} \dot\theta\hat{\mathbf{z}}_0 \\ \mathbf{0} \end{Bmatrix}_O = C\dot\theta$$

The total power is then found to be

$$\mathbb{P}_{\bar{1}\to 1/0} = -\frac{1}{12}\mu a^3 b\dot\theta^2 + C\dot\theta$$

■

Example 12.2 Consider the system of Example 11.5. Disk 1 moves on a horizontal plane Π of a referential 0 so that the extremity O of its massless axle remains fixed in plane Π. Furthermore friction between the disk and the plane Π prevents slipping at both contact points O and I. See example 11.5 for notations.

Find the power $\mathbb{P}_{\bar{1}\to 1/0}$ generated by all external actions on disk 1. ■

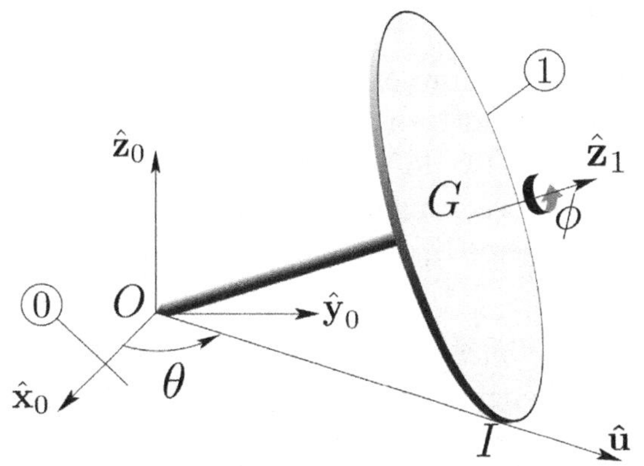

Figure 12.4

Accounting for the contact forces at point O and I, and neglecting rolling and spinning friction, the external action screw exerted on body 1 takes the expression

$$\{\mathcal{A}_{\bar{1}\to 1}\} = \begin{Bmatrix} \mathbf{R}_O \\ \mathbf{0} \end{Bmatrix}_O + \begin{Bmatrix} \mathbf{R}_I \\ \mathbf{0} \end{Bmatrix}_I + \begin{Bmatrix} -mg\hat{\mathbf{e}}_3 \\ \mathbf{0} \end{Bmatrix}_C$$

Furthermore the kinematic screw of body 1 takes the expression, taking into account the no-slip conditions at O and I:

$$\{\mathcal{V}_{1/0}\} = \begin{Bmatrix} -\dot{\theta}\hat{\mathbf{u}} \\ \mathbf{0} \end{Bmatrix}_O = \begin{Bmatrix} -\dot{\theta}\hat{\mathbf{u}} \\ \mathbf{0} \end{Bmatrix}_I = \begin{Bmatrix} -\dot{\theta}\hat{\mathbf{u}} \\ \frac{r}{\sqrt{2}}\dot{\theta}\hat{\mathbf{v}} \end{Bmatrix}_C$$

Then applying formulas (12.11) and (12.12) we find

$$\mathbb{P}_{\bar{1}\to 1/0} = \begin{Bmatrix} \mathbf{R}_O \\ \mathbf{0} \end{Bmatrix}_O \cdot \begin{Bmatrix} -\dot{\theta}\hat{\mathbf{u}} \\ \mathbf{0} \end{Bmatrix}_O + \begin{Bmatrix} \mathbf{R}_I \\ \mathbf{0} \end{Bmatrix}_I \cdot \begin{Bmatrix} -\dot{\theta}\hat{\mathbf{u}} \\ \mathbf{0} \end{Bmatrix}_I + \begin{Bmatrix} -mg\hat{\mathbf{e}}_3 \\ \mathbf{0} \end{Bmatrix}_C \cdot \begin{Bmatrix} -\dot{\theta}\hat{\mathbf{u}} \\ \frac{r}{\sqrt{2}}\dot{\theta}\hat{\mathbf{v}} \end{Bmatrix}_C = 0$$

■

Denote by $\Sigma = \{\mathcal{B}_1, \mathcal{B}_2, \ldots, \mathcal{B}_N\}$ a system of N rigid bodies. Consider a material system Σ_1 external to system Σ ($\Sigma_1 \subset \overline{\Sigma}$) which acts upon each rigid body $\mathcal{B}_j$: denote by $\{\mathcal{A}_{\Sigma_1\to\mathcal{B}_j}\}$ the corresponding action screw. We can then write:

$$\mathbb{P}_{\Sigma_1\to\Sigma/\mathcal{E}} = \sum_{j=1}^{N} \mathbb{P}_{\Sigma_1\to\mathcal{B}_j/\mathcal{E}} = \sum_{j=1}^{N} \left\{\mathcal{A}_{\Sigma_1\to\mathcal{B}_j}\right\} \cdot \left\{\mathcal{V}_{\mathcal{B}_j/\mathcal{E}}\right\}$$

If the exterior $\overline{\Sigma}$ is comprised of M material systems Σ_1, Σ_2, ..., Σ_M, then the total external power is found to be

$$\mathbb{P}_{\overline{\Sigma}\to\Sigma/\mathcal{E}} = \sum_{j=1}^{N} \mathbb{P}_{\overline{\Sigma}\to\mathcal{B}_j/\mathcal{E}} = \sum_{i=1}^{M}\sum_{j=1}^{N} \mathbb{P}_{\Sigma_i\to\mathcal{B}_j/\mathcal{E}}$$

12.3 Power of Internal Actions

We saw in Section 12.1 that the sum of the powers generated by the internal forces acting between any two particles P_i and P_j of a system does not vanish, but is in fact independent of the choice of referential relative to which the motion of these particles is observed. This power was denoted $\mathbb{P}_{i\leftrightarrow j}$. We seek a similar property for the case of material systems.

Consider two material systems Σ_1 and Σ_2 of a system Σ in motion relative to a referential $\mathcal{E}$.

Definition 12.2 The *power of interaction* between two material systems Σ_1 and Σ_2 is defined as the sum of the powers generated by the action $\{\mathcal{A}_{\Sigma_1\to\Sigma_2}\}$ and by the reaction $\{\mathcal{A}_{\Sigma_2\to\Sigma_1}\}$ relative to $\mathcal{E}$:

$$\mathbb{P}_{\Sigma_1\leftrightarrow\Sigma_2} = \mathbb{P}_{\Sigma_1\to\Sigma_2/\mathcal{E}} + \mathbb{P}_{\Sigma_2\to\Sigma_1/\mathcal{E}} \tag{12.13}$$

Theorem 12.3 The power of interaction $\mathbb{P}_{\Sigma_1\leftrightarrow\Sigma_2}$ is *independent* of the choice of referential $\mathcal{E}$.

Proof. Consider two referentials $\mathcal{E}$ and $\mathcal{F}$. To compare the powers of action and reaction in $\mathcal{E}$ and $\mathcal{F}$, we determine the difference

$$\underbrace{\left(\mathbb{P}_{\Sigma_1\to\Sigma_2/\mathcal{E}} + \mathbb{P}_{\Sigma_2\to\Sigma_1/\mathcal{E}}\right)}_{\Sigma_1\leftrightarrow\Sigma_2/\mathcal{E}} - \underbrace{\left(\mathbb{P}_{\Sigma_1\to\Sigma_2/\mathcal{F}} + \mathbb{P}_{\Sigma_2\to\Sigma_1/\mathcal{F}}\right)}_{\Sigma_1\leftrightarrow\Sigma_2/\mathcal{F}}$$

We can simplify the power difference $(\mathbb{P}_{\Sigma_1\to\Sigma_2/\mathcal{E}} - \mathbb{P}_{\Sigma_1\to\Sigma_2/\mathcal{F}})$ assuming that the action $\{\mathcal{A}_{\Sigma_1\to\Sigma_2}\}$ (and the reaction) is the result of contact forces $\mathbf{f}^c_{1\to 2}(Q)$

$$\mathbb{P}_{\Sigma_1\to\Sigma_2/\mathcal{E}} - \mathbb{P}_{\Sigma_1\to\Sigma_2/\mathcal{F}} = \int_{\partial\Sigma_2} \mathbf{f}^c_{1\to 2}(Q)\cdot(\mathbf{v}_{Q/\mathcal{E}} - \mathbf{v}_{Q/\mathcal{F}})dA$$
$$= \int_{\partial\Sigma_2} \mathbf{f}^c_{1\to 2}(Q)\cdot \mathbf{v}_{Q\in\mathcal{F}/\mathcal{E}}dA = \{\mathcal{A}^c_{\Sigma_1\to\Sigma_2}\}\cdot\{\mathcal{V}_{\mathcal{F}/\mathcal{E}}\}$$

This last result also applies for gravitational interactions. Consequently, we have

$$\mathbb{P}_{\Sigma_1\leftrightarrow\Sigma_2/\mathcal{E}} - \mathbb{P}_{\Sigma_1\leftrightarrow\Sigma_2/\mathcal{F}} = \{\mathcal{A}_{\Sigma_1\to\Sigma_2}\}\cdot\{\mathcal{V}_{\mathcal{F}/\mathcal{E}}\} + \underbrace{\{\mathcal{A}_{\Sigma_2\to\Sigma_1}\}}_{-\{\mathcal{A}_{\Sigma_1\to\Sigma_2}\}}\cdot\{\mathcal{V}_{\mathcal{F}/\mathcal{E}}\} = 0$$

This shows that the sum of the powers generated by the action $\{\mathcal{A}_{\Sigma_1\to\Sigma_2}\}$ and the reaction $\{\mathcal{A}_{\Sigma_2\to\Sigma_1}\}$ is independent of the chosen referential $\mathcal{E}$ relative to which the motions of Σ_1 and Σ_2 are observed. ■

This last theorem can be used to determine the power of interaction between two rigid bodies $\mathcal{B}_1$ and $\mathcal{B}_2$ of a system Σ.

Theorem 12.4 The power of interaction between two rigid bodies $\mathcal{B}_1$ and $\mathcal{B}_2$ of a system Σ can be found as follows

$$\begin{aligned}\mathbb{P}_{\mathcal{B}_1\leftrightarrow\mathcal{B}_2} &= \mathbb{P}_{\mathcal{B}_1\to\mathcal{B}_2/\mathcal{B}_1} = \{\mathcal{A}_{\mathcal{B}_1\to\mathcal{B}_2}\}\cdot\{\mathcal{V}_{\mathcal{B}_2/\mathcal{B}_1}\}\\ &= \mathbb{P}_{\mathcal{B}_2\to\mathcal{B}_1/\mathcal{B}_2} = \{\mathcal{A}_{\mathcal{B}_2\to\mathcal{B}_1}\}\cdot\{\mathcal{V}_{\mathcal{B}_1/\mathcal{B}_2}\}\end{aligned} \tag{12.14}$$

Remark 2. We will often denote power $\mathbb{P}_{\mathcal{B}_1\leftrightarrow\mathcal{B}_2}$ simply $\mathbb{P}_{1\leftrightarrow 2}$.

Remark 3. Formula (12.14) offers a practical way to determine powers of interaction between rigid bodies.

Example 12.3 A cylindrical pipe 2 is pulled by a conveyor belt 1 in translational motion at velocity $v_1\hat{\mathbf{x}}_1$ relative to a referential 0. Neglect rolling frictional effects.
Find the expression of

a. the external power $\mathbb{P}^c_{1\to 2/0}$ of the contact action exerted by body 1 on body 2,

b. the (internal) power $\mathbb{P}^c_{1\leftrightarrow 2}$ of interaction between body 1 and body 2,

Simplify these expressions when body 2 rolls without slipping on body 1. ■

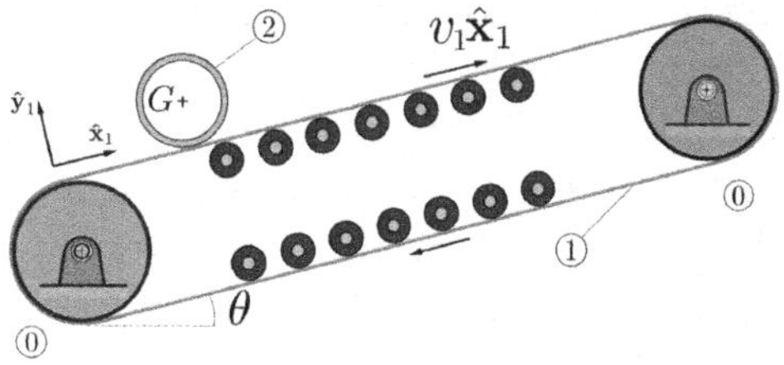

Figure 12.5

With the notations of Figures 12.5 and 12.6, we write the contact action screw of body 1 on body 2 in the following form

$$\{\mathcal{A}^c_{1\to 2}\} = \begin{Bmatrix} N_{12}\hat{\mathbf{y}}_1 + F_{12}\hat{\mathbf{x}}_1 \\ \mathbf{0}\end{Bmatrix}_I$$

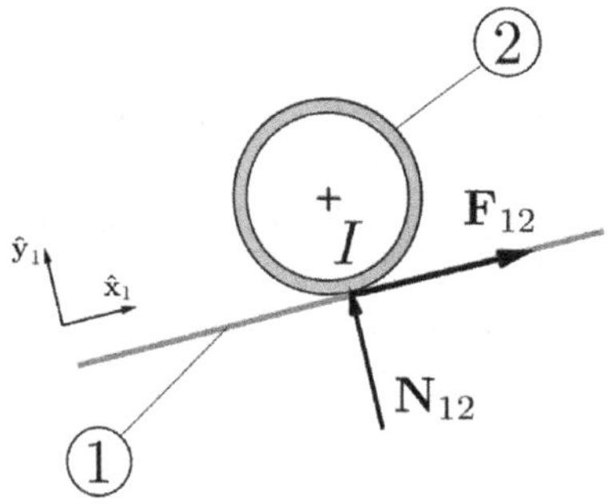

Figure 12.6

From the point of view of body 2, this action is external: its power relative to referential 0 is found as

$$\mathbb{P}^c_{1\to 2/0} = \{\mathcal{A}^c_{1\to 2}\} \cdot \{\mathcal{V}_{2/0}\} = \begin{Bmatrix} N_{12}\hat{\mathbf{y}}_1 + F_{12}\hat{\mathbf{x}}_1 \\ \mathbf{0} \end{Bmatrix}_I \cdot \begin{Bmatrix} \boldsymbol{\omega}_{2/0} \\ \mathbf{v}_{I\in 2/0} \end{Bmatrix}$$

This gives the expression

$$\mathbb{P}^c_{1\to 2/0} = (N_{12}\hat{\mathbf{y}}_1 + F_{12}\hat{\mathbf{x}}_1) \cdot \mathbf{v}_{I\in 2/0}$$

From the point of view of system $\Sigma = \{1,2\}$, this action is internal. The (internal) power of interaction is given by

$$\mathbb{P}^c_{1\leftrightarrow 2} = \mathbb{P}^c_{1\to 2/1} = \{\mathcal{A}^c_{1\to 2}\} \cdot \{\mathcal{V}_{2/1}\} = (N_{12}\hat{\mathbf{y}}_1 + F_{12}\hat{\mathbf{x}}_1) \cdot \mathbf{v}_{I\in 2/1}$$

This gives the expression

$$\mathbb{P}^c_{1\leftrightarrow 2} = F_{12}\hat{\mathbf{x}}_1 \cdot \mathbf{v}_{I\in 2/1}$$

since the slip velocity $\mathbf{v}_{I\in 2/1}$ is directed along $\hat{\mathbf{x}}_1$. Note that this power is always negative, since the friction force $F_{12}\hat{\mathbf{x}}_1$ is always opposed to the slip velocity $\mathbf{v}_{I\in 2/1}$. We do not know the sign of power $\mathbb{P}^c_{1\to 2/0}$.

When body 2 rolls without slipping, we have $\mathbf{v}_{I\in 2/1} = \mathbf{0}$, leading to

$$\mathbb{P}^c_{1\leftrightarrow 2} = 0$$

Using the kinematic identity $\mathbf{v}_{I\in 2/0} = \mathbf{v}_{I\in 2/1} + \mathbf{v}_{I\in 1/0} = v_1\hat{\mathbf{x}}_1$, and

$$\mathbb{P}^c_{1\to 2/0} = (N_{12}\hat{\mathbf{y}}_1 + F_{12}\hat{\mathbf{x}}_1) \cdot v_1\hat{\mathbf{x}}_1 = v_1 F_{12}$$

■

Example 12.4 A system of two rigid bodies $\Sigma = \{1,2\}$ is in motion in a referential $0(O, \hat{\mathbf{x}}_0, \hat{\mathbf{y}}_0, \hat{\mathbf{z}}_0)$. Unit vector $\hat{\mathbf{z}}_0$ represents the direction of the vertical directed upward. See Figure 12.7. Rigid body $1(O, \hat{\mathbf{x}}_1, \hat{\mathbf{y}}_1, \hat{\mathbf{z}}_0)$ is in rotation about axis $(O, \hat{\mathbf{z}}_0)$ relative to 0 with angular velocity $\boldsymbol{\omega}_{1/0} = \dot{\theta}_1\hat{\mathbf{z}}_0$. The motion of body $2(A, \hat{\mathbf{x}}_2, \hat{\mathbf{y}}_1, \hat{\mathbf{z}}_2)$ relative to 1 is a rotation about axis $(A, \hat{\mathbf{y}}_1)$ of 1 with angular velocity $\boldsymbol{\omega}_{2/1} = -\dot{\theta}_2\hat{\mathbf{y}}_1$. Point A is defined by $\mathbf{r}_{OA} = a\hat{\mathbf{x}}_1$. The location of mass centers G_1 and G_2 of bodies 1 and 2 is given by $\mathbf{r}_{AG_1} = -l_1\hat{\mathbf{x}}_1$and $\mathbf{r}_{AG_2} = l_2\hat{\mathbf{x}}_2$.

Body 1 is subjected to the following action

$$\{\mathcal{A}_{0\to 1}\} = \left\{ \begin{array}{c} -m_1 g \hat{\mathbf{z}}_0 \\ \mathbf{0} \end{array} \right\}_{G_1} + \left\{ \begin{array}{c} \mathbf{0} \\ C_{01}\hat{\mathbf{z}}_0 \end{array} \right\}_{O} + \{\mathcal{A}^c_{0\to 1}\}$$

where the first two terms represent the gravitational action and the action due to motor $\mathcal{M}_{01}$ mounted between 0 and 1. The action $\{\mathcal{A}^c_{0\to 1}\}$ represents the contact action due to the frictionless pivot mounted between 0 and 1.

Body 2 is subjected to the following action

$$\{\mathcal{A}_{\bar{2}\to 2}\} = \left\{ \begin{array}{c} -m_2 g \hat{\mathbf{z}}_0 \\ \mathbf{0} \end{array} \right\}_{G_2} + \left\{ \begin{array}{c} F_{12}\hat{\mathbf{u}} \\ \mathbf{0} \end{array} \right\}_{G_1} + \{\mathcal{A}^c_{1\to 2}\}$$

where the second term represents the action of a massless linear actuator $\mathcal{L}_{12}$ mounted between 1 and 2 directed along unit vector $\hat{\mathbf{u}}$ such that $\mathbf{r}_{G_1G_2} = \rho(t)\hat{\mathbf{u}}$. The action $\{\mathcal{A}^c_{1\to 2}\}$ represents the contact action due the pivot between 1 and 2: it is assumed to satisfy the property $\mathbf{M}^c_{A,1\to 2} \cdot \hat{\mathbf{y}}_1 = G(\dot{\theta}_2)$ (where G is a given function).

a. Find powers $\mathbb{P}_{\bar{1}\to 1/0}$ and $\mathbb{P}_{\bar{2}\to 2/0}$.

b. Find the power of interaction $\mathbb{P}_{1\leftrightarrow 2}$.

c. Find the total power $\mathbb{P}_{\bar{\Sigma}\to\Sigma/0}$. ■

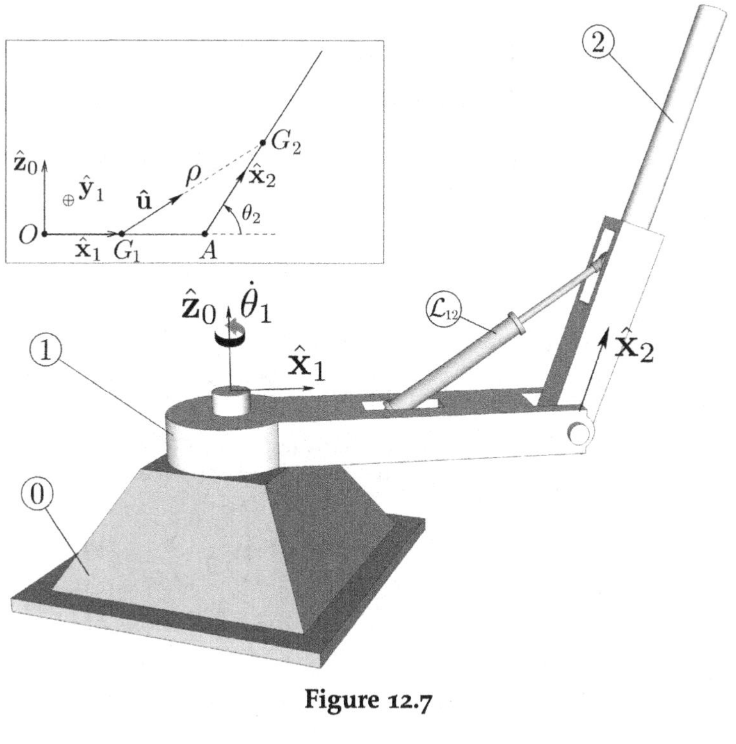

Figure 12.7

a. To find power $\mathbb{P}_{\bar{1}\to 1/0}$ we need the expression of kinematic screw $\{\mathcal{V}_{1/0}\}$:

$$\{\mathcal{V}_{1/0}\} = \begin{Bmatrix} \dot{\theta}_1\hat{\mathbf{z}}_0 \\ \mathbf{0} \end{Bmatrix}_O = \begin{Bmatrix} \dot{\theta}_1\hat{\mathbf{z}}_0 \\ (a-l_1)\dot{\theta}_1\hat{\mathbf{y}}_1 \end{Bmatrix}_{G_1} = \begin{Bmatrix} \dot{\theta}_1\hat{\mathbf{z}}_0 \\ a\dot{\theta}_1\hat{\mathbf{y}}_1 \end{Bmatrix}_A$$

We then obtain

$$\begin{aligned}
\mathbb{P}_{\bar{1}\to 1/0} =& \{\mathcal{A}_{0\to 1}\}\cdot\{\mathcal{V}_{1/0}\} + \{\mathcal{A}_{2\to 1}\}\cdot\{\mathcal{V}_{1/0}\} \\
=& (\begin{Bmatrix} -m_1 g\hat{\mathbf{z}}_0 \\ \mathbf{0} \end{Bmatrix}_{G_1} + \begin{Bmatrix} \mathbf{0} \\ C_{01}\hat{\mathbf{z}}_0 \end{Bmatrix}_O + \{\mathcal{A}_{0\to 1}\}^c - \begin{Bmatrix} F_{12}\hat{\mathbf{u}} \\ \mathbf{0} \end{Bmatrix}_{G_1} + \{\mathcal{A}^c_{2\to 1}\})\cdot\{\mathcal{V}_{1/0}\} \\
=& -m_1 g\hat{\mathbf{z}}_0\cdot\mathbf{v}_{G_1/0} + C_{01}\dot{\theta}_1 + \mathbf{M}^c_{O,0\to 1}\cdot\dot{\theta}_1\hat{\mathbf{z}}_0 - F_{12}\hat{\mathbf{u}}\cdot\mathbf{v}_{G_1/0} + (\mathbf{R}^c_{2\to 1}\cdot l_1\dot{\theta}_1\hat{\mathbf{y}}_1 + \mathbf{M}^c_{A,2\to 1}\cdot\dot{\theta}_1\hat{\mathbf{z}}_0) \\
=& C_{01}\dot{\theta}_1 + \dot{\theta}_1(l_1\mathbf{R}^c_{2\to 1}\cdot\hat{\mathbf{y}}_1 + \mathbf{M}^c_{A,2\to 1}\cdot\hat{\mathbf{z}}_0)
\end{aligned}$$

where we have used $\hat{\mathbf{z}}_0\cdot\mathbf{v}_{G_1/0} = \hat{\mathbf{u}}\cdot\mathbf{v}_{G_1/0} = 0$ and $\hat{\mathbf{z}}_0\cdot\mathbf{M}^c_{O,0\to 1} = 0$. Note that the contribution of action $\{\mathcal{A}^c_{2\to 1}\}$ to power $\mathbb{P}_{\bar{1}\to 1/0}$ would still be non-zero had the joint between 1 and 2 been assumed frictionless.

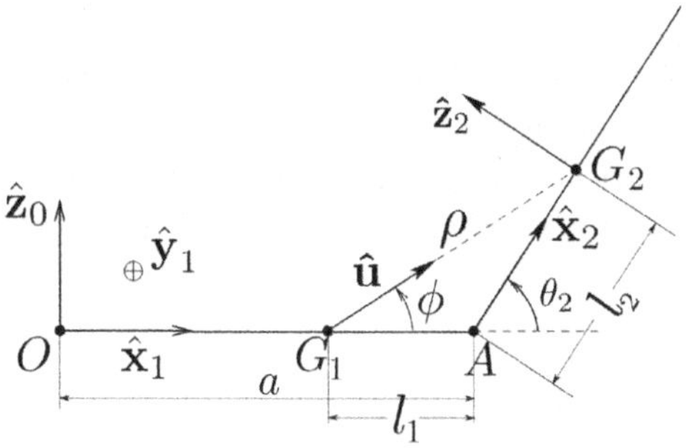

Figure 12.8

To find power $\mathbb{P}_{\bar{2}\to 2/0}$ we need the expression of kinematic screw $\{\mathcal{V}_{2/0}\}$:

$$\{\mathcal{V}_{2/0}\} = \begin{Bmatrix} \dot{\theta}_1\hat{\mathbf{z}}_0 - \dot{\theta}_2\hat{\mathbf{y}}_1 \\ a\dot{\theta}_1\hat{\mathbf{y}}_1 \end{Bmatrix}_A = \begin{Bmatrix} \dot{\theta}_1\hat{\mathbf{z}}_0 - \dot{\theta}_2\hat{\mathbf{y}}_1 \\ (a + l_2\cos\theta_2)\dot{\theta}_1\hat{\mathbf{y}}_1 + l_2\dot{\theta}_2\hat{\mathbf{z}}_2 \end{Bmatrix}_{G_2}$$

We obtain:

$$\begin{aligned}
\mathbb{P}_{\bar{2}\to 2/0} &= (\begin{Bmatrix} -m_2 g\hat{\mathbf{z}}_0 \\ \mathbf{0} \end{Bmatrix}_{G_2} + \begin{Bmatrix} F_{12}\hat{\mathbf{u}} \\ \mathbf{0} \end{Bmatrix}_{G_1} + \{\mathcal{A}^c_{1\to 2}\})\cdot\{\mathcal{V}_{2/0}\} \\
&= -m_2 g l_2\dot{\theta}_2\cos\theta_2 + F_{12}\hat{\mathbf{u}}\cdot l_2\dot{\theta}_2\hat{\mathbf{z}}_2 + \mathbf{M}^c_{A,1\to 2}\cdot(\dot{\theta}_1\hat{\mathbf{z}}_0 - \dot{\theta}_2\hat{\mathbf{y}}_1) + \mathbf{R}^c_{1\to 2}\cdot l_1\dot{\theta}_1\hat{\mathbf{y}}_1 \\
&= -m_2 g l_2\dot{\theta}_2\cos\theta_2 - l_2\dot{\theta}_2 F_{12}\sin(\theta_2 - \phi) + \mathbf{R}^c_{1\to 2}\cdot l_1\dot{\theta}_1\hat{\mathbf{y}}_1 + \mathbf{M}^c_{A,1\to 2}\cdot(\dot{\theta}_1\hat{\mathbf{z}}_0 - \dot{\theta}_2\hat{\mathbf{y}}_1)
\end{aligned}$$

where angle ϕ is the angle $(\hat{\mathbf{x}}_1, \hat{\mathbf{u}})$. Note that the power generated by the actuator on body 1 is not equal to the power generated by the reaction on body 2:

$$-\begin{Bmatrix} F_{12}\hat{\mathbf{u}} \\ \mathbf{0} \end{Bmatrix}_{G_1}\cdot\{\mathcal{V}_{1/0}\} \neq \begin{Bmatrix} F_{12}\hat{\mathbf{u}} \\ \mathbf{0} \end{Bmatrix}_{G_2}\cdot\{\mathcal{V}_{2/0}\}$$

b. To find power of interaction $\mathbb{P}_{1\leftrightarrow 2}$ we need the expressions of kinematic screw $\{\mathcal{V}_{2/1}\}$:

$$\{\mathcal{V}_{2/1}\} = \begin{Bmatrix} -\dot{\theta}_2\hat{\mathbf{y}}_1 \\ \mathbf{0} \end{Bmatrix}_A = \begin{Bmatrix} -\dot{\theta}_2\hat{\mathbf{y}}_1 \\ l_2\dot{\theta}_2\hat{\mathbf{z}}_2 \end{Bmatrix}_{G_2}$$

and of the action screw

$$\{\mathcal{A}_{1\to 2}\} = \begin{Bmatrix} F_{12}\hat{\mathbf{u}} \\ \mathbf{0} \end{Bmatrix}_{G_2} + \{\mathcal{A}^c_{1\to 2}\}$$

We obtain:

$$\mathbb{P}_{1\leftrightarrow 2} = \begin{Bmatrix} F_{12}\hat{\mathbf{u}} \\ \mathbf{0} \end{Bmatrix}_{G_2} \cdot \begin{Bmatrix} -\dot{\theta}_2\hat{\mathbf{y}}_1 \\ l_2\dot{\theta}_2\hat{\mathbf{z}}_2 \end{Bmatrix}_{G_2} + \{\mathcal{A}^c_{1\to 2}\} \cdot \begin{Bmatrix} -\dot{\theta}_2\hat{\mathbf{y}}_1 \\ \mathbf{0} \end{Bmatrix}_{A} = -l_2\dot{\theta}_2 F_{12}\sin(\theta_2 - \phi) - \mathbf{M}^c_{A,1\to 2}\cdot\dot{\theta}_2\hat{\mathbf{y}}_1$$
$$= \dot{\rho}F_{12} - \dot{\theta}_2 G(\dot{\theta}_2)$$

where we have used $\dot{\rho} = -l_2\dot{\theta}_2\sin(\theta_2 - \phi)$.

c. To find the total power $\mathbb{P}_{\bar{\Sigma}\to\Sigma/0}$ we determine the powers of all actions external to system Σ:

$$\mathbb{P}_{\bar{\Sigma}\to\Sigma/0} = -m_1 g\hat{\mathbf{z}}_0\cdot\mathbf{v}_{G_1/0} + \mathcal{C}_{01}\dot{\theta}_1 + \mathbf{M}^c_{O,0\to 1}\cdot\dot{\theta}_1\hat{\mathbf{z}}_0 - m_2 g\hat{\mathbf{z}}_0\cdot\mathbf{v}_{G_2/0}$$
$$= \mathcal{C}_{01}\dot{\theta}_1 - m_2 g l_2\dot{\theta}_2\cos\theta_2$$

■

12.4 Potential Energy

We generalize in this section the notion of potential energy to the case of material systems subjected to mechanical actions. Consider two material systems Σ_1 and Σ_2 in motion relative to a referential $\mathcal{E}$.

12.4.1 Potential Energy Associated with External Actions

Definition 12.3 Material system Σ_2 is said to possess a potential energy due to the action $\{\mathcal{A}_{\Sigma_1\to\Sigma_2}\}$ relative to referential $\mathcal{E}$ if the corresponding power $\mathbb{P}_{\Sigma_1\to\Sigma_2/\mathcal{E}}$ can be written as:

$$\mathbb{P}_{\Sigma_1\to\Sigma_2/\mathcal{E}} = -\frac{d}{dt}\mathbb{U}_{\Sigma_1\to\Sigma_2/\mathcal{E}} \tag{12.15}$$

The action $\{\mathcal{A}_{\Sigma_1\to\Sigma_2}\}$ is then said to *derive* from **potential energy** $\mathbb{U}_{\Sigma_1\to\Sigma_2/\mathcal{E}}$ relative to referential $\mathcal{E}$ (within an arbitrary additive constant).

Note that an action $\{\mathcal{A}_{\Sigma_1\to\Sigma_2}\}$ may derive from a potential $\mathbb{U}_{\Sigma_1\to\Sigma_2/\mathcal{E}}$ relative to a referential $\mathcal{E}$, but not relative to another referential $\mathcal{F}$.

Example 12.5 Assuming that the Earth's gravitational field can be modeled by a constant gravitational acceleration $\mathbf{g}$, show that the corresponding potential energy $\mathbb{U}^g_{\text{Earth}\to\Sigma/\mathcal{E}}$ can be expressed as:

$$\mathbb{U}^g_{\text{Earth}\to\Sigma/\mathcal{E}} = -m_\Sigma\,\mathbf{g}\cdot\mathbf{r}_{OG_\Sigma}$$

relative to a referential $\mathcal{E}$ (of origin O) attached to Earth. ■

If the local force $\mathbf{F}^g_{\text{Earth}\to\Sigma}(P)$ at every point P of Σ takes the expression $\rho(P)\mathbf{g}$ (where ρ is the mass density), then the power $\mathbb{P}^g_{\text{Earth}\to\Sigma/\mathcal{E}}$ is given by

$$\mathbb{P}^g_{\text{Earth}\to\Sigma/\mathcal{E}} = \int_\Sigma \rho(P)\mathbf{g}\cdot\mathbf{v}_{P/\mathcal{E}}dV = \int_\Sigma \frac{d}{dt}(\mathbf{g}\cdot\mathbf{r}_{OP})dm = \frac{d}{dt}(m_\Sigma\mathbf{g}\cdot\mathbf{r}_{OG_\Sigma})$$

leading to the expression $\mathbb{U}^g_{\text{Earth}\to\Sigma/\mathcal{E}} = -m_\Sigma\,\mathbf{g}\cdot\mathbf{r}_{OG_\Sigma}$. ■

Example 12.6 Figure 12.9 shows a wheel 1 of center C and radius R which rolls along the axis $(O, \hat{\mathbf{x}}_0)$ of a referential $0(O, \hat{\mathbf{x}}_0, \hat{\mathbf{y}}_0, \hat{\mathbf{z}}_0)$. A rigid body 2 is constrained to slide along a groove of 1 along the line $(C, \hat{\mathbf{z}}_1)$. The position of this system is defined by the variables $x(t) = \mathbf{r}_{OC} \cdot \hat{\mathbf{x}}_0$, angle $\theta(t) = (\hat{\mathbf{z}}_0, \hat{\mathbf{z}}_1)$ and $l(t) = \mathbf{r}_{CA} \cdot \hat{\mathbf{z}}_1$ where A is a point attached to 2. Body 2 is subjected to the following action

$$\{\mathcal{A}^s_{1\to 2}\} = \begin{Bmatrix} -k(l - l_0)\hat{\mathbf{z}}_1 \\ \mathbf{0} \end{Bmatrix}_A$$

due to the presence of a massless helicoidal spring mounted between 1 and 2 along line $(C, \hat{\mathbf{z}}_1)$ (k and l_0 are constants).

a. Show that action $\{\mathcal{A}^s_{1\to 2}\}$ derive from a potential $\mathbb{U}^s_{1\to 2/1}$.

b. Show that the power $\mathbb{P}^s_{1\to 2/0}$ cannot be determined from a potential $\mathbb{U}^s_{1\to 2/0}$. ■

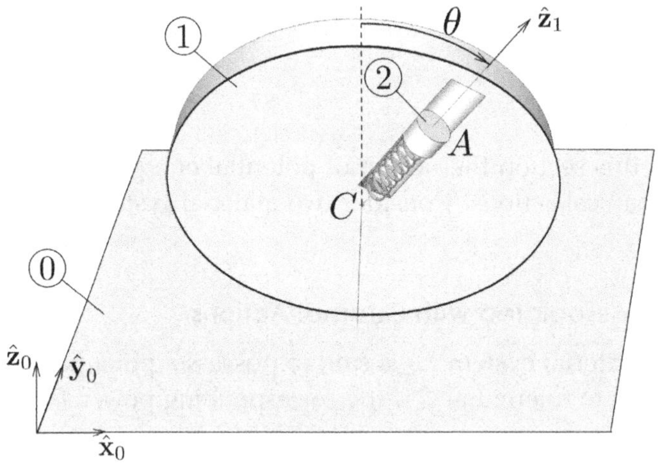

Figure 12.9

a. We can easily determine the power $\mathbb{P}^s_{1\to 2/1}$ as follows:

$$\mathbb{P}^s_{1\to 2/1} = \{\mathcal{A}^s_{1\to 2}\} \cdot \{\mathcal{V}_{2/1}\} = \begin{Bmatrix} -k(l - l_0)\hat{\mathbf{z}}_1 \\ \mathbf{0} \end{Bmatrix}_A \cdot \begin{Bmatrix} \mathbf{0} \\ \dot{l}\hat{\mathbf{z}}_1 \end{Bmatrix}_A = -k(l - l_0)\dot{l} = -\frac{d}{dt}\left(\frac{k}{2}(l - l_0)^2\right)$$

which shows that potential $\mathbb{U}^s_{1\to 2/1}$ exists and is given by

$$\mathbb{U}^s_{1\to 2/1} = \frac{k}{2}(l - l_0)^2$$

b. We proceed as in the previous case to find power $\mathbb{P}^s_{1\to 2/0}$:

$$\mathbb{P}^s_{1\to 2/0} = \{\mathcal{A}^s_{1\to 2}\} \cdot \{\mathcal{V}_{2/0}\} = \begin{Bmatrix} -k(l - l_0)\hat{\mathbf{z}}_1 \\ \mathbf{0} \end{Bmatrix}_A \cdot \begin{Bmatrix} \dot{\theta}\hat{\mathbf{y}}_0 \\ \dot{x}\hat{\mathbf{x}}_0 + \dot{l}\hat{\mathbf{z}}_1 + l\frac{d\hat{\mathbf{z}}_1}{dt} \end{Bmatrix}_A$$
$$= -k(l - l_0)(\dot{x}\cos\theta + \dot{l}) = -k(l - l_0)\dot{x}\cos\theta - \frac{d}{dt}\left(\frac{k}{2}(l - l_0)^2\right)$$

using the fact that $\hat{\mathbf{z}}_1 \cdot d\hat{\mathbf{z}}_1/dt = 0$. We see that in this case we cannot define a potential $\mathbb{U}^s_{1\to 2/0}$.
■

12.4.2 Potential Energy of Interaction

Definition 12.4 Two interacting material systems Σ_1 and Σ_2 are said to possess a *potential energy of interaction* if the corresponding power of interaction $\mathbb{P}_{\Sigma_1 \leftrightarrow \Sigma_2}$ can be expressed in the form

$$\mathbb{P}_{\Sigma_1 \leftrightarrow \Sigma_2} = -\frac{d}{dt}\mathbb{U}_{\Sigma_1 \leftrightarrow \Sigma_2} \tag{12.16}$$

The interaction between Σ_1 and Σ_2 is then said to *derive* from potential energy $\mathbb{U}_{\Sigma_1 \leftrightarrow \Sigma_2}$.

Note that as power $\mathbb{P}_{\Sigma_1 \leftrightarrow \Sigma_2}$, potential $\mathbb{U}_{\Sigma_1 \leftrightarrow \Sigma_2}$ is independent of the referential $\mathcal{E}$ relative to which both material systems are observed.

Example 12.7 Show that the potential energy associated with the gravitational interactions between Σ_1 and Σ_2 is given by:

$$\mathbb{U}^g_{\Sigma_1 \leftrightarrow \Sigma_2} = -G\int_{\Sigma_1}\int_{\Sigma_2} \frac{dm(P_1)dm(P_2)}{|\mathbf{r}_{P_1P_2}|}.$$

■

According to definition (12.14) we can express $\mathbb{P}_{\Sigma_1 \leftrightarrow \Sigma_2}$ as the sum $\mathbb{P}^g_{\Sigma_1 \to \Sigma_2/\mathcal{E}} + \mathbb{P}^g_{\Sigma_2 \to \Sigma_1/\mathcal{E}}$ relative to some arbitrary referential $\mathcal{E}$:

$$\mathbb{P}^g_{\Sigma_1 \leftrightarrow \Sigma_2} = \int_{\Sigma_2} \mathbf{F}^g_{1\to 2}(P_2)\cdot \mathbf{v}_{P_2/\mathcal{E}}dV(P_2) + \int_{\Sigma_1} \mathbf{F}^g_{2\to 1}(P_1)\cdot \mathbf{v}_{P_1/\mathcal{E}}dV(P_1)$$

with

$$\mathbf{F}^g_{1\to 2}(P_2) = -G\rho(P_2)\int_{\Sigma_1} \frac{\mathbf{r}_{P_1P_2}}{|\mathbf{r}_{P_1P_2}|^3}dm(P_1), \quad \mathbf{F}^g_{2\to 1}(P_1) = -G\rho(P_1)\int_{\Sigma_2} \frac{\mathbf{r}_{P_2P_1}}{|\mathbf{r}_{P_1P_2}|^3}dm(P_2)$$

leading to

$$\begin{aligned}
\mathbb{P}^g_{\Sigma_1 \leftrightarrow \Sigma_2} &= -G\int_{\Sigma_1}\int_{\Sigma_2} \frac{\mathbf{r}_{P_1P_2}}{|\mathbf{r}_{P_1P_2}|^3}\cdot(\mathbf{v}_{P_2/\mathcal{E}} - \mathbf{v}_{P_1/\mathcal{E}})dm(P_1)dm(P_2) \\
&= -G\int_{\Sigma_1}\int_{\Sigma_2} \frac{\mathbf{r}_{P_1P_2}}{|\mathbf{r}_{P_1P_2}|^3}\cdot\frac{d\mathbf{r}_{P_1P_2}}{dt}dm(P_1)dm(P_2)
\end{aligned}$$

As expected the integrand is independent of the choice of referential $\mathcal{E}$ and can be expressed as

$$\frac{\mathbf{r}_{P_1P_2}}{|\mathbf{r}_{P_1P_2}|^3}\cdot\frac{d}{dt}\mathbf{r}_{P_1P_2} = -\frac{d}{dt}\left(\frac{1}{|\mathbf{r}_{P_1P_2}|}\right)$$

leading to the expression

$$\mathbb{P}_{\Sigma_1 \leftrightarrow \Sigma_2} = \frac{d}{dt}\int_{\Sigma_1}\int_{\Sigma_2} G\frac{dm(P_1)dm(P_2)}{|\mathbf{r}_{P_1P_2}|}$$

This gives the result sought. ■

12.5 Ideal Joints

We wish here to generalize the notion of frictionless joint introduced in Section 10.4. Recall that frictionless joints interconnecting rigid bodies are defined by assuming that the local contact force is normal to the coinciding surfaces (or lines) in direct contact. We can enlarge this family of joints by including interconnections which do not necessitate direct contact but rather involve intermediary mechanisms of negligible mass, such as ball bearings, lubricating fluid, etc. After all, true technological joints are not conceived by direct physical contact of rigid bodies. This enlarged family will be called *ideal joints* and is defined as follows.

Definition 12.5 — Ideal joint. A joint between two rigid bodies $\mathcal{B}_1$ and $\mathcal{B}_2$ is said to be *ideal* if the corresponding contact action screw $\{\mathcal{A}^c_{\mathcal{B}_1\to\mathcal{B}_2}\}$ satisfies

$$\mathbb{P}^c_{\mathcal{B}_1\leftrightarrow\mathcal{B}_2} = 0 \tag{12.17}$$

for all possible relative motions between $\mathcal{B}_1$ and $\mathcal{B}_2$ allowed by the joint.

This definition is independent of the eventual interconnections which may exist between $\mathcal{B}_1$ or $\mathcal{B}_2$ and other rigid bodies. Indeed, since the power of interaction $\mathbb{P}^c_{\mathcal{B}_1\leftrightarrow\mathcal{B}_2}$ only involves the kinematics of $\mathcal{B}_2$ relative to $\mathcal{B}_1$ (or vice versa), the motion of $\mathcal{B}_1$ and $\mathcal{B}_2$ relative to some referential $\mathcal{E}$ is irrelevant in equation (12.17).

Remark 4. If the joint allows a mobility of size M defined by M independent coordinates $(q_1, q_2, \dots, q_M)$, equation (12.17) leads to M scalar relationships: we may write the kinematic screw $\{\mathcal{V}_{2/1}\}$ as

$$\{\mathcal{V}_{2/1}\} = \dot{q}_1\{\mathcal{V}^{q_1}_{2/1}\} + \dot{q}_2\{\mathcal{V}^{q_2}_{2/1}\} + \cdots + \dot{q}_M\{\mathcal{V}^{q_M}_{2/1}\}$$

Then the condition $\mathbb{P}^c_{\mathcal{B}_1\leftrightarrow\mathcal{B}_2} = 0$ leads to M conditions of the type

$$\{\mathcal{V}^{q_k}_{2/1}\}\cdot\{\mathcal{A}^c_{1\to 2}\} = 0, \qquad k = 1, 2, \cdots, M \tag{12.18}$$

Remark 5. A joint achieved by direct frictionless contact between two rigid bodies $\mathcal{B}_1$ and $\mathcal{B}_2$ is of course ideal:

$$\mathbb{P}^c_{\mathcal{B}_1\leftrightarrow\mathcal{B}_2} = \int_{\partial\mathcal{B}_1\cap\partial\mathcal{B}_2} \mathbf{f}^c_{1\to 2}(Q)\cdot\mathbf{v}_{Q\in 2/1}\,dA(Q)$$

assuming without loss of generality a surface of contact between $\mathcal{B}_1$ and $\mathcal{B}_2$. Recall that the local contact force $\mathbf{f}^c_{1\to 2}(Q)$ is directed along the unit normal vector $\hat{\mathbf{n}}_{12}(Q)$ to the surface of contact, and that the slip velocity $\mathbf{v}_{Q\in 2/1}$ is always perpendicular to $\hat{\mathbf{n}}_{12}(Q)$: for all $Q\in\partial\mathcal{B}_1\cap\partial\mathcal{B}_2$ we have $\mathbf{f}^c_{1\to 2}(Q)\cdot\mathbf{v}_{Q\in 2/1} = 0$. Therefore, $\mathbb{P}^c_{\mathcal{B}_1\leftrightarrow\mathcal{B}_2} = 0$. Hence, frictionless joints are ideal joint. However, it is important to realize that ideal joints are not necessarily realized by direct frictionless contact.

Remark 6. The notion of ideal joints allows the designer to resolve the indeterminations which inevitably arise whenever rigid bodies are interconnected. It also leads to the determination of contact action screw $\{\mathcal{A}^c_{\mathcal{B}_1\to\mathcal{B}_2}\}$ without specifying the technological solution of a physical realization of the joint between $\mathcal{B}_1$ and $\mathcal{B}_2$.

Example 12.8 Derive the condition that must be satisfied by the action screw $\{\mathcal{A}^c_{1\to 2}\}$ for two rigid bodies connected by an ideal helical joint. ■

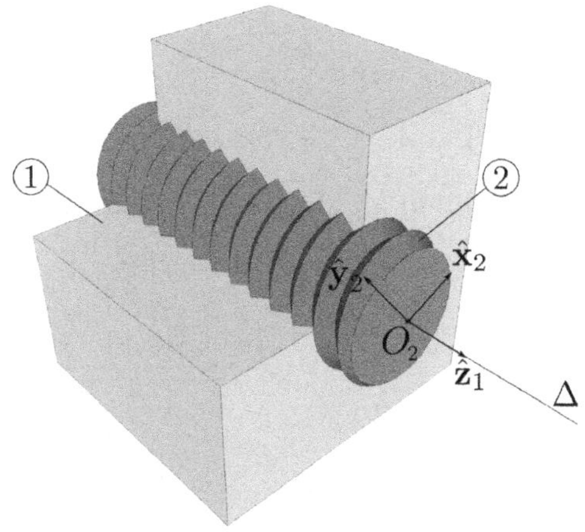

Denote by $(O_2, \hat{\mathbf{z}}_1)$ the axis which define the helical joint. Recall that the corresponding kinematic screw takes the following form

$$\{\mathcal{V}_{2/1}\} = \left\{ \begin{array}{c} \omega_z \hat{\mathbf{z}}_1 \\ \frac{p}{2\pi}\omega_z \hat{\mathbf{z}}_1 \end{array} \right\}_{\forall A \in (O_2, \hat{\mathbf{z}}_1)}$$

Then the condition $\mathbb{P}^c_{1\leftrightarrow 2} = 0$ can be written as

$$\{\mathcal{V}_{2/1}\} \cdot \{\mathcal{A}^c_{1\to 2}\} = \frac{p}{2\pi}\omega_z \mathbf{R}^c_{1\to 2} \cdot \hat{\mathbf{z}}_1 + \mathbf{M}^c_{A,1\to 2} \cdot \omega_z \hat{\mathbf{z}}_1 = 0$$

for all possible values of ω_z. This leads to the condition

$$\frac{p}{2\pi}\mathbf{R}^c_{1\to 2} \cdot \hat{\mathbf{z}}_1 + \mathbf{M}^c_{A,1\to 2} \cdot \hat{\mathbf{z}}_1 = 0$$

for any point A of axis $(O_2, \hat{\mathbf{z}}_1)$. This is the same condition that we stated without proof in Section 10.4. ■

Example 12.9 Derive the condition that must be satisfied by the action screw $\{\mathcal{A}^c_{1\to 2}\}$ corresponding to the frictionless contact between a sphere and the interior of a toroidal surface. See Figure 12.10. ■

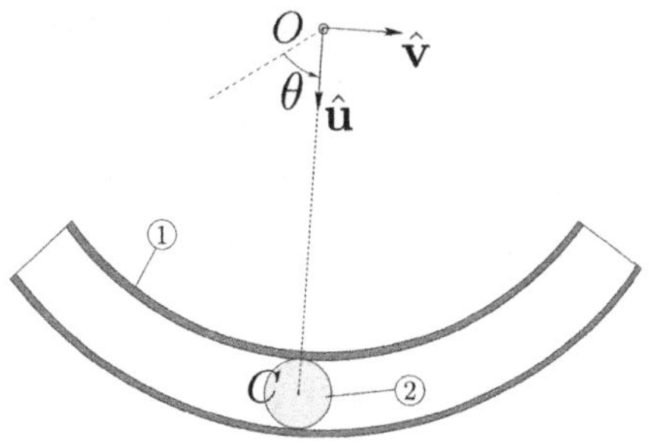

Figure 12.10

Denote by C the center of the sphere 2, and by O the center of the torus 1. Then the kinematic screw of 2 relative to 1 takes the following form

$$\{\mathcal{V}_{2/1}\} = \left\{ \begin{array}{c} \omega_{2/1} \\ R\dot{\theta}\hat{\mathbf{v}} \end{array} \right\}_C$$

The condition $\mathbb{P}^c_{1\leftrightarrow 2} = 0$ can be written as

$$\{\mathcal{V}_{2/1}\} \cdot \{\mathcal{A}^c_{1\to 2}\} = R\dot{\theta}\hat{\mathbf{v}} \cdot \mathbf{R}^c_{1\to 2} + \omega_{2/1} \cdot \mathbf{M}^c_{C,1\to 2} = 0$$

In order to satisfy this condition for all possible motions between 1 and 2, we must impose

$$\hat{\mathbf{v}} \cdot \mathbf{R}^c_{1\to 2} = 0, \qquad \mathbf{M}^c_{C,1\to 2} = 0$$

■

12.6 The Kinetic Energy Theorem

We generalize in this section the Kinetic Energy Theorem (KET) to rigid bodies.

12.6.1 Case 1: Single Rigid Body

Consider a rigid body $\mathcal{B}$ in motion relative to a Newtonian referential $\mathcal{E}$ under the effect of gravitational and contact mechanical actions. Let us apply D'Alembert Principle of Virtual Power by choosing the actual velocity field $P \in \mathcal{B} \mapsto \mathbf{v}_{P/\mathcal{E}}$ for the virtual velocity field $P \mapsto \mathbf{v}^*_P$ (since $\mathcal{B}$ is a rigid body, this vector field defines a screw):

$$\int_{\mathcal{B}} \mathbf{v}_{P/\mathcal{E}} \cdot \mathbf{F}^g_{\overline{\mathcal{B}}\to\mathcal{B}}(P)\, dV + \int_{\partial\mathcal{B}} \mathbf{v}_{Q/\mathcal{E}} \cdot \mathbf{f}^c_{\overline{\mathcal{B}}\to\mathcal{B}}(Q)\, dA = \int_{\mathcal{B}} \mathbf{v}_{P/\mathcal{E}} \cdot \mathbf{a}_{P/\mathcal{E}}\, dm$$

In the left-hand-side of this equation, we recognize the powers $\mathbb{P}^g_{\overline{\mathcal{B}}\to\mathcal{B}/\mathcal{E}}$ and $\mathbb{P}^c_{\overline{\mathcal{B}}\to\mathcal{B}/\mathcal{E}}$ generated by the gravitational and contact forces during the motion of $\mathcal{B}$ relative to $\mathcal{E}$: we can denote the sum of these two contributions simply as $\mathbb{P}_{\overline{\mathcal{B}}\to\mathcal{B}/\mathcal{E}}$. In the right-hand-side, we recognize the rate-of-change of the kinetic energy of $\mathcal{B}$

$$\int_{\mathcal{B}} \mathbf{v}_{P/\mathcal{E}} \cdot \mathbf{a}_{P/\mathcal{E}}\, dm = \frac{d}{dt}\int_{\mathcal{B}} \frac{1}{2}\mathbf{v}^2_{P/\mathcal{E}}\, dm = \frac{d}{dt}\mathbb{K}_{\mathcal{B}/\mathcal{E}}$$

We conclude with the following theorem.

Theorem 12.5 — Kinetic Energy Theorem (Single Body). The power generated by all external mechanical actions exerted on rigid body $\mathcal{B}$ is equal to the time rate-of-change of the kinetic energy of $\mathcal{B}$:

$$\frac{d}{dt}\mathbb{K}_{\mathcal{B}/\mathcal{E}} = \mathbb{P}_{\overline{\mathcal{B}}\to\mathcal{B}/\mathcal{E}} \tag{12.19}$$

relative to Newtonian referential $\mathcal{E}$.

Remark. A simple way to derive the KET consists of taking the scalar product of both sides of the FTD by the kinematic screw $\{\mathcal{V}_{\mathcal{B}/\mathcal{E}}\}$:

$$\{\mathcal{D}_{\mathcal{B}/\mathcal{E}}\} \cdot \{\mathcal{V}_{\mathcal{B}/\mathcal{E}}\} = \{\mathcal{A}_{\overline{\mathcal{B}}\to\mathcal{B}}\} \cdot \{\mathcal{V}_{\mathcal{B}/\mathcal{E}}\}$$

The term $\{\mathcal{A}_{\overline{\mathcal{B}}\to\mathcal{B}}\} \cdot \{\mathcal{V}_{\mathcal{B}/\mathcal{E}}\}$ is of course the power $\mathbb{P}_{\overline{\mathcal{B}}\to\mathcal{B}/\mathcal{E}}$. It is also straightforward to show that the scalar term $\{\mathcal{D}_{\mathcal{B}/\mathcal{E}}\} \cdot \{\mathcal{V}_{\mathcal{B}/\mathcal{E}}\}$ is nothing but $\frac{d}{dt}\mathbb{K}_{\mathcal{B}/\mathcal{E}}$ (see Section 9.7).

12.6.2 Case 2: System of Rigid Bodies

Now consider a system $\Sigma = \{\mathcal{B}_1, \mathcal{B}_2, \dots, \mathcal{B}_N\}$ of N rigid bodies in motion relative to a Newtonian referential $\mathcal{E}$, and let us apply again D'Alembert Principle of Virtual Power to Σ, by choosing the virtual velocity field $\mathbf{v}^*$ as follows:

$$\mathbf{v}_P^* = \mathbf{v}_{P\in\mathcal{B}_j/\mathcal{E}} \qquad \text{if } P \in \mathcal{B}_j$$

Then, we obtain

$$\frac{d}{dt}\mathbb{K}_{\Sigma/\mathcal{E}} = \sum_{j=1}^{N} \{\mathcal{A}_{\overline{\mathcal{B}}_j\to\mathcal{B}_j}\} \cdot \{\mathcal{V}_{\mathcal{B}_j/\mathcal{E}}\}$$

which amounts to summing the N equations obtained by applying the KET to each rigid body of the system. Next, we decompose each action screw $\{\mathcal{A}_{\overline{\mathcal{B}}_j\to\mathcal{B}_j}\}$ as the sum $\{\mathcal{A}_{\overline{\Sigma}\to\mathcal{B}_j}\} + \sum_{i\neq j}\{\mathcal{A}_{\mathcal{B}_i\to\mathcal{B}_j}\}$ of external and internal contributions to system Σ. This leads to two terms:

- a term associated to the external actions on Σ:

$$\sum_{j=1}^{N} \{\mathcal{A}_{\overline{\Sigma}\to\mathcal{B}_j}\} \cdot \{\mathcal{V}_{\mathcal{B}_j/\mathcal{E}}\},$$

  which is recognized as the power $\mathbb{P}_{\overline{\Sigma}\to\Sigma/\mathcal{E}}$ generated by the external actions exerted on Σ,

- a term associated to all possible internal actions, that is, the actions (and reactions) between all possible parts of Σ:

$$\sum_{i,j}^{N} P_{B_i \to B_j} = \sum_{\substack{i,j=1\\ i<j}}^{N} \{\mathcal{A}_{\mathcal{B}_i\to\mathcal{B}_j}\} \cdot \underbrace{\left(\{\mathcal{V}_{\mathcal{B}_j/\mathcal{E}}\} - \{\mathcal{V}_{\mathcal{B}_i/\mathcal{E}}\}\right)}_{\{\mathcal{V}_{\mathcal{B}_j/\mathcal{B}_i}\}}$$

  power of interaction; ← relative motion of B_j & B_i

  which is recognized as the sum of all powers $\mathbb{P}_{\mathcal{B}_i\leftrightarrow\mathcal{B}_j}$ of interactions within Σ.

In conclusion, Theorem 12.5 becomes

> **Theorem 12.6 — Kinetic Energy Theorem (Systems).** The Kinetic Energy Theorem applied to system Σ takes the following form:
>
> $$\frac{d}{dt}\mathbb{K}_{\Sigma/\mathcal{E}} = \mathbb{P}_{\overline{\Sigma}\to\Sigma/\mathcal{E}} + \sum_{\substack{i,j=1\\ i<j}}^{N} \mathbb{P}_{\mathcal{B}_i\leftrightarrow\mathcal{B}_j} \qquad (12.20)$$
>
> relative to Newtonian referential $\mathcal{E}$.

A fundamental difference with the FTD is that the internal interactions between the rigid bodies of a system Σ must be accounted for.

Remark 7. The integrated forms of the KET is known as the Work-Energy Theorem: integration of (12.20) over time gives

First integral

$$\Delta\mathbb{K}_{\Sigma/\mathcal{E}} = \int_0^T \mathbb{P}_{\overline{\Sigma}\to\Sigma/\mathcal{E}}\,dt + \sum_{\substack{i,j=1\\ i<j}}^{N} \int_0^T \mathbb{P}_{\mathcal{B}_i\leftrightarrow\mathcal{B}_j}\,dt \qquad (12.21)$$

Hence the variation of the system's kinetic energy is equal to the work done by all external and internal actions.

Remark 8. A first integral governing the motion of system Σ can be found if the following conditions are satisfied:

(i) if the external actions either generate no power or derive from a total potential $\mathbb{U}_{\bar{\Sigma}\to\Sigma/\mathcal{E}}$,

(ii) if the internal interactions either generate no power or derive from a total potential $\sum_{i<j}\mathbb{U}_{i\leftrightarrow j}$,

then the system's mechanical energy $\mathbb{E}_{\Sigma/\mathcal{E}} = \mathbb{K}_{\Sigma/\mathcal{E}} + \mathbb{U}_{\bar{\Sigma}\to\Sigma/\mathcal{E}} + \sum_{i<j}\mathbb{U}_{i\leftrightarrow j}$ is conserved.

12.7 Examples

Example 12.10 Consider rigid body 1 of Example 12.1 Using the same assumptions regarding the forces acting on body 1, apply the KET to find a scalar equation. How does this equation relate to the FTD? ■

We found the total external power $\mathbb{P}_{\bar{1}\to 1/0}$ in Example 12.1.

$$\mathbb{P}_{\bar{1}\to 1/0} = -\frac{1}{12}\mu a^3 b\dot{\theta}^2 + C\dot{\theta}$$

Furthermore the kinetic energy of body 1 is given by

$$\mathbb{K}_{1/0} = \tfrac{1}{2}\omega_{1/0}\cdot\mathcal{I}_O(\omega_{1/0}) = \frac{m}{12}a^2\dot{\theta}^2$$

Application of the KET to the motion of body 1 gives

$$\frac{d}{dt}\left(\frac{m}{12}a^2\dot{\theta}^2\right) = -\frac{1}{12}\mu a^3 b\dot{\theta}^2 + C\dot{\theta} \quad [1]$$

To show the relationship between this result and the FTD, recall that the KET can be written in the following form:

$$\{\mathcal{D}_{1/0}\}\cdot\{\mathcal{V}_{1/0}\} = \{\mathcal{A}_{\bar{1}\to 1}\}\cdot\{\mathcal{V}_{1/0}\}$$

which gives

$$\dot{\theta}\hat{\mathbf{z}}_0\cdot\mathbf{D}_{O,1/0} = \dot{\theta}\hat{\mathbf{z}}_0\cdot\mathbf{M}_{O,\bar{1}\to 1}$$

In other words, equation [1] is nothing but the $\hat{\mathbf{z}}_0$-component of the dynamic moment equation about O premultiplied by $\dot{\theta}$. ■

Example 12.11 A spinning top $1(O,\hat{\mathbf{x}}_1,\hat{\mathbf{y}}_1,\hat{\mathbf{z}}_1)$ of mass center G and mass m is in motion in a referential 0 $(O,\hat{\mathbf{x}}_0,\hat{\mathbf{y}}_0,\hat{\mathbf{z}}_0)$ in such a way that its tip O remains stationary relative to 0. The connection between 0 and 1 is equivalent to a frictionless spherical joint. The upward vertical is directed along $\hat{\mathbf{z}}_0$. The orientation of body 1 relative to 0 is defined in terms of the three angles (ψ,θ,ϕ) according the following sequence of rotations:

$$(\hat{\mathbf{x}}_0,\hat{\mathbf{y}}_0,\hat{\mathbf{z}}_0)\xrightarrow{\mathcal{R}_{\psi,\hat{\mathbf{z}}_0}}(\hat{\mathbf{u}},\hat{\mathbf{v}},\hat{\mathbf{z}}_0)\xrightarrow{\mathcal{R}_{\theta,\hat{\mathbf{u}}}}(\hat{\mathbf{u}},\hat{\mathbf{w}},\hat{\mathbf{z}}_1)\xrightarrow{\mathcal{R}_{\phi,\hat{\mathbf{z}}_1}}(\hat{\mathbf{x}}_1,\hat{\mathbf{y}}_1,\hat{\mathbf{z}}_1)$$

The top is axisymmetric about axis $(O,\hat{\mathbf{z}}_1)$. The position of its mass center is defined by $\mathbf{r}_{OG} = l\hat{\mathbf{z}}_1$. Its inertia operator about O is entirely defined by its axial moment of inertia $C = \hat{\mathbf{z}}_1\cdot\mathcal{I}_O(\hat{\mathbf{z}}_1)$ and its transverse moment of inertia $A = \hat{\mathbf{x}}_1\cdot\mathcal{I}_O(\hat{\mathbf{x}}_1) = \hat{\mathbf{y}}_1\cdot\mathcal{I}_O(\hat{\mathbf{y}}_1)$. The top is under the sole effect of gravity and contact forces, neglecting rolling and pivoting friction.

Apply the Kinetic Energy Theorem to body 1 and find a first-integral of motion. ■

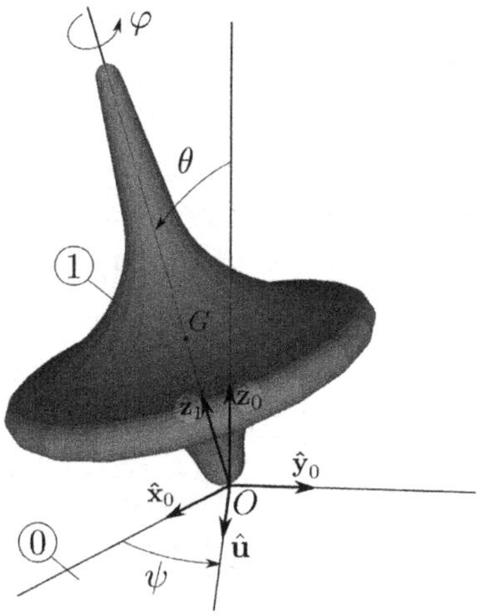

Figure 12.11

Step 1: kinematics. With $\boldsymbol{\omega}_{1/0} = \dot{\psi}\hat{\mathbf{z}}_0 + \dot{\theta}\hat{\mathbf{u}} + \dot{\phi}_0\hat{\mathbf{z}}_1$ and $\mathbf{v}_{O\in 1/0} = \mathbf{0}$, we find the expression of the kinematic screw of the top

$$\{\mathcal{V}_{1/0}\} = \begin{Bmatrix} \dot{\psi}\hat{\mathbf{z}}_0 + \dot{\theta}\hat{\mathbf{u}} + \dot{\phi}_0\hat{\mathbf{z}}_1 \\ \mathbf{0} \end{Bmatrix}_O$$

Step 2: kinetic energy. We find the KE of the top as a body rotating about fixed point O by representing inertia operator $\mathcal{I}_O$ on basis $b(\hat{\mathbf{u}}, \hat{\mathbf{w}}, \hat{\mathbf{z}}_1)$ (using $\boldsymbol{\omega}_{1/0} \cdot \hat{\mathbf{z}}_1 = \dot{\psi}\cos\theta + \dot{\phi}$, $\boldsymbol{\omega}_{1/0} \cdot \hat{\mathbf{w}} = \dot{\psi}\sin\theta$, and $\boldsymbol{\omega}_{1/0} \cdot \hat{\mathbf{u}} = \dot{\theta}$):

$$2\mathbb{K}_{1/0} = \boldsymbol{\omega}_{1/0} \cdot \mathcal{I}_O(\boldsymbol{\omega}_{1/0}) = \boldsymbol{\omega}_{1/0} \cdot \begin{bmatrix} A & 0 & 0 \\ 0 & A & 0 \\ 0 & 0 & C \end{bmatrix}_b \begin{bmatrix} \dot{\theta} \\ \dot{\psi}\sin\theta \\ \dot{\psi}\cos\theta + \dot{\phi} \end{bmatrix}_b = A(\dot{\psi}^2 \sin^2\theta + \dot{\theta}^2) + C(\dot{\psi}\cos\theta + \dot{\phi})^2$$

Step 3: action screw. We find the contributions to action screw $\{\mathcal{A}_{\bar{1}\to 1}\}$

$$\{\mathcal{A}_{\bar{1}\to 1}\} = \begin{Bmatrix} -mg\hat{\mathbf{z}}_0 \\ \mathbf{0} \end{Bmatrix}_G + \begin{Bmatrix} \mathbf{R}_O \\ \mathbf{0} \end{Bmatrix}_O = \begin{Bmatrix} \mathbf{R}_O - mg\hat{\mathbf{z}}_0 \\ mgl\sin\theta\hat{\mathbf{u}} \end{Bmatrix}_O$$

Step 4: We find the power $\mathbb{P}_{\bar{1}\to 1/0}$:

$$\mathbb{P}_{\bar{1}\to 1/0} = mgl\sin\theta\hat{\mathbf{u}} \cdot \boldsymbol{\omega}_{1/0} = mgl\dot{\theta}\sin\theta = -\frac{d}{dt}(mgl\cos\theta)$$

Step 5: We apply the KET $\frac{d}{dt}\mathbb{K}_{1/0} = \mathbb{P}_{\bar{1}\to 1/0}$ to find

$$\frac{d}{dt}\Big(A(\dot{\psi}^2 \sin^2\theta + \dot{\theta}^2) + C(\dot{\psi}\cos\theta + \dot{\phi})^2\Big) = -\frac{d}{dt}(2mgl\cos\theta)$$

which yield a first-integral of motion (conservation of mechanical energy):

$$A(\dot{\psi}^2 \sin^2\theta + \dot{\theta}^2) + C(\dot{\psi}\cos\theta + \dot{\phi})^2 + 2mgl\cos\theta = Cst$$

Note that we could have used the potential energy $\mathbb{U}_{earth\to 1/0} = mgl\cos\theta$. ■

Example 12.12 Figure 12.12 shows a system Σ comprised of two rigid bodies 1 and 2 in motion relative to a referential 0 assumed Newtonian. The vertical is defined by the axis $(O, \hat{\mathbf{z}}_0)$ directed upward. Rigid body 1 is connected to a fixed housing by an ideal pivot of axis $(O, \hat{\mathbf{z}}_0)$. Rigid body 2 is free to rotate relative to body 1 about axis $(O, \hat{\mathbf{z}}_0)$. The corresponding joint is not ideal due to frictional effects. The two bodies are given the initial angular velocity $\boldsymbol{\omega}_{1/0} = \omega_{01}\hat{\mathbf{z}}_0$ and $\boldsymbol{\omega}_{2/0} = \omega_{02}\hat{\mathbf{z}}_0$ (ω_{01} and ω_{02} are two positive constants). After a certain time T, it is observed that the two bodies rotate at the same angular velocity $\boldsymbol{\omega}_{1/0} = \boldsymbol{\omega}_{2/0} = \Omega \hat{\mathbf{z}}_0$. Denote by I_1 and I_2 the moment of inertia of bodies 1 and 2 about axis $(O, \hat{\mathbf{z}}_0)$.

a. Find the angular velocity Ω in terms of ω_{01}, ω_{02} and the constants I_1 and I_2.

b. Find the variation of the kinetic energies $\mathbb{K}_{1/0}$, $\mathbb{K}_{2/0}$ and $\mathbb{K}_{\Sigma/0}$ during during the time interval T. Justify the sign of these three quantities. ■

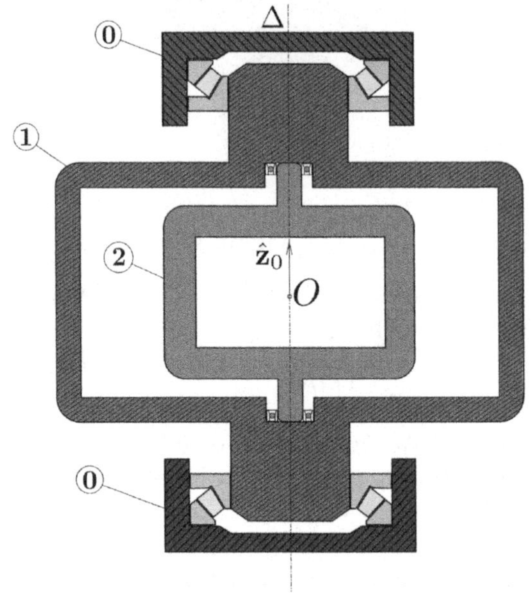

Figure 12.12

a. Since the pivot connections between 0 and 1 are frictionless, the contact forces exerted on body 1 satisfy $\mathbf{M}^c_{O,0\to 1} \cdot \hat{\mathbf{z}}_0 = 0$. Furthermore the only other external forces acting on the system are the gravitational forces acting on both bodies directed along $\hat{\mathbf{z}}_0$. This necessarily implies that the resultant external moment about O satisfies $\mathbf{M}_{O,\overline{\Sigma}\to\Sigma} \cdot \hat{\mathbf{z}}_0 = 0$. According to the dynamic moment equation (Euler's second principle) applied to system Σ, this leads to

$$\frac{d}{dt}(\mathbf{H}_{O,\Sigma/0} \cdot \hat{\mathbf{z}}_0) = 0$$

Hence, the $\hat{\mathbf{z}}_0$-component of the system's angular momentum $\mathbf{H}_{O,\Sigma/0}$ is conserved:

$$\mathbf{H}_{O,\Sigma/0} \cdot \hat{\mathbf{z}}_0 = \mathbf{H}_{O,1/0} \cdot \hat{\mathbf{z}}_0 + \mathbf{H}_{O,2/0} \cdot \hat{\mathbf{z}}_0 = \text{constant}$$

with $\mathbf{H}_{O,1/0} \cdot \hat{\mathbf{z}}_0 + \mathbf{H}_{O,2/0} \cdot \hat{\mathbf{z}}_0 = (I_1 + I_2)\Omega$ at time $t = T$ and $\mathbf{H}_{O,1} \cdot \hat{\mathbf{z}}_0 = I_1\omega_{01}$, $\mathbf{H}_{O,2} \cdot \hat{\mathbf{z}}_0 = I_2\omega_{02}$ at time $t = 0$. This gives angular velocity Ω in terms of ω_{01}, ω_{02}:

$$\Omega = \frac{I_1\omega_{01} + I_2\omega_{02}}{I_1 + I_2}$$

b. For bodies in rotation about axis Δ, the kinetic energies $\mathbb{K}_{1/0}$, $\mathbb{K}_{2/0}$ and $\mathbb{K}_{\Sigma/0}$ are given by

$$\mathbb{K}_{1/0} = \tfrac{1}{2}I_1\omega_1^2, \qquad \mathbb{K}_{2/0} = \tfrac{1}{2}I_2\omega_2^2, \qquad \mathbb{K}_{\Sigma/0} = \tfrac{1}{2}I_1\omega_1^2 + \tfrac{1}{2}I_2\omega_2^2$$

The variations of these quantities during during the time interval T are then found to be:

$$\Delta\mathbb{K}_1 = \tfrac{1}{2}I_1(\Omega^2 - \omega_{01}^2) = \tfrac{1}{2}\frac{I_1 I_2}{(I_1+I_2)^2}(\omega_{02}-\omega_{01})[(2I_1+I_2)\omega_{01}+I_2\omega_{02}]$$

$$\Delta\mathbb{K}_2 = \tfrac{1}{2}I_2(\Omega^2 - \omega_{02}^2) = \tfrac{1}{2}\frac{I_1 I_2}{(I_1+I_2)^2}(\omega_{01}-\omega_{02})[(2I_2+I_1)\omega_{02}+I_1\omega_{01}]$$

leading to

$$\Delta\mathbb{K}_{\Sigma/0} = \Delta\mathbb{K}_{1/0} + \Delta\mathbb{K}_{2/0} = -\tfrac{1}{2}\frac{I_1 I_2}{(I_1+I_2)}(\omega_{02}-\omega_{01})^2$$

First, we see that $\Delta\mathbb{K}_\Sigma < 0$: this can be explained by the Work-Energy Theorem applied to system Σ during time interval $0 \le t \le T$:

$$\Delta\mathbb{K}_{\Sigma/0} = \int_0^T \mathbb{P}_{\overline{\Sigma}\to\Sigma/0}dt + \int_0^T \mathbb{P}_{1\leftrightarrow 2}dt = \int_0^T \mathbb{P}_{1\leftrightarrow 2}dt$$

where the work done by the external actions (the gravitational and contact forces $0\to 1$) vanishes. The work done by the internal forces takes the expression

$$\int_0^T \mathbb{P}_{1\leftrightarrow 2}dt = \int_0^T \omega_{2/1}\cdot\mathbf{M}^c_{O,1\to 2}dt = \int_0^T (\omega_2-\omega_1)\hat{\mathbf{z}}_0\cdot\mathbf{M}^c_{O,1\to 2}dt$$

where $(\omega_2-\omega_1)\hat{\mathbf{z}}_0\cdot\mathbf{M}^c_{O,1\to 2} < 0$ at any time since the frictional forces exerted by 1 on 2 must oppose the rotation of 2 relative to 1. This justifies that $\Delta\mathbb{K}_\Sigma < 0$.

The variations $\Delta\mathbb{K}_1$ and $\Delta\mathbb{K}_2$ of the kinetic energies of bodies 1 and 2 can be positive or negative depending on the sign of $\omega_{01}-\omega_{02}$: application of the work-energy theorem to body 1, then body 2 gives

$$\Delta\mathbb{K}_{1/0} = -\int_0^T \omega_1\hat{\mathbf{z}}_0\cdot\mathbf{M}^c_{O,1\to 2}\,dt$$

$$\Delta\mathbb{K}_{2/0} = \int_0^T \omega_2\hat{\mathbf{z}}_0\cdot\mathbf{M}^c_{O,1\to 2}\,dt$$

Assume that $\omega_{02} > \omega_{01} > 0$ then $\hat{\mathbf{z}}_0\cdot\mathbf{M}^c_{O,1\to 2} < 0$ from $t=0$ until $t=T$: this implies that $\int_0^T \hat{\mathbf{z}}_0\cdot\mathbf{M}_{O,1\to 2}\,dt$ is negative

$$\Delta\mathbb{K}_{1/0} > 0, \qquad \Delta\mathbb{K}_{2/0} < 0$$

Conversely, if $\omega_{02} > \omega_{01} > 0$ at $t=0$, then $\Delta\mathbb{K}_{1/0} < 0$ and $\Delta\mathbb{K}_{2/0} > 0$. ■

Example 12.13 Figure 12.13 shows a truncated right-circular cone 2 of half-angle θ, uniformly-distributed mass m, and mass center G. It is in motion relative to a horizontal support 1 in such a way that (i) one of its generatrix lines is in contact with 1, and (ii) its axis always passes through fixed point O of 1, (iii) it does not slip relative to 1.

Its motion relative to 1 is entirely specified by the angles ψ and ϕ. Denote by I_1 the moment of inertia of 1 about axis OZ, by A_2 and C_2 the transverse and axial moments of inertia which characterize the inertia operator $\mathcal{I}_{O,2}$ of body 2.

a. Assume that support 1 is stationary. Apply the KET to body 2 relative to body 1.

b. Now assume that support 1 is in rotation about vertical axis OZ at angular velocity Ω under the action of a motor of couple C mounted between 1 and the supporting frame 0. Apply the KET to 2 relative to 0, and then to the system Σ ={1, 2} relative to 0. Assume that the connection between 1 and 0 is an ideal pivot of axis OZ. ■

a. If body 1 is stationary, we can apply the KET to body 2 relative to body 1: $d\mathbb{K}_{2/1}/dt =$

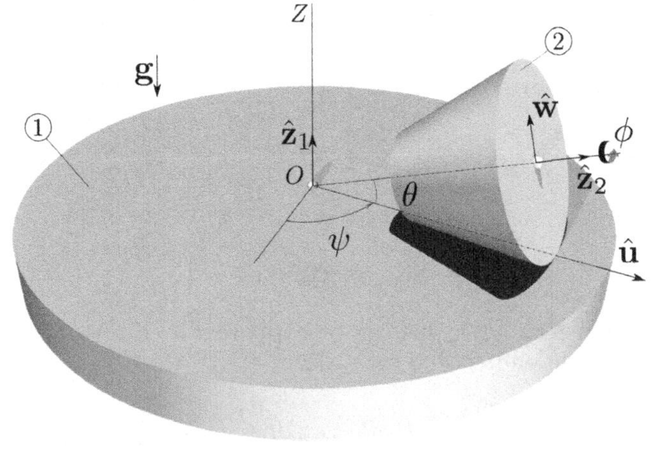

Figure 12.13

$\mathbb{P}_{\bar{2}\to 2/1}$. To find power $\mathbb{P}_{\bar{2}\to 2/1}$ we first note that $\{\mathcal{A}_{\bar{2}\to 2}\} = \{\mathcal{A}^g_{\text{Earth}\to 2}\} + \{\mathcal{A}^c_{1\to 2}\}$:

$$\mathbb{P}_{\bar{2}\to 2/1} = \underbrace{-mg\hat{\mathbf{z}}_1 \cdot \mathbf{v}_{G/1}}_{0} + \underbrace{\int_{l_A}^{l_B} (N\hat{\mathbf{z}}_1 + F_u\hat{\mathbf{u}} + F_v\hat{\mathbf{v}}) \cdot \mathbf{v}_{Q\in 2/1}\, dl}_{0} = 0$$

where we have accounted for contact forces distributed along the contact line AB (with $\hat{\mathbf{v}} = \hat{\mathbf{z}}_1 \times \hat{\mathbf{u}}$), and the no-slip kinematic condition $\mathbf{v}_{Q\in 2/1} = \mathbf{0}$. It results that $\mathbb{K}_{2/1}$ remains constant during the motion (this results in a first-integral of motion). To find $\mathbb{K}_{2/1}$, we first find angular velocity $\boldsymbol{\omega}_{2/1} = \dot{\psi}\hat{\mathbf{z}}_1 + \dot{\phi}\hat{\mathbf{z}}_2$. Imposing the no-slip condition at Q gives the condition $\dot{\psi} = -\dot{\phi}\sin\theta$ and $\boldsymbol{\omega}_{2/1} = -\dot{\psi}\cot\theta\hat{\mathbf{z}}_1$. The kinetic energy $\mathbb{K}_{2/1}$ is then given by

$$\mathbb{K}_{2/1} = \tfrac{1}{2}\boldsymbol{\omega}_{2/1} \cdot \mathcal{I}_{O,2}(\boldsymbol{\omega}_{2/1}) = \tfrac{1}{2}(A_2 + C_2\cot^2\theta)\dot{\psi}^2\cos^2\theta = Cst$$

This implies that $\dot{\psi}$ = constant (or $\dot{\phi}$ = constant).

b. If body 1 is in rotation, we cannot apply the KET to 2 relative to 1 which is no longer Newtonian. We find power $\mathbb{P}_{\bar{2}\to 2/0}$ as in question a):

$$\frac{d}{dt}\mathbb{K}_{2/0} = \mathbb{P}_{\bar{2}\to 2/0} = \underbrace{-mg\hat{\mathbf{z}}_1 \cdot \mathbf{v}_{G/0}}_{0} + \int_{l_A}^{l_B} (N\hat{\mathbf{z}}_1 + T_u\hat{\mathbf{u}} + T_v\hat{\mathbf{v}}) \cdot \mathbf{v}_{Q\in 2/0}\, dl$$
$$= \int_{l_A}^{l_B} T_v l\Omega\, dl \neq 0$$

where we have used $\mathbf{v}_{Q\in 2/0} = \mathbf{v}_{Q\in 2/1} + \mathbf{v}_{Q\in 1/0} = \mathbf{v}_{Q\in 1/0} = \Omega l\hat{\mathbf{v}}$ (denoting $l = |OQ|$). We end up with an integral expression whose value cannot be explicitly written in terms of the motion variables (Ω, ψ, ϕ).

The situation is different if we apply the KET to the system Σ ={1,2} relative to 0:

$$\frac{d}{dt}(\mathbb{K}_{1/0} + \mathbb{K}_{2/0}) = \underbrace{\mathbb{P}^g_{\text{Earth}\to\Sigma/0}}_{0} + \underbrace{\mathbb{P}^c_{0\to 1/0}}_{0} + \underbrace{\mathbb{P}_{\text{Motor}\to 1/0}}_{C\Omega} + \underbrace{\mathbb{P}^c_{1\leftrightarrow 2}}_{0} = C\Omega$$

Note here that we have to account for the internal interaction between 1 and 2 in the term $\mathbb{P}^c_{1\leftrightarrow 2}$ which is in fact identical to $\mathbb{P}^c_{1\to 2/1} = 0$. The kinetic energy of the system is given by

$$\mathbb{K}_{\Sigma/0} = \mathbb{K}_{1/0} + \mathbb{K}_{2/0} = \tfrac{1}{2}I_1\Omega^2 + \tfrac{1}{2}A_2(\dot{\psi} + \Omega)^2\cos^2\theta + \tfrac{1}{2}C_2[(\dot{\psi} + \Omega)\sin\theta + \dot{\phi}]^2$$

with $\dot{\phi} = -\dot{\psi}/\sin\theta$. ∎

Example 12.14 Consider Example 11.8. Show that the energy of system Σ is conserved. Then re-derive the expressions of the angular velocities reached by bodies 1 and 2 just before body 2 hits the end of the screw, that is, when the value $z = 0$ is reached. Assume that the joints $0 \leftrightarrow 1$ and $1 \leftrightarrow 2$ are ideal. ■

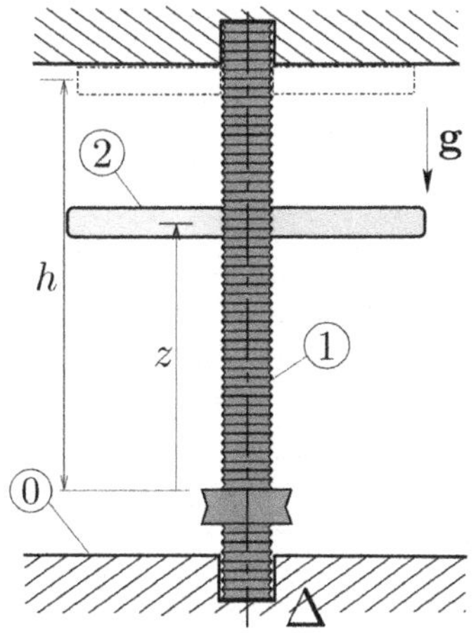

Figure 12.14

Application of the KET to system Σ gives the following equation

$$\frac{d}{dt}(\mathbb{K}_{1/0} + \mathbb{K}_{2/0}) = \mathbb{P}^c_{0\to 1/0} + \mathbb{P}^g_{\text{Earth}\to\Sigma} + \mathbb{P}^c_{1\leftrightarrow 2} \tag{1}$$

Since the joints $0 \leftrightarrow 1$ and $1 \leftrightarrow 2$ are ideal, we have

$$\mathbb{P}^c_{0\to 1/0} = \mathbb{P}^c_{0\leftrightarrow 1} = 0, \qquad \mathbb{P}^c_{1\leftrightarrow 2} = 0.$$

Furthermore, the power $\mathbb{P}^g_{\text{Earth}\to\Sigma}$ can be rewritten in terms of potential energy $\mathbb{U}^g_{\text{Earth}\to\Sigma/0}$:

$$\mathbb{P}^g_{\text{Earth}\to\Sigma/0} = -\frac{d}{dt}\mathbb{U}^g_{\text{Earth}\to\Sigma/0} = -\frac{d}{dt}(m_2 g z)$$

where z denote the height reached by the mass center of body 2. We then see that equation (1) is equivalent to

$$\mathbb{K}_{1/0} + \mathbb{K}_{2/0} + m_2 g z = \text{constant} = m_2 g h$$

which states that the mechanical energy of system Σ is conserved. With $\mathbb{K}_{1/0} = \frac{1}{2}J_1\omega_1^2$ and $\mathbb{K}_{2/0} = \frac{1}{2}J_1\omega_2^2 + \frac{1}{2}m_2\dot{z}^2$, we obtain

$$J_1\omega_1^2 + J_1\omega_2^2 + m_2\frac{p^2}{4\pi^2}(\omega_2 - \omega_1)^2 = m_2 g(h - z)$$

where we have used $\dot{z} = (p/2\pi)(\omega_2 - \omega_1)$. At the end of the downward motion of 2, we impose $z = 0$, and the angular velocities reach the values $\omega_{1,*}$ and $\omega_{2,*}$ which satisfy:

$$J_1\omega_{1,*}^2 + J_1\omega_{2,*}^2 + m_2\frac{p^2}{4\pi^2}(\omega_{2,*} - \omega_{1,*})^2 = m_2 g h$$

After taking account equation $J_1\omega_{1,*} + J_2\omega_{2,*} = 0$ obtained by conservation of angular momentum, we obtain the same result obtained in Example 11.8. ■

Example 12.15 Consider the system Σ of Example 12.4. Recall that it is comprised of two rigid bodies:

- rigid body 1 has mass m_1, mass center G_1 and moment of inertia I_1 about axis of rotation $(O, \hat{\mathbf{z}}_0)$.
- rigid body 2 has mass m_2, mass center G_2 and inertia matrix

$$[\mathcal{I}_{G_2,2}]_{b_2} = \begin{bmatrix} A_2 & 0 & 0 \\ 0 & B_2 & 0 \\ 0 & 0 & C_2 \end{bmatrix}_{b_2}$$

on basis $b_2(\hat{\mathbf{x}}_2, \hat{\mathbf{y}}_1, \hat{\mathbf{z}}_2)$.

a. Apply the KET to rigid body 1, then to rigid body 2.
b. Apply the KET to system Σ. ■

a. The KET applied to rigid body 1 states that $\frac{d}{dt}\mathbb{K}_{1/0} = \mathbb{P}_{\bar{1}\to 1/0}$ where the expression of power $\mathbb{P}_{\bar{1}\to 1/0}$ was found in Example 12.4. The expression of $\mathbb{K}_{1/0}$ is easily found to be $\frac{1}{2}I_1\dot{\theta}_1^2$. We obtain the equation:

$$\frac{d}{dt}\Big(\frac{1}{2}I_1\dot{\theta}_1^2\Big) = \mathcal{C}_{01}\dot{\theta}_1 + \underbrace{(\mathbf{R}^c_{2\to 1}\cdot l_1\dot{\theta}_1\hat{\mathbf{y}}_1 + \mathbf{M}^c_{A,2\to 1}\cdot\dot{\theta}_1\hat{\mathbf{z}}_0)}_{\mathbb{P}^c_{2\to 1/0}} \tag{1}$$

As was noted previously, power $\mathbb{P}^c_{2\to 1/0}$ would still not be zero for an ideal pivot $1 \leftrightarrow 2$.

Similarly for rigid body 2 we can state $\frac{d}{dt}\mathbb{K}_{2/0} = \mathbb{P}_{\bar{2}\to 2/0}$ with $\mathbb{K}_{2/0} = \frac{1}{2}\boldsymbol{\omega}_{2/0}\cdot\mathcal{I}_{G_2,2}(\boldsymbol{\omega}_{2/0}) + \frac{1}{2}\mathbf{v}^2_{G_2/0}$:

$$\mathbb{K}_{2/0} = \frac{1}{2}(B_2 + m_2(a + l_2\cos\theta_2)^2)\dot{\theta}_1^2 + \frac{1}{2}(A_2\cos^2\theta_2 + C_2\sin^2\theta_2 + m_2 l_2^2)\dot{\theta}_2^2$$

leading to

$$\frac{d}{dt}\left[\frac{1}{2}(B_2 + m_2(a + l_2\cos\theta_2)^2)\dot{\theta}_1^2 + \frac{1}{2}(A_2\cos^2\theta_2 + C_2\sin^2\theta_2 + m_2 l_2^2)\dot{\theta}_2^2\right] =$$
$$-m_2 g l_2\dot{\theta}_2\cos\theta_2 + \dot{\rho}F_{12} + \underbrace{(\mathbf{R}^c_{1\to 2}\cdot l_1\dot{\theta}_1\hat{\mathbf{y}}_1 + \mathbf{M}^c_{A,1\to 2}\cdot(\dot{\theta}_1\hat{\mathbf{z}}_0 - \dot{\theta}_2\hat{\mathbf{y}}_1))}_{\mathbb{P}^c_{1\to 2/0}} \tag{2}$$

The two equations obtained are not very useful due to the presence of unknown power terms.

b. To apply the KET to system Σ we need to write

$$\frac{d}{dt}(\mathbb{K}_{1/0} + \mathbb{K}_{2/0}) = \mathbb{P}_{\bar{\Sigma}\to 2/0} + \mathbb{P}_{\bar{\Sigma}\to 2/0} + \mathbb{P}_{1\leftrightarrow 2}$$

We find

$$\frac{d}{dt}\left[\frac{1}{2}(I_1 + B_2 + m_2(a + l_2\cos\theta_2)^2)\dot{\theta}_1^2 + \frac{1}{2}(A_2\cos^2\theta_2 + C_2\sin^2\theta_2 + m_2 l_2^2)\dot{\theta}_2^2\right] =$$
$$\underbrace{\mathcal{C}_{01}\dot{\theta}_1 - m_2 g l_2\dot{\theta}_2\cos\theta_2}_{\mathbb{P}_{\bar{\Sigma}\to\Sigma/0}} + \underbrace{\dot{\rho}F_{12} - \dot{\theta}_2 G(\dot{\theta}_2)}_{\mathbb{P}_{1\leftrightarrow 2}}$$

This equation is much more useful since the unknown power terms of equations (1) and (2) have disappeared. However application of the KET to system Σ is not sufficient to find all equations of motion. ■

Example 12.16 In the speed reducer shown in Figure 12.15, input shaft 1 terminates in a gear wheel of radius r_1. It is coupled to the output shaft 3 by a satellite gear 2 whose axis is mounted on the carrier rigidly connected to shaft 3. Gear 2 is also meshed to a stationary ring gear 4. The dimension of the gear train is defined by the parameters r_1 and r_2. A motor exerts a couple $C_i\hat{\mathbf{x}}_0$ on shaft 1. The output shaft exerts a couple $C_o\hat{\mathbf{x}}_0$ to an output device. Denote by I_1 and I_3 the moments of inertia of shafts 1 and 3 about axis $(O, \hat{\mathbf{x}}_0)$. Gear 2 has mass m_2, mass center G_2 and moment of inertia I_2 about axis $(G_2, \hat{\mathbf{x}}_0)$. Assume that all pivots are ideal and neglect the effect of gravity.

a. Find the ratio of angular velocities ω_3/ω_1 by using kinematic arguments.

b. Find the equation which governs the angular velocity $\omega_1(t)$ as a function of couple C_i and C_o and the system's parameters. ■

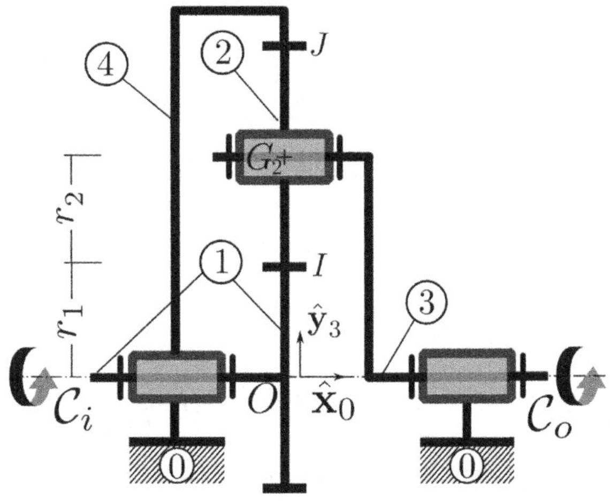

Figure 12.15

a. Using unit vectors $(\hat{\mathbf{x}}_0, \hat{\mathbf{y}}_3, \hat{\mathbf{z}}_3 = \hat{\mathbf{y}}_3 \times \hat{\mathbf{x}}_0)$, the relationship between ω_3 and ω_1 is found by writing the no-slip conditions at I (between 1 and 2) and at J (between 4 and 2):

$$\underbrace{\omega_1\hat{\mathbf{x}}_0 \times r_1\hat{\mathbf{y}}_3}_{\mathbf{v}_{I\in 1/0}} = r_1\omega_1\hat{\mathbf{z}}_3 = \underbrace{\mathbf{v}_{G_2} + \omega_2\hat{\mathbf{x}}_0 \times (-r_2\hat{\mathbf{y}}_3)}_{\mathbf{v}_{I\in 2/0}} = \mathbf{v}_{G_2} - r_2\omega_2\hat{\mathbf{z}}_3 \tag{1}$$

$$\underbrace{\mathbf{0}}_{\mathbf{v}_{J\in 4/0}} = \underbrace{\mathbf{v}_{G_2} + \omega_2\hat{\mathbf{x}}_0 \times (r_2\hat{\mathbf{y}}_3)}_{\mathbf{v}_{J\in 2/0}} = \mathbf{v}_{G_2} + r_2\omega_2\hat{\mathbf{z}}_3 \tag{2}$$

with $\mathbf{v}_{G_2} = (r_1 + r_2)\omega_3\hat{\mathbf{z}}_3$. Comparing (1) and (2) gives

$$\frac{\omega_3}{\omega_1} = \frac{r_1}{2(r_1 + r_2)} \tag{3}$$

Also note that equations (1-2) also give $\omega_2 = -\frac{r_1+r_2}{r_2}\omega_3 = -\frac{r_1}{2r_2}\omega_1$.

b. Denote by Σ the system $\{1, 2, 3\}$. To find the equation which governs the angular velocity $\omega_1(t)$, we apply the KET to system Σ, that is:

$$\frac{d}{dt}\mathbb{K}_{\Sigma/0} = \mathbb{P}_{\overline{\Sigma}\to\Sigma/0} + \mathbb{P}_{1\leftrightarrow 2} + \mathbb{P}_{2\leftrightarrow 3} \tag{4}$$

To find the kinetic energy of the system, we find the kinetic energy of each body:

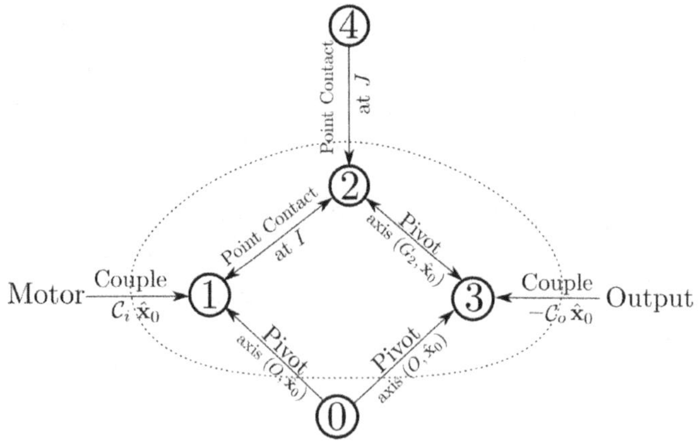

Figure 12.16

- body 1 in rotation about axis $(O, \hat{\mathbf{x}}_0)$:

$$\mathbb{K}_{1/0} = \tfrac{1}{2} I_1 \omega_1^2$$

- body 2 in instantaneous rotation about axis $(J, \hat{\mathbf{x}}_0)$:

$$\mathbb{K}_{2/0} = \tfrac{1}{2}(I_2 + m_2 r_2^2)\omega_2^2 = \frac{1}{8}(I_2 + m_2 r_2^2)\frac{r_1^2}{r_2^2}\omega_1^2$$

- body 3 in rotation about axis $(O, \hat{\mathbf{x}}_0)$:

$$\mathbb{K}_{3/0} = \tfrac{1}{2} I_3 \omega_2^2 = \frac{1}{8} I_3 \frac{r_1^2}{(r_1 + r_2)^2}\omega_1^2$$

To find the external power $\mathbb{P}_{\overline{\Sigma}\to\Sigma/0}$ and the powers of interaction $\mathbb{P}_{1\leftrightarrow 2}$ and $\mathbb{P}_{2\leftrightarrow 3}$, we sketch in Figure 12.16 the diagram showing all external and internal actions (gravity is neglected). The external actions contribute to the power $\mathbb{P}_{\overline{\Sigma}\to\Sigma/0}$:

$$\begin{aligned}\mathbb{P}_{\overline{\Sigma}\to\Sigma/0} &= \underbrace{C_i\omega_1}_{\text{input motor}} \underbrace{-C_o\omega_3}_{\text{output device}} + \underbrace{\omega_1\hat{\mathbf{x}}_0 \cdot \mathbf{M}^c_{O,0\to 1}}_{\text{pivot connection}} + \underbrace{\omega_3\hat{\mathbf{x}}_0 \cdot \mathbf{M}^c_{O,0\to 3}}_{\text{pivot connection}} + \underbrace{\mathbf{R}^c_{4\to 2}\cdot \mathbf{v}_{J\in 2/4}}_{\text{point contact at } J} \\ &= (C_i - \frac{r_1}{2(r_1+r_2)}C_o)\omega_1\end{aligned}$$

where we have used (3) and the fact that (i) the pivots connections $0 \leftrightarrow 1$ and $0 \leftrightarrow 2$ are ideal: $\hat{\mathbf{x}}_0 \cdot \mathbf{M}^c_{O,0\to 1} = \hat{\mathbf{x}}_0 \cdot \mathbf{M}^c_{O,0\to 2} = 0$ and (ii) there is no-slip at J: $\mathbf{v}_{J\in 2/4} = \mathbf{0}$.

The powers of interactions are given by

$$\mathbb{P}_{1\leftrightarrow 2} + \mathbb{P}_{2\leftrightarrow 3} = \underbrace{\mathbf{R}^c_{1\to 2}\cdot \mathbf{v}_{I\in 2/1}}_{\text{point contact at } I} + \underbrace{\omega_{2/3}\hat{\mathbf{x}}_0 \cdot \mathbf{M}^c_{G_2,3\to 2}}_{\text{pivot connection}} = 0$$

where we have used the fact that (i) the pivot connection $2 \leftrightarrow 3$ is ideal: $\hat{\mathbf{x}}_0 \cdot \mathbf{M}_{G_2,3\to 2} = 0$ and (ii) there is no-slip at I: $\mathbf{v}_{I\in 2/1} = \mathbf{0}$.

Now equation (4) becomes

$$\left(I_1 + \frac{r_1^2}{4r_2^2}I_2 + \frac{1}{4}m_2 r_1^2 + \frac{r_1^2}{4(r_1+r_2)^2}I_3\right)\frac{d\omega_1}{dt} = C_i - \frac{r_1}{2(r_1+r_2)}C_o$$

This final result shows the benefit of the energy approach over the use of Newton-Euler vectorial method for a single-degree-of-freedom system. ■

12.8 Problems

Problem 12.1 A system Σ comprised of a frame 1 supporting a cylinder 2 is in motion relative to a referential 0. More specifically, frame 1 is free to rotate about a frictionless vertical axis Δ. Cylinder 2 is connected to frame 1 by a pivot of axis AB. The frictional forces between 1 and 2 are taken into account.

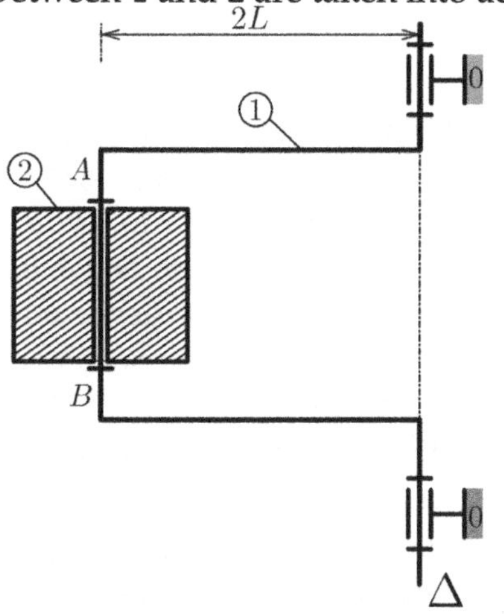

Cylinder 2 has mass m and moment of inertia $\frac{1}{2}mR^2$ about axis AB. Frame 1 has mass M and moment of inertia I_Δ about axis Δ.

At $t = 0$, the frame is immobile, and the cylinder is given an initial angular velocity ω_0. One observes that the cylinder comes to rest relative to the frame at some time $t = t_1$ due to the effect of friction.

a. Find the angular velocity reached by frame 1 at time t_1.

b. Find the work done by the frictional forces between 1 and 2 from time $t = 0$ to time $t = t_1$. Verify that this work is negative.

Problem 12.2 Consider a right-circular cylinder C of radius R and height $2\pi R$, which can rotate without friction about axis OZ of a Newtonian referential of Cartesian axes $OXYZ$. The axis $Oz \equiv OZ$ is directed downward, and the upper base Oxy of C is horizontal. The axes Ox and Oy attached to the cylinder initially coincides with OX and OY.

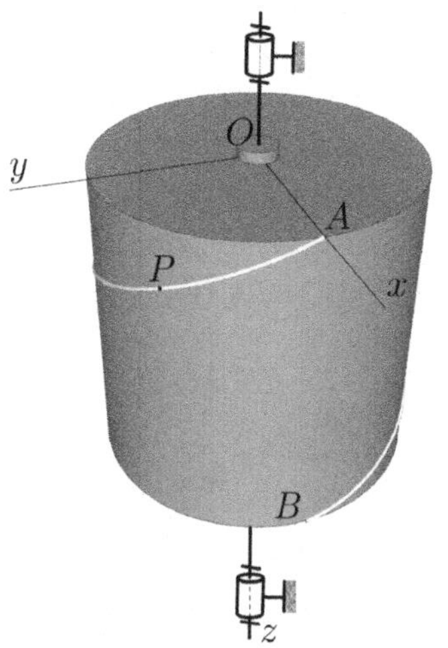

A helical tube of negligible cross-section, and negligible mass is attached to the lateral surface of the cylinder. A small ball P of mass m, modeled as a particle, can move inside this tube without friction under the action of gravity. Its trajectory relative to C can be defined in the following parametric form

$$x = R\cos\theta, \quad y = R\sin\theta, \quad z = R\theta$$

with $0 \leq \theta \leq 2\pi$, point A corresponding to $\theta = 0$ and point B to $\theta = 2\pi$. Particle P is dropped at point A without initial velocity. The cylinder is initially at rest. Its moment of inertia about axis Oz is denoted as I.

a. Find two quantities which are conserved during the motion and which allow the determination of both the cylinder's angular velocity and $\dot{\theta}$.

b. Find the time taken by P to reach point B. Determine the velocity of P with respect to $OXYZ$ at this instant.

Problem 12.3 We consider in this problem the motion of a system Σ relative to a referential $0(O, \hat{\mathbf{x}}_0, \hat{\mathbf{y}}_0, \hat{\mathbf{z}}_0)$. Referential 0 is attached to the Earth, and considered Newtonian. Axis $(O, \hat{\mathbf{z}}_0)$ is directed upward ($\mathbf{g} = -g\hat{\mathbf{z}}_0$). The system Σ comprises two rigid bodies 1 and 2 described as follows:
Body 1 is a torus-shaped body, of homoge-

neous density, center O, radius R, and mass m_1. A basis attached to 1 is $b_1(\hat{\mathbf{x}}_1, \hat{\mathbf{y}}_1, \hat{\mathbf{z}}_1 = \hat{\mathbf{z}}_0)$ as defined in the figure. The plane $(O, \hat{\mathbf{x}}_1, \hat{\mathbf{z}}_1)$ is a plane of symmetry. It is connected to frame 0 by an ideal pivot of axis $(O, \hat{\mathbf{z}}_0)$, and its position is defined by angle $\psi = (\hat{\mathbf{x}}_0, \hat{\mathbf{x}}_1) = (\hat{\mathbf{y}}_0, \hat{\mathbf{y}}_1)$. Denote by I_1 the moment of inertia of body 1 about axis $(O, \hat{\mathbf{z}}_0)$.

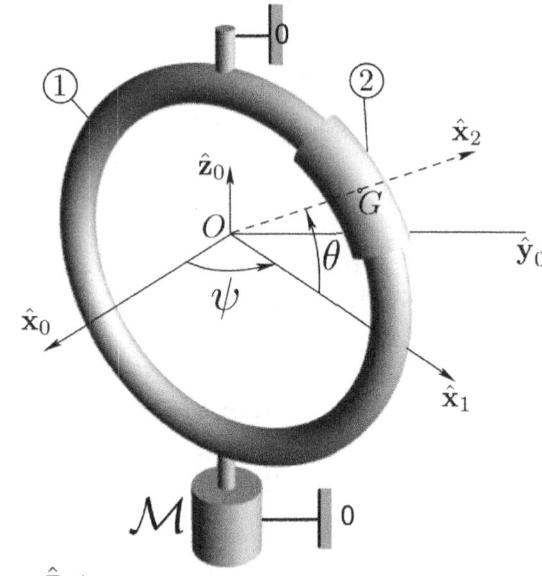

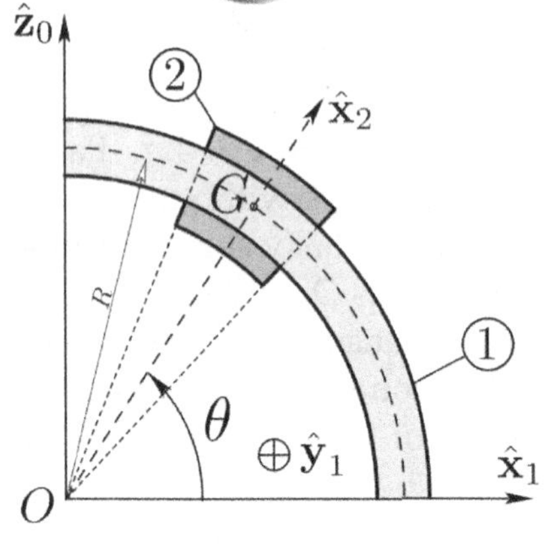

Body 2 is a truncated hollow torus-shaped body of mass center G, mass m_2, and basis $b_2(\hat{\mathbf{x}}_2, \hat{\mathbf{y}}_2 = \hat{\mathbf{y}}_1, \hat{\mathbf{z}}_2 = \hat{\mathbf{x}}_2 \times \hat{\mathbf{y}}_2)$ such that $\mathbf{r}_{OG} = R\hat{\mathbf{x}}_2$. The external surface of 1 is in contact with the internal surface of 2: body 2 is free to "slide" relative to 1, and its motion relative to 1 is entirely parametrized by angle $\theta = (\hat{\mathbf{x}}_1, \hat{\mathbf{x}}_2) = (\hat{\mathbf{z}}_0, \hat{\mathbf{z}}_2)$. Its inertia operator about G is represented by:

$$[\mathcal{I}_{G,2}]_{b_2} = \begin{bmatrix} A_2 & 0 & 0 \\ 0 & B_2 & 0 \\ 0 & 0 & C_2 \end{bmatrix}_{b_2}$$

The direct contact between 1 and 2 is assumed frictionless. The corresponding contact action screw $\{\mathcal{A}^c_{1\to 2}\}$ must satisfy the condition

$$\mathbf{M}^c_{O,1\to 2} \cdot \hat{\mathbf{y}}_1 = 0$$

A motor $\mathcal{M}$ is mounted between 0 and 1, and imposes a prescribed angle $\psi(t)$. The action of $\mathcal{M}$ on 1 is equivalent to a couple $C\hat{\mathbf{z}}_0$. All aerodynamics effects are neglected.

a. Justify the form of inertia matrix $[\mathcal{I}_{G,2}]_{b_2}$.

b. Derive the two equations extracted from the Fundamental Theorem of Dynamics in order to find the unknown couple C and angle $\theta(t)$.

c. Apply the Kinetic Energy Theorem to system Σ. How is this result related to the equations derived in **b.**?

Problem 12.4 In this speed reducer, the carrier 1 supports the double satellite gear 3 which is meshed with two co-axial ring gears 2 and 4. Ring gear 4 is stationary.

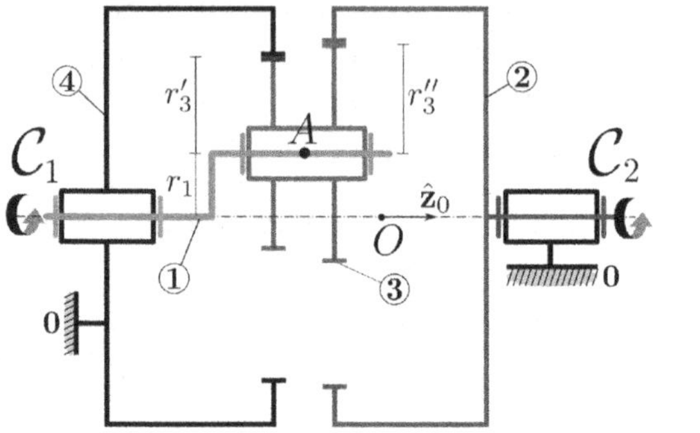

A motor exerts a couple $C_1\hat{\mathbf{z}}_0$ on the shaft of carrier 1. The output shaft of ring gear 2 exerts a couple $C_2\hat{\mathbf{z}}_0$ to an output device. Carrier 1 has moment of inertia I_1 about axis $(O, \hat{\mathbf{z}}_0)$. Satellite gear 3 has moment of inertia I_3 about axis $(A, \hat{\mathbf{z}}_0)$, mass m_3, and mass center A. Gear 2 has moment of inertia I_2 about axis $(O, \hat{\mathbf{z}}_0)$. All pivots are assumed ideal and the effect of gravity is neglected.

a. Find the ratio of angular velocities ω_2/ω_1 in terms of the parameters r_1, r'_3 and r''_3.

b. Find the equation which governs the angular velocity $\omega_1(t)$ as a function of couple C_1 and C_2 and the system's parameters. Deduce the ratio C_2/C_1 in steady-state regime.

Problem 12.5 Figure 12.17 displayed below shows a schematic of a three-degree-of-freedom human centrifuge. Denote by Σ the system of three rigid bodies 1, 2, 3 in motion in a Newtonian referential 0.

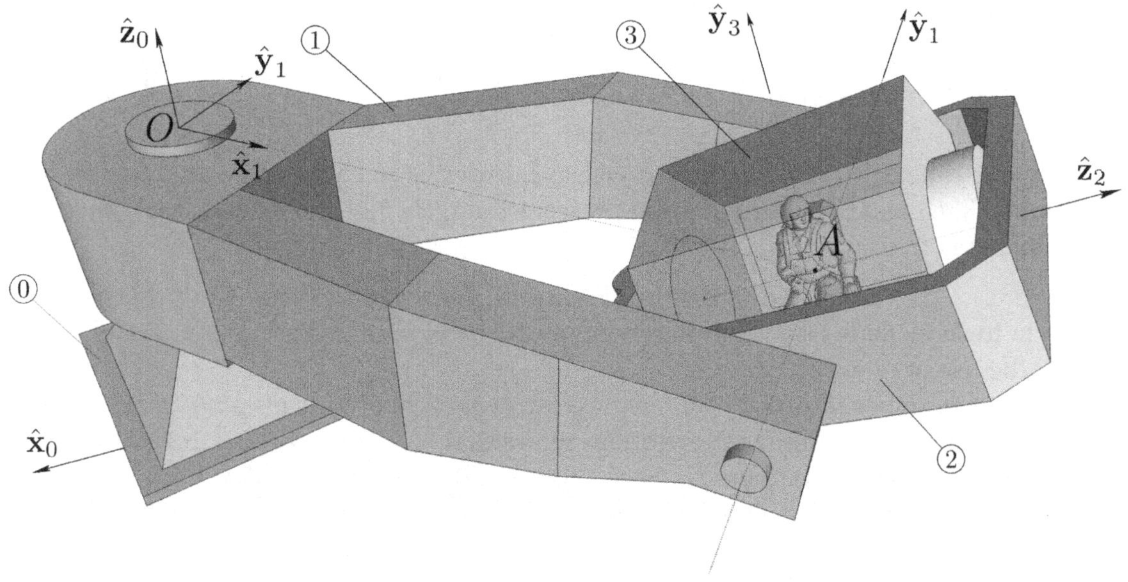

Figure 12.17

Body 1 is the main arm of the centrifuge. Its motion relative to 0 is a rotation about vertical axis $(O, \hat{\mathbf{z}}_0)$. A basis attached to 1 is denoted $b_1(\hat{\mathbf{x}}_1, \hat{\mathbf{y}}_1, \hat{\mathbf{z}}_0)$ whose orientation relative to a basis $(\hat{\mathbf{x}}_0, \hat{\mathbf{y}}_0, \hat{\mathbf{z}}_0)$ of 0 is defined by angle $\theta_1(t) = (\hat{\mathbf{x}}_0, \hat{\mathbf{x}}_1) = (\hat{\mathbf{y}}_0, \hat{\mathbf{y}}_1)$. Its mass center G_1 location is given by $\mathbf{r}_{OG_1} = L_1\hat{\mathbf{x}}_1$. Its moment of inertia about axis $(O, \hat{\mathbf{z}}_0)$ is denoted I_1.
Body 2 is the fork of the centrifuge. Its motion relative to 1 is a rotation about axis $(A, \hat{\mathbf{y}}_1)$. A basis attached to 2 is denoted $b_2(\hat{\mathbf{x}}_2, \hat{\mathbf{y}}_1, \hat{\mathbf{z}}_2)$ whose orientation relative to basis $(\hat{\mathbf{x}}_1, \hat{\mathbf{y}}_1, \hat{\mathbf{z}}_0)$ is defined by angle $\theta_2(t) = (\hat{\mathbf{x}}_1, \hat{\mathbf{x}}_2) = (\hat{\mathbf{z}}_0, \hat{\mathbf{z}}_2)$. Its mass center A is defined by $\mathbf{r}_{OA} = L_2\hat{\mathbf{x}}_1$. Its mass is m_2 and its inertia operator about A takes the form

$$[\mathcal{I}_{A,2}]_{b_2} = \begin{bmatrix} I_2 & 0 & 0 \\ 0 & J_2 & 0 \\ 0 & 0 & K_2 \end{bmatrix}_{b_2}$$

Body 3 is the cab of the centrifuge, including the passenger. Its motion relative to 2 is a rotation about axis $(A, \hat{\mathbf{z}}_2)$. A basis attached to 3 is denoted $b_3(\hat{\mathbf{x}}_3, \hat{\mathbf{y}}_3, \hat{\mathbf{z}}_2)$ whose orientation relative to basis $(\hat{\mathbf{x}}_2, \hat{\mathbf{y}}_1, \hat{\mathbf{z}}_2)$ is defined by angle $\theta_3(t) = (\hat{\mathbf{x}}_2, \hat{\mathbf{x}}_3) = (\hat{\mathbf{y}}_1, \hat{\mathbf{y}}_3)$. Its mass center is

A, its mass m_3, and its inertia operator about A

$$[\mathcal{I}_{A,3}]_{b_3} = \begin{bmatrix} I_3 & P_3 & Q_3 \\ P_3 & J_3 & R_3 \\ Q_3 & R_3 & K_3 \end{bmatrix}_{b_3}$$

Assume that all interconnections can be modeled as ideal joints. The three degrees of freedom $\theta_1(t)$, $\theta_2(t)$ and $\theta_3(t)$ are controlled by three motors (assumed massless) $\mathcal{M}_1$ (mounted between 0 and 1), $\mathcal{M}_2$ (mounted between 1 and 2), and $\mathcal{M}_3$ (mounted between 2 and 3), whose actions are modeled as

$$\{\mathcal{A}_{\mathcal{M}_1\to 1}\} = \left\{ \begin{matrix} \mathbf{0} \\ C_1\hat{\mathbf{z}}_0 \end{matrix} \right\} \qquad \{\mathcal{A}_{\mathcal{M}_2\to 2}\} = \left\{ \begin{matrix} \mathbf{0} \\ C_2\hat{\mathbf{y}}_1 \end{matrix} \right\} \qquad \{\mathcal{A}_{\mathcal{M}_3\to 3}\} = \left\{ \begin{matrix} \mathbf{0} \\ C_3\hat{\mathbf{z}}_2 \end{matrix} \right\}$$

Apply the Kinetic Energy Theorem to system Σ to derive an equation governing the unknown couples C_1, C_2 and C_3 in terms of the prescribed angles $\theta_1(t)$, $\theta_2(t)$ and $\theta_3(t)$, and all other parameters of the systems.

Problem 12.6 The sketch displayed in Figure 12.18 shows a mechanism proposed by Lord Kelvin to show that elastic energy can be produced by rigid body motion, more specifically with the use of gyrostatic devices.

The figure shows four identical massless bars connected by pivots at A and B, C and D to form a frame in motion in a Newtonian referential $0(A, \hat{\mathbf{x}}_0, \hat{\mathbf{y}}_0, \hat{\mathbf{z}}_0)$ (with $\hat{\mathbf{z}}_0$ directed along the vertical downward). This frame is suspended to a hinge so that the plane $(A, \hat{\mathbf{x}}_s, \hat{\mathbf{z}}_0)$ containing the figure $ABCD$ is free to rotate about the vertical diagonal AC. At the center of each bar is placed a flywheel whose axis of rotation coincides with the line of the bar. The axisymmetric flywheels 1,2,3,4 are identical, each of mass M, of axial moment of inertia I, and of transverse moment of inertia J. They are given the same axial angular velocity

$$\Omega = -\boldsymbol{\omega}_{1/0} \cdot \hat{\mathbf{x}}_1 = \boldsymbol{\omega}_{2/0} \cdot \hat{\mathbf{x}}_2 = \boldsymbol{\omega}_{3/0} \cdot \hat{\mathbf{x}}_3 = -\boldsymbol{\omega}_{4/0} \cdot \hat{\mathbf{x}}_4$$

Connected to lower pivot C is a body 5 of mass m_5. Body 5 is also connected to fixed support 0 by a slider-pivot, while its mass center G_5 moves along axis $(A, \hat{\mathbf{z}}_s)$. We denote the system composed by the frame, the flywheels and body 5 as Σ. The position of system Σ is defined by the angles θ and ψ. All joints between the rigid bodies and the support are assumed ideal. The geometry of the system is defined by $\mathbf{r}_{AB} = 2a\hat{\mathbf{x}}_1$, $\mathbf{r}_{AG_1} = a\hat{\mathbf{x}}_1$, $\mathbf{r}_{CB} = 2a\hat{\mathbf{x}}_2$, $\mathbf{r}_{CG_2} = a\hat{\mathbf{x}}_2$, etc.

Lord Kelvin called this device "gyrostatic spring balance". The goal of this problem is to find out whether this device does behave like a balance and to compare it to a balance equipped with a linear spring connecting A to C.

a. Find the two equations of motion governing angles θ and ψ in terms of M, m_5, a, I, J, and Ω.

b. Show that the system can attain an equilibrium position. Find the period of small amplitude oscillations about the equilibrium. Investigate the change of length of diagonal AC under a change of mass m_5 and compare this result to that for a standard spring balance. Comment.

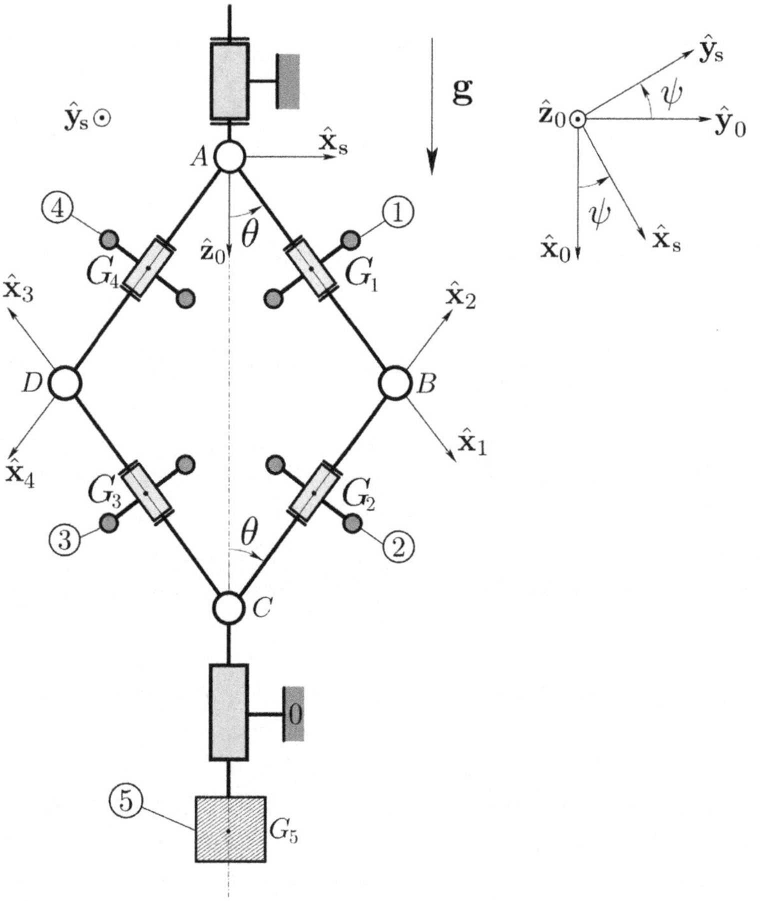
g
$\hat{\mathbf{y}}_s$
$\hat{\mathbf{z}}_0$
$\hat{\mathbf{y}}_0$
ψ
$\hat{\mathbf{x}}_0$
$\hat{\mathbf{x}}_s$
A
B
C
D
G_1
G_2
G_3
G_4
G_5
θ
$\hat{\mathbf{x}}_1$
$\hat{\mathbf{x}}_2$
$\hat{\mathbf{x}}_3$
$\hat{\mathbf{x}}_4$
1
2
3
4
5
0

Figure 12.18

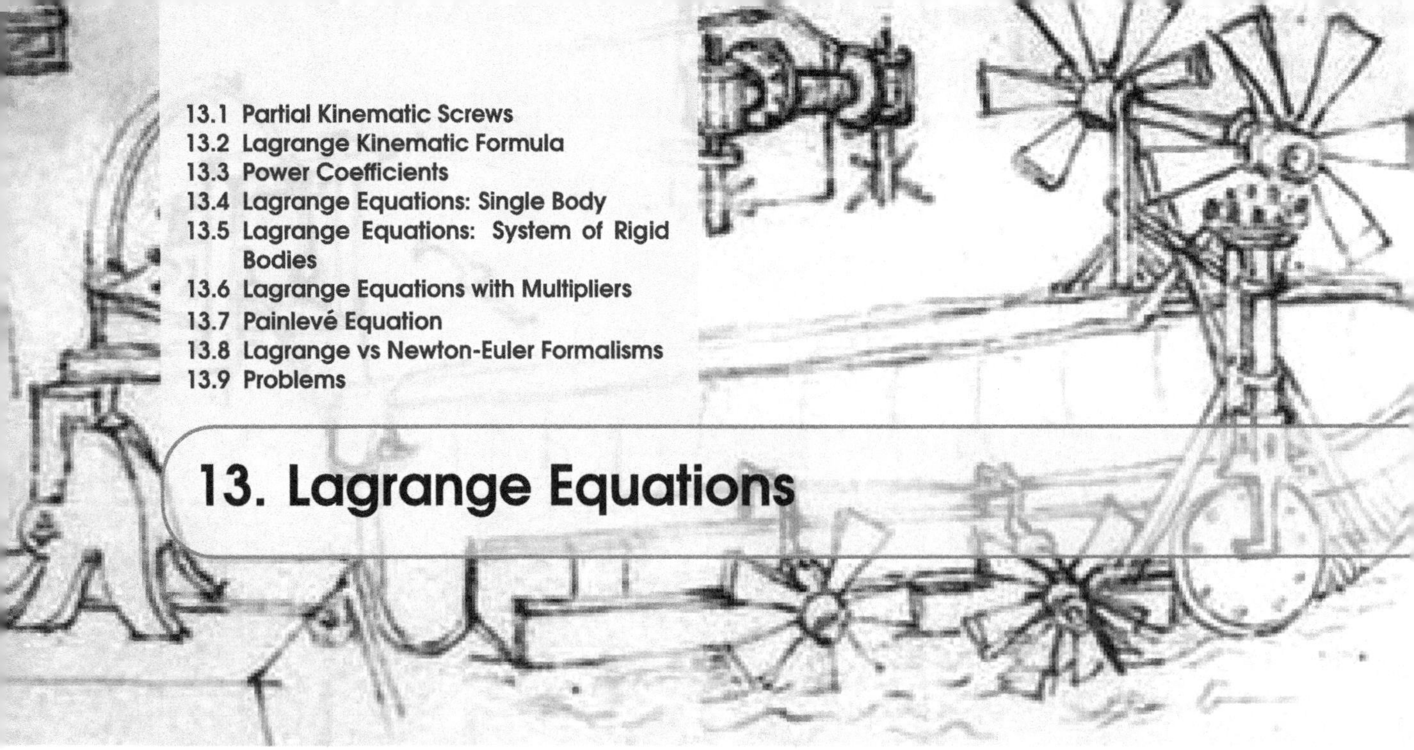

13. Lagrange Equations

LAGRANGE FORMALISM constitutes the foundation of *analytical mechanics*, a term coined by Lagrange himself [1]. Lagrange method provides another tool to derive the same equations found by applying Newton-Euler formalism, and hence brings about nothing fundamentally new. Lagrange himself stated in the preface of his first edition "*There already exist several treatises on mechanics, but the purpose of this one is entirely new. I propose to condense the theory of this science and the method of solving the related problems to general formulas whose simple application produces all the necessary equations for the solution of each problem. I hope that my presentation achieves this purpose and leaves nothing lacking.*

In addition, this work will have another use. The various principles presently available will be assembled and presented from a single point of view in order to facilitate the solution of the problems of mechanics. Moreover, it will also show their interdependence and mutual dependence and will permit the evaluation of their validity and scope."

However, contrary to the Newton-Euler formalism, Lagrange method takes a unified, global view of the system. The advantages of Lagrange equations are well known: their wide range and ease of applicability, the freedom of choice of coordinates to describe the system, the elimination of forces and moments of constraint. Hence, when the Newton-Euler formalism requires a careful and often difficult strategy to find the equations of motion so as to avoid unwanted equations, Lagrange method will yield these equations in an automatic and systematic way. The two formalisms are also different in an important way. Newton-Euler formalism is vectorial, while Lagrange formalism is scalar: the contribution of the inertial effects is found from the system's kinetic energy while the contribution of the mechanical actions is expressed through their virtual power. It is also important to point out that Lagrange equations do not yield a solution for the complete analysis of a dynamic system. Their use is also problematic for kinematically constrained systems or for the determination of the unknown contact actions which take place through the system's geometric joints.

To derive Lagrange equations, we take the same approach adopted to derive the Kinetic Energy Theorem: we choose a specific virtual velocity field and apply D'Alembert Principle of Virtual Power. In order to obtain as many equations as the body's degrees of freedom, the kinematic screw of a rigid body is decomposed into components with respect to the body's coordinates, known as the body's *partial kinematic screws*. Then, two types of terms are obtained: the virtual power of volume and surface forces leads to *power coefficients*, whereas the virtual power of inertial forces is related to the body's kinetic energy by *Lagrange kinematic formula*. The derivation of Lagrange equations is first done for a single body, then for a system of rigid bodies. A special case is considered to take into account the holonomic and non-holonomic constraint equations to arrive at Lagrange equations with *multipliers*. Finally, we derive Painlevé equation which can lead to a first integral under certain conditions.

13.1 Partial Kinematic Screws

In the Lagrangian formalism, the configuration of a system Σ of one or more rigid bodies is assumed to be defined by $(n+1)$ *independent* coordinates [2] $(q_1, q_2, \ldots, q_n, t)$ so that the position of any point of Σ relative to a referential $\mathcal{E}$ (of origin O) can be viewed as a vector function $\mathbf{r}_{OP}(q_1, q_2, \ldots, q_n, t)$ of these $(n+1)$ variables. Hence the velocity of P relative to $\mathcal{E}$ can be evaluated as follows:

$$\mathbf{v}_{P/\mathcal{E}} = \sum_{i=1}^{n} \frac{\partial \mathbf{r}_{OP}}{\partial q_i} \dot{q}_i + \frac{\partial \mathbf{r}_{OP}}{\partial t} \tag{13.1}$$

Equation (13.1) shows that the velocity of any point P of the system can be defined by the values of $(2n+1)$ variables $(\mathbf{q}, \dot{\mathbf{q}}, t)$, denoting by $\dot{\mathbf{q}}$ the set of variables $(\dot{q}_1, \ldots, \dot{q}_n)$. The Lagrangian formulation hinges on the following assumption

$(\mathbf{q}, \dot{\mathbf{q}}, t)$ form a set of independent variables. (13.2)

Remark 1. This assumption is pivotal to Lagrange formulation, and it has important consequences in practice.

Remark 2. In (13.1), the partial derivatives $\partial \mathbf{r}_{OP}/\partial q_i$ or $\partial \mathbf{r}_{OP}/\partial t$ depend on the choice of referential $\mathcal{E}$ and should be denoted $(\partial \mathbf{r}_{OP}/\partial q_i)_\mathcal{E}$ and $(\partial \mathbf{r}_{OP}/\partial t)_\mathcal{E}$, respectively. In what follows, we omit this dependence for simplicity.

One key consequence is the following identity:

$$\frac{\partial \mathbf{v}_{P/\mathcal{E}}}{\partial \dot{q}_i} = \frac{\partial \mathbf{r}_{OP}}{\partial q_i} \tag{13.3}$$

for $i = 1, \ldots, n$, leading to the following result.

[1] J.L. LAGRANGE "Mécanique Analytique" first published in 1788. The second edition was completed by de Prony, Garnier and Binet and it appeared posthumously in 1815. An edition was translated in 1997 by A. Boissonnade & V.N. Vagliente, Kluwer Academic Publishers.

[2] In the Lagrangian formalism, the variables $\mathbf{q} = (q_1, \ldots, q_n)$ are often called *generalized coordinates* of the system. But this terminology is archaic dating back from an era when the term coordinate would only refer to Cartesian coordinates. The variable t is present if the position of the system is explicitly parametrized by time.

Corollary 13.1 — Partial Kinematic Screw. Given a rigid body $\mathcal{B}$ parametrized by $(q_1, q_2, \cdots q_n)$ satisfying assumption (13.2), the vector fields

$$P \in \mathcal{B} \mapsto \frac{\partial \mathbf{r}_{OP}}{\partial q_i} \qquad (i = 1, \ldots, n)$$

and

$$P \in \mathcal{B} \mapsto \frac{\partial \mathbf{r}_{OP}}{\partial t}$$

define screws denoted as $\{\mathcal{V}^{q_i}_{B/\mathcal{E}}\}$ and $\{\mathcal{V}^{t}_{B/\mathcal{E}}\}$. The kinematic screw of body $\mathcal{B}$ can then be expressed as

$$\{\mathcal{V}_{B/\mathcal{E}}\} = \dot{q}_1\{\mathcal{V}^{q_1}_{B/\mathcal{E}}\} + \cdots + \dot{q}_n\{\mathcal{V}^{q_n}_{B/\mathcal{E}}\} + \{\mathcal{V}^{t}_{B/\mathcal{E}}\} \tag{13.4}$$

$\{\mathcal{V}^{q_i}_{B/\mathcal{E}}\}$ is called *partial kinematic screw* of $\mathcal{B}$ with respect to coordinate q_i.

Proof. For any two points P and Q attached to $\mathcal{B}$, we take the partial derivative of both sides of equation $\mathbf{v}_Q = \mathbf{v}_P + \boldsymbol{\omega}_{\mathcal{B}} \times \mathbf{r}_{PQ}$ w.r.t. variable $\dot{q}_i$ (for a given $i = 1, \ldots, n$) to find

$$\frac{\partial \mathbf{v}_Q}{\partial \dot{q}_i} = \frac{\partial \mathbf{v}_P}{\partial \dot{q}_i} + \frac{\partial \boldsymbol{\omega}_{\mathcal{B}}}{\partial \dot{q}_i} \times \mathbf{r}_{PQ}$$

since vector $\mathbf{r}_{PQ}$ does not depend upon $\dot{q}_i$. This shows that the field $P \in \mathcal{B} \mapsto \frac{\partial \mathbf{v}_P}{\partial \dot{q}_i} = \frac{\partial \mathbf{r}_{OP}}{\partial q_i}$ is a screw of resultant $\frac{\partial \boldsymbol{\omega}_{\mathcal{B}}}{\partial \dot{q}_i}$. Equation (13.1) implies that the field $P \in \mathcal{B} \mapsto \frac{\partial \mathbf{r}_{OP}}{\partial t}$ also defines a screw. Equation (13.4) is then equivalent to (13.1). ■

The following examples illustrate the calculation of partial kinematic screws $\{\mathcal{V}^{q_i}_{B/\mathcal{E}}\}$ in accordance with assumption (13.2).

Example 13.1 Consider the planar motion of plate 1 in referential 0. Its lower edge A remains in contact with a horizontal support $(O, \hat{\mathbf{x}}_0, \hat{\mathbf{z}}_0)$ while remaining in contact with a vertical step of height h. The configuration of the plate is defined by the coordinates $\mathbf{q} = (x, \theta)$ as shown in Figure 13.1.

Find the corresponding partial kinematic screws $\{\mathcal{V}^{x}_{1/0}\}$ and $\{\mathcal{V}^{\theta}_{1/0}\}$. ■

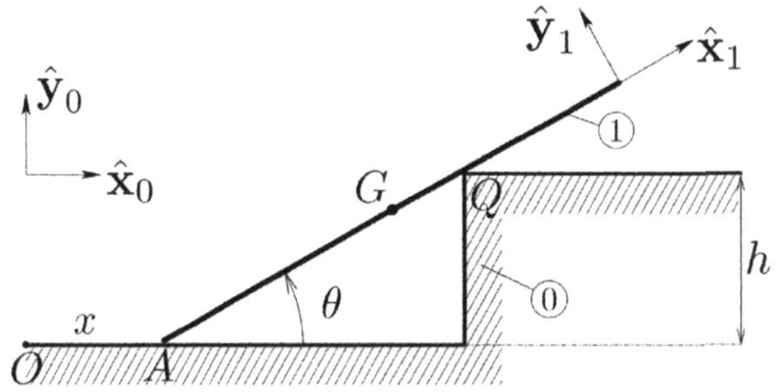

Figure 13.1

The velocity $\mathbf{v}_A = \dot{x}\hat{\mathbf{x}}_0$ of A and the angular velocity $\omega_{1/0} = \dot{\theta}\hat{\mathbf{z}}_0$ give the expression of kinematic screw $\{\mathcal{V}_{1/0}\}$ of body 1

$$\{\mathcal{V}_{1/0}\} = \begin{Bmatrix} \dot{\theta}\hat{\mathbf{z}}_0 \\ \dot{x}\hat{\mathbf{x}}_0 \end{Bmatrix}_A = \dot{\theta}\begin{Bmatrix} \hat{\mathbf{z}}_0 \\ \mathbf{0} \end{Bmatrix}_A + \dot{x}\begin{Bmatrix} \mathbf{0} \\ \hat{\mathbf{x}}_0 \end{Bmatrix}_A$$

This gives the expressions of partial kinematic screws $\{\mathcal{V}^x_{1/0}\}$ and $\{\mathcal{V}^\theta_{1/0}\}$:

$$\{\mathcal{V}^x_{1/0}\} = \begin{Bmatrix} \mathbf{0} \\ \hat{\mathbf{x}}_0 \end{Bmatrix}_A, \qquad \{\mathcal{V}^\theta_{1/0}\} = \begin{Bmatrix} \hat{\mathbf{z}}_0 \\ \mathbf{0} \end{Bmatrix}_A$$

Note that there exists a holonomic constraint between the coordinates (x, θ):

$$x + h\cot\theta = \text{const.}$$

which guarantees contact at Q and leads to the velocity $\mathbf{v}_{Q\in 1/0} = \dot{x}\cos\theta\hat{\mathbf{x}}_1$. This constraint must be ignored since it violates the requirement that $(x, \theta, \dot{x}, \dot{\theta})$ be independent variables. The slip velocity at Q compatible with this requirement is given by $\mathbf{v}_{Q\in 1/0} = \dot{x}\hat{\mathbf{x}}_0 + \dot{\theta}\frac{h}{\sin\theta}\hat{\mathbf{y}}_1$ according to the expression of $\{\mathcal{V}_{1/0}\}$. ■

Example 13.2 A sphere 1 of center G and radius r rolls without slipping on a horizontal plane $(O, \hat{\mathbf{x}}_0, \hat{\mathbf{y}}_0)$ of a referential 0. Its configuration is defined by the Cartesian coordinates (x, y) of center G and the Euler angles (ψ, θ, ϕ) as defined in Figure 13.2.

Find the corresponding partial kinematic screws $\{\mathcal{V}^{q_i}_{1/0}\}$ for $q = x, y, \psi, \theta, \phi$. ■

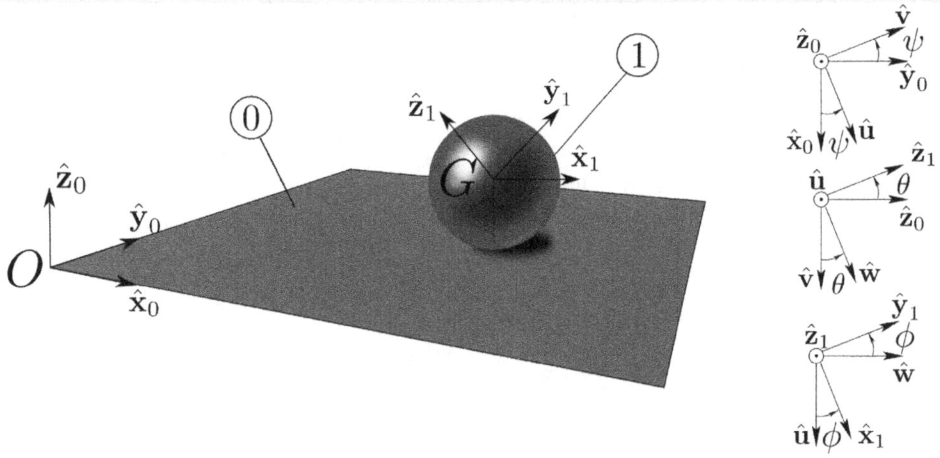

Figure 13.2

The velocity $\mathbf{v}_G = \dot{x}\hat{\mathbf{x}}_0 + \dot{y}\hat{\mathbf{y}}_0$ of G and the angular velocity $\omega_{1/0} = \dot{\psi}\hat{\mathbf{z}}_0 + \dot{\theta}\hat{\mathbf{u}} + \dot{\phi}\hat{\mathbf{z}}_1$ give the expression of kinematic screw $\{\mathcal{V}_{1/0}\}$

$$\{\mathcal{V}_{1/0}\} = \begin{Bmatrix} \dot{\psi}\hat{\mathbf{z}}_0 + \dot{\theta}\hat{\mathbf{u}} + \dot{\phi}\hat{\mathbf{z}}_1 \\ \dot{x}\hat{\mathbf{x}}_0 + \dot{y}\hat{\mathbf{y}}_0 \end{Bmatrix}_G = \dot{x}\begin{Bmatrix} \mathbf{0} \\ \hat{\mathbf{x}}_0 \end{Bmatrix}_G + \dot{y}\begin{Bmatrix} \mathbf{0} \\ \hat{\mathbf{x}}_0 \end{Bmatrix}_G + \dot{\psi}\begin{Bmatrix} \hat{\mathbf{z}}_0 \\ \mathbf{0} \end{Bmatrix}_G + \dot{\theta}\begin{Bmatrix} \hat{\mathbf{u}} \\ \mathbf{0} \end{Bmatrix}_G + \dot{\phi}\begin{Bmatrix} \hat{\mathbf{z}}_1 \\ \hat{\mathbf{x}}_0 \end{Bmatrix}_G$$

This gives the expressions of the partial kinematic screws $\{\mathcal{V}^q_{1/0}\}$ for $q = x, y, \psi, \theta, \phi$:

$$\{\mathcal{V}^x_{1/0}\} = \begin{Bmatrix} \mathbf{0} \\ \hat{\mathbf{x}}_0 \end{Bmatrix}_G, \{\mathcal{V}^y_{1/0}\} = \begin{Bmatrix} \mathbf{0} \\ \hat{\mathbf{y}}_0 \end{Bmatrix}_G, \{\mathcal{V}^\psi_{1/0}\} = \begin{Bmatrix} \hat{\mathbf{z}}_0 \\ \mathbf{0} \end{Bmatrix}_G, \{\mathcal{V}^\theta_{1/0}\} = \begin{Bmatrix} \hat{\mathbf{u}} \\ \mathbf{0} \end{Bmatrix}_G, \{\mathcal{V}^\phi_{1/0}\} = \begin{Bmatrix} \hat{\mathbf{z}}_1 \\ \mathbf{0} \end{Bmatrix}_G$$

Note that the no-slip condition $\mathbf{v}_{I\in 1/0} = \mathbf{0}$ at contact point I must not be taken into account in accordance with the requirement that the variables

$$(x, y, \psi, \theta, \phi, \dot{x}, \dot{y}, \dot{\psi}, \dot{\theta}, \dot{\phi})$$

be independent. Then velocity $\mathbf{v}_{I\in 1/0}$ takes the expression

$$\mathbf{v}_{I\in 1/0} = \dot{x}\hat{\mathbf{x}}_0 + \dot{y}\hat{\mathbf{y}}_0 + r(\dot{\theta}\hat{\mathbf{v}} + \dot{\phi}\sin\theta\hat{\mathbf{u}}) \neq \mathbf{0}$$

■

THESE EXAMPLES demonstrate that it is always possible to guarantee assumption (13.2) even in the case of holonomic or non-holonomic constraint equations between the variables $(\mathbf{q}, \dot{\mathbf{q}}, t)$.

Care must then be taken to consistently ignore these constraints. This last point will be emphasized in the remaining formulation.

13.2 Lagrange Kinematic Formula

The following formula is pivotal to the Lagrange formulation.

Theorem 13.1 — Lagrange Kinematic Formula. Given a system Σ whose position is parametrized by $(n+1)$ variables $(\mathbf{q}, t)$, the acceleration of an arbitrary point P of the system satisfies

$$\mathbf{a}_P \cdot \frac{\partial \mathbf{r}_{OP}}{\partial q_i} = \left[\frac{d}{dt}\left(\frac{\partial}{\partial \dot{q}_i}\right) - \frac{\partial}{\partial q_i}\right]\frac{\mathbf{v}_P^2}{2} \tag{13.5}$$

where the variables $(\mathbf{q}, \dot{\mathbf{q}}, t)$ satisfy assumption (13.2).

Proof. We seek to find the scalar quantity $\mathbf{a}_P \cdot \frac{\partial \mathbf{r}_{OP}}{\partial q_i}$ for a given coordinate q_i. Here P represents an arbitrary point of the system. By using (13.3) we find

$$\mathbf{a}_P \cdot \frac{\partial \mathbf{r}_{OP}}{\partial q_i} = \mathbf{a}_P \cdot \frac{\partial \mathbf{v}_P}{\partial \dot{q}_i} = \frac{d}{dt}\left(\mathbf{v}_P \cdot \frac{\partial \mathbf{v}_P}{\partial \dot{q}_i}\right) - \mathbf{v}_P \cdot \frac{d}{dt}\left(\frac{\partial \mathbf{r}_{OP}}{\partial q_i}\right)$$

The first term can be written as

$$\frac{d}{dt}\left(\mathbf{v}_P \cdot \frac{\partial \mathbf{v}_P}{\partial \dot{q}_i}\right) = \frac{1}{2}\frac{d}{dt}\left(\frac{\partial \mathbf{v}_P^2}{\partial \dot{q}_i}\right)$$

As for the second term, we cannot permute the operators $\frac{d}{dt}$ and $\frac{\partial}{\partial q_i}$: as we did for equation (13.1) we consider $\frac{\partial \mathbf{r}_{OP}}{\partial q_i}$ as a function of $(\mathbf{q}, t)$ to find

$$\frac{d}{dt}\left(\frac{\partial \mathbf{r}_{OP}}{\partial q_i}\right) = \sum_{j=1}^{n} \frac{\partial^2 \mathbf{r}_{OP}}{\partial q_j \partial q_i}\dot{q}_j + \frac{\partial^2 \mathbf{r}_{OP}}{\partial t \partial q_i} = \frac{\partial}{\partial q_i}\left(\sum_{j=1}^{n} \frac{\partial \mathbf{r}_{OP}}{\partial q_j}\dot{q}_j + \frac{\partial \mathbf{r}_{OP}}{\partial t}\right) = \frac{\partial \mathbf{v}_P}{\partial q_i}$$

Now we can write $\mathbf{v}_P \cdot \frac{d}{dt}\left(\frac{\partial \mathbf{r}_{OP}}{\partial q_i}\right)$ as $\frac{1}{2}\frac{\partial}{\partial q_i}\mathbf{v}_P^2$. ■

13.3 Power Coefficients

RECALL that the power generated by the action screw $\{\mathcal{A}_{\overline{\mathcal{B}}\to\mathcal{B}}\}$ exerted on a rigid body $\mathcal{B}$ relative to a referential $\mathcal{E}$ is given by

$$\mathbb{P}_{\overline{\mathcal{B}}\to\mathcal{B}/\mathcal{E}} = \{\mathcal{A}_{\overline{\mathcal{B}}\to\mathcal{B}}\} \cdot \{\mathcal{V}_{\mathcal{B}/\mathcal{E}}\}$$

Assuming that body $\mathcal{B}$ belongs to a system Σ whose configuration is defined by $(n+1)$ coordinates $(\mathbf{q}, t)$, we can use the expansion (13.17) of the kinematic screw $\{\mathcal{V}_{\mathcal{B}/\mathcal{E}}\}$ into its partial kinematic screws (under assumption 13.2) to find the expression

$$\mathbb{P}_{\overline{\mathcal{B}}\to\mathcal{B}/\mathcal{E}} = \sum_{i=1}^{n} \dot{q}_i \{\mathcal{A}_{\overline{\mathcal{B}}\to\mathcal{B}}\} \cdot \{\mathcal{V}^{q_i}_{\mathcal{B}/\mathcal{E}}\} + \{\mathcal{A}_{\overline{\mathcal{B}}\to\mathcal{B}}\} \cdot \{\mathcal{V}^{t}_{\mathcal{B}/\mathcal{E}}\}$$

This result leads to the following definition:

Definition 13.1 — Power Coefficient. We call *power coefficient* of the action $\{\mathcal{A}_{\overline{\mathcal{B}}\to\mathcal{B}}\}$ with respect to coordinate q_i $(i = 1, \ldots, n)$ and variable t satisfying assumption (13.2) the following scalar quantities:

$$\mathrm{Q}^{q_i}_{\overline{\mathcal{B}}\to\mathcal{B}/\mathcal{E}} = \{\mathcal{A}_{\overline{\mathcal{B}}\to\mathcal{B}}\} \cdot \{\mathcal{V}^{q_i}_{\mathcal{B}/\mathcal{E}}\} \tag{13.6}$$

$$\mathrm{Q}^{t}_{\overline{\mathcal{B}}\to\mathcal{B}/\mathcal{E}} = \{\mathcal{A}_{\overline{\mathcal{B}}\to\mathcal{B}}\} \cdot \{\mathcal{V}^{t}_{\mathcal{B}/\mathcal{E}}\} \tag{13.7}$$

Remark 3. Power coefficients are usually referred to as *generalized forces* in the mechanics or physics literature when the variables $(q_1, \ldots, q_n)$ are called *generalized coordinates.*

Remark 4. In practice, the q_i-power coefficient of a particular action is found by resolving both screws $\{\mathcal{A}_{\overline{\mathcal{B}}\to\mathcal{B}}\}$ and $\{\mathcal{V}^{q_i}_{\mathcal{B}/\mathcal{E}}\}$ about the same point:

$$\mathrm{Q}^{q_i}_{\overline{\mathcal{B}}\to\mathcal{B}/\mathcal{E}} = \mathbf{R}_{\overline{\mathcal{B}}\to\mathcal{B}} \cdot \frac{\partial}{\partial \dot{q}_i}\mathbf{v}_{A\in\mathcal{B}/\mathcal{E}} + \mathbf{M}_{A,\overline{\mathcal{B}}\to\mathcal{B}} \cdot \frac{\partial}{\partial \dot{q}_i}\boldsymbol{\omega}_{\mathcal{B}/\mathcal{E}} \tag{13.8}$$

Corollary 13.2 The power $\mathbb{P}_{\overline{\mathcal{B}}\to\mathcal{B}/\mathcal{E}}$ can be expressed in terms of the corresponding power coefficients according to the equation

$$\mathbb{P}_{\overline{\mathcal{B}}\to\mathcal{B}/\mathcal{E}} = \sum_{i=1}^{n} \dot{q}_i \mathrm{Q}^{q_i}_{\overline{\mathcal{B}}\to\mathcal{B}/\mathcal{E}} + \mathrm{Q}^{t}_{\overline{\mathcal{B}}\to\mathcal{B}/\mathcal{E}} \tag{13.9}$$

Remark 5. Equation (13.9) justifies the name of "power coefficient" given to $\mathrm{Q}_{\overline{\mathcal{B}}\to\mathcal{B}/\mathcal{E}}$.

In view of equation (13.9) it is tempting to find each q_i-power coefficient from the corresponding power according to

$$\mathrm{Q}^{q_i}_{\overline{\mathcal{B}}\to\mathcal{B}/\mathcal{E}} = \frac{\partial}{\partial \dot{q}_i}\mathbb{P}_{\overline{\mathcal{B}}\to\mathcal{B}/\mathcal{E}}$$

However, this is risky and often incorrect since the power term may have been determined without consideration of assumption (13.2). For instance, $\mathbb{P}_{\overline{\mathcal{B}}\to\mathcal{B}/\mathcal{E}}$ may be found to vanish, yet the corresponding power coefficients may not be zero!

Remark 6. If a particular action $\{\mathcal{A}_{\Sigma_1\to\mathcal{B}}\}$ derives from a potential energy $\mathbb{U}_{\Sigma_1\to\mathcal{B}/\mathcal{E}}$ relatice to $\mathcal{E}$, then it is possible to determine the corresponding power coefficients $\mathbb{Q}^{q_i}_{\Sigma_1\to\mathcal{B}/\mathcal{E}}$ from $\mathbb{U}_{\Sigma_1\to\mathcal{B}/\mathcal{E}}$. Assuming that the configuration of $\mathcal{B}$ relative to $\mathcal{E}$ can be defined by n coordinates $(q_1,\dots,q_n)$ and time t, then power $\mathbb{P}_{\Sigma_1\to\mathcal{B}/\mathcal{E}}$ can be written as

$$\mathbb{P}_{\Sigma_1\to\mathcal{B}/\mathcal{E}} = -\frac{d}{dt}\mathbb{U}_{\Sigma_1\to\mathcal{B}/\mathcal{E}} = -\sum_{i=1}^{n}\dot{q}_i\frac{\partial\mathbb{U}}{\partial q_i} - \frac{\partial\mathbb{U}}{\partial t} \tag{13.10}$$

Comparison of equations (13.9) and (13.10) shows that

$$\mathbb{Q}^{q_i}_{\Sigma_1\to\mathcal{B}/\mathcal{E}} = -\frac{\partial}{\partial q_i}\mathbb{U}_{\Sigma_1\to\mathcal{B}/\mathcal{E}}, \qquad \mathbb{Q}^{t}_{\Sigma_1\to\mathcal{B}/\mathcal{E}} = -\frac{\partial}{\partial t}\mathbb{U}_{\Sigma_1\to\mathcal{B}/\mathcal{E}} \tag{13.11}$$

For instance, the action of Earth constant gravitational acceleration $\mathbf{g}$ can be accounted by

$$\mathbb{Q}_{\text{Earth}\to\mathcal{B}/\mathcal{E}} = m\mathbf{g}\cdot\frac{\partial}{\partial q_i}\mathbf{r}_{OG} \tag{13.12}$$

The following examples illustrate the calculation of power coefficients.

Example 13.3 The plate 1 of Example 13.1 is subject to a force $F_A\hat{\mathbf{x}}_0$ applied at point A where the contact is friction-free. The contact of the plate with the corner point Q of the step is assumed with friction and characterized by (kinetic) friction coefficient μ. The position of mass center G is given by $\mathbf{r}_{AG} = l\hat{\mathbf{x}}_1$.

a. Find the total power $\mathbb{P}_{\bar{1}\to 1/0}$ of external action on body 1.

b. Find the power coefficients $\mathbb{Q}^{q}_{\bar{1}\to 1/0}$ for $q = x, \theta$. ■

a. We start by giving the expression of the total action screw $\{\mathcal{A}_{\bar{1}\to 1/0}\}$ (denoting by $N_Q\hat{\mathbf{y}}_1$ the normal force and $F_Q\hat{\mathbf{x}}_1$ the friction force at Q)

$$\{\mathcal{A}_{\bar{1}\to 1/0}\} = \begin{Bmatrix} F_A\hat{\mathbf{x}}_0 + N_A\hat{\mathbf{y}}_0 \\ \mathbf{0} \end{Bmatrix}_A + \begin{Bmatrix} -mg\hat{\mathbf{y}}_0 \\ \mathbf{0} \end{Bmatrix}_G + \begin{Bmatrix} N_Q\hat{\mathbf{y}}_1 + F_Q\hat{\mathbf{x}}_1 \\ \mathbf{0} \end{Bmatrix}_Q$$

and of the kinematic screw $\{\mathcal{V}_{1/0}\}$

$$\{\mathcal{V}_{1/0}\} = \begin{Bmatrix} \dot{\theta}\hat{\mathbf{z}}_0 \\ \dot{x}\hat{\mathbf{x}}_0 \end{Bmatrix}_A = \begin{Bmatrix} \dot{\theta}\hat{\mathbf{z}}_0 \\ \dot{x}\hat{\mathbf{x}}_0 + l\dot{\theta}\hat{\mathbf{y}}_1 \end{Bmatrix}_G = \begin{Bmatrix} \dot{\theta}\hat{\mathbf{z}}_0 \\ \dot{x}\hat{\mathbf{x}}_0 + \frac{h}{\sin\theta}\dot{\theta}\hat{\mathbf{y}}_1 \end{Bmatrix}_Q$$

Power $\mathbb{P}_{\bar{1}\to 1/0}$ is then found by treating each action screw separately

$$\begin{aligned}\mathbb{P}_{\bar{1}\to 1/0} = {} & \begin{Bmatrix} F_A\hat{\mathbf{x}}_0 + N_A\hat{\mathbf{y}}_0 \\ \mathbf{0} \end{Bmatrix}_A \cdot \begin{Bmatrix} \dot{\theta}\hat{\mathbf{z}}_0 \\ \dot{x}\hat{\mathbf{x}}_0 \end{Bmatrix}_A + \begin{Bmatrix} -mg\hat{\mathbf{y}}_0 \\ \mathbf{0} \end{Bmatrix}_G \cdot \begin{Bmatrix} \dot{\theta}\hat{\mathbf{z}}_0 \\ \dot{x}\hat{\mathbf{x}}_0 + l\dot{\theta}\hat{\mathbf{y}}_1 \end{Bmatrix}_G + \\ & \begin{Bmatrix} N_Q\hat{\mathbf{y}}_1 + F_Q\hat{\mathbf{x}}_1 \\ \mathbf{0} \end{Bmatrix}_Q \cdot \begin{Bmatrix} \dot{\theta}\hat{\mathbf{z}}_0 \\ \dot{x}\hat{\mathbf{x}}_0 + \frac{h}{\sin\theta}\dot{\theta}\hat{\mathbf{y}}_1 \end{Bmatrix}_Q\end{aligned}$$

giving

$$\begin{aligned}\mathbb{P}_{\bar{1}\to 1/0} &= F_A\dot{x} - mgl\dot{\theta}\cos\theta + N_Q(-\dot{x}\sin\theta + \frac{h\dot{\theta}}{\sin\theta}) + F_Q\dot{x}\cos\theta \\ &= F_A\dot{x} - mgl\dot{\theta}\cos\theta + F_Q\dot{x}\cos\theta\end{aligned}$$

where the power of normal force $N_Q\hat{\mathbf{y}}_1$ vanishes due to the constraint $\mathbf{v}_{Q\in 1/0}\cdot\hat{\mathbf{y}}_1 = 0$.

b. We find the power coefficients by using the expressions of $\{\mathcal{V}^q_{1/0}\}$ found in Example 13.1. Each power coefficient $\mathbb{Q}^q_{\bar{1}\to 1/0}$ is found by treating each contribution of the total action screw individually.

$$\mathbb{Q}^x_{\bar{1}\to 1/0} = \begin{Bmatrix} F_A\hat{\mathbf{x}}_0 + N_A\hat{\mathbf{y}}_0 \\ \mathbf{0} \end{Bmatrix}_A \cdot \begin{Bmatrix} \mathbf{0} \\ \hat{\mathbf{x}}_0 \end{Bmatrix}_A + \begin{Bmatrix} -mg\hat{\mathbf{y}}_0 \\ \mathbf{0} \end{Bmatrix}_G \cdot \begin{Bmatrix} \mathbf{0} \\ \hat{\mathbf{x}}_0 \end{Bmatrix}_G + \begin{Bmatrix} N_Q\hat{\mathbf{y}}_1 + F_Q\hat{\mathbf{x}}_1 \\ \mathbf{0} \end{Bmatrix}_Q \cdot \begin{Bmatrix} \mathbf{0} \\ \hat{\mathbf{x}}_0 \end{Bmatrix}_Q$$
$$= F_A - N_Q\sin\theta + F_Q\cos\theta$$

$$\mathbb{Q}^\theta_{\bar{1}\to 1/0} = \begin{Bmatrix} F_A\hat{\mathbf{x}}_0 + N_A\hat{\mathbf{y}}_0 \\ \mathbf{0} \end{Bmatrix}_A \cdot \begin{Bmatrix} \hat{\mathbf{z}}_0 \\ \mathbf{0} \end{Bmatrix}_A + \begin{Bmatrix} -mg\hat{\mathbf{y}}_0 \\ \mathbf{0} \end{Bmatrix}_G \cdot \begin{Bmatrix} \hat{\mathbf{z}}_0 \\ l\hat{\mathbf{y}}_1 \end{Bmatrix}_G + \begin{Bmatrix} N_Q\hat{\mathbf{y}}_1 + F_Q\hat{\mathbf{x}}_1 \\ \mathbf{0} \end{Bmatrix}_Q \cdot \begin{Bmatrix} \hat{\mathbf{z}}_0 \\ \frac{h}{\sin\theta}\hat{\mathbf{y}}_1 \end{Bmatrix}_Q$$
$$= -mgl\cos\theta + \frac{h}{\sin\theta}N_Q$$

We can verify here that the power coefficients cannot be found by using $\frac{\partial}{\partial\dot{q}}\mathbb{P}_{\bar{1}\to 1/0}$ from the expression $\mathbb{P}_{\bar{1}\to 1/0} = F_A\dot{x} - mgl\dot{\theta}\cos\theta - \mu\dot{x}N_Q\cos\theta$. Indeed, this result was found by taking into account the constraint between coordinates x and θ in violation [3] of assumption (13.2). ■

Example 13.4 The sphere (of mass m) 1 of Example 13.2 is subject to the total external action

$$\{\mathcal{A}_{\bar{1}\to 1/0}\} = \begin{Bmatrix} -mg\hat{\mathbf{z}}_0 \\ \mathbf{0} \end{Bmatrix}_G + \begin{Bmatrix} F_u\hat{\mathbf{u}} + F_v\hat{\mathbf{v}} + N\hat{\mathbf{z}}_0 \\ \mathbf{0} \end{Bmatrix}_I$$

where I is the contact point and $F_u\hat{\mathbf{u}} + F_v\hat{\mathbf{v}}$ is the friction force acting on the sphere. Hence, rolling and pivoting friction are neglected.

a. Find the total power $\mathbb{P}_{\bar{1}\to 1/0}$ of the actions exerted on body 1.

b. Find the power coefficients $\mathbb{Q}^q_{\bar{1}\to 1/0}$ for $q = x, y, \psi, \theta, \phi$. ■

a. Since $\mathbf{v}_{I\in 1/0} = \mathbf{0}$, we easily find $\mathbb{P}_{\bar{1}\to 1/0} = 0$.

b. The variables $(q = x, y, \psi, \theta, \phi)$ are now required to satisfy the assumption (13.2): we must ignore the kinematic condition $\mathbf{v}_{I\in 1/0} = \mathbf{0}$. Instead we must use the expressions of the partial kinematic screws $\{\mathcal{V}^q_{1/0}\}$ found in Example 13.2. We then find

$$\mathbb{Q}^x_{\bar{1}\to 1/0} = \begin{Bmatrix} F_u\hat{\mathbf{u}} + F_v\hat{\mathbf{v}} + (N - mg)\hat{\mathbf{z}}_0 \\ \mathbf{0} \end{Bmatrix}_I \cdot \begin{Bmatrix} \mathbf{0} \\ \hat{\mathbf{x}}_0 \end{Bmatrix}_I = F_u\cos\psi - F_v\sin\psi$$

$$\mathbb{Q}^y_{\bar{1}\to 1/0} = \begin{Bmatrix} F_u\hat{\mathbf{u}} + F_v\hat{\mathbf{v}} + (N - mg)\hat{\mathbf{z}}_0 \\ \mathbf{0} \end{Bmatrix}_I \cdot \begin{Bmatrix} \mathbf{0} \\ \hat{\mathbf{y}}_0 \end{Bmatrix}_I = F_u\sin\psi + F_v\cos\psi$$

$$\mathbb{Q}^\psi_{\bar{1}\to 1/0} = \begin{Bmatrix} F_u\hat{\mathbf{u}} + F_v\hat{\mathbf{v}} + (N - mg)\hat{\mathbf{z}}_0 \\ \mathbf{0} \end{Bmatrix}_I \cdot \begin{Bmatrix} \hat{\mathbf{z}}_0 \\ \mathbf{0} \end{Bmatrix}_I = 0$$

$$\mathbb{Q}^\theta_{\bar{1}\to 1/0} = \begin{Bmatrix} F_u\hat{\mathbf{u}} + F_v\hat{\mathbf{v}} + (N - mg)\hat{\mathbf{z}}_0 \\ \mathbf{0} \end{Bmatrix}_I \cdot \begin{Bmatrix} \hat{\mathbf{u}} \\ r\hat{\mathbf{v}} \end{Bmatrix}_I = rF_v$$

[3] It is of course possible to find the expression of power $\mathbb{P}_{\bar{1}\to 1/0}$ without violating the requirement that $(x, \theta, \dot{x}, \dot{\theta})$ be independent.

$$\mathcal{Q}^{\phi}_{\bar{1}\to 1/0} = \begin{Bmatrix} F_u\hat{\mathbf{u}} + F_v\hat{\mathbf{v}} + (N - mg)\hat{\mathbf{z}}_0 \\ \mathbf{0} \end{Bmatrix}_I \cdot \begin{Bmatrix} \hat{\mathbf{z}}_1 \\ r\sin\theta\hat{\mathbf{u}} \end{Bmatrix}_I = rF_u \sin\theta$$

Note that we have to resolve the partial kinematic screws $\{\mathcal{V}^q_{1/0}\}$ at contact point I. ∎

In each of the previous examples, it appears that the power coefficient $\mathcal{Q}^q_{\overline{\mathcal{B}}\to\mathcal{B}/\mathcal{E}}$ could have been found by finding $\frac{\partial}{\partial \dot{q}}\mathbb{P}_{\overline{\mathcal{B}}\to\mathcal{B}/\mathcal{E}}$, had the expression of the power been determined in accordance with the assumption (13.2) imposed on the coordinates. However, it is straightforward to construct an example of an action for which the power is zero, yet the corresponding power coefficients are non-zero without violating the assumption (13.2): consider the notional action exerted on a rigid body $\mathcal{B}$ in the form of couple

$$\{\mathcal{A}_{\mathcal{B}_1\to\mathcal{B}}\} = \begin{Bmatrix} \mathbf{0} \\ c(\dot{q}_1\hat{\mathbf{v}} - \dot{q}_2\hat{\mathbf{u}}) \end{Bmatrix}$$

where c is a constant and $\hat{\mathbf{u}}$ and $\hat{\mathbf{v}}$ are two unit vectors satisfying $\hat{\mathbf{u}}\cdot\hat{\mathbf{v}} = 0$. The kinematic screw $\{\mathcal{V}_{\mathcal{B}/\mathcal{E}}\}$ is assumed of the form

$$\{\mathcal{V}_{\mathcal{B}/\mathcal{E}}\} = \begin{Bmatrix} \dot{q}_1\hat{\mathbf{u}} + \dot{q}_2\hat{\mathbf{v}} \\ \mathbf{v}_A \end{Bmatrix}$$

(the expression of velocity $\mathbf{v}_A$ is unimportant). The coordinates (q_1, q_2) satisfy the assumption (13.2). It is easy to find $\mathbb{P}_{\mathcal{B}_1\to\mathcal{B}/\mathcal{E}} = 0$ yet $\mathcal{Q}^{q_1}_{\mathcal{B}_1\to\mathcal{B}/\mathcal{E}} = -c\dot{q}_2$ and $\mathcal{Q}^{q_2}_{\mathcal{B}_1\to\mathcal{B}/\mathcal{E}} = c\dot{q}_1$.

In conclusion, it is best to find each power coefficient $\mathcal{Q}^q_{\overline{\mathcal{B}}\to\mathcal{B}/\mathcal{E}}$ by a careful determination of the partial kinematic screws $\{\mathcal{V}^q_{\mathcal{B}/\mathcal{E}}\}$ without violating assumption (13.2).

Another type of power coefficient can be defined, corresponding to an interaction between two rigid bodies $\mathcal{B}_1$ and $\mathcal{B}_2$ of a system Σ. Recall that if two bodies are interacting, a power of interaction $\mathbb{P}_{\mathcal{B}_1\leftrightarrow\mathcal{B}_2}$ can be defined as

$$\mathbb{P}_{\mathcal{B}_1\leftrightarrow\mathcal{B}_2} = \{\mathcal{A}_{\mathcal{B}_1\to\mathcal{B}_2}\}\cdot\{\mathcal{V}_{\mathcal{B}_2/\mathcal{B}_1}\} = \{\mathcal{A}_{\mathcal{B}_2\to\mathcal{B}_1}\}\cdot\{\mathcal{V}_{\mathcal{B}_1/\mathcal{B}_2}\}$$

Suppose that the set of variables $(q_1, q_2, \cdots, q_n, t)$ satisfies assumption (13.2): we can then write

$$\mathbb{P}_{\mathcal{B}_1\leftrightarrow\mathcal{B}_2} = \{\mathcal{A}_{\mathcal{B}_1\to\mathcal{B}_2}\}\cdot\Big(\dot{q}_1\{\mathcal{V}^{q_1}_{\mathcal{B}_2/\mathcal{B}_1}\} + \dot{q}_2\{\mathcal{V}^{q_2}_{\mathcal{B}_2/\mathcal{B}_1}\} + \cdots + \dot{q}_n\{\mathcal{V}^{q_n}_{\mathcal{B}_2/\mathcal{B}_1}\} + \{\mathcal{V}^{t}_{\mathcal{B}_2/\mathcal{B}_1}\}\Big)$$

with $\{\mathcal{V}^{q_i}_{\mathcal{B}_2/\mathcal{B}_1}\} = \{\mathcal{V}^{q_i}_{\mathcal{B}_2/\mathcal{E}}\} - \{\mathcal{V}^{q_i}_{\mathcal{B}_1/\mathcal{E}}\}$. This result leads to the following definition:

Definition 13.2 — Power Coefficient of Interaction. The *power coefficient of interaction* between two rigid bodies $\mathcal{B}_1$ and $\mathcal{B}_2$ of a system Σ whose configuration is defined coordinates $(q_1, \ldots, q_n)$ and time t are the following scalar quantities:

$$\mathcal{Q}^{q_i}_{\mathcal{B}_1\leftrightarrow\mathcal{B}_2} = \{\mathcal{A}_{\mathcal{B}_1\to\mathcal{B}_2}\}\cdot\{\mathcal{V}^{q_i}_{\mathcal{B}_2/\mathcal{B}_1}\} = \{\mathcal{A}_{\mathcal{B}_2\to\mathcal{B}_1}\}\cdot\{\mathcal{V}^{q_i}_{\mathcal{B}_1/\mathcal{B}_2}\} \qquad (13.13)$$

where the variables $(\mathbf{q}, \dot{\mathbf{q}}, t)$ satisfy assumption (13.2).

Remark 7. The non-zero power coefficients $\mathcal{Q}^{q_i}_{\mathcal{B}_1\leftrightarrow\mathcal{B}_2}$ are those associated with the coordinates q_i which define the relative motion between $\mathcal{B}_1$ and $\mathcal{B}_2$.

Remark 8. If the interaction between rigid bodies $\mathcal{B}_1$ and $\mathcal{B}_2$ derives from the potential energy $\mathbb{U}_{\mathcal{B}_1\leftrightarrow\mathcal{B}_2}$, then the power coefficient $\mathbb{Q}^{q_i}_{\mathcal{B}_1\leftrightarrow\mathcal{B}_2}$ can be determined as

$$\mathbb{Q}^{q_i}_{\mathcal{B}_1\leftrightarrow\mathcal{B}_2} = -\frac{\partial}{\partial q_i}\mathbb{U}_{\mathcal{B}_1\leftrightarrow\mathcal{B}_2} \tag{13.14}$$

Remark 9. (**Power coefficients of interaction for an ideal joint**) Recall that if there exists a joint between bodies $\mathcal{B}_1$ and $\mathcal{B}_2$ which satisfies

$$\mathbb{P}^c_{1\leftrightarrow 2} = 0$$

for all allowable motions between the two bodies, then the corresponding joint is said to be *ideal*. We saw in Section 12.5 that this condition leads to the equations:

$$\{\mathcal{V}^{\tilde{q}_k}_{2/1}\}\cdot\{\mathcal{A}^c_{1\rightarrow 2}\} = 0, \qquad (k = 1, 2, \cdots, M)$$

for all *independent* coordinates $\tilde{q}_1, \ldots, \tilde{q}_M$ ($M < 6$) defining the configuration of $\mathcal{B}_2$ relative to $\mathcal{B}_1$. These equations are recognized as the conditions:

$$\mathbb{Q}^{\tilde{q}_k}_{\mathcal{B}_1\leftrightarrow\mathcal{B}_2} = 0 \qquad (k = 1, 2, \ldots, M) \tag{13.15}$$

Remark 10. Power coefficients of interaction are relevant to the formulation of Lagrange equations for systems of rigid bodies.

13.4 Lagrange Equations: Single Body

Consider a rigid body in motion in a Newtonian referential $\mathcal{E}$. Assume that its configuration is defined by n coordinates $(q_1, \ldots, q_n)$ and time t satisfying the assumption (13.2). Recall from section 11.1 that D'Alembert Principle of Virtual Power takes the form:

$$\{\mathcal{D}_{\mathcal{B}/\mathcal{E}}\}\cdot\{\mathcal{V}^*\} = \{\mathcal{A}_{\overline{\mathcal{B}}\rightarrow\mathcal{B}}\}\cdot\{\mathcal{V}^*\} \tag{13.16}$$

for any virtual kinematic screw $\{\mathcal{V}^*\}$. Lagrange equations are found by choosing the virtual kinematic screw as a linear combination of the partial kinematic screws of $\mathcal{B}$:

$$\mathbf{v}^*_P = \dot{q}^*_1\frac{\partial \mathbf{v}_P}{\partial \dot{q}_1} + \cdots + \dot{q}^*_n\frac{\partial \mathbf{v}_P}{\partial \dot{q}_n}$$

which is equivalent to choosing $\{\mathcal{V}^*\}$ as

$$\{\mathcal{V}^*\} = \dot{q}^*_1\{\mathcal{V}^{q_1}_{\mathcal{B}/\mathcal{E}}\} + \cdots + \dot{q}^*_n\{\mathcal{V}^{q_n}_{\mathcal{B}/\mathcal{E}}\} \tag{13.17}$$

The scalars $(\dot{q}^*_1, \ldots, \dot{q}^*_n)$, known as *virtual speeds*, are arbitrary. Now equation (13.16) becomes

$$\sum_{i=1}^{n}\dot{q}^*_i\{\mathcal{D}_{\mathcal{B}/\mathcal{E}}\}\cdot\{\mathcal{V}^{q_i}_{\mathcal{B}/\mathcal{E}}\} = \sum_{i=1}^{n}\dot{q}^*_i\{\mathcal{A}_{\overline{\mathcal{B}}\rightarrow\mathcal{B}}\}\cdot\{\mathcal{V}^{q_i}_{\mathcal{B}/\mathcal{E}}\} \tag{13.18}$$

The coefficients in the left-hand-side are found by using Lagrange kinematic formula (13.5)

$$\{\mathcal{D}_{\mathcal{B}/\mathcal{E}}\} \cdot \{\mathcal{V}^{q_i}_{\mathcal{B}/\mathcal{E}}\} = \int_{\mathcal{B}} \mathbf{a}_P \cdot \frac{\partial \mathbf{v}_P}{\partial \dot{q}_i} dm = \int_{\mathcal{B}} \mathbf{a}_P \cdot \frac{\partial \mathbf{r}_{OP}}{\partial q_i} dm$$
$$= \int_{\mathcal{B}} \left[\frac{d}{dt}\left(\frac{\partial}{\partial \dot{q}_i}\right) - \frac{\partial}{\partial q_i}\right] \frac{\mathbf{v}_P^2}{2} dm = \left[\frac{d}{dt}\left(\frac{\partial}{\partial \dot{q}_i}\right) - \frac{\partial}{\partial q_i}\right] \mathbb{K}_{\mathcal{B}/\mathcal{E}}$$

where $\mathbb{K}_{\mathcal{B}/\mathcal{E}}$ is the kinetic energy of $\mathcal{B}$. The right-hand-side of (13.18) is the virtual power $\mathbb{P}^*_{\overline{\mathcal{B}}\to\mathcal{B}/\mathcal{E}}$ and can be expressed in terms of the power coefficients of the external action $\{\mathcal{A}_{\overline{\mathcal{B}}\to\mathcal{B}}\}$

$$\mathbb{P}^*_{\overline{\mathcal{B}}\to\mathcal{B}/\mathcal{E}} = \sum_{i=1}^{n} \dot{q}_i^* \{\mathcal{A}_{\overline{\mathcal{B}}\to\mathcal{B}}\} \cdot \{\mathcal{V}^{q_i}_{\mathcal{B}/\mathcal{E}}\} = \sum_{i=1}^{n} \dot{q}_i^* \mathbb{Q}^{q_i}_{\overline{\mathcal{B}}\to\mathcal{B}/\mathcal{E}}$$

Now equation (13.18) can be written as

$$\sum_{i=1}^{n} \dot{q}_i^* \left(\frac{d}{dt}\frac{\partial \mathbb{K}_{\mathcal{B}/\mathcal{E}}}{\partial \dot{q}_i} - \frac{\partial \mathbb{K}_{\mathcal{B}/\mathcal{E}}}{\partial q_i} - \mathbb{Q}^{q_i}_{\overline{\mathcal{B}}\to\mathcal{B}/\mathcal{E}}\right) = 0 \qquad (13.19)$$

Since the virtual speeds $(\dot{q}_1^*, \dots, \dot{q}_n^*)$ are arbitrary, we can equate the ith coefficients of (13.19) to zero, yielding Lagrange equations (denoted $\mathcal{L}^{q_i}_{\mathcal{B}/\mathcal{E}}$).

Theorem 13.2 — Lagrange Equations (Single Body). The motion of a rigid body $\mathcal{B}$ relative to a Newtonian referential $\mathcal{E}$ defined by n coordinates $\mathbf{q} = (q_1, \dots, q_n)$ and time t is governed by the n Lagrange equations

$$\mathcal{L}^{q_i}_{\mathcal{B}/\mathcal{E}}: \quad \frac{d}{dt}\frac{\partial \mathbb{K}_{\mathcal{B}/\mathcal{E}}}{\partial \dot{q}_i} - \frac{\partial \mathbb{K}_{\mathcal{B}/\mathcal{E}}}{\partial q_i} = \mathbb{Q}^{q_i}_{\overline{\mathcal{B}}\to\mathcal{B}/\mathcal{E}} \qquad (i = 1, 2, \dots, n) \qquad (13.20)$$

where the variables $(\mathbf{q}, \dot{\mathbf{q}}, t)$ satisfy assumption (13.2).

There are as many Lagrange equations as the number of coordinates chosen to parametrize the configuration of $\mathcal{B}$ relative to $\mathcal{E}$. Before establishing guidelines for the derivation of Lagrange equations, we examine the solution of two examples.

Example 13.5 Derive Lagrange equations $\mathcal{L}^x_{1/0}$ and $\mathcal{L}^\theta_{1/0}$ for the plate of Example 13.3. ■

To find these equations, we use the results found in Examples 13.1 and 13.3. We first need to find the kinetic energy $\mathbb{K}_{1/0}$ in a manner compatible with assumption (13.2) which must be imposed to coordinates (x, θ): recall that this is equivalent to ignoring the geometric constraint equation between the coordinates x and θ which guarantees contact at corner point Q. This leads to the velocity

$$\mathbf{v}_G = \mathbf{v}_A + \dot{\theta}\hat{\mathbf{z}}_0 \times l\hat{\mathbf{x}}_1 = \dot{x}\hat{\mathbf{x}}_0 + l\dot{\theta}\hat{\mathbf{y}}_1$$

We can now find the expression of kinetic energy $\mathbb{K}_{1/0}$:

$$2\mathbb{K}_{1/0} = m\mathbf{v}_G^2 + I_{Gy}\dot{\theta}^2 = m(\dot{x}\hat{\mathbf{x}}_0 + l\dot{\theta}\hat{\mathbf{y}}_1)^2 + \tfrac{1}{3}ml^2\dot{\theta}^2 = m\dot{x}^2 - 2ml\dot{x}\dot{\theta}\sin\theta + \tfrac{4}{3}ml^2\dot{\theta}^2$$

This leads to

$$\left[\frac{d}{dt}\left(\frac{\partial}{\partial \dot{x}}\right) - \frac{\partial}{\partial x}\right] \mathbb{K}_{1/0} = \frac{d}{dt}(m\dot{x} - ml\dot{\theta}\sin\theta) = m\ddot{x} - ml\ddot{\theta}\sin\theta - ml\dot{\theta}^2\cos\theta$$

$$\left[\frac{d}{dt}\left(\frac{\partial}{\partial\dot\theta}\right)-\frac{\partial}{\partial\theta}\right]\mathbb{K}_{1/0}=\frac{d}{dt}(\tfrac{4}{3}ml^2\dot\theta-ml\dot x\sin\theta)+ml\dot x\dot\theta\cos\theta=\tfrac{4}{3}ml^2\ddot\theta-ml\ddot x\sin\theta$$

The two equations $\mathcal{L}^x_{1/0}$ and $\mathcal{L}^\theta_{1/0}$ are then found by using the expressions of the power coefficients $Q^x_{\bar{1}\to 1/0}$ and $Q^\theta_{\bar{1}\to 1/0}$:

$$\mathcal{L}^x_{1/0}: \quad m\ddot x-ml\ddot\theta\sin\theta-ml\dot\theta^2\cos\theta=F_A-N_Q\sin\theta+F_Q\cos\theta \tag{1}$$

$$\mathcal{L}^\theta_{1/0}: \quad \tfrac{4}{3}ml^2\ddot\theta-ml\ddot x\sin\theta=-mgl\cos\theta+\frac{h}{\sin\theta}N_Q \tag{2}$$

With F_A given, we have found two equations governing four unknowns: x, θ, F_Q and N_Q. Hence, two additional equations must be given to complete the solution. The first equation is the geometric constraint equation

$$x+h\cot\theta=\text{const.} \tag{3}$$

and the relationship between F_Q and N_Q

$$|F_Q|=\mu N_Q \tag{4}$$

according to Coulomb law. The sign of F_Q is such that frictional force $F_Q\hat{\mathbf{x}}_1$ opposes the slip velocity $\mathbf{v}_{Q\in 1/0}$. ■

Example 13.6 Derive the five Lagrange equations $\mathcal{L}^q_{1/0}$ governing the motion of the sphere of Example 13.4 for $q=x,y,\psi,\theta,\phi$. ■

We can use the expressions of the power coefficients $Q^q_{\bar{1}\to 1/0}$ which were found in Example 13.4 by enforcing assumption (13.2) imposed on the coordinates (x,y,ψ,θ,ϕ): this is equivalent to ignoring the kinematic constraint $\mathbf{v}_{I\in 1/0}=\mathbf{0}$ which guarantees no-slip at contact point I. It remains to find the kinetic energy $\mathbb{K}_{1/0}$ without violating assumption (13.2): we use the following expressions

$$\mathbf{v}_G=\dot x\hat{\mathbf{x}}_0+\dot y\hat{\mathbf{y}}_0, \qquad \boldsymbol{\omega}_{1/0}=\dot\psi\hat{\mathbf{z}}_0+\dot\theta\hat{\mathbf{u}}+\dot\phi\hat{\mathbf{z}}_1$$

to find

$$2\mathbb{K}_{1/0}=m\mathbf{v}_G^2+\tfrac{2}{5}mr^2\boldsymbol{\omega}_{1/0}^2=m(\dot x^2+\dot y^2)+\tfrac{2}{5}mr^2(\dot\psi^2+\dot\theta^2+\dot\phi^2+2\dot\psi\dot\phi\cos\theta)$$

This leads to

$$\left[\frac{d}{dt}\left(\frac{\partial}{\partial\dot x}\right)-\frac{\partial}{\partial x}\right]\mathbb{K}_{1/0}=m\ddot x$$

$$\left[\frac{d}{dt}\left(\frac{\partial}{\partial\dot y}\right)-\frac{\partial}{\partial y}\right]\mathbb{K}_{1/0}=m\ddot y$$

$$\left[\frac{d}{dt}\left(\frac{\partial}{\partial\dot\psi}\right)-\frac{\partial}{\partial\psi}\right]\mathbb{K}_{1/0}=\tfrac{2}{5}mr^2\frac{d}{dt}(\dot\psi+\dot\phi\cos\theta)$$

$$\left[\frac{d}{dt}\left(\frac{\partial}{\partial\dot\theta}\right)-\frac{\partial}{\partial\theta}\right]\mathbb{K}_{1/0}=\tfrac{2}{5}mr^2(\ddot\theta+\dot\psi\dot\phi\sin\theta)$$

$$\left[\frac{d}{dt}\left(\frac{\partial}{\partial\dot\phi}\right)-\frac{\partial}{\partial\phi}\right]\mathbb{K}_{1/0}=\tfrac{2}{5}mr^2\frac{d}{dt}(\dot\phi+\dot\psi\cos\theta)$$

The five Lagrange equations $\mathcal{L}^q_{1/0}$ are then found by using the expressions of the power coefficients $Q^q_{\bar{1}\to 1/0}$ determined in Example 13.4:

$$\mathcal{L}^x_{1/0}: \qquad m\ddot{x} = F_u \cos\psi - F_v \sin\psi \tag{1}$$
$$\mathcal{L}^y_{1/0}: \qquad m\ddot{y} = F_u \sin\psi + F_v \cos\psi \tag{2}$$
$$\mathcal{L}^\psi_{1/0}: \qquad \tfrac{2}{5}mr^2 \frac{d}{dt}(\dot{\psi} + \dot{\phi}\cos\theta) = 0 \tag{3}$$
$$\mathcal{L}^\theta_{1/0}: \qquad \tfrac{2}{5}mr^2(\ddot{\theta} + \dot{\psi}\dot{\phi}\sin\theta) = rF_v \tag{4}$$
$$\mathcal{L}^\phi_{1/0}: \qquad \tfrac{2}{5}mr^2 \frac{d}{dt}(\dot{\phi} + \dot{\psi}\cos\theta) = rF_u \sin\theta \tag{5}$$

We have found five equations governing seven unknowns $(x, y, \psi, \theta, \phi, F_u, F_v)$. Hence, we are missing two equations. These equations are found by setting $\mathbf{v}_{I\in 1/0} = \mathbf{0}$: [4]

$$\dot{x} = r\dot{\theta}\sin\psi - r\dot{\phi}\sin\theta\cos\psi \tag{6}$$
$$\dot{y} = -r\dot{\theta}\cos\psi - r\dot{\phi}\sin\theta\sin\psi \tag{7}$$

The solution is now complete. ∎

WE CAN now provide basic guidelines for the proper and efficient implementation of Lagrange equations.

1. Identify all coordinates q_i which define the configuration of the rigid body. The larger the set of coordinates, the better since more equations will be obtained. In particular, if a particular coordinate is an explicit function of time, it will advantageous to ignore this relationship: an additional Lagrange equation will be gained. [5]
2. Guarantee the assumption (13.2): this consists of ignoring all holonomic and non-holonomic equations which may exist between the coordinates.
3. Find all partial kinematic screws $\{\mathcal{V}^q_{\mathcal{B}/\mathcal{E}}\}$ in a manner consistent the assumption (13.2).
4. Identify all actions exerted on $\mathcal{B}$: for each action, find the corresponding power coefficients Q^q for all q's.
5. Determine the kinetic energy $\mathbb{K}_{\mathcal{B}/\mathcal{E}}$ in a manner consistent with assumption (13.2).
6. Derive Lagrange equations and bring back all constraint equations.

To emphasize point 2, we return to Examples 13.5 and 13.6. In Example 13.5 it can be seen that the unknown normal reaction N_A is missing from the solution. This is due to the fact that the parametrization of the plate takes into account the contact at A: $\mathbf{r}_{OA} \cdot \hat{\mathbf{y}}_0 = y = 0$. We can alter the solution by ignoring the constraint $y = 0$ at A. We have now three coordinates (x, y, θ) assumed to satisfy assumption (13.2): we can verify that this does not change the expression of the power coefficients $\mathrm{Q}^x_{\bar{1}\to 1/0}$ and $\mathrm{Q}^\theta_{\bar{1}\to 1/0}$. It is easy to show that the power coefficient $\mathrm{Q}^y_{\bar{1}\to 1/0}$ takes the expression $N_A + N_Q\cos\theta + F_Q\sin\theta - mg$. Similarly, the kinetic energy $\mathbb{K}_{1/0}$ must be corrected by the term $\frac{m}{2}(\dot{y}^2 + 2l\dot{y}\dot{\theta}\cos\theta)$. Lagrange equation $\mathcal{L}^y_{1/0}$ takes

[4] Once the Lagrange equations have been determined, the holonomic or non-holonomic equations can be brought back to the fore!

[5] Only "true" coordinates which determine the configuration of the body (such as measures of distance or angle) are eligible. The components (p, q, r) of the body's angular velocity ω on some particular basis are not eligible as potential coordinates q_i!

the form [6]

$$m\frac{d}{dt}(\dot{y} + l\dot{\theta}\cos\theta) = N_A + N_Q\cos\theta + F_Q\sin\theta - mg$$

We can now impose $y = 0$ and find $N_A = mg - N_Q\cos\theta - F_Q\sin\theta$.

In a similar manner, we can add Cartesian coordinate $z = \hat{\mathbf{z}}_0 \cdot \mathbf{r}_{OG}$ for sphere 1 of Example 13.6 and ignore geometric constraint $z = r$. This new coordinate leaves equations $\mathcal{L}^q_{1/0}$ unchanged for $q = x, y, \psi, \theta, \phi$. However, a new equation is found:

$$\mathcal{L}^z_{1/0}: \qquad m\ddot{z} = N - mg$$

After imposing $z = r$, we find $N = mg$.

Of course, the procedure consisting of introducing "fictitious" coordinates to derive additional Lagrange equations is clumsy and can significantly complicate the solution. It can also be argued that this destroys the elegance of Lagrange formalism which in fact eliminates the presence of non-working mechanical action thanks to vanishing power coefficients. If equations are missing to solve for particular unknown quantities, it is best to return to the Newton-Euler methodology and extract one or more equations from the Fundamental Theorem of Dynamics, as we have learned in Chapter 11.

Finally, an important point can be made about holonomic systems such as Example 13.5: if a rigid body $\mathcal{B}$ satisfies a holonomic constraint of the form

$$f(q_1, q_2, \ldots, q_n, t) = 0$$

it is always possible to eliminate one (or more, given additional constraint equations) coordinate, say q_n, from the parametrization of $\mathcal{B}$. Then the position of any point P of $\mathcal{B}$ can be viewed as a function of $(q_1, q_2, \ldots, q_{n-1}, t)$:

$$\mathbf{r}_{OP} = \mathbf{r}\,(q_1, q_2, \ldots, q_{n-1}, q_n(q_1, \ldots, q_{n_1}, t), t) = \tilde{\mathbf{r}}(q_1, q_2, \ldots, q_{n-1}, t)$$

It is then possible to derive $(n-1)$ Lagrange equations by assuming that coordinates $(q_1, q_2, \ldots, q_{n-1})$ satisfy assumption (13.2). In this case, the Lagrange equations are said to be compatible with the holonomic constraints. *We shall see in section 13.6 that this procedure is fundamentally not possible for non-holonomic systems.*

Here are two example problems whose solution follows the aforementioned guidelines.

Example 13.7 Figure 13.3 shows a plate $1(G, \hat{\mathbf{x}}_1, \hat{\mathbf{y}}_1, \hat{\mathbf{z}}_1)$ in motion in a Newtonian referential 0 $(O, \hat{\mathbf{x}}_0, \hat{\mathbf{y}}_0, \hat{\mathbf{z}}_0)$. Plate 1 has a straight edge (directed along $\hat{\mathbf{x}}_1$) which can slide freely on the smooth plane $(O, \hat{\mathbf{x}}_0, \hat{\mathbf{y}}_0)$ of upward normal $\hat{\mathbf{z}}_0$. Its mass is m and mass center G. Its inertia matrix about G takes the form

$$[\mathcal{I}_G]_{b_1} = \begin{bmatrix} A & F & 0 \\ F & B & 0 \\ 0 & 0 & C \end{bmatrix}_{b_1}$$

on basis $b_1(\hat{\mathbf{x}}_1, \hat{\mathbf{y}}_1, \hat{\mathbf{z}}_1)$. Unit vector $\hat{\mathbf{z}}_1$ is normal to the plate. The point H of the sliding

[6] It turns out that the extra term $ml\dot{y}\dot{\theta}\cos\theta$ will lead to an extra term in equation $\mathcal{L}^\theta_{1/0}$. However this term will vanish once $y = 0$ is imposed.

edge is defined by $\mathbf{r}_{HG} = h\hat{\mathbf{y}}_1$. The configuration of the plate is defined by five coordinates:
- the Cartesian coordinates (x, y, z) of G: $\mathbf{r}_{OG} = x\hat{\mathbf{x}}_0 + y\hat{\mathbf{y}}_0 + z\hat{\mathbf{z}}_0$,
- the two angles ψ and θ which define the orientation of basis $(\hat{\mathbf{x}}_1, \hat{\mathbf{y}}_1, \hat{\mathbf{z}}_1)$ relative to basis $(\hat{\mathbf{x}}_0, \hat{\mathbf{y}}_0, \hat{\mathbf{z}}_0)$.

a. Find a holonomic constraint equation.

b. Find the conditions which guarantee that the joint $0 \leftrightarrow 1$ is ideal.

c. Derive the five Lagrange equations.

d. If the plate is released from rest, under what conditions will the edge slip without changing direction? ■

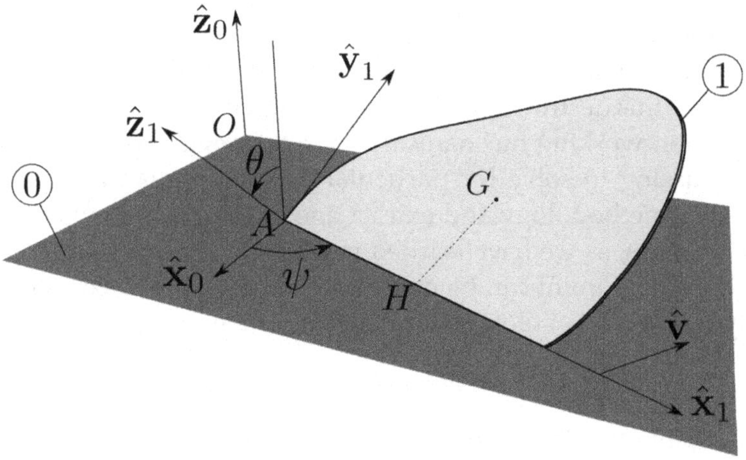

Figure 13.3

a. There exists a relationship between coordinates z and θ. To find it, we set $\mathbf{r}_{OG} \cdot \hat{\mathbf{z}}_0 = \mathbf{r}_{HG} \cdot \hat{\mathbf{z}}_0$ with $\mathbf{r}_{OG} \cdot \hat{\mathbf{z}}_0 = z$ and $\mathbf{r}_{HG} \cdot \hat{\mathbf{z}}_0 = h\hat{\mathbf{y}}_1 \cdot \hat{\mathbf{z}}_0 = h \sin\theta$. The holonomic constraint equation is then

$$z = h \sin\theta \tag{1}$$

b. The joint $0 \leftrightarrow 1$ is defined by four degrees of freedom described by the four independent coordinates (x, y, ψ, θ). To guarantee that this joint is ideal, we must impose the conditions

$$\mathcal{Q}^x_{0\leftrightarrow 1} = \mathcal{Q}^y_{0\leftrightarrow 1} = \mathcal{Q}^\psi_{0\leftrightarrow 1} = \mathcal{Q}^\theta_{0\leftrightarrow 1} = 0$$

assuming that the set (x, y, ψ, θ) satisfies the assumption (13.2). To express these conditions, it is best to resolve both the partial kinematic screws and the contact action screw $\{\mathcal{A}^c_{0\to 1}\}$ at point H. With $\boldsymbol{\omega}_{1/0} = \dot{\psi}\hat{\mathbf{z}}_0 + \dot{\theta}\hat{\mathbf{x}}_1$ and $\mathbf{v}_{H\in 1/0} = \dot{x}\hat{\mathbf{x}}_0 + \dot{y}\hat{\mathbf{y}}_0$ we find the partial kinematic screws

$$\{\mathcal{V}^x_{1/0}\} = \begin{Bmatrix} \mathbf{0} \\ \hat{\mathbf{x}}_0 \end{Bmatrix}_H, \{\mathcal{V}^y_{1/0}\} = \begin{Bmatrix} \mathbf{0} \\ \hat{\mathbf{y}}_0 \end{Bmatrix}_H, \{\mathcal{V}^\psi_{1/0}\} = \begin{Bmatrix} \hat{\mathbf{z}}_0 \\ \mathbf{0} \end{Bmatrix}_H, \{\mathcal{V}^\theta_{1/0}\} = \begin{Bmatrix} \hat{\mathbf{x}}_1 \\ \mathbf{0} \end{Bmatrix}_H$$

The contact action screw $\{\mathcal{A}^c_{0\to 1}\}$ resolved at H is expressed in the following form

$$\{\mathcal{A}^c_{0\to 1}\} = \begin{Bmatrix} X\hat{\mathbf{x}}_0 + Y\hat{\mathbf{y}}_0 + Z\hat{\mathbf{z}}_0 \\ L\hat{\mathbf{x}}_1 + M\hat{\mathbf{v}} + N\hat{\mathbf{z}}_0 \end{Bmatrix}_H$$

The conditions $\mathcal{Q}^q_{0\leftrightarrow 1} = 0$ for $q = x, y, \psi, \theta$ immediately give

$$X = Y = 0, \qquad L = N = 0$$

c. We now assume that the five coordinates (x, y, z, ψ, θ) satisfy the assumption (13.2): hence we must ignore equation (1). With $\mathbf{v}_{G/0} = \dot{x}\hat{\mathbf{x}}_0 + \dot{y}\hat{\mathbf{y}}_0 + \dot{z}\hat{\mathbf{z}}_0$, we can find the expression of the five corresponding partial kinematic screws resolved at point G:

$$\{\mathcal{V}^x_{1/0}\} = \begin{Bmatrix} \mathbf{0} \\ \hat{\mathbf{x}}_0 \end{Bmatrix}_G, \{\mathcal{V}^y_{1/0}\} = \begin{Bmatrix} \mathbf{0} \\ \hat{\mathbf{y}}_0 \end{Bmatrix}_G, \{\mathcal{V}^z_{1/0}\} = \begin{Bmatrix} \mathbf{0} \\ \hat{\mathbf{z}}_0 \end{Bmatrix}_G, \{\mathcal{V}^\psi_{1/0}\} = \begin{Bmatrix} \hat{\mathbf{z}}_0 \\ \mathbf{0} \end{Bmatrix}_G, \{\mathcal{V}^\theta_{1/0}\} = \begin{Bmatrix} \hat{\mathbf{x}}_1 \\ \mathbf{0} \end{Bmatrix}_G$$

This leads to the expressions of the five power coefficients $Q^q_{\bar{1}\to 1/0}$:

$$Q^x_{\bar{1}\to 1/0} = \begin{Bmatrix} Z\hat{\mathbf{z}}_0 \\ M\hat{\mathbf{v}} \end{Bmatrix}_H \cdot \begin{Bmatrix} \mathbf{0} \\ \hat{\mathbf{x}}_0 \end{Bmatrix}_H + \begin{Bmatrix} -mg\hat{\mathbf{z}}_0 \\ \mathbf{0} \end{Bmatrix}_G \cdot \begin{Bmatrix} \mathbf{0} \\ \hat{\mathbf{x}}_0 \end{Bmatrix}_G = 0$$

$$Q^y_{\bar{1}\to 1/0} = \begin{Bmatrix} Z\hat{\mathbf{z}}_0 \\ M\hat{\mathbf{v}} \end{Bmatrix}_H \cdot \begin{Bmatrix} \mathbf{0} \\ \hat{\mathbf{y}}_0 \end{Bmatrix}_H + \begin{Bmatrix} -mg\hat{\mathbf{z}}_0 \\ \mathbf{0} \end{Bmatrix}_G \cdot \begin{Bmatrix} \mathbf{0} \\ \hat{\mathbf{y}}_0 \end{Bmatrix}_G = 0$$

$$Q^z_{\bar{1}\to 1/0} = \begin{Bmatrix} Z\hat{\mathbf{z}}_0 \\ M\hat{\mathbf{v}} \end{Bmatrix}_H \cdot \begin{Bmatrix} \mathbf{0} \\ \hat{\mathbf{z}}_0 \end{Bmatrix}_H + \begin{Bmatrix} -mg\hat{\mathbf{z}}_0 \\ \mathbf{0} \end{Bmatrix}_G \cdot \begin{Bmatrix} \mathbf{0} \\ \hat{\mathbf{z}}_0 \end{Bmatrix}_G = Z - mg$$

$$Q^\psi_{\bar{1}\to 1/0} = \begin{Bmatrix} Z\hat{\mathbf{z}}_0 \\ M\hat{\mathbf{v}} \end{Bmatrix}_H \cdot \begin{Bmatrix} \hat{\mathbf{z}}_0 \\ h\cos\theta\hat{\mathbf{x}}_1 \end{Bmatrix}_H + \begin{Bmatrix} -mg\hat{\mathbf{z}}_0 \\ \mathbf{0} \end{Bmatrix}_G \cdot \begin{Bmatrix} \hat{\mathbf{z}}_0 \\ \mathbf{0} \end{Bmatrix}_G = 0$$

$$Q^\theta_{\bar{1}\to 1/0} = \begin{Bmatrix} Z\hat{\mathbf{z}}_0 \\ M\hat{\mathbf{v}} \end{Bmatrix}_H \cdot \begin{Bmatrix} \hat{\mathbf{x}}_1 \\ -h\hat{\mathbf{z}}_1 \end{Bmatrix}_H + \begin{Bmatrix} -mg\hat{\mathbf{z}}_0 \\ \mathbf{0} \end{Bmatrix}_G \cdot \begin{Bmatrix} \hat{\mathbf{x}}_1 \\ \mathbf{0} \end{Bmatrix}_G = -hZ\cos\theta$$

Next we find the expression of the kinetic energy $\mathbb{K}_{1/0}$:

$$2\mathbb{K}_{1/0} = m\mathbf{v}^2_{G/0} + \boldsymbol{\omega}_{1/0}\cdot\mathcal{I}_G(\boldsymbol{\omega}_{1/0}) = m(\dot{x}^2+\dot{y}^2+\dot{z}^2) + A\dot{\theta}^2 + 2F\dot{\psi}\dot{\theta}\sin\theta + \dot{\psi}^2(B\sin^2\theta + C\cos^2\theta)$$

leading to

$$\left[\frac{d}{dt}\left(\frac{\partial}{\partial\dot{x}}\right) - \frac{\partial}{\partial x}\right]\mathbb{K}_{1/0} = m\ddot{x}$$

$$\left[\frac{d}{dt}\left(\frac{\partial}{\partial\dot{y}}\right) - \frac{\partial}{\partial y}\right]\mathbb{K}_{1/0} = m\ddot{y}$$

$$\left[\frac{d}{dt}\left(\frac{\partial}{\partial\dot{z}}\right) - \frac{\partial}{\partial z}\right]\mathbb{K}_{1/0} = m\ddot{z}$$

$$\left[\frac{d}{dt}\left(\frac{\partial}{\partial\dot{\psi}}\right) - \frac{\partial}{\partial \psi}\right]\mathbb{K}_{1/0} = \frac{d}{dt}\Big(\dot{\psi}(B\sin^2\theta + C\cos^2\theta) + F\dot{\theta}\sin\theta\Big)$$

$$\left[\frac{d}{dt}\left(\frac{\partial}{\partial\dot{\theta}}\right) - \frac{\partial}{\partial \theta}\right]\mathbb{K}_{1/0} = \frac{d}{dt}(A\dot{\theta} + F\dot{\psi}\sin\theta) - F\dot{\psi}\dot{\theta}\cos\theta - \dot{\psi}^2(B-C)\cos\theta\sin\theta$$

We can now combine these equations with the expressions of the power coefficients to obtain five Lagrange equations:

$$\mathcal{L}^x_{1/0}: \quad m\ddot{x} = 0 \tag{2}$$

$$\mathcal{L}^y_{1/0}: \quad m\ddot{y} = 0 \tag{3}$$

$$\mathcal{L}^z_{1/0}: \quad m\ddot{z} = Z - mg \tag{4}$$

$$\mathcal{L}^\psi_{1/0}: \quad \frac{d}{dt}\Big(\dot{\psi}(B\sin^2\theta + C\cos^2\theta) + F\dot{\theta}\sin\theta\Big) = 0 \tag{5}$$

$$\mathcal{L}^\theta_{1/0}: \quad A\ddot{\theta} + F\ddot{\psi}\sin\theta - \dot{\psi}^2(B-C)\cos\theta\sin\theta = -hZ\cos\theta \tag{6}$$

We can now append equation (1) to equations (2-6) which solve for the six unknowns $(x, y, z, \psi, \theta, Z)$. However, moment M remains unknown. Note that we have obtained 3 first integrals of motion:

$$\dot{x} = const, \quad \dot{y} = const, \quad \dot{\psi}(B\sin^2\theta + C\cos^2\theta) + F\dot{\theta}\sin\theta = const.$$

We could have modeled this system by using the four coordinates (x, y, ψ, θ): we would have obtained four corresponding Lagrange equations. Unknown Z would be absent from these equations.

d. If the plate is released from rest, then we can write equation (5) as

$$\dot{\psi}(B\sin^2\theta + C\cos^2\theta) + F\dot{\theta}\sin\theta = 0$$

The plate's edge will slide without changing direction if angle ψ satisfies $\dot{\psi} = 0$ at all time: this leads to

$$F\dot{\theta}\sin\theta = 0$$

which holds for all time if the condition $F = 0$ is satisfied. This implies that the unit vectors $(\hat{\mathbf{x}}_1, \hat{\mathbf{y}}_1)$ are principal directions for the inertia operator $\mathcal{I}_G$. ■

Example 13.8 — **Chaplygin sleigh.** Consider the planar motion of a rigid body 1 of mass m supported by a horizontal plane $(O, \hat{\mathbf{x}}_0, \hat{\mathbf{y}}_0)$ at points A and B due to the presence of legs which slide freely over the support, and at C due to a blade which constrains the direction of the motion. More specifically, the velocity $\mathbf{v}_{C\in 1/0}$ of C is always directed along unit vector $\hat{\mathbf{x}}_1$ of the sleigh. The position of the body is specified by the horizontal coordinates, x and y, of the point of contact C and by the angle θ that the axis $(C, \hat{\mathbf{x}}_1)$ fixed to the body makes with the axis $(O, \hat{\mathbf{x}}_0)$ fixed in referential 0. See Figure 13.4. Denote by G the mass center of the body located on line $(C, \hat{\mathbf{x}}_1)$, by b the distance $|CG|$ and by I_C the moment of inertia about axis $(C, \hat{\mathbf{z}}_0)$. The joint at C is assumed frictionless.

a. Express the non-holonomic constraint equation in terms of $(\dot{x}, \dot{y}, \dot{\theta})$.

b. Express the conditions which guarantee that the joint at C is ideal.

c. Derive the three Lagrange equations $\mathcal{L}^q_{1/0}$ for $q = x, y, \theta$. Deduce the equations of motion of the body. ■

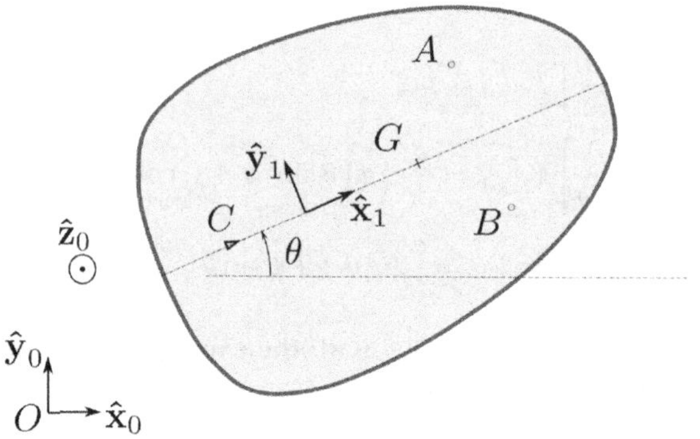

Figure 13.4

a. We impose that the velocity of C is directed along $\hat{\mathbf{x}}_1$ to find

$$\mathbf{v}_{C\in 1/0} \cdot \hat{\mathbf{y}}_1 = -\dot{x}\sin\theta + \dot{y}\cos\theta = 0 \tag{1}$$

Equation (1) represents a non-integrable non-holonomic constraint equation. The kinematic screw of body 1 takes the following expression in terms of coordinates x, y, θ:

$$\{\mathcal{V}_{1/0}\} = \begin{Bmatrix} \dot{\theta}\hat{\mathbf{z}}_0 \\ \dot{x}\hat{\mathbf{x}}_0 + \dot{y}\hat{\mathbf{y}}_0 \end{Bmatrix}_C = \begin{Bmatrix} \dot{\theta}\hat{\mathbf{z}}_0 \\ v_C\hat{\mathbf{x}}_1 \end{Bmatrix}_C$$

with v_C given by $v_C = \dot{x}\cos\theta + \dot{y}\sin\theta$.

b. The action screw at contact point C must satisfy

$$\begin{Bmatrix} \dot{\theta}\hat{\mathbf{z}}_0 \\ v_C\hat{\mathbf{x}}_1 \end{Bmatrix}_C \cdot \begin{Bmatrix} X\hat{\mathbf{x}}_0 + Y\hat{\mathbf{y}}_0 + Z\hat{\mathbf{z}}_0 \\ L\hat{\mathbf{x}}_0 + M\hat{\mathbf{y}}_0 + N\hat{\mathbf{z}}_0 \end{Bmatrix}_C = N\dot{\theta} + v_C(X\cos\theta + Y\sin\theta) = 0$$

for all possible values of $\dot{\theta}$ and v_C: this leads to the conditions

$$N = 0, \qquad X\cos\theta + Y\sin\theta = 0 \tag{2-3}$$

c. To derive the three Lagrange equations $\mathcal{L}^q_{1/0}$ for $q = x, y, \theta$, we must assume Lagrange assumption that $(x, y, \theta, \dot{x}, \dot{y}, \dot{\theta})$ are independent variables. We must ignore equation (1). Accordingly, the kinematic screw is written in the form

$$\{\mathcal{V}_{1/0}\} = \begin{Bmatrix} \dot{\theta}\hat{\mathbf{z}}_0 \\ \dot{x}\hat{\mathbf{x}}_0 + \dot{y}\hat{\mathbf{y}}_0 \end{Bmatrix}_C = \dot{\theta}\begin{Bmatrix} \hat{\mathbf{z}}_0 \\ \mathbf{0} \end{Bmatrix}_C + \dot{x}\begin{Bmatrix} \mathbf{0} \\ \hat{\mathbf{x}}_0 \end{Bmatrix}_C + \dot{y}\begin{Bmatrix} \mathbf{0} \\ \hat{\mathbf{y}}_0 \end{Bmatrix}_C$$

leading to the expressions of the partial kinematic screws:

$$\{\mathcal{V}^x_{1/0}\} = \begin{Bmatrix} \mathbf{0} \\ \hat{\mathbf{x}}_0 \end{Bmatrix}_C, \quad \{\mathcal{V}^y_{1/0}\} = \begin{Bmatrix} \mathbf{0} \\ \hat{\mathbf{y}}_0 \end{Bmatrix}_C, \quad \{\mathcal{V}^\theta_{1/0}\} = \begin{Bmatrix} \hat{\mathbf{z}}_0 \\ \mathbf{0} \end{Bmatrix}_C$$

and the expression of the kinetic energy (using equation 9.28)

$$\begin{aligned} 2\mathbb{K}_{1/0} &= m\mathbf{v}^2_{C\in 1/0} + 2m\mathbf{v}_{C\in 1/0} \cdot (\dot{\theta}\hat{\mathbf{z}}_0 \times b\hat{\mathbf{x}}_1) + I_C\dot{\theta}^2 \\ &= m(\dot{x}^2 + \dot{y}^2) + 2mb\dot{\theta}(-\dot{x}\sin\theta + \dot{y}\cos\theta) + I_C\dot{\theta}^2 \end{aligned}$$

From this last expression, we obtain

$$\left[\frac{d}{dt}\frac{\partial}{\partial\dot{x}} - \frac{\partial}{\partial x}\right]\mathbb{K}_{1/0} = m\frac{d}{dt}(\dot{x} - b\dot{\theta}\sin\theta)$$

$$\left[\frac{d}{dt}\frac{\partial}{\partial\dot{y}} - \frac{\partial}{\partial y}\right]\mathbb{K}_{1/0} = m\frac{d}{dt}(\dot{y} + b\dot{\theta}\cos\theta)$$

$$\left[\frac{d}{dt}\frac{\partial}{\partial\dot{\theta}} - \frac{\partial}{\partial\theta}\right]\mathbb{K}_{1/0} = \frac{d}{dt}(I_C\dot{\theta} - mb\dot{x}\sin\theta + mb\dot{y}\cos\theta) - mb\dot{\theta}(-\dot{x}\cos\theta - \dot{y}\sin\theta)$$

The expressions of the power coefficients $\mathbb{Q}^q_{\bar{1}\to 1/0}$ are found as follows

$$\mathbb{Q}^x_{\bar{1}\to 1/0} = \{\mathcal{V}^x_{1/0}\} \cdot \begin{Bmatrix} X\hat{\mathbf{x}}_0 + Y\hat{\mathbf{y}}_0 + Z\hat{\mathbf{z}}_0 \\ L\hat{\mathbf{x}}_0 + M\hat{\mathbf{y}}_0 + N\hat{\mathbf{z}}_0 \end{Bmatrix}_C = X$$

$$\mathbb{Q}^y_{\bar{1}\to 1/0} = \{\mathcal{V}^y_{1/0}\} \cdot \begin{Bmatrix} X\hat{\mathbf{x}}_0 + Y\hat{\mathbf{y}}_0 + Z\hat{\mathbf{z}}_0 \\ L\hat{\mathbf{x}}_0 + M\hat{\mathbf{y}}_0 + N\hat{\mathbf{z}}_0 \end{Bmatrix}_C = Y$$

$$\mathbb{Q}^\theta_{\bar{1}\to 1/0} = \{\mathcal{V}^\theta_{1/0}\} \cdot \begin{Bmatrix} X\hat{\mathbf{x}}_0 + Y\hat{\mathbf{y}}_0 + Z\hat{\mathbf{z}}_0 \\ L\hat{\mathbf{x}}_0 + M\hat{\mathbf{y}}_0 + N\hat{\mathbf{z}}_0 \end{Bmatrix}_C = N$$

The effect of gravity and the reactions at A and B do not contribute to these energy coefficients. These expressions lead to three Lagrange equations:

$$\mathcal{L}^x_{1/0}: \quad m\tfrac{d}{dt}(\dot{x} - b\dot{\theta}\sin\theta) = X \tag{4}$$
$$\mathcal{L}^y_{1/0}: \quad m\tfrac{d}{dt}(\dot{y} + b\dot{\theta}\cos\theta) = Y \tag{5}$$
$$\mathcal{L}^\theta_{1/0}: \quad I_C\ddot{\theta} + mb(-\ddot{x}\sin\theta + \ddot{y}\cos\theta) = N \tag{6}$$

Equations (1-6) allow for the determination of (x, y, θ, X, Y, N). By eliminating (X, Y, N) we obtain the equations of motions after a few manipulations:

$$\begin{aligned} \ddot{x} &= b\dot{\theta}^2\cos\theta - \dot{x}\dot{\theta}\tan\theta \\ \ddot{y} &= b\dot{\theta}^2\sin\theta + \dot{x}\dot{\theta} \\ I_C\ddot{\theta} &= -mb\dot{\theta}(\dot{x}\cos\theta + \dot{y}\sin\theta) \end{aligned}$$

Remark 11. The incorrect way to proceed is to use the expressions

$$\{\mathcal{V}_{1/0}\} = \begin{Bmatrix} \dot{\theta}\hat{\mathbf{z}}_0 \\ (\dot{x}\cos\theta + \dot{y}\sin\theta)\hat{\mathbf{x}}_1 \end{Bmatrix}_C$$

$$\{\mathcal{V}^x_{1/0}\} = \begin{Bmatrix} \mathbf{0} \\ \cos\theta\hat{\mathbf{x}}_1 \end{Bmatrix}_C, \quad \{\mathcal{V}^y_{1/0}\} = \begin{Bmatrix} \mathbf{0} \\ \sin\theta\hat{\mathbf{x}}_1 \end{Bmatrix}_C, \quad \{\mathcal{V}^\theta_{1/0}\} = \begin{Bmatrix} \hat{\mathbf{z}}_0 \\ \mathbf{0} \end{Bmatrix}_C$$

since this clearly violates the requirement that $(x, y, \theta, \dot{x}, \dot{y}, \dot{\theta})$ be independent variables. Similarly, the kinetic energy can be written as

$$2\mathbb{K}_{1/0} = m(\dot{x}^2 + \dot{y}^2) + I_C\dot{\theta}^2$$

This expression is correct, but it cannot be used for the purpose of deriving Lagrange equations since, once again, the requirement that $(x, y, \theta, \dot{x}, \dot{y}, \dot{\theta})$ be independent variables is not satisfied. Using these expressions one would find the erroneous equations

$$\begin{aligned} \ddot{x} &= \cos\theta(X\cos\theta + Y\sin\theta) = 0 \\ \ddot{y} &= \sin\theta(X\cos\theta + Y\sin\theta) = 0 \\ I_C\ddot{\theta} &= N = 0 \end{aligned}$$

Remark 12. In Section 13.6, we shall learn how to derive Lagrange equations by taking into account the non-holonomic constraint (1).

■

13.5 Lagrange Equations: System of Rigid Bodies

CONSIDER a system Σ of p rigid bodies $(\mathcal{B}_1, \ldots, \mathcal{B}_p)$ in motion in a Newtonian referential $\mathcal{E}$. The configuration of the system is defined by n coordinates $(q_1, \ldots, q_n)$ and by time t satisfying assumption (13.2). All holonomic and non-holonomic equations which may govern these coordinates are therefore ignored. The simplest way to derive the n Lagrange equations governing Σ is to add the p equations written for each rigid body $\mathcal{B}_j$: we obtain for a given coordinate q_i[7]

[7] To simplify notations, as we have done in Chapter 12, referential $\mathcal{E}$ and rigid body $\mathcal{B}_j$ will be indexed as 0 and j: $\mathbb{K}_{\mathcal{B}_j/\mathcal{E}}$ becomes $\mathbb{K}_{j/0}$, $\mathbb{Q}^q_{\mathcal{B}_k\leftrightarrow\mathcal{B}_j}$ becomes $\mathbb{Q}^q_{k\leftrightarrow j}$, etc.

$$\left[\frac{d}{dt}\left(\frac{\partial}{\partial \dot{q}_i}\right) - \frac{\partial}{\partial q_i}\right](\mathbb{K}_{1/0} + \mathbb{K}_{2/0} + \cdots + \mathbb{K}_{p/0}) = \sum_{j=1}^{p} \mathbb{Q}^{q_i}_{\bar{j}\to j/0} \qquad (13.21)$$

We then write the actions on body $\mathcal{B}_j$ as a sum of contributions internal and external to the system

$$\{\mathcal{A}_{\bar{j}\to j}\} = \{\mathcal{A}_{\bar{\Sigma}\to j}\} + \sum_{k=1}^{p}\{\mathcal{A}_{k\to j}\}$$

Then equation (13.21) becomes

$$\left[\frac{d}{dt}\left(\frac{\partial}{\partial \dot{q}_i}\right) - \frac{\partial}{\partial q_i}\right]\mathbb{K}_{\Sigma/0} = \mathbb{Q}^{q_i}_{\bar{\Sigma}\to\Sigma/0} + \sum_{j,k=1}^{p} \mathbb{Q}^{q_i}_{k\to j/0}$$

where we have written the system's kinetic energy as $\mathbb{K}_{\Sigma/0} = \mathbb{K}_{1/0} + \cdots + \mathbb{K}_{p/0}$. Consider a pair of interacting bodies $\mathcal{B}_j$ and $\mathcal{B}_k$ (fixing q_i): we recognize the sum $\mathbb{Q}^{q_i}_{k\to j/0} + \mathbb{Q}^{q_i}_{j\to k/0}$ as the q_i-power coefficient of interaction between $\mathcal{B}_j$ and $\mathcal{B}_k$:

$$\begin{aligned}
\mathbb{Q}^{q_i}_{k\to j/0} + \mathbb{Q}^{q_i}_{j\to k/0} &= \{\mathcal{A}_{k\to j}\}\cdot\{\mathcal{V}^{q_i}_{j/0}\} + \{\mathcal{A}_{j\to k}\}\cdot\{\mathcal{V}^{q_i}_{k/0}\} \\
&= \{\mathcal{A}_{k\to j}\}\cdot\left(\{\mathcal{V}^{q_i}_{j/0}\} - \{\mathcal{V}^{q_i}_{k/0}\}\right) = \{\mathcal{A}_{k\to j}\}\cdot\{\mathcal{V}^{q_i}_{j/k}\} \\
&= \mathbb{Q}^{q_i}_{k\leftrightarrow j}
\end{aligned}$$

Then we write the sum of internal terms as a pairwise sum

$$\sum_{j,k=1}^{p} \mathbb{Q}^{q_i}_{k\to j/0} = \sum_{1\le j<k\le p} \mathbb{Q}^{q_i}_{k\leftrightarrow j}$$

In conclusion, the Lagrange equations for system Σ can be stated as follows:

Theorem 13.3 — Lagrange Equations (System). The motion of a system Σ of p rigid bodies relative to a Newtonian referential $\mathcal{E}$ whose configuration is defined by n coordinates $(q_1, \ldots, q_n)$ and the time variable t, is governed by the n Lagrange equations

$$\mathcal{L}^{q_i}_{\Sigma/0}: \quad \left[\frac{d}{dt}\left(\frac{\partial}{\partial \dot{q}_i}\right) - \frac{\partial}{\partial q_i}\right]\mathbb{K}_{\Sigma/0} = \mathbb{Q}^{q_i}_{\bar{\Sigma}\to\Sigma/0} + \sum_{1\le j<k\le p} \mathbb{Q}^{q_i}_{k\leftrightarrow j} \quad (i = 1, \ldots, n) \qquad (13.22)$$

where the variables $(\mathbf{q}, \dot{\mathbf{q}}, t)$ satisfy the assumption (13.2).

Remark 13. A special case of Theorem 13.3 can be formulated as follows:

(i) if all joints between the bodies of system Σ are ideal,

(ii) if all joints between Σ and external bodies which are either fixed or whose motions are prescribed, are ideal,

(iii) if all other actions, whether external or internal, derive from potential energies $\mathbb{U} = \mathbb{U}_{\bar{\Sigma}\to\Sigma/0} + \sum_{j<k}\mathbb{U}_{k\leftrightarrow j}$,

then Lagrange equations can be stated as follows:

$$\left[\frac{d}{dt}\left(\frac{\partial}{\partial \dot{q}_i}\right) - \frac{\partial}{\partial q_i}\right]\mathbb{L}_{\Sigma/0} = 0 \tag{13.23}$$

where $\mathbb{L}_{\Sigma/0} = \mathbb{K}_{\Sigma/0} - \mathbb{U}$ is known as the *Lagrangian* of the system.

Remark 14. It is possible that one (or more) Lagrange equation leads to a first integral of motion if the following conditions are met:

(i) all external actions satisfy $\mathbb{Q}^{q_1}_{\overline{\Sigma}\to\Sigma/0} = 0$,

(ii) all internal interactions satisfy $\mathbb{Q}^{q_1}_{k\leftrightarrow j} = 0$,

(iii) the kinetic energy $\mathbb{K}_{\Sigma/0}$ is not explicitly a function of q_1,

then Lagrange equation $\mathcal{L}^{q_1}_{\Sigma/0}$ leads to

$$\frac{\partial}{\partial \dot{q}_1}\mathbb{K}_{\Sigma/0} = \text{Cst}$$

Here is an illustration of Lagrange equations (13.22).

Example 13.9 We consider the motion of a system Σ comprised of an axisymmetric body 2 connected to a ring-like rigid body 1 in motion on a fixed horizontal plane $\Pi(O, \hat{\mathbf{x}}_0, \hat{\mathbf{y}}_0)$. More specifically, body 1 (of mass center G, of mass m_1) rolls without slipping on plane Π in such a way as to remain vertical. We denote by $(G, \hat{\mathbf{y}}_1)$ the axis of 1. Unit vector $\hat{\mathbf{z}}_1$ shown in Figure 13.5 is directed along a particular diameter of 1 which coincides with the axis of body 2. Let I be the contact point of body 1 with Π, and let (x, y, R) be the Cartesian coordinates of G relative to referential $0(O, \hat{\mathbf{x}}_0, \hat{\mathbf{y}}_0, \hat{\mathbf{z}}_0)$. The orientation of 1 relative to 0 is defined by

1. angle ψ which defines the orientation of the vertical plane containing 1 relative to 0,
2. angle θ which defines the orientation of axis $(G, \hat{\mathbf{z}}_1)$ relative to the vertical plane containing 1.

The inertia matrix of body 1 about G takes the form

$$[\mathcal{I}_{G,1}]_{b_1} = \begin{bmatrix} I_1 & 0 & 0 \\ 0 & J_1 & 0 \\ 0 & 0 & I_1 \end{bmatrix}_{b_1}$$

on basis $b_1(\hat{\mathbf{x}}_1, \hat{\mathbf{y}}_1, \hat{\mathbf{z}}_1)$.

Body 2 (of mass center G, mass m_2) is mounted on the diameter $(G, \hat{\mathbf{z}}_1)$ through a frictionless pivot about which it is free to rotate. Denote by ϕ the angle of rotation of 2 relative to 1 measured about axis $(G, \hat{\mathbf{z}}_1)$. Its inertia matrix about G takes the form

$$[\mathcal{I}_{G,2}]_{b_2} = \begin{bmatrix} I_2 & 0 & 0 \\ 0 & I_2 & 0 \\ 0 & 0 & J_2 \end{bmatrix}_{b_2}$$

on basis $b_2(\hat{\mathbf{x}}_2, \hat{\mathbf{y}}_2, \hat{\mathbf{z}}_1)$ attached body 2.

a. Find the equations which express the no-slip condition of body 1 at point I.

b. Assume that the contact at I is realized with (sliding) friction (neglecting spinning and rolling friction), and that the corresponding action screw takes the form

$$\{\mathcal{A}_{\Pi\to 1}\}^c = \begin{Bmatrix} X\hat{\mathbf{x}}_0 + Y\hat{\mathbf{y}}_0 + Z\hat{\mathbf{z}}_0 \\ M\hat{\mathbf{u}} \end{Bmatrix}_I$$

where the (unknown) couple $M\hat{\mathbf{u}}$ accounts for the fact that 1 is maintained vertical. Find the five Lagrange equations $\mathcal{L}^q_{\Sigma/0}$ with respect to coordinates $q = x, y, \psi, \theta, \phi$. Can unknown couple M be found?

c. A massless motor is mounted between bodies 1 and 2 to exert a couple $C\hat{\mathbf{z}}_1$: find the corresponding change in the Lagrange equations found in question b). ■

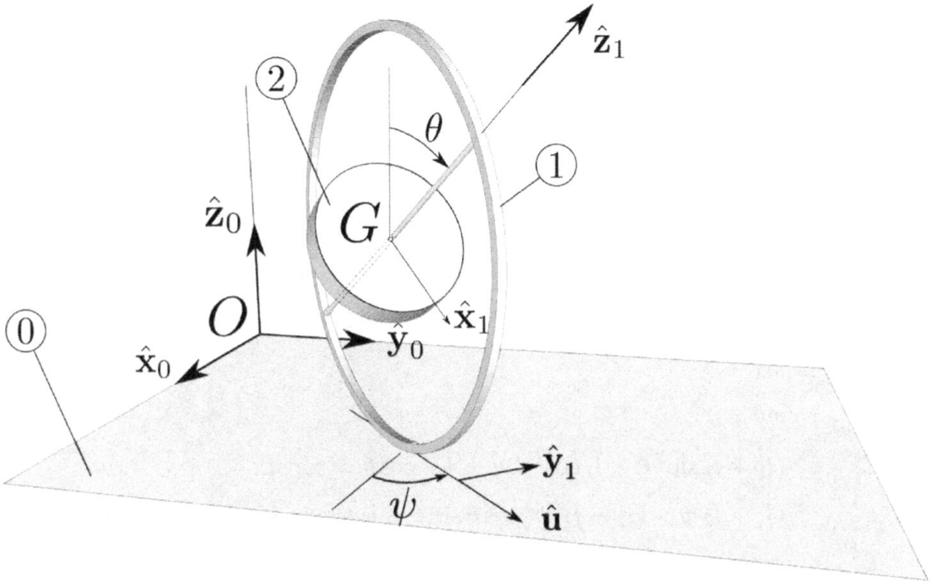

Figure 13.5

a. We find the slip velocity at I according to $\mathbf{v}_{I\in 1/0} = \mathbf{v}_{G/0} + \boldsymbol{\omega}_{1/0} \times \mathbf{r}_{GI}$:

$$\mathbf{v}_{I\in 1/0} = \dot{x}\hat{\mathbf{x}}_0 + \dot{y}\hat{\mathbf{y}}_0 + (\dot{\psi}\hat{\mathbf{z}}_0 + \dot{\theta}\hat{\mathbf{y}}_1) \times (-R\hat{\mathbf{z}}_0) = \dot{x}\hat{\mathbf{x}}_0 + \dot{y}\hat{\mathbf{y}}_0 - R\dot{\theta}\hat{\mathbf{u}}$$

The no-slip condition then gives two equations

$$\dot{x} = R\dot{\theta}\cos\psi \qquad (1)$$
$$\dot{y} = R\dot{\theta}\sin\psi \qquad (2)$$

b. We assume that the coordinates $(x, y, \psi, \theta, \phi)$ satisfy the assumption (13.2). We then find the kinematic screws $\{\mathcal{V}_{1/0}\}$, $\{\mathcal{V}_{2/1}\}$ and $\{\mathcal{V}_{2/0}\}$

$$\{\mathcal{V}_{1/0}\} = \begin{Bmatrix} \dot{\psi}\hat{\mathbf{z}}_0 + \dot{\theta}\hat{\mathbf{y}}_1 \\ \dot{x}\hat{\mathbf{x}}_0 + \dot{y}\hat{\mathbf{y}}_0 \end{Bmatrix}_G = \begin{Bmatrix} \dot{\psi}\hat{\mathbf{z}}_0 + \dot{\theta}\hat{\mathbf{y}}_1 \\ \dot{x}\hat{\mathbf{x}}_0 + \dot{y}\hat{\mathbf{y}}_0 - R\dot{\theta}\hat{\mathbf{u}} \end{Bmatrix}_I$$

$$\{\mathcal{V}_{2/1}\} = \begin{Bmatrix} \dot{\phi}\hat{\mathbf{z}}_1 \\ \mathbf{0} \end{Bmatrix}_G \qquad \{\mathcal{V}_{2/0}\} = \{\mathcal{V}_{2/1}\} + \{\mathcal{V}_{1/0}\} = \begin{Bmatrix} \dot{\psi}\hat{\mathbf{z}}_0 + \dot{\theta}\hat{\mathbf{y}}_1 + \dot{\phi}\hat{\mathbf{z}}_1 \\ \dot{x}\hat{\mathbf{x}}_0 + \dot{y}\hat{\mathbf{y}}_0 \end{Bmatrix}_G$$

We can then determine the expression of the partial kinematic screws $\{\mathcal{V}^q_{1/0}\}$, $\{\mathcal{V}^q_{2/1}\}$ and $\{\mathcal{V}^q_{2/0}\}$ for $q = x, y, \psi, \theta, \phi$. The power coefficients $\mathbb{Q}^q_{\bar{1}\to 1/0}$, $\mathbb{Q}^q_{\bar{2}\to 2/0}$, and $\mathbb{Q}^q_{1\leftrightarrow 2}$ are then found to be

$$\mathbb{Q}^q_{\bar{1}\to 1/0} = \begin{Bmatrix} X\hat{\mathbf{x}}_0 + Y\hat{\mathbf{y}}_0 + (Z - mg)\hat{\mathbf{z}}_0 \\ M\hat{\mathbf{u}} \end{Bmatrix}_I \cdot \frac{\partial}{\partial \dot{q}} \begin{Bmatrix} \dot{\psi}\hat{\mathbf{z}}_0 + \dot{\theta}\hat{\mathbf{y}}_1 \\ \dot{x}\hat{\mathbf{x}}_0 + \dot{y}\hat{\mathbf{y}}_0 - R\dot{\theta}\hat{\mathbf{u}} \end{Bmatrix}_I$$

leading to

$$\mathbb{Q}^q_{\bar{1}\to 1/0} = \begin{cases} X & , \quad q = x \\ Y & , \quad q = y \\ 0 & , \quad q = \psi, \phi \\ -R(X\cos\psi + Y\sin\psi) & , \quad q = \theta \end{cases}$$

$$\mathbb{Q}^q_{\bar{2}\to 2/0} = \begin{Bmatrix} -mg\hat{\mathbf{z}}_0 \\ \mathbf{0} \end{Bmatrix}_G \cdot \frac{\partial}{\partial \dot{q}} \begin{Bmatrix} \dot{\psi}\hat{\mathbf{z}}_0 + \dot{\theta}\hat{\mathbf{y}}_1 + \dot{\phi}\hat{\mathbf{z}}_1 \\ \dot{x}\hat{\mathbf{x}}_0 + \dot{y}\hat{\mathbf{y}}_0 \end{Bmatrix}_G = 0, \quad q = x, y, \psi, \theta, \phi$$

$$\mathbb{Q}^q_{1\leftrightarrow 2} = \{\mathcal{A}_{1\to 2}\}^c \cdot \frac{\partial}{\partial \dot{q}} \begin{Bmatrix} \dot{\phi}\hat{\mathbf{z}}_1 \\ \mathbf{0} \end{Bmatrix}_G = \begin{cases} 0 & , \quad q = x, y, \psi, \theta \\ \mathbf{M}^c_{G,1\to 2}\cdot\hat{\mathbf{z}}_1 = 0 & , \quad q = \phi \end{cases}$$

The next step is to find the kinetic energy of the system:

$$\begin{aligned} 2\mathbb{K}_{\Sigma/0} &= (m_1 + m_2)\mathbf{v}^2_{G/0} + \boldsymbol{\omega}_{1/0}\cdot\mathcal{I}_{G,1}(\boldsymbol{\omega}_{1/0}) + \boldsymbol{\omega}_{2/0}\cdot\mathcal{I}_{G,2}(\boldsymbol{\omega}_{2/0}) \\ &= (m_1 + m_2)(\dot{x}^2 + \dot{y}^2) + (I_1 + I_2\sin^2\theta + J_2\cos^2\theta)\dot{\psi}^2 + (J_1 + I_2)\dot{\theta}^2 + J_2\dot{\phi}^2 + 2J_2\dot{\phi}\dot{\psi}\cos\theta \end{aligned}$$

We can now apply (13.22) for system Σ to find seven Lagrange equations:

$$\mathcal{L}^x_{\Sigma/0}: \quad m\ddot{x} = X \tag{3}$$

$$\mathcal{L}^y_{\Sigma/0}: \quad m\ddot{y} = Y \tag{4}$$

$$\mathcal{L}^\psi_{\Sigma/0}: \quad (I_1 + I_2\sin^2\theta + J_2\cos^2\theta)\dot{\psi} + J_2\dot{\phi}\cos\theta = const. \tag{5}$$

$$\mathcal{L}^\theta_{\Sigma/0}: \quad (J_1 + I_2)\ddot{\theta} - (I_2 - J_2)\dot{\psi}^2\cos\theta\sin\theta + J_2\dot{\phi}\dot{\psi}\sin\theta = -R(X\cos\psi + Y\sin\psi) \tag{6}$$

$$\mathcal{L}^\phi_{\Sigma/0}: \quad \dot{\phi} + \dot{\psi}\cos\theta = const. \tag{7}$$

Equations (1-7) solve for seven unknowns $(x, y, \psi, \theta, \phi, X, Y)$. However moment M remains unknown. To find it, it is best to use the Newton-Euler approach: it is immediately seen that the following dynamic moment equation solves for M

$$\mathbf{D}_{I,\Sigma/0}\cdot\hat{\mathbf{u}} = M = \mathbf{D}_{I,1/0}\cdot\hat{\mathbf{u}} + \mathbf{D}_{I,2/0}\cdot\hat{\mathbf{u}}$$

with

$$\begin{aligned} \mathbf{D}_{I,1/0}\cdot\hat{\mathbf{u}} &= \hat{\mathbf{u}}\cdot\left(\frac{d}{dt}\mathbf{H}_{G,1/0} + \mathbf{r}_{IG}\times m_1\mathbf{a}_{G/0}\right) \\ &= \hat{\mathbf{u}}\cdot\frac{d}{dt}(I_1\dot{\psi}\hat{\mathbf{z}}_0 + J_1\dot{\theta}\hat{\mathbf{y}}_1) + \hat{\mathbf{u}}\cdot R\hat{\mathbf{z}}_0\times m_1R(\ddot{\theta}\hat{\mathbf{u}} + R\dot{\theta}^2\hat{\mathbf{y}}_1) \\ &= -(J_1 + m_1R^2)\dot{\theta}^2 \end{aligned}$$

and

$$\mathbf{D}_{I,2/0} \cdot \hat{\mathbf{u}} = \hat{\mathbf{u}} \cdot \left(\frac{d}{dt} \mathbf{H}_{G,2/0} + \mathbf{r}_{IG} \times m_2 \mathbf{a}_{G/0} \right)$$

$$= \hat{\mathbf{u}} \cdot \frac{d}{dt} [-I_2 \dot{\psi} \sin\theta \hat{\mathbf{x}}_1 + I_2 \dot{\theta} \hat{\mathbf{y}}_1 + J_2(\dot{\phi} + \dot{\psi}\cos\theta)\hat{\mathbf{z}}_1] - m_2 R^2 \dot{\theta}^2$$

$$= -(I_2 + m_2 R^2)\dot{\theta}^2 + \frac{d}{dt}[J_2 \dot{\phi} + (J_2 - I_2)\cos\theta \sin\theta]$$

This gives the expression of M:

$$M = -(J_1 + I_2 + (m_1 + m_2)R^2)\dot{\theta}^2 + \frac{d}{dt}[J_2\dot{\phi} + (J_2 - I_2)\cos\theta\sin\theta]$$

c. The addition of the motor between bodies 1 and 2 contributes to an additional term for the power coefficient of interaction $Q^{\phi}_{1\leftrightarrow 2}$

$$Q^{\phi}_{1\leftrightarrow 2} = \{\mathcal{A}_{1\to 2}\}^c \cdot \frac{\partial}{\partial \dot{\phi}} \begin{Bmatrix} \dot{\phi}\hat{\mathbf{z}}_1 \\ \mathbf{0} \end{Bmatrix}_G = (C\hat{\mathbf{z}}_1 + \mathbf{M}^c_{G,1\to 2}) \cdot \hat{\mathbf{z}}_1 = C$$

The only modified Lagrange equation is $\mathcal{L}^{\phi}_{\Sigma/0}$:

$$\mathcal{L}^{\phi}_{\Sigma/0}: \qquad C = J_2 \frac{d}{dt}(\dot{\phi} + \dot{\psi}\cos\theta) \tag{7'}$$

■

13.6 Lagrange Equations with Multipliers

We saw in Section 13.4 that it is always possible to derive Lagrange equations for systems which satisfy holonomic or non-holonomic constraint equations by simply ignoring these constraints and thereby guaranteeing that the chosen coordinates $\mathbf{q}$ satisfy assumption (13.2). The corresponding virtual velocity field is then defined as

$$\mathbf{v}^*_P = \sum_{i=1}^{n} \frac{\partial \mathbf{r}_{OP}}{\partial q_i} \dot{q}^*_i = \sum_{i=1}^{n} \frac{\partial \mathbf{v}_P}{\partial \dot{q}_i} \dot{q}^*_i$$

where the virtual speeds $\dot{\mathbf{q}}^* = (\dot{q}^*_1, \dot{q}^*_2, \ldots, \dot{q}^*_n)$ take arbitrary values.

We examine here how to derive Lagrange equations which take into account non-holonomic constraints: suppose that the coordinates $\mathbf{q}$ are known to satisfy $l < n$ constraint (time-independent) equations of the type

$$\sum_{j=1}^{n} a_{ij}(\mathbf{q})\dot{q}_j + b_i(\mathbf{q}) = 0, \qquad (i = 1, 2, \ldots, l) \tag{13.24}$$

These equations, linear in the $\dot{q}_j$, are assumed non-integrable, that is, it is not possible to express l coordinates, say, $(q_{m+1}, q_{m+2}, \ldots, q_n)$ as an explicit function of the $m = n - l$ remaining independent coordinates $(q_1, q_2, \ldots, q_m)$. However we assume that the linear system of equations (13.24) in the unknowns $(\dot{q}_{m+1}, \dot{q}_{m+2}, \ldots, \dot{q}_n)$ is invertible to give

$$\dot{q}_{m+i} = \sum_{j=1}^{m} \tilde{a}_{ij}(\mathbf{q})\dot{q}_j + \tilde{b}_i(\mathbf{q}), \qquad (i = 1, 2, \ldots, l) \tag{13.25}$$

We then ask if it is possible to derive m Lagrange equations w.r.t. the independent coordinates $(q_1, q_2, \ldots, q_m)$. We start with equation (13.1) and substitute each $\dot{q}_{m+i}$ for $i = 1, 2, \ldots, l$ according to (13.25): we find

$$\mathbf{v}_P = \sum_{i=1}^{m} \mathbf{w}_P^{q_i} \dot{q}_i + \mathbf{w}_P^0 \tag{13.26}$$

with

$$\mathbf{w}_P^{q_i} = \frac{\partial \mathbf{r}_{OP}}{\partial q_i} + \sum_{j=1}^{l} \tilde{a}_{ji} \frac{\partial \mathbf{r}_{OP}}{\partial q_{m+j}}$$

and

$$\mathbf{w}_P^0 = \sum_{j=1}^{l} \tilde{b}_j \frac{\partial \mathbf{r}_{OP}}{\partial q_{m+j}}$$

We find from (13.26) the relationship

$$\mathbf{w}_P^{q_i} = \frac{\partial}{\partial \dot{q}_i} \mathbf{v}_P \qquad (i = 1, \ldots, m) \tag{13.27}$$

Note however that

$$\mathbf{w}_P^{q_i} \neq \frac{\partial \mathbf{r}_{OP}}{\partial q_i} \qquad (i = 1, \ldots, m) \tag{13.28}$$

We now introduce the following virtual velocity field

$$\mathbf{v}_P^* = \sum_{i=1}^{m} \dot{q}_i^* \, \mathbf{w}_P^{q_i} \tag{13.29}$$

where $\dot{\mathbf{q}}^* = (\dot{q}_1^*, \dot{q}_2^*, \ldots, \dot{q}_m^*)$ is an arbitrary element of $\mathbb{R}^m$. It is easy to see, with equation (13.27), that this virtual velocity field defines a screw. The derivation of Lagrange equations from D'Alembert Principle of Virtual Power hinges on the Lagrange kinematic formula (13.5). Hence, we seek to find a generalization of Lagrange kinematic formula compatible with the virtual velocity field (13.29):

$$\mathbf{a}_P \cdot \mathbf{w}_P^{q_i} = \frac{d}{dt} \left(\mathbf{v}_P \cdot \frac{\partial}{\partial \dot{q}_i} \mathbf{v}_P \right) - \mathbf{v}_P \cdot \frac{d}{dt} \mathbf{w}_P^{q_i} \tag{13.30}$$

On one hand, the first term of (13.30) can be put in the form $\frac{d}{dt} \frac{\partial}{\partial \dot{q}_i} \frac{1}{2} \mathbf{v}_P^2$ found in Lagrange kinematic formula (13.5). On the other hand, the second term $\mathbf{v}_P \cdot \frac{d}{dt} \mathbf{w}_P^{q_i}$ is problematic since $\mathbf{w}_P^{q_i} \neq \frac{\partial \mathbf{r}_{OP}}{\partial q_i}$. In fact it is easy to show that $\frac{d}{dt} \mathbf{w}_P^{q_i}$ cannot possibly be equal to $\frac{\partial}{\partial q_i} \mathbf{v}_P$. This shows that it is *not possible* to evaluate the integral

$$\int_{\mathcal{B}} \mathbf{a}_P \cdot \frac{\partial \mathbf{v}_P}{\partial \dot{q}_i} dm$$

as

$$\frac{d}{dt} \left(\frac{\partial \mathbb{K}_{\mathcal{B}/\mathcal{E}}}{\partial \dot{q}_i} \right) - \frac{\partial \mathbb{K}_{\mathcal{B}/\mathcal{E}}}{\partial q_i} \qquad (i = 1, \ldots, m)$$

This makes non-holonomic systems fundamentally different from holonomic systems in the Lagrangian formalism.

In conclusion, it is not possible to derive Lagrange equations for non-holonomic systems with respect to the reduced set of independent coordinates $(q_1, q_2, \cdots, q_m)$.

We verify this important fact by re-examining the solution of Example 13.6.

Example 13.10 Derive the three Lagrange equations $\mathcal{L}^q_{1/0}$ governing the motion of the sphere of Example 13.6 for $q = \psi, \theta, \phi$ by taking into account the no-slip constraint equations. Show that these equations are meaningless. ■

We can express $(\dot{x}, \dot{y})$ in terms of $(\dot{\psi}, \dot{\theta}, \dot{\phi})$ by relating $\mathbf{v}_{G/0}$ to $\mathbf{v}_{I\in 1/0} = \mathbf{0}$:

$$\mathbf{v}_{G/0} = \dot{x}\hat{\mathbf{x}}_0 + \dot{y}\hat{\mathbf{y}}_0 = -r(\dot{\theta}\hat{\mathbf{v}} + \dot{\phi}\sin\theta\hat{\mathbf{u}})$$

leading to the non-holonomic equations

$$\dot{x} = r\dot{\theta}\sin\psi - r\dot{\phi}\sin\theta\cos\psi$$
$$\dot{y} = -r\dot{\theta}\cos\psi - r\dot{\phi}\sin\theta\sin\psi$$

The kinetic energy $\mathbb{K}_{1/0}$ can now be expressed in terms of $q = \psi, \theta, \psi$ and their time-derivative

$$2\mathbb{K}_{1/0} = mr^2(\dot{\theta}\hat{\mathbf{v}} + \dot{\phi}\sin\theta\hat{\mathbf{u}})^2 + \tfrac{2}{5}mr^2(\dot{\psi}\hat{\mathbf{z}}_0 + \dot{\theta}\hat{\mathbf{u}} + \dot{\phi}\hat{\mathbf{z}}_1)^2$$
$$= \tfrac{2}{5}mr^2\left(\dot{\psi}^2 + \tfrac{7}{2}\dot{\theta}^2 + \dot{\phi}^2(1 + \tfrac{5}{2}\sin^2\theta) + 2\dot{\psi}\dot{\phi}\cos\theta\right)$$

Furthermore, if we take into account the no-slip velocity at I, the power coefficients $\mathbb{Q}^q_{\bar{1}\to 1/0}$ vanish for $q = \psi, \theta, \psi$. The 3 Lagrange equations would then take the expression

$$\mathcal{L}^{\psi}_{1/0}: \quad \dot{\psi} + \dot{\phi}\cos\theta = const. \tag{1}$$
$$\mathcal{L}^{\theta}_{1/0}: \quad \tfrac{7}{2}\ddot{\theta} - \tfrac{5}{2}\dot{\phi}^2\sin\theta\cos\theta + \dot{\psi}\dot{\phi}\sin\theta = 0 \tag{2}$$
$$\mathcal{L}^{\phi}_{1/0}: \quad \dot{\phi}(1 + \tfrac{5}{2}\sin^2\theta) + \dot{\psi}\cos\theta = const. \tag{3}$$

Although equation $\mathcal{L}^{\psi}$ is correct, equations $\mathcal{L}^{\theta}$ and $\mathcal{L}^{\phi}$ do not match the results found in Example 13.6. For instance, for equation (2) to match equation (4) of Example 13.6 one would have to equate F_v to $mr(\dot{\phi}^2\sin\theta\cos\theta - \ddot{\theta})$. It is possible to find the expression of F_v from equations (1-7) of Example 13.6:

$$F_v = -mr(\ddot{\theta} + \dot{\phi}\dot{\psi}\sin\theta) = mr(\dot{\phi}^2\sin\theta\cos\theta - \ddot{\theta} - C_1\dot{\phi}\sin\theta)$$

where C_1 denotes the constant $\dot{\psi} + \dot{\phi}\cos\theta$. This last extra term leads to a discrepancy. This procedure is incorrect, as expected. ■

The correct way to proceed is to assume that the coordinates $(q_1, q_2, \ldots, q_n)$ satisfy assumption (13.2): hence the coordinates $(\mathbf{q}, \dot{\mathbf{q}})$ are assumed independent. However the virtual speeds $(q_1^*, q_2^*, \ldots, q_n^*)$ which define the virtual velocity field $P \mapsto \mathbf{v}_P^*$ as

$$\{\mathcal{V}^*\} = \dot{q}_1^*\{\mathcal{V}^{q_1}_{B/\mathcal{E}}\} + \dot{q}_2^*\{\mathcal{V}^{q_2}_{B/\mathcal{E}}\} + \cdots + \dot{q}_n^*\{\mathcal{V}^{q_n}_{B/\mathcal{E}}\} \tag{13.31}$$

are no longer arbitrary element of $\mathbb{R}^n$, but rather, are assumed to satisfy the homogeneous equations

$$\sum_{j=1}^{n} a_{ij}(\mathbf{q})\dot{q}_j^* = 0, \qquad (i = 1, 2, \ldots, l) \tag{13.32}$$

The virtual speeds $(q_1^*, q_2^*, \ldots, q_n^*)$ are then said to be compatible with the non-holonomic constraints. Application of D'Alembert Principle of Virtual Power with the choice (13.31) for virtual velocity gives

$$\sum_{i=1}^{n} \dot{q}_i^* \{\mathcal{D}_{\mathcal{B}/\mathcal{E}}\} \cdot \{\mathcal{V}_{\mathcal{B}/\mathcal{E}}^{q_i}\} = \sum_{i=1}^{n} \dot{q}_i^* \{\mathcal{A}_{\overline{\mathcal{B}}\to\mathcal{B}}\} \cdot \{\mathcal{V}_{\mathcal{B}/\mathcal{E}}^{q_i}\} \tag{13.33}$$

Given that the coordinates satisfy assumption (13.2), the coefficients in the left-hand-side are unchanged, and are determined from the kinetic energy of $\mathcal{B}$ by using Lagrange kinematic formula:

$$\{\mathcal{D}_{\mathcal{B}/\mathcal{E}}\} \cdot \{\mathcal{V}_{\mathcal{B}/\mathcal{E}}^{q_i}\} = \int_{\mathcal{B}} \mathbf{a}_P \cdot \frac{\partial \mathbf{v}_P}{\partial \dot{q}_i} dm = \left[\frac{d}{dt}\left(\frac{\partial}{\partial \dot{q}_i}\right) - \frac{\partial}{\partial q_i}\right] \mathbb{K}_{\mathcal{B}/\mathcal{E}}$$

The right-hand-side of (13.33) is the virtual power of external action $\{\mathcal{A}_{\overline{\mathcal{B}}\to\mathcal{B}}\}$

$$\mathbb{P}_{\overline{\mathcal{B}}\to\mathcal{B}/\mathcal{E}}^* = \{\mathcal{A}_{\overline{\mathcal{B}}\to\mathcal{B}}\} \cdot \{\mathcal{V}^*\} = \sum_{i=1}^{n} \dot{q}_i^* \overline{\mathbb{Q}}_{\overline{\mathcal{B}}\to\mathcal{B}/\mathcal{E}}^{q_i} \tag{13.34}$$

and gives the expression of power coefficients $\overline{\mathbb{Q}}_{\overline{\mathcal{B}}\to\mathcal{B}/\mathcal{E}}^{q_i}$. Note that these power coefficients are in general not equal to the standard power coefficients $\mathbb{Q}_{\overline{\mathcal{B}}\to\mathcal{B}/\mathcal{E}}^{q_i}$ found by assuming independent virtual speeds, since now the virtual speeds satisfy the equations (13.32).

Equation (13.33) becomes

$$\sum_{i=1}^{n} \dot{q}_i^* \left\{ \frac{d}{dt}\frac{\partial \mathbb{K}_{\mathcal{B}/\mathcal{E}}}{\partial \dot{q}_i} - \frac{\partial \mathbb{K}_{\mathcal{B}/\mathcal{E}}}{\partial q_i} - \overline{\mathbb{Q}}_{\overline{\mathcal{B}}\to\mathcal{B}/\mathcal{E}}^{q_i} \right\} = 0 \tag{13.35}$$

To solve equation (13.35) with the virtual speeds satisfying (13.32), we use a theorem of linear algebra: a *linear form* [8] is a linear combination of a finite number of linear forms f_1, f_2,..., f_l if and only if its *kernel* contains the intersection of the kernels of the f_i's. This implies that the linear form defined by (13.35) is necessarily a linear combination of the l linear forms defined by (13.32): there must exist l scalars $\lambda_1, \lambda_2, \ldots, \lambda_l$ such that

$$\sum_{i=1}^{n} \dot{q}_i^* \left\{ \frac{d}{dt}\frac{\partial \mathbb{K}_{\mathcal{B}/\mathcal{E}}}{\partial \dot{q}_i} - \frac{\partial \mathbb{K}_{\mathcal{B}/\mathcal{E}}}{\partial q_i} - \overline{\mathbb{Q}}_{\overline{\mathcal{B}}\to\mathcal{B}/\mathcal{E}}^{q_i} \right\} = \sum_{k=1}^{l} \lambda_k \sum_{j=1}^{n} a_{ij}(\mathbf{q}) \dot{q}_j^* \tag{13.36}$$

for all $\dot{\mathbf{q}}^* \in \mathbb{R}^n$. This gives n Lagrange equations for rigid body $\mathcal{B}$ in the following form.

Theorem 13.4 — Lagrange Equations with Multipliers. The motion of a rigid body $\mathcal{B}$ relative to a Newtonian referential $\mathcal{E}$ defined by n coordinates $(q_1, \ldots, q_n)$ is governed by the n Lagrange equations

$$\mathcal{L}_{\mathcal{B}/\mathcal{E}}^{q_i}: \quad \frac{d}{dt}\frac{\partial \mathbb{K}_{\mathcal{B}/\mathcal{E}}}{\partial \dot{q}_i} - \frac{\partial \mathbb{K}_{\mathcal{B}/\mathcal{E}}}{\partial q_i} = \overline{\mathbb{Q}}_{\overline{\mathcal{B}}\to\mathcal{B}/\mathcal{E}}^{q_i} + \sum_{j=1}^{l} \lambda_j a_{ji}(\mathbf{q})$$

where the coordinates $(q_1, \ldots, q_n)$ satisfy assumption (13.2). The unknown real parameters $\lambda_1, \lambda_2, \ldots, \lambda_l$, called *Lagrange multipliers*, are associated with the l non-holonomic

[8] A linear form f of $\mathbb{R}^n$ is linear map from $\mathbb{R}^n$ to $\mathbb{R}$:

$$\dot{\mathbf{q}}^* \in \mathbb{R}^n \mapsto f(\dot{\mathbf{q}}^*) = c_1 \dot{q}_1^* + \ldots + c_n \dot{q}_n^*$$

The kernel $\ker(f)$ of f is the set of elements $\dot{\mathbf{q}}^* \in \mathbb{R}^n$ satisfying $f(\dot{\mathbf{q}}^*) = 0$.

constraint equations:

$$\sum_{j=1}^{n} a_{ij}(\mathbf{q})\dot{q}_j + b_i(\mathbf{q}) = 0, \qquad (i = 1, 2, \ldots, l)$$

These equations are readily extended to the case of a system Σ of p rigid bodies by accounting for the power coefficients of interactions $\overline{\mathbb{Q}}_{j\leftrightarrow h}$ between pairs of rigid bodies:

$$\mathcal{L}^{q_i}_{\Sigma/0}: \qquad \frac{d}{dt}\frac{\partial \mathbb{K}_{\Sigma/0}}{\partial \dot{q}_i} - \frac{\partial \mathbb{K}_{\Sigma/0}}{\partial q_i} = \overline{\mathbb{Q}}^{q_i}_{\overline{\Sigma}\to\Sigma/\mathcal{E}} + \sum_{1\le j<h\le p} \overline{\mathbb{Q}}^{q_i}_{j\leftrightarrow h} + \sum_{j=1}^{l} \lambda_j a_{ji}(\mathbf{q})$$

In practice, Lagrange equations with multipliers are implemented as follows:

1. Identify the n coordinates $(q_1, q_2, \ldots, q_n)$ which parametrize the configuration of system Σ.
2. Identify all holonomic and non-holonomic constraint equations to be taken into account by the virtual velocity field.[9]
3. Determine the kinetic energy of Σ in a manner consistent with assumption (13.2) satisfied by the coordinates: hence this must be done by ignoring all holonomic and non-holonomic equations.
4. Define the virtual velocity field $\{\mathcal{V}^*\}$ compatible with all holonomic and non-holonomic constraint equations.
5. For all external actions or interactions, find the corresponding virtual powers $\mathbb{P}^*_{\overline{\Sigma}\to\Sigma/\mathcal{E}}$ or $\mathbb{P}^*_{j\leftrightarrow h}$ in terms of the virtual speeds $(\dot{q}^*_1, \dot{q}^*_2, \ldots, \dot{q}^*_n)$ compatible with the constraints. The corresponding power coefficients are the coefficients in the virtual speeds of the virtual power.
6. Derive Lagrange equations by including l Lagrange multipliers to account for l constraint equations.
7. Once the Lagrange equations are determined, we retrieve all holonomic and non-holonomic constraint equations.

We first illustrate this implementation on the holonomic system examined in Example 13.5.

Example 13.11 Derive Lagrange equations $\mathcal{L}^{x}_{1/0}$ and $\mathcal{L}^{\theta}_{1/0}$ for Example 13.5 by considering virtual speeds compatible with the holonomic constraint equation governing coordinates (x, θ). See Figure 13.1. ■

We know that coordinates (x, θ) satisfy the geometric constraint

$$x + h\cot\theta = \text{const.}$$

which can be differentiated w.r.t. time to give

$$-\dot{x}\sin\theta + h\frac{\dot{\theta}}{\sin\theta} = 0 \qquad (1)$$

[9]Holonomic equations of the type $f(q_1, \ldots, q_n, t) = 0$ can be included to the set of non-holonomic equations in the form of

$$\frac{\partial f}{\partial q_1}\dot{q}_1 + \cdots + \frac{\partial f}{\partial q_n}\dot{q}_n + \frac{\partial f}{\partial t} = 0$$

We choose virtual speeds $(\dot{x}^*, \dot{\theta}^*)$ compatible with this constraint, that is, such that

$$-\dot{x}^* \sin\theta + h\frac{\dot{\theta}^*}{\sin\theta} = 0 \tag{2}$$

Assuming that (x, θ) satisfy assumption (13.2), the virtual velocity field takes the form

$$\{\mathcal{V}^*\} = \dot{x}^*\{\mathcal{V}^x_{\bar{1}/0}\} + \dot{\theta}^*\{\mathcal{V}^\theta_{\bar{1}/0}\} = \dot{x}^*\begin{Bmatrix} \mathbf{0} \\ \hat{\mathbf{x}}_0 \end{Bmatrix}_A + \dot{\theta}^*\begin{Bmatrix} \hat{\mathbf{z}}_0 \\ \mathbf{0} \end{Bmatrix}_A = \dot{x}^*\begin{Bmatrix} \mathbf{0} \\ \hat{\mathbf{x}}_0 \end{Bmatrix}_Q + \dot{\theta}^*\begin{Bmatrix} \hat{\mathbf{z}}_0 \\ \frac{h}{\sin\theta}\hat{\mathbf{y}}_1 \end{Bmatrix}_Q$$

The kinetic energy $\mathbb{K}_{1/0}$ takes the same expression found in Example 13.5:

$$2\mathbb{K}_{1/0} = m\dot{x}^2 - 2ml\dot{x}\dot{\theta}\sin\theta + \tfrac{4}{3}ml^2\dot{\theta}^2$$

We then find the virtual power of all external actions:

$$\begin{aligned}\mathbb{P}^*_{\bar{1}\to 1/0} = &\begin{Bmatrix} F_A\hat{\mathbf{x}}_0 + N_A\hat{\mathbf{y}}_0 \\ \mathbf{0} \end{Bmatrix}_A \cdot \begin{Bmatrix} \dot{\theta}^*\hat{\mathbf{z}}_0 \\ \dot{x}^*\hat{\mathbf{x}}_0 \end{Bmatrix}_A + \begin{Bmatrix} -mg\hat{\mathbf{y}}_0 \\ \mathbf{0} \end{Bmatrix}_G \cdot \begin{Bmatrix} \dot{\theta}^*\hat{\mathbf{z}}_0 \\ \dot{x}^*\hat{\mathbf{x}}_0 + l\dot{\theta}^*\hat{\mathbf{y}}_1 \end{Bmatrix}_G + \\ &\begin{Bmatrix} N_Q\hat{\mathbf{y}}_1 + F_Q\hat{\mathbf{x}}_1) \\ \mathbf{0} \end{Bmatrix}_Q \cdot \begin{Bmatrix} \dot{\theta}^*\hat{\mathbf{z}}_0 \\ \dot{x}^*\hat{\mathbf{x}}_0 + \frac{h}{\sin\theta}\dot{\theta}^*\hat{\mathbf{y}}_1 \end{Bmatrix}_Q \\ = &F_A\dot{x}^* - mgl\dot{\theta}^*\cos\theta + N_Q(-\dot{x}^*\sin\theta + \frac{h\dot{\theta}^*}{\sin\theta}) + F_Q\dot{x}^*\cos\theta \\ = &F_A\dot{x}^* - mgl\dot{\theta}^*\cos\theta + \dot{x}^*F_Q\cos\theta\end{aligned}$$

where the virtual power of normal force $N_Q\hat{\mathbf{y}}_1$ is seen to vanish due to equation (2) satisfied by the virtual speeds. We can now obtain the power coefficients from the expression of the virtual power:

$$\overline{\mathbb{Q}}^x_{\bar{1}\to 1/0} = F_A + F_Q\cos\theta$$
$$\overline{\mathbb{Q}}^\theta_{\bar{1}\to 1/0} = -mgl\cos\theta$$

The two equations $\mathcal{L}^x_{1/0}$ and $\mathcal{L}^\theta_{1/0}$ are then found by introducing the Lagrange multiplier λ associated with constraint (2):

$$\mathcal{L}^x_{1/0}: \quad m\ddot{x} - ml\ddot{\theta}\sin\theta - ml\dot{\theta}^2\cos\theta = F_A + F_Q\cos\theta - \lambda\sin\theta \tag{3}$$
$$\mathcal{L}^\theta_{1/0}: \quad \tfrac{4}{3}ml^2\ddot{\theta} - ml\ddot{x}\sin\theta = -mgl\cos\theta + \lambda\frac{h}{\sin\theta} \tag{4}$$

To equations (3) and (4) we now add equation (1): we have 3 equations to solve for 4 unknowns $(x, \theta, F_Q, \lambda)$. We cannot use the relationship $|F_Q| = \mu N_Q$ without knowledge of N_Q. Comparison with equations (1) and (2) of Example 13.5 shows that the multiplier λ can be identified with

$$\lambda = N_Q$$

We can see on this example that Lagrange equations with multipliers are less than satisfying. ∎

Although the multipliers can be determined, their physical interpretation is problematic in practice. The following examples illustrate Lagrange equations with multipliers for non-holonomic systems. These examples will show that the method has no advantage over the Lagrange equations without multipliers.

Example 13.12 Derive the five Lagrange equations $\mathcal{L}^q_{1/0}$ of Example 13.6 for $q = x, y, \psi, \theta, \phi$ by taking into account the no-slip constraint equations with Lagrange multipliers. Interpret the physical meaning of the multipliers. ■

The non-holonomic equations expressing the no-slip condition at I were found in Example 13.6:

$$r\dot{\phi}\sin\theta + \dot{x}\cos\psi + \dot{y}\sin\psi = 0 \tag{1}$$
$$r\dot{\theta} - \dot{x}\sin\psi + \dot{y}\cos\psi = 0 \tag{2}$$

The virtual speeds $(\dot{x}^*, \dot{y}^*, \dot{\psi}^*, \dot{\theta}^*, \dot{\phi}^*)$ compatible with constraint equations (1-2) satisfy the equations

$$r\dot{\phi}^*\sin\theta + \dot{x}^*\cos\psi + \dot{y}^*\sin\psi = 0 \tag{3}$$
$$r\dot{\theta}^* - \dot{x}^*\sin\psi + \dot{y}^*\cos\psi = 0 \tag{4}$$

The virtual velocity field $\{\mathcal{V}^*\}$ is then chosen as

$$\{\mathcal{V}^*\} = \dot{x}^*\{\mathcal{V}^x_{1/0}\} + \dot{y}^*\{\mathcal{V}^y_{1/0}\} + \dot{\psi}^*\{\mathcal{V}^\psi_{1/0}\} + \dot{\theta}^*\{\mathcal{V}^\theta_{1/0}\} + \dot{\phi}^*\{\mathcal{V}^\phi_{1/0}\}$$
$$= \begin{Bmatrix} \dot{\psi}^*\hat{\mathbf{z}}_0 + \dot{\theta}^*\hat{\mathbf{u}} + \dot{\phi}^*\hat{\mathbf{z}}_1 \\ \dot{x}^*\hat{\mathbf{x}}_0 + \dot{y}^*\hat{\mathbf{y}}_0 \end{Bmatrix}_G = \begin{Bmatrix} \dot{\psi}^*\hat{\mathbf{z}}_0 + \dot{\theta}^*\hat{\mathbf{u}} + \dot{\phi}^*\hat{\mathbf{z}}_1 \\ \mathbf{0} \end{Bmatrix}_I$$

where the last expression of $\{\mathcal{V}^*\}$ has been found by taking into account (3-4). We can now find the virtual power of all external actions:

$$\mathbb{P}^*_{\bar{1}\to 1/0} = \begin{Bmatrix} F_u\hat{\mathbf{u}} + F_v\hat{\mathbf{v}} + (N - mg)\hat{\mathbf{z}}_0 \\ \mathbf{0} \end{Bmatrix}_I \cdot \begin{Bmatrix} \dot{\psi}^*\hat{\mathbf{z}}_0 + \dot{\theta}^*\hat{\mathbf{u}} + \dot{\phi}^*\hat{\mathbf{z}}_1 \\ \mathbf{0} \end{Bmatrix}_I = 0$$

This shows that all power coefficients $\overline{\mathbb{Q}}^q_{\bar{1}\to 1/0}$ are zero. The kinetic energy $\mathbb{K}_{1/0}$ takes the same expression as found in Example 13.6

$$2\mathbb{K}_{1/0} = mr^2(\dot{x}^2 + \dot{y}^2) + \tfrac{2}{5}mr^2(\dot{\psi}^2 + \dot{\theta}^2 + \dot{\phi}^2 + 2\dot{\psi}\dot{\phi}\cos\theta)$$

We can now write five Lagrange equations with two multipliers (λ_1, λ_2) associated with constraint equations (3-4):

$$\mathcal{L}^x_{1/0}: \quad m\ddot{x} = \lambda_1\cos\psi - \lambda_2\sin\psi \tag{5}$$
$$\mathcal{L}^y_{1/0}: \quad m\ddot{y} = \lambda_1\sin\psi + \lambda_2\cos\psi \tag{6}$$
$$\mathcal{L}^\psi_{1/0}: \quad \tfrac{2}{5}mr^2\frac{d}{dt}(\dot{\psi} + \dot{\phi}\cos\theta) = 0 \tag{7}$$
$$\mathcal{L}^\theta_{1/0}: \quad \tfrac{2}{5}mr^2(\ddot{\theta} + \dot{\psi}\dot{\phi}\sin\theta) = r\lambda_2 \tag{8}$$
$$\mathcal{L}^\phi_{1/0}: \quad \tfrac{2}{5}mr^2\frac{d}{dt}(\dot{\phi} + \dot{\psi}\cos\theta) = r\lambda_1\sin\theta \tag{9}$$

The seven equations (1-2) and (5-9) solves for seven unknowns $(x, y, \psi, \theta, \phi, \lambda_1, \lambda_2)$. Comparison with equations (1-5) of Example 13.6 shows that $\lambda_1 = F_u$ and $\lambda_2 = F_v$. With this identification, Lagrange equations with and without multipliers then become identical: however, identifying the physical meaning of multipliers is an issue. ■

Example 13.13 Derive the Lagrange equations with multiplier for Chaplygin sleigh of Example 13.8 ($q = x, y, \theta$). ■

The (non-integrable) non-holonomic constraint equation was found in Example 13.8 to be given by

$$\dot{y} = \dot{x} \tan\theta \qquad [1]$$

The virtual speeds $(\dot{x}^*, \dot{y}^*, \dot{\theta}^*)$ compatible with constraint equations [1] must satisfy the equation

$$\dot{y}^* = \dot{x}^* \tan\theta \qquad [2]$$

The virtual velocity field $\{\mathcal{V}^*\}$ is then chosen as

$$\{\mathcal{V}^*\} = \dot{x}^*\{\mathcal{V}^x_{1/0}\} + \dot{y}^*\{\mathcal{V}^y_{1/0}\} + \dot{\theta}^*\{\mathcal{V}^\theta_{1/0}\} = \begin{Bmatrix} \dot{\theta}^*\hat{\mathbf{z}}_0 \\ \dot{x}^*\hat{\mathbf{x}}_0 + \dot{y}^*\hat{\mathbf{y}}_0 \end{Bmatrix}_C = \begin{Bmatrix} \dot{\theta}^*\hat{\mathbf{z}}_0 \\ (\dot{x}^*\cos\theta + \dot{y}^*\sin\theta)\hat{\mathbf{x}}_1 \end{Bmatrix}_C$$

where we have taken into account the constraint equation [2]. The virtual power of all external actions is then given by:

$$\begin{aligned} \mathbb{P}^*_{\bar{1}\to 1/0} &= \begin{Bmatrix} \dot{\theta}^*\hat{\mathbf{z}}_0 \\ (\dot{x}^*\cos\theta + \dot{y}^*\sin\theta)\hat{\mathbf{x}}_1 \end{Bmatrix}_C \cdot \begin{Bmatrix} X\hat{\mathbf{x}}_0 + Y\hat{\mathbf{y}}_0 + Z\hat{\mathbf{z}}_0 \\ L\hat{\mathbf{x}}_0 + M\hat{\mathbf{y}}_0 + N\hat{\mathbf{z}}_0 \end{Bmatrix}_C \\ &= N\dot{\theta}^* + (\dot{x}^*\cos\theta + \dot{y}^*\sin\theta)(X\cos\theta + Y\sin\theta) = 0 \end{aligned}$$

since $N = 0$ and $X\cos\theta + Y\sin\theta = 0$. Hence all power coefficients $\overline{\mathbb{Q}}^q_{\bar{1}\to 1/0}$ are zero. Assuming that the variables $(x, y, \theta, \dot{x}, \dot{y}, \dot{\theta})$ are independent, the kinetic energy of the body takes the same expression as found in Example 13.8:

$$2\mathbb{K}_{1/0} = m(\dot{x}^2 + \dot{y}^2) + 2mb\dot{\theta}(-\dot{x}\sin\theta + \dot{y}\cos\theta) + I_C\dot{\theta}^2$$

Hence we can now state that for all $\dot{q}^* = \dot{x}^*, \dot{y}^*, \dot{\theta}^*$ satisfying [2]

$$\sum_{i=1}^{3} \dot{q}_i^* \left[\frac{d}{dt}\frac{\partial \mathbb{K}_{1/0}}{\partial \dot{q}_i} - \frac{\partial \mathbb{K}_{1/0}}{\partial q_i}\right] = 0$$

or equivalently, that there exists a scalar λ such that

$$\sum_{i=1}^{3} \dot{q}_i^* \left[\frac{d}{dt}\frac{\partial \mathbb{K}_{1/0}}{\partial \dot{q}_i} - \frac{\partial \mathbb{K}_{1/0}}{\partial q_i}\right] = \lambda(\dot{y}^* - \dot{x}^*\tan\theta)$$

for arbitrary values of $\dot{q}^* = \dot{x}^*, \dot{y}^*, \dot{\theta}^*$. This leads to 3 equations:

$$\begin{aligned} \mathcal{L}^x_{1/0}: &\quad m\tfrac{d}{dt}(\dot{x} - b\dot{\theta}\sin\theta) = -\lambda\tan\theta &\quad [3] \\ \mathcal{L}^y_{1/0}: &\quad m\tfrac{d}{dt}(\dot{y} + b\dot{\theta}\cos\theta) = \lambda &\quad [4] \\ \mathcal{L}^\theta_{1/0}: &\quad I_C\ddot{\theta} + mb(-\ddot{x}\sin\theta + \ddot{y}\cos\theta) = 0 &\quad [5] \end{aligned}$$

Equations [1] and [3-5] solve for the unknowns (x, y, θ, λ). Comparison of equations [3-5] with equations [5-6] of Example 13.8 shows that multiplier λ can be identified with

$$\lambda = Y = -X\cot\theta$$

Once again, the physical identification of the multiplier can be safely made only by comparison with Lagrange equations without multipliers. ■

13.7 Painlevé Equation

Consider a rigid body $\mathcal{B}$ whose position relative to a Newtonian referential $\mathcal{E}$ is defined by the $(n+1)$ independent coordinates $(q_1, q_2, \dots q_n, t)$. Assume that the variables $(\mathbf{q}, t)$ are independent. The kinetic energy can be viewed in general as a quadratic form in the variables $(\dot{q}_1, \dot{q}_2, \ldots, \dot{q}_n)$. This can be shown as follows:

$$\mathbf{v}^2_{P/\mathcal{E}} = \left(\frac{d\mathbf{r}}{dt}\right)^2 = \left(\dot{q}_1\frac{\partial \mathbf{r}}{\partial q_1} + \cdots + \dot{q}_n\frac{\partial \mathbf{r}}{\partial q_n} + \frac{\partial \mathbf{r}}{\partial t}\right)^2 = \dot{q}_i\dot{q}_j\frac{\partial \mathbf{r}}{\partial q_i}\cdot\frac{\partial \mathbf{r}}{\partial q_j} + \dot{q}_i\frac{\partial \mathbf{r}}{\partial q_i}\cdot\frac{\partial \mathbf{r}}{\partial t} + \left(\frac{\partial \mathbf{r}}{\partial t}\right)^2$$

denoting $\mathbf{r} = \mathbf{r}_{OP}$ and using the summation convention for repeated indices. This leads to the following decomposition:

Corollary 13.3 The kinetic energy $\mathbb{K}_{\mathcal{B}/\mathcal{E}}$ of a rigid body $\mathcal{B}$ whose position relative to a referential $\mathcal{E}$ is parametrized by the $(n+1)$ independent variables $(q_1, q_2, \ldots q_n, t)$ can be written as the sum of three terms:

$$\mathbb{K}_{\mathcal{B}/\mathcal{E}} = \mathbb{K}^{(2)}_{\mathcal{B}/\mathcal{E}} + \mathbb{K}^{(1)}_{\mathcal{B}/\mathcal{E}} + \mathbb{K}^{(0)}_{\mathcal{B}/\mathcal{E}}$$

with

$$\mathbb{K}^{(2)}_{\mathcal{B}/\mathcal{E}} = \tfrac{1}{2}\dot{q}_i\dot{q}_j\int_{\mathcal{B}}\frac{\partial \mathbf{r}}{\partial q_i}\cdot\frac{\partial \mathbf{r}}{\partial q_j}dm$$

$$\mathbb{K}^{(1)}_{\mathcal{B}/\mathcal{E}} = \tfrac{1}{2}\dot{q}_i\int_{\mathcal{B}}\frac{\partial \mathbf{r}}{\partial q_i}\cdot\frac{\partial \mathbf{r}}{\partial t}dm$$

$$\mathbb{K}^{(0)}_{\mathcal{B}/\mathcal{E}} = \tfrac{1}{2}\int_{\mathcal{B}}\left(\frac{\partial \mathbf{r}}{\partial t}\right)^2 dm$$

Remark 15. $\mathbb{K}^{(k)}_{\mathcal{B}/\mathcal{E}}$ is of degree k in the variables $\dot{q}_i$.

Remark 16. In practice, the kth-order contribution of the kinetic energy is found by first determining the expression $\mathbb{K}_{\mathcal{B}/\mathcal{E}}$ (making sure that $q_1, q_2, \ldots q_n, t$ are treated as independent variables) and collecting all term in $\dot{q}_i$ of order k in this expression.

Painlevé equation can be found by following the now familiar approach: we choose the following virtual velocity field

$$\mathbf{v}^*_P = \dot{q}_1\frac{\partial \mathbf{r}}{\partial q_1} + \cdots + \dot{q}_n\frac{\partial \mathbf{r}}{\partial q_n}$$

assuming that the variables $(q_1, \ldots q_n, \dot{q}_1, \ldots, \dot{q}_n, t)$ are independent. This field defines a screw since it is a linear combinations of screws. We then apply the principle of virtual power: this leads to the determination of two virtual power terms:

(i) the virtual power of inertial forces $\int_{\mathcal{B}} \mathbf{v}^*_P \cdot (-\mathbf{a}_P)dm$,

(ii) the virtual powers of external body forces $\int_{\mathcal{B}} \mathbf{v}^*_P \cdot \mathbf{F}_P dV$ and contact forces $\int_{\partial\mathcal{B}} \mathbf{v}^*_Q \cdot \mathbf{f}_Q dA$. These terms involve the power coefficients $\mathcal{Q}^{q_i}_{\bar{\mathcal{B}}\to\mathcal{B}/\mathcal{E}}$ of the external actions:

$$\sum_{i=1}^{n} \dot{q}_i \mathcal{Q}^{q_i}_{\bar{\mathcal{B}}\to\mathcal{B}/\mathcal{E}} \tag{13.37}$$

To find the virtual power of inertial forces, we must find an expression of the $\mathbf{v}^*_P \cdot \mathbf{a}_P$:

$$\begin{aligned}\mathbf{v}_P^* \cdot \mathbf{a}_P &= \dot{q}_i \frac{\partial \mathbf{r}}{\partial q_i} \cdot \frac{d}{dt}\left(\dot{q}_j \frac{\partial \mathbf{r}}{\partial q_j} + \frac{\partial \mathbf{r}}{\partial t}\right) = \dot{q}_i \frac{\partial \mathbf{r}}{\partial q_i} \cdot \frac{d}{dt}\left(\dot{q}_j \frac{\partial \mathbf{r}}{\partial q_j}\right) + \dot{q}_i \frac{\partial \mathbf{r}}{\partial q_i} \cdot \frac{d}{dt}\left(\frac{\partial \mathbf{r}}{\partial t}\right) \\ &= \underbrace{\frac{d}{dt}\left(\tfrac{1}{2}\dot{q}_i \dot{q}_j \frac{\partial \mathbf{r}}{\partial q_i}\frac{\partial \mathbf{r}}{\partial q_j}\right)}_{\text{term \#1}} + \underbrace{\dot{q}_i \frac{\partial \mathbf{r}}{\partial q_i} \cdot \frac{d}{dt}\left(\frac{\partial \mathbf{r}}{\partial t}\right)}_{\text{term \#2}}\end{aligned}$$

Upon integrating over $\mathcal{B}$ three kinetic energy terms are obtained:
(i) in the term #1 we recognize the kinetic energy of order 2: it leads to $\frac{d}{dt}\mathbb{K}^{(2)}_{\mathcal{B}/\mathcal{E}}$
(ii) term #2 is transformed as follows:

$$\dot{q}_i \frac{\partial \mathbf{r}}{\partial q_i} \cdot \frac{d}{dt}\left(\frac{\partial \mathbf{r}}{\partial t}\right) = \left(\mathbf{v}_P - \frac{\partial \mathbf{r}}{\partial t}\right) \cdot \frac{d}{dt}\left(\frac{\partial \mathbf{r}}{\partial t}\right) = \underbrace{\mathbf{v}_P \cdot \frac{d}{dt}\left(\frac{\partial \mathbf{r}}{\partial t}\right)}_{\text{term \#2.1}} - \underbrace{\frac{d}{dt}\left(\tfrac{1}{2}\frac{\partial \mathbf{r}}{\partial t} \cdot \frac{\partial \mathbf{r}}{\partial t}\right)}_{\text{term \#2.2}}$$

The term #2.1 can be written as follows

$$\mathbf{v}_P \cdot \left(\dot{q}_i \frac{\partial^2 \mathbf{r}}{\partial q_i \partial t} + \frac{\partial^2 \mathbf{r}}{\partial t^2}\right) = \mathbf{v}_P \cdot \frac{\partial}{\partial t}\mathbf{v}_P = \frac{\partial}{\partial t}\left(\tfrac{1}{2}\mathbf{v}_P^2\right)$$

and its integration over $\mathcal{B}$ leads to $\frac{\partial}{\partial t}\mathbb{K}_{\mathcal{B}/\mathcal{E}}$. Finally, the integration of term #2.2 leads to $\frac{d}{dt}\mathbb{K}^{(0)}_{\mathcal{B}/\mathcal{E}}$. By collecting all the terms we arrive at Painlevé equation:

Theorem 13.5 — Painlevé equation. The motion of a rigid body $\mathcal{B}$ whose position relative to a Newtonian referential $\mathcal{E}$ is parametrized by $(n+1)$ independent variables $(q_1, q_2, \ldots q_n, t)$ satisfies the equation

$$\frac{d}{dt}(\mathbb{K}^{(2)}_{\mathcal{B}/\mathcal{E}} - \mathbb{K}^{(0)}_{\mathcal{B}/\mathcal{E}}) + \frac{\partial}{\partial t}\mathbb{K}_{\mathcal{B}/\mathcal{E}} = \sum_{i=1}^{n} \dot{q}_i \mathbf{Q}^{q_i}_{\overline{\mathcal{B}}\to\mathcal{B}/\mathcal{E}} \qquad (13.38)$$

where the variables $(q_1, \ldots q_n, \dot{q}_1, \ldots, \dot{q}_n, t)$ are assumed independent.

It is possible to generalize Painlevé equation (13.38) to a system Σ of p rigid bodies

$$\frac{d}{dt}(\mathbb{K}^{(2)}_{\Sigma/\mathcal{E}} - \mathbb{K}^{(0)}_{\Sigma/\mathcal{E}}) + \frac{\partial}{\partial t}\mathbb{K}_{\Sigma/\mathcal{E}} = \sum_{i=1}^{n} \dot{q}_i \mathbf{Q}^{q_i}_{\overline{\Sigma}\to\Sigma/\mathcal{E}} + \sum_{i=1}^{n} \sum_{1\le k<l\le p} \dot{q}_i \mathbf{Q}^{q_i}_{k\leftrightarrow l} \qquad (13.39)$$

An interesting corollary follows from Painlevé equation:

Corollary 13.4 — Painlevé first integral. Let Σ be a system parametrized in a Newtonian referential $\mathcal{E}$ by the $(n+1)$ variables $(q_1, \ldots, q_n, t)$. Assuming the variables $(q_1, \ldots q_n, \dot{q}_1, \ldots, \dot{q}_n, t)$ independent, then the motion of Σ in $\mathcal{E}$ satisfies the first integral

$$\mathbb{K}^{(2)}_{\Sigma/\mathcal{E}} - \mathbb{K}^{(0)}_{\Sigma/\mathcal{E}} + \mathbb{U} = Cst \qquad (13.40)$$

if the following conditions are satisfied:
(i) all geometric joints between the bodies of Σ or between Σ and some external bodies which are either fixed or whose motions relative to $\mathcal{E}$ are prescribed, are ideal,

(ii) all external actions or interactions between the bodies of Σ other than those generated by the geometric constraints derive from a potential energy $\mathbb{U}$,

(iii) the kinetic energy of Σ and the potential energy $\mathbb{U}$ are not explicitly functions of time, that is,

$$\frac{\partial}{\partial t}\mathbb{K}_{\Sigma/\mathcal{E}} = \frac{\partial}{\partial t}\mathbb{U} = 0$$

Proof. The proof stems from the assumptions (i)-(iii): all power coefficients $\mathbb{Q}^{q_i}_{\overline{\Sigma}\to\Sigma/\mathcal{E}}$ and $\mathbb{Q}^{q_i}_{k\leftrightarrow l}$ are either zero by assumption (i) or can be expressed in the form $-\partial\mathbb{U}/\partial q_i$. With $\partial\mathbb{K}_{\Sigma/\mathcal{E}}/\partial t = 0$ and $\partial\mathbb{U}/\partial t = 0$ we obtain (13.40). ■

The following problem illustrates the use of Painlevé equation.

Example 13.14 We consider the motion of a system Σ relative to a Newtonian referential $0(O, \hat{\mathbf{x}}_0, \hat{\mathbf{y}}_0, \hat{\mathbf{z}}_0)$. Axis $(O, \hat{\mathbf{z}}_0)$ is directed upward ($\mathbf{g} = -g\hat{\mathbf{z}}_0$). The system Σ is comprised of two rigid bodies 1 and 2 described as follows:
Body $1(O, \hat{\mathbf{x}}_1, \hat{\mathbf{y}}_1, \hat{\mathbf{z}}_0)$ is a torus-shaped body, of homogeneous density, mass center O, radius R, and mass m_1. The plane $(O, \hat{\mathbf{x}}_1, \hat{\mathbf{z}}_1)$ is a plane of symmetry. Body 1 is connected to referential 0 by an ideal pivot of axis $(O, \hat{\mathbf{z}}_0)$, and its position is defined by angle $\psi = (\hat{\mathbf{x}}_0, \hat{\mathbf{x}}_1) = (\hat{\mathbf{y}}_0, \hat{\mathbf{y}}_1)$. Denote by I_1 the moment of inertia of body 1 about axis $(O, \hat{\mathbf{z}}_0)$.

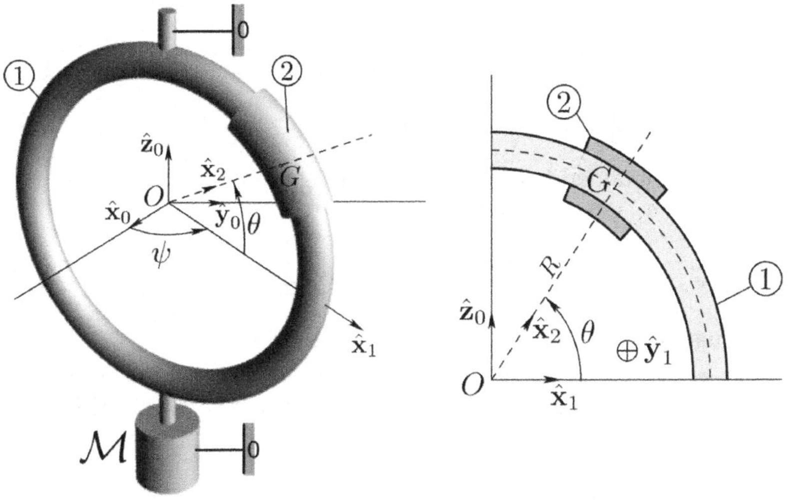

Figure 13.6

Body $2(G, \hat{\mathbf{x}}_2, \hat{\mathbf{y}}_2 = \hat{\mathbf{y}}_1, \hat{\mathbf{z}}_2)$ is a truncated toroidal shell of mass m_2 and mass center G with $\mathbf{r}_{OG} = R\hat{\mathbf{x}}_2$. The exterior surface of body 1 is in contact with the interior surface of body 2: body 2 is free to "slide" relative to body 1, and its motion relative to 1 is parametrized by angle $\theta = (\hat{\mathbf{x}}_1, \hat{\mathbf{x}}_2) = (\hat{\mathbf{z}}_0, \hat{\mathbf{z}}_2)$. Its inertia operator about G is represented by:

$$[\mathcal{I}_{G,2}]_{b_2} = \begin{bmatrix} A_2 & 0 & 0 \\ 0 & B_2 & 0 \\ 0 & 0 & C_2 \end{bmatrix}_{b_2}$$

on basis $b_2(\hat{\mathbf{x}}_2, \hat{\mathbf{y}}_2, \hat{\mathbf{z}}_2)$.
The joint between 1 and 2 is assumed ideal. A motor $\mathcal{M}$ is mounted between 0 and 1, and imposes a prescribed angle $\psi(t) = \Omega t$ where Ω is a positive constant. The action of $\mathcal{M}$ on 1 is equivalent to a couple $C\hat{\mathbf{z}}_0$.
a. Determine Painlevé equation applied to system Σ. Does it lead to a first integral?
b. Determine Lagrange equations applied to system Σ w.r.t. $q = \psi, \theta$. Recover the results of a). ∎

The position of system Σ is parametrized by angle θ and time t. The kinematic screws of bodies 1 and 2 are written as

$$\{\mathcal{V}_{1/0}\} = \{\mathcal{V}^t_{1/0}\} = \begin{Bmatrix} \Omega\hat{\mathbf{z}}_0 \\ \mathbf{0} \end{Bmatrix}_O, \quad \{\mathcal{V}_{2/0}\} = \dot{\theta}\{\mathcal{V}^{\theta}_{2/0}\} + \{\mathcal{V}^t_{2/0}\} = \dot{\theta}\begin{Bmatrix} -\hat{\mathbf{y}}_1 \\ \mathbf{0} \end{Bmatrix}_O + \begin{Bmatrix} \Omega\hat{\mathbf{z}}_0 \\ \mathbf{0} \end{Bmatrix}_O$$

where we have used $\omega_{2/0} = \Omega\hat{\mathbf{z}}_0 - \dot{\theta}\hat{\mathbf{y}}_1$ and $\mathbf{v}_{O\in 2/0} = \mathbf{0}$. The kinetic energy of the system is found as follows

$$\begin{aligned}
\mathbb{K}_{\Sigma/0} &= \mathbb{K}^{(0)}_{\Sigma/0} + \mathbb{K}^{(1)}_{\Sigma/0} + \mathbb{K}^{(2)}_{\Sigma/0} = \tfrac{1}{2}I_1\Omega^2 + \tfrac{1}{2}\omega_{2/0}\cdot\mathcal{I}_{O,2}(\omega_{2/0}) \\
&= \tfrac{1}{2}I_1\Omega^2 + \tfrac{1}{2}\begin{bmatrix} \Omega\sin\theta \\ -\dot{\theta} \\ \Omega\cos\theta \end{bmatrix}\cdot\begin{bmatrix} A_2 & 0 & 0 \\ 0 & B_2 + mR^2 & 0 \\ 0 & 0 & C_2 + mR^2 \end{bmatrix}_{b_2}\begin{bmatrix} \Omega\sin\theta \\ -\dot{\theta} \\ \Omega\cos\theta \end{bmatrix} \\
&= \tfrac{1}{2}I_1\Omega^2 + \tfrac{1}{2}A_2\Omega^2\sin^2\theta + \tfrac{1}{2}(B_2 + mR^2)\dot{\theta}^2 + \tfrac{1}{2}(C_2 + mR^2)\Omega^2\cos^2\theta
\end{aligned}$$

where $[\mathcal{I}_{O,2}]_{b_2}$ is obtained from $[\mathcal{I}_{G,2}]_{b_2}$ by using the Parallel Axis theorem. This leads to the expression of $\mathbb{K}^{(0)}_{\Sigma/0}$, $\mathbb{K}^{(1)}_{\Sigma/0}$ and $\mathbb{K}^{(2)}_{\Sigma/0}$:

$$\mathbb{K}^{(0)}_{\Sigma/0} = \tfrac{1}{2}I_1\Omega^2 + \tfrac{1}{2}A_2\Omega^2\sin^2\theta + \tfrac{1}{2}(C_2 + mR^2)\Omega^2\cos^2\theta, \quad \mathbb{K}^{(1)}_{\Sigma/0} = 0, \quad \mathbb{K}^{(2)}_{\Sigma/0} = \tfrac{1}{2}(B_2 + mR^2)\dot{\theta}^2$$

Painlevé equation applied to system Σ can be written as

$$\frac{d}{dt}(\mathbb{K}^{(2)}_{\Sigma/0} - \mathbb{K}^{(0)}_{\Sigma/0}) + \frac{\partial}{\partial t}\mathbb{K}_{\Sigma/0} = \dot{\theta}\mathbb{Q}^{\theta}_{\overline{\Sigma}\to\Sigma/0} + \dot{\theta}\mathbb{Q}^{\theta}_{1\leftrightarrow 2} \qquad [1]$$

with

$$\mathbb{Q}^{\theta}_{\overline{\Sigma}\to\Sigma/0} = \underbrace{\mathbb{Q}^{\theta}_{\overline{\Sigma}\to 1/0}}_{0} + \mathbb{Q}^{\theta}_{\overline{\Sigma}\to 2/0} = -\frac{\partial\mathbb{U}}{\partial\theta} = -mgR\cos\theta$$

using the gravitational potential $\mathbb{U} = mgR\sin\theta$, and

$$\mathbb{Q}^{\theta}_{1\leftrightarrow 2} = \{\mathcal{V}^{\theta}_{2/1}\}\cdot\{\mathcal{A}^c_{1\to 2}\} = -\hat{\mathbf{y}}_1\cdot\mathbf{M}^c_{O,1\to 2} = 0$$

The last result is a consequence of the fact that the joint between bodies 1 and 2 is ideal. Since the kinetic energy is not an explicit function of time, we find

$$\frac{\partial}{\partial t}\mathbb{K}_{\Sigma/0} = 0$$

Finally equation [1] becomes

$$\frac{d}{dt}(\mathbb{K}^{(2)}_{\Sigma/0} - \mathbb{K}^{(0)}_{\Sigma/0}) = -\dot{\theta}\frac{\partial \mathbb{U}}{\partial \theta} = -\frac{d\mathbb{U}}{dt}$$

This leads to Painlevé first integral

$$\mathbb{K}^{(2)}_{\Sigma/0} - \mathbb{K}^{(0)}_{\Sigma/0} + \mathbb{U} = Cst$$

or

$$(B_2 + mR^2)\dot{\theta}^2 - \Big(I_1 + A_2 \sin^2\theta + (C_2 + mR^2)\cos^2\theta\Big)\Omega^2 + 2mgR\sin\theta = Cst \qquad [2]$$

b. We can apply Lagrange equations to system Σ w.r.t. variables (ψ, θ): we then assume that the variables $(\psi, \theta, \dot{\psi}, \dot{\theta})$ are independent and must ignore the relationship $\psi = \Omega t$. Now the kinetic energy of the system takes the expression

$$\mathbb{K}_{\Sigma/0} = \tfrac{1}{2}\Big(I_1 + A_2 \sin^2\theta + (C_2 + mR^2)\cos^2\theta\Big)\dot{\psi}^2 + \tfrac{1}{2}(B_2 + mR^2)\dot{\theta}^2$$

Lagrange equation $\mathcal{L}^{\psi}_{\Sigma/0}$ is given by

$$\frac{d}{dt}\Big((I_1 + A_2\sin^2\theta + (C_2 + mR^2)\cos^2\theta)\dot{\psi}\Big) = \mathbb{Q}^{\psi}_{\overline{\Sigma}\to\Sigma/0} + \mathbb{Q}^{\psi}_{1\leftrightarrow 2}$$

with

$$\mathbb{Q}^{\psi}_{\overline{\Sigma}\to\Sigma/0} = \mathcal{C}, \qquad \mathbb{Q}^{\psi}_{1\leftrightarrow 2} = 0$$

This equation becomes:

$$\mathcal{L}^{\psi}_{\Sigma/0}: \qquad \frac{d}{dt}\Big((I_1 + A_2\sin^2\theta + (C_2 + mR^2)\cos^2\theta)\dot{\psi}\Big) = \mathcal{C} \qquad [3]$$

Similarly, Lagrange equation $\mathcal{L}^{\theta}_{\Sigma/0}$ is given by

$$(B_2 + mR^2)\ddot{\theta} - \Big(A_2 \sin\theta\cos\theta - (C_2 + mR^2)\cos\theta\sin\theta\Big)\dot{\psi}^2 = \mathbb{Q}^{\theta}_{\overline{\Sigma}\to\Sigma/0} + \mathbb{Q}^{\theta}_{1\leftrightarrow 2}$$

with

$$\mathbb{Q}^{\theta}_{\overline{\Sigma}\to\Sigma/0} = -mgR\cos\theta, \qquad \mathbb{Q}^{\theta}_{1\leftrightarrow 2} = 0$$

giving

$$\mathcal{L}^{\theta}_{\Sigma/0}: \ (B_2 + mR^2)\ddot{\theta} - \Omega^2(A_2 - C_2 - mR^2)\sin\theta\cos\theta = -mgR\cos\theta \qquad [4]$$

after substitution of $\dot{\psi} = \Omega$. It is easy to show that [4] can be obtained by taking the time-derivative of [2]. ∎

13.8 Lagrange vs Newton-Euler Formalisms

It is of interest to relate Lagrange equations and to those obtained by applying the Fundamental Theorem of Dynamics. Recall from section 13.4 that the Lagrange equation with respect to coordinate q_i applied to rigid body $\mathcal{B}$ (of mass m, mass center G) is equivalent to the equation

$$\{\mathcal{D}_{\mathcal{B}/\mathcal{E}}\} \cdot \{\mathcal{V}^{q_i}_{\mathcal{B}/\mathcal{E}}\} = \{\mathcal{A}_{\overline{\mathcal{B}}\to\mathcal{B}}\} \cdot \{\mathcal{V}^{q_i}_{\mathcal{B}/\mathcal{E}}\} \qquad (13.41)$$

Hence, it is seen that Lagrange equation $\mathcal{L}^{q_i}_{\mathcal{B}/\mathcal{E}}$ can be obtained by "projection" (in the sense of screws) of the Fundamental Theorem of Dynamics $\{\mathcal{D}_{\mathcal{B}/\mathcal{E}}\} = \{\mathcal{A}_{\overline{\mathcal{B}}\to\mathcal{B}}\}$ onto partial kinematic screw $\{\mathcal{V}^{q_i}_{\mathcal{B}/\mathcal{E}}\}$:

$$\underbrace{\frac{\partial \omega}{\partial \dot{q}_i} \cdot \mathbf{D}_A + \frac{\partial \mathbf{v}_{A \in \mathcal{B}}}{\partial \dot{q}_i} \cdot m\mathbf{a}_G}_{\frac{d}{dt}\frac{\partial \mathbb{K}}{\partial \dot{q}_i} - \frac{\partial \mathbb{K}}{\partial q_i}} = \underbrace{\frac{\partial \omega}{\partial \dot{q}_i} \cdot \mathbf{M}_{B,\overline{\mathcal{B}} \to \mathcal{B}} + \frac{\partial \mathbf{v}_{B \in \mathcal{B}}}{\partial \dot{q}_i} \cdot \mathbf{R}_{\overline{\mathcal{B}} \to \mathcal{B}}}_{Q^{q_i}_{\overline{\mathcal{B}} \to \mathcal{B}}} \tag{13.42}$$

where A and B are arbitrary points. A similar equation is obtained for a system of p rigid bodies by summation of the p Lagrange equations $\mathcal{L}^{q_i}_{j/0}$, $j = 1, ..., p$. Equation (13.42) demonstrates that in order to obtain equation $\mathcal{L}^{q_i}_{\mathcal{B}/\mathcal{E}}$ a complicated (linear) combination of equations extracted from the Fundamental Theorem of Dynamics must be devised. We see here the significant advantage offered by Lagrange equations: while an equation of motion or a first integral can readily be obtained in an automatic and systematic way with the Lagrange formalism, use of the Newton-Euler formalism requires a careful and often difficult, if not fruitless, strategy.

Example 13.15 Using the system Σ of Example 13.14 show how the Lagrange equations $\mathcal{L}^{\psi}_{\Sigma/0}$ and $\mathcal{L}^{\theta}_{\Sigma/0}$ relate to equations extracted from the Fundamental Theorem of Dynamics. ■

With the results of Example 13.14, Lagrange equation $\mathcal{L}^{\psi}_{\Sigma/0}$ is obtained as follows:

$$\{\mathcal{D}_{1/0}\} \cdot \{\mathcal{V}^{\psi}_{1/0}\} + \{\mathcal{D}_{2/0}\} \cdot \{\mathcal{V}^{\psi}_{2/0}\} = \{\mathcal{A}_{\bar{1} \to 1}\} \cdot \{\mathcal{V}^{\psi}_{1/0}\} + \{\mathcal{A}_{\bar{2} \to 2}\} \cdot \{\mathcal{V}^{\psi}_{2/0}\}$$

with the partial kinematic screws

$$\{\mathcal{V}^{\psi}_{1/0}\} = \{\mathcal{V}^{\psi}_{2/0}\} = \begin{Bmatrix} \hat{\mathbf{z}}_0 \\ \mathbf{0} \end{Bmatrix}_O,$$

we find

$$\hat{\mathbf{z}}_0 \cdot \underbrace{(\mathbf{D}_{O,1/0} + \mathbf{D}_{O,2/0})}_{\mathbf{D}_{O,\Sigma/0}} = \hat{\mathbf{z}}_0 \cdot \underbrace{(\mathbf{M}_{O,\bar{1} \to 1} + \mathbf{M}_{O,\bar{2} \to 2})}_{\mathbf{M}_{O,\bar{\Sigma} \to \Sigma}}$$

Hence Lagrange equation $\mathcal{L}^{\psi}_{\Sigma/0}$ is equivalent to extracting from $\{\mathcal{D}_{\Sigma/0}\} = \{\mathcal{A}_{\bar{\Sigma} \to \Sigma}\}$ the dynamic moment equation about O along $\hat{\mathbf{z}}_0$. Likewise, Lagrange equation $\mathcal{L}^{\theta}_{\Sigma/0}$ is obtained as follows:

$$\{\mathcal{D}_{1/0}\} \cdot \{\mathcal{V}^{\theta}_{1/0}\} + \{\mathcal{D}_{2/0}\} \cdot \{\mathcal{V}^{\theta}_{2/0}\} = \{\mathcal{A}_{\bar{1} \to 1}\} \cdot \{\mathcal{V}^{\theta}_{1/0}\} + \{\mathcal{A}_{\bar{2} \to 2}\} \cdot \{\mathcal{V}^{\theta}_{2/0}\}$$

with the partial kinematic screws

$$\{\mathcal{V}^{\theta}_{1/0}\} = \{0\}, \qquad \{\mathcal{V}^{\psi}_{2/0}\} = \begin{Bmatrix} -\hat{\mathbf{y}}_1 \\ \mathbf{0} \end{Bmatrix}_O$$

giving

$$\hat{\mathbf{y}}_1 \cdot \mathbf{D}_{O,2/0} = \hat{\mathbf{y}}_1 \cdot \mathbf{M}_{O,\bar{2} \to 2}$$

This shows that $\mathcal{L}^{\theta}_{\Sigma/0}$ is equivalent to extracting from $\{\mathcal{D}_{2/0}\} = \{\mathcal{A}_{\bar{2} \to 2}\}$ the dynamic moment equation about O along $\hat{\mathbf{y}}_1$. ■

13.9 Problems

Problem 13.1 Consider a rigid body $\mathcal{B}$ whose position relative to a Newtonian referential $\mathcal{E}$ is defined by $(n+1)$ independent variables $(q_1, q_2, \ldots q_n, t)$. Assume that the variables $(q_1, \ldots q_n, \dot{q}_1, \ldots, \dot{q}_n, t)$ are independent. Use the field $P \in \mathcal{B} \mapsto \mathbf{v}_P^* = \frac{\partial \mathbf{r}_{OP}}{\partial t}$ as the virtual velocity field in D'Alembert Principle of Virtual Power to show the following equation

$$\frac{d}{dt}(\mathbb{K}^{(1)} + 2\mathbb{K}^{(0)}) - \frac{\partial \mathbb{K}}{\partial t} = Q^t_{\bar{\mathcal{B}} \to \mathcal{B}/\mathcal{E}}$$

where $\mathbb{K}^{(k)}$ is the kinetic energy of $\mathcal{B}$ of order k ($\mathbb{K} = \mathbb{K}^{(0)} + \mathbb{K}^{(1)} + \mathbb{K}^{(2)}$). Generalize this equation for a system of p rigid bodies.

Problem 13.2 A small spherical ball 2 of mass m fits loosely in the interior of a vertical hoop 1 of center C and radius r which is driven in rotation about a vertical axis Oz at constant angular velocity Ω. The position of ball 2 relative to the hoop is defined by angle ϕ. The contact is assumed frictionless. Denote by $R = |OC|$ and by I_1 the moment of inertia of body 1 about axis Oz. The pivot connection is assumed ideal.

a. Find Painlevé equation applied to system $\Sigma = \{1, 2\}$. Deduce that ball 2 moves in an effective one-dimensional potential $\mathbb{U}_{eff}(\phi)$ given by

$$\mathbb{U}_{eff}(\phi) = -\tfrac{1}{2} m R \Omega^2 (R + r\cos\phi)^2 + mgr\sin\phi$$

Find the equilibrium positions and discuss their stability. Then discuss the nature of the non-equilibrium solutions.

b. Find the couple C needed to set the system in rotation about axis Oz.

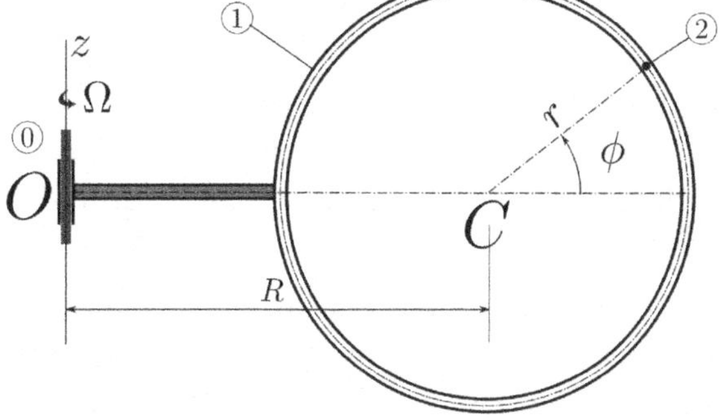

Figure 13.7

Problem 13.3 Figure 13.8 is a schematic of a centrifugal governor: it is made of two identical rod-ball assemblies 2 and 2′ each of mass m connected to a rotating vertical shaft 1 at the pivot O about which they can rotate. Two slender massless rods 3 and 3′ maintain the assemblies 2 and 2′ at the same inclination angle θ. The rotation of the shaft is defined by angle ϕ. The role of the governor is stabilize the shaft's rotation which fluctuates due to variations of the load applied to the system. When the shaft's angular speed increases, the spheres separate from the shaft. The increased inertia of the system, in turn, tends to bring back the angular speed to its initial value. The goal of this problem is to verify this behavior.

The matrix of inertia of body 2 on basis $b_2(\hat{\mathbf{x}}_1, \hat{\mathbf{y}}_2, \hat{\mathbf{z}}_2)$ is assumed to be of the form

$$[\mathcal{I}_{O,2}] = \begin{bmatrix} J & 0 & 0 \\ 0 & I & 0 \\ 0 & 0 & J \end{bmatrix}_{b_2}$$

with $I < J$ and its mass center G_2 is defined by $\mathbf{r}_{OG_2} = l\hat{\mathbf{y}}_2$. Assume that all joints are ideal.

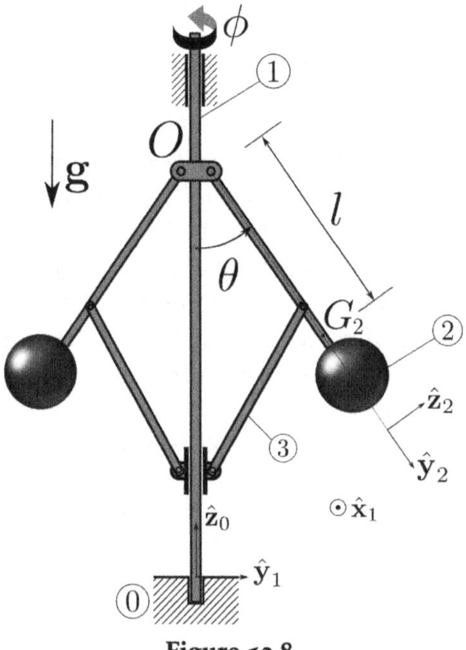

Figure 13.8

a. Find the kinetic and potential energy of body 2.
b. Find Lagrange equations for body 2 w.r.t. coordinates ϕ and θ.
c. Assume $\dot{\phi} = \Omega$ constant, find the positions of equilibrium $\theta = \theta_e$ of the system. Discuss the stability of the system by introducing $\epsilon(t) = \theta(t) - \theta_e$ for $I = 0$ and $J = ml^2$.

Problem 13.4 Figure 13.9 shows a schematic of an open-flow, sea-bed mounted device Σ used to harvest marine current power. The system is observed in a Newtonian referential $0(O, \hat{\mathbf{x}}_0, \hat{\mathbf{y}}_0, \hat{\mathbf{z}}_0)$ with unit vector $\hat{\mathbf{z}}_0$ directed upward. It is comprised of the following bodies:
-the arm $1(O, \hat{\mathbf{x}}_0, \hat{\mathbf{y}}_1, \hat{\mathbf{z}}_1)$ is modeled as a uniform slender rod of length $2l_1$ and mass m_1: its orientation is defined by angle $\theta_1 = (\hat{\mathbf{y}}_0, \hat{\mathbf{y}}_1)$.
-the wing $2(O, \hat{\mathbf{x}}_0, \hat{\mathbf{y}}_2, \hat{\mathbf{z}}_2)$ is modeled a uniform plate of dimensions $2b$ (along $\hat{\mathbf{x}}_0$) and $2c$ (along $\hat{\mathbf{y}}_2$), of mass m_2, mass center G_2 ($\mathbf{r}_{DG_2} = c\hat{\mathbf{y}}_2$). It is in rotation about axis $(D, \hat{\mathbf{x}}_0)$ relative to arm 1: its orientation relative to arm 1 is defined by angle $\theta_2 = (\hat{\mathbf{y}}_1, \hat{\mathbf{y}}_2)$.
-the two hydraulic cylinders 3 and 4 mounted between the fixed referential (at pivots A and B) and the arm 1 at pivot C ($|OA| = |OB| = H$ and $|OC| = L$). Their mass is assumed negligible.
The action of the surrounding water current on each element dl at point P of rod 1 is defined by a resistive viscous force $d\mathbf{f} = -k\mathbf{v}_P dl$. The action of the surrounding water current on

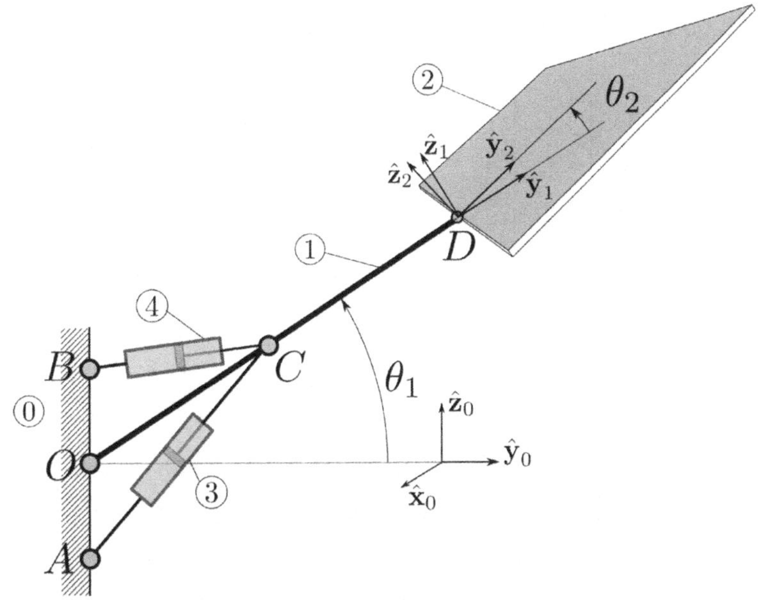

Figure 13.9

wing 2 is defined by the action screw

$$\{\mathcal{A}_{\text{fluid}\to 2}\} = \begin{Bmatrix} F_{wy}\hat{\mathbf{y}}_2 + F_{wz}\hat{\mathbf{z}}_2 \\ \mathbf{0} \end{Bmatrix}_E, \qquad \mathbf{r}_{DE} = \frac{c}{2}\hat{\mathbf{y}}_2$$

Finally the actions of the hydraulic cylinders on the arm is modeled as

$$\{\mathcal{A}_{3\to 1}\} = \begin{Bmatrix} F_3\hat{\mathbf{u}}_3 \\ \mathbf{0} \end{Bmatrix}_C, \qquad \{\mathcal{A}_{4\to 1}\} = \begin{Bmatrix} F_4\hat{\mathbf{u}}_4 \\ \mathbf{0} \end{Bmatrix}_C$$

with $\hat{\mathbf{u}}_3 = \frac{\mathbf{r}_{AC}}{|AC|}$ and $\hat{\mathbf{u}}_4 = \frac{\mathbf{r}_{BC}}{|BC|}$.
a. Find the kinetic energy $\mathbb{K}_{\Sigma/0}$ of system Σ.
b. Find the virtual power due the action of water current on bodies 1 and 2 corresponding to virtual speeds (θ_1^*, θ_2^*) compatible with the geometric constraints of the system.
c. Find the virtual power due the action of the hydraulic cylinders on body 1 corresponding to virtual speeds $(\dot{\theta}_1^*, \dot{\theta}_2^*)$ compatible with the geometric constraints of the system.
d. Derive Lagrange equations $\mathcal{L}^q_{\Sigma/0}$ for the coordinates $q = \theta_1, \theta_2$.

Problem 13.5 In Newtonian referential $\mathcal{E}(O, \hat{\mathbf{x}}_0, \hat{\mathbf{y}}_0, \hat{\mathbf{z}}_0)$ consider the material plane $\Pi(O, \hat{\mathbf{x}}_0, \hat{\mathbf{y}}_0)$ and a fixed rigid rod of negligible cross-section coinciding with axis $(O, \hat{\mathbf{z}}_0)$. A rigid body 1 is assembled by joining a massless slender rod with a uniform disk of radius r, mass m and mass center G so that the rod coincides with the axis $(G, \hat{\mathbf{z}}_1)$ of the disk. It is in motion in $\mathcal{E}$ in the following way: (i) the axis $(G, \hat{\mathbf{z}}_1)$ is in contact at a point A with axis (O, z_0), (ii) the rim of the disk is in contact at a point I without friction with horizontal plane Π. See Figure 13.10. The joint are A is bilateral and ideal.
The position of the body is defined the distance $\rho = |OI|$ and the Euler angles (ψ, θ, ϕ).
a. Find the equations of motion by deriving the four Lagrange equations $\mathcal{L}^q_{1/0}$ for $q = (\eta = \rho + r\cos\theta, \psi, \theta, \phi)$.

b. Can motions be found for which angle θ or distance ρ remain constant?

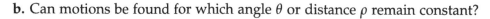

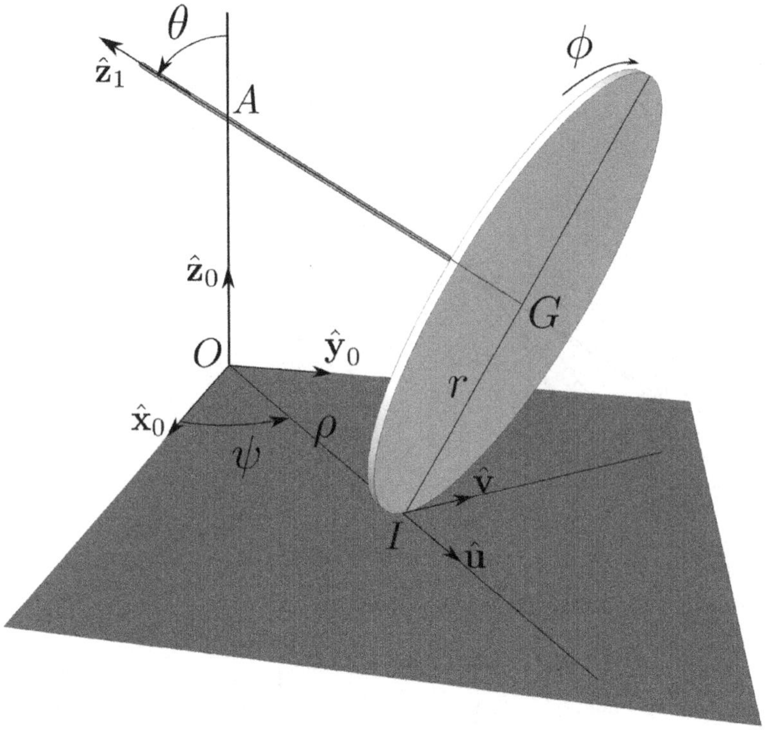

Figure 13.10

Problem 13.6 We continue the analysis of problem 13.5 by assuming that the contact at I is achieved without slipping. Denote by (X, Y, Z) and (X_1, Y_1, Z_1) the components on basis $(\hat{\mathbf{u}}, \hat{\mathbf{v}}, \hat{\mathbf{z}}_0)$ of the reactions of support Π and of the joint at A on the body, respectively.

a. Show that the no-slip condition at I yields two holonomic constraint equations in the coordinates $(\rho, \psi, \theta, \phi)$.

b. Find the equations of motion by deriving the four Lagrange equations $\mathcal{L}^q_{1/0}$ for $q = (\rho, \psi, \theta, \phi)$. Show that angles θ and ψ can be obtained by two quadratures.

c. Find the reaction components (X, Y, Z) and (X_1, Y_1, Z_1).

Problem 13.7 The rigid body 1 of problem 13.6 is again assumed to roll without slipping relative to fixed support Π. A cylinder 2 of mass M, radius R, and height h is constrained to fixed axis $(O, \hat{\mathbf{z}}_0)$ about which it can slide and rotate. It is placed in contact at a point J with body 1, as shown in Figure 13.11. The position of the mass center G_2 of body 2 is defined by $\mathbf{r}_{OG_2} = \zeta \hat{\mathbf{z}}_0$ and the orientation of body 2 is defined by angle α about $(O, \hat{\mathbf{z}}_0)$. The contact at J is achieved without slipping. Denote by (X_2, Y_2, Z_2) the components on basis $(\hat{\mathbf{u}}, \hat{\mathbf{v}}, \hat{\mathbf{z}}_0)$ of the reaction of body 2 on body 1.

a. Show that the contact at J yields a holonomic constraint equations in the coordinates (ζ, θ).

b. Find the equations of motion of the system $\Sigma = \{1, 2\}$ by deriving the four Lagrange equations $\mathcal{L}^q_{\Sigma/0}$ for $q = (\psi, \theta, \zeta, \alpha)$. Find the reaction forces at A, I and J.

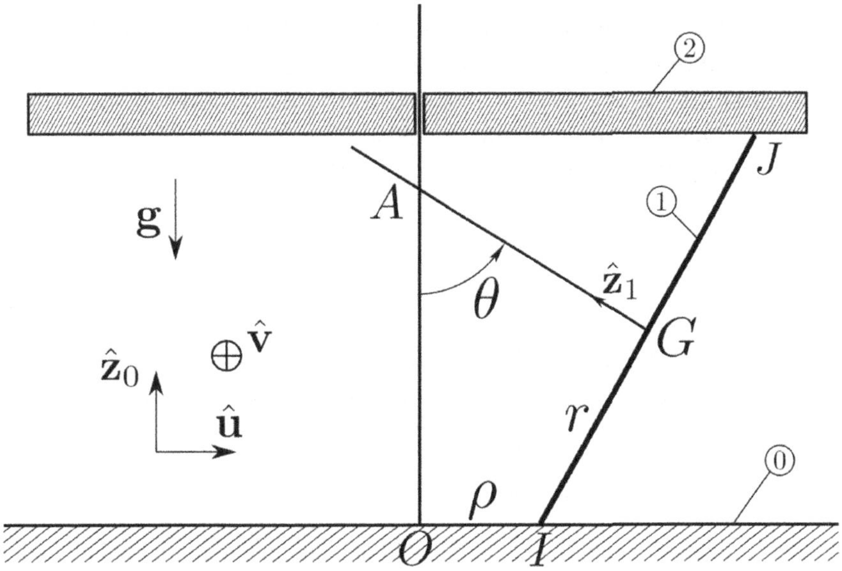

Figure 13.11

Problem 13.8 The goal of this problem is to study the behavior of a gyroscopic instrument mounted on aircraft, known as attitude indicator or artificial horizon. It provides a vertical reference irrespective of the position or motion of its support. Its working principle is based on conservation of angular momentum: its axis of rotation remains fixed relative to a Newtonian referential in the absence of perturbative effects. In realistic environments these effects cannot be neglected. A stability analysis can give the precise conditions under which the attitude indicator works properly.

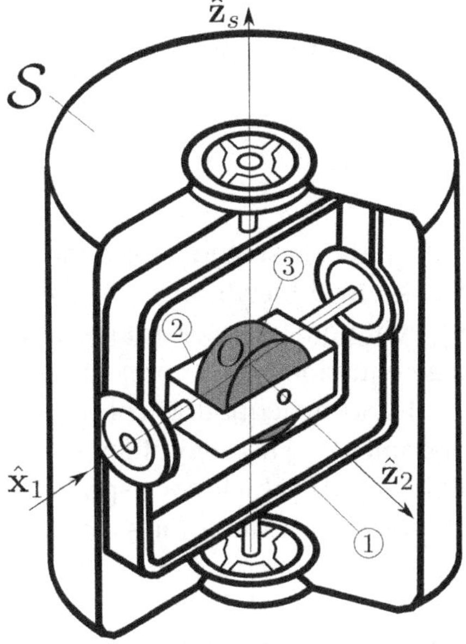

Figure 13.12

The system Σ is comprised of three bodies mounted in a case $\mathcal{S}(O, \hat{\mathbf{x}}_s, \hat{\mathbf{y}}_s, \hat{\mathbf{z}}_s)$ attached to the stationary or moving support (the aircraft):

-the outer gimbal $1(O, \hat{\mathbf{x}}_1, \hat{\mathbf{y}}_1, \hat{\mathbf{z}}_s)$ is mounted to the case by pivots of axis $(O, \hat{\mathbf{z}}_s)$. Its mass center is located on axis $(O, \hat{\mathbf{z}}_s)$. Denote by L its moment of inertia about its axis of rotation.
-the inner gimbal $2(O, \hat{\mathbf{x}}_1, \hat{\mathbf{y}}_2, \hat{\mathbf{z}}_2)$ is mounted to the outer gimbal 1 by pivots of axis $(O, \hat{\mathbf{x}}_1)$. Its mass center is O and its inertia matrix about O is assumed of the form (its inertia operator about O has spherical symmetry)

$$[\mathcal{I}_{O,2}]_b = \begin{bmatrix} K & 0 & 0 \\ 0 & K & 0 \\ 0 & 0 & K \end{bmatrix}_b$$

-the rotor $3(O, \hat{\mathbf{x}}_3, \hat{\mathbf{y}}_3, \hat{\mathbf{z}}_2)$ mounted to the inner gimbal 2 by pivots of axis $(O, \hat{\mathbf{z}}_2)$. Its mass is M, its mass center G is located on axis $(O, \hat{\mathbf{z}}_2)$ with $\mathbf{r}_{OG} = a\hat{\mathbf{z}}_2$ $(a > 0)$, and its inertia matrix about O on basis $b_3(\hat{\mathbf{x}}_3, \hat{\mathbf{y}}_3, \hat{\mathbf{z}}_2)$ is given by

$$[\mathcal{I}_{O,3}]_{b_3} = \begin{bmatrix} A & 0 & 0 \\ 0 & A & 0 \\ 0 & 0 & C \end{bmatrix}_{b_3}$$

The system has three degrees of freedom described by the angles ψ, θ, ϕ and the corresponding transformations:

$$(\hat{\mathbf{x}}_s, \hat{\mathbf{y}}_s, \hat{\mathbf{z}}_s) \xrightarrow{\mathcal{R}_{\psi,\hat{\mathbf{z}}_s}} (\hat{\mathbf{x}}_1, \hat{\mathbf{y}}_1, \hat{\mathbf{z}}_s) \xrightarrow{\mathcal{R}_{\theta,\hat{\mathbf{x}}_1}} (\hat{\mathbf{x}}_1, \hat{\mathbf{y}}_2, \hat{\mathbf{z}}_2) \xrightarrow{\mathcal{R}_{\phi,\hat{\mathbf{z}}_2}} (\hat{\mathbf{x}}_3, \hat{\mathbf{y}}_3, \hat{\mathbf{z}}_2)$$

The rotation of the rotor relative to the inner gimbal is maintained uniform thanks to a small motor $\mathcal{M}$ of negligible mass resulting in the time relationship

$$\phi = \omega t, \qquad \omega = Cst$$

The action of the motor on the rotor is represented by the screw

$$\{\mathcal{A}_{\mathcal{M}\to 3}\} = \begin{Bmatrix} \mathbf{0} \\ \mathcal{C}\hat{\mathbf{z}}_2 \end{Bmatrix}$$

All joints are assumed ideal. In this first study, the vehicle is assumed fixed relative to Earth so that referential $\mathcal{S}$ can be assumed Newtonian. The vertical directed downward is defined by unit vector $\hat{\mathbf{x}}_s$ and the gravitational acceleration is given by $\mathbf{g} = g\hat{\mathbf{x}}_s$.
a. Derive the three Lagrange equations $\mathcal{L}^q_{\Sigma/\mathcal{S}}$ for $q = \psi, \theta, \phi$ to find two equations of motion (governing angles ψ and θ) and an equation solving for couple $\mathcal{C}$. Discuss how these equations relate to the Fundamental Theorem of Dynamics of the Newton-Euler formalism.
b. Find the values of angles (ψ, θ) which correspond to stationary positions of the axis $(O, \hat{\mathbf{z}}_2)$ of the rotor. Which position of the rotor's axis corresponds to the value $\psi = -\pi/2$ and $\theta = \pi/2$?
c. Define the variables $\alpha = \psi + \pi/2$ and $\beta = \theta - \pi/2$. Linearize the two o.d.e.'s governing α and β. Find the characteristic equation corresponding to these equations and deduce the condition of stability of the position $\psi = -\pi/2$ and $\theta = \pi/2$. Find the minimal value of angular velocity ω guaranteeing stability as a function of the parameters (L, K, A, C, M, a, g). Find the numerical value of ω_{min} for $A = 400$ g.cm^2, $C = 900$ g.cm^2, $L = 2000$ g.cm^2, $K = 1600$ g.cm^2, $a = 4$ cm, $M = 200$ g and $g = 9.81$ m/s^2.

Problem 13.9 In this problem we continue the stability study of problem 13.8 by taking into account the motion of the aircraft.

Part 1. The aircraft $\mathcal{S}$ is undergoing a turn relative to Earth $\mathcal{E}(O_0, \hat{\mathbf{x}}_0, \hat{\mathbf{y}}_0, \hat{\mathbf{z}}_0)$ considered Newtonian (where $\hat{\mathbf{z}}_0$ is directed along the vertical upward). Point O of $\mathcal{S}$ describes a circular path of center O_0 and radius R given by

$$\mathbf{r}_{O_0O} = R(\hat{\mathbf{x}}_0 \cos \Omega t + \hat{\mathbf{y}}_0 \sin \Omega t), \qquad \Omega = Cst$$

The basis attached to referential $\mathcal{S}$ is defined as follows: $\hat{\mathbf{y}}_s$ is directed along $\Omega \hat{\mathbf{z}}_0 \times \mathbf{r}_{O_0O}$, $\hat{\mathbf{x}}_s$ is directed along $\mathbf{g} + \Omega^2 \mathbf{r}_{O_0O}$, $\hat{\mathbf{z}}_s = \hat{\mathbf{y}}_s \times \hat{\mathbf{x}}_s$. Define the constant angle δ according to

$$\cos \delta = \frac{g}{(g^2 + R^2\Omega^4)^{1/2}}, \qquad \sin \delta = \frac{R\Omega^2}{(g^2 + R^2\Omega^4)^{1/2}}$$

Assume angle δ small: $\frac{R\Omega^2}{g} \ll 1$.

1a. Find corrections to the equations of motion found in problem 13.8 by keeping only linear terms in Ω.

1b. Find stationary solutions, that is, corresponding to $\dot{\phi} = \omega$, $\dot{\psi} = \dot{\theta} = 0$. Can the unperturbed directions $\hat{\mathbf{z}}_2 = \pm \hat{\mathbf{z}}_0$ of the rotor be maintained?

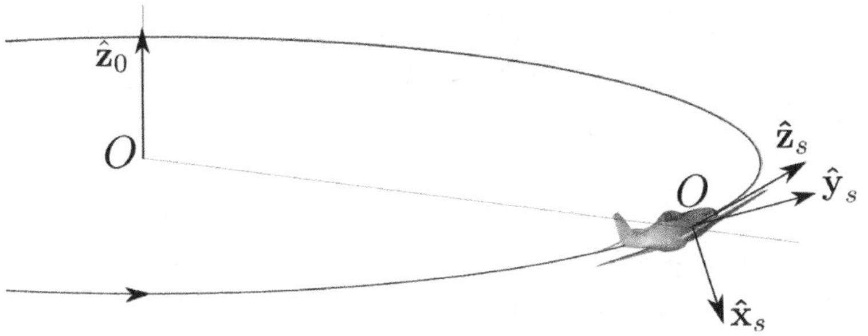

Figure 13.13

Part 2. The aircraft $\mathcal{S}$ is in rectilinear translation in $\mathcal{E}(O_0, \hat{\mathbf{x}}_0, \hat{\mathbf{y}}_0, \hat{\mathbf{z}}_0)$ with unit vector $\hat{\mathbf{x}}_s$ directed downward: $\mathbf{g} = g\hat{\mathbf{x}}_s$. The motion of O in $\mathcal{E}$ is described by

$$\mathbf{r}_{O_0O} = (vt + \epsilon \sin \Omega t)\hat{\mathbf{z}}_s$$

with v, Ω, ϵ are constant, and ϵ is assumed small.

2a. Find corrections to the equations of motion found in problem 13.8 by keeping only linear terms in ϵ.

2b. Discuss the stability of the motions of the rotor's axis $(O, \hat{\mathbf{z}}_2)$ near the stationary unperturbed position $\psi = -\pi/2$ and $\theta = \pi/2$ (for $\epsilon = 0$). Then find the two values of Ω corresponding to resonances which would destabilize the gyroscope by using the values $A = 400$ g.cm^2, $C = 900$ g.cm^2, $L = 2000$ g.cm^2, $K = 1600$ g.cm^2, $a = 4$ cm, $M = 200$ g and $\Omega = 20$ rev/s.

Problem 13.10 Consider three particles P_1 of mass m_1, P_2 of mass m_2 and P_3 of mass m_3 in planar motion and under the sole effect of their mutual gravitational interactions. Denote by

(x_k, y_k) the Cartesian coordinates of particle P_k in some rectangular axes $(O, \hat{\mathbf{x}}, \hat{\mathbf{y}})$ fixed in a Newtonian referential $\mathcal{E}$. Denote by r_1, r_2 and r_3 their mutual distances:

$$r_1 = |P_2P_3|, \qquad r_2 = |P_1P_3|, \qquad r_3 = |P_1P_2|$$

For simplicity, assume that a system of normalization is chosen so as to make the gravitational constant equal to unity.

a. Find the Lagrangian of the system $\Sigma = \{P_1, P_2, P_3\}$. Then derive the corresponding Lagrange equations $\mathcal{L}^q_{\Sigma/\mathcal{E}}$, for $q = (x_1, x_2, x_3, y_1, y_2, y_3)$. Denote this system of equations (S).

b. Show that (S) implies conservation of the energy of system Σ.

c. Show that (S) implies conservation of angular momentum about O of system Σ.

d. Characterize the motion of the mass center G of Σ. Conclude that the referential $(G, \hat{\mathbf{x}}, \hat{\mathbf{y}})$ is Newtonian.

e. By combining the first three equations of (S), then the last three remaining equations, find two additional first integrals of motion.

f. Since the motion of the mass center is known, it is possible to study the system in the centroidal referential $\mathcal{E}^*(G, \hat{\mathbf{x}}, \hat{\mathbf{y}})$ relative to which the system has four degrees of freedom. The system can be studied in terms of the Jacobian coordinates $\mathbf{q} = (q_1, q_2, q_3, q_4)$ defined as follows: (q_1, q_2) are the components of position vector $\mathbf{r}_{P_1P_2}$ and (q_3, q_4) are the components of position vector $\mathbf{r}_{G_{12}P_3}$ where G_{12} is the center of mass of system $\{P_1, P_2\}$.

f1. Express the coordinates (q_1, q_2, q_3, q_4) in terms of coordinates (x_k, y_k) $(k = 1, 2, 3)$.

f2. Show that the kinetic energy of the system can be expressed in terms of the Jacobian coordinates as

$$\mathbb{K} = \tfrac{1}{2}\mu_1(\dot{q}_1^2 + \dot{q}_2^2) + \tfrac{1}{2}\mu_2(\dot{q}_3^2 + \dot{q}_4^2)$$

Find the expressions of reduced masses μ_1 and μ_2. Then express the Lagrangian $\mathbb{L}(\mathbf{q}, \dot{\mathbf{q}})$ of the system in terms of the Jacobian coordinates and their time-derivatives.

g. Define the variables p_k according to

$$p_k = \frac{\partial \mathbb{L}}{\partial \dot{q}_k} \qquad (k = 1, 2, 3, 4)$$

Show that Lagrange equations generated by $\mathbb{L}(\mathbf{q}, \dot{\mathbf{q}})$ are equivalent to the equations

$$\dot{q}_k = \frac{\partial \mathbb{L}}{\partial p_k}, \qquad \dot{p}_k = -\frac{\partial \mathbb{L}}{\partial q_k} \qquad (k = 1, 2, 3, 4) \qquad (SH)$$

known as Hamilton equations, where $\mathbb{H}$ (the Hamiltonian of the system) is defined as

$$\mathbb{H}(\mathbf{q}, \mathbf{p}) = \mathbb{K}(\mathbf{p}) - \mathbb{U}(\mathbf{q})$$

Show that $\mathbb{H}$ is a first integral of system (SH).

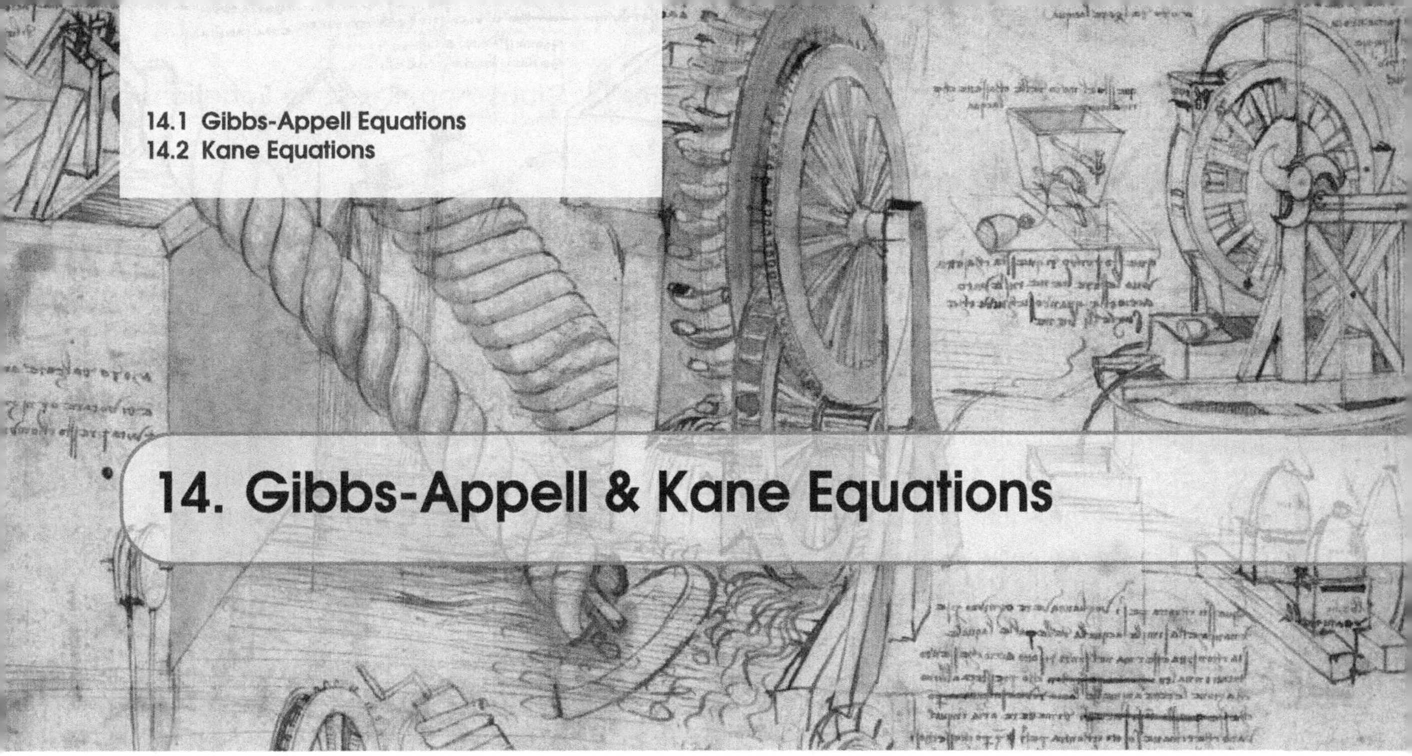

14. Gibbs-Appell & Kane Equations

IN THIS CHAPTER we continue our treatment of analytical dynamics by presenting two methods: Gibbs-Appell[1] and Kane[2] equations.

We saw in Chapter 13 that the calculation of the virtual power of inertial forces from the system's kinetic energy requires a separate treatment whether variables $(\mathbf{q}, \dot{\mathbf{q}}, t)$ are independent or not. We shall see that in the Gibbs-Appell formalism, this separate treatment is avoided by considering the energy of acceleration instead of the kinetic energy. All systems whether holonomic or non-holonomic can be treated uniformly. Unfortunately, these equations require the rather burdensome determination of the energy of acceleration.

One of the drawbacks of both Lagrange or Gibbs-Appell equations is the determination of partial derivatives $\frac{\partial}{\partial q_i}$ and $\frac{\partial}{\partial \dot{q}_i}$ of the kinetic energy (for Lagrange equations) and $\frac{\partial}{\partial \ddot{q}_i}$ of the energy of acceleration. This determination requires tedious algebraic manipulations and does not lead to differential systems of equations in a form amenable to numerical integration by standard techniques. These methods also require the use of physical coordinates and their time-derivatives which can be problematic for coordinates such as Euler angles. To address these issues, Kane introduced *generalized speeds* which need not be defined as the derivatives of coordinates. We shall see that Kane equations are obtained by projection (in the sense of screws) of the Fundamental Theorem of Dynamics on the *generalized partial kinematic screws*. The corresponding generalized inertial forces are, in general, not determined from the system's kinetic energy or other scalar function. Instead, they require the determination of the dynamic screw of each body.

[1] P. Appell, *Sur une forme générale des équations de la dynamique*, Mémorial des sciences mathématiques, fascicule 1, Gauthiers-Villars, Paris, 1925.

[2] T.R. Kane & D.A. Levinson, *Dynamics: Theory and Applications*, McGraw Hill, 1985.

14.1 Gibbs-Appell Equations

In Gibbs-Appell equations, the calculation of the virtual power of inertial forces relies on the system's energy of acceleration (a.k.a. Gibbs S-function).

14.1.1 Gibbs Energy of Acceleration

RECALL that, in the formulation of Lagrange equations, the quantity $\mathbf{a}_P \cdot \frac{\partial \mathbf{r}_{OP}}{\partial q_i}$ comes about by application of D'Alembert Principle of Virtual Power with the use of the field $P \mapsto \frac{\partial \mathbf{r}_{OP}}{\partial q_i}$ as a virtual velocity field. We return to Lagrange kinematic formula to provide an alternate formulation of the scalar product $\mathbf{a}_P \cdot \frac{\partial \mathbf{r}_{OP}}{\partial q_i}$ where the position vector $\mathbf{r}_{OP}$ of points attached to a rigid body is viewed as a function of n independent coordinates $(q_1, q_2, \ldots, q_n)$ and time t: we can take the time-derivative of velocity $\mathbf{v}_P$ (relative to a referential $\mathcal{E}$) written as

$$\mathbf{v}_P = \sum_{i=1}^{n} \frac{\partial \mathbf{r}_{OP}}{\partial q_i} \dot{q}_i + \frac{\partial \mathbf{r}_{OP}}{\partial t}$$

to obtain the acceleration of P in the form

$$\mathbf{a}_P = \sum_{i=1}^{n} \frac{\partial \mathbf{r}_{OP}}{\partial q_i} \ddot{q}_i + \sum_{i,j=1}^{n} \frac{\partial^2 \mathbf{r}_{OP}}{\partial q_i \partial q_j} \dot{q}_i \dot{q}_j + 2 \sum_{i=1}^{n} \frac{\partial^2 \mathbf{r}_{OP}}{\partial t \partial q_i} \dot{q}_i + \frac{\partial^2 \mathbf{r}_{OP}}{\partial t^2} \tag{14.1}$$

If we view the acceleration of P as a function of the independent variables $(\mathbf{q}, \dot{\mathbf{q}}, \ddot{\mathbf{q}}, t)$ we can obtain the following result

$$\frac{\partial \mathbf{a}_P}{\partial \ddot{q}_i} = \frac{\partial \mathbf{r}_{OP}}{\partial q_i} \tag{14.2}$$

for $i = 1, \ldots, n$. This leads to an alternate way of obtaining $\mathbf{a}_P \cdot \frac{\partial \mathbf{r}_{OP}}{\partial q_i}$ by using (14.2)

$$\mathbf{a}_P \cdot \frac{\partial \mathbf{r}_{OP}}{\partial q_i} = \frac{1}{2} \frac{\partial}{\partial \ddot{q}_i} \mathbf{a}_P^2 \tag{14.3}$$

and to the definition of Gibbs energy of acceleration.

Definition 14.1 — Gibbs energy of acceleration. We call Gibbs *energy of acceleration* (or simply Gibbs *S-function*) of rigid body $\mathcal{B}$ the following quantity

$$S_{\mathcal{B}/\mathcal{E}} = \frac{1}{2} \int_{\mathcal{B}} \mathbf{a}_{P/\mathcal{E}}^2 \, dm \tag{14.4}$$

More generally, Gibbs S-function for a system Σ of p rigid bodies is defined by

$$S_{\Sigma/0} = S_{1/0} + S_{2/0} + \cdots + S_{p/0} \tag{14.5}$$

Gibbs S-function can then be related to the coefficient $\int_{\mathcal{B}} \mathbf{a}_P \cdot \frac{\partial \mathbf{r}_{OP}}{\partial q_i} dm$ according to

$$\int_{\mathcal{B}} \mathbf{a}_P \cdot \frac{\partial \mathbf{r}_{OP}}{\partial q_i} dm = \frac{\partial S_{\mathcal{B}/\mathcal{E}}}{\partial \ddot{q}_i} \tag{14.6}$$

where function $\mathcal{S}$ is viewed as a function of the independent variables $(\mathbf{q}, \dot{\mathbf{q}}, \ddot{\mathbf{q}}, t)$. The S-function will play the role in Gibbs-Appell equations that the kinetic energy plays in Lagrange equations. Before deriving these equations, we must learn how to determine the S-function.

14.1.2 Determination of Gibbs S-function.

To find the general expression of the S-function, we relate the acceleration $\mathbf{a}_P$ to that of mass center G of body $\mathcal{B}$:

$$\mathbf{a}_P = \mathbf{a}_G + \boldsymbol{\alpha} \times \mathbf{r}_{GP} + \boldsymbol{\omega} \times (\boldsymbol{\omega} \times \mathbf{r}_{GP})$$

where $\boldsymbol{\omega} = \boldsymbol{\omega}_{\mathcal{B}/\mathcal{E}}$ and $\boldsymbol{\alpha} = \boldsymbol{\alpha}_{\mathcal{B}/\mathcal{E}}$. Substituting this expression in the expression of $\mathcal{S}$ we obtain six terms:

$$\mathcal{S}_1 = \tfrac{1}{2}\int_{\mathcal{B}} \mathbf{a}_G^2 dm = \tfrac{1}{2} m \mathbf{a}_G^2$$

$$\mathcal{S}_2 = \tfrac{1}{2}\int_{\mathcal{B}} (\boldsymbol{\alpha} \times \mathbf{r}_{GP})^2 dm = \tfrac{1}{2}\boldsymbol{\alpha} \cdot \int_{\mathcal{B}} \mathbf{r}_{GP} \times (\boldsymbol{\alpha} \times \mathbf{r}_{GP}) dm = \tfrac{1}{2}\boldsymbol{\alpha} \cdot \mathcal{I}_G(\boldsymbol{\alpha})$$

$$\begin{aligned}\mathcal{S}_3 &= \int_{\mathcal{B}} (\boldsymbol{\alpha} \times \mathbf{r}_{GP}) \cdot (\boldsymbol{\omega} \times (\boldsymbol{\omega} \times \mathbf{r}_{GP})) dm = (\boldsymbol{\alpha} \times \boldsymbol{\omega}) \cdot \int_{\mathcal{B}} \mathbf{r}_{GP} \times (\boldsymbol{\omega} \times \mathbf{r}_{GP}) dm \\ &= (\boldsymbol{\alpha} \times \boldsymbol{\omega}) \cdot \mathcal{I}_G(\boldsymbol{\omega})\end{aligned}$$

using the identity

$$(\mathbf{A} \times \mathbf{B}) \cdot (\mathbf{C} \times \mathbf{D}) = (\mathbf{A} \times \mathbf{C}) \cdot (\mathbf{B} \times \mathbf{D}) + (\mathbf{A} \cdot \mathbf{C})(\mathbf{B} \cdot \mathbf{D}) - (\mathbf{A} \cdot \mathbf{B})(\mathbf{C} \cdot \mathbf{D})$$

$$\mathcal{S}_4 = \tfrac{1}{2}\int_{\mathcal{B}} (\boldsymbol{\omega} \times (\boldsymbol{\omega} \times \mathbf{r}_{GP}))^2 dm = \tfrac{1}{2}\omega^2 \int_{\mathcal{B}} (\boldsymbol{\omega} \times \mathbf{r}_{GP})^2 dm = \tfrac{1}{2}\omega^2 (\boldsymbol{\omega} \cdot \mathcal{I}_G(\boldsymbol{\omega}))$$

using the identity $(\mathbf{A} \times \mathbf{B})^2 = \mathbf{A}^2\mathbf{B}^2 - (\mathbf{A} \cdot \mathbf{B})^2$,

$$\mathcal{S}_5 = \int_{\mathcal{B}} \mathbf{a}_G \cdot \boldsymbol{\alpha} \times \mathbf{r}_{GP} dm = \mathbf{a}_G \cdot \boldsymbol{\alpha} \times \int_{\mathcal{B}} \mathbf{r}_{GP} dm = 0$$

$$\mathcal{S}_6 = \int_{\mathcal{B}} \mathbf{a}_G \cdot \boldsymbol{\omega} \times (\boldsymbol{\omega} \times \mathbf{r}_{GP}) dm = \mathbf{a}_G \cdot \boldsymbol{\omega} \times (\boldsymbol{\omega} \times \int_{\mathcal{B}} \mathbf{r}_{GP} dm) = 0$$

where $\mathcal{I}_G$ denotes the inertia operator of $\mathcal{B}$ about G. We can now write the general expression of the energy of acceleration:

Theorem 14.1 The energy of acceleration of a rigid body $\mathcal{B}$ of mass m, mass center G, inertia operator $\mathcal{I}_G$ about G takes the expression

$$\mathcal{S}_{\mathcal{B}/\mathcal{E}} = \tfrac{1}{2} m \mathbf{a}_G^2 + \tfrac{1}{2}\boldsymbol{\alpha} \cdot \mathcal{I}_G(\boldsymbol{\alpha}) + (\boldsymbol{\alpha} \times \boldsymbol{\omega}) \cdot \mathcal{I}_G(\boldsymbol{\omega}) + \tfrac{1}{2}\omega^2 (\boldsymbol{\omega} \cdot \mathcal{I}_G(\boldsymbol{\omega})) \quad (14.7)$$

Remark 1. Inspection of (14.7) shows that the S-function will require significantly more effort than the kinetic energy of $\mathcal{B}$ due to the need to determine the accelerations $\mathbf{a}_G$ and $\boldsymbol{\alpha}$.

Remark 2. In general, the first two terms $\mathcal{S}_1$ and $\mathcal{S}_2$ in (14.7) are quadratic in the $\ddot{q}_i$'s, while the third term $\mathcal{S}_3$ is linear in the $\ddot{q}_i$'s. The last term, $\mathcal{S}_4$, is not a function of the $\ddot{q}_i$'s and its determination can be omitted in Gibbs-Appell formulation.

If $\mathcal{B}$ admits a fixed point O in referential $\mathcal{E}$, the S-function of $\mathcal{B}$ is determined by using $\mathbf{a}_P = \boldsymbol{\alpha} \times \mathbf{r}_{OP} + \boldsymbol{\omega} \times (\boldsymbol{\omega} \times \mathbf{r}_{OP})$. It is readily shown that it is given by

$$S_{\mathcal{B}/\mathcal{E}} = \tfrac{1}{2}\boldsymbol{\alpha} \cdot \mathcal{I}_O(\boldsymbol{\alpha}) + (\boldsymbol{\alpha} \times \boldsymbol{\omega}) \cdot \mathcal{I}_O(\boldsymbol{\omega}) + \tfrac{1}{2}\omega^2(\boldsymbol{\omega} \cdot \mathcal{I}_O(\boldsymbol{\omega})) \tag{14.8}$$

where $\mathcal{I}_O$ is the inertia operator of $\mathcal{B}$ about O.
The following examples illustrate the use of the formula (14.7) or (14.8) for the determination of S.

Example 14.1 An homogeneous sphere 1 of center G, radius r, and mass m is in motion on a horizontal plane $(O, \hat{\mathbf{x}}_0, \hat{\mathbf{y}}_0)$ of a referential 0. Its configuration is defined by the Cartesian coordinates (x, y) of center G and the Euler angles (ψ, θ, ϕ).
Find Gibbs S-function of body 1 in terms of $q = x, y, \psi, \theta, \phi$ and their derivatives. ■

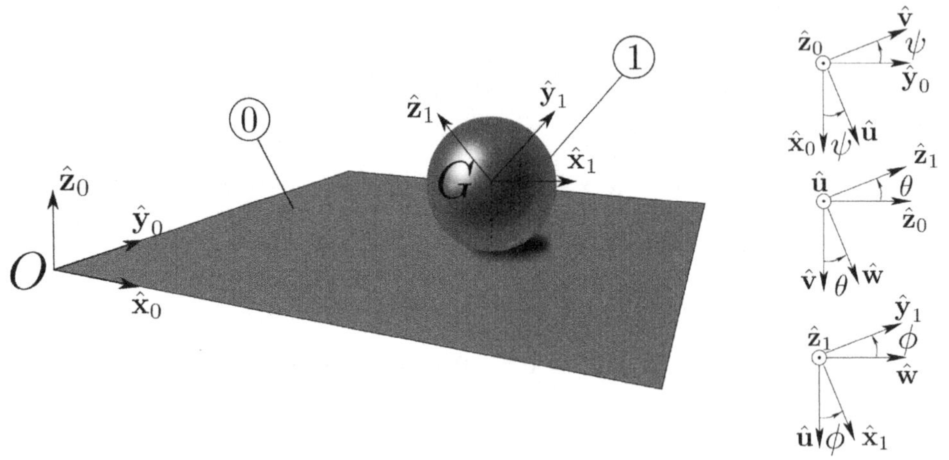

Figure 14.1

Starting with velocity $\mathbf{v}_G = \dot{x}\hat{\mathbf{x}}_0 + \dot{y}\hat{\mathbf{y}}_0$ and the angular velocity $\boldsymbol{\omega} = \dot{\psi}\hat{\mathbf{z}}_0 + \dot{\theta}\hat{\mathbf{u}} + \dot{\phi}\hat{\mathbf{z}}_1$, we find acceleration $\mathbf{a}_G$ and angular acceleration $\boldsymbol{\alpha}$:

$$\mathbf{a}_G = \ddot{x}\hat{\mathbf{x}}_0 + \ddot{y}\hat{\mathbf{y}}_0, \qquad \boldsymbol{\alpha} = \ddot{\psi}\hat{\mathbf{z}}_0 + \ddot{\theta}\hat{\mathbf{u}} + \ddot{\phi}\hat{\mathbf{z}}_1 + \dot{\psi}\dot{\theta}\hat{\mathbf{v}} + \dot{\phi}(\dot{\psi}\sin\theta\hat{\mathbf{u}} - \dot{\theta}\hat{\mathbf{w}})$$

where we have used $d\hat{\mathbf{z}}_1/dt = (\dot{\psi}\sin\theta\hat{\mathbf{u}} - \dot{\theta}\hat{\mathbf{w}})$. Denoting by $A = \frac{2}{5}mr^2$, we have $\mathcal{I}_G(\boldsymbol{\omega}) = A\boldsymbol{\omega}$: this implies that the term $S_3 = (\boldsymbol{\alpha} \times \boldsymbol{\omega}) \cdot \mathcal{I}_G(\boldsymbol{\omega})$ is zero. We are left with the following expression by application of (14.7)

$$\begin{aligned} S = \tfrac{1}{2}m(\ddot{x}^2 + \ddot{y}^2) &+ \tfrac{1}{2}A\big((\ddot{\theta} + \dot{\psi}\dot{\phi}\sin\theta)^2 + (\dot{\psi}\dot{\theta} - \ddot{\phi}\sin\theta - \dot{\theta}\dot{\phi}\cos\theta)^2 \\ &+ (\ddot{\psi} + \ddot{\phi}\cos\theta - \dot{\theta}\dot{\phi}\sin\theta)^2\big) + \tfrac{1}{2}A(\dot{\psi}^2 + \dot{\theta}^2 + \dot{\phi}^2 + 2\dot{\psi}\dot{\phi}\cos\theta)^2 \end{aligned}$$

Note that the last term is not a function of $(\ddot{\psi}, \ddot{\theta}, \ddot{\phi})$ and hence will not contribute to $\frac{\partial S}{\partial \ddot{q}}$. ■

Example 14.2 A gyroscope $1(G, \hat{\mathbf{x}}_1, \hat{\mathbf{y}}_1, \hat{\mathbf{z}}_1)$ of mass center G and mass m is maintained in motion about a fixed point O by a spherical joint fixed in a referential $0(O, \hat{\mathbf{x}}_0, \hat{\mathbf{y}}_0, \hat{\mathbf{z}}_0)$. Its configuration relative to referential 0 is defined by the Euler angles (ψ, θ, ϕ) as shown in

Figure 14.1. Its inertia operator about O is represented by the matrix

$$[\mathcal{I}_O]_{b_1} = \begin{bmatrix} A & 0 & 0 \\ 0 & A & 0 \\ 0 & 0 & C \end{bmatrix}_{b_1}$$

on basis $b_1(\hat{\mathbf{x}}_1, \hat{\mathbf{y}}_1, \hat{\mathbf{z}}_1)$.
Find the scalars $\frac{\partial \mathcal{S}}{\partial \ddot{q}}$ for $q = \psi, \theta, \phi$ where $\mathcal{S}$ is Gibbs S-function of body 1. ■

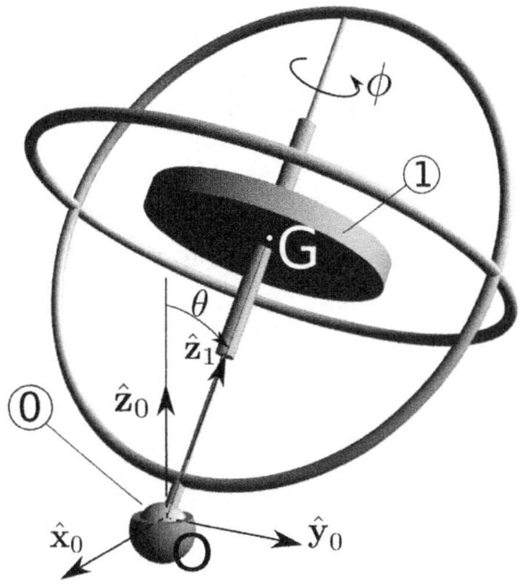

Figure 14.2

Since O is a fixed point of body 1, we can apply (14.7). Thus we need the expression of the angular velocity $\boldsymbol{\omega} = \dot{\psi}\hat{\mathbf{z}}_0 + \dot{\theta}\hat{\mathbf{u}} + \dot{\phi}\hat{\mathbf{z}}_1$ and angular acceleration $\boldsymbol{\alpha} = \ddot{\psi}\hat{\mathbf{z}}_0 + \ddot{\theta}\hat{\mathbf{u}} + \ddot{\phi}\hat{\mathbf{z}}_1 + \dot{\psi}\dot{\theta}\hat{\mathbf{v}} + \dot{\phi}(\dot{\psi}\sin\theta\hat{\mathbf{u}} - \dot{\theta}\hat{\mathbf{w}})$ found in Example 14.1. To find the quantities $\frac{\partial \mathcal{S}}{\partial \ddot{q}}$, we could first find $\mathcal{S}$. However, this proves very tedious. It is preferable to proceed by applying the operator $\frac{\partial}{\partial \ddot{q}}$ on each term of $\mathcal{S}$ depending on $\ddot{q}$. Consider the term $(\boldsymbol{\alpha} \times \boldsymbol{\omega}) \cdot \mathcal{I}_O(\boldsymbol{\omega})$: since the only term dependent upon $\ddot{q}$ is $\boldsymbol{\alpha}$ we can write:

$$\frac{\partial}{\partial \ddot{q}}((\boldsymbol{\alpha} \times \boldsymbol{\omega}) \cdot \mathcal{I}_O(\boldsymbol{\omega})) = (\frac{\partial \boldsymbol{\alpha}}{\partial \ddot{q}} \times \boldsymbol{\omega}) \cdot \mathcal{I}_O(\boldsymbol{\omega})$$

We easily find

$$\frac{\partial}{\partial \ddot{\phi}}((\boldsymbol{\alpha} \times \boldsymbol{\omega}) \cdot \mathcal{I}_O(\boldsymbol{\omega})) = (\hat{\mathbf{z}}_1 \times \boldsymbol{\omega}) \cdot \mathcal{I}_O(\boldsymbol{\omega}) = (-\dot{\psi}\sin\theta\hat{\mathbf{u}} + \dot{\theta}\hat{\mathbf{w}}) \cdot \mathcal{I}_O(\boldsymbol{\omega}) = 0$$

$$\begin{aligned}\frac{\partial}{\partial \ddot{\psi}}((\boldsymbol{\alpha} \times \boldsymbol{\omega}) \cdot \mathcal{I}_O(\boldsymbol{\omega})) &= (\hat{\mathbf{z}}_0 \times \boldsymbol{\omega}) \cdot \mathcal{I}_O(\boldsymbol{\omega}) = (\dot{\theta}\hat{\mathbf{v}} + \dot{\phi}\sin\theta\hat{\mathbf{u}}) \cdot \mathcal{I}_O(\boldsymbol{\omega}) \\ &= (A - C)(\dot{\phi} + \dot{\psi}\cos\theta)\dot{\theta}\sin\theta\end{aligned}$$

$$\begin{aligned}\frac{\partial}{\partial \ddot{\theta}}((\boldsymbol{\alpha} \times \boldsymbol{\omega}) \cdot \mathcal{I}_O(\boldsymbol{\omega})) &= (\hat{\mathbf{u}} \times \boldsymbol{\omega}) \cdot \mathcal{I}_O(\boldsymbol{\omega}) = -(\dot{\psi}\hat{\mathbf{v}} + \dot{\phi}\hat{\mathbf{w}}) \cdot \mathcal{I}_O(\boldsymbol{\omega}) \\ &= (C - A)(\dot{\phi} + \dot{\psi}\cos\theta)\dot{\psi}\sin\theta\end{aligned}$$

Again for the term $\frac{1}{2}\boldsymbol{\alpha}\cdot\mathcal{I}_O(\boldsymbol{\alpha})$, the only dependence upon $\ddot{q}$ is due to $\boldsymbol{\alpha}$:

$$\frac{\partial}{\partial\ddot{q}}(\tfrac{1}{2}\boldsymbol{\alpha}\cdot\mathcal{I}_O(\boldsymbol{\alpha})) = \boldsymbol{\alpha}\cdot\mathcal{I}_O\left(\frac{\partial\boldsymbol{\alpha}}{\partial\ddot{q}}\right) = \frac{\partial\boldsymbol{\alpha}}{\partial\ddot{q}}\cdot\mathcal{I}_O(\boldsymbol{\alpha})$$

exploiting the symmetry of operator $\mathcal{I}_0$. This leads to the following results

$$\begin{aligned}
\frac{\partial}{\partial\ddot{\phi}}(\tfrac{1}{2}\boldsymbol{\alpha}\cdot\mathcal{I}_O(\boldsymbol{\alpha})) &= \boldsymbol{\alpha}\cdot\mathcal{I}_O\left(\frac{\partial\boldsymbol{\alpha}}{\partial\ddot{\phi}}\right) = \boldsymbol{\alpha}\cdot\mathcal{I}_O(\hat{\mathbf{z}}_1) = \boldsymbol{\alpha}\cdot C\hat{\mathbf{z}}_1 \\
&= C(\ddot{\psi}\cos\theta - \dot{\psi}\dot{\theta}\sin\theta + \ddot{\phi}) = C\frac{d}{dt}(\dot{\phi} + \dot{\psi}\cos\theta) \\
\frac{\partial}{\partial\ddot{\psi}}(\tfrac{1}{2}\boldsymbol{\alpha}\cdot\mathcal{I}_O(\boldsymbol{\alpha})) &= \boldsymbol{\alpha}\cdot\mathcal{I}_O\left(\frac{\partial\boldsymbol{\alpha}}{\partial\ddot{\psi}}\right) = \boldsymbol{\alpha}\cdot\mathcal{I}_O(\hat{\mathbf{z}}_0) = \boldsymbol{\alpha}\cdot(A\sin\theta\hat{\mathbf{w}} + C\cos\theta\hat{\mathbf{z}}_1) \\
&= (A\sin^2\theta + C\cos^2\theta)\ddot{\psi} + (A-C)\dot{\psi}\dot{\theta}\sin\theta\cos\theta - A\dot{\phi}\dot{\theta}\sin\theta + C\ddot{\phi}\cos\theta \\
\frac{\partial}{\partial\ddot{\theta}}(\tfrac{1}{2}\boldsymbol{\alpha}\cdot\mathcal{I}_O(\boldsymbol{\alpha})) &= \boldsymbol{\alpha}\cdot\mathcal{I}_O\left(\frac{\partial\boldsymbol{\alpha}}{\partial\ddot{\theta}}\right) = \boldsymbol{\alpha}\cdot\mathcal{I}_O(\hat{\mathbf{u}}) = \boldsymbol{\alpha}\cdot A\hat{\mathbf{u}} = A(\ddot{\theta} + \dot{\psi}\dot{\theta}\sin\theta)
\end{aligned}$$

Now we add both terms to obtain $\frac{\partial\mathbb{S}}{\partial\ddot{q}}$ keeping in mind that the contribution of the last term $\frac{1}{2}\omega^2(\boldsymbol{\omega}\cdot\mathcal{I}_O(\boldsymbol{\omega}))$ is zero:

$$\frac{\partial\mathbb{S}}{\partial\ddot{\phi}} = C\frac{d}{dt}(\dot{\phi} + \dot{\psi}\cos\theta)$$

$$\begin{aligned}
\frac{\partial\mathbb{S}}{\partial\ddot{\psi}} &= (A\sin^2\theta + C\cos^2\theta)\ddot{\psi} + 2(A-C)\dot{\psi}\dot{\theta}\sin\theta\cos\theta + C(\ddot{\phi}\cos\theta - \dot{\phi}\dot{\theta}\sin\theta) \\
&= \frac{d}{dt}((A\sin^2\theta + C\cos^2\theta)\dot{\psi} + C\dot{\phi}\cos\theta) \\
\frac{\partial\mathbb{S}}{\partial\ddot{\theta}} &= (C-A)(\dot{\phi} + \dot{\psi}\cos\theta)\dot{\psi}\sin\theta + A(\ddot{\theta} + \dot{\psi}\dot{\theta}\sin\theta) \\
&= A\ddot{\theta} + (C-A)\dot{\psi}^2\sin\theta\cos\theta + C\dot{\psi}\dot{\phi}\sin\theta
\end{aligned}$$

■

In the last example, it is arguably simpler and faster to find $\frac{\partial\mathbb{S}}{\partial\ddot{q}}$ by applying Lagrange kinematic formula:

$$\int_{\mathcal{B}} \mathbf{a}_P\cdot\frac{\partial\mathbf{r}_{OP}}{\partial q_i}dm = \frac{\partial\mathbb{S}}{\partial\ddot{q}_i} = \frac{d}{dt}\frac{\partial\mathbb{T}}{\partial\dot{q}_i} - \frac{\partial\mathbb{T}}{\partial q_i}$$

Thus the advantage of Gibbs-Appell approach over Lagrange equations will find its origin elsewhere.

14.1.3 Gibbs-Appell Equations: Single Rigid Body

To derive Gibbs-Appell equations, we proceed as we did for Lagrange equations in Section 13.4. Given a rigid body $\mathcal{B}$ whose configuration is defined by the n coordinates $(q_1, q_2, \ldots q_n)$, we apply D'Alembert Principle of Virtual Power by choosing the virtual kinematic screw as a linear combination of the partial kinematic screws of $\mathcal{B}$, assuming that the variables $(\mathbf{q}, \dot{\mathbf{q}})$ are independent

$$\{\mathcal{V}^*\} = \dot{q}_1^*\{\mathcal{V}_{\mathcal{B}/\mathcal{E}}^{q_1}\} + \cdots + \dot{q}_n^*\{\mathcal{V}_{\mathcal{B}/\mathcal{E}}^{q_n}\} \quad (14.9)$$

where the virtual speeds $(\dot{q}_1^*, \ldots, \dot{q}_n^*)$ are arbitrary. This gives the equation

$$\sum_{i=1}^{n} \dot{q}_i^* \int_{\mathcal{B}} \mathbf{a}_P \cdot \frac{\partial \mathbf{r}_{OP}}{\partial q_i} dm = \sum_{i=1}^{n} \dot{q}_i^* \{\mathcal{A}_{\overline{\mathcal{B}} \to \mathcal{B}}\} \cdot \{\mathcal{V}_{\mathcal{B}/\mathcal{E}}^{q_i}\} \tag{14.10}$$

Assuming that the variables $(\mathbf{q}, \dot{\mathbf{q}}, \ddot{\mathbf{q}})$ are independent, we can use formula (14.6) to obtain Gibbs-Appell equations in terms of Gibbs S-function and the power coefficients of external actions.

Theorem 14.2 — Gibbs-Appell equations. The motion of a rigid body $\mathcal{B}$ whose configuration relative to a Newtonian referential $\mathcal{E}$ is defined by n coordinates $(q_1, \ldots, q_n)$ is governed by the n Gibbs-Appell equations

$$\frac{\partial S_{\mathcal{B}/\mathcal{E}}}{\partial \ddot{q}_i} = \mathcal{Q}^{q_i}_{\overline{\mathcal{B}} \to \mathcal{B}/\mathcal{E}} \qquad (i = 1, 2, \ldots, n) \tag{14.11}$$

where the variables $(\mathbf{q}, \dot{\mathbf{q}}, \ddot{\mathbf{q}})$ are assumed independent.

Remark 3. Since the variables $(\mathbf{q}, \dot{\mathbf{q}})$ are assumed independent (assumption (13.2) of the Lagrange formulation), all holonomic and non-holonomic constraint equations, which may exist, must be ignored.

Remark 4. The time variable t can be explicitly present in Gibbs-Appell formulation through the explicit dependency of a coordinate upon t. However, as in Lagrange equations, it is best to ignore this dependency and append an extra coordinate to the set $(q_1, q_2, \ldots, q_n)$.

Remark 5. Gibbs S-function must be viewed as a function of $(\mathbf{q}, \dot{\mathbf{q}}, \ddot{\mathbf{q}})$: hence terms not explicitly function of $\ddot{\mathbf{q}}$ drop out of Gibbs-Appell equations. In particular, the term $\frac{1}{2}\omega^2(\omega \cdot \mathcal{I}_G(\omega))$ of the general expression (14.7) should never be determined.

Remark 6. The power coefficients $\mathcal{Q}^{q_i}_{\overline{\mathcal{B}} \to \mathcal{B}/\mathcal{E}}$ are determined as in Lagrange equations: this is done by determining all partial kinematic screws $\{\mathcal{V}^{q}_{\mathcal{B}/\mathcal{E}}\}$ in a manner consistent with the requirement that $(\mathbf{q}, \dot{\mathbf{q}})$ be independent variables.

Example 14.3 Use the results of Example 14.1 to derive the five Gibbs-Appell equations corresponding to coordinates $(x, y, \psi, \theta, \phi)$. Assume that the sphere is subject to the following action screw

$$\{\mathcal{A}_{\overline{1} \to 1/0}\} = \begin{Bmatrix} -mg\hat{\mathbf{z}}_0 \\ \mathbf{0} \end{Bmatrix}_G + \begin{Bmatrix} F_u\hat{\mathbf{u}} + F_v\hat{\mathbf{v}} + N\hat{\mathbf{z}}_0 \\ \mathbf{0} \end{Bmatrix}_I$$

where I is the contact point of the sphere with the horizontal support and $F_u\hat{\mathbf{u}} + F_v\hat{\mathbf{v}}$ is the friction force acting on the sphere. ■

With $\mathbf{q} = (x, y, \psi, \theta, \phi)$, we must assume that the variables $(\mathbf{q}, \dot{\mathbf{q}}, \ddot{\mathbf{q}})$ are independent. We then consider the Gibbs S-function found in Example 14.1 as a function of 15 variables. Then we find

$$\begin{aligned}
\frac{\partial \mathbb{S}}{\partial \ddot{x}} &= m\ddot{x} \\
\frac{\partial \mathbb{S}}{\partial \ddot{y}} &= m\ddot{y} \\
\frac{\partial \mathbb{S}}{\partial \ddot{\psi}} &= A(\ddot{\psi} + \ddot{\phi}\cos\theta - \dot{\theta}\dot{\phi}\sin\theta) \\
\frac{\partial \mathbb{S}}{\partial \ddot{\theta}} &= A(\ddot{\theta} + \dot{\psi}\dot{\phi}\sin\theta) \\
\frac{\partial \mathbb{S}}{\partial \ddot{\phi}} &= -A(\dot{\psi}\dot{\theta} - \ddot{\phi}\sin\theta - \dot{\theta}\dot{\phi}\cos\theta)\sin\theta + A(\ddot{\psi} + \ddot{\phi}\cos\theta - \dot{\theta}\dot{\phi}\sin\theta)\cos\theta \\
&= A(\ddot{\phi} + \ddot{\psi}\cos\theta - \dot{\psi}\dot{\theta}\sin\theta)
\end{aligned}$$

with $A = \frac{2}{5}mr^2$. The expressions of the power coefficients can be found from Example 13.4:

$$\mathbb{Q}^x_{\bar{1}\to 1/0} = F_u\cos\psi - F_v\sin\psi, \qquad \mathbb{Q}^y_{\bar{1}\to 1/0} = F_u\sin\psi + F_v\cos\psi$$
$$\mathbb{Q}^\psi_{\bar{1}\to 1/0} = 0, \qquad \mathbb{Q}^\theta_{\bar{1}\to 1/0} = rF_v, \qquad \mathbb{Q}^\phi_{\bar{1}\to 1/0} = rF_u\sin\theta$$

We then find the five Gibbs-Appell equations corresponding to coordinates $(x, y, \psi, \theta, \phi)$:

$$\begin{aligned}
m\ddot{x} &= F_u\cos\psi - F_v\sin\psi & (1)\\
m\ddot{y} &= F_u\sin\psi + F_v\cos\psi & (2)\\
A(\ddot{\psi} + \ddot{\phi}\cos\theta - \dot{\theta}\dot{\phi}\sin\theta) &= 0 & (3)\\
A(\ddot{\theta} + \dot{\psi}\dot{\phi}\sin\theta) &= rF_v & (4)\\
A(\ddot{\phi} + \ddot{\psi}\cos\theta - \dot{\psi}\dot{\theta}\sin\theta) &= rF_u\sin\theta & (5)
\end{aligned}$$

We can verify that equations (1-5) are identical to the five Lagrange equations found in Example 13.6. However we note that the first integral found from equation (3) appears more directly in Lagrange formulation as $\frac{\partial \mathbb{K}}{\partial \dot{\psi}} = constant$ thanks to the fact that $\frac{\partial \mathbb{K}}{\partial \psi} = 0$. ■

Example 14.4 Use the results of Example 14.2 to derive the three Gibbs-Appell equations corresponding to Euler angles (ψ, θ, ϕ). Assume that the spherical joint between sphere 1 and referential 0 is ideal. The unit vector $\hat{\mathbf{z}}_0$ defines the upward vertical direction. The position of mass center G is defined by $\mathbf{r}_{OG} = l\hat{\mathbf{z}}_1$ where l is a constant parameter. ■

With $\mathbf{q} = (\psi, \theta, \phi)$ and assuming that variables $(\mathbf{q}, \dot{\mathbf{q}}, \ddot{\mathbf{q}})$ are independent, we found in Example 14.2 the partial derivatives $\frac{\partial \mathbb{S}}{\partial \ddot{q}}$. Since the spherical joint between sphere 1 and referential 0 is ideal, the power coefficients $\mathbb{Q}^q_{0\leftrightarrow 1} = \mathbb{Q}^q_{0\to 1/0}$ associated with the contact action screw $\{\mathcal{A}^c_{0\to 1}\}$ are all zero, for $q = \psi, \theta, \phi$. For the effect of gravity, we can find the power coefficients from the potential energy $\mathbb{U}^g_{\bar{1}\to 1/0} = -m\mathbf{g}\cdot\mathbf{r}_{OG} = mgl\hat{\mathbf{z}}_0\cdot\hat{\mathbf{z}}_1 = mgl\cos\theta$:

$$\mathbb{Q}^{\psi,\phi}_{gravity\to 1/0} = 0, \qquad \mathbb{Q}^\theta_{gravity\to 1/0} = -\frac{\partial}{\partial\theta}(mgl\cos\theta) = mgl\sin\theta$$

This gives the three Gibbs-Appell equations

$$C\frac{d}{dt}(\dot{\phi} + \dot{\psi}\cos\theta) = 0$$
$$\frac{d}{dt}((A\sin^2\theta + C\cos^2\theta)\dot{\psi} + C\dot{\phi}\cos\theta) = 0$$
$$A\ddot{\theta} + (C - A)\dot{\psi}^2\sin\theta\cos\theta + C\dot{\psi}\dot{\phi}\sin\theta = mgl\sin\theta$$

We obtain two first integrals: the component $r = \dot{\phi} + \dot{\psi}\cos\theta$ of angular velocity ω is a constant. We can use this constant to write the three equations in the form

$$\dot{\phi} + \dot{\psi}\cos\theta = r_0 \quad (1)$$
$$A\dot{\psi}\sin^2\theta + Cr_0\cos\theta = p_0 \quad (2)$$
$$A\ddot{\theta} - A\dot{\psi}^2\sin\theta\cos\theta + Cr_0\dot{\psi}\sin\theta = mgl\sin\theta \quad (3)$$

where r_0 and p_0 are two constants of integration. ■

14.1.4 Gibbs-Appell Equations for Non-Holonomic Systems

We saw in Section 13.6 that it is not possible to derive Lagrange equations for a reduced set of independent coordinates obtained by taking into account the non-holonomic constraints. We show in this section that this is not the case in the method of Gibbs-Appell equations. There lies its advantage over Lagrange formalism which requires special treatment for non-holonomic systems via the use of multipliers.

Suppose that the coordinates $\mathbf{q}$ are known to satisfy $l < n$ constraint equations of the type

$$\sum_{j=1}^{n} a_{ij}(\mathbf{q}, t)\dot{q}_j + b_i(\mathbf{q}, t) = 0, \qquad (i = 1, 2, \ldots, l) \tag{14.12}$$

We assume that the component of $\mathbf{q}$ have been ordered in such a way that the unknowns $(\dot{q}_{m+1}, \dot{q}_{m+2}, \ldots, \dot{q}_n)$ can be expressed in terms of $m = n - l$ independent variables $(\dot{q}_1, \dot{q}_2, \ldots, \dot{q}_m)$ in the form

$$\dot{q}_{m+i} = \sum_{j=1}^{m} \tilde{a}_{ij}(\mathbf{q}, t)\dot{q}_j + \tilde{b}_i(\mathbf{q}, t), \qquad (i = 1, 2, \ldots, l) \tag{14.13}$$

We saw in Section 13.6 that the velocity of P can then be expressed as

$$\mathbf{v}_P = \sum_{i=1}^{m} \mathbf{w}_P^{q_i}(\mathbf{q}, t)\,\dot{q}_i + \mathbf{w}_P^0(\mathbf{q}, t) \tag{14.14}$$

leading to the relationships

$$\mathbf{w}_P^{q_i} = \frac{\partial}{\partial \dot{q}_i}\mathbf{v}_P \tag{14.15}$$

for $i = 1, 2, \ldots, m$. We can differentiate $\mathbf{v}_P$ to find

$$\mathbf{a}_P = \sum_{i=1}^{m} \mathbf{w}_P^{q_i}\,\ddot{q}_i + \sum_{i=1}^{m} \dot{q}_i \frac{d}{dt}\mathbf{w}_P^{q_i} + \frac{d\mathbf{w}_P^0}{dt} \tag{14.16}$$

which gives

$$\mathbf{w}_P^{q_i} = \frac{\partial \mathbf{a}_P}{\partial \ddot{q}_i} \tag{14.17}$$

We now introduce the following virtual velocity field

$$\mathbf{v}_P^* = \mathbf{w}_P^{q_1}\,\dot{q}_1^* + \mathbf{w}_P^{q_2}\,\dot{q}_2^* + \ldots + \mathbf{w}_P^{q_m}\,\dot{q}_m^* \tag{14.18}$$

where $\dot{\mathbf{q}}^* = (\dot{q}_1^*, \dot{q}_2^*, \ldots, \dot{q}_m^*)$ is an arbitrary element of $\mathbb{R}^m$. This field defines a screw in light of equation (14.15).
Next we apply D'Alembert Principle of Virtual Power with virtual velocity field (14.18) to find

$$\sum_{i=1}^{m} \dot{q}_i^* \int_{\mathcal{B}} \mathbf{a}_P \cdot \mathbf{w}_P^{q_i} dm = \sum_{i=1}^{m} \dot{q}_i^*\, \mathcal{Q}^{q_i}_{\overline{\mathcal{B}}\to\mathcal{B}/\mathcal{B}} \tag{14.19}$$

where the power coefficients $\mathcal{Q}^{q_i}_{\overline{\mathcal{B}}\to\mathcal{B}/\mathcal{B}}$ are found exactly as in the Lagrange formulation in light of equation (14.15). Now taking into account (14.17), we find

$$\int_{\mathcal{B}} \mathbf{a}_P \cdot \mathbf{w}_P^{q_i} dm = \int_{\mathcal{B}} \mathbf{a}_P \cdot \frac{\partial \mathbf{a}_P}{\partial \ddot{q}_i} dm = \frac{\partial \mathcal{S}}{\partial \ddot{q}_i}$$

Since the virtual speeds are arbitrary, we find the same Gibbs-Appell equations as found in Section 14.1.3.

$$\frac{\partial \mathcal{S}_{\mathcal{B}/\mathcal{E}}}{\partial \ddot{q}_i} = \mathcal{Q}^{q_i}_{\overline{\mathcal{B}}\to\mathcal{B}/\mathcal{E}} \qquad (i = 1, 2, \ldots, m) \tag{14.20}$$

In conclusion, non-holonomic systems do not require a special treatment to derive their Gibbs-Appell equations, as is needed for Lagrange equations.

Example 14.5 In Example 13.10, Lagrange equations were found to be incorrect with respect to coordinates $\mathbf{q} = (\psi, \theta, \phi)$ for sphere 1 rolling without slipping on plane $(O, \hat{\mathbf{x}}_0, \hat{\mathbf{y}}_0)$. Use Gibbs S-function expressed in terms of $(\mathbf{q}, \dot{\mathbf{q}}, \ddot{\mathbf{q}})$ to find three Gibbs-Appell equations. ■

If the no-slip condition at I is assumed, we can express $\mathbf{a}_G$ in terms of $\mathbf{q}$ and its derivatives:

$$\mathbf{a}_G = -r\frac{d}{dt}(\dot{\theta}\hat{\mathbf{v}} + \dot{\phi}\sin\theta\hat{\mathbf{u}}) = -r(\ddot{\phi}\sin\theta + \dot{\phi}\dot{\theta}\cos\theta - \dot{\psi}\dot{\theta})\hat{\mathbf{u}} - r(\ddot{\theta} + \dot{\psi}\dot{\phi}\sin\theta)\hat{\mathbf{v}}$$

This leads to

$$\frac{\partial}{\partial \ddot{\psi}}\mathbf{a}_G = 0 \qquad\qquad \frac{\partial}{\partial \ddot{\psi}}\boldsymbol{\alpha} = \hat{\mathbf{z}}_0$$

$$\frac{\partial}{\partial \ddot{\theta}}\mathbf{a}_G = -r\hat{\mathbf{v}} \qquad\qquad \frac{\partial}{\partial \ddot{\theta}}\boldsymbol{\alpha} = \hat{\mathbf{u}}$$

$$\frac{\partial}{\partial \ddot{\phi}}\mathbf{a}_G = -r\sin\theta\hat{\mathbf{u}} \qquad\qquad \frac{\partial}{\partial \ddot{\phi}}\boldsymbol{\alpha} = \hat{\mathbf{z}}_1$$

and

$$\mathbf{a}_G \cdot \frac{\partial}{\partial \ddot{\psi}}\mathbf{a}_G = 0 \qquad\qquad \boldsymbol{\alpha} \cdot \frac{\partial}{\partial \ddot{\psi}}\boldsymbol{\alpha} = \ddot{\psi} + \ddot{\phi}\cos\theta - \dot{\theta}\dot{\phi}\sin\theta$$

$$\mathbf{a}_G \cdot \frac{\partial}{\partial \ddot{\theta}}\mathbf{a}_G = r^2(\ddot{\theta} + \dot{\psi}\dot{\phi}\sin\theta) \qquad\qquad \boldsymbol{\alpha} \cdot \frac{\partial}{\partial \ddot{\theta}}\boldsymbol{\alpha} = \ddot{\theta} + \dot{\psi}\dot{\phi}\sin\theta$$

$$\mathbf{a}_G \cdot \frac{\partial}{\partial \ddot{\phi}}\mathbf{a}_G = r^2\sin\theta(\ddot{\phi}\sin\theta + \dot{\phi}\dot{\theta}\cos\theta - \dot{\psi}\dot{\theta}) \qquad\qquad \boldsymbol{\alpha} \cdot \frac{\partial}{\partial \ddot{\phi}}\boldsymbol{\alpha} = \ddot{\psi}\cos\theta + \ddot{\phi} - \dot{\psi}\dot{\theta}\sin\theta$$

Now we can find $\frac{\partial S}{\partial \ddot{q}} = m\mathbf{a}_G \cdot \frac{\partial \mathbf{a}_G}{\partial \ddot{q}} + \frac{2}{5}mr^2\boldsymbol{\alpha} \cdot \frac{\partial \boldsymbol{\alpha}}{\partial \ddot{q}}$:

$$\frac{\partial S}{\partial \ddot{\psi}} = \tfrac{2}{5}mr^2(\ddot{\psi} + \ddot{\phi}\cos\theta - \dot{\theta}\dot{\phi}\sin\theta)$$
$$\frac{\partial S}{\partial \ddot{\theta}} = mr^2(\ddot{\theta} + \dot{\psi}\dot{\phi}\sin\theta) + \tfrac{2}{5}mr^2(\ddot{\theta} + \dot{\psi}\dot{\phi}\sin\theta)$$
$$\frac{\partial S}{\partial \ddot{\phi}} = mr^2\sin\theta(\ddot{\phi}\sin\theta + \dot{\phi}\dot{\theta}\cos\theta - \dot{\psi}\dot{\theta}) + \tfrac{2}{5}mr^2(\ddot{\psi}\cos\theta + \ddot{\phi} - \dot{\psi}\dot{\theta}\sin\theta)$$

As was seen in Example 13.10, the power coefficients $Q^q_{\bar{1}\to 1/0}$ are all zero since they are found by taking into account the condition $\mathbf{v}_{I\in 1/0} = \mathbf{0}$. We can now state the three Gibbs-Appell equations:

$$\dot{\psi} + \dot{\phi}\cos\theta = p_0 \qquad (1)$$
$$\ddot{\theta} + \dot{\psi}\dot{\phi}\sin\theta = 0 \qquad (2)$$
$$(\tfrac{2}{5} + \sin^2\theta)\ddot{\phi} + \dot{\phi}\dot{\theta}\cos\theta\sin\theta - \tfrac{7}{5}\dot{\psi}\dot{\theta}\sin\theta + \tfrac{2}{5}\ddot{\psi}\cos\theta = 0 \qquad (3)$$

where p_0 is a constant of integration. Equation (3) can lead to a first integral by substituting $\ddot{\psi} = -\ddot{\phi}\cos\theta + \dot{\theta}\dot{\phi}\sin\theta$:

$$\ddot{\phi}\sin^2\theta + (\dot{\phi}\cos\theta - \dot{\psi})\dot{\theta}\sin\theta = 0$$

which gives

$$\dot{\phi}\sin^2\theta + p_0\cos\theta = q_0 \qquad (3')$$

where q_0 is a constant of integration. ∎

Example 14.6 Figure 14.3 shows a sphere $1(G, \hat{\mathbf{x}}_1, \hat{\mathbf{y}}_1, \hat{\mathbf{z}}_1)$ (of radius R, mass center G, mass m) supported by a plate $2(A, \hat{\mathbf{x}}_0, \hat{\mathbf{y}}_0, \hat{\mathbf{z}}_0)$ (of mass M). Plate 2 is constrained to slide along a fixed plane $(O, \hat{\mathbf{x}}_0, \hat{\mathbf{y}}_0)$ of referential $0(O, \hat{\mathbf{x}}_0, \hat{\mathbf{y}}_0, \hat{\mathbf{z}}_0)$. Hence, its motion is translational and its configuration is entirely defined by the Cartesian coordinates $(x_A, y_A, z_A = 0)$ of point A: $\mathbf{r}_{OA} = x_A\hat{\mathbf{x}}_0 + y_A\hat{\mathbf{y}}_0$. The goal of this problem is to find out how to control the motion of A so as to impose a particular motion of center G, while sphere 1 rolls without slipping on 2.
We denote by (x_G, y_G, p, q, r) the components of $\mathbf{r}_{OG} = x_A\hat{\mathbf{x}}_0 + y_A\hat{\mathbf{y}}_0 + R\hat{\mathbf{z}}_0$ and of angular velocity $\boldsymbol{\omega}_{1/0} = p\hat{\mathbf{x}}_0 + q\hat{\mathbf{y}}_0 + r\hat{\mathbf{z}}_0$.

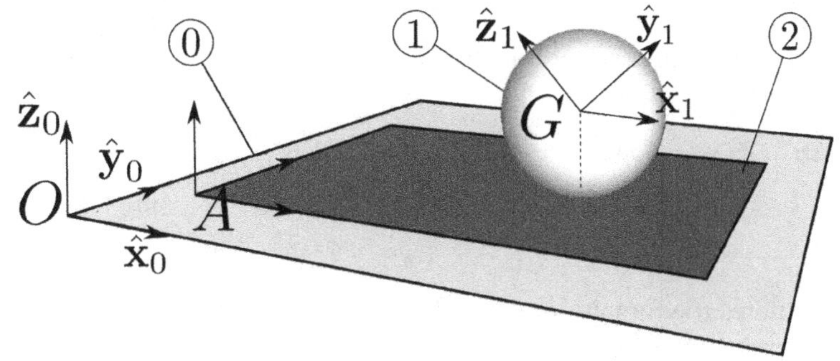

Figure 14.3

a. Express the no-slip condition of sphere 1 relative to plate 2.
b. If G is to have a circular motion relative to 0 about axis $(O, \hat{\mathbf{z}}_0)$ at constant angular speed Ω, find $(\dot{x}_G, \dot{y}_G)$ in terms of (x_G, y_G) and Ω.
c. Define three fictitious angles (α, β, γ) by the relationships

$$\dot{\alpha} = p, \quad \dot{\beta} = q, \quad \dot{\gamma} = r$$

Find the five Gibbs-Appell equations corresponding to $\mathbf{q} = (x_G, y_G, x_A, y_A, \gamma)$.
d. Use these equations to solve for the trajectory of A with initial conditions $x_A = y_A = 0$ and $\dot{x}_A = \dot{y}_A = 0$ at $t = 0$ in terms of angular speed Ω and the radius ρ of the circular trajectory of G.
e. Assume that the planar joint 0-2 is ideal: find the force $\mathbf{F}_A$ applied at A necessary to control the circular motion of G. ∎

a. The no-slip condition at the contact point I between 1 and 2 can stated as

$$\mathbf{v}_{I\in 1/0} = \mathbf{v}_{I\in 2/0}$$

with $\mathbf{v}_{I\in 1/0} = \mathbf{v}_{G/0} + \boldsymbol{\omega}_{1/0} \times \mathbf{r}_{GI}$ and $\mathbf{v}_{I\in 2/0} = \mathbf{v}_{A/0}$. We obtain

$$\dot{x}_G \hat{\mathbf{x}}_0 + \dot{y}_G \hat{\mathbf{y}}_0 + R(p\hat{\mathbf{y}}_0 - q\hat{\mathbf{x}}_0) = \dot{x}_A \hat{\mathbf{x}}_0 + \dot{y}_A \hat{\mathbf{y}}_0$$

which yields two equations:

$$\dot{x}_G - Rq = \dot{x}_A \qquad (1)$$
$$\dot{y}_G + Rp = \dot{y}_A \qquad (2)$$

b. The rotation of G about axis $(O, \hat{\mathbf{z}}_0$ at angular velocity Ω leads to the velocity $\mathbf{v}_{G/0} = \Omega \hat{\mathbf{z}}_0 \times \mathbf{r}_{OG}$: this gives two equations

$$\dot{x}_G = \Omega y_G \qquad (3)$$
$$\dot{y}_G = -\Omega x_G \qquad (4)$$

c. With the angles α, β, γ, the no-slip equations (1-2) can now be expressed as

$$\dot{x}_G - R\dot{\beta} = \dot{x}_A \qquad (1')$$
$$\dot{y}_G + R\dot{\alpha} = \dot{y}_A \qquad (2')$$

By taking into account constraint equations (1′-2′), two coordinates can be eliminated from the set $(x_A, y_A, x_G, y_G, \alpha, \beta, \gamma)$: if we choose to eliminate α and β, then we can obtain five Gibbs-Appell equations corresponding to the reduced set of coordinates $\mathbf{q} = (x_A, y_A, x_G, y_G, \gamma)$. First, we express Gibbs S-function of the sphere 1 in terms of $(\mathbf{q}, \dot{\mathbf{q}}, \ddot{\mathbf{q}})$ assumed independent (hence equations (3-4) are ignored):

$$\begin{aligned} 2\mathcal{S} = 2\mathcal{S}_{1/0} &= m\mathbf{a}_{G/0} + \tfrac{2}{5} mR^2 \boldsymbol{\alpha}_{1/0}^2 + \tfrac{2}{5} mR^2 \boldsymbol{\omega}_{1/0}^4 \\ &= m(\ddot{x}_G^2 + \ddot{y}_G^2) + \tfrac{2}{5} mR^2 (\ddot{\alpha}^2 + \ddot{\beta}^2 + \ddot{\gamma}^2) + \tfrac{2}{5} mR^2 (\dot{\alpha}^2 + \dot{\beta}^2 + \dot{\gamma}^2)^2 \\ &= m(\ddot{x}_G^2 + \ddot{y}_G^2) + \tfrac{2}{5} m(\ddot{y}_A - \ddot{y}_G)^2 + \tfrac{2}{5} m(\ddot{x}_A - \ddot{x}_G)^2 + \tfrac{2}{5} mR^2 \ddot{\gamma}^2 + \mathcal{S}_3 \end{aligned}$$

where $\mathcal{S}_3$ denotes the remainder of $\mathcal{S}$ which is independent of $\ddot{\mathbf{q}}$. The action screw exerted on the sphere takes the form

$$\{\mathcal{A}_{\bar{1}\to 1/0}\} = \begin{Bmatrix} -mg\hat{\mathbf{z}}_0 \\ \mathbf{0} \end{Bmatrix}_G + \begin{Bmatrix} X\hat{\mathbf{x}}_0 + Y\hat{\mathbf{y}}_0 + Z\hat{\mathbf{z}}_0 \\ \mathbf{0} \end{Bmatrix}_I$$

To find the corresponding power coefficients, we need to find the partial kinematic screws

$\{\mathcal{V}_{1/0}^{q_i}\}$ for $q_i = x_A, y_A, x_G, y_G, \gamma$: we start with the expression of $\{\mathcal{V}_{1/0}\}$ by taking into account the no-slip condition at I

$$\{\mathcal{V}_{1/0}\} = \begin{Bmatrix} \boldsymbol{\omega}_{1/0} \\ \mathbf{v}_{I\in 1/0} \end{Bmatrix}_I = \begin{Bmatrix} \boldsymbol{\omega}_{1/0} \\ \mathbf{v}_{I\in 2/0} \end{Bmatrix}_I = \begin{Bmatrix} \frac{1}{R}(\dot{y}_A - \dot{y}_G)\hat{\mathbf{x}}_0 + \frac{1}{R}(\dot{x}_G - \dot{x}_A)\hat{\mathbf{y}}_0 + \dot{\gamma}\hat{\mathbf{z}}_0 \\ \dot{x}_A\hat{\mathbf{x}}_0 + \dot{y}_A\hat{\mathbf{y}}_0 \end{Bmatrix}_I$$

which yields

$$\{\mathcal{V}_{1/0}^{x_A}\} = \begin{Bmatrix} -\frac{1}{R}\hat{\mathbf{y}}_0 \\ \hat{\mathbf{x}}_0 \end{Bmatrix}_I, \quad \{\mathcal{V}_{1/0}^{y_A}\} = \begin{Bmatrix} \frac{1}{R}\hat{\mathbf{x}}_0 \\ \hat{\mathbf{y}}_0 \end{Bmatrix}_I$$

$$\{\mathcal{V}_{1/0}^{x_G}\} = \begin{Bmatrix} \frac{1}{R}\hat{\mathbf{y}}_0 \\ \mathbf{0} \end{Bmatrix}_I, \quad \{\mathcal{V}_{1/0}^{y_G}\} = \begin{Bmatrix} -\frac{1}{R}\hat{\mathbf{x}}_0 \\ \mathbf{0} \end{Bmatrix}_I, \quad \{\mathcal{V}_{1/0}^{\gamma}\} = \begin{Bmatrix} \hat{\mathbf{z}}_0 \\ \mathbf{0} \end{Bmatrix}_I$$

We can now find the power coefficients corresponding to $\{\mathcal{A}_{\bar{1}\to 1/0}\}$

$$Q_{\bar{1}\to 1/0}^{x_A} = X, \quad Q_{\bar{1}\to 1/0}^{y_A} = Y, \quad Q_{\bar{1}\to 1/0}^{x_G} = 0, \quad Q_{\bar{1}\to 1/0}^{y_G} = 0, \quad Q_{\bar{1}\to 1/0}^{\gamma} = 0$$

The five Gibbs-Appell equations are found as follows:

$$\frac{\partial \mathcal{S}}{\partial \ddot{x}_A} = \tfrac{2}{5}m(\ddot{x}_A - \ddot{x}_G) = X \tag{5}$$

$$\frac{\partial \mathcal{S}}{\partial \ddot{y}_A} = \tfrac{2}{5}m(\ddot{y}_A - \ddot{y}_G) = Y \tag{6}$$

$$\frac{\partial \mathcal{S}}{\partial \ddot{x}_G} = m\ddot{x}_G - \tfrac{2}{5}m(\ddot{x}_A - \ddot{x}_G) = 0 \tag{7}$$

$$\frac{\partial \mathcal{S}}{\partial \ddot{y}_G} = m\ddot{y}_G - \tfrac{2}{5}m(\ddot{y}_A - \ddot{y}_G) = 0 \tag{8}$$

$$\frac{\partial \mathcal{S}}{\partial \ddot{\gamma}} = \tfrac{2}{5}m\ddot{\gamma} = 0 \tag{9}$$

These five equations must be complemented with equations (1′-2′) and (3-4): we have thus nine equations to solve for nine unknowns $(x_A, y_A, x_G, y_G, \alpha, \beta, \gamma, X, Y)$.

d. We can always assume that the trajectory of G is described by

$$x_G(t) = \rho\cos\Omega t, \qquad y_G(t) = \rho\sin\Omega t$$

Equations (7-8) give by integration

$$x_A(t) = \tfrac{7}{2}x_A(t) + at + b, \qquad y_A(t) = \tfrac{7}{2}y_A(t) + ct + d$$

where the constants of integration are found by imposing $x_A = y_A = 0$ and $\dot{x}_A = \dot{y}_A = 0$ at $t = 0$:

$$a = 0, \qquad b = -\tfrac{7}{2}\rho, \qquad c = -\tfrac{7}{2}\rho\Omega, \qquad d = 0$$

This gives the coordinates (x_A, y_A) versus time:

$$x_A(t) = \tfrac{7}{2}\rho(\cos\Omega t - 1), \qquad y_A(t) = \tfrac{7}{2}\rho(\sin\Omega t - \Omega t)$$

The trajectory of A shown in Figure 14.4 is a cycloid.

e. We can use the resultant equation of the FTD (Euler's first principle) applied to body 2 to find force $\mathbf{F}_A$

$$M\mathbf{a}_{A/0} = \mathbf{F}_A + \mathbf{F}_{0\to 2}^c - Mg\hat{\mathbf{z}}_0 - (X\hat{\mathbf{x}}_0 + Y\hat{\mathbf{y}}_0)$$

If the planar joint 0–2 is ideal, then the force $\mathbf{F}_{0\to 2}^c$ of contact between the plate and the plane

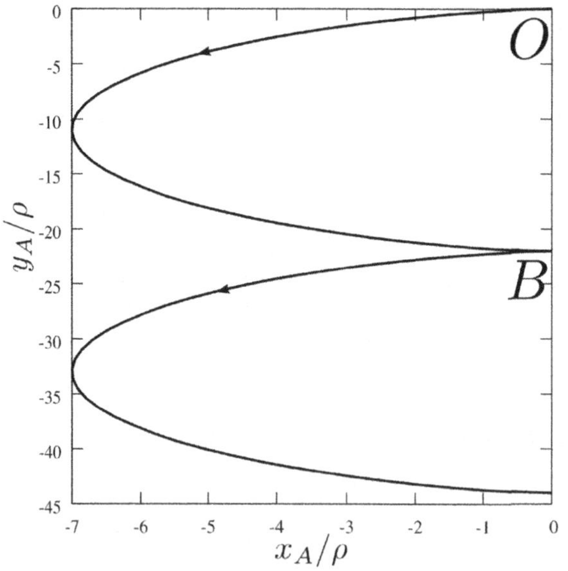

Figure 14.4 – *Point A moves along a cycloid: after a full revolution of center G, A starts at origin O and ends at B.*

of support satisfies $\mathbf{F}^c_{0\to2}\cdot\hat{\mathbf{x}}_0 = \mathbf{F}^c_{0\to2}\cdot\hat{\mathbf{y}}_0 = 0$. This gives $\mathbf{F}_A$ as

$$\mathbf{F}_A = M\mathbf{a}_{A/0} + X\hat{\mathbf{x}}_0 + Y\hat{\mathbf{y}}_0 = \tfrac{7}{2}M\mathbf{a}_{G/0} + X\hat{\mathbf{x}}_0 + Y\hat{\mathbf{y}}_0$$

where (X, Y) are solution of (5-6): $X\hat{\mathbf{x}}_0 + Y\hat{\mathbf{y}}_0 = \frac{2}{5}m(\mathbf{a}_{A/0} - \mathbf{a}_{G/0}) = m\mathbf{a}_{G/0}$ (as expected!):

$$\mathbf{F}_A = (m + \tfrac{7}{2}M)\mathbf{a}_{G/0} = -(m + \tfrac{7}{2}M)\Omega^2\mathbf{r}_{OG}$$

■

14.2 Kane Equations

Kane equations hinge on the definition of generalized speeds and the corresponding generalized partial kinematic screws.

14.2.1 Generalized Partial Kinematic Screws

To define the formulation of Kane equations for a rigid body $\mathcal{B}$ whose configuration is defined by n coordinates $\mathbf{q} = (q_1, q_2, \ldots, q_n)$, we proceed as we did in Section 13.6. We assume that the coordinates $\mathbf{q}$ satisfy $l < n$ (holonomic or non-holonomic) constraint equations of the type [2]

$$\sum_{j=1}^{n} a_{ij}(\mathbf{q}, t)\dot{q}_j + b_i(\mathbf{q}, t) = 0, \qquad (i = 1, 2, \ldots, l) \tag{14.21}$$

We assume that the coordinates $q_1, q_2, \ldots, q_n$ have been ordered so that the unknowns $(\dot{q}_{m+1}, \dot{q}_{m+2}, \ldots, \dot{q}_n)$ can be expressed in terms of $m = n - l$ independent variables $(\dot{q}_1, \dot{q}_2, \ldots, \dot{q}_m)$:

[2] Recall that holonomic equations of the type $f(q_1, \ldots, q_n, t) = 0$ can always be included to the set of non-holonomic equations in the form of $\frac{\partial f}{\partial q_1}\dot{q}_1 + \cdots + \frac{\partial f}{\partial q_n}\dot{q}_n + \frac{\partial f}{\partial t} = 0$.

$$\dot{q}_{m+i} = \sum_{j=1}^{m} \tilde{a}_{ij}(\mathbf{q},t)\dot{q}_j + \tilde{b}_i(\mathbf{q},t), \qquad (i = 1,2,\ldots,l) \tag{14.22}$$

Starting with equation (13.1) and substituting the dependent variables $\dot{q}_{m+i}$ for $i = 1,2,\ldots,l$ in terms of the independent variables $(\dot{q}_1, \dot{q}_2, \ldots, \dot{q}_m)$, we can express the velocity of any point P of rigid body $\mathcal{B}$ as

$$\mathbf{v}_{P/\mathcal{E}} = \sum_{i=1}^{m} \mathbf{v}_P^{q_i}\,\dot{q}_i + \tilde{\mathbf{v}}_P^0 \tag{14.23}$$

with

$$\mathbf{v}_P^{q_i} = \frac{\partial \mathbf{r}_{OP}}{\partial q_i} + \sum_{j=1}^{l} \tilde{a}_{ji}\frac{\partial \mathbf{r}_{OP}}{\partial q_{m+j}}, \qquad \tilde{\mathbf{v}}_P^0 = \frac{\partial \mathbf{r}_{OP}}{\partial t} + \sum_{j=1}^{l} \tilde{b}_j\frac{\partial \mathbf{r}_{OP}}{\partial q_{m+j}}$$

The formulation of Kane's equations hinges upon the definition of m *generalized speeds* $(u_1, u_2, \ldots, u_m)$ according to the equation

$$u_i = \sum_{i=1}^{m} c_{ij}(\mathbf{q},t)\dot{q}_j + u_i^0(\mathbf{q},t) \qquad (i = 1,2,\ldots,m) \tag{14.24}$$

in terms of the m independent variables $(\dot{q}_1, \dot{q}_2, \ldots, \dot{q}_m)$. Equations (14.24) are assumed invertible to obtain $(\dot{q}_1, \dot{q}_2, \ldots, \dot{q}_m)$ as a function of the generalized speeds $(u_1, u_2, \ldots, u_m)$

$$\dot{q}_i = \sum_{i=1}^{m} \tilde{c}_{ij}(\mathbf{q})(u_j - u_j^0) \qquad (i = 1,2,\ldots,m) \tag{14.25}$$

Thus it is possible to express $(\dot{q}_{m+1}, \dot{q}_{m+1}, \ldots, \dot{q}_n)$ in terms of the generalized speeds $(u_1, u_2, \ldots, u_m)$ by combined use of (14.22) and (14.25).

More importantly, we can express $\mathbf{v}_P$ in terms of the generalized speeds:

$$\mathbf{v}_P = \sum_{i=1}^{m} \mathbf{v}_P^{u_i}\,u_i + \mathbf{v}_P^0 \tag{14.26}$$

with

$$\mathbf{v}_P^{u_i} = \sum_{j=1}^{m} \tilde{c}_{ji}\mathbf{v}_P^{q_j}, \qquad \mathbf{v}_P^0 = \mathbf{w}_P^0 - \sum_{i,j=1}^{m} \tilde{c}_{ij}u_j^0\mathbf{v}_P^{q_i}$$

We find the relationship

$$\mathbf{v}_P^{u_i} = \frac{\partial \mathbf{v}_P}{\partial u_i} \tag{14.27}$$

This leads to the following definition:

Definition 14.2 — Generalized Partial Kinematic Screws. Given m *generalized speeds* $(u_1, u_2, \ldots, u_m)$ defined by

$$u_i = \sum_{i=1}^{m} c_{ij}(\mathbf{q},t)\dot{q}_j + u_i^0(\mathbf{q},t) \qquad (i = 1,2,\ldots,m) \tag{14.28}$$

each vector field $P \in \mathcal{B} \mapsto \mathbf{v}_P^{u_i} = \frac{\partial \mathbf{v}_P}{\partial u_i}$ $(i = 1,2,\ldots,m)$ defines a screw called *generalized partial kinematic screws* and denoted

$$\{\mathcal{V}^{u_i}_{\mathcal{B}/\mathcal{E}}\} = \left\{ \begin{array}{c} \frac{\partial}{\partial u_i}\omega_{\mathcal{B}/\mathcal{E}} \\ \\ \frac{\partial}{\partial u_i}\mathbf{v}_{A\in\mathcal{B}/\mathcal{E}} \end{array} \right\} \tag{14.29}$$

Then the kinematic screw of body $\mathcal{B}$ can be *uniquely* expressed as

$$\{\mathcal{V}_{\mathcal{B}/\mathcal{E}}\} = u_1\{\mathcal{V}^{u_1}_{\mathcal{B}/\mathcal{E}}\} + u_2\{\mathcal{V}^{u_2}_{\mathcal{B}/\mathcal{E}}\} + \cdots + u_m\{\mathcal{V}^{u_m}_{\mathcal{B}/\mathcal{E}}\} + \{\mathcal{V}^{t}_{\mathcal{B}/\mathcal{E}}\} \tag{14.30}$$

The quantities $\frac{\partial}{\partial u_i}\omega_{\mathcal{B}/\mathcal{E}}$ and $\frac{\partial}{\partial u_i}\mathbf{v}_{A\in\mathcal{B}/\mathcal{E}}$ are called *partial angular velocity* of $\mathcal{B}$ and *partial velocity* of point A w.r.t. u_i.

Remark 7. The generalized partial kinematic screws become the standard partial kinematic screws whenever $u_i = \dot{q}_i$, $(i = 1, 2, \ldots, m)$.

Remark 8. The screw $\{\mathcal{V}^{t}_{\mathcal{B}/\mathcal{E}}\}$ is simply the remainder of the expansion of $\{\mathcal{V}_{\mathcal{B}/\mathcal{E}}\}$ into the generalized partial screws $\{\mathcal{V}^{u_i}_{\mathcal{B}/\mathcal{E}}\}$: in other words, it represents the term of (14.30) which is independent of the u_i's.

14.2.2 Derivation of Kane's Equations

Kane's equations can be found by applying D'Alembert Principle of Virtual Power with the following choice of virtual velocity field

$$\mathbf{v}^*_P = \mathbf{v}^{u_1}_P\, u^*_1 + \mathbf{v}^{u_2}_P\, u^*_2 + \cdots + \mathbf{v}^{u_m}_P\, u^*_m \tag{14.31}$$

where the virtual generalized speeds $(u^*_1, u^*_2, \ldots, u^*_m)$ take arbitrary values. This is equivalent to the equation

$$\{\mathcal{D}_{\mathcal{B}/\mathcal{E}}\} \cdot \{\mathcal{V}^*\} = \{\mathcal{A}_{\overline{\mathcal{B}}\to\mathcal{B}}\} \cdot \{\mathcal{V}^*\} \tag{14.32}$$

with

$$\{\mathcal{V}^*\} = u^*_1\{\mathcal{V}^{u_1}_{\mathcal{B}/\mathcal{E}}\} + u^*_2\{\mathcal{V}^{u_2}_{\mathcal{B}/\mathcal{E}}\} + \cdots + u^*_m\{\mathcal{V}^{u_m}_{\mathcal{B}/\mathcal{E}}\} \tag{14.33}$$

This leads to m equations

$$\{\mathcal{A}_{\overline{\mathcal{B}}\to\mathcal{B}}\} \cdot \{\mathcal{V}^{u_i}_{\mathcal{B}/\mathcal{E}}\} - \{\mathcal{D}_{\mathcal{B}/\mathcal{E}}\} \cdot \{\mathcal{V}^{u_i}_{\mathcal{B}/\mathcal{E}}\} = 0 \tag{14.34}$$

This brings us to the following definitions:

Definition 14.3 — Generalized Active Forces. Given m independent generalized speeds $(u_1, u_2, \ldots, u_m)$ as defined by equation (14.24), we call *total generalized active force* w.r.t. generalized speed u_i the following m scalar quantities $(i = 1, 2, \ldots, m)$

$$\begin{aligned} F^{u_i}_{\overline{\mathcal{B}}\to\mathcal{B}} &= \{\mathcal{A}_{\overline{\mathcal{B}}\to\mathcal{B}}\} \cdot \{\mathcal{V}^{u_i}_{\mathcal{B}/\mathcal{E}}\} \\ &= \mathbf{R}_{\overline{\mathcal{B}}\to\mathcal{B}} \cdot \frac{\partial}{\partial u_i}\mathbf{v}_{A\in\mathcal{B}/\mathcal{E}} + \mathbf{M}_{A,\overline{\mathcal{B}}\to\mathcal{B}} \cdot \frac{\partial}{\partial u_i}\omega_{\mathcal{B}/\mathcal{E}} \end{aligned} \tag{14.35}$$

where $\{\mathcal{A}_{\overline{\mathcal{B}}\to\mathcal{B}}\}$ is the total action screw exerted on $\mathcal{B}$.

Remark 9. In practice, the total generalized active force is found by breaking down the total action screw into individual contributions.

Definition 14.4 — Generalized Inertial Forces. We call *generalized inertial force* w.r.t. generalized speed u_i the following m scalar quantities ($i = 1, 2, \ldots, m$)

$$\begin{aligned} \tilde{F}^{u_i}_{\mathcal{B}/\mathcal{E}} &= -\{\mathcal{D}_{\mathcal{B}/\mathcal{E}}\} \cdot \{\mathcal{V}^{u_i}_{\mathcal{B}/\mathcal{E}}\} \\ &= -m\mathbf{a}_{G/\mathcal{E}} \cdot \frac{\partial}{\partial u_i}\mathbf{v}_{A\in\mathcal{B}/\mathcal{E}} - \mathbf{D}_{A,\overline{\mathcal{B}}/\mathcal{B}} \cdot \frac{\partial}{\partial u_i}\omega_{\mathcal{B}/\mathcal{E}} \end{aligned} \tag{14.36}$$

where $\{\mathcal{D}_{\mathcal{B}/\mathcal{E}}\}$ is dynamic screw of $\mathcal{B}$ relative to $\mathcal{E}$.

Remark 10. If mass center G is chosen to resolve all screws, then the generalized inertial force are found according to equation:

$$\tilde{F}^{u_i}_{\mathcal{B}/\mathcal{E}} = -m\mathbf{a}_{G/\mathcal{E}} \cdot \frac{\partial}{\partial u_i}\mathbf{v}_{G/\mathcal{E}} - \frac{d}{dt}\mathbf{H}_{G,\mathcal{B}/\mathcal{E}} \cdot \frac{\partial}{\partial u_i}\omega_{\mathcal{B}/\mathcal{E}}$$

where $\mathbf{H}_{G,\mathcal{B}/\mathcal{E}}$ is the angular momentum of body $\mathcal{B}$ about G.

We can now express Kane equations as follows:

Theorem 14.3 — Kane equations. The motion of a rigid body $\mathcal{B}$ in a Newtonian referential $\mathcal{E}$ described by m independent generalized speed u_i is governed by the m equations

$$F^{u_i}_{\overline{\mathcal{B}}\to\mathcal{B}} + \tilde{F}^{u_i}_{\mathcal{B}/\mathcal{E}} = 0 \qquad (i = 1, 2, \ldots, m) \tag{14.37}$$

known as Kane equations.

Equation (14.34) shows that Kane equations are obtained by "projection" of the FTD $\{\mathcal{D}_{\mathcal{B}/\mathcal{E}}\} = \{\mathcal{A}_{\overline{\mathcal{B}}\to\mathcal{B}}\}$ onto each generalized partial kinematic screws. In fact when the generalized speeds are chosen to be $u_i = \dot{q}_i$ ($i = 1, \ldots, m$), Kane equation (14.37) are identical to equation (13.42)

$$\frac{\partial\omega}{\partial\dot{q}_i} \cdot \mathbf{D}_A + \frac{\partial\mathbf{v}_{A\in\mathcal{B}}}{\partial\dot{q}_i} \cdot m\mathbf{a}_G = \underbrace{\frac{\partial\omega}{\partial\dot{q}_i} \cdot \mathbf{M}_{B,\overline{\mathcal{B}}\to\mathcal{B}} + \frac{\partial\mathbf{v}_{B\in\mathcal{B}}}{\partial\dot{q}_i} \cdot \mathbf{R}_{\overline{\mathcal{B}}\to\mathcal{B}}}_{Q^{q_i}_{\overline{\mathcal{B}}\to\mathcal{B}}} \tag{14.38}$$

where A and B are arbitrary points. Keep in mind that the r.h.s. of equation (14.38) cannot be evaluated as $\frac{d}{dt}\frac{\partial\mathbb{K}}{\partial\dot{q}_i} - \frac{\partial\mathbb{K}}{\partial q_i}$ due to the constraint equations (14.21). However, it can be obtained from the S-function as $\frac{\partial\mathbb{S}_{\mathcal{B}/\mathcal{E}}}{\partial\ddot{q}_i}$: in this case, Kane equations are identical to Gibbs-Appell equations and the generalized active forces $F^{u_i}_{\overline{\mathcal{B}}\to\mathcal{B}}$ coincide with the power coefficients $Q^{q_i}_{\overline{\mathcal{B}}\to\mathcal{B}}$.

In general, the generalized speeds are not chosen as $u_i = \dot{q}_i$: in that case, the corresponding Kane equations will be quite different from Gibbs-Appell equations and must be considered a more general method. Before we give some general guidelines for their application, we illustrate Kane's method on some example problems.

Example 14.7 A circular disk 1 of mass center G, radius R and uniform mass is in motion on a planar support $(O, \hat{\mathbf{x}}_0, \hat{\mathbf{y}}_0)$ in a referential $0(O, \hat{\mathbf{x}}_0, \hat{\mathbf{y}}_0, \hat{\mathbf{z}}_0)$. See Figure 14.5. An auxiliary basis $b_3(\hat{\mathbf{x}}_3, \hat{\mathbf{y}}_3, \hat{\mathbf{z}}_3)$ is defined as follows:

- the line $(I, \hat{\mathbf{x}}_3)$ is the tangent at the point of contact I to the edge of the disk.

- the line $(I, \hat{\mathbf{y}}_3)$ is the line connecting I and G.
- the line $(G, \hat{\mathbf{z}}_3)$ is normal to the plane of the disk.

Basis $(\hat{\mathbf{x}}_1, \hat{\mathbf{y}}_1, \hat{\mathbf{z}}_1 = \hat{\mathbf{z}}_3)$ is attached to the disk. The orientation of basis $(\hat{\mathbf{x}}_3, \hat{\mathbf{y}}_3, \hat{\mathbf{z}}_3)$ relative to 0 is defined by the angles $\psi = (\hat{\mathbf{x}}_0, \hat{\mathbf{x}}_2)$ and $\theta = (\hat{\mathbf{z}}_0, \hat{\mathbf{z}}_3)$. The position of the contact point I is defined by its coordinates x, y on the axes $(O, \hat{\mathbf{x}}_0)$ and $(O, \hat{\mathbf{y}}_0)$. The orientation of the disk relative to basis b_3 is characterized by the angle $\phi = (\hat{\mathbf{x}}_3, \hat{\mathbf{x}}_1) = (\hat{\mathbf{y}}_3, \hat{\mathbf{y}}_1)$.

Assume that the initial conditions are such that the disk initially rolls without slipping on the horizontal plane. Rolling and pivoting friction is neglected. By taking into account the non-holonomic equations, we select the coordinates $\mathbf{q} = (\psi, \theta, \phi)$ and the generalized speeds (u_1, u_2, u_3) as the components of angular velocity $\omega_{1/0}$ on basis b_3.

a. Derive the two non-holonomic equations and the three equations expressing $\dot{\mathbf{q}}$ in terms of (u_1, u_2, u_3).

b. Derive the three Kane equations w.r.t. (u_1, u_2, u_3). ■

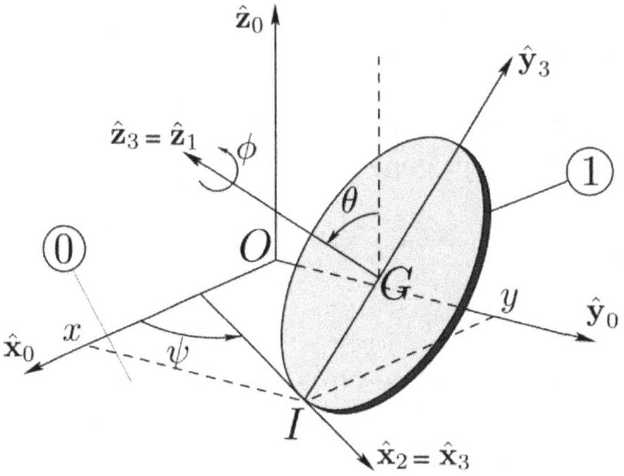

Figure 14.5

a. The orientation of basis $(\hat{\mathbf{x}}_1, \hat{\mathbf{y}}_1, \hat{\mathbf{z}}_1)$ attached to the disk relative to basis $(\hat{\mathbf{x}}_0, \hat{\mathbf{y}}_0, \hat{\mathbf{z}}_0)$ attached to referential 0 is defined by the following transformations

$$(\hat{\mathbf{x}}_0, \hat{\mathbf{y}}_0, \hat{\mathbf{z}}_0) \xrightarrow{\mathcal{R}_{\psi,\hat{\mathbf{z}}_0}} (\hat{\mathbf{x}}_2, \hat{\mathbf{y}}_2, \hat{\mathbf{z}}_2 = \hat{\mathbf{z}}_0) \xrightarrow{\mathcal{R}_{\theta,\hat{\mathbf{x}}_2}} (\hat{\mathbf{x}}_3 = \hat{\mathbf{x}}_2, \hat{\mathbf{y}}_3, \hat{\mathbf{z}}_3) \xrightarrow{\mathcal{R}_{\phi,\hat{\mathbf{z}}_3}} (\hat{\mathbf{x}}_1, \hat{\mathbf{y}}_1, \hat{\mathbf{z}}_1 = \hat{\mathbf{z}}_3)$$

The kinematic screw of the disk relative to referential 0 is represented by

$$\{\mathcal{V}_{1/0}\} = \begin{Bmatrix} \dot{\phi}\hat{\mathbf{z}}_3 + \dot{\theta}\hat{\mathbf{x}}_2 + \dot{\psi}\hat{\mathbf{z}}_0 \\ \mathbf{0} \end{Bmatrix}_I = \begin{Bmatrix} \dot{\phi}\hat{\mathbf{z}}_3 + \dot{\theta}\hat{\mathbf{x}}_2 + \dot{\psi}\hat{\mathbf{z}}_0 \\ R\dot{\theta}\hat{\mathbf{z}}_3 - R(\dot{\phi} + \dot{\psi}\cos\theta)\hat{\mathbf{x}}_3 \end{Bmatrix}_G$$

taking into account the no-slip condition at I. The equality $\omega_{1/0} = u_1\hat{\mathbf{x}}_3 + u_2\hat{\mathbf{y}}_3 + u_3\hat{\mathbf{z}}_3 = \dot{\phi}\hat{\mathbf{z}}_3 + \dot{\theta}\hat{\mathbf{x}}_2 + \dot{\psi}\hat{\mathbf{z}}_0$ yields

$$u_1 = \dot{\theta}, \quad u_2 = \dot{\psi}\sin\theta, \quad u_3 = \dot{\psi}\cos\theta + \dot{\phi}$$

and

$$\dot{\psi} = \frac{u_2}{\sin\theta}, \qquad \dot{\theta} = u_1, \qquad \dot{\phi} = u_3 - u_2\cot\theta \qquad (1-3)$$

We can then express the velocity of mass center G in terms of (u_2, u_2, u_3):

$$\mathbf{v}_{G/0} = R(u_1\hat{\mathbf{z}}_3 - u_3\hat{\mathbf{x}}_3)$$

Setting the velocity $\mathbf{v}_{I/0} = \dot{x}\hat{\mathbf{x}}_0 + \dot{y}\hat{\mathbf{y}}_0$ equal to $\mathbf{v}_{I/1} = -R\dot{\phi}\hat{\mathbf{x}}_3 = -R(u_3 - u_2 \cot\theta)\hat{\mathbf{x}}_3$ (due to $\mathbf{v}_{I\in 1/0} = \mathbf{0}$) gives $(\dot{x}, \dot{y})$ in terms of (u_2, u_2, u_3) and $\mathbf{q}$:

$$\dot{x} = -R(u_3 - u_2 \cot\theta)\cos\psi, \qquad \dot{y} = -R(u_3 - u_2\cot\theta)\sin\psi \qquad (4-5)$$

We also give the expressions of the generalized partial screws:

$$\{\mathcal{V}_{1/0}^{u_1}\} = \begin{Bmatrix} \hat{\mathbf{x}}_3 \\ \mathbf{0} \end{Bmatrix}_I \qquad \{\mathcal{V}_{1/0}^{u_2}\} = \begin{Bmatrix} \hat{\mathbf{y}}_3 \\ \mathbf{0} \end{Bmatrix}_I \qquad \{\mathcal{V}_{1/0}^{u_3}\} = \begin{Bmatrix} \hat{\mathbf{z}}_3 \\ \mathbf{0} \end{Bmatrix}_I$$

b. To find Kane equations w.r.t. (u_1, u_2, u_3), we first determine the generalized active forces $F_{\bar{1}\to 1}^{u_i} = \{\mathcal{V}_{1/0}^{u_i}\} \cdot \{\mathcal{A}_{\bar{1}\to 1}\}$

$$F_{\bar{1}\to 1}^{u_1} = \begin{Bmatrix} \hat{\mathbf{x}}_3 \\ \mathbf{0} \end{Bmatrix}_I \cdot \begin{Bmatrix} \mathbf{R}_{\bar{1}\to 1} \\ -mgR\cos\theta\hat{\mathbf{x}}_3 \end{Bmatrix}_I = -mgR\cos\theta$$

$$F_{\bar{1}\to 1}^{u_2} = \begin{Bmatrix} \hat{\mathbf{y}}_3 \\ \mathbf{0} \end{Bmatrix}_I \cdot \begin{Bmatrix} \mathbf{R}_{\bar{1}\to 1} \\ -mgR\cos\theta\hat{\mathbf{x}}_3 \end{Bmatrix}_I = 0$$

$$F_{\bar{1}\to 1}^{u_3} = \begin{Bmatrix} \hat{\mathbf{z}}_3 \\ \mathbf{0} \end{Bmatrix}_I \cdot \begin{Bmatrix} \mathbf{R}_{\bar{1}\to 1} \\ -mgR\cos\theta\hat{\mathbf{x}}_3 \end{Bmatrix}_I = 0$$

To find the generalized inertial forces $\tilde{F}_{1/0}^{u_i} = -\{\mathcal{D}_{1/0}\} \cdot \{\mathcal{V}_{1/0}^{u_i}\}$ w.r.t. generalized speed u_i we need to determine the rate of change of the angular momentum $\mathbf{H}_I = \mathbf{H}_{I,1/0} = \frac{1}{4}mR^2(5u_1\hat{\mathbf{x}}_3 + u_2\hat{\mathbf{y}}_3 + 6u_3\hat{\mathbf{z}}_3)$:

$$\begin{aligned}
\frac{d}{dt}\mathbf{H}_I &= \frac{1}{4}mR^2\Big[(5\dot{u}_1\hat{\mathbf{x}}_3 + \dot{u}_2\hat{\mathbf{y}}_3 + 6\dot{u}_3\hat{\mathbf{z}}_3) + 5u_1(u_1\hat{\mathbf{x}}_3 + u_2\hat{\mathbf{y}}_3 + u_2\cot\theta\hat{\mathbf{z}}_3)\times\hat{\mathbf{x}}_3 \\
&\quad + u_2(u_1\hat{\mathbf{x}}_3 + u_2\hat{\mathbf{y}}_3 + u_2\cot\theta\hat{\mathbf{z}}_3)\times\hat{\mathbf{y}}_3 + 6u_3(u_1\hat{\mathbf{x}}_3 + u_2\hat{\mathbf{y}}_3 + u_2\cot\theta\hat{\mathbf{z}}_3)\times\hat{\mathbf{z}}_3\Big] \\
&= \frac{1}{4}mR^2\Big[(5\dot{u}_1 - u_2^2\cot\theta + 6u_2u_3)\hat{\mathbf{x}}_3 + (\dot{u}_2 + 5u_1u_2\cot\theta - 6u_1u_3)\hat{\mathbf{y}}_3 \\
&\quad + (6\dot{u}_3 - 4u_1u_2)\hat{\mathbf{z}}_3\Big]
\end{aligned}$$

where we have used $\boldsymbol{\omega}_{3/0} = u_1\hat{\mathbf{x}}_3 + u_2\hat{\mathbf{y}}_3 + u_2\cot\theta\hat{\mathbf{z}}_3$. This leads to the expression of dynamic moment $\mathbf{D}_I$:

$$\begin{aligned}
\mathbf{D}_I &= \frac{d}{dt}\mathbf{H}_I + \mathbf{v}_I \times m\mathbf{v}_G = \frac{d}{dt}\mathbf{H}_I + mR^2u_1(u_3 - u_2\cot\theta)\hat{\mathbf{y}}_3 \\
&= \frac{1}{4}mR^2\Big[(5\dot{u}_1 - u_2^2\cot\theta + 6u_2u_3)\hat{\mathbf{x}}_3 + (\dot{u}_2 + u_1u_2\cot\theta - 2u_1u_3)\hat{\mathbf{y}}_3 \\
&\quad + (6\dot{u}_3 - 4u_1u_2)\hat{\mathbf{z}}_3\Big]
\end{aligned}$$

and to the following expression of

$$\tilde{F}_{1/0}^{u_i} = -\{\mathcal{D}_{1/0}\} \cdot \{\mathcal{V}_{1/0}^{u_i}\} = -\begin{Bmatrix} m\mathbf{a}_G \\ \mathbf{D}_I \end{Bmatrix}_I \cdot \begin{Bmatrix} \frac{\partial\boldsymbol{\omega}_{1/0}}{\partial u_i} \\ \mathbf{0} \end{Bmatrix}_I = -\mathbf{D}_I \cdot \frac{\partial\boldsymbol{\omega}_{1/0}}{\partial u_i}$$

giving the generalized inertial forces

$$\begin{aligned}\tilde{F}^{u_1}_{1/0} &= -\frac{1}{4}mR^2(5\dot{u}_1 - u_2^2\cot\theta + 6u_2u_3)\\ \tilde{F}^{u_2}_{1/0} &= -\frac{1}{4}mR^2(\dot{u}_2 + u_1u_2\cot\theta - 2u_1u_3)\end{aligned}$$

$$\tilde{F}^{u_3}_{1/0} = -\frac{1}{4}mR^2(6\dot{u}_3 - 4u_1u_2)$$

Finally we obtain the three Kane equations

$$5\dot{u}_1 - u_2^2\cot\theta + 6u_2u_3 = -\frac{4g}{R}\cos\theta \tag{6}$$

$$\dot{u}_2 + u_1u_2\cot\theta - 2u_1u_3 = 0 \tag{7}$$

$$3\dot{u}_3 - 2u_1u_2 = 0 \tag{8}$$

Equations (1-8) constitute a set of eight first-order o.d.e.'s governing the eight unknown functions $(x, y, \psi, \theta, \phi, u_1, u_2, u_3)$. ■

Example 14.8 Derive Kane equations for Chaplygin sleigh of Example 13.8 by choosing coordinates $\mathbf{q} = (x, y, \theta)$ and the generalized speeds $(u_1 = \dot{\theta}, u_2 = \hat{\mathbf{x}}_1 \cdot \mathbf{v}_C)$. ■

Recall from Example 13.8 that the body is subject to the (non-integrable) non-holonomic constraint equation given by

$$\dot{y} = \dot{x}\tan\theta \tag{1}$$

Taking (1) into account, the velocity of C is given by

$$\mathbf{v}_{C/0} = u_2\hat{\mathbf{x}}_1 = (\dot{x}\cos\theta + \dot{y}\sin\theta)\dot{x}_1$$

We can express $\dot{\mathbf{q}} = (\dot{x}, \dot{y}, \dot{\theta})$ in terms of the generalized speeds (u_1, u_2):

$$\dot{\theta} = u_1, \qquad \dot{x} = u_2\cos\theta, \qquad \dot{y} = u_2\sin\theta \tag{2-4}$$

To find Kane equations w.r.t. (u_1, u_2) we first need to find the generalized partial kinematic screws:

$$\{\mathcal{V}_{1/0}\} = \begin{Bmatrix} u_1\hat{\mathbf{z}}_0 \\ u_2\hat{\mathbf{x}}_1 \end{Bmatrix}_C = u_1\{\mathcal{V}^{u_1}_{1/0}\} + u_2\{\mathcal{V}^{u_2}_{1/0}\}$$

giving

$$\{\mathcal{V}^{u_1}_{1/0}\} = \begin{Bmatrix} \hat{\mathbf{z}}_0 \\ \mathbf{0} \end{Bmatrix}_C, \qquad \{\mathcal{V}^{u_2}_{1/0}\} = \begin{Bmatrix} \mathbf{0} \\ \hat{\mathbf{x}}_1 \end{Bmatrix}_C$$

We first determine the generalized active forces $F^{u_i}_{\bar{1}\to 1} = \{\mathcal{V}^{u_i}_{1/0}\} \cdot \{\mathcal{A}_{\bar{1}\to 1}\}$

$$F^{u_1}_{\bar{1}\to 1} = \begin{Bmatrix} \hat{\mathbf{z}}_0 \\ \mathbf{0} \end{Bmatrix}_C \cdot \begin{Bmatrix} X\hat{\mathbf{x}}_0 + Y\hat{\mathbf{y}}_0 + Z\hat{\mathbf{z}}_0 \\ L\hat{\mathbf{x}}_0 + M\hat{\mathbf{y}}_0 + N\hat{\mathbf{z}}_0 \end{Bmatrix}_C = \hat{\mathbf{z}}_0 \cdot (L\hat{\mathbf{x}}_0 + M\hat{\mathbf{y}}_0 + N\hat{\mathbf{z}}_0) = 0$$

$$F^{u_2}_{\bar{1}\to 1} = \begin{Bmatrix} \mathbf{0} \\ \hat{\mathbf{x}}_1 \end{Bmatrix} \cdot \begin{Bmatrix} X\hat{\mathbf{x}}_0 + Y\hat{\mathbf{y}}_0 + Z\hat{\mathbf{z}}_0 \\ L\hat{\mathbf{x}}_0 + M\hat{\mathbf{y}}_0 + N\hat{\mathbf{z}}_0 \end{Bmatrix}_C = \hat{\mathbf{x}}_1 \cdot (X\hat{\mathbf{x}}_0 + Y\hat{\mathbf{y}}_0) = 0$$

where we have used the fact that $X\cos\theta + Y\sin\theta = 0$ and $N = 0$. Next we find the generalized inertial forces $\tilde{F}^{u_i}_{1/0} = -\{\mathcal{D}_{1/0}\} \cdot \{\mathcal{V}^{u_i}_{1/0}\}$ w.r.t. generalized speed u_i: using $\hat{\mathbf{z}}_0 \cdot \mathbf{H}_C = I_C u_1$,

$\mathbf{v}_{C/0} = u_2\hat{\mathbf{x}}_1$ and $\mathbf{v}_{G/0} = u_2\hat{\mathbf{x}}_1 + bu_1\hat{\mathbf{y}}_1$ we find

$$\tilde{F}_{1/0}^{u_1} = -\hat{\mathbf{z}}_0 \cdot \mathbf{D}_C = -\hat{\mathbf{z}}_0 \cdot (\frac{d}{dt}\mathbf{H}_C + m\mathbf{v}_C \cdot \mathbf{v}_G) = -(I_C\dot{u}_1 + mbu_1u_2)$$

$$\tilde{F}_{1/0}^{u_2} = -\hat{\mathbf{x}}_1 \cdot m\mathbf{a}_G = -\hat{\mathbf{x}}_1 \cdot (\dot{u}_2\hat{\mathbf{x}}_1 + b\dot{u}_1\hat{\mathbf{y}}_1 - bu_1^2\hat{\mathbf{x}}_1) = -(\dot{u}_2 - bu_1^2)$$

Finally we obtain the two Kane equations

$$I_C\dot{u}_1 + mbu_1u_2 = 0 \tag{5}$$

$$\dot{u}_2 - bu_1^2 = 0 \tag{6}$$

Equations (2-6) constitute a set of five first-order o.d.e.'s governing the five unknown functions (x, y, θ, u_1, u_2). The same equations of motion are found. ∎

We can make a few remarks from these examples:

Remark 11. As in the method of Gibbs-Appell, the non-holonomic equations are taken into account without the use of multipliers if the generalized speeds are independent. It is however possible to generalize Kane equations for dependent generalized speeds: assume that the n generalized speeds $(u_1, u_2, \ldots, u_n)$ satisfy l equations of the type

$$\sum_{i=1}^{n} A_{ij}(\mathbf{q}, t)u_j + B_i(\mathbf{q}, t) = 0, \qquad (i = 1, 2, \ldots, l)$$

then the n Kane equations are given by

$$F_{\overline{\mathcal{B}}\to\mathcal{B}}^{u_i} + \tilde{F}_{\mathcal{B}/\mathcal{E}}^{u_i} = \sum_{j=1}^{l} \lambda_j A_{ji} \qquad (i = 1, 2, \ldots, n) \tag{14.39}$$

where $\lambda_1, \lambda_2, \ldots, \lambda_l$ are l multipliers.

Remark 12. The examples show that the method eliminates non-working constraint forces.

Remark 13. The method leads directly to first-order differential equations, which is a convenient form for numerical integration.

Kane's method can be generalized to systems of rigid bodies: consider a system Σ of p bodies $\mathcal{B}_1, \mathcal{B}_2, \ldots, \mathcal{B}_p$ whose position is defined by n coordinates $\mathbf{q} = (q_1, q_2, \ldots, q_n)$ and time t satisfying m constraint equations (14.21). Assuming that the motion of the system is described by m independent generalized speeds u_i, each body is governed by the m Kane equations

$$F_{\bar{k}\to k}^{u_i} + \tilde{F}_{k/0}^{u_i} = 0 \qquad (i = 1, 2, \ldots, m)$$

for $k = 1, \ldots, p$. Kane equations for system Σ are then obtained by summing the p equations (14.2.2):

$$\underbrace{\sum_{k=1}^{p} F_{\overline{\Sigma}\to k}^{u_i}}_{F_{\overline{\Sigma}\to\Sigma}^{u_i}} + \sum_{k=1}^{p}\sum_{l=1}^{p} F_{l\to k}^{u_i} + \underbrace{\sum_{k=1}^{p} \tilde{F}_{k/0}^{u_i}}_{\tilde{F}_{\Sigma/0}^{u_i}} = 0$$

where we have broken the generalized active force on the kth body into an external contribution $F_{\overline{\Sigma}\to k}^{u_i}$ and a sum of internal contributions $F_{l\to k}^{u_i}$. Then we use the law of action and reaction to write

$$\sum_{k=1}^{p}\sum_{l=1}^{p} F^{u_i}_{l\to k} = \sum_{1\le k<l\le p} (F^{u_i}_{l\to k} + F^{u_i}_{k\to l}) = \sum_{1\le k<l\le p} \{\mathcal{A}_{k\to l}\}\cdot\{\mathcal{V}^{u_i}_{l/k}\}$$

where we have used the identity

$$\{\mathcal{V}^{u_i}_{l/0}\} - \{\mathcal{V}^{u_i}_{k/0}\} = \{\mathcal{V}^{u_i}_{l/k}\}$$

This leads to the following definition.

Definition 14.5 — Generalized Active Force of Interaction. Given m independent generalized speeds $(u_1, u_2, \ldots, u_m)$, we call *generalized active force of interaction* w.r.t. generalized speed u_i the following m scalar quantities $(i = 1, 2, \ldots, m)$

$$\begin{aligned} F^{u_i}_{k\leftrightarrow j} &= F^{u_i}_{k\to j} + F^{u_i}_{j\to k} \\ &= \{\mathcal{A}_{j\to k}\}\cdot\{\mathcal{V}^{u_i}_{k/j}\} = \{\mathcal{A}_{k\to j}\}\cdot\{\mathcal{V}^{u_i}_{j/k}\} \end{aligned} \tag{14.40}$$

where $\{\mathcal{A}_{j\to k}\} = -\{\mathcal{A}_{k\to j}\}$ is the action screw exerted on body $\mathcal{B}_k$ by body $\mathcal{B}_j$.

Remark 14. The generalized active forces of interaction $F^{u_i}_{k\leftrightarrow j}$ play the same role as the power coefficients of interactions $Q^{q_i}_{k\leftrightarrow j}$ in Lagrange equations.

This leads to the following result:

Theorem 14.4 — Kane equations (System). The motion of a system Σ of p rigid bodies $\mathcal{B}_1, \mathcal{B}_2, \ldots, \mathcal{B}_p$ in a Newtonian referential $\mathcal{E}$ described by m independent generalized speed u_i is governed by the m equations

$$F^{u_i}_{\overline{\Sigma}\to\Sigma} + \sum_{1\le k<j\le p} F^{u_i}_{k\leftrightarrow j} + \tilde{F}^{u_i}_{\Sigma/0} = 0 \qquad (i = 1, 2, \ldots, m) \tag{14.41}$$

Kane's method applied to a system Σ of p rigid bodies $\mathcal{B}_1, \mathcal{B}_2, \ldots, \mathcal{B}_p$ consists of the following procedure:

1. Define n coordinates $\mathbf{q} = (q_1, q_2, \ldots, q_n)$ parametrizing the system's configuration. Derive all holonomic and non-holonomic equations governing $\mathbf{q}$ and $\dot{\mathbf{q}}$.
2. Define m independent generalized speed $\mathbf{u}(u_1, u_2, \ldots, u_m)$. Express $\dot{\mathbf{q}}$ in terms of $\mathbf{q}$ and $\mathbf{u}$.
3. For each body $\mathcal{B}_j$, express the kinematic screw $\{\mathcal{V}_{j/0}\}$ in terms of $\mathbf{u}$ and $\mathbf{q}$. Deduce the expressions of the generalized partial kinematic screws $\{\mathcal{V}^{u_i}_{j/0}\}$ for $i = 1, ..., m$ and $j = 1, ..., p$.
4. For each body $\mathcal{B}_j$, express the dynamic screw $\{\mathcal{D}_{j/0}\}$ in terms of $\mathbf{u}$ and $\mathbf{q}$.
5. For each body $\mathcal{B}_j$ and each generalized speed u_i, find the generalized inertial forces $\tilde{F}^{u_i}_{j/0} = -\{\mathcal{D}_{j/0}\}\cdot\{\mathcal{V}^{u_i}_{j/0}\}$: deduce the expression of the system's generalized inertial forces $\tilde{F}^{u_i}_{\Sigma/0}$.
6. For each contribution of the external action screw $\{\mathcal{A}_{\overline{\Sigma}\to j}\}$ exerted on body $\mathcal{B}_j$, find the generalized external active force $F^{u_i}_{\overline{\Sigma}\to j} = \{\mathcal{A}_{\overline{\Sigma}\to j}\}\cdot\{\mathcal{V}^{u_i}_{j/0}\}$: deduce the expression of the total external generalized active force $F^{u_i}_{\overline{\Sigma}\to\Sigma}$ w.r.t. generalized speed u_i.

7. For each internal action $\{\mathcal{A}_{j\to k}\}$ between two interacting bodies $\mathcal{B}_j$ and $\mathcal{B}_k$ determine the generalized active forces of interaction $F^{u_i}_{j\leftrightarrow k} = \{\mathcal{A}_{j\to k}\} \cdot \{\mathcal{V}^{u_i}_{k/j}\}$ w.r.t. generalized speed u_i.
8. Write m Kane equations in the form

$$F^{u_i}_{\overline{\Sigma}\to\Sigma} + \sum_{1\leq k<j\leq p} F^{u_i}_{j\leftrightarrow k} + \tilde{F}^{u_i}_{\Sigma/0} = 0$$

   w.r.t. generalized speed u_i, $i = 1, ..., m$.
9. If the generalized speeds are not independent, correct Kane equation by introducing multipliers.

This procedure is illustrated with the following problem:

Example 14.9 Figure 14.6 shows a schematic of a system $\Sigma = \{1,2\}$ in motion in a referential $0(O, \hat{\mathbf{x}}_0, \hat{\mathbf{y}}_0, \hat{\mathbf{z}}_0)$ assumed Newtonian. The cart 1 of mass M slides along the axis $(O, \hat{\mathbf{y}}_0)$. The pendulum 2 is connected to cart 1 by a pivot of axis $(A, \hat{\mathbf{z}}_0)$. Its mass is m, its mass center is located at G with $\mathbf{r}_{AG} = l\hat{\mathbf{x}}_1$, and its moment of inertia about axis $(A, \hat{\mathbf{z}}_0)$ is I_A. The system's configuration is defined by Cartesian coordinate $y(t) = \hat{\mathbf{y}}_0 \cdot \mathbf{r}_{OA}$ and angle $\theta(t) = (\hat{\mathbf{x}}_0, \hat{\mathbf{x}}_1)$. The cart is connected to the support by a spring of constant k and unstretched length l_0. The action of body 1 on body 2 is characterized by

$$\hat{\mathbf{z}}_0 \cdot \mathbf{M}_{A,1\to 2} = -c\theta$$

due to a torsion spring (c is a positive constant). All joints are assumed ideal.

a. Find Kane equations applied to system Σ for $\mathbf{q} = (y, \theta)$ and $\mathbf{u} = (u_1, u_2) = (\dot{y}, \dot{\theta})$.

b. Find the equilibrium positions and discuss their stability. ■

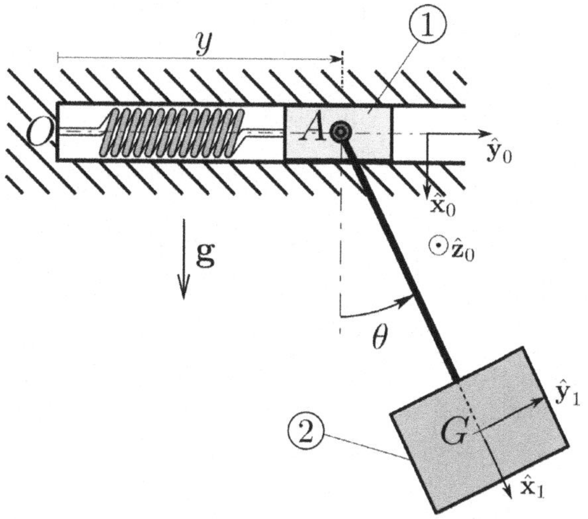

Figure 14.6

a. The kinematics of system Σ is described by

$$\{\mathcal{V}_{1/0}\} = \left\{ \begin{matrix} \mathbf{0} \\ u_1\hat{\mathbf{y}}_0 \end{matrix} \right\} = u_1\{\mathcal{V}^{u_1}_{1/0}\}$$

$$\{\mathcal{V}_{2/0}\} = \begin{Bmatrix} u_2\hat{\mathbf{z}}_0 \\ u_1\hat{\mathbf{y}}_0 \end{Bmatrix}_A = u_1\{\mathcal{V}_{2/0}^{u_1}\} + u_2\{\mathcal{V}_{2/0}^{u_2}\}$$

The dynamic screw $\{\mathcal{D}_{\Sigma/0}\}$ of the system can be expressed in terms of $\mathbf{u}$ and $\mathbf{q}$:

$$\{\mathcal{D}_{1/0}\} = \begin{Bmatrix} M\mathbf{a}_A \\ \mathbf{0} \end{Bmatrix}_A = \begin{Bmatrix} M\dot{u}_1\hat{\mathbf{y}}_0 \\ \mathbf{0} \end{Bmatrix}_A$$

$$\{\mathcal{D}_{2/0}\} = \begin{Bmatrix} m\mathbf{a}_G \\ \frac{d}{dt}\mathbf{H}_{A,2} + \mathbf{v}_A \times m\mathbf{v}_G \end{Bmatrix}_A = \begin{Bmatrix} m(\dot{u}_1\hat{\mathbf{y}}_0 + l\dot{u}_2\hat{\mathbf{y}}_1 - lu_2^2\hat{\mathbf{x}}_1) \\ (I_A\dot{u}_2 + mlu_1u_2\sin\theta)\hat{\mathbf{z}}_0 \end{Bmatrix}_A$$

This leads to the generalized inertial forces $\tilde{F}_{j/0}^{u_i} = -\{\mathcal{D}_{j/0}\}\cdot\{\mathcal{V}_{j/0}^{u_i}\}$:

$$\tilde{F}_{1/0}^{u_1} = -\begin{Bmatrix} M\dot{u}_1\hat{\mathbf{y}}_0 \\ \mathbf{0} \end{Bmatrix}_A \cdot \begin{Bmatrix} \mathbf{0} \\ \hat{\mathbf{y}}_0 \end{Bmatrix} = -M\dot{u}_1 \qquad \tilde{F}_{1/0}^{u_2} = 0$$

$$\tilde{F}_{2/0}^{u_1} = -\begin{Bmatrix} m(\dot{u}_1\hat{\mathbf{y}}_0 + l\dot{u}_2\hat{\mathbf{y}}_1 - lu_2^2\hat{\mathbf{x}}_1) \\ (I_A\dot{u}_2 + mlu_1u_2\sin\theta)\hat{\mathbf{z}}_0 \end{Bmatrix}_A \cdot \begin{Bmatrix} \mathbf{0} \\ \hat{\mathbf{y}}_0 \end{Bmatrix} = -m(\dot{u}_1 + l\dot{u}_2\cos\theta - lu_2^2\sin\theta)$$

$$\tilde{F}_{2/0}^{u_2} = -\begin{Bmatrix} m(\dot{u}_1\hat{\mathbf{y}}_0 + l\dot{u}_2\hat{\mathbf{y}}_1 - lu_2^2\hat{\mathbf{x}}_1) \\ (I_A\dot{u}_2 + mlu_1u_2\sin\theta)\hat{\mathbf{z}}_0 \end{Bmatrix}_A \cdot \begin{Bmatrix} \hat{\mathbf{z}}_0 \\ \mathbf{0} \end{Bmatrix}_A = -(I_A\dot{u}_2 + mlu_1u_2\sin\theta)$$

Next we determine the external generalized active forces

$$F_{\overline{\Sigma}\to\Sigma}^{u_1} = \{\mathcal{A}_{\overline{\Sigma}\to 1}\}\cdot\{\mathcal{V}_{1/0}^{u_1}\} + \{\mathcal{A}_{\overline{\Sigma}\to 2}\}\cdot\{\mathcal{V}_{2/0}^{u_1}\} = \hat{\mathbf{y}}_0\cdot\mathbf{R}_{\overline{\Sigma}\to 1} + \hat{\mathbf{y}}_0\cdot\mathbf{R}_{\overline{\Sigma}\to 2} = -k(y - l_0)$$

$$F_{\overline{\Sigma}\to\Sigma}^{u_2} = \{\mathcal{A}_{\overline{\Sigma}\to 1}\}\cdot\{\mathcal{V}_{1/0}^{u_2}\} + \{\mathcal{A}_{\overline{\Sigma}\to 2}\}\cdot\{\mathcal{V}_{2/0}^{u_2}\} = \hat{\mathbf{z}}_0\cdot\mathbf{M}_{A,\overline{\Sigma}\to 2} = -mgl\sin\theta$$

Finally we find the generalized active forces of interaction $F_{1\leftrightarrow 2}^{u_i}$:

$$F_{1\leftrightarrow 2}^{u_1} = \{\mathcal{A}_{1\to 2}\}\cdot\{\mathcal{V}_{2/1}^{u_1}\} = 0$$

$$F_{1\leftrightarrow 2}^{u_2} = \{\mathcal{A}_{1\to 2}\}\cdot\{\mathcal{V}_{2/1}^{u_2}\} = \hat{\mathbf{z}}_0\cdot\mathbf{M}_{A,1\to 2} = -c\theta$$

We can now write the two Kane equations $F_{\overline{\Sigma}\to\Sigma}^{u_i} + F_{1\leftrightarrow 2}^{u_i} + \tilde{F}_{\Sigma/0}^{u_i} = 0$

$$(m+M)\dot{u}_1 + ml\dot{u}_2\cos\theta - mlu_2^2\sin\theta = -k(y - l_0) \qquad [1]$$

$$I_A\dot{u}_2 + mlu_1u_2\sin\theta = -mgl\sin\theta - c\theta \qquad [2]$$

b. The equilibrium positions $\mathbf{q}_e = (y_e, \theta_e)$ corresponds to $u_1 = u_2 = 0$ in [1-2]:

$$y_e = l_0, \qquad -mgl\sin\theta - c\theta = 0$$

The only solution is given by $(y_e, \theta_e) = (l_0, 0)$. To study the stability of $\mathbf{q}_e$ we introduce the small perturbations $(\epsilon_1, \epsilon_2) = (y - y_e, \theta)$ and linearize the equations [1-2] in (ϵ_1, ϵ_2): we find

$$(m+M)\ddot{\epsilon}_1 + ml\ddot{\epsilon}_2 + k\epsilon_1 = 0, \qquad I_A\ddot{\epsilon}_2 + (mgl + c)\epsilon_2 = 0 \qquad [3-4]$$

We seek solutions of the type $(\epsilon_1, \epsilon_2) = e^{\Omega t}(\epsilon_{01}, \epsilon_{02})$ and find the characteristic equation $\big((m+M)\Omega^2 + k\big)\big(I_A\Omega^2 + k\big) = 0$ whose roots are $\Omega_1^2 = -k/(m+M)$ and $\Omega_2^2 = -k/I_A$. We conclude that the equilibrium position $(y_e, \theta_e) = (l_0, 0)$ is stable since the perturbations (ϵ_1, ϵ_2) remain near $(0, 0)$. ■

Example 14.10 Consider a system Σ of two rigid bodies 1 and 2. Body 1 (of moment of inertia J_1 about Δ) is free to rotate about a vertical axis $\Delta(O, \hat{\mathbf{z}}_0)$ of referential 0. A uniform disk 2 (of mass center A, mass m_2 and moment of inertia J_2 about Δ) is constrained to 1 by a helical joint of axis Δ and constant pitch p. The system is initially at rest. Assume that the two joints $0 \leftrightarrow 1$ and $1 \leftrightarrow 2$ are ideal. See Figure 14.7.

a. Express the conditions which guarantee that the two joints $0 \leftrightarrow 1$ and $1 \leftrightarrow 2$ are ideal. Deduce a choice of coordinates (q_1, q_2) and generalized speeds (u_1, u_2).

b. Find the corresponding Kane equations. ■

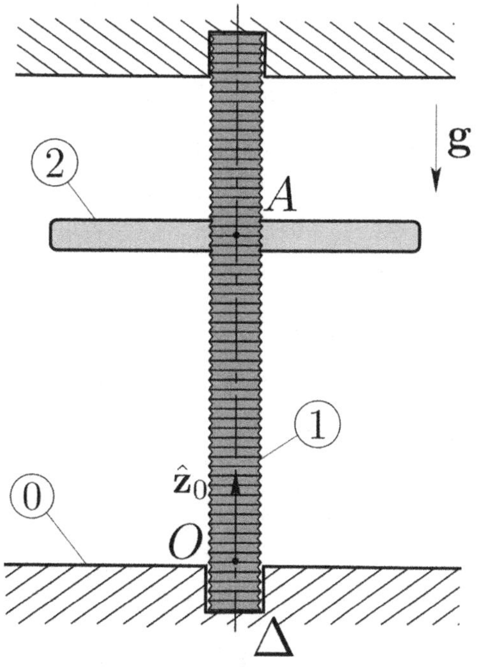

Figure 14.7

a. Two coordinates are sufficient to define the configuration of the system at any given time: the angle θ defining the rotation of body 1 about $(O, \hat{\mathbf{z}}_0)$ and $z = \hat{\mathbf{z}}_0 \cdot \mathbf{r}_{OA}$ defining the position of mass center A.

The revolute joint $0 \leftrightarrow 1$ is ideal if the condition

$$\{\mathcal{V}_{1/0}\} \cdot \{\mathcal{A}^c_{0\to 1}\} = \begin{Bmatrix} \omega_{1/0}\hat{\mathbf{z}}_0 \\ 0 \end{Bmatrix}_O \cdot \{\mathcal{A}^c_{0\to 1}\} = 0$$

is satisfied. Similarly, the helical joint $1 \leftrightarrow 2$ is ideal if the condition

$$\{\mathcal{V}_{2/1}\} \cdot \{\mathcal{A}^c_{1\to 2}\} = \begin{Bmatrix} \omega_{2/1}\hat{\mathbf{z}}_0 \\ \frac{p}{2\pi}\omega_{2/1}\hat{\mathbf{z}}_0 \end{Bmatrix}_A \cdot \{\mathcal{A}^c_{1\to 2}\} = 0$$

is satisfied. These conditions give us a possible choice for the generalized speeds

$$u_1 = \omega_{1/0}, \qquad u_2 = \omega_{2/1} \tag{14.42}$$

Then the kinematic screws are expressed in the following form

$$\{\mathcal{V}_{1/0}\} = u_1 \begin{Bmatrix} \hat{\mathbf{z}}_0 \\ 0 \end{Bmatrix}_O = u_1\{\mathcal{V}^{u_1}_{1/0}\} \tag{14.43}$$

$$\{\mathcal{V}_{2/0}\} = u_2 \begin{Bmatrix} \hat{\mathbf{z}}_0 \\ \frac{p}{2\pi}\hat{\mathbf{z}}_0 \end{Bmatrix}_A + u_1 \begin{Bmatrix} \hat{\mathbf{z}}_0 \\ 0 \end{Bmatrix}_A = u_1\{\mathcal{V}^{u_1}_{2/0}\} + u_2\{\mathcal{V}^{u_2}_{2/0}\} \tag{14.44}$$

We can relate the coordinates (θ, z) to the generalized speeds by the relations

$$\dot{\theta} = u_1, \qquad \dot{z} = \frac{p}{2\pi}u_2 \tag{1 – 2}$$

b. Kane equation w.r.t. generalized speed u_k $(k = 1, 2)$ can be stated as

$$F^{u_k}_{\overline{\Sigma}\to 1} + F^{u_k}_{\overline{\Sigma}\to 2} + F^{u_k}_{1\leftrightarrow 2} = -\tilde{F}^{u_k}_{1/0} - \tilde{F}^{u_k}_{2/0}$$

It is equivalent to the equation

$$\{\mathcal{A}_{\overline{\Sigma}\to 1}\}\cdot\{\mathcal{V}^{u_k}_{1/0}\} + \{\mathcal{A}_{\overline{\Sigma}\to 2}\}\cdot\{\mathcal{V}^{u_k}_{2/0}\} + \{\mathcal{A}_{1\to 2}\}\cdot\{\mathcal{V}^{u_k}_{2/1}\} = \{\mathcal{D}_{1/0}\}\cdot\{\mathcal{V}^{u_k}_{1/0}\} + \{\mathcal{D}_{2/0}\}\cdot\{\mathcal{V}^{u_k}_{2/0}\}$$

With the expressions of (i) the action screws

$$\{\mathcal{A}_{\overline{\Sigma}\to 1}\} = \{\mathcal{A}^g_{\overline{\Sigma}\to 1}\} + \underbrace{\{\mathcal{A}^c_{0\to 1}\}}_{\{\mathcal{A}^c_{0\to 1}\}\cdot\{\mathcal{V}^{u_1}_{1/0}\} = 0}, \quad \{\mathcal{A}_{\overline{\Sigma}\to 2}\} = \{\mathcal{A}^g_{\overline{\Sigma}\to 2}\}, \quad \{\mathcal{A}_{1\to 2}\} = \underbrace{\{\mathcal{A}^c_{1\to 2}\}}_{\{\mathcal{A}^c_{1\to 2}\}\cdot\{\mathcal{V}^{u_2}_{2/1}\} = 0}$$

(ii) the dynamic screws

$$\{\mathcal{D}_{1/0}\} = \begin{Bmatrix} \mathbf{0} \\ I_1\dot{u}_1\hat{\mathbf{z}}_0 \end{Bmatrix}_O \qquad \{\mathcal{D}_{2/0}\} = \begin{Bmatrix} m_2\frac{p}{2\pi}\dot{u}_2\hat{\mathbf{z}}_0 \\ I_2(\dot{u}_1 + \dot{u}_2)\hat{\mathbf{z}}_0 \end{Bmatrix}_A$$

and (iii) the generalized partial kinematic screws $\{\mathcal{V}^{u_k}_{1/0}\}$ and $\{\mathcal{V}^{u_k}_{2/0}\}$ found in a), we easily find Kane equation for $u = u_1$:

$$I_2(\dot{u}_1 + \dot{u}_2) + I_1\dot{u}_1 = 0 \tag{3}$$

and for $u = u_2$:

$$m_2\frac{p^2}{4\pi^2}\dot{u}_2 + I_2(\dot{u}_1 + \dot{u}_2) = -\frac{p}{2\pi}m_2 g \tag{4}$$

Equations (1-4) constitute a set of four first-order o.d.e.'s governing the unknowns (z, θ, u_1, u_2). These equations can be integrated to obtain first integrals. ∎

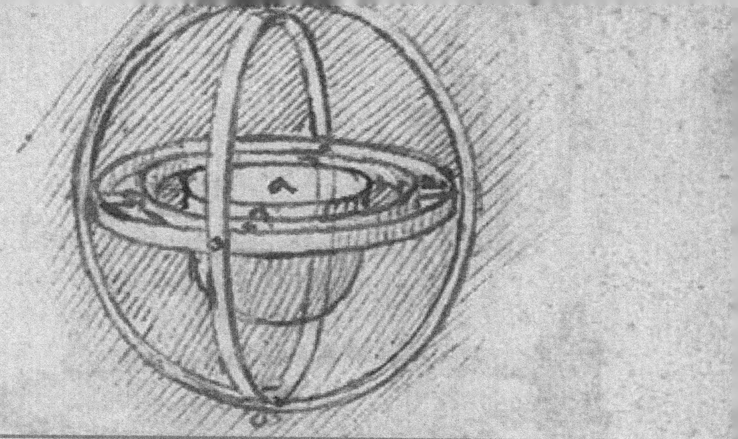

15. Gyroscopic Phenomena

THE GYROSCOPIC EFFECT is the tendency of an axisymmetric rigid body undergoing a rapid rotation about its axis to oppose all mechanical efforts which aim at altering the direction of its axis of rotation. Gyroscopic effects lead to counter-intuitive and even paradoxical dynamic behavior.

Consider the experiment shown in Figure 15.1. The experimenter holds a bicycle wheel which has been given a large spin about its axle. Upon trying to tilt the orientation of the axle, the experimenter immediately feels a strong resistance: this is known as *gyroscopic stiffness*. Moreover, if he applies to the wheel a couple directed upward, thereby attempting to rotate the plane of the wheel to his left, the wheel then immediately reacts by rotating about a horizontal axis! This motion of the wheel is referred to as the *gyroscopic precession*.

The goal of this chapter is to analyze the general laws which govern gyroscopic motions, as well as to illustrate gyroscopic phenomena taking place in mechanical systems.

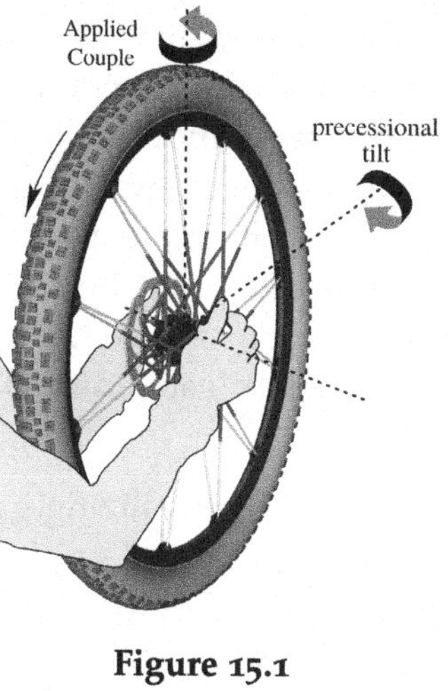

Figure 15.1

15.1 Examples of Gyroscopic Phenomena

Engineers take advantage of gyroscopic effects in many industrial applications, such as in guidance and navigation systems of ships, airplanes and spacecraft or in motion stabilizers. Gyroscopic effects can also be detrimental and even dangerous to the proper behavior of vehicles or machinery.

EXAMPLE 1: ROTARY ENGINES ON AIRPLANES. Rotary engines were early types of internal combustion engines, in which the crankshaft remained stationary in operation, with the entire crankcase and its cylinders rotating around it as a unit. Rotary engines were mounted on WWI biplane fighter aircrafts such as the Sopwith Camel. This large rotating mass behaved like a gyroscope and was the cause of stability and control problems in aircraft. Due to the direction of the engine's rotation, left turns required effort and happened relatively slowly, combined with a tendency to nose up, while right turns were almost instantaneous, with a tendency for the nose to drop. The Sopwith Camel behavior caused inexperienced pilots to crash or stall during takeoff. See Figure 15.2 (left).

EXAMPLE 2: GYROSCOPIC EFFECT OF PROPELLER ON LIGHT AIRCRAFT. The propeller of a single-engine light aircraft acts as a gyroscope: during a turn, the propeller causes the plane to tilt about the pitch axis. In a right turn and for an anti-clockwise rotation of the propeller (viewed from the pilot), the plane will have a tendency to rise. See Figure 15.2 (right).

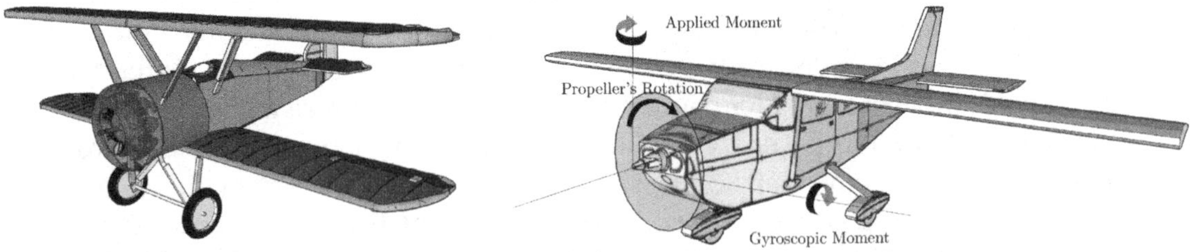

Figure 15.2 – *Sopwith Camel and its rotary engine (left). Precessional moment acting on a single-engine light aircraft (right).*

EXAMPLE 3: STABILITY AND COUNTERSTEERING OF MOTORCYCLES. Above 20 km/h, the wheels of a motocycle traveling along a straight path endow the vehicle great stability: the rider can do all kinds of tricks without destabilizing the motocycle. Above 35 km/h, the axes of the wheels become so stiff, that it becomes impossible to turn the handlebar. Countersteering must be used by the rider to initiate a turn toward a given direction by momentarily steering counter to the desired direction. To negotiate a turn successfully, the combined center of mass of the rider and motorcycle must first be leaned in the direction of the turn, and steering briefly in the opposite direction causes that lean. The slight pressure applied by the rider on the right side of the handlebar leads to the leaning of the front wheel on his right side.

EXAMPLE 4: ANTI-ROLLING GYROS. Ship stabilizing gyroscopes are a technology developed in the 19th century and early 20th century and used to stabilize roll motions in ocean-going ships such as the ocean liner SS Conte di Savoia, or the USS Henderson. Since the 1990s, interest in this technology has reemerged for low speed roll stabilization of vessels.

EXAMPLE 5: GYROCOMPASSES. Gyrocompasses are navigation tools. Since gyroscopes maintain their direction, if they are mounted into a device that allows them to move freely, the gyroscope will still point in the same direction, irrespective of the motion of the body it is mounted on. The angular positions of the gyroscope can then be measured: it then acts like a compass. Gyrocompasses are commonly used in ships and aircraft. They can also be used as artificial horizon gauges to indicate the position of an aircraft relative to the horizon, that is, the pitch of the aircraft.

EXAMPLE 6: ATTITUDE CONTROL OF SATELLITES WITH GYRODYNES. These actuators are called gyrodynes or Control Moment Gyros. They exert a gyroscopic couple about mobile axes. Their use is very complex. A minimum of two gyrodynes is needed to achieve a control moment about a fixed axis. For arbitrary attitude control in 3D, an architecture of 4 gyrodynes with concurrent axes is needed. Such systems have a propensity to reach singular configurations where they lose their capacity. Special control laws must be devised to show that any configuration can be reached.
OTHER USES. Gyroscopes can be used to provide stability for the Segway. In Virtual Reality, gyroscopes are used in headsets and other VR products. Gyroscopes are used to keep complex robots upright. They are also present in smart phones, and hand-held video camera.

15.2 Gyroscope

We start with a general definition of gyroscope.

Definition 15.1 We call *gyroscope* a rigid body $\mathcal{B}$ in motion in a referential $\mathcal{E}$ with the following properties

- $\mathcal{B}$ is an axisymmetric rigid body with respect to some axis $(G, \hat{\mathbf{z}})$ passing through its mass center G. Its inertia operator about G is characterized by an axial moment of inertia C, and a transverse moment of inertia A:

$$\mathcal{I}_G(\mathbf{u}) = A(\mathbf{u} - (\mathbf{u} \cdot \hat{\mathbf{z}})\hat{\mathbf{z}}) + C(\mathbf{u} \cdot \hat{\mathbf{z}})\hat{\mathbf{z}} \tag{15.1}$$

  for any vector $\mathbf{u}$.
- the moment about axis $(G, \hat{\mathbf{z}})$ of the external forces acting on $\mathcal{B}$ is zero:

$$\mathbf{M}_{G,\overline{\mathcal{B}}\to\mathcal{B}} \cdot \hat{\mathbf{z}} = 0. \tag{15.2}$$

- $\mathcal{B}$ rotates with a large angular velocity $\omega_z = \boldsymbol{\omega}_{\mathcal{B}/\mathcal{E}} \cdot \hat{\mathbf{z}}$ about its axis.

Remark 1. The axial angular velocity ω_z is large compared to the transverse component of $\boldsymbol{\omega}_{\mathcal{B}/\mathcal{E}} = \omega_z \hat{\mathbf{z}} + \boldsymbol{\Omega}_\perp$: $|\boldsymbol{\Omega}_\perp| \ll |\omega_z|$. However ω_z may not necessarily be large if the axial moment of inertia C is itself much larger than transverse moment of inertia A. In all cases, the magnitude of the axial angular momentum $C|\omega_z|$ remains much larger than that of the transverse angular momentum $A|\boldsymbol{\Omega}_\perp|$.

Remark 2. A typical realization is shown in Figure 15.3 (left): an axisymmetric body $\mathcal{B}$ of axis Gz is connected by a frictionless pivots to another body $\mathcal{B}_1$ which serves as a housing of the gyroscope. Body $\mathcal{B}_1$ is itself in motion relative to a referential $\mathcal{E}$. If the external actions

exerted on $\mathcal{B}$ amount to the forces of gravity and the contact reaction forces acting on the pivots, then these external forces satisfy $\mathbf{M}_{G,\overline{\mathcal{B}}\to\mathcal{B}} \cdot \hat{\mathbf{z}} = 0$.
Another realization shown in Figure 15.3 (right) amounts to constrain the axle Gz of $\mathcal{B}$ to body $\mathcal{B}_1$ by a frictionless spherical joint of center O_1 located on the axis Gz of $\mathcal{B}$. Then once again the condition $\mathbf{M}_{G,\overline{\mathcal{B}}\to\mathcal{B}} \cdot \hat{\mathbf{z}} = 0$ is satisfied.

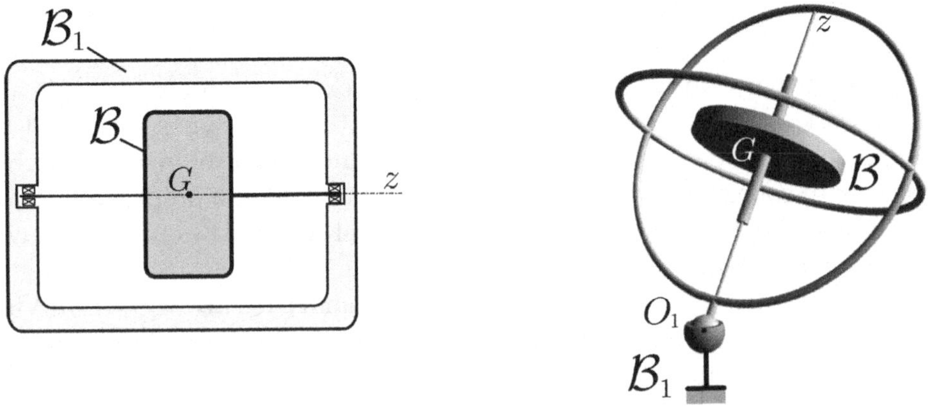

Figure 15.3

15.3 Dynamic Characterization of Gyroscopes

We first attempt to derive general properties pertaining to the motion of a gyroscope $\mathcal{B}$ relative to a Newtonian referential $\mathcal{E}$. We can express the angular velocity $\boldsymbol{\Omega} = \omega_{\mathcal{B}/\mathcal{E}}$ of body $\mathcal{B}$ in terms of unit vector $\hat{\mathbf{z}}$ and its time rate of change relative $\mathcal{E}$. Since unit vector $\hat{\mathbf{z}}$ is attached to $\mathcal{B}$ we have [1]

$$\frac{d\hat{\mathbf{z}}}{dt} = \boldsymbol{\Omega} \times \hat{\mathbf{z}} \tag{15.3}$$

This equation can be solved to give $\boldsymbol{\Omega}$ by taking the cross-product of both sides of (15.3) with $\hat{\mathbf{z}}$: using $\hat{\mathbf{z}} \times (\boldsymbol{\Omega} \times \hat{\mathbf{z}}) = \boldsymbol{\Omega} - (\hat{\mathbf{z}}. \cdot \boldsymbol{\Omega})\hat{\mathbf{z}}$ we find

$$\boldsymbol{\Omega} = \omega_z \hat{\mathbf{z}} + \hat{\mathbf{z}} \times \frac{d\hat{\mathbf{z}}}{dt} \tag{15.4}$$

where $\omega_z = \boldsymbol{\Omega} \cdot \hat{\mathbf{z}}$ is the *axial* angular velocity of $\mathcal{B}$. Hence vector $\hat{\mathbf{z}} \times \frac{d\hat{\mathbf{z}}}{dt}$ represents its *transverse* angular velocity $\boldsymbol{\Omega}_\perp$. We are generally interested in the effect of "large" values of ω_z on the general motion of $\mathcal{B}$, that is, $|\omega_z| \gg |\boldsymbol{\Omega}_\perp|$.

From (15.1) and (15.4) we can determine the angular momentum $\mathbf{H}_G = \mathbf{H}_{G,\mathcal{B}/\mathcal{E}}$ of $\mathcal{B}$ about G:

$$\mathbf{H}_G = \mathcal{I}_G(\boldsymbol{\Omega}) = A\hat{\mathbf{z}} \times \frac{d\hat{\mathbf{z}}}{dt} + C\omega_z \hat{\mathbf{z}} \tag{15.5}$$

The dynamic moment equation about the mass center G (Euler's second principle) gives

$$\frac{d}{dt}\mathbf{H}_G = \mathbf{M}_G \tag{15.6}$$

[1] All time-derivatives are performed with respect to $\mathcal{E}$.

where we have denoted by $\mathbf{M}_G \equiv \mathbf{M}_{G,\overline{\mathcal{B}}\to\mathcal{B}}$ the moment of the external actions about G. Recall that the moment about axis $(G, \hat{\mathbf{z}})$ of these forces is assumed to be zero. This implies that

$$\hat{\mathbf{z}} \cdot \frac{d}{dt}\mathbf{H}_G = \frac{d}{dt}(\hat{\mathbf{z}} \cdot \mathbf{H}_G) - \mathbf{H}_G \cdot \frac{d\hat{\mathbf{z}}}{dt} = C\frac{d\omega_z}{dt} = 0$$

where we have used (15.5) and the fact that $\hat{\mathbf{z}} \cdot (d\hat{\mathbf{z}}/dt) = 0$.

Corollary 15.1 The axial component $\omega_z = \mathbf{\Omega} \cdot \hat{\mathbf{z}}$ of a gyroscope's angular velocity $\mathbf{\Omega}$ remains constant.

We can then simplify the dynamic moment about G:

$$\mathbf{D}_G = \frac{d}{dt}\mathbf{H}_G = C\omega_z\frac{d\hat{\mathbf{z}}}{dt} + A\hat{\mathbf{z}} \times \frac{d^2\hat{\mathbf{z}}}{dt^2}$$

Corollary 15.2 The equation of motion of the gyroscope axis $(G, \hat{\mathbf{z}})$ is given by

$$A\hat{\mathbf{z}} \times \frac{d^2\hat{\mathbf{z}}}{dt^2} = \mathbf{M}_G + \mathbf{\Gamma}_g \tag{15.7}$$

where $\mathbf{\Gamma}_g = -C\omega_z\frac{d\hat{\mathbf{z}}}{dt}$ is called *gyroscopic couple.*

There are two ways of interpreting this equation:

1. The equation (15.7) can be interpreted as the equation that would govern a slender rod directed along $(G, \hat{\mathbf{z}})$ having the same mass center G, the same transverse moment of inertia A (about G), and subjected to the same external moment $\mathbf{M}_G$ as well as the fictitious gyroscopic couple $\mathbf{\Gamma}_g = -C\omega_z\frac{d\hat{\mathbf{z}}}{dt}$.

Proof. The angular momentum of a slender rod directed along line $(G, \hat{\mathbf{z}})$ and of transverse moment of inertia A about its mass center G is $A\hat{\mathbf{z}} \times (d\hat{\mathbf{z}}/dt)$, thus leading to (15.7) if the rod is subject to external moment $\mathbf{M}_G$ and gyroscopic couple $\mathbf{\Gamma}_g$ by application of Euler second principle. ■

2. The equation (15.7) can be interpreted as the equation of motion of a fictitious particle P defined by the position vector $\mathbf{r}_{OP} = \hat{\mathbf{z}}$ (with respect to some arbitrary origin O of $\mathcal{E}$), of fictitious mass A, and constrained to move on the unit sphere of center O according to the equation

$$A(\mathbf{a}_P - (\hat{\mathbf{z}} \cdot \mathbf{a}_P)\hat{\mathbf{z}}) = \mathbf{M}_G \times \hat{\mathbf{z}} + C\omega_z \hat{\mathbf{z}} \times \frac{d\hat{\mathbf{z}}}{dt} \tag{15.8}$$

where $\mathbf{a}_P - (\hat{\mathbf{z}} \cdot \mathbf{a}_P)\hat{\mathbf{z}}$ is the tangential acceleration of P. Hence particle P is subject to the two tangential "forces" $\mathbf{M}_G \times \hat{\mathbf{z}}$ and $C\omega_z\hat{\mathbf{z}} \times \frac{d\hat{\mathbf{z}}}{dt}$.

Proof. Particle P is constrained to move on the unit sphere of center O: its velocity $\mathbf{v}_P = d\hat{\mathbf{z}}/dt$ is tangential to the sphere, its acceleration $\mathbf{a}_P = d^2\hat{\mathbf{z}}/dt^2$ however has both a component tangential and normal to the sphere. Equation (15.8) is then obtained by taking the cross-product of both sides of (15.7) with $\hat{\mathbf{z}}$. ■

15.4 Motion of a Gyroscope about a Fixed Point

To continue our study of the motion of gyroscope's axis, we consider the particular case of a gyroscope whose axis $(G, \hat{\mathbf{z}})$ possesses a point O fixed in Newtonian referential $\mathcal{E}(O, \hat{\mathbf{x}}_0, \hat{\mathbf{y}}_0, \hat{\mathbf{z}}_0)$. See Figure 15.4. A physical realization would consist of a spinning top in contact with a horizontal plane at a fixed point O or a gyroscope constrained to $\mathcal{E}$ by a frictionless spherical joint.

Denote $\mathbf{M}_O$ the moment of the external forces about point O. The assumption $\mathbf{M}_G \cdot \hat{\mathbf{z}} = 0$ implies $\mathbf{M}_O \cdot \hat{\mathbf{z}} = 0$, since $\mathbf{r}_{OG}$ is collinear to $\hat{\mathbf{z}}$. Denote by a the distance from O to G, that is, $\mathbf{r}_{OG} = a\hat{\mathbf{z}}$ and by $I = A + ma^2$ the moment of inertia about an axis perpendicular to $(O, \hat{\mathbf{z}})$. Since $d\mathbf{H}_O/dt = \mathbf{M}_O$, the equation of motion of axis $(O, \hat{\mathbf{z}})$ is obtained from (15.7) by substituting $\mathbf{M}_G$ with $\mathbf{M}_O$ and A with I.

$$I\hat{\mathbf{z}} \times \frac{d^2\hat{\mathbf{z}}}{dt^2} = \mathbf{M}_O - C\omega_z \frac{d\hat{\mathbf{z}}}{dt}. \tag{15.9}$$

where the axial angular velocity $\omega_z = \boldsymbol{\Omega} \cdot \hat{\mathbf{z}}$ remains constant during the motion. When the only perturbing effect is that due to gravitational forces, we have $\mathbf{M}_O = mga\hat{\mathbf{z}}_0 \times \hat{\mathbf{z}}$.

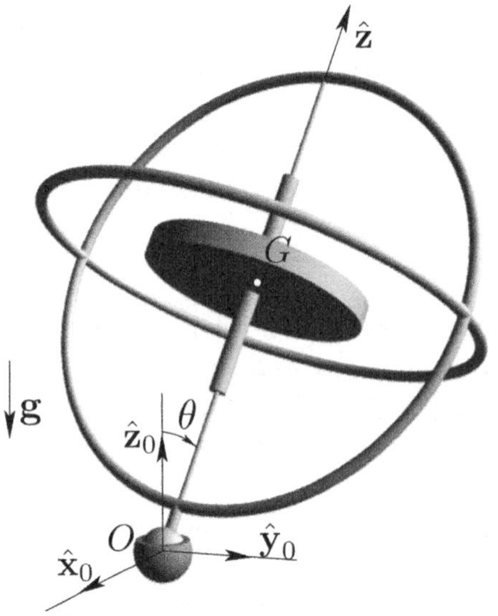

Figure 15.4

The motion of the gyroscope's axis can be visualized by considering the fictitious particle P of fictitious mass I defined by position vector $\mathbf{r}_{OP} = \hat{\mathbf{z}}$ and moving on the unit sphere of center O according to

$$I(\mathbf{a}_P - (\hat{\mathbf{z}} \cdot \mathbf{a}_P)\hat{\mathbf{z}}) = \mathbf{M}_O \times \hat{\mathbf{z}} + C\omega_z \hat{\mathbf{z}} \times \frac{d\hat{\mathbf{z}}}{dt} \tag{15.10}$$

Remark 3. A particular case of equation (15.9) corresponds to an axisymmetric body in Euler-Poinsot motion considered in Section 11.4.2. In this case $\mathbf{M}_O = \mathbf{0}$, and equation (15.9) can be integrated to give $I\hat{\mathbf{z}} \times \frac{d\hat{\mathbf{z}}}{dt} + C\omega_z\hat{\mathbf{z}} = \mathbf{h}_0 =$ constant, implying that $\mathbf{H}_O \cdot \hat{\mathbf{z}} = C\omega_z$: particle P moves uniformly around a circular trajectory in a plane perpendicular to constant vector $\mathbf{h}_0$.

Now let us consider the feasibility of a particular motion of the gyroscope's axis under the destabilizing action of gravity, that is, for $\mathbf{M}_O = mga\hat{\mathbf{z}}_0 \times \hat{\mathbf{z}}$. We ask whether the *steady precession* of this axis is possible, that is, whether this axis can rotate about the vertical $(O, \hat{\mathbf{z}}_0)$ with constant angular speed ω while maintaining a constant angle θ_0 with the vertical. This amounts to answering the question: can a value of ω be found satisfying the conditions

$$\frac{d\hat{\mathbf{z}}}{dt} = \omega\hat{\mathbf{z}}_0 \times \hat{\mathbf{z}}, \qquad \hat{\mathbf{z}}_0 \cdot \hat{\mathbf{z}} = \cos\theta_0$$

such that equation (15.9) can be satisfied? Upon replacing $d\hat{\mathbf{z}}/dt$ by $\omega\hat{\mathbf{z}}_0 \times \hat{\mathbf{z}}$ and $d^2\hat{\mathbf{z}}/dt^2$ by $\omega^2(\cos\theta_0\hat{\mathbf{z}}_0 - \hat{\mathbf{z}})$ into (15.9) we find

$$I\hat{\mathbf{z}} \times \omega^2(\cos\theta_0\hat{\mathbf{z}}_0 - \hat{\mathbf{z}}) = mga\hat{\mathbf{z}}_0 \times \hat{\mathbf{z}} - C\omega_z\omega\hat{\mathbf{z}}_0 \times \hat{\mathbf{z}}$$

leading to the following quadratic equation in ω

$$I\omega^2\cos\theta_0 - C\omega_z\omega + mga = 0. \tag{15.11}$$

If the condition

$$C\omega_z > (4Imga\cos\theta_0)^{1/2}$$

is satisfied then two real solutions are found:

$$\omega_{1,2} = \frac{C\omega_z}{2I\cos\theta_0}\left[1 \pm \left(1 - \frac{4Imga\cos\theta_0}{C^2\omega_z^2}\right)^{1/2}\right]$$

do Taylor expansion

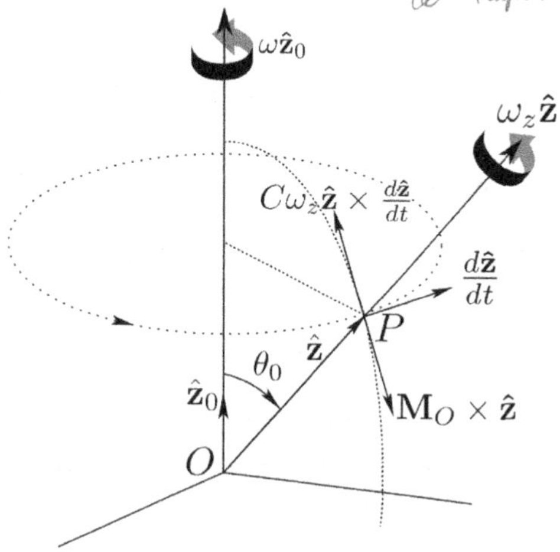

Figure 15.5

We are interested in the case of very large spin angular speed ω_z, more specifically when the condition

$$C\omega_z \gg (4Imga\cos\theta_0)^{1/2} \tag{15.12}$$

is satisfied. Then, the precession angular velocity ω can reach a slow steady value

$$\omega_1 = \frac{mga}{C\omega_z} \tag{15.13}$$

and a fast value

$$\omega_2 = \frac{C\omega_z}{I\cos\theta_0}$$

If the initial velocity $d\hat{\mathbf{z}}/dt$ is zero, then it is the slow precession speed ω_1 that is attained by the gyroscope's axis. Moreover we see from (15.13) that *the larger the spin angular speed* ω_z*, the slower the precessional motion about* $(O, \hat{\mathbf{z}})$. In this regime, we see that the angular momentum about any point Q of the gyroscope axis $(G, \hat{\mathbf{z}})$ is approximately given by $\mathbf{H}_{Q,\mathcal{B}/\mathcal{E}} = C\omega_z\hat{\mathbf{z}}$, since the transverse term $A\hat{\mathbf{z}} \times d\hat{\mathbf{z}}/dt$ being of the order $1/\omega_z$ is negligible. Moreover, the fictitious particle P governed by equation (15.10) rotates uniformly around the circular trajectory of axis $(O, \hat{\mathbf{z}}_0)$ at a slow constant angular velocity $\omega\hat{\mathbf{z}}_0$ which is solution of:

$$\mathbf{M}_O \times \hat{\mathbf{z}} + C\omega_z\, \hat{\mathbf{z}} \times \frac{d\hat{\mathbf{z}}}{dt} = \mathbf{0}$$

where the inertia term $I(\mathbf{a}_P - (\hat{\mathbf{z}} \cdot \mathbf{a}_P)\hat{\mathbf{z}})$ of order $1/\omega_z^2$ is negligible, or equivalently

$$\mathbf{M}_O - C\omega_z \frac{d\hat{\mathbf{z}}}{dt} = \mathbf{0} \tag{15.14}$$

The precessional motion of axis $(O, \hat{\mathbf{z}})$ *can be obtained as if the external applied moment* $\mathbf{M}_O$ *is in balance at all time with the gyroscopic couple* $\boldsymbol{\Gamma}_g = -C\omega_z \frac{d\hat{\mathbf{z}}}{dt}$.

To study the stability of the precessional motion we consider the particular motion corresponding to the initial condition $d\hat{\mathbf{z}}/dt = 0$ at $\theta = \theta_0$. We are only interested in very large values of $C\omega_z$, that is, we assume that $C\omega_z$ satisfies condition (15.12). To parametrize the orientation of the gyroscope axis $(O, \hat{\mathbf{z}})$, we adopt Euler angles ψ (the precessional angle) and θ (the nutational angle) according to the transformations (see Figure 15.6)

$$(\hat{\mathbf{x}}_0, \hat{\mathbf{y}}_0, \hat{\mathbf{z}}_0) \xrightarrow{\mathcal{R}_{\psi,\hat{\mathbf{z}}_0}} (\hat{\mathbf{u}}, \hat{\mathbf{v}}, \hat{\mathbf{z}}_0) \xrightarrow{\mathcal{R}_{\theta,\hat{\mathbf{u}}}} (\hat{\mathbf{u}}, \hat{\mathbf{w}}, \hat{\mathbf{z}})$$

This leads to the expression of $d\hat{\mathbf{z}}/dt$ in terms of $\dot{\phi}$ and $\dot{\theta}$:

$$\frac{d\hat{\mathbf{z}}}{dt} = (\dot{\psi}\hat{\mathbf{z}}_0 + \dot{\theta}\hat{\mathbf{u}}) \times \hat{\mathbf{z}} = \dot{\psi}\sin\theta\hat{\mathbf{u}} - \dot{\theta}\hat{\mathbf{w}}$$

From the equation of motion (15.9) two first integrals can be obtained: (i) the energy of body $\mathcal{B}$ is conserved, (ii) the component of angular momentum $\mathbf{H}_O$ about O on unit vector $\hat{\mathbf{z}}_0$ is conserved. The first equation is obtained by finding the kinetic energy $\mathbb{K}$ of body $\mathcal{B}$:

$$\mathbb{K} = \tfrac{1}{2}\boldsymbol{\omega} \cdot \mathcal{I}_O(\boldsymbol{\omega}) = \frac{I}{2}(\hat{\mathbf{z}} \times \frac{d\hat{\mathbf{z}}}{dt})^2 + \frac{C}{2}(\omega_z\hat{\mathbf{z}})^2 = \frac{I}{2}(\dot{\psi}^2\sin^2\theta + \dot{\theta}^2) + \frac{C}{2}\omega_z^2$$

Then conservation of energy $\mathbb{K} + mga\cos\theta = \text{Cst}$ gives the equation:

$$\frac{I}{2}(\dot{\psi}^2\sin^2\theta + \dot{\theta}^2) = mga(\cos\theta_0 - \cos\theta) \tag{15.15}$$

(recall that $\omega_z = \text{Cst}$). The second equation is obtained by taking the scalar product of equation (15.9) with $\hat{\mathbf{z}}_0$:

$$\hat{\mathbf{z}}_0 \cdot \left(I\hat{\mathbf{z}} \times \frac{d\hat{\mathbf{z}}}{dt} \right) = -C\omega_z \hat{\mathbf{z}}_0 \cdot \frac{d\hat{\mathbf{z}}}{dt}$$

leading to first integral

$$I\dot{\psi} \sin^2\theta = C\omega_z(\cos\theta_0 - \cos\theta) \tag{15.16}$$

We can use equation (15.16) to substitute $\dot{\psi}^2$ in equation (15.15) to obtain

$$\dot{\theta}^2 = \frac{2mga}{I}(\cos\theta_0 - \cos\theta) - \frac{C^2\omega_z^2}{I^2}\left(\frac{\cos\theta - \cos\theta_0}{\sin\theta}\right)^2$$

By introducing the variable $u = \cos\theta$, the gyroscope's behavior can be studied from the equation

$$\dot{u}^2 = f(u), \qquad f(u) = \beta(u_0 - u)(1 - u^2) - \alpha(u - u_0)^2 \tag{15.17}$$

with $\beta = 2mga/I$ and $\alpha = C^2\omega_z^2/I^2$. The behavior of the gyroscope about O can be determined by listing the properties of function $f(u)$ (a cubic polynomial) :

(i) $f(u) \sim \beta u^3$ as $|u| \to \infty$,

(ii) $f(\pm 1) < 0$ and $f(u_0) = 0$,

(iii) for a physically realizable motion of body $\mathcal{B}$, $f(u)$ has necessarily three real roots u_0, u_1 and u_2 satisfying $-1 < u_1 < u_0 < 1 < u_2$,

(iv) $\dot{u}^2 > 0$ imposes the bounds $u_1 \leq u \leq u_0$.

We conclude that angle θ must evolve periodically between two bounds: $\theta_1 \leq \theta \leq \theta_0$ (corresponding to the values u_1 and u_0). This property corresponds to the *nutational oscillations* of the gyroscope's axis. It is easy to see that, as $\omega_z \to \infty$, root u_1 tends to u_0:

$$u_0 - u_1 = \frac{2Imga}{C^2\omega_z^2}(1 - u_0^2)$$

leading to the asymptotic result

$$\theta_0 - \theta_1 = \frac{2Imga}{C^2\omega_z^2}\sin\theta_0 \qquad \omega_z \to \infty$$

The difference $\theta_0 - \theta_1$ behaves like $1/(C\omega_z)^2$ for large values of $C\omega_z$: the axis will exhibit nutational oscillations of very small amplitude $(\theta_0 - \theta_1)/2$ and very large frequency. We can then recover the slow precessional speed of equation (15.13) by finding the average of $\dot{\psi}$ using (15.16)

$$\langle\dot{\psi}\rangle \approx \frac{C\omega_z}{I\sin^2\theta_0}\langle u_0 - u\rangle \approx \frac{mga}{C\omega_z}$$

where the average $\langle u_0 - u\rangle$ is taken to be $\frac{1}{2}(u_0 - u_1)$. We can now characterize the motion of fictitious point P described by (15.10) on the unit sphere: P stays within a distance of the order $1/(C\omega_z)^2$ from an average path described by the circle $\theta = \theta_0$ with the angular speed of the order $1/(C\omega_z)$.

Period of nutation oscilations is very small

$$\int_{u_0}^{u_1} \frac{du}{f(u)} = \int_0^{T/2} dt$$

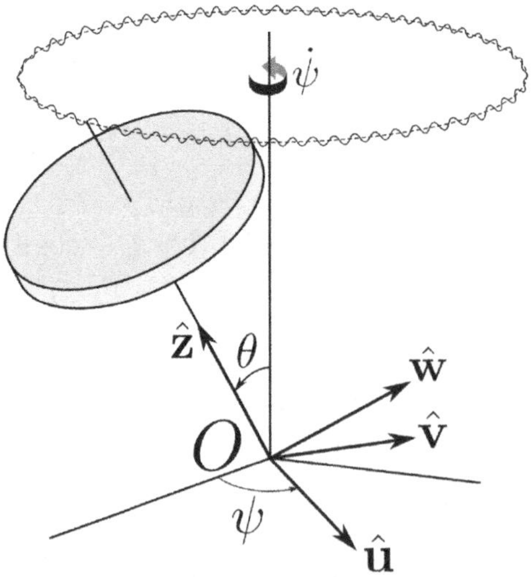

Figure 15.6 – *The precessional and nutational motions of a gyroscope about a fixed point.*

In conclusion, this study of gyroscopic effects underscores the following characteristics:

1. The velocity $d\hat{\mathbf{z}}/dt$ whose magnitude gives a measure of the angular speed of the gyroscope's axis is proportional to the moment $\mathbf{M}_O$ of the applied forces with the coefficient of proportionality $1/C\omega_z$: if $\mathbf{M}_O$ does not become excessive, the angular displacement of the axis remains very slow. This characteristic is called *gyroscopic stiffness*: the gyroscope's axis keeps a direction which is sensibly constant despite the perturbing forces which tend to modify its direction.
2. The perturbing forces despite their weakness act in a non-intuitive manner: the "force" $\mathbf{F} = \mathbf{M}_O \times \hat{\mathbf{z}}$ sets in motion fictitious particle P in a direction perpendicular to $\mathbf{F}$! There lies the paradox of gyroscopic effects: the applied moment $\mathbf{M}_O$ does not produce a rotation of the gyroscope about the direction of $\mathbf{M}_O$, but rather about a direction 90 degrees from the expected direction.

15.5 The Gyroscopic Approximation

The conclusions drawn in Section 15.4 were specific to a gyroscope possessing a fixed point O under the destabilizing effect of gravity and with an axis initially at rest. Similar conclusions could be made under more general conditions. They can also be generalized for a gyroscope governed by equation (15.7): for a general perturbing moment $\mathbf{M}_G$ and for sufficiently small initial conditions, the change of orientation of its axis, quantified by the magnitude of $d\hat{\mathbf{z}}/dt$, remains very slow, of the order of $1/C\omega_z$, as long as the axial angular speed ω_z is given a very large value. Furthermore, the axis is subject to high frequency nutational oscillations whose amplitude is of order $1/\omega_z^2$.

In general, the analysis would be greatly simplified if the nutational effects were neglected. It is then tempting to neglect the inertial term $A\hat{\mathbf{z}} \times \frac{d^2\hat{\mathbf{z}}}{dt^2}$ present in the equation of motion (15.7). However it is easy to see that vector $\frac{d^2\hat{\mathbf{z}}}{dt^2}$ is of the same order of magnitude as $C\omega_z \frac{d\hat{\mathbf{z}}}{dt}$ (both are of order 1 in ω_z) and hence cannot be neglected at any given time. However vector $\frac{d^2\hat{\mathbf{z}}}{dt^2}$ oscillates rapidly about a slowly-varying direction, and hence, on average becomes negligible. The gyroscope's average motion can then be predicted by using the following approximation:

Theorem 15.1 — Gyroscopic Approximation. The average precessional motion of a gyroscope of axis $(G, \hat{\mathbf{z}})$ can be predicted by expressing that the external moments applied on the gyroscope are balanced by the gyroscopic couple (relative to a Newtonian referential):

$$\mathbf{M}_G - C\omega_z \frac{d\hat{\mathbf{z}}}{dt} = 0 \tag{15.18}$$

where $\mathbf{M}_G = \mathbf{M}_{G,\overline{\mathcal{B}}\to\mathcal{B}}$ satisfies $\mathbf{M}_G \cdot \hat{\mathbf{z}} = 0$, and $\omega_z = \boldsymbol{\omega} \cdot \hat{\mathbf{z}}$ remains constant during the motion.

Remark 4. To create a gyroscopic couple, the gyroscope's axis must exhibit a rotation transverse to the axis. The resulting motion is often called *gyroscopic drift*.

Remark 5. The gyroscopic drift is detrimental whenever the gyroscope must maintain a fixed direction, such as in inertial navigation systems.

Remark 6. The gyroscopic drift effects can be exploited to detect external perturbations or to measure rotational motions.

The following example illustrates the use of the gyroscopic approximation. It demonstrates the unexpected behavior of gyroscopes.

Example 15.1 Consider a gyroscope 3 mounted on two massless gimbals 1 and 2 in motion in a Newtonian referential 0. The outer gimbal 1 is connected to 0 by a frictionless pivot of vertical axis $(O, \hat{\mathbf{z}}_0)$ with corresponding angular velocity $\boldsymbol{\omega}_{1/0} = \dot{\psi}\hat{\mathbf{z}}_0$. The inner gimbal 2 is connected to outer gimbal 1 by a frictionless pivot of horizontal axis $(O, \hat{\mathbf{u}})$ with corresponding angular velocity $\boldsymbol{\omega}_{2/1} = \dot{\theta}\hat{\mathbf{u}}$. Finally gyroscope 3 of mass center O is mounted on 2 by a frictionless pivot of axis $(O, \hat{\mathbf{z}})$ about which it rotates at angular velocity $\boldsymbol{\omega}_{3/2} = \dot{\phi}\hat{\mathbf{z}}$.

The gyroscopic assumptions are made: owing to the absence of axial moment $\mathbf{M}_{O,\bar{3}\to 3} \cdot \hat{\mathbf{z}} = 0$ and to the large axial angular velocity $\dot{\phi}$, the angular momentum of body 3 about O can be approximated as $\mathbf{H}_O = C\dot{\phi}\hat{\mathbf{z}}$, where $\dot{\phi}$ remains constant and where C is the axial moment of inertia of body 3. In the absence of external perturbations, the axis $(O, \hat{\mathbf{z}})$ remains fixed relative to referential 0, its position given by constant angles $\theta = \theta_0$ and $\psi = \psi_0$.

a. The system is subjected to an external perturbation in the form of a force $F_P\hat{\mathbf{z}} \times \hat{\mathbf{u}} = F_P\hat{\mathbf{w}}$ of constant magnitude F_P applied at point P of the gyroscope's axis defined by $\mathbf{r}_{OP} = -r\hat{\mathbf{z}}$ (r is a positive constant). Describe the dynamic response of the system to this perturbation.

b. The system is now perturbed by applying a force $F_Q\hat{\mathbf{z}}_0 \times \hat{\mathbf{u}} = F_Q\hat{\mathbf{v}}$ of constant magnitude F_Q applied at point Q of gimbal 1 defined by $\mathbf{r}_{OQ} = R\hat{\mathbf{u}}$ (R is a positive constant). Describe the dynamic response of the system to this new perturbation. ■

a. Force $F_P\hat{\mathbf{w}}$ creates an external moment $\mathbf{M}_O = -r\hat{\mathbf{z}} \times F_P\hat{\mathbf{w}} = rF_P\hat{\mathbf{u}}$ applied to body 3. Application of the dynamic moment equation $d\mathbf{H}_O/dt = \mathbf{M}_{O,\bar{3}\to 3}$ gives

$$C\dot{\phi}\frac{d\hat{\mathbf{z}}}{dt} = rF_P\hat{\mathbf{u}} + \mathbf{M}^c_{O,2\to 3}$$

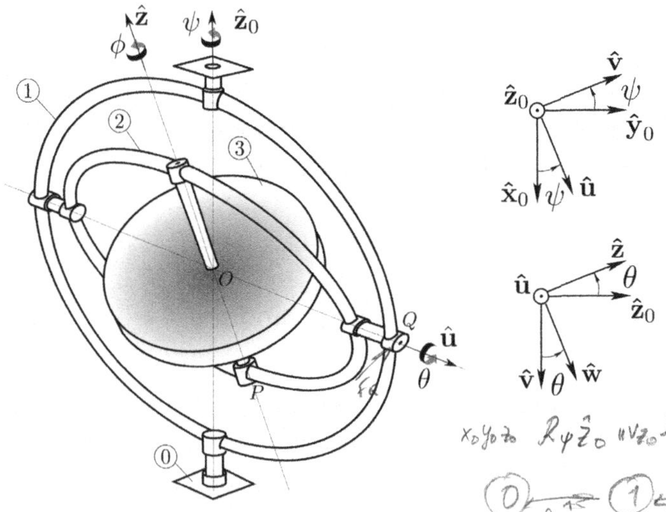

Figure 15.7

To evaluate $d\hat{\mathbf{z}}/dt$ we use the angular velocity $\boldsymbol{\omega}_{2/0} = \dot{\psi}\hat{\mathbf{z}}_0 + \dot{\theta}\hat{\mathbf{u}}$:

$$\frac{d\hat{\mathbf{z}}}{dt} = (\dot{\psi}\hat{\mathbf{z}}_0 + \dot{\theta}\hat{\mathbf{u}}) \times \hat{\mathbf{z}} = \dot{\psi}\sin\theta\hat{\mathbf{u}} - \dot{\theta}\hat{\mathbf{w}}$$

Hence we obtain

$$C\dot{\phi}(\dot{\psi}\sin\theta\hat{\mathbf{u}} - \dot{\theta}\hat{\mathbf{w}}) = rF_P\hat{\mathbf{u}} + \mathbf{M}^c_{O,2\to 3} \tag{1}$$

Before resolving (1) on basis $(\hat{\mathbf{u}}, \hat{\mathbf{w}}, \hat{\mathbf{z}})$ we need the components of $\mathbf{M}^c_{O,2\to 3} = L\hat{\mathbf{u}} + M\hat{\mathbf{w}}$ (the component on $\hat{\mathbf{z}}$ is zero since the pivot between 2 and 3 is frictionless). They can be found by writing the "equilibrium" of (massless) body 2:

$$\mathbf{M}^c_{O,3\to 2} + \mathbf{M}^c_{O,1\to 2} = \mathbf{0}$$

Since $\mathbf{M}^c_{O,1\to 2} \cdot \hat{\mathbf{u}} = 0$, this gives $L = 0$. Then equilibrium of body 1 gives

$$\mathbf{M}^c_{O,0\to 1} + \mathbf{M}^c_{O,2\to 1} = \mathbf{0}$$

Again the condition $\mathbf{M}^c_{O,0\to 1} \cdot \hat{\mathbf{z}}_0 = 0$ (the pivot between 0 and 1 is frictionless) necessarily implies $M = 0$. Therefore, after taking into account $L = M = 0$, equation (1) now leads to

$$\dot{\theta} = 0, \qquad C\dot{\phi}\dot{\psi}\sin\theta = rF_P$$

This shows that angle θ remains constant, and that the gyroscope slowly precesses at constant angular velocity

$$\dot{\psi} = \frac{rF_P}{C\dot{\phi}\sin\theta_0}$$

about axis $(O, \hat{\mathbf{z}}_0)$. *One would expect that application of force F_P would lead to a rotation about axis $(O, \hat{\mathbf{u}})$. But in fact the gyroscope precesses at a right angle to the applied force.*

b. Force $F_Q\hat{\mathbf{v}}$ leads to a moment $R\hat{\mathbf{u}} \times F_Q\hat{\mathbf{v}} = RF_Q\hat{\mathbf{z}}_0$ about O acting on body 1. Equilibrium of gimbal 1 translates into

$$RF_Q\hat{\mathbf{z}}_0 + \mathbf{M}^c_{O,0\to 1} + \mathbf{M}^c_{O,2\to 1} = \mathbf{0}$$

Since $\hat{\mathbf{z}}_0 \cdot \mathbf{M}^c_{O,0\to 1} = 0$, this leads to the equation

$$RF_Q + (M_{12}\hat{\mathbf{w}} + N_{12}\hat{\mathbf{z}}) \cdot \hat{\mathbf{z}}_0 = 0 \tag{2}$$

where we have written $\mathbf{M}^c_{O,2\to 1} = M_{12}\hat{\mathbf{w}} + N_{12}\hat{\mathbf{z}}$ (the component on $\hat{\mathbf{u}}$ is zero). On the other hand, equilibrium of body 2 implies that

$$\mathbf{M}^c_{O,3\to 2} + \mathbf{M}^c_{O,1\to 2} = \mathbf{0} \tag{3}$$

Since $\mathbf{M}_{O,3\to 2} \cdot \hat{\mathbf{z}} = 0$ this leads to $N_{12} = 0$. Equation (2) then gives $RF_Q = -M_{12}\sin\theta$. Finally we obtain from (3)

$$\mathbf{M}^c_{O,2\to 3} = -\mathbf{M}^c_{O,2\to 1} = -M_{12}\hat{\mathbf{w}} = \frac{RF_Q}{\sin\theta}\hat{\mathbf{w}}$$

Now as in a), we apply the dynamic moment equation $d\mathbf{H}_O/dt = \mathbf{M}_{0,\bar{3}\to 3}$ to obtain

$$C\dot{\phi}(\dot{\psi}\sin\theta\hat{\mathbf{u}} - \dot{\theta}\hat{\mathbf{w}}) = \mathbf{M}^c_{O,2\to 3} = \frac{RF_Q}{\sin\theta}\hat{\mathbf{w}}$$

leading to

$$C\dot{\phi}\dot{\psi}\sin\theta = 0, \qquad C\dot{\phi}\dot{\theta} = -\frac{RF_Q}{\sin\theta}$$

This shows that angular velocity $\dot{\psi}$ is zero: *the moment $RF_Q\hat{\mathbf{z}}_0$ exerted on gimbal 1 does not lead to the rotation of gimbal 1 about axis $(O,\hat{\mathbf{z}}_0)$! Instead it produces the rotation of gimbal 2 about axis $(O,\hat{\mathbf{u}})$ with angular velocity*

$$\dot{\theta} = -\frac{RF_Q}{C\dot{\phi}\sin\theta}$$

This equation can be integrated to give

$$\cos\theta = \cos\theta_0 + \frac{RF_Q}{C\dot{\phi}}t$$

which shows that angle θ decreases toward the value $\theta = 0$: gimbal 2 eventually reaches the vertical position, its plane coinciding with that of gimbal 1. At this point, the axes $(O,\hat{\mathbf{z}}_0)$ and $(O,\hat{\mathbf{z}})$ coincide, the gyroscopic effect ceases, and the rotation of gimbal 1 proceeds. ■

15.6 Applications

Example 15.2 — The Precession of the Equinoxes. The precession of the equinoxes is a phenomenon that has been known since the Greek antiquity. It is due to the periodic precession of the Earth's axis of rotation with a corresponding period of about 26,000 years. The precession can be predicted as the gyroscopic effect created by the gravitational forces of the Sun and the Moon on the Earth: due to the oblate spheroidal shape of the Earth, and to its axial tilt relative to its ecliptic plane, these forces create a non-zero moment about the mass center of the Earth acting perpendicularly to the axis of rotation. This moment thus leads to the axis' precession which we propose to study here.

Figure 15.8 shows the Earth $\mathcal{E}$ of mass center O, mass m_E, radius R_E and angular velocity Ω_E about axis of rotation Oz. The Cartesian axes $OXYZ$ are chosen so that axis OZ is perpendicular to the Earth's ecliptic plane OXY, with axis OX perpendicular to the plane OZz. Axis of rotation Oz is assumed inclined with a constant angle θ_0 relative to axis OZ. The Earth's gravitational potential at a point P of spherical coordinates (r,ϕ,θ) located at a distance $r \gg R_E$ from O can be shown to be given by

$$\mathbb{U} = -\frac{Gm_E}{r} - (C - A)\frac{G}{2r^3}[1 - 3(\sin\theta\sin\phi\sin\theta_0 + \cos\theta\cos\theta_0)^2]$$

where C is the axial moment of inertia, and A the equatorial moment of inertia of the Earth.

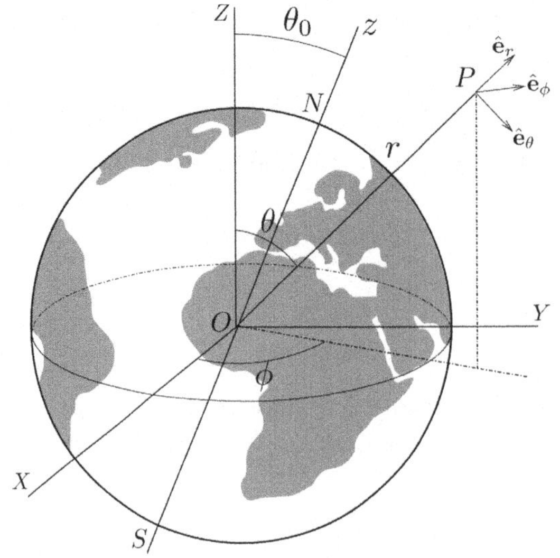

Figure 15.8

a. Show that the Earth's gravitational field at a point P located in the ecliptic plane $(\theta = \pi/2)$ is given by

$$\mathbf{G}_P = (C - A)\frac{3G}{2r^4}[\sin 2\theta_0 \sin\phi\,\hat{\mathbf{e}}_\theta - \sin^2\theta_0 \sin 2\phi\,\hat{\mathbf{e}}_\phi]$$

Deduce that a celestial body of mass M_P located at P exerts on Earth an average moment about O given by

$$\mathbf{M}_O = (C - A)\frac{3GM_P}{4r^3}\sin 2\theta_0 \hat{\mathbf{e}}_X$$

b. By including the contribution of the Sun (mass M_s, distance r_s) and the Moon (mass M_m, distance r_m) in the expression of $\mathbf{M}_O$, show that the axis of rotation Oz precesses (relative to the Heliocentric referential) at the rate

$$\omega = -\frac{C-A}{C}\frac{3G\cos\theta_0}{2\Omega_E}\left(\frac{M_s}{r_s^3} + \frac{M_m}{r_m^3}\right)\hat{\mathbf{e}}_Z$$

With $(C - A)/C = 1/308$, $\theta_0 = 23°27'$, $M_m/r_m^3 = 2.17 M_s/r_s^3$, $M_s/r_s^3 = 4\pi^2/GT^2$ (according Kepler's 3rd law, with T the period of revolution of $\mathcal{E}$ around the Sun), find numerically (in time unit of years) the corresponding period of the precessional motion. ∎

a. The Earth's gravitational field at a point P is found from the potential $\mathbb{U}$ according to $\mathbf{G}_P = -\nabla\mathbb{U}$, which gives in spherical coordinates (r, θ, ϕ):

$$\mathbf{G}_P = -\frac{\partial\mathbb{U}}{\partial r}\hat{\mathbf{e}}_r - \frac{1}{r}\frac{\partial\mathbb{U}}{\partial\theta}\hat{\mathbf{e}}_\theta - \frac{1}{r\sin\theta}\frac{\partial\mathbb{U}}{\partial\phi}\hat{\mathbf{e}}_\phi$$

This gives the components

$$G_\theta = -6(C-A)\frac{G}{2r^4}(\sin\theta\sin\phi\sin\theta_0 + \cos\theta\cos\theta_0)(\cos\theta\sin\phi\sin\theta_0 - \sin\theta\cos\theta_0)$$

$$G_\phi = -6(C-A)\frac{G}{2r^4}(\sin\theta\sin\phi\sin\theta_0 + \cos\theta\cos\theta_0)\cos\phi\sin\theta_0$$

In the ecliptic plane, $\theta = \pi/2$, the G_θ and G_ϕ components simplify to

$$G_\theta = 3(C-A)\frac{G}{2r^4}\sin\phi\sin 2\theta_0, \qquad G_\phi = -3(C-A)\frac{G}{2r^4}\sin 2\phi\sin^2\theta_0$$

The moment $\mathbf{M}_O$ of the forces exerted on Earth by a celestial body of mass M_P located at P is the opposite of the moment $\mathbf{r}_{OP} \times M_P\mathbf{G}_P$ which Earth exerts on P: it is given by

$$\begin{aligned}\mathbf{M}_O &= -r\hat{\mathbf{e}}_r \times M_P(G_r\hat{\mathbf{e}}_r + G_\theta\hat{\mathbf{e}}_\theta + G_\phi\hat{\mathbf{e}}_\phi) = -M_P r(G_\theta\hat{\mathbf{e}}_\phi - G_\phi\hat{\mathbf{e}}_\theta)\\ &= -M_P r(-G_\theta\sin\phi\hat{\mathbf{e}}_X + G_\theta\cos\phi\hat{\mathbf{e}}_Y + G_\phi\hat{\mathbf{e}}_Z)\\ &= 3(C-A)\frac{GM_P}{2r^3}(\sin^2\phi\sin 2\theta_0\hat{\mathbf{e}}_X - \sin\phi\cos\phi\sin 2\theta_0\hat{\mathbf{e}}_Y + \sin 2\phi\sin^2\theta_0\hat{\mathbf{e}}_Z)\end{aligned}$$

When Earth rotates, the angle ϕ exhibits rapid variations and the moment $\mathbf{M}_O$ can be averaged by taking into account $\langle\sin^2\phi\rangle = 1/2$ and $\langle\sin\phi\cos\phi\rangle = 0$: this gives the average value

$$\mathbf{M}_O = 3(C-A)\frac{GM_P}{4r^3}\sin 2\theta_0\hat{\mathbf{e}}_X \tag{1}$$

b. In the geocentric referential, the Earth rotates at angular velocity $\Omega_E\hat{\mathbf{e}}_z$. The gyroscopic effect due to the gravitation perturbation is predicted as a balance of moment $\mathbf{M}_O$ and the gyroscopic couple $\mathbf{\Gamma}_g = -C\Omega_E\frac{d\hat{\mathbf{z}}}{dt}$:

$$\frac{3}{4}G(C-A)(\frac{M_s}{r_s^3} + \frac{M_m}{r_m^3})\sin 2\theta_0\hat{\mathbf{e}}_X - C\Omega_E\frac{d\hat{\mathbf{z}}}{dt} = \mathbf{0}$$

using the expression (1) of $\mathbf{M}_O$ for the contributions of the Sun and the Moon. This equation shows that $\mathbf{M}_O$ causes a slow precessional rotation about axis OZ at angular velocity $\boldsymbol{\omega} = \omega\hat{\mathbf{e}}_Z$ such that

$$\frac{d\hat{\mathbf{z}}}{dt} = \omega\hat{\mathbf{e}}_Z \times \hat{\mathbf{e}}_z = -\omega\sin\theta_0\hat{\mathbf{e}}_X$$

This gives $\boldsymbol{\omega}$:

$$\boldsymbol{\omega} = -\left(\frac{C-A}{C}\right)\frac{3G\cos\theta_0}{2\Omega_E}(\frac{M_s}{r_s^3} + \frac{M_m}{r_m^3})\hat{\mathbf{e}}_Z$$

Numerically, this formula gives the period of precession $T = \frac{2\pi}{\omega} = 25{,}699T_E \approx 257$ centuries. This compares very well with the measured value of T. ■

Example 15.3 — Gyrocompass. A gyrocompass is a non-magnetic compass which is based on the a fast-spinning axisymmetric suspended rotor and the rotation of the Earth to automatically find geographical direction. Gyrocompasses are widely used as a navigation tool on ships for their ability to find true north and for being unaffected by ferromagnetic materials. The gyrocompass is modeled as a system Σ consisting of a rotor 2 suspended by two gimbals. The rotation of the inner gimbal is blocked relative to the outer gimbal: the two rigidly connected gimbals, denoted 1, are allowed to rotate about a vertical axis $(O, \hat{\mathbf{z}}_0)$. The system $\Sigma = \{1, 2\}$ is located at a point O

of the Earth $\mathcal{E}(O, \hat{\mathbf{x}}_0, \hat{\mathbf{y}}_0, \hat{\mathbf{z}}_0)$ at latitude λ. The Earth is assumed to rotate relative to the geocentric referential $\mathcal{G}$ at constant angular velocity Ω_E. The axis of the rotor $(O, \hat{\mathbf{z}})$ lies in a horizontal plane $(O, \hat{\mathbf{x}}_0, \hat{\mathbf{y}}_0)$ with axis $(O, \hat{\mathbf{x}}_0)$ pointing southward. Its orientation is defined by the angle ψ as follows

$$(\hat{\mathbf{x}}_0, \hat{\mathbf{y}}_0, \hat{\mathbf{z}}_0) \xrightarrow{\mathcal{R}_{\psi, \hat{\mathbf{z}}_0}} (\hat{\mathbf{z}}, \hat{\mathbf{w}}, \hat{\mathbf{z}}_0)$$

The mass centers of both bodies 1 and 2 coincide with O. The rotor is given a large angular velocity $\dot{\phi}\hat{\mathbf{z}}$ about its axis so that its angular momentum about O (relative to $\mathcal{E}$) can be approximated as $C\dot{\phi}\hat{\mathbf{z}}$, assuming $\dot{\phi}$ a positive constant and denoting C the axial moment of inertia of the rotor. Denote by I_1 the moment of inertia of body 1 about axis $(O, \hat{\mathbf{z}}_0)$. Assume that all joints are frictionless.

a. Find the expression of the rate of change of the component $\hat{\mathbf{z}}_0 \cdot \mathbf{H}_{O,\Sigma/\mathcal{G}}$ of the system's angular momentum about O relative to the geocentric referential $\mathcal{G}$.

b. Show that the axis of the rotor exhibits precessional oscillations about the equilibrium position $\psi_e = \pi$. Find the period of these oscillations. Conclude that, in the presence of friction, the axis points to the north. ■

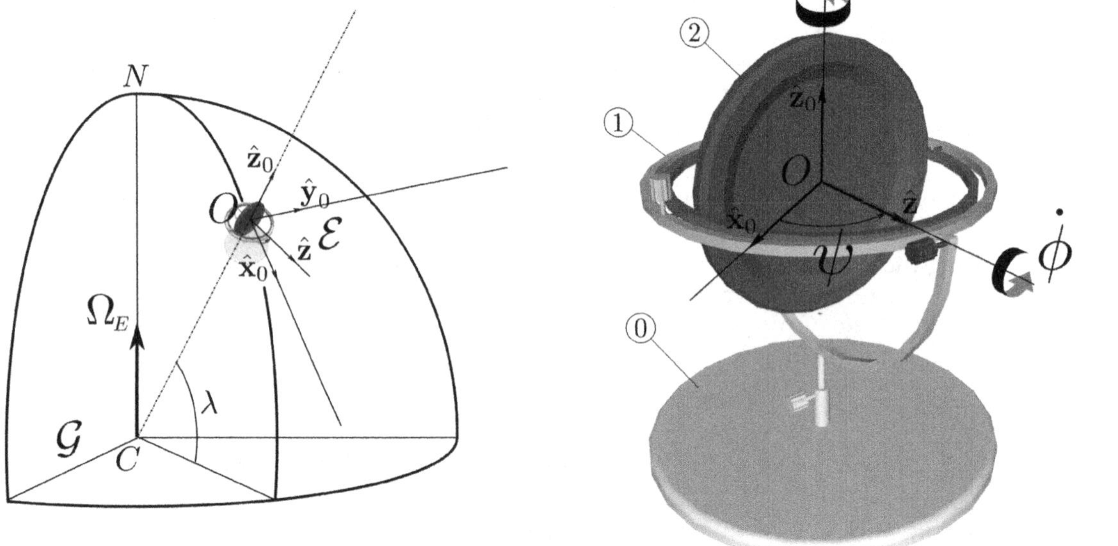

Figure 15.9

a. First we can relate the system's angular momentum $\mathbf{H}_{O,\Sigma/\mathcal{G}}$ relative to referential $\mathcal{G}$ to its angular momentum relative to $\mathcal{E}$:

$$\begin{aligned}
\mathbf{H}_{O,\Sigma/\mathcal{G}} &= \int_\Sigma \mathbf{r}_{OP} \times \mathbf{v}_{P/\mathcal{G}} dm = \int_\Sigma \mathbf{r}_{OP} \times (\mathbf{v}_{P/\mathcal{E}} + \mathbf{v}_{P\in\mathcal{E}/\mathcal{G}}) dm \\
&= \mathbf{H}_{O,\Sigma/\mathcal{E}} + \int_\Sigma \mathbf{r}_{OP} \times R\Omega_E \cos\lambda\, \hat{\mathbf{y}}_0 \, dm = \mathbf{H}_{O,\Sigma/\mathcal{E}}
\end{aligned}$$

where we have used the fact that O is the mass center of Σ. We then relate the rate of change of $\mathbf{H}_{O,\Sigma/\mathcal{G}}$ relative to $\mathcal{G}$ to that relative to $\mathcal{E}$:

$$\left(\frac{d}{dt}\mathbf{H}_{O,\Sigma/\mathcal{G}}\right)_{\mathcal{G}} = \left(\frac{d}{dt}\mathbf{H}_{O,\Sigma/\mathcal{G}}\right)_{\mathcal{E}} + \boldsymbol{\omega}_{\mathcal{E}/\mathcal{G}} \times \mathbf{H}_{O,\Sigma/\mathcal{G}}$$

with

$$\mathbf{H}_{O,\Sigma/\mathcal{G}} = \mathbf{H}_{O,\Sigma/\mathcal{E}} = \mathbf{H}_{O,1/\mathcal{E}} + \mathbf{H}_{O,2/\mathcal{E}} = I_1\dot{\psi}\hat{\mathbf{z}}_0 + C\dot{\phi}\hat{\mathbf{z}}$$

First we obtain $\left(\frac{d}{dt}\mathbf{H}_{O,\Sigma/\mathcal{G}}\right)_{\mathcal{E}}$:

$$\left(\frac{d}{dt}\mathbf{H}_{O,\Sigma/\mathcal{G}}\right)_{\mathcal{E}} = \left(\frac{d}{dt}(I_1\dot{\psi}\hat{\mathbf{z}}_0 + C\dot{\phi}\hat{\mathbf{z}})\right)_{\mathcal{E}} = I_1\ddot{\psi}\hat{\mathbf{z}}_0 + C\dot{\phi}\dot{\psi}\hat{\mathbf{w}}$$

Next, we find $\boldsymbol{\omega}_{\mathcal{E}/\mathcal{G}} \times \mathbf{H}_{O,\Sigma/\mathcal{G}}$:

$$\Omega_E(-\cos\lambda\hat{\mathbf{x}}_0 + \sin\lambda\hat{\mathbf{z}}_0) \times (I_1\dot{\psi}\hat{\mathbf{z}}_0 + C\dot{\phi}\hat{\mathbf{z}}) = \Omega_E\cos\lambda(I_1\dot{\psi}\hat{\mathbf{y}}_0 - C\dot{\phi}\sin\psi\hat{\mathbf{z}}_0) + (\Omega_E\sin\lambda)C\dot{\phi}\hat{\mathbf{w}}$$

The final expression is then given by

$$\left(\frac{d}{dt}\mathbf{H}_{O,\Sigma/\mathcal{G}}\right)_{\mathcal{G}} = (I_1\ddot{\psi} - C\Omega_E\dot{\phi}\cos\lambda\sin\psi)\hat{\mathbf{z}}_0 + (\Omega_E\cos\lambda)I_1\dot{\psi}\hat{\mathbf{y}}_0 + (\Omega_E\sin\lambda)C\dot{\phi}\hat{\mathbf{w}} \quad (1)$$

b. We apply the dynamic moment equation of the FTD (Euler's second principle) to system Σ relative to referential $\mathcal{G}$ (since $\mathcal{E}$ cannot be assumed Newtonian):

$$\left(\frac{d}{dt}\mathbf{H}_{O,\Sigma/\mathcal{G}}\right)_{\mathcal{G}} = \mathbf{M}_{O,\bar{\Sigma}\to\Sigma}$$

Since O is the mass center of system Σ and the connection with the support 0 is frictionless, the external moment about O satisfies $\hat{\mathbf{z}}_0 \cdot \mathbf{M}_{O,\bar{\Sigma}\to\Sigma} = 0$. This leads to the equation, using (1)

$$I_1\ddot{\psi} - C\Omega_E\dot{\phi}\cos\lambda\sin\psi = 0 \quad (2)$$

Two equilibrium positions are found: $\psi = 0$ (the axis points to the south) and $\psi = \pi$ (the axis points to the south). The position $\psi = 0$ is unstable (note that $\dot{\phi} > 0$). The position $\psi = \pi$ is stable. The small amplitude oscillations about $\psi = \pi$ are governed by

$$I_1\ddot{\epsilon} + (C\Omega_E\dot{\phi}\cos\lambda)\epsilon = 0$$

with $\epsilon = \psi - \pi$. The corresponding period of these oscillations is given by

$$T = 2\pi\sqrt{\frac{I_1}{C\Omega_E\dot{\phi}\cos\lambda}}$$

With the presence of friction, we expect $\hat{\mathbf{z}}_0 \cdot \mathbf{M}_{O,\bar{\Sigma}\to\Sigma} \neq 0$ (proportional to $\dot{\psi}$ for viscous damping): the precessional oscillations will be dampened and the axis of the rotor will point toward the north. ■

Example 15.4 — **Attitude Stabilization of Projectiles.** Consider a projectile modeled as an axisymmetric body $\mathcal{B}$ of mass center G, axis $(G, \hat{\mathbf{z}})$, axial moment of inertia C, and transverse moment of inertia A. This study is limited to an analysis of the stability of the projectile attitude under the effect of aerodynamic forces. To simplify the analysis we assume that the motion of mass center G is uniform and rectilinear. The basis $(\hat{\mathbf{x}}_0, \hat{\mathbf{y}}_0, \hat{\mathbf{z}}_0)$ is fixed relative to the Newtonian referential $\mathcal{E}$, with $\hat{\mathbf{z}}_0$ directed along velocity $\mathbf{v}_G = v_G\hat{\mathbf{z}}_0$, and $\hat{\mathbf{y}}_0$ normal to the vertical plane $(G, \hat{\mathbf{z}}_0, \hat{\mathbf{x}}_0)$. Under these assumptions, the aerodynamic action screw is represented by a moment about G given by

$$\mathbf{M}_{G,\text{air}\to\mathcal{B}} = \mu\hat{\mathbf{z}}_0 \times \hat{\mathbf{z}}, \qquad \mu = \frac{1}{8}C_M \rho v_G^2 r^3$$

where r is a characteristic cross-sectional length, ρ is the air mass density, and C_M is an empirical constant. Denote by θ the attitude (or yaw), that is, the angle between the projective flight path $(G, \hat{\mathbf{z}}_0)$ and the projectile axis $(G, \hat{\mathbf{z}})$. Denote by P the point of $\mathcal{B}$ defined by $\mathbf{r}_{GP} = \hat{\mathbf{z}}$ and by $x = \hat{\mathbf{x}}_0 \cdot \mathbf{r}_{GP}$ and $y = \hat{\mathbf{y}}_0 \cdot \mathbf{r}_{GP}$ the coordinates of the projection Q of P on plane $(G, \hat{\mathbf{x}}_0, \hat{\mathbf{y}}_0)$.

a. Show that the motion of axis $(G, \hat{\mathbf{z}})$ is governed by the equations

$$C\frac{d\omega}{dt} = 0, \qquad C\omega\frac{d\hat{\mathbf{z}}}{dt} + A\hat{\mathbf{z}} \times \frac{d^2\hat{\mathbf{z}}}{dt^2} = \mu\hat{\mathbf{z}}_0 \times \hat{\mathbf{z}}$$

with $\omega = \hat{\mathbf{z}} \cdot \boldsymbol{\omega}_{\mathcal{B}/\mathcal{E}}$.

b. Deduce the equations governing (x, y) assuming that angle θ is small. To integrate these equations, define complex number $\zeta = x + iy$ $(i^2 = -1)$. Find ζ versus t and derive a condition for the stability of the attitude of $\mathcal{B}$. Sketch the trajectory of Q. ■

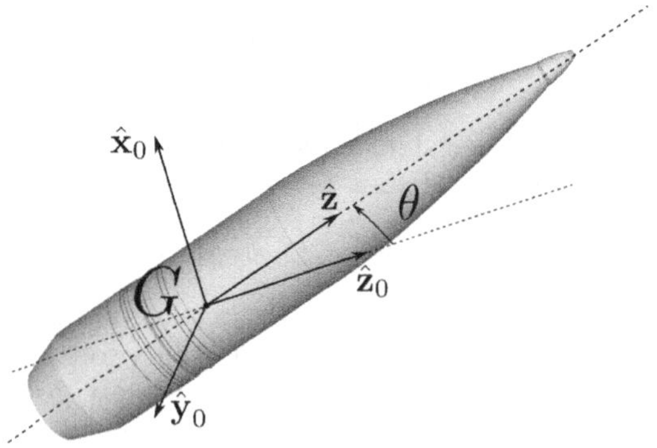

Figure 15.10

a. The angular velocity of $\mathcal{B}$ can be expressed as

$$\boldsymbol{\omega} = \omega\hat{\mathbf{z}} + \hat{\mathbf{z}} \times \frac{d\hat{\mathbf{z}}}{dt}$$

This leads to the following expression of the angular momentum $\mathbf{H}_G$:

$$\mathbf{H}_G = C\omega\hat{\mathbf{z}} + A\hat{\mathbf{z}} \times \frac{d\hat{\mathbf{z}}}{dt}$$

and its rate of change

$$\frac{d}{dt}\mathbf{H}_G = C\frac{d\omega}{dt}\hat{\mathbf{z}} + C\omega\frac{d\hat{\mathbf{z}}}{dt} + A\hat{\mathbf{z}} \times \frac{d^2\hat{\mathbf{z}}}{dt^2}$$

Application of Euler's second principle gives

$$C\frac{d\omega}{dt}\hat{\mathbf{z}} + A\hat{\mathbf{z}} \times \frac{d^2\hat{\mathbf{z}}}{dt^2} = \mathbf{M}_{\overline{\mathcal{B}}\to\mathcal{B}} = \mathbf{M}_{G,\text{air}\to\mathcal{B}} = \mu\hat{\mathbf{z}}_0 \times \hat{\mathbf{z}}$$

This yields two equations: first along $\hat{\mathbf{z}}$

$$C\frac{d\omega}{dt} = 0 \tag{1}$$

and along the normals to $\hat{\mathbf{z}}$

$$C\omega\frac{d\hat{\mathbf{z}}}{dt} + A\hat{\mathbf{z}} \times \frac{d^2\hat{\mathbf{z}}}{dt^2} = \mu\hat{\mathbf{z}}_0 \times \hat{\mathbf{z}} \tag{2}$$

b. Equation (1) gives $\omega = Cst$. Equation (2) can be expressed in terms of (x,y) and its derivatives

$$C\omega(\dot{x}\hat{\mathbf{x}}_0 + \dot{y}\hat{\mathbf{y}}_0) + A(-\ddot{y}\hat{\mathbf{x}}_0 + \ddot{x}\hat{\mathbf{y}}_0) = \mu(-y\hat{\mathbf{x}}_0 + x\hat{\mathbf{y}}_0)$$

yielding two differential equations governing x and y:

$$A\ddot{y} - C\omega\dot{x} - \mu y = 0$$

$$A\ddot{x} + C\omega\dot{y} - \mu x = 0$$

With $\zeta = x + iy$, we find

$$A\ddot{\zeta} = A\ddot{x} + iA\ddot{y} = i(C\omega\dot{x} + \mu y) + (-C\omega\dot{y} + \mu x) = C\omega(-\dot{y} + i\dot{x}) + \mu(x + iy)$$

We obtain a linear equation governing ζ:

$$A\ddot{\zeta} - iC\omega\dot{\zeta} - \mu\zeta = 0$$

Seeking solutions of the type $\zeta_0 e^{rt}$, we find the characteristic equation

$$Ar^2 - iC\omega r - \mu = 0$$

whose roots are $r_{1,2} = (iC\omega \pm (-C^2\omega^2 + 4A\mu)^{1/2})/2A = i\Omega_{1,2}$. For stable solutions we need to impose the condition

$$C^2\omega^2 > 4A\mu \tag{3}$$

otherwise the solution (x,y) will be unbounded functions of time. The general solution is then

$$\zeta(t) = \alpha_1 e^{i(\Omega_1 t + \beta_1)} + \alpha_2 e^{i(\Omega_2 t + \beta_2)}$$

where $(\alpha_1, \alpha_2, \beta_1, \beta_2)$ are constants of integration. In the limit $C^2\omega^2 \gg 4A\mu$, the frequency $\Omega_1 = 2\mu/C\omega$ corresponds to the slow precessional rotation of the axis $(G, \hat{\mathbf{z}})$ about $(G, \hat{\mathbf{z}}_0)$, while frequency $\Omega_2 = C\omega/A$ corresponds to the fast nutational perturbations. The motion of Q projection of P on plane $(O, \hat{\mathbf{x}}_0, \hat{\mathbf{y}}_0)$ is an epicycloid: an example is shown in Figure 15.11.

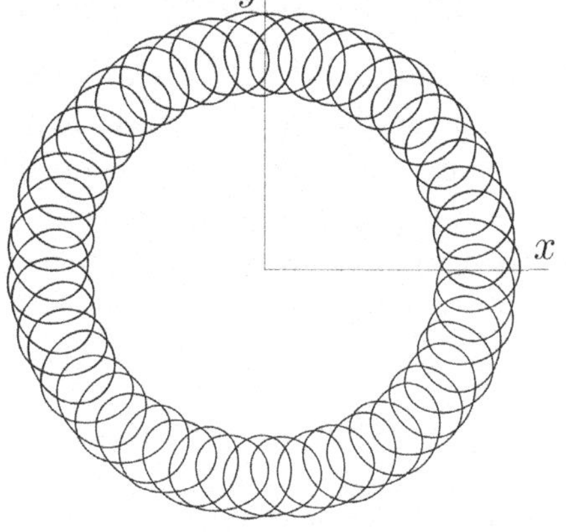

Figure 15.11

■

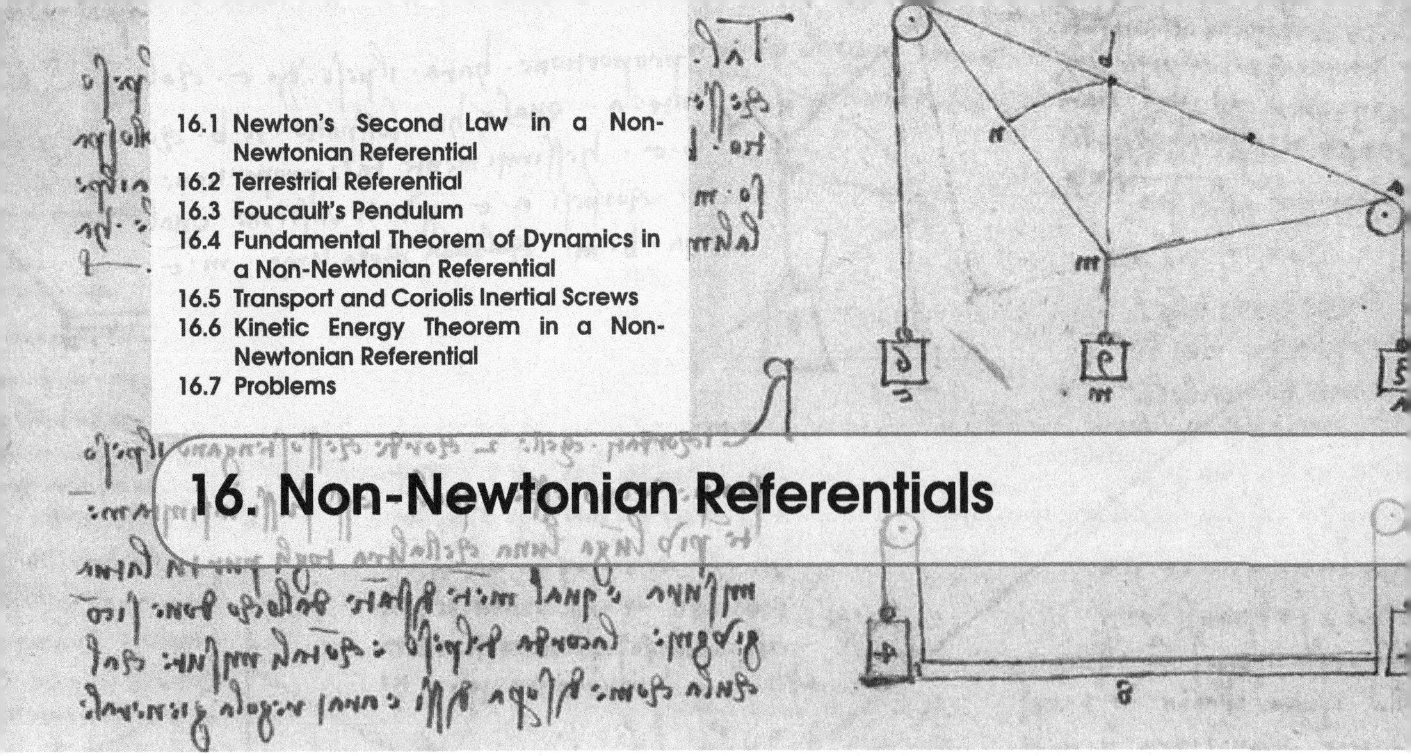

16. Non-Newtonian Referentials

THE MAIN TASK of this chapter is to generalize the Fundamental Theorem of Dynamics relative to a non-Newtonian referential. This generalization is fundamental to the study of the effect of Earth's rotation on the motion of material systems. For the motion of particles, Newton's second law is modified by the appearance of inertial forces of two types: transport and Coriolis forces. More generally, for material systems, the FTD is modified by inertial action screws. We shall learn how to determine the transport and Coriolis inertial screws for rigid bodies. These closed-form expressions will be useful to derive a generalization of the Kinetic Energy Theorem relative to non-Newtonian referentials. In particular, we shall show that the Coriolis inertial forces are non-working forces.

16.1 Newton's Second Law in a Non-Newtonian Referential

Consider a referential $\mathcal{F}$ whose motion is known relative to referential $\mathcal{E}$ assumed Newtonian. We wish to extend Newton's second law for a particle P in motion relative to $\mathcal{F}$. On one hand, Newton's second law states that $m\mathbf{a}_{P/\mathcal{E}} = \mathbf{F}$, denoting by $\mathbf{F}$ the resultant force acting on P, On the other hand, the acceleration of P relative to $\mathcal{E}$ can be determined from that relative to $\mathcal{F}$ according to the change of referential formula (6.5)

$$\mathbf{a}_{P/\mathcal{E}} = \mathbf{a}_{P/\mathcal{F}} + \mathbf{a}_{P\in\mathcal{F}/\mathcal{E}} + 2\boldsymbol{\omega}_{\mathcal{F}/\mathcal{E}} \times \mathbf{v}_{P/\mathcal{F}}$$

This leads to the following generalization of Newton's second law to non-Newtonian referentials.

Theorem 16.1 Newton's second law can be written relative to a non-Newtonian referential $\mathcal{F}$ as if $\mathcal{F}$ were Newtonian, as long as *inertial forces* $\tilde{\mathbf{F}}_i$ (proportional to the mass m of P)

are added to the resultant force $\mathbf{F}$ acting on P

$$m\mathbf{a}_{P/\mathcal{F}} = \mathbf{F} + \tilde{\mathbf{F}}_i \tag{16.1}$$

where the inertial forces are of two types:
(i) force $\tilde{\mathbf{F}}_{trp} = -m\mathbf{a}_{P\in\mathcal{F}/\mathcal{E}}$ is called *transport force,*
(ii) force $\tilde{\mathbf{F}}_{cor} = -2m\boldsymbol{\omega}_{\mathcal{F}/\mathcal{E}} \times \mathbf{v}_{P/\mathcal{F}}$ is called *Coriolis force.*

Equation (16.1) plays a fundamental role in evaluating whether a referential can be considered adequately Newtonian or not. If both inertial forces $\tilde{\mathbf{F}}_{trp}$ and $\tilde{\mathbf{F}}_{cor}$ are negligible relative to resultant force $\mathbf{F}$, then referential $\mathcal{F}$ can be considered Newtonian for the motion of P. Equation (16.1) can also be used to evaluate the effect of inertial forces on a rigid body.

Remark 1. Inertial forces are pseudoforces: they do not originate from the action of a material system. Hence, they do not satisfy the law of action and reaction. However, they should not be qualified as fictitious since they do lead to real effects.

Remark 2. In general, if P is at rest relative to referential $\mathcal{F}$, the Coriolis force vanishes. However, the transport force must be taken into account to express the equilibrium of P in $\mathcal{F}$:

$$\mathbf{F} + \tilde{\mathbf{F}}_{trp} = \mathbf{0}$$

Remark 3. If $\mathcal{F}$ is in pure translation relative to $\mathcal{E}$, then all points attached to $\mathcal{F}$ have the same acceleration, say $\mathbf{a}_F$, relative to $\mathcal{E}$. We can then write (16.1) in the form

$$m\mathbf{a}_{P/\mathcal{F}} = \mathbf{F} - m\mathbf{a}_F \tag{16.2}$$

for any particle P.

Remark 4. If $\mathcal{F}$ is in pure rotation relative to $\mathcal{E}$ at constant angular velocity $\omega\hat{\mathbf{e}}_z$ about an axis $\Delta(O, \hat{\mathbf{e}}_z)$ fixed in $\mathcal{E}$, the inertial force $\mathbf{F}_e$ is commonly referred to as the *centrifugal force.* This force takes the following expression

$$\tilde{\mathbf{F}}_{trp} = -m\mathbf{a}_{P\in\mathcal{F}/\mathcal{E}} = m\omega^2\mathbf{r}_{HP} \tag{16.3}$$

where H is the projection of P onto axis Δ. Furthermore, the Coriolis force

$$\tilde{\mathbf{F}}_{cor} = -2m\omega\hat{\mathbf{e}}_z \times \mathbf{v}_{P/\mathcal{F}}$$

is non-zero.

16.2 Terrestrial Referential

Consider a particle P in motion, observed in a terrestrial referential $\mathcal{E}$ attached at a point O of Earth at colatitude ϕ, with Cartesian axes $Oxyz$ defined as follows:

- axis Ox is tangent to the meridian at O and directed southward,
- axis Oy is tangent to the parallel at O and directed eastward,
- axis Oz is directed upward, that is, along the vertical as defined by a plumb line experiment at O (see Section 10.2.4).

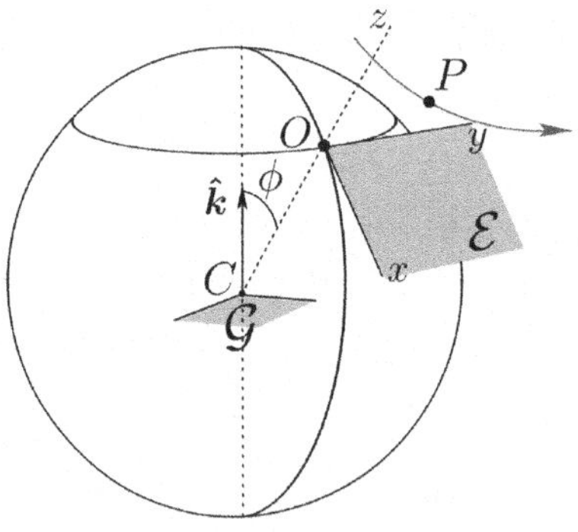

Figure 16.1

Newton's second law applied to particle P (of mass m) is given by equation (16.1) taking into account the inertial forces induced by the rotation of $\mathcal{E}$ about axis $(C, \hat{\mathbf{k}})$ of Geocentric referential $\mathcal{G}$

$$m\mathbf{a}_{P/\mathcal{E}} = \mathbf{F} - m\mathbf{a}_{P\in\mathcal{E}/\mathcal{G}} - 2m\boldsymbol{\omega}_{\mathcal{E}/\mathcal{G}} \times \mathbf{v}_{P/\mathcal{E}} \tag{16.4}$$

with $\boldsymbol{\omega}_{\mathcal{E}/\mathcal{G}} = \omega_E \hat{\mathbf{k}}$. Denoting by $\mathbf{G}_P$ the gravitational field at P, we can write the resultant force $\mathbf{F}$ acting on P as the sum of $m\mathbf{G}_P + \mathbf{F}'$. Then, the motion of P relative to $\mathcal{E}$ is governed by the equation

$$m\mathbf{a}_{P/\mathcal{E}} = \mathbf{F}' + m\mathbf{g}_P - 2m\omega\hat{\mathbf{k}} \times \mathbf{v}_{P/\mathcal{E}} \tag{16.5}$$

where we have denoted by $\mathbf{g}_P = \mathbf{G}_P - \mathbf{a}_{P\in\mathcal{E}/\mathcal{G}}$ the gravitational acceleration at point P relative to $\mathcal{E}$. In most applications, we may treat the gravitational acceleration as the constant vector $\mathbf{g}_P \approx \mathbf{G}_O - \mathbf{a}_{O\in\mathcal{E}/\mathcal{G}} \approx -g\hat{\mathbf{e}}_z$ parallel to axis Oz with $g = 9.81$ m/s^2 as long as the extent of the motion is small compared to the distances over which $\mathbf{g}_P$ varies appreciably. In this case, we can write the equations governing the Cartesian coordinates $(x(t), y(t), z(t))$ of P relatives to $Oxyz$:

$$\begin{aligned} m\ddot{x} &= F'_x + 2m\omega_E \dot{y}\cos\phi \\ m\ddot{y} &= F'_y - 2m\omega_E(\dot{x}\cos\phi + \dot{z}\sin\phi) \\ m\ddot{z} &= F'_x - mg + 2m\omega_E \dot{y}\sin\phi \end{aligned} \tag{16.6}$$

where (F'_x, F'_y, F'_z) are the components of $\mathbf{F}'$ on $(\hat{\mathbf{e}}_x, \hat{\mathbf{e}}_y, \hat{\mathbf{e}}_z)$. The effect of Coriolis inertial forces on the motion of a particle was first demonstrated by Foucault's experiment. This experiment can be modeled by equations (16.6). See Section 16.3.

Example 16.1 Consider a particle P of mass m in motion relative to a terrestrial referential $\mathcal{E}$ of Cartesian coordinate axes $Oxyz$ where axis Ox points to the South, axis Oy points to the East, and axis Oz points upward. P moves under the sole effect of a constant gravitational acceleration $\mathbf{g} = -g\hat{\mathbf{e}}_z$ and of Coriolis inertial force due to Earth's rotation.

a. Show that the position vector $\mathbf{r} = \mathbf{r}_{OP}$ of P is solution of the equation

$$\frac{d\mathbf{r}}{dt} = \mathbf{v}_0 + \mathbf{g}t + 2\omega_E \hat{\mathbf{k}} \times (\mathbf{r}(0) - \mathbf{r}(t)) \tag{1}$$

where $\mathbf{r}(0)$ is the initial value of $\mathbf{r}$, and $\mathbf{v}_0$ is the initial velocity of P relative to $\mathcal{E}$.

b. In order to find of solution of equation [1], we can take advantage of the small value of ω_E and seek an approximate solution in the form

$$\mathbf{r}(t) = \mathbf{r}_0(t) + \omega_E \mathbf{r}_1(t) + \omega_E^2 \mathbf{r}_2(t) + \cdots$$

Find the expressions of $\mathbf{r}_0(t)$, $\mathbf{r}_1(t)$ and $\mathbf{r}_2(t)$ as functions of time.

c. Assume that P is dropped without initial speed from a height h directly above O. Find the eastward and southward deviation from O of the impact location of P into the horizontal plane Oxy. Find the deviations of P for $h = 200$ m at colatitude $\phi = 45°$. ▪

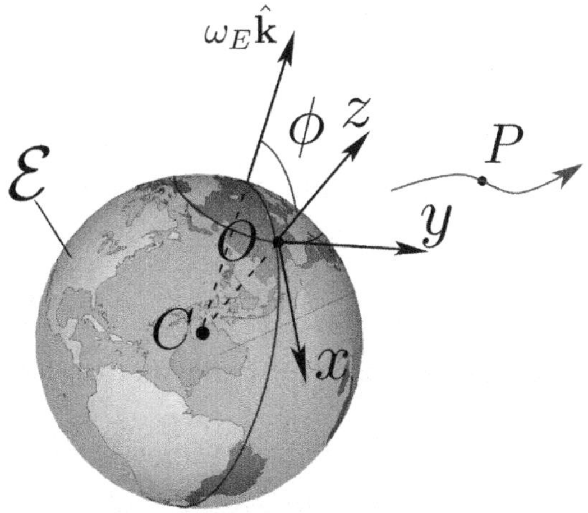

Figure 16.2

a. We apply the Newton's second law in (non-Newtonian) referential $\mathcal{E}$ by accounting for Coriolis inertial force (and neglecting the centrifugal force) to find

$$\frac{d\mathbf{v}_P}{dt} = \mathbf{g} - 2\omega_E \hat{\mathbf{k}} \times \mathbf{v}_P$$

Since $\hat{\mathbf{k}}$ is fixed relative to $\mathcal{E}$, we can integrate this equation to find

$$\mathbf{v}_P = \frac{d\mathbf{r}}{dt} = \mathbf{v}_0 + \mathbf{g}t - 2\omega_E \hat{\mathbf{k}} \times (\mathbf{r}(t) - \mathbf{r}(0)) \qquad [1]$$

taking into account the initial conditions $\mathbf{v}_P = \mathbf{v}_0$ at $t = 0$.

b. An exact solution of equation [1] is possible. But it is more practical to solve it in terms of an expansion in powers of ω_E:

$$\mathbf{r}(t) = \mathbf{r}_0(t) + \omega_E \mathbf{r}_1(t) + \omega_E^2 \mathbf{r}_2(t) + \cdots \qquad [2]$$

The leading term $\mathbf{r}_0$ is found by substituting [2] in [1] and collecting all terms in $\omega_E^0 = 1$: we find

$$\frac{d\mathbf{r}_0}{dt} = \mathbf{v}_0 + \mathbf{g}t$$

whose integration gives

$$\mathbf{r}_0 = \mathbf{r}(0) + \mathbf{v}_0 t + \frac{1}{2}\mathbf{g}t^2$$

This solution corresponds to neglecting Coriolis force, and would be the exact parabolic trajectory if referential $\mathcal{E}$ is assumed Newtonian.

At the next order, we collect all terms in powers of ω_E and find

$$\frac{d\mathbf{r}_1}{dt} = -2\hat{\mathbf{k}} \times [\mathbf{r}_0(t) - \mathbf{r}(0)] = -2\hat{\mathbf{k}} \times [\mathbf{v}_0 t + \frac{1}{2}\mathbf{g}t^2]$$

whose integration gives

$$\mathbf{r}_1 = -\hat{\mathbf{k}} \times [\mathbf{v}_0 t^2 + \frac{1}{3}\mathbf{g}t^3]$$

since $\mathbf{r}_1(0) = \mathbf{0}$.

Finally at order 2, we find

$$\frac{d\mathbf{r}_2}{dt} = -2\hat{\mathbf{k}} \times \mathbf{r}_1(t) = 2\hat{\mathbf{k}} \times \left[\hat{\mathbf{k}} \times (\mathbf{v}_0 t^2 + \frac{1}{3}\mathbf{g}t^3)\right]$$

whose integration gives

$$\mathbf{r}_2 = \frac{2}{3}\hat{\mathbf{k}} \times \left[\hat{\mathbf{k}} \times (\mathbf{v}_0 t^3 + \frac{1}{4}\mathbf{g}t^4)\right]$$

c. With $\mathbf{v}_0 = \mathbf{0}$ and $\mathbf{r}(0) = h\hat{\mathbf{e}}_z$, we find from the previous results

$$\mathbf{r}(t) = h\hat{\mathbf{e}}_z + \frac{1}{2}\mathbf{g}t^2 - \frac{1}{3}\omega_E\hat{\mathbf{k}} \times \mathbf{g}t^3 + \frac{1}{6}\omega_E^2\hat{\mathbf{k}} \times (\hat{\mathbf{k}} \times \mathbf{g})t^4 + O(\omega_E^3)$$

We may project $\mathbf{r}$ on axes $Oxyz$ to find the Cartesian coordinates

$$x(t) = \frac{1}{6}g\omega_E^2(\sin\phi\cos\phi)t^4, \quad y(t) = \frac{1}{3}g\omega_E(\sin\phi)t^3, \quad z(t) = h - \frac{1}{2}gt^2 - \frac{1}{6}g\omega_E^2(\sin^2\phi)t^4$$

The expressions of $x(t)$ and $y(t)$ show that P is deflected toward the east and south directions, the southward deflection being much smaller by the eastward deflection. We find the time t_i of impact by neglecting the ω^2 term in the expression of $z(t)$:

$$t_i = \sqrt{\frac{2h}{g}}$$

Then, the southward and eastward deflections at impact are given by

$$x_i = \frac{2h}{3g}\omega_E^2 \sin\phi\cos\phi, \qquad y_i = \frac{2}{3}\omega_E \sin\phi\sqrt{\frac{2h^3}{g}}$$

For $g = 9.8$ m/s^2, $\phi = 45°$ and $h = 200$ m, we find the values $x_i \approx \mathbf{3.6 \times 10^{-8}}$ m and $y_i \approx 44$ mm. Only the eastward deviation would be measurable experimentally. [1] ■

16.3 Foucault's Pendulum

Foucault's pendulum experiment was first demonstrated in 1852 by hanging a heavy mass from Paris' Panthéon at latitude $\lambda = \pi/2 - \phi = 48.85°$. The pendulum's length was chosen to be $L = 67$ m, the mass was released without initial speed at a distance of 3m from its equilibrium position. The experiments revealed that the oscillations do not take place in a fixed vertical plane of $\mathcal{E}$, as it should if the only forces acting on P are the string's tension and the force of gravity. Rather P exhibits a more complex motion whereby the

[1] The eastward deviation was first observed by Ferdinand Reich in 1833: an object was dropped in a 158 m deep mine shaft in Freiberg, Germany. He measured a 28 mm deviation in agreement with the expression of y_i for $\phi = 39°$.

plane of oscillations rotates slowly about axis Oz with a period of 31 hours and 47 minutes. These results cannot be explained if referential $\mathcal{E}$ is assumed Newtonian. Hence Foucault's pendulum demonstrated the non-Newtonian character of referential $\mathcal{E}$. This experiment is now replicated in many science museums around the world where the motion of the pendulum is maintained indefinitely by electromagnetic forces to compensate its gradual slowing down due to frictional forces.

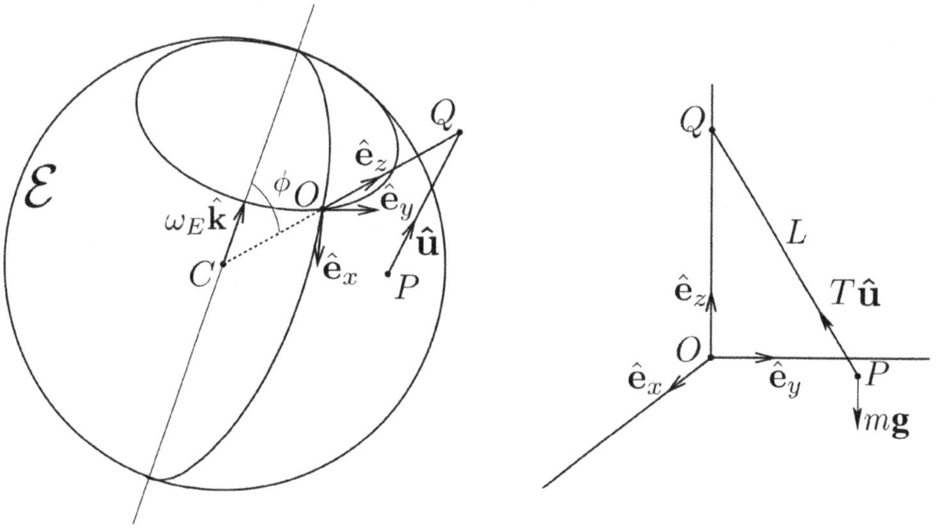

Figure 16.3 – *Foucault's pendulum*

To predict the motion of P, we use equations (16.6) to account for the Earth's rotation. With the notations of Figure 16.3, assume that the coordinates of attachment point Q are $(0, 0, L)$, and that the coordinates of initial position P_0 are $(0, y_0, z_0)$ with $z_0 \ll L$. Denote by $\mathbf{T} = T\hat{\mathbf{u}}$ the string's tension, where $\hat{\mathbf{u}}$ is the unit vector defined by

$$\hat{\mathbf{u}} = \frac{1}{L}\mathbf{r}_{PQ} = -\frac{x}{L}\hat{\mathbf{e}}_x - \frac{y}{L}\hat{\mathbf{e}}_y - \frac{z-L}{L}\hat{\mathbf{e}}_z$$

We neglect all possible frictional forces. Now equations (16.6) become

$$m\ddot{x} = -T\frac{x}{L} + 2m\omega_E\dot{y}\cos\phi \tag{16.7}$$

$$m\ddot{y} = -T\frac{y}{L} - 2m\omega_E(\dot{x}\cos\phi + \dot{z}\sin\phi) \tag{16.8}$$

$$m\ddot{z} = -T\frac{z-L}{L} - mg + 2m\omega_E\dot{y}\sin\phi \tag{16.9}$$

To simplify these equations we note that we expect that the motion to be essentially contained in a horizontal plane, given the small initial deviation of P from its equilibrium position. Hence $z \ll L$ and that $\ddot{z} - 2\omega_E\dot{y}\sin\phi \ll g$, which shows that the tension remains sensibly constant: equation (16.9) becomes

$$T \approx mg$$

leading to $z = z_0 \approx 0$. Furthermore, if point O is located sufficiently far from the equator ($\phi \neq \pi/2$) then we expect $\dot{x}\cos\phi \approx \dot{y}\cos\phi \gg \dot{z}\sin\phi$. This leads to the simplified system of linear homogeneous o.d.e.'s

$$\ddot{x} + \omega_0^2 x = 2\omega_E \dot{y} \cos\phi \qquad (16.10)$$

$$\ddot{y} + \omega_0^2 y = -2\omega_E \dot{x} \cos\phi \qquad (16.11)$$

where we have denoted $\omega_0^2 = g/L$. Note that ω_0 is the frequency of small amplitude oscillations of the pendulum in the absence of Coriolis forces. We expect $\omega_E \ll \omega_0$. This system is easily integrated by introducing the complex variable $Z(t) = x(t) + iy(t)$. Then we have

$$\ddot{Z} = \ddot{x} + i\ddot{y} = -\omega_0^2(x + iy) + 2\omega_E \cos\phi(\dot{y} + i\dot{x}) = -\omega_0^2 Z - 2i\omega_E \cos\phi Z$$

This o.d.e. admits two solutions of the type $\exp(st)$ with s solution of the quadratic equation $s^2 + 2i(\omega_E \cos\phi)s + \omega_0^2 = 0$:

$$s_{1,2} = -i\omega_E \cos\phi \pm i(\omega_0^2 + \omega_E^2 \cos^2\phi) \approx -i\omega_E \cos\phi \pm i\omega_0$$

Hence, the solution is of the form

$$Z(t) = x(t) + iy(t) = e^{-i(\omega_E \cos\phi)t}\left(ae^{i\omega_0 t} + be^{-i\omega_0 t}\right)$$

where the constants of integration are found by imposing the initial conditions: at $t = 0$, we impose $\dot{Z} = 0$ leading to

$$b/a = (\omega_0 - \omega_E \cos\phi)/(\omega_0 + \omega_E \cos\phi) \approx 1$$

and $Z = iy_0$ leading to $a = b = iy_0/2$.

The final solution is then given by

$$\begin{aligned} Z(t) &= x(t) + iy(t) = iy_0 \cos(\omega_0 t)e^{-i(\omega_E \cos\phi)t} \\ &= y_0 \cos(\omega_0 t)\left[-\sin(\omega_E t \cos\phi) + i\cos(\omega_E t \cos\phi)\right] \end{aligned} \qquad (16.12)$$

From this result, we can conclude that

1. over a short time scale $T_0 = 2\pi/\omega_0$, the effect of Coriolis forces on the motion of P is negligible: indeed
$$Z(t + T_0) = Z(t)e^{-i(\omega_E \cos\phi)T_0} \approx Z(t)$$
since $\omega_E T_0$ is a very small number. Hence over a time scale T_0, the pendulum oscillates in a vertical plane fixed in $\mathcal{E}$.
2. over a much larger time scale $T_E = 2\pi/\omega_E \gg T_0$, the effect of Coriolis forces is seen to cause a rotation of the plane of oscillations about vertical axis Oz with constant angular velocity $\omega = -\omega_E \cos\phi$: this plane completes a full rotation over a period $T = T_E/\cos\phi$. This rotation is clockwise when seen by an observer looking down on plane Oxy in the northern hemisphere. The rotation is anticlockwise in the southern hemisphere.

Numerically, we find $T_0 = 16.4$ seconds, and $T = 31$ hours 47 mn, in total agreement with the experimental measurements. This agreement supports the hypothesis that the geocentric referential $\mathcal{G}$ is a better approximation of a Newtonian referential than the terrestrial referential $\mathcal{E}$. For motions taking place over sufficiently short time intervals (particularly near the equator), $\mathcal{E}$ can still be considered as a satisfactory approximation to a Newtonian referential. Furthermore, these conclusions do not mean that Geocentric referential $\mathcal{G}$ is always a good approximation of a Newtonian referential.

16.4 Fundamental Theorem of Dynamics in a Non-Newtonian Referential

Here, we wish to extend the FTD to a non-Newtonian referential $\mathcal{F}$ whose motion relative to a Newtonian referential $\mathcal{E}$ is entirely known. Starting with the FTD relative to $\mathcal{E}$, $\{\mathcal{D}_{\Sigma/\mathcal{E}}\} = \{\mathcal{A}_{\overline{\Sigma}\to\Sigma}\}$, we can relate the dynamic screws $\{\mathcal{D}_{\Sigma/\mathcal{E}}\}$ and $\{\mathcal{D}_{\Sigma/\mathcal{F}}\}$ by using the formula

$$\mathbf{a}_{P/\mathcal{E}} = \mathbf{a}_{P/\mathcal{F}} + \mathbf{a}_{P\in\mathcal{F}/\mathcal{E}} + 2\boldsymbol{\omega}_{\mathcal{F}/\mathcal{E}} \times \mathbf{v}_{P/\mathcal{F}} \tag{16.13}$$

Recall that the field of acceleration $P \mapsto \mathbf{a}_{P/\mathcal{E}}$ leads to the dynamic screw $\{\mathcal{D}_{\Sigma/\mathcal{E}}\}$. Hence equation (16.13) shows that the dynamic screw $\{\mathcal{D}_{\Sigma/\mathcal{E}}\}$ relative to $\mathcal{E}$ can be related to that relative to $\mathcal{F}$. This gives us a generalization of the Fundamental Theorem of Dynamics.

Theorem 16.2 — FTD in a non-Newtonian Referential. The fields of transport acceleration $P \mapsto \mathbf{a}_{P\in\mathcal{F}/\mathcal{E}}$ and Coriolis acceleration $P \mapsto 2\boldsymbol{\omega}_{\mathcal{F}/\mathcal{E}} \times \mathbf{v}_{P/\mathcal{F}}$ generate two action screws called *transport inertial screw* and *Coriolis inertial screw*, respectively. Then the Fundamental Theorem of Dynamics applied to a material Σ of constant mass relative to non-Newtonian referential $\mathcal{F}$ can be stated as follows

$$\{\mathcal{D}_{\Sigma/\mathcal{F}}\} = \{\mathcal{A}_{\overline{\Sigma}\to\Sigma}\} - \begin{Bmatrix} \int_\Sigma \mathbf{a}_{P\in\mathcal{F}/\mathcal{E}}\, dm \\ \int_\Sigma \mathbf{r}_{AP} \times \mathbf{a}_{P\in\mathcal{F}/\mathcal{E}}\, dm \end{Bmatrix} - \begin{Bmatrix} \int_\Sigma 2\boldsymbol{\omega}_{\mathcal{F}/\mathcal{E}} \times \mathbf{v}_{P/\mathcal{F}}\, dm \\ \int_\Sigma \mathbf{r}_{AP} \times (2\boldsymbol{\omega}_{\mathcal{F}/\mathcal{E}} \times \mathbf{v}_{P/\mathcal{F}})\, dm \end{Bmatrix} \tag{16.14}$$

In section 16.5, we derive general expressions of the inertial screws in the case of a *rigid body* and for arbitrary motion between $\mathcal{F}$ and $\mathcal{E}$. First we consider the following example.

Example 16.2 A rigid spherical ball $\mathcal{S}$ of radius a, uniform mass m and mass center C is set in motion on a rotating turntable $\mathcal{F}$ constrained to rotate uniformly about a vertical axis $(O, \hat{\mathbf{e}}_z)$ which remains fixed in some Newtonian referential $\mathcal{E}$. We denote by
(i) $(\hat{\mathbf{f}}_x, \hat{\mathbf{f}}_y, \hat{\mathbf{f}}_z = \hat{\mathbf{e}}_z)$ a basis which rotates with $\mathcal{F}$,
(ii) $\omega\hat{\mathbf{e}}_z$ the prescribed constant angular velocity of turntable $\mathcal{F}$ relative to $\mathcal{E}$,
(iii) $\boldsymbol{\Omega} \equiv \boldsymbol{\omega}_{\mathcal{S}/\mathcal{F}} = p\hat{\mathbf{f}}_x + q\hat{\mathbf{f}}_y + r\hat{\mathbf{e}}_z$ the unknown angular velocity of $\mathcal{S}$ relative to $\mathcal{F}$,
(iv) $\mathbf{v}_C \equiv \mathbf{v}_{C/\mathcal{F}} = \dot{x}_C\hat{\mathbf{f}}_x + \dot{y}_C\hat{\mathbf{f}}_y$ the velocity of its mass center C relative to $\mathcal{F}$.

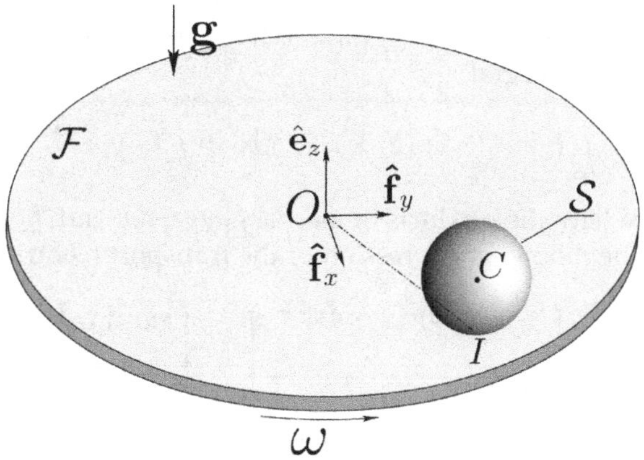

Figure 16.4

The ball is assumed to roll and spin without slipping. We neglect rolling and spinning friction. The moment of inertia of $\mathcal{S}$ about one of its diameters is $\frac{2}{5}ma^2$. The goal of this problem is to apply the FTD relative to *non-Newtonian* referential $\mathcal{F}$ and to determine the trajectory of center C relative to $\mathcal{F}$.

a. Find an expression of the transport inertial screw of the ball.

b. Find an expression of the Coriolis inertial screw of the ball.

c. Apply the FTD to ball $\mathcal{S}$ relative to $\mathcal{F}$ to find six equations governing (x_C, y_C, p, q, r) and the unknown reaction force of $\mathcal{F}$ on $\mathcal{S}$.

d. Assume that $\mathcal{S}$ does not slip relative to $\mathcal{F}$: derive the two equations of motion governing the components (x_C, y_C) of center C. Integrate these equations with the initial conditions $x_C(0) = x_0$, $y_C(0) = 0$, $\dot{x}_C(0) = \dot{x}_0$ and $\dot{y}_C(0) = \dot{y}_0$. Plot the trajectory of C for $\dot{x}_0 = \dot{x}_0 = 0$. ∎

a. The transport inertial screw resolved about arbitrary point A takes the form

$$\begin{Bmatrix} -\int_{\mathcal{S}} \mathbf{a}_{P\in\mathcal{F}/\mathcal{E}}\, dm \\ -\int_{\mathcal{S}} \mathbf{r}_{AP} \times \mathbf{a}_{P\in\mathcal{F}/\mathcal{E}}\, dm \end{Bmatrix}$$

where the transport acceleration is given by

$$\mathbf{a}_{P\in\mathcal{F}/\mathcal{E}} = \omega\hat{\mathbf{e}}_z \times (\omega\hat{\mathbf{e}}_z \times \mathbf{r}_{OP})$$

since referential $\mathcal{F}$ is in rotation about axis $(O, \hat{\mathbf{e}}_z)$. We start with the expression of the resultant of this screw:

$$-\int_{\mathcal{S}} \mathbf{a}_{P\in\mathcal{F}/\mathcal{E}} dm = -\omega\hat{\mathbf{e}}_z \times (\omega\hat{\mathbf{e}}_z \times \int_{\mathcal{S}} \mathbf{r}_{OP} dm) = -m\omega^2\hat{\mathbf{e}}_z \times (\hat{\mathbf{e}}_z \times \mathbf{r}_{OC})$$

Since C is the mass center of $\mathcal{S}$ with $\mathbf{r}_{OC} = x_C\hat{\mathbf{f}}_x + y_C\hat{\mathbf{f}}_y + a\hat{\mathbf{e}}_z$ we find

$$-\int_{\mathcal{S}} \mathbf{a}_{P\in\mathcal{F}/\mathcal{E}} dm = m\omega^2(x_C\hat{\mathbf{f}}_x + y_C\hat{\mathbf{f}}_y)$$

Next, to take advantage of the symmetry of $\mathcal{S}$, we seek to find the expression of the moment of the transport inertial screw about point C:

$$\int_{\mathcal{S}} \mathbf{r}_{CP} \times \mathbf{a}_{P\in\mathcal{F}/\mathcal{E}} dm = \omega^2 \int_{\mathcal{S}} \mathbf{r}_{CP} \times [\hat{\mathbf{e}}_z \times (\hat{\mathbf{e}}_z \times (\mathbf{r}_{OC} + \mathbf{r}_{CP}))] dm = \omega^2 \int_{\mathcal{S}} \mathbf{r}_{CP} \times [\hat{\mathbf{e}}_z \times (\hat{\mathbf{e}}_z \times \mathbf{r}_{CP})] dm$$

where we have used the fact $\int_{\mathcal{S}} \mathbf{r}_{CP} dm = \mathbf{0}$. Next we write $\mathbf{r}_{CP} = x_P\hat{\mathbf{f}}_x + y_P\hat{\mathbf{f}}_y + z_P\hat{\mathbf{f}}_z$ and we can simplify the last integral

$$\int_{\mathcal{S}} \mathbf{r}_{CP} \times [\hat{\mathbf{e}}_z \times (\hat{\mathbf{e}}_z \times \mathbf{r}_{CP})] dm = \int_{\mathcal{S}} (-y_P z_P \hat{\mathbf{f}}_x + x_P z_P \hat{\mathbf{f}}_y) dm$$

By symmetry, we have the products of inertia $\int_{\mathcal{S}} y_P z_P dm$ and $\int_{\mathcal{S}} x_P z_P dm$ vanish. In conclusion, we have found the following expression of the transport (centrifugal) inertial screw

$$\begin{Bmatrix} -\int_{\mathcal{S}} \mathbf{a}_{P\in\mathcal{F}/\mathcal{E}}\, dm \\ -\int_{\mathcal{S}} \mathbf{r}_{CP} \times \mathbf{a}_{P\in\mathcal{F}/\mathcal{E}}\, dm \end{Bmatrix} = \begin{Bmatrix} m\omega^2(x_C\hat{\mathbf{f}}_x + y_C\hat{\mathbf{f}}_y) \\ \mathbf{0} \end{Bmatrix}_C$$

b. The Coriolis inertial screw resolved about arbitrary point A takes the form

$$-\begin{Bmatrix} \int_{\mathcal{S}} 2\boldsymbol{\omega}_{\mathcal{F}/\mathcal{E}} \times \mathbf{v}_{P/\mathcal{F}}\, dm \\ \int_{\mathcal{S}} \mathbf{r}_{AP} \times (2\boldsymbol{\omega}_{\mathcal{F}/\mathcal{E}} \times \mathbf{v}_{P/\mathcal{F}})\, dm \end{Bmatrix}$$

First we find the expression of the resultant:

$$-\int_{\mathcal{S}} 2\boldsymbol{\omega}_{\mathcal{F}/\mathcal{E}} \times \mathbf{v}_{P/\mathcal{F}} dm = -2\omega\hat{\mathbf{e}}_z \times \int_{\mathcal{S}} \mathbf{v}_{P/\mathcal{F}} dm = -2\omega\hat{\mathbf{e}}_z \times m\mathbf{v}_{C/\mathcal{F}} = -2m\omega(\dot{y}_C\hat{\mathbf{f}}_x - \dot{x}_C\hat{\mathbf{f}}_y)$$

where we have used $\int_{\mathcal{S}} \mathbf{v}_{P/\mathcal{F}} dm = m\mathbf{v}_{C/\mathcal{F}}$. Again to take advantage of symmetries, we find the expression of the moment about point C:

$$\int_{\mathcal{S}} \mathbf{r}_{CP} \times (2\boldsymbol{\omega}_{\mathcal{F}/\mathcal{E}} \times \mathbf{v}_{P/\mathcal{F}}) dm = \int_{\mathcal{S}} \mathbf{r}_{CP} \times [2\omega\hat{\mathbf{e}}_z \times (\mathbf{v}_{C/\mathcal{F}} + \boldsymbol{\Omega} \times \mathbf{r}_{CP})] dm$$

The first integral vanishes since $\int_{\mathcal{S}} \mathbf{r}_{CP} dm = \mathbf{0}$. So we need to simplify the integral $J = \int_{\mathcal{S}} \mathbf{r}_{CP} \times [\hat{\mathbf{e}}_z \times (\boldsymbol{\Omega} \times \mathbf{r}_{CP})] dm$

$$\begin{aligned}
J &= \int_{\mathcal{S}} \mathbf{r}_{CP} \times [\hat{\mathbf{e}}_z \times ((qz_P - ry_P)\hat{\mathbf{f}}_x + (-pz_P + rx_P)\hat{\mathbf{f}}_y)] dm \\
&= \int_{\mathcal{S}} \mathbf{r}_{CP} \times [(qz_P - ry_P)\hat{\mathbf{f}}_y - (-pz_P + rx_P)\hat{\mathbf{f}}_x] dm \\
&= \int_{\mathcal{S}} [(-qz_P^2 + ry_P z_P)\hat{\mathbf{f}}_x + (pz_P^2 - rx_P z_P)\hat{\mathbf{f}}_y + (qx_P z_P - py_P z_P)\hat{\mathbf{f}}_z \\
&= I(-q\hat{\mathbf{f}}_x + p\hat{\mathbf{f}}_y)
\end{aligned}$$

where we have used $\int_{\mathcal{S}} x_P z_P dm = \int_{\mathcal{S}} y_P z_P dm = 0$ and we have denoted $I = \int_{\mathcal{S}} z_P^2 dm$. By symmetry we find that the moment of inertia I can be expressed as

$$I = \int_{\mathcal{S}} z_P^2 dm = \frac{1}{2}\int_{\mathcal{S}} (x_P^2 + y_P^2) dm = \frac{1}{5} m a^2$$

In conclusion we have found the following expression of the Coriolis inertial screw

$$-\left\{\begin{matrix} \int_{\mathcal{S}} 2\boldsymbol{\omega}_{\mathcal{F}/\mathcal{E}} \times \mathbf{v}_{P/\mathcal{F}}\, dm \\ \int_{\mathcal{S}} \mathbf{r}_{CP} \times (2\boldsymbol{\omega}_{\mathcal{F}/\mathcal{E}} \times \mathbf{v}_{P/\mathcal{F}})\, dm \end{matrix}\right\} = \left\{\begin{matrix} 2m\omega(\dot{y}_C\hat{\mathbf{f}}_x - \dot{x}_C\hat{\mathbf{f}}_y) \\ \frac{2}{5} m a^2 \omega (q\hat{\mathbf{f}}_x - p\hat{\mathbf{f}}_y) \end{matrix}\right\}_C$$

c. Now we can apply the FTD relative to $\mathcal{F}$ taking into account the effect of inertial forces

$$\{\mathcal{D}_{\mathcal{S}/\mathcal{F}}\} = \{\mathcal{A}_{\bar{\mathcal{S}}\to\mathcal{S}}\} + \left\{\begin{matrix} m\omega^2(x_C\hat{\mathbf{f}}_x + y_C\hat{\mathbf{f}}_y) \\ \mathbf{0} \end{matrix}\right\}_C + \left\{\begin{matrix} 2m\omega(\dot{y}_C\hat{\mathbf{f}}_x - \dot{x}_C\hat{\mathbf{f}}_y) \\ \frac{2}{5} m a^2 \omega (q\hat{\mathbf{f}}_x - p\hat{\mathbf{f}}_y) \end{matrix}\right\}_C$$

Taking into account contact and gravitational forces, the external action screw exerted on $\mathcal{S}$ is the sum $\{\mathcal{A}^c_{\mathcal{F}\to\mathcal{S}}\} + \{\mathcal{A}^g_{\text{Earth}\to\mathcal{S}}\}$:

$$\{\mathcal{A}_{\bar{\mathcal{S}}\to\mathcal{S}}\} = \left\{\begin{matrix} R_x\hat{\mathbf{f}}_x + R_y\hat{\mathbf{f}}_y + R_z\hat{\mathbf{e}}_z \\ \mathbf{0} \end{matrix}\right\}_I + \left\{\begin{matrix} -mg\hat{\mathbf{e}}_z \\ \mathbf{0} \end{matrix}\right\}_C$$

The dynamic screw of $\mathcal{S}$ relative to $\mathcal{F}$ takes the form

$$\{\mathcal{D}_{\mathcal{S}/\mathcal{F}}\} = \left\{\begin{matrix} m\mathbf{a}_{C/\mathcal{F}} \\ \mathbf{D}_{C,\mathcal{S}/\mathcal{F}} \end{matrix}\right\} = \left\{\begin{matrix} m(\ddot{x}_C\hat{\mathbf{f}}_x + \ddot{y}_C\hat{\mathbf{f}}_y) \\ \frac{2}{5} m a^2 (\dot{p}\hat{\mathbf{f}}_x + \dot{q}\hat{\mathbf{f}}_y + \dot{r}\hat{\mathbf{e}}_z) \end{matrix}\right\}_C$$

Using the results of a) and b) we find that application of the FTD relative to $\mathcal{F}$ gives the following equations:

$$m\ddot{x}_C = m\omega^2 x_C + 2m\omega\dot{y}_C + R_x, \quad m\ddot{y}_C = m\omega^2 y_C - 2m\omega\dot{x}_C + R_y, \quad 0 = R_z - mg \qquad [1-3]$$

$$2ma\dot{p} = 2ma\omega q + 5R_x, \quad 2ma\dot{q} = -2ma\omega p - 5R_y, \quad \dot{r} = 0 \qquad [4-6]$$

d. The no-slip condition $\mathbf{v}_{I\in S/\mathcal{F}} = \mathbf{v}_C + \mathbf{\Omega} \times a\hat{\mathbf{e}}_z = \mathbf{0}$ gives the two additional equations

$$\dot{x}_C = aq, \qquad \dot{y}_C = -ap \tag{7-8}$$

We can derive the equations of motion as follows: first we use [4] and [5] to substitute R_x and R_y into [1] and [2]. Then we use [7] and [8] to eliminate p and q to find

$$7\ddot{x}_C = 5\omega^2 x_C + 12\omega\dot{y}_C, \qquad 7\ddot{y}_C = 5\omega^2 y_C - 12\omega\dot{x}_C \tag{9-10}$$

Equations [9-10] are linear o.d.e.'s. They are easily integrated by introducing the complex variable $\zeta = x_C + iy_C$ ($i^2 = -1$) which is solution of

$$7\ddot{\zeta} + 12i\omega\dot{\zeta} - 5\omega^2\zeta = 0$$

We seek solutions of the type $\zeta = \zeta_0 \exp(st)$: then s is solution of the quadratic equation $7s^2 + 12i\omega s - 5\omega^2 s = 0$. We find $s_1 = i\omega$ and $s_2 = \frac{5}{7}i\omega$. Hence the solution $\zeta(t)$ takes the form

$$\zeta(t) = \zeta_{0,1}e^{i\omega t} + \zeta_{0,2}e^{\frac{5}{7}i\omega t}$$

where constants $\zeta_{0,1}$ and $\zeta_{0,2}$ are found by imposing the initial conditions

$$\zeta_{0,1} = (-\frac{5}{2}x_0 + \frac{7}{2\omega}\dot{y}_0) - i\frac{7}{2\omega}\dot{x}_0, \quad \zeta_{0,2} = (\frac{7}{2}x_0 - \frac{7}{2\omega}\dot{y}_0) + i\frac{7}{2\omega}\dot{x}_0$$

The trajectory of C is then given by the equations

$$x_C(t) = (-\tfrac{5}{2}x_0 + \tfrac{7}{2\omega}\dot{y}_0)\cos\omega t + \tfrac{7}{2\omega}\dot{x}_0 \sin\omega t + (\tfrac{7}{2}x_0 - \tfrac{7}{2\omega}\dot{y}_0)\cos\tfrac{5}{7}\omega t - \tfrac{7}{2\omega}\dot{x}_0 \sin\tfrac{5}{7}\omega t$$

$$y_C(t) = (-\tfrac{5}{2}x_0 + \tfrac{7}{2\omega}\dot{y}_0)\sin\omega t - \tfrac{7}{2\omega}\dot{x}_0 \cos\omega t + (\tfrac{7}{2}x_0 - \tfrac{7}{2\omega}\dot{y}_0)\sin\tfrac{5}{7}\omega t + \tfrac{7}{2\omega}\dot{x}_0 \cos\tfrac{5}{7}\omega t$$

The trajectory of C is shown in Figure 16.2: it is a closed trajectory of period $T = 14\pi/\omega$.

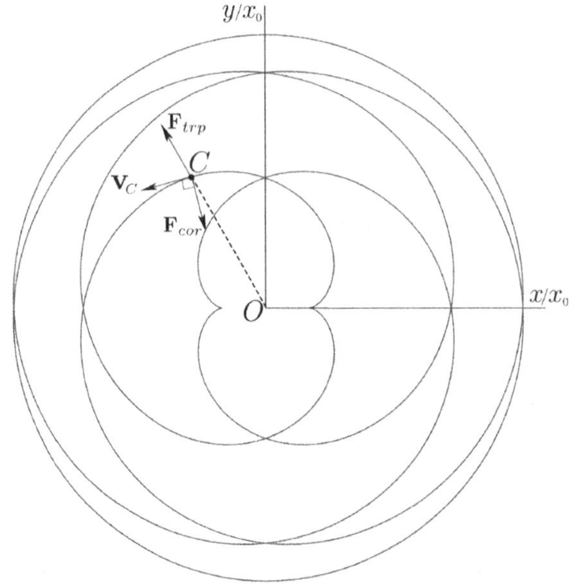

Figure 16.5 – *The trajectory of center C relative to rotating turntable $\mathcal{F}$ starting at $(x_0, 0)$ without initial velocity. The ball is subject to the centrifugal and Coriolis inertial forces $\mathbf{F}_{trp} = m\omega^2\mathbf{r}_{OC}$ and $\mathbf{F}_{cor} = 2\omega\hat{\mathbf{e}}_z \times m\mathbf{v}_C$ shown in the figure for $\omega > 0$. Note that the moment of the Coriolis inertial forces about mass center C is not zero.*

■

16.5 Transport and Coriolis Inertial Screws

Example 16.2 shows that analytical expressions of the transport and Coriolis inertial screws exerted on a rigid body $\mathcal{B}$ may be found in terms of

(i) the kinematic characteristics of the motion of $\mathcal{F}$ relative to $\mathcal{E}$,
(ii) the "relative" kinematics of $\mathcal{B}$,
(iii) the inertia characteristics of $\mathcal{B}$.

More specifically assume that the motion of $\mathcal{F}$ relative to $\mathcal{E}$ is characterized by angular velocity $\boldsymbol{\omega}_{\mathcal{F}/\mathcal{E}}$, velocity $\mathbf{v}_{O_F/\mathcal{E}}$ of an "origin" O_F of $\mathcal{F}$, angular acceleration $\boldsymbol{\alpha}_{\mathcal{F}/\mathcal{E}}$, and acceleration $\mathbf{a}_{O_F/\mathcal{E}}$. Recall for all points P we have

$$\mathbf{a}_{P\in\mathcal{F}/\mathcal{E}} = \mathbf{a}_{O_F/\mathcal{E}} + \boldsymbol{\alpha}_{\mathcal{F}/\mathcal{E}} \times \mathbf{r}_{O_F P} + \boldsymbol{\omega}_{\mathcal{F}/\mathcal{E}} \times (\boldsymbol{\omega}_{\mathcal{F}/\mathcal{E}} \times \mathbf{r}_{O_F P})$$

Assume that the kinematics of $\mathcal{B}$ relative to $\mathcal{F}$ is described by kinematic screw:

$$\{\mathcal{V}_{\mathcal{B}/\mathcal{F}}\} = \begin{Bmatrix} \boldsymbol{\Omega}_{\mathcal{B}/\mathcal{F}} \\ \mathbf{v}_{G/\mathcal{F}} \end{Bmatrix}$$

where G is the mass center of $\mathcal{B}$, where we have denoted $\boldsymbol{\Omega}_{\mathcal{B}/\mathcal{F}}$ the "relative" angular velocity of $\mathcal{B}$ to distinguish it from angular velocity $\boldsymbol{\omega}_{\mathcal{F}/\mathcal{E}}$. Assume that $\mathcal{B}$ is of mass m and denote by $\mathcal{I}_G$ its inertia operator about G. The transport inertial screw takes the expression

$$-\begin{Bmatrix} \int_{\mathcal{B}} \mathbf{a}_{P\in\mathcal{F}/\mathcal{E}} dm \\ \int_{\mathcal{B}} \mathbf{r}_{GP} \times \mathbf{a}_{P\in\mathcal{F}/\mathcal{E}} dm \end{Bmatrix}_G = -\begin{Bmatrix} \int_{\mathcal{B}} [\mathbf{a}_{O_F/\mathcal{E}} + \boldsymbol{\alpha}_{\mathcal{F}/\mathcal{E}} \times \mathbf{r}_{O_F P} + \boldsymbol{\omega}_{\mathcal{F}/\mathcal{E}} \times (\boldsymbol{\omega}_{\mathcal{F}/\mathcal{E}} \times \mathbf{r}_{O_F P})] dm \\ \int_{\mathcal{B}} \mathbf{r}_{GP} \times [\mathbf{a}_{O_F/\mathcal{E}} + \boldsymbol{\alpha}_{\mathcal{F}/\mathcal{E}} \times \mathbf{r}_{O_F P} + \boldsymbol{\omega}_{\mathcal{F}/\mathcal{E}} \times (\boldsymbol{\omega}_{\mathcal{F}/\mathcal{E}} \times \mathbf{r}_{O_F P})] dm \end{Bmatrix}_G$$

The resultant of this screw can be simplified to

$$-m(\mathbf{a}_{O_F/\mathcal{E}} + \boldsymbol{\alpha}_{\mathcal{F}/\mathcal{E}} \times \mathbf{r}_{O_F G} + \boldsymbol{\omega}_{\mathcal{F}/\mathcal{E}} \times (\boldsymbol{\omega}_{\mathcal{F}/\mathcal{E}} \times \mathbf{r}_{O_F G}) = -m\mathbf{a}_{G\in\mathcal{F}/\mathcal{E}}$$

Likewise, the moment about G can be simplified to yield two terms

$$-\int_{\mathcal{B}} \mathbf{r}_{GP} \times (\boldsymbol{\alpha}_{\mathcal{F}/\mathcal{E}} \times \mathbf{r}_{GP}) dm - \int_{\mathcal{B}} \mathbf{r}_{GP} \times [\boldsymbol{\omega}_{\mathcal{F}/\mathcal{E}} \times (\boldsymbol{\omega}_{\mathcal{F}/\mathcal{E}} \times \mathbf{r}_{GP})] dm$$

The first integral is recognized as $\mathcal{I}_G(\boldsymbol{\alpha}_{\mathcal{F}/\mathcal{E}})$. To simplify the second integral, we use the identity $\mathbf{U} \times (\mathbf{V} \times \mathbf{W}) = (\mathbf{U} \times \mathbf{V}) \times \mathbf{W} + \mathbf{V} \times (\mathbf{U} \times \mathbf{W})$. This integral then becomes

$$-\boldsymbol{\omega}_{\mathcal{F}/\mathcal{E}} \times \int_{\mathcal{B}} \mathbf{r}_{GP} \times (\boldsymbol{\omega}_{\mathcal{F}/\mathcal{E}} \times \mathbf{r}_{GP}) dm = -\boldsymbol{\omega}_{\mathcal{F}/\mathcal{E}} \times \mathcal{I}_G(\boldsymbol{\omega}_{\mathcal{F}/\mathcal{E}})$$

We conclude with the following result

Theorem 16.3 The transport inertial screw exerted on a rigid body $\mathcal{B}$ of mass m, mass center G during its motion in a non-Newtonian referential $\mathcal{F}$ takes the expression

$$\begin{Bmatrix} -m\mathbf{a}_{G\in\mathcal{F}/\mathcal{E}} \\ -\mathcal{I}_G(\boldsymbol{\alpha}_{\mathcal{F}/\mathcal{E}}) - \boldsymbol{\omega}_{\mathcal{F}/\mathcal{E}} \times \mathcal{I}_G(\boldsymbol{\omega}_{\mathcal{F}/\mathcal{E}}) \end{Bmatrix}_G \tag{16.15}$$

Likewise, we simplify the expression of the Coriolis inertial screw exerted on $\mathcal{B}$ by taking into account that the velocity field of points of $\mathcal{B}$ satisfies $\mathbf{v}_{P/\mathcal{F}} = \mathbf{v}_{G/\mathcal{F}} + \mathbf{\Omega}_{\mathcal{B}/\mathcal{F}} \times \mathbf{r}_{GP}$:

$$\begin{Bmatrix} -\int_{\mathcal{B}} 2\boldsymbol{\omega}_{\mathcal{F}/\mathcal{E}} \times \mathbf{v}_{P/\mathcal{F}} dm \\ -\int_{\mathcal{B}} \mathbf{r}_{GP} \times [2\boldsymbol{\omega}_{\mathcal{F}/\mathcal{E}} \times (\mathbf{v}_{G/\mathcal{F}} + \mathbf{\Omega}_{\mathcal{B}/\mathcal{F}} \times \mathbf{r}_{GP})] dm \end{Bmatrix}_G = \begin{Bmatrix} -2\boldsymbol{\omega}_{\mathcal{F}/\mathcal{E}} \times m\mathbf{v}_{G/\mathcal{F}} \\ -2\int_{\mathcal{B}} \mathbf{r}_{GP} \times [\boldsymbol{\omega}_{\mathcal{F}/\mathcal{E}} \times (\mathbf{\Omega}_{\mathcal{B}/\mathcal{F}} \times \mathbf{r}_{GP})] dm \end{Bmatrix}_G$$

To simplify the expression of the moment about G we use the identity

$$\begin{aligned} \mathbf{r}_{GP} \times [\boldsymbol{\omega}_{\mathcal{F}/\mathcal{E}} \times (\mathbf{\Omega}_{\mathcal{B}/\mathcal{F}} \times \mathbf{r}_{GP})] &= [\mathbf{r}_{GP} \cdot (\mathbf{\Omega}_{\mathcal{B}/\mathcal{F}} \times \mathbf{r}_{GP})]\boldsymbol{\omega}_{\mathcal{B}/\mathcal{F}} - (\mathbf{r}_{GP} \cdot \boldsymbol{\omega}_{\mathcal{F}/\mathcal{E}})(\mathbf{\Omega}_{\mathcal{B}/\mathcal{F}} \times \mathbf{r}_{GP}) \\ &= (\mathbf{r}_{GP} \cdot \boldsymbol{\omega}_{\mathcal{F}/\mathcal{E}})(\mathbf{r}_{GP} \times \mathbf{\Omega}_{\mathcal{B}/\mathcal{F}}) \end{aligned}$$

Now we obtain the integral

$$2\mathbf{\Omega}_{\mathcal{B}/\mathcal{F}} \times \int_{\mathcal{B}} (\mathbf{r}_{GP} \times \boldsymbol{\omega}_{\mathcal{F}/\mathcal{E}}) \mathbf{r}_{GP} dm$$

This last integral appears to be related to the inertia operator $\mathcal{I}_G$: indeed we have the identity

$$\mathbf{r}_{GP} \times (\boldsymbol{\omega}_{\mathcal{F}/\mathcal{E}} \times \mathbf{r}_{GP}) = \mathbf{r}_{GP}^2 \boldsymbol{\omega}_{\mathcal{F}/\mathcal{E}} - (\mathbf{r}_{GP} \cdot \boldsymbol{\omega}_{\mathcal{F}/\mathcal{E}})\mathbf{r}_{GP}$$

which leads to

$$\int_{\mathcal{B}} (\mathbf{r}_{GP} \times \boldsymbol{\omega}_{\mathcal{F}/\mathcal{E}}) \mathbf{r}_{GP} dm = \boldsymbol{\omega}_{\mathcal{F}/\mathcal{E}} \int_{\mathcal{B}} \mathbf{r}_{GP}^2 dm - \mathcal{I}_G(\boldsymbol{\omega}_{\mathcal{F}/\mathcal{E}})$$

The integral $\int_{\mathcal{B}} \mathbf{r}_{GP}^2 dm$ can be expressed in terms of inertia operator $\mathcal{I}_G$ in the following way: given an arbitrary basis $(\hat{\mathbf{x}}, \hat{\mathbf{y}}, \hat{\mathbf{z}})$ we can write

$$\int_{\mathcal{B}} \mathbf{r}_{GP}^2 dm = \int_{\mathcal{B}} (x^2 + y^2 + z^2) dm = \frac{1}{2}(I_{Gx} + I_{Gy} + I_{Gz}) = \frac{1}{2}\mathrm{tr}(\mathcal{I}_G)$$

where $\mathrm{tr}(\mathcal{I}_G)$ is the trace[2] of operator $\mathcal{I}_G$. In conclusion,

Theorem 16.4 The Coriolis inertial screw exerted on a rigid body $\mathcal{B}$ of mass m, mass center G during its motion in a non-Newtonian referential $\mathcal{F}$ takes the expression

$$\begin{Bmatrix} -2\boldsymbol{\omega}_{\mathcal{F}/\mathcal{E}} \times m\mathbf{v}_{G/\mathcal{F}} \\ (2\mathcal{I}_G(\boldsymbol{\omega}_{\mathcal{F}/\mathcal{E}}) - \mathrm{tr}(\mathcal{I}_G)\boldsymbol{\omega}_{\mathcal{F}/\mathcal{E}}) \times \mathbf{\Omega}_{\mathcal{B}/\mathcal{F}} \end{Bmatrix}_G \tag{16.16}$$

We can now restate the Fundamental Theorem of Dynamics in $\mathcal{F}$.

Theorem 16.5 The Fundamental Theorem of Dynamics applied to a rigid body $\mathcal{B}$ in

[2]The trace of operator $\mathcal{I}_G$ is an invariant, that is, is independent of the choice of basis $(\hat{\mathbf{x}}, \hat{\mathbf{y}}, \hat{\mathbf{z}})$: it can be obtained as the sum of the principal moments about G.

motion relative to non-Newtonian referential $\mathcal{F}$ takes the form

$$\{\mathcal{D}_{\mathcal{B}/\mathcal{F}}\} = \{\mathcal{A}_{\overline{\mathcal{B}}\to\mathcal{B}}\} + \underbrace{\begin{Bmatrix} -m\mathbf{a}_{G\in\mathcal{F}/\mathcal{E}} \\ -\mathcal{I}_G(\boldsymbol{\alpha}_{\mathcal{F}/\mathcal{E}}) - \boldsymbol{\omega}_{\mathcal{F}/\mathcal{E}} \times \mathcal{I}_G(\boldsymbol{\omega}_{\mathcal{F}/\mathcal{E}}) \end{Bmatrix}_G}_{\text{transport inertial screw}} + \underbrace{\begin{Bmatrix} -2\boldsymbol{\omega}_{\mathcal{F}/\mathcal{E}} \times m\mathbf{v}_{G/\mathcal{F}} \\ (2\mathcal{I}_G(\boldsymbol{\omega}_{\mathcal{F}/\mathcal{E}}) - \text{tr}(\mathcal{I}_G)\boldsymbol{\omega}_{\mathcal{F}/\mathcal{E}}) \times \boldsymbol{\Omega}_{\mathcal{B}/\mathcal{F}} \end{Bmatrix}_G}_{\text{Coriolis inertial screw}} \tag{16.17}$$

where the motion of $\mathcal{F}$ is known relative to a Newtonian referential $\mathcal{E}$.

We can verify that the expressions of the transport and Coriolis inertial screws found in Example 16.2 are in agreement with the general expressions (16.15) and (16.16).

16.6 Kinetic Energy Theorem in a Non-Newtonian Referential

We wish here to generalize the KET to a non-Newtonian referential. With the assumptions of Section 16.4, recall that the KET applied to rigid body $\mathcal{B}$ in motion relative to Newtonian referential $\mathcal{E}$ can be stated as

$$\frac{d}{dt}\mathbb{K}_{\mathcal{B}/\mathcal{E}} = \mathbb{P}_{\overline{\mathcal{B}}\to\mathcal{B}/\mathcal{E}} \tag{16.18}$$

To express the KET relative to non-Newtonian referential $\mathcal{F}$ we proceed as in Section 12.6.1: we apply D'Alembert Principle of Virtual Power by choosing as virtual velocity field the field $P \in \mathcal{B} \mapsto \mathbf{v}_{P/\mathcal{F}}$. This equivalent to taking the scalar product of both sides of the FTD relative to $\mathcal{E}$ with the kinematic screw $\{\mathcal{V}_{\mathcal{B}/\mathcal{F}}\}$:

$$\{\mathcal{D}_{\mathcal{B}/\mathcal{E}}\} \cdot \{\mathcal{V}_{\mathcal{B}/\mathcal{F}}\} = \{\mathcal{A}_{\overline{\mathcal{B}}\to\mathcal{B}}\} \cdot \{\mathcal{V}_{\mathcal{B}/\mathcal{F}}\} \tag{16.19}$$

The term on the right-hand-side of (16.19) is the power of the external action relative to $\mathcal{F}$: we denote this term $\mathbb{P}_{\overline{\mathcal{B}}\to\mathcal{B}/\mathcal{F}}$. For the left-hand-side expression, we adopt we same approach as in Section 16.4 by relating the dynamic screw of $\mathcal{B}$ relative to $\mathcal{E}$ to that relative to $\mathcal{F}$:

$$\{\mathcal{D}_{\mathcal{B}/\mathcal{E}}\} = \{\mathcal{D}_{\mathcal{B}/\mathcal{F}}\} + \begin{Bmatrix} \int_{\mathcal{B}} \mathbf{a}_{P\in\mathcal{F}/\mathcal{E}}\, dm \\ \int_{\Sigma} \mathbf{r}_{AP} \times \mathbf{a}_{P\in\mathcal{F}/\mathcal{E}}\, dm \end{Bmatrix} + \begin{Bmatrix} \int_{\Sigma} 2\boldsymbol{\omega}_{\mathcal{F}/\mathcal{E}} \times \mathbf{v}_{P/\mathcal{F}}\, dm \\ \int_{\Sigma} \mathbf{r}_{AP} \times (2\boldsymbol{\omega}_{\mathcal{F}/\mathcal{E}} \times \mathbf{v}_{P/\mathcal{F}})\, dm \end{Bmatrix}$$

This leads to three terms:
(i) the term $\{\mathcal{D}_{\mathcal{B}/\mathcal{F}}\} \cdot \{\mathcal{V}_{\mathcal{B}/\mathcal{F}}\}$ is given by the time rate of change of kinetic energy:

$$\{\mathcal{D}_{\mathcal{B}/\mathcal{F}}\} \cdot \{\mathcal{V}_{\mathcal{B}/\mathcal{F}}\} = \frac{d}{dt}\mathbb{K}_{\mathcal{B}/\mathcal{F}}$$

(ii) the term involving Coriolis accelerations vanishes:

$$\begin{Bmatrix} \int_{\Sigma} 2\boldsymbol{\omega}_{\mathcal{F}/\mathcal{E}} \times \mathbf{v}_{P/\mathcal{F}}\, dm \\ \int_{\Sigma} \mathbf{r}_{AP} \times (2\boldsymbol{\omega}_{\mathcal{F}/\mathcal{E}} \times \mathbf{v}_{P/\mathcal{F}})\, dm \end{Bmatrix} \cdot \{\mathcal{V}_{\mathcal{B}/\mathcal{F}}\} = \int_{\mathcal{B}} 2\mathbf{v}_{P/\mathcal{F}} \cdot (\boldsymbol{\omega}_{\mathcal{F}/\mathcal{E}} \times \mathbf{v}_{P/\mathcal{F}})\, dm = 0$$

which shows that the inertial Coriolis forces are non-working forces.
(iii) the term involving transport accelerations can be found by using the expression (16.15) of the transport action screw

$$\begin{Bmatrix} m\mathbf{a}_{G\in\mathcal{F}/\mathcal{E}} \\ \mathcal{I}_G(\boldsymbol{\alpha}_{\mathcal{F}/\mathcal{E}}) + \boldsymbol{\omega}_{\mathcal{F}/\mathcal{E}} \times \mathcal{I}_G(\boldsymbol{\omega}_{\mathcal{F}/\mathcal{E}}) \end{Bmatrix}_G \cdot \begin{Bmatrix} \boldsymbol{\omega}_{\mathcal{B}/\mathcal{F}} \\ \mathbf{v}_{G/\mathcal{F}} \end{Bmatrix}_G = \mathbf{v}_{G/\mathcal{F}} \cdot m\mathbf{a}_{G\in\mathcal{F}/\mathcal{E}} + \boldsymbol{\omega}_{\mathcal{B}/\mathcal{F}} \cdot (\mathcal{I}_G(\boldsymbol{\alpha}_{\mathcal{F}/\mathcal{E}}) + \boldsymbol{\omega}_{\mathcal{F}/\mathcal{E}} \times \mathcal{I}_G(\boldsymbol{\omega}_{\mathcal{F}/\mathcal{E}}))$$

By collecting all terms we can state the KET in non-Newtonian referential $\mathcal{F}$:

Theorem 16.6 — **Kinetic Energy Theorem (Single Body).** The time rate-of-change of the kinetic energy of $\mathcal{B}$ relative to $\mathcal{F}$ is equal to the power in $\mathcal{F}$ of the external mechanical actions and the transport inertial action exerted on rigid body $\mathcal{B}$:

$$\frac{d}{dt}\mathbb{K}_{\mathcal{B}/\mathcal{F}} = \mathbb{P}_{\overline{\mathcal{B}}\to\mathcal{B}/\mathcal{F}} + \mathbb{P}_{\mathcal{B}\in\mathcal{F}/\mathcal{E}} \tag{16.20}$$

where the power $\mathbb{P}_{\mathcal{B}\in\mathcal{F}/\mathcal{E}}$ of the transport inertial forces is found from the formula

$$\mathbb{P}_{\mathcal{B}\in\mathcal{F}/\mathcal{E}} = -\mathbf{v}_{G/\mathcal{F}} \cdot m\mathbf{a}_{G\in\mathcal{F}/\mathcal{E}} - \boldsymbol{\omega}_{\mathcal{B}/\mathcal{F}} \cdot (\mathcal{I}_G(\boldsymbol{\alpha}_{\mathcal{F}/\mathcal{E}}) + \boldsymbol{\omega}_{\mathcal{F}/\mathcal{E}} \times \mathcal{I}_G(\boldsymbol{\omega}_{\mathcal{F}/\mathcal{E}})) \tag{16.21}$$

This theorem can be generalized to systems of rigid bodies.

16.7 Problems

Problem 16.1 We consider in this problem the attitude stabilization of a satellite Σ modeled as two point masses P_1 and P_2 of identical mass m connected by a rigid massless rod of length $2l$. The mass center G of Σ describes a circular path of center C (Earth's center) and radius $r_0 \gg l$ relative to the Geocentric referential $\mathcal{G}$ assumed Newtonian. The rectangular axes $CXYZ$ are attached to $\mathcal{G}$ (OXY is the orbital plane of the satellite). We assume that P_1 and P_2 both lie in plane OXY. The rectangular axes $Cxyz$ are in rotation with G at constant angular velocity Ω relative to $\mathcal{G}$. These axes define a referential $\mathcal{F}$. Relative to $\mathcal{F}$, the satellite's orientation is defined by angle θ. We are interested in the equilibrium positions of Σ in $\mathcal{F}$ and their stability.

a. Show that the Coriolis forces acting on Σ relative to referential $\mathcal{F}$ amount to a vanishing screw (show that their resultant is zero and that their moment about G is zero).

b. Show that the gravitational forces and the transport forces give rise to a couple $-\Gamma\hat{\mathbf{e}}_z$ on Σ with

$$\Gamma = 6GmM\frac{l^2}{r_0^3}\sin\theta\cos\theta$$

c. Deduce the differential equation governing angle θ: find the equilibrium positions and discuss their stability.

d. Find the period of small amplitude oscillations about the stable equilibria in terms of the orbital period.

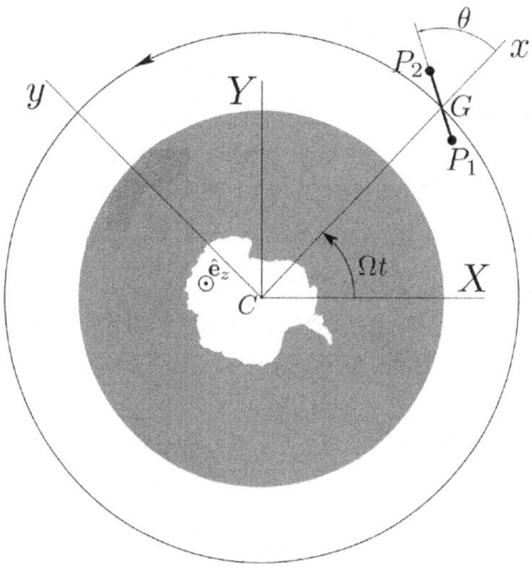

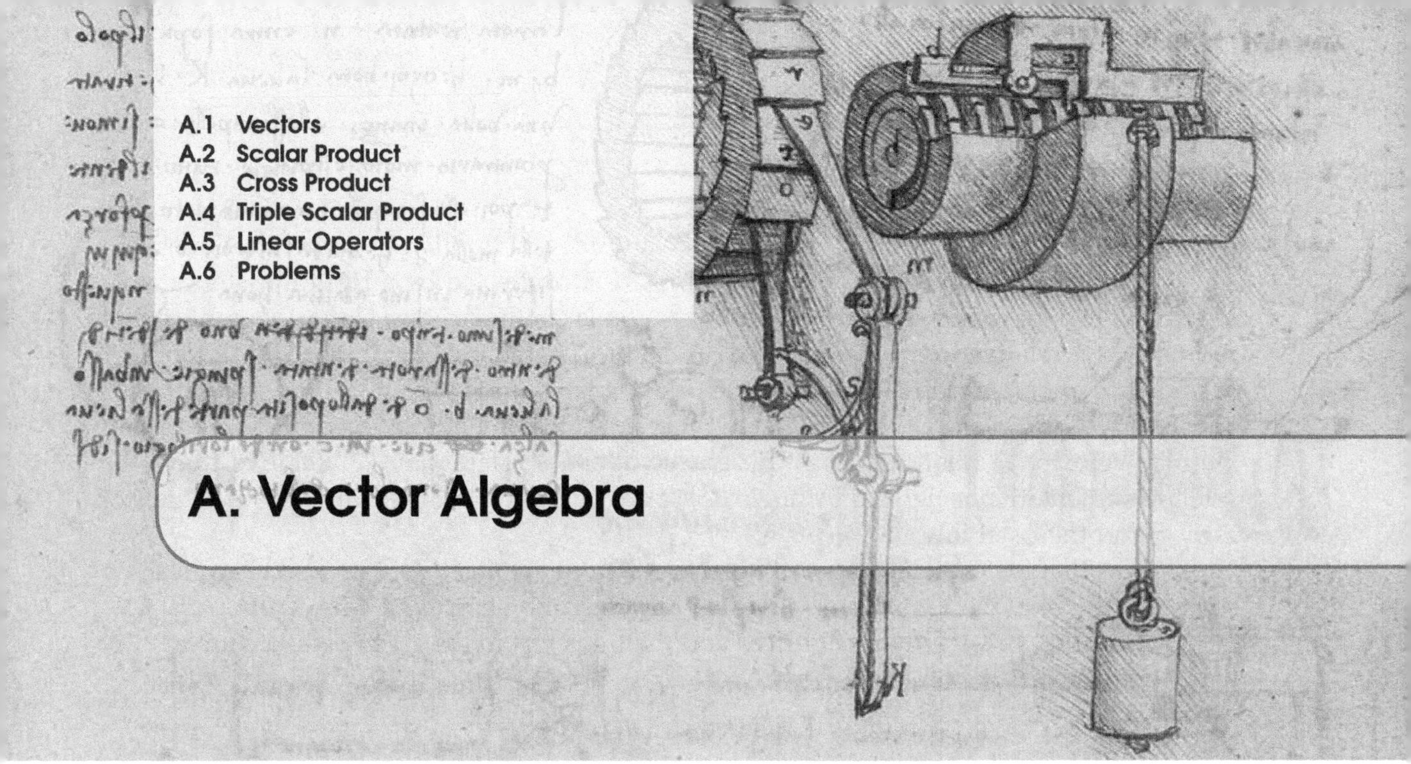

A. Vector Algebra

A.1 Vectors

We can define vectors in an intuitive manner as a directed line segment. Hence, a vector **U** [1] is characterized by its magnitude, denoted $|\mathbf{U}|$, and by its direction. On a more abstract level, vectors are defined as equivalent classes of ordered pairs of points (A, B) of a three-dimensional space: two ordered pairs (A, B) and (C, D) are equipollent if (i) their supports are parallel, (ii) they have the same order, (iii) they have the same magnitude. The equivalence $(A, B) \sim (C, D)$ is denoted $\overrightarrow{AB} = \overrightarrow{CD}$. All ordered pairs equivalent to (A, B) are then defined as vector $\mathbf{U} = \overrightarrow{AB}$. See Figure A.1.

Hence two vectors **U** and **V** are equal if and only if they are parallel, have the same direction and the same magnitude: we then write $\mathbf{U} = \mathbf{V}$. The starting points of vectors are thus immaterial.

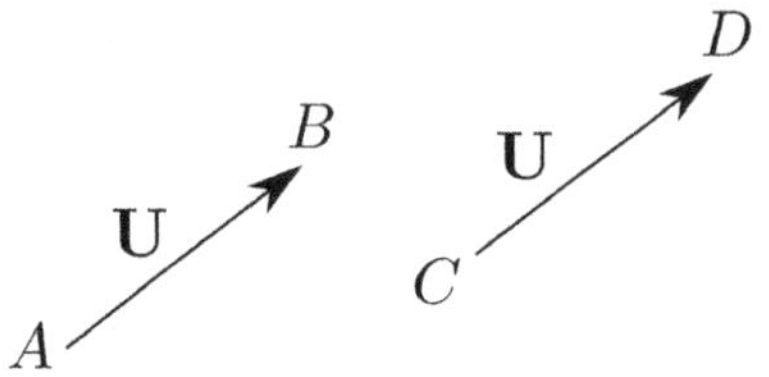

Figure A.1

We can then define two operations which make the set of vectors a *vector space* E over the set of real numbers $\mathbb{R}$:

1. Multiplication by a scalar (the identity element is the real number 1): the product of scalar λ and vector **U** is a vector parallel to **U**, of magnitude $|\lambda||\mathbf{U}|$, in the same

[1] We represent vectors by arrows and use boldface type to distinguish vectorial quantities from scalar quantities.

direction as **U** if $\lambda > 0$, opposed to **U** if $\lambda < 0$.

2. Addition of vectors (the identity element is the zero vector **0**): the sum of two vectors **U** and **V** is obtained by constructing a triangle with **U** and **V** forming two sides, **V** adjoined to **U**: then the sum $\mathbf{U}+\mathbf{V}$ is the vector starting at the origin of **U** and ending at the arrow of **V**. See Figure A.2

To qualify as a vector space, the set E and the operations of addition and multiplication must adhere to the following axioms: given three vectors **U**, **V**, and **W**, and two real scalars λ and μ,

$$\begin{aligned} \mathbf{U}+\mathbf{V} &= \mathbf{V}+\mathbf{U} & 1\mathbf{U} &= \mathbf{U} \\ (\mathbf{U}+\mathbf{V})+\mathbf{W} &= \mathbf{U}+(\mathbf{V}+\mathbf{W}) & \lambda(\mathbf{U}+\mathbf{V}) &= \lambda\mathbf{U}+\lambda\mathbf{V} \\ \mathbf{U}+\mathbf{0} &= \mathbf{U} & (\lambda+\mu)\mathbf{U} &= \lambda\mathbf{U}+\mu\mathbf{U} \\ \mathbf{U}+(-\mathbf{U}) &= \mathbf{0} & \lambda(\mu\mathbf{U}) &= \lambda\mu\mathbf{U} \end{aligned}$$

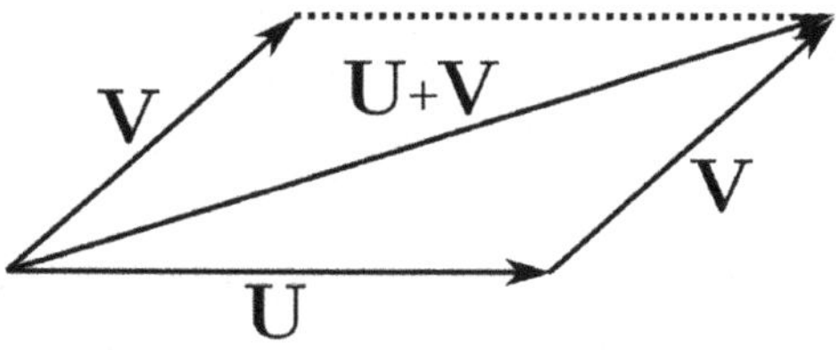

Figure A.2

Definition A.1 Two vectors **U** and **V** are said to be *collinear* if there exists a non-zero scalar λ such that $\mathbf{V} = \lambda\mathbf{U}$

Definition A.2 Two vectors **U** and **V** are said to be *linearly independent* if $\lambda\mathbf{U}+\mu\mathbf{V} = \mathbf{0}$ implies $\lambda = \mu = 0$.

Definition A.3 Three vectors $(\mathbf{U}_1, \mathbf{U}_2, \mathbf{U}_3)$ are said to form a *basis* of E if they are linearly independent. Then any vector $\mathbf{V} \in E$ can be written uniquely in the form

$$\mathbf{V} = V_1\mathbf{U}_1 + V_2\mathbf{U}_2 + V_3\mathbf{U}_3$$

The scalars V_1, V_2 and V_3 are the *components* of **V** on basis $(\mathbf{U}_1, \mathbf{U}_2, \mathbf{U}_3)$.

A.2 Scalar Product

Definition A.4 The *scalar product* (or *dot product*) between vectors **U** and **V** is the scalar defined by $\mathbf{U}\cdot\mathbf{V} = |\mathbf{U}||\mathbf{V}|\cos\alpha$, where $\alpha \in [0, \pi]$ is the angle measured between **U** and **V**.

Properties:

1. Distributivity: $\mathbf{U}\cdot(\mathbf{V}+\mathbf{W}) = \mathbf{U}\cdot\mathbf{V}+\mathbf{V}\cdot\mathbf{W}$
2. Multiplication by a scalar λ: $\mathbf{U}\cdot(\lambda\mathbf{V}) = \lambda\mathbf{U}\cdot\mathbf{V}$

3. If $\mathbf{U} \cdot \mathbf{V} = 0$, the non-zero vectors $\mathbf{U}$ and $\mathbf{V}$ are said to be orthogonal.
4. The scalar $|\mathbf{U}| = (\mathbf{U} \cdot \mathbf{U})^{1/2}$ is the magnitude or *norm* of $\mathbf{U}$[2].
5. The orthogonal projection of vector $\mathbf{U}$ on the line $\Delta = \{\lambda \mathbf{V} | \lambda \in \mathbb{R}\}$ is the vector (see Figure A.3)

$$\text{proj}_{\mathbf{V}}(\mathbf{U}) = \frac{\mathbf{U} \cdot \mathbf{V}}{\mathbf{V}^2} \mathbf{V}$$

6. The orthogonal projection of vector $\mathbf{W}$ on the plane spanned by two linear independent vectors $\mathbf{U}$ and $\mathbf{V}$ is the vector

$$\text{proj}_{(\mathbf{U},\mathbf{V})}(\mathbf{W}) = \frac{\mathbf{W} \cdot \mathbf{U}}{\mathbf{U}^2} \mathbf{U} + \frac{\mathbf{W} \cdot \mathbf{V}}{\mathbf{V}^2} \mathbf{V}$$

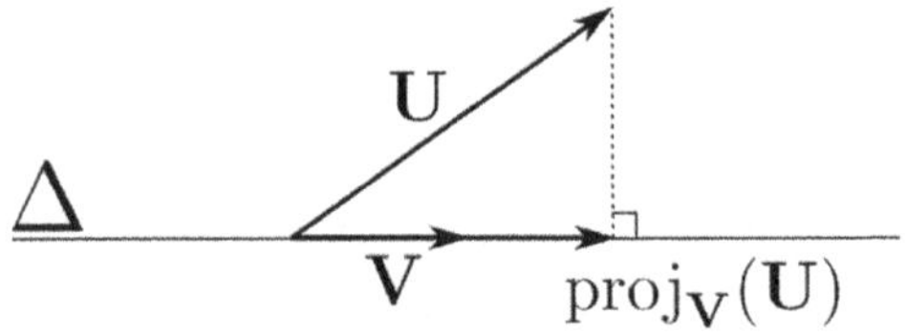

Figure A.3

7. A unit vector is a vector of magnitude 1 and denoted $\hat{\mathbf{u}}$.
8. A orthonormal basis $b(\hat{\mathbf{e}}_1, \hat{\mathbf{e}}_2, \hat{\mathbf{e}}_3)$ is a basis satisfying $\hat{\mathbf{e}}_i \cdot \hat{\mathbf{e}}_j = 0$ if $i \neq j$ and $\hat{\mathbf{e}}_i \cdot \hat{\mathbf{e}}_i = 1$. Vector space E equipped with the scalar product is a *Euclidean* space of dimension 3. Any vector $\mathbf{U}$ of E can then be written on basis b as

$$\mathbf{U} = (\hat{\mathbf{e}}_1 \cdot \mathbf{U})\hat{\mathbf{e}}_1 + (\hat{\mathbf{e}}_2 \cdot \mathbf{U})\hat{\mathbf{e}}_2 + (\hat{\mathbf{e}}_3 \cdot \mathbf{U})\hat{\mathbf{e}}_3$$

9. Consider another basis $b'(\hat{\mathbf{e}}'_1, \hat{\mathbf{e}}'_2, \hat{\mathbf{e}}'_3)$ of E and define the coefficients $c_{ij} = \hat{\mathbf{e}}_i \cdot \hat{\mathbf{e}}'_j$. Consider the 3×3 matrix $[C] = [c_{ij}]$: the jth column of $[C]$ is composed of the components of $\hat{\mathbf{e}}'_j$ on basis b. It is easily seen that $[C]$ gives the components of vector $\mathbf{U}$ from one basis to the other: more specifically, if $\mathbf{U} = \sum U_i \hat{\mathbf{e}}_i = \sum U'_i \hat{\mathbf{e}}'_i$ then

$$U_i = \sum c_{ij} U'_j$$

A.3 Cross Product

Definition A.5 The *cross product* between two vectors $\mathbf{U}$ and $\mathbf{V}$ is the vector denoted $\mathbf{U} \times \mathbf{V}$ such that (see Figure A.4):

- $\mathbf{U} \times \mathbf{V}$ is orthogonal to the plane spanned by $\mathbf{U}$ and $\mathbf{V}$,
- $(\mathbf{U}, \mathbf{V}, \mathbf{U} \times \mathbf{V})$ is oriented in the right-handed direction[3],
- its magnitude is given by $|\mathbf{U} \times \mathbf{V}| = |\mathbf{U}||\mathbf{V}| \sin \alpha$, where $\alpha \in [0, \pi]$ is the angle between $\mathbf{U}$ and $\mathbf{V}$.

Properties:

1. Skew-symmetry: $\mathbf{U} \times \mathbf{V} = -\mathbf{V} \times \mathbf{U}$, and hence $\mathbf{U} \times \mathbf{U} = \mathbf{0}$

[2]We will often denote $\mathbf{U} \cdot \mathbf{U}$ as $\mathbf{U}^2$.

[3]When the right hand is turned so as to bring $\mathbf{U}$ toward $\mathbf{V}$, the thumb points in the direction of $\mathbf{U} \times \mathbf{V}$.

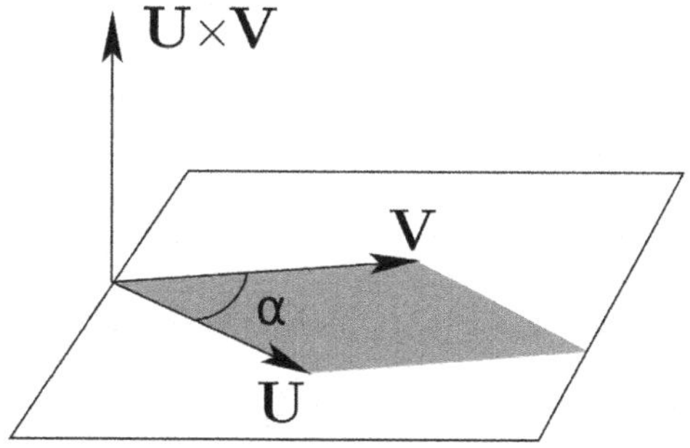

Figure A.4

2. Distributivity: $\mathbf{U} \times (\mathbf{V} + \mathbf{W}) = \mathbf{U} \times \mathbf{V} + \mathbf{V} \times \mathbf{W}$

3. Multiplication by a scalar λ: $\mathbf{U} \times (\lambda \mathbf{V}) = \lambda \mathbf{U} \times \mathbf{V}$

4. If three vectors satisfy the equality $\mathbf{U} \times \mathbf{V} = \mathbf{U} \times \mathbf{W}$, then $\mathbf{V} = \mathbf{W} + \lambda \mathbf{U}$ where λ is an indeterminate scalar.

5. Given a right-handed orthonormal basis $(\hat{\mathbf{e}}_1, \hat{\mathbf{e}}_2, \hat{\mathbf{e}}_3)$, we have the following relationships

$$\hat{\mathbf{e}}_1 = \hat{\mathbf{e}}_2 \times \hat{\mathbf{e}}_3, \qquad \hat{\mathbf{e}}_2 = \hat{\mathbf{e}}_3 \times \hat{\mathbf{e}}_1, \qquad \hat{\mathbf{e}}_3 = \hat{\mathbf{e}}_1 \times \hat{\mathbf{e}}_2$$

Then, the cross product between $\mathbf{U} = U_1 \hat{\mathbf{e}}_1 + U_2 \hat{\mathbf{e}}_2 + U_3 \hat{\mathbf{e}}_3$ and $\mathbf{V} = V_1 \hat{\mathbf{e}}_1 + V_2 \mathbf{V}_2 + V_3 \hat{\mathbf{e}}_3$ can be calculated according to

$$\mathbf{U} \times \mathbf{V} = \begin{vmatrix} \hat{\mathbf{e}}_1 & \hat{\mathbf{e}}_2 & \hat{\mathbf{e}}_3 \\ U_1 & U_2 & U_3 \\ V_1 & V_2 & V_3 \end{vmatrix} = (U_2 V_3 - U_3 V_2) \hat{\mathbf{e}}_1 + (U_3 V_1 - U_1 V_3) \hat{\mathbf{e}}_2 + (U_1 V_2 - U_2 V_1) \hat{\mathbf{e}}_3$$

6. $|\mathbf{U} \times \mathbf{V}|$ represents the area of the parallelogram formed by the two vectors.

7. Given three vectors $\mathbf{U}$, $\mathbf{V}$ and $\mathbf{W}$, the triple vector product $\mathbf{U} \times (\mathbf{V} \times \mathbf{W})$ can be found according to the formula

$$\mathbf{U} \times (\mathbf{V} \times \mathbf{W}) = (\mathbf{U} \cdot \mathbf{W}) \mathbf{V} - (\mathbf{U} \cdot \mathbf{V}) \mathbf{W}$$

In general, $\mathbf{U} \times (\mathbf{V} \times \mathbf{W})$ is not equal to $(\mathbf{U} \times \mathbf{V}) \times \mathbf{W}$. In fact, we have

$$\mathbf{U} \times (\mathbf{V} \times \mathbf{W}) = (\mathbf{U} \times \mathbf{V}) \times \mathbf{W} + \mathbf{V} \times (\mathbf{U} \times \mathbf{W})$$

8. Given two vectors $\mathbf{U}$ and $\mathbf{V}$ we have (Lagrange formula)

$$(\mathbf{U} \cdot \mathbf{V})^2 + (\mathbf{U} \times \mathbf{V})^2 = \mathbf{U}^2 \, \mathbf{V}^2$$

A.4 Triple Scalar Product

Definition A.6 The *triple scalar product* between three vectors $\mathbf{U}$, $\mathbf{V}$, and $\mathbf{W}$ is the scalar denoted $(\mathbf{U}, \mathbf{V}, \mathbf{W})$ and defined as

$$(\mathbf{U}, \mathbf{V}, \mathbf{W}) = (\mathbf{U} \times \mathbf{V}) \cdot \mathbf{W}$$

Properties:

1. The triple scalar product $(\mathbf{U}, \mathbf{V}, \mathbf{W})$ is the volume of the parallelepiped formed by the three vectors.

2. Under circular permutation of the vectors, the triple scalar product remains unchanged

$$(\mathbf{U}, \mathbf{V}, \mathbf{W}) = (\mathbf{V}, \mathbf{W}, \mathbf{U}) = (\mathbf{W}, \mathbf{U}, \mathbf{V})$$

3. The triple scalar product changes sign under the permutation of any two vectors,

$$(\mathbf{U}, \mathbf{V}, \mathbf{W}) = -(\mathbf{V}, \mathbf{U}, \mathbf{W}) = -(\mathbf{U}, \mathbf{W}, \mathbf{V})$$

4. Given three non-zero vectors, $(\mathbf{U}, \mathbf{V}, \mathbf{W})$ is zero if two of the three vectors are collinear. Conversely, if the triple product $(\mathbf{U}, \mathbf{V}, \mathbf{W})$ is zero, two of the vectors are collinear or all three vectors are coplanar.

5. The triple scalar product can be calculated by resolving each vector on a right-handed orthonormal basis $(\hat{\mathbf{e}}_1, \hat{\mathbf{e}}_2, \hat{\mathbf{e}}_3)$, that is, $\mathbf{U} = U_1\hat{\mathbf{e}}_1 + U_2\hat{\mathbf{e}}_2 + U_3\hat{\mathbf{e}}_3$, $\mathbf{V} = V_1\hat{\mathbf{e}}_1 + V_2\hat{\mathbf{e}}_2 + V_3\hat{\mathbf{e}}_3$, and $\mathbf{W} = W_1\hat{\mathbf{e}}_1 + W_2\hat{\mathbf{e}}_2 + W_3\hat{\mathbf{e}}_3$. Then, we have

$$(\mathbf{U}, \mathbf{V}, \mathbf{W}) = \begin{vmatrix} U_1 & V_1 & W_1 \\ U_2 & V_2 & W_2 \\ U_3 & V_3 & W_3 \end{vmatrix}$$

6. The following identity can be proven

$$(\mathbf{U} \times \mathbf{V}) \cdot (\mathbf{W} \times \mathbf{X}) = (\mathbf{U} \cdot \mathbf{W})(\mathbf{V} \cdot \mathbf{X}) - (\mathbf{U} \cdot \mathbf{X})(\mathbf{V} \cdot \mathbf{W})$$

A.5 Linear Operators

Definition A.7 An operator $\mathcal{L} : E \to E$ is *linear* if the following two conditions are satisfied:

$$\mathcal{L}(\lambda \mathbf{U}) = \lambda \mathcal{L}(\mathbf{U})$$

$$\mathcal{L}(\mathbf{U} + \mathbf{V}) = \mathcal{L}(\mathbf{U}) + \mathcal{L}(\mathbf{V})$$

for any $\lambda \in \mathbb{R}$ and any two vectors $\mathbf{U}$ and $\mathbf{V}$. The identity operator $\mathcal{I}$ is the operator satisfying $\mathcal{I}(\mathbf{U}) = \mathbf{U}$.

Definition A.8 A linear operator $\mathcal{L}$ is said to be *invertible* if there exists an operator denoted $\mathcal{L}^{-1}$, called the *inverse* of $\mathcal{L}$, such that $\mathcal{L}^{-1} \circ \mathcal{L} = \mathcal{L} \circ \mathcal{L}^{-1} = \mathcal{I}$.

Properties:

1. If $\mathcal{L}_1$ and $\mathcal{L}_2$ of E are two linear operators, then $\mathcal{L}_1 \circ \mathcal{L}_2$ is a linear operator. In general $\mathcal{L}_1 \circ \mathcal{L}_2 \neq \mathcal{L}_2 \circ \mathcal{L}_1$.

2. All linear operators satisfy $\mathcal{L}(\mathbf{0}) = \mathbf{0}$.

3. The *kernel* of linear operator $\mathcal{L}$ is the subset $\ker(\mathcal{L}) = \{\mathbf{X} \in E \mid \mathcal{L}(\mathbf{X}) = \mathbf{0}\}$. The *range* of $\mathcal{L}$ is the subset $\mathcal{L}(E)$. In general, we have $\dim(\ker(\mathcal{L})) + \dim(\mathcal{L}(E)) = \dim(E)$.

4. A linear operator $\mathcal{L}$ is entirely defined by the mapping by $\mathcal{L}$ of basis vectors. Given a right-handed orthonormal basis $b(\hat{\mathbf{e}}_1, \hat{\mathbf{e}}_2, \hat{\mathbf{e}}_3)$, let λ_{ij} be the scalars defined by

$$\mathcal{L}(\hat{\mathbf{e}}_j) = \sum_{i=1}^{3} \lambda_{ij} \hat{\mathbf{e}}_i \qquad (j = 1, 2, 3)$$

The scalars $(\lambda_{ij})_{i,j=1,2,3}$ define the matrix of $\mathcal{L}$ on basis b: it is denoted $[\mathcal{L}]_b$ and written in the form of a 3×3 array

$$[\mathcal{L}]_b = \begin{pmatrix} \lambda_{11} & \lambda_{12} & \lambda_{13} \\ \lambda_{21} & \lambda_{22} & \lambda_{23} \\ \lambda_{31} & \lambda_{32} & \lambda_{33} \end{pmatrix}_b$$

The jth column of matrix $[\mathcal{L}]_b$ represents the components of vector $\mathcal{L}(\hat{\mathbf{e}}_j)$ on basis b. The mapping by $\mathcal{L}$ of vector $\mathbf{U}$ can then be obtained as the product $[\mathcal{L}]_b[\mathbf{U}]_b$ where $[\mathbf{U}]_b$ represent vector $\mathbf{U}$ on basis b:

$$\mathcal{L}(\mathbf{U}) = [\mathcal{L}]_b[\mathbf{U}]_b = \begin{pmatrix} \lambda_{11} & \lambda_{12} & \lambda_{13} \\ \lambda_{21} & \lambda_{22} & \lambda_{23} \\ \lambda_{31} & \lambda_{32} & \lambda_{33} \end{pmatrix}_b \begin{pmatrix} U_1 \\ U_2 \\ U_3 \end{pmatrix}_b = \sum_{i=1}^{3}\sum_{j=1}^{3} \lambda_{ij} U_j \hat{\mathbf{e}}_i$$

5. Given two linear operators $\mathcal{L}_1$ and $\mathcal{L}_2$ and a basis b, we have

$$[\mathcal{L}_1 \circ \mathcal{L}_2]_b = [\mathcal{L}_1]_b\,[\mathcal{L}_2]_b$$

Definition A.9 The *adjoint* $\mathcal{L}^*$ of operator $\mathcal{L}$ of E is the linear operator satisfying

$$\mathbf{U} \cdot \mathcal{L}(\mathbf{V}) = \mathcal{L}^*(\mathbf{U}) \cdot \mathbf{V}$$

for all vectors $\mathbf{U}$ and $\mathbf{V}$ of E. The operator $\mathcal{L}$ is said to be *symmetric* if $\mathcal{L}^* = \mathcal{L}$.

Definition A.10 The symmetric and skew-symmetric parts of linear operator $\mathcal{L} : E \to E$ are the operators defined respectively by

$$\mathcal{L}_+ = \tfrac{1}{2}(\mathcal{L} + \mathcal{L}^*), \qquad \mathcal{L}_- = \tfrac{1}{2}(\mathcal{L} - \mathcal{L}^*)$$

Properties:

1. The matrix representation of $\mathcal{L}^*$ on basis b is the transpose of matrix $[\mathcal{L}]_b^T$:

$$\lambda^*_{ij} = \lambda_{ji}$$

2. It is easy to prove that

$$\mathcal{L} = (\mathcal{L}_+ + \mathcal{L}_-), \qquad \mathcal{L}^*_+ = \mathcal{L}_+, \qquad \mathcal{L}^*_- = -\mathcal{L}_-$$

Definition A.11 The *trace* of a linear operator $\mathcal{L}$, denoted $\mathrm{tr}(\mathcal{L})$, is the scalar $\lambda_{11} + \lambda_{22} + \lambda_{33}$, where $\lambda_{ii} = \hat{\mathbf{e}}_i \cdot \mathcal{L}(\hat{\mathbf{e}}_i)$. It is independent of the choice of basis b.

Properties:

1. The trace satisfies the property $\mathrm{tr}(\mathcal{L}_1 \circ \mathcal{L}_2) = \mathrm{tr}(\mathcal{L}_2 \circ \mathcal{L}_1)$.
2. Given an invertible linear operator $\mathcal{L}_1$, $\mathrm{tr}(\mathcal{L}_1^{-1} \circ \mathcal{L}_2 \circ \mathcal{L}_1) = \mathrm{tr}(\mathcal{L}_2)$.

Definition A.12 A linear operator $\mathcal{L}$ of E is said to be *orthogonal* if it satisfies one the following three equivalent properties:
(i) $\mathcal{L}(\mathbf{U}) \cdot \mathcal{L}(\mathbf{V}) = \mathbf{U} \cdot \mathbf{V}$ for all $\mathbf{U}$ and $\mathbf{V}$ of E,
(ii) $|\mathcal{L}(\mathbf{U})| = |\mathbf{U}|$ for all $\mathbf{U}$ of E,
(iii) $\mathcal{L}^* \circ \mathcal{L} = \mathcal{I}$.
The set of orthogonal operators forms a group, called *orthogonal group* of E.

Properties:

1. Given an orthonormal basis b, the matrix of $\mathcal{L}$ in basis b is *orthogonal*, that is, it satisfies $[\mathcal{L}]_b^T[\mathcal{L}]_b = [\mathcal{I}]_b$.

2. Orthogonal operators satisfy the property $\det[\mathcal{L}]_b = \pm 1$. The orthogonal operators satisfying $\det[\mathcal{L}]_b = 1$ form a subgroup denoted $SO(3)$.

3. For each orthogonal operator $\mathcal{L}$, there exists an orthonormal basis $b(\hat{\mathbf{e}}_1, \hat{\mathbf{e}}_2, \hat{\mathbf{e}}_3)$ such that the matrix of $\mathcal{L}$ on b takes the form

$$[\mathcal{L}]_b = \begin{pmatrix} \cos\theta & -\sin\theta & 0 \\ \sin\theta & \cos\theta & 0 \\ 0 & 0 & \epsilon \end{pmatrix}_b$$

with $\epsilon = \pm 1$. For $\epsilon = 1$, $\det[\mathcal{L}]_b = 1$ and $\mathcal{L}$ is a *rotation* about $\hat{\mathbf{e}}_3$ of angle θ, denoted $\mathcal{R}_{\theta,\hat{\mathbf{e}}_3}$. Note that $\text{tr}(\mathcal{R}_{\theta,\hat{\mathbf{e}}_3}) = 2\cos\theta + 1$.

A.6 Problems

Problem A.1 Prove Jacobi's identity: given three arbitrary vectors in an oriented vector space

$$(\mathbf{U} \times \mathbf{V}) \times \mathbf{W} + (\mathbf{V} \times \mathbf{W}) \times \mathbf{U} + (\mathbf{W} \times \mathbf{U}) \times \mathbf{V} = \mathbf{0}$$

Problem A.2 Given four vectors $\mathbf{A}$, $\mathbf{B}$, $\mathbf{C}$ and $\mathbf{D}$, prove the identity

$$(\mathbf{A} \times \mathbf{B}) \cdot (\mathbf{C} \times \mathbf{D}) = (\mathbf{A} \times \mathbf{C}) \cdot (\mathbf{B} \times \mathbf{D}) + (\mathbf{A} \cdot \mathbf{C})(\mathbf{B} \cdot \mathbf{D}) - (\mathbf{A} \cdot \mathbf{B})(\mathbf{C} \cdot \mathbf{D})$$

Problem A.3 Find the conditions satisfied by three non-zero vectors $\mathbf{U}$, $\mathbf{V}$ and $\mathbf{W}$ to guarantee the following equality

$$(\mathbf{U} \times \mathbf{V}) \times \mathbf{W} = \mathbf{U} \times (\mathbf{V} \times \mathbf{W})$$

Problem A.4 Given four arbitrary points P, Q, R and S prove the identity

$$\mathbf{r}_{QR} \times \mathbf{r}_{QS} = \mathbf{r}_{PQ} \times \mathbf{r}_{PR} + \mathbf{r}_{PR} \times \mathbf{r}_{PS} + \mathbf{r}_{PS} \times \mathbf{r}_{PQ}$$

where $\mathbf{r}_{AB}$ is the vector which points from A to B.

Problem A.5 In a Euclidean vector space E, a linear operator $\mathcal{L} : \mathbf{U} \mapsto \mathcal{L}(\mathbf{U})$ is said to be skew-symmetric if and only if $\mathcal{L}(\mathbf{U}) \cdot \mathbf{V} = -\mathbf{U} \cdot \mathcal{L}(\mathbf{V})$.

a. Show that any skew-symmetric operator $\mathcal{L}$ is represented by a skew-symmetric matrix relative to any orthonormal basis, that is, satisfying

$$[\mathcal{L}]_b^T = -[\mathcal{L}]_b$$

Conversely, show that to a skew-symmetric matrix corresponds a skew-symmetric linear operator.

b. Show that, given a non-zero vector $\mathbf{U}$, the linear operator $\mathbf{X} \mapsto \mathbf{U} \times \mathbf{X}$ is skew-symmetric. Conversely, show that all skew-symmetric operator are of the form $\mathbf{X} \mapsto \mathbf{U} \times \mathbf{X}$.

Problem A.6 Given two non-zero vectors **A** and **B**, find the set of vectors **X** solution of the equation

$$\mathbf{A} \times \mathbf{X} = \mathbf{B}$$

Problem A.7 Given a non-zero vector **Y**, consider the linear operator $\mathcal{L}_{\mathbf{Y}}$ defined by

$$\mathcal{L}_{\mathbf{Y}}(\mathbf{X}) = \mathbf{X} \times \mathbf{Y}$$

a. Find the matrix of $\mathcal{L}_{\mathbf{Y}}$ on right-handed orthonormal basis $b(\hat{\mathbf{e}}_1, \hat{\mathbf{e}}_2, \hat{\mathbf{e}}_3)$.
b. Show that $\mathcal{L}_{\mathbf{Y}}^3 = -\mathbf{Y}^2 \mathcal{L}_{\mathbf{Y}}$.
c. Deduce an expression of operator $\exp(\mathcal{L}_{\mathbf{Y}}) = \mathcal{I} + \mathcal{L}_{\mathbf{Y}} + \frac{1}{2!}\mathcal{L}_{\mathbf{Y}}^2 + \frac{1}{3!}\mathcal{L}_{\mathbf{Y}}^3 + \cdots$.

B. Tables of Moment of Inertia

Here we list the inertia properties of bodies of standard shape. In all cases, a particular set of axes $Axyz$ is chosen so as to take into account the body's symmetries. The mass density is assumed uniform throughout the body. All products of inertia are zero unless stated otherwise.

One-dimensional bodies

Slender rod of length l

$$I_{Gx} = I_{Gy} = \tfrac{1}{12} m l^2$$

$$I_{Gz} = 0$$

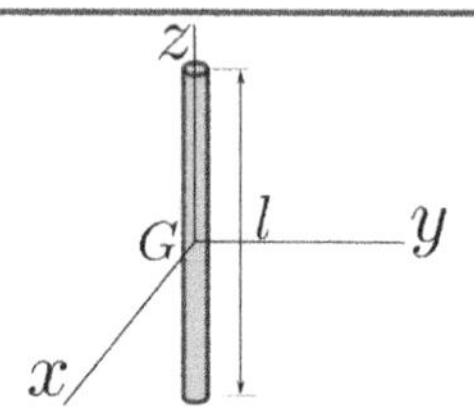

Circle of radius R

$$I_{Gx} = I_{Gy} = \tfrac{1}{2} m R^2$$

$$I_{Gz} = m R^2$$

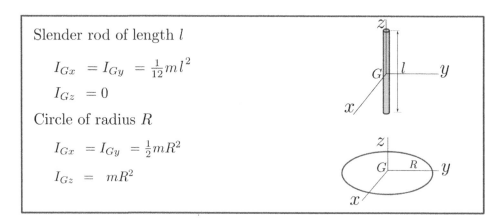

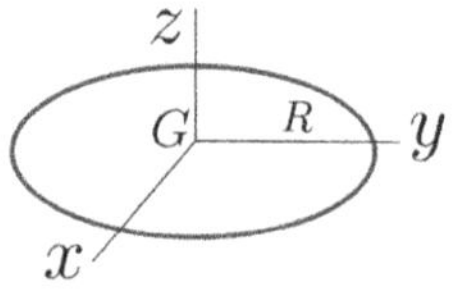

Two-dimensional bodies

Spherical shell of radius R

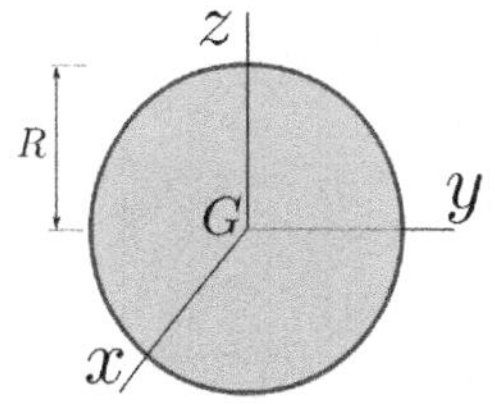

$$I_{Gx} = I_{Gy} = I_{Gz} = \tfrac{2}{3}mR^2$$

Disk of radius R

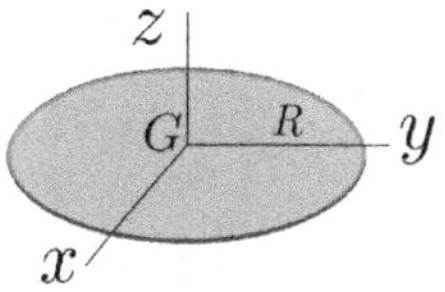

$$I_{Gx} = I_{Gy} = \tfrac{1}{4}mR^2$$

$$I_{Gz} = \tfrac{1}{2}mR^2$$

Rectangular plate of side lengths (a, b)

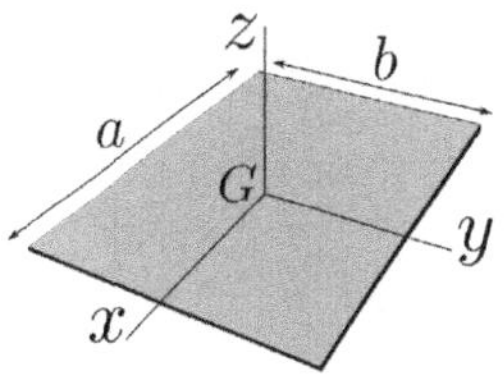

$$I_{Gx} = \tfrac{1}{12}mb^2$$

$$I_{Gy} = \tfrac{1}{12}ma^2$$

$$I_{Gz} = \tfrac{1}{12}m(a^2 + b^2)$$

Right triangular plate

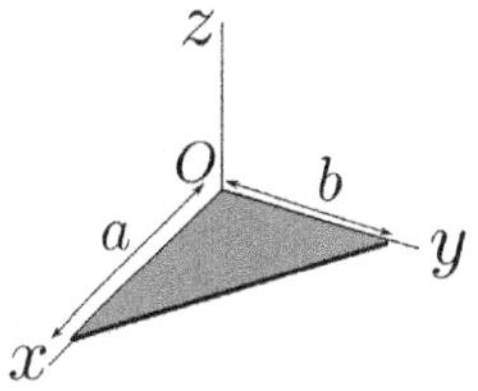

$$I_{Ox} = \tfrac{1}{6}mb^2$$

$$I_{Oy} = \tfrac{1}{6}ma^2$$

$$I_{Oz} = \tfrac{1}{6}m(a^2 + b^2)$$

$$I_{Oxy} = -\tfrac{1}{12}mab$$

Three-dimensional bodies

Sphere of radius R

$$I_{Gx} = I_{Gy} = I_{Gz} = \tfrac{2}{5}mR^2$$

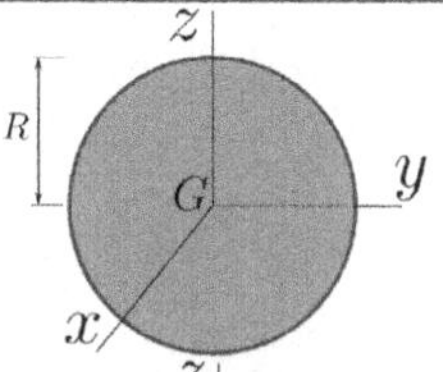

Hollow sphere of inner radius r
outer radius R

$$I_{Gx} = I_{Gy} = I_{Gz} = \tfrac{2}{5}mR^2\frac{1-\frac{r^5}{R^5}}{1-\frac{r^3}{R^3}}$$

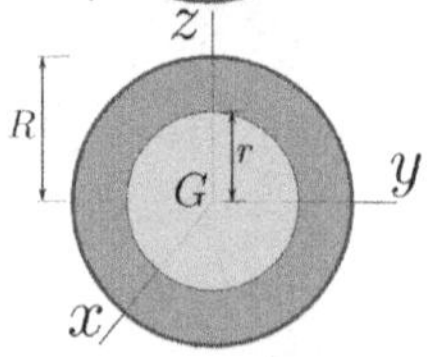

Cuboid of side lengths (a, b, c)

$$I_{Gx} = \tfrac{1}{12}m(b^2 + c^2)$$
$$I_{Gy} = \tfrac{1}{12}m(a^2 + c^2)$$
$$I_{Gz} = \tfrac{1}{12}m(a^2 + b^2)$$

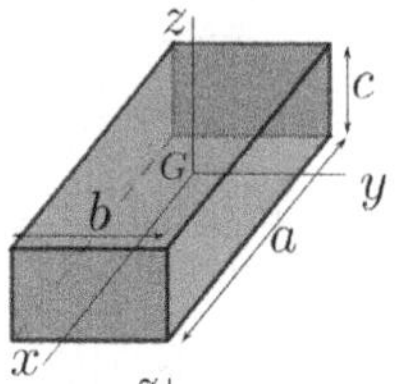

Cylinder of radius R and height H

$$I_{Gx} = I_{Gy} = \tfrac{1}{4}mR^2 + \tfrac{1}{12}mH^2$$
$$I_{Gz} = \tfrac{1}{2}mR^2$$

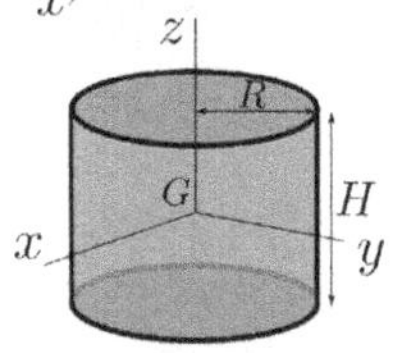

Cone of height H and base radius R

$$I_{Ox} = I_{Oy} = \tfrac{3}{10}m(2H^2 + \tfrac{1}{2}R^2)$$
$$I_{Oz} = \tfrac{3}{10}mR^2$$

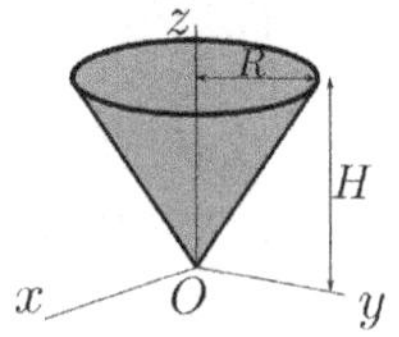

Hollow cylinder of inner radius r outer radius R
height H

$$I_{Gx} = I_{Gy} = \tfrac{1}{4}m(r^2 + R^2) + \tfrac{1}{12}mH^2$$
$$I_{Gz} = \tfrac{1}{2}m(R^2 + r^2)$$

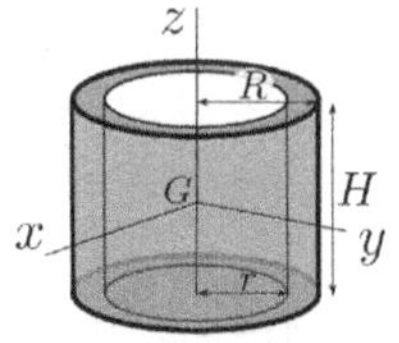

Torus of radii (r, R)

$$I_{Gx} = I_{Gy} = m(R^2 + \tfrac{5}{8}r^2)$$
$$I_{Gz} = m(R^2 + \tfrac{3}{4}r^2)$$

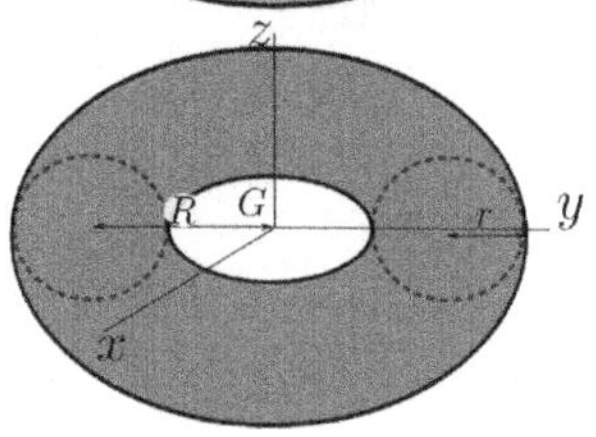

Index

63929165R00269

Made in the USA
Middletown, DE
28 August 2019